HANDBOOK OF
Community
Mental Health

THE CENTURY PSYCHOLOGY SERIES

HANDBOOK OF
Community
Mental Health

EDITED BY

Stuart E. Golann AND Carl Eisdorfer
University of Massachusetts   University of Washington

New York
APPLETON-CENTURY-CROFTS
Educational Division
MEREDITH CORPORATION

to
Erica
Jason
Marc
Evan
and to all the others

Contributors

Daniel Adelson, Ph.D.
Associate Professor of Psychology in Residence
University of California at San Francisco
San Francisco, California

Khazan C. Agrawal, M.S.
Chief of Data Processing, Assessment and Evaluation Section
Woodlawn Mental Health Center;
Research Associate, Department of Psychiatry
University of Chicago
Chicago, Illinois

Melvin E. Allerhand, Ph.D.
Consulting Psychologist, REM Associates and
Case Western Reserve and Cleveland State Universities
Cleveland, Ohio

John Altrocchi, Ph.D.
Professor of Behavioral Sciences, School of Medical Sciences, and Professor of Psychology
University of Nevada
Reno, Nevada

Franklyn N. Arnhoff, Ph.D.
John Edward Fowler Professor of Psychology and Professor of Psychiatry
University of Virginia School of Medicine
Charlottesville, Virginia

J. A. Baldwin, M.A., M.D., M.R.C. Psych., M.F.C.M.
Director, Unit of Clinical Epidemiology and Oxford Record Linkage Study
University of Oxford, England;
formerly Scottish Hospital Endowments Research Trust Fellow
Research Unit, Department of Mental Health
University of Aberdeen, Scotland

Arnold Bernstein, Ph.D.
Professor of Psychology
Queens College of the City University of New York
Queens, New York

Bernard L. Bloom, Ph.D.
Professor, Department of Psychology
University of Colorado
Boulder, Colorado

C. Alan Boneau, Ph.D.
Director, Programs & Planning
American Psychological Association
Washington, D.C.

Eli M. Bower, Ed.D.
Professor, Educational Psychology
School of Education
University of California at Berkeley
Berkeley, California

Jeannette D. Branch, M.A.
Director, Woodlawn Mental Health Center, and Field Work Assistant Professor of Psychiatry
University of Chicago
Chicago, Illinois

Dennis E. Breiter, Ph.D.
Captain, Medical Service Corps; Assistant Chief, Psychology Service
Fort Ord, California

Thomas R. Brigante, Ph.D.
Consulting Psychologist
Claremont, California

Bertram M. Brown, M.D.
Director, National Institute of Mental Health
Rockville, Maryland

Donald S. Carter, Ph.D.
Executive Director, Community Consultants, Inc.
Washington, D.C.

Caroline A. Chandler, M.D.
Assistant Professor of Pediatrics
The Johns Hopkins University School of Medicine;
Special Lecturer in Child Health and Development
The George Washington University School of Medicine

Raquel E. Cohen, M.D.
Associate Professor of Psychiatry and Associate Director, Laboratory of Community Psychiatry
Department of Psychiatry
Harvard Medical School
Boston, Massachusetts

Shlomo I. Cohen, Ph.D.
President, Center for Behavior Change and Development
Greenbelt, Maryland

Barbara Snell Dohrenwend, Ph.D.
Professor, Department of Psychology
The City College of the City University of New York
New York, New York

Bruce P. Dohrenwend, Ph.D.
Professor of Social Science, Department of Psychiatry
Columbia University College of Physicians & Surgeons
New York, New York

Carl Eisdorfer, Ph.D., M.D.
Professor & Chairman, Department of Psychiatry
University of Washington
Seattle, Washington

Leon J. Epstein, M.D., Ph.D.
Professor and Vice Chairman, Department of Psychiatry;
Associate Medical Director, Langley Porter Neuropsychiatric Institute
University of California School of Medicine
San Francisco, California

John C. Glidewell, Ph.D.
Professor, Department of Education
University of Chicago
Chicago, Illinois

Stuart E. Golann, Ph.D.
Associate Professor and Coordinator, Community Programs
Department of Psychology
University of Massachusetts
Amherst, Massachusetts

Gerald Goodman, Ph.D.
Assistant Professor of Clinical & Community Psychology
Department of Psychology
University of California at Los Angeles
Los Angeles, California

Margaret E. Grabill, M.A.
Staff Sociologist, Assessment and Evaluation Section
Woodlawn Mental Health Center
University of Chicago
Chicago, Illinois

Anthony M. Graziano, Ph.D.
Associate Professor of Psychology
State University of New York at Buffalo
Buffalo, New York

Frances Kaplan Grossman, Ph.D.
Associate Professor, Department of Psychology
Boston University
Boston, Massachusetts

Ralph G. Hirschowitz, M.B., Ch.B.
Assistant Professsor of Psychiatry, Laboratory of Community Psychiatry
Harvard Medical School
Boston, Massachusetts;
Director, Office of Prevention
Commonwealth of Massachusetts Department of Mental Health

Hans R. Huessy, M.D.
Professor of Psychiatry
University of Vermont College of Medicine
Burlington, Vermont

Ira Iscoe, Ph.D.
Professor of Psychology and Education
Director, Graduate Training in Community Mental Health
University of Texas
Austin, Texas

Earl J. Janda, Ph.D.
Consulting Psychologist
Kensington, Maryland

Edward S. Katkin, Ph.D.
Professor of Psychology
State University of New York at Buffalo
Buffalo, New York

Sheppard G. Kellam, M.D.
Director, Assessment and Evaluation Section, and Chief Consultant Psychiatrist, Woodlawn Mental Health Center;
Associate Professor of Psychiatry
University of Chicago
Chicago, Illinois

James G. Kelly, Ph.D.
Professor of Psychology
University of Michigan
Ann Arbor, Michigan

William L. Kissick, M.D.
George S. Pepper Professor of Community Medicine, Department of Community Medicine
University of Pennsylvania School of Medicine
Philadelphia, Pennsylvania

Goldie Lake, M.A.
Coordinator, Manpower Programs, and Director, Geriatric Outreach Worker Program, Center for Continuing Education
Case Western Reserve University
Cleveland, Ohio

Henry L. Lennard, Ph.D.
Professor of Medical Sociology, (Psychiatry) In Residence
University of California at San Francisco
San Francisco, California

Alan I. Levenson, M.D.
Professor and Head, Department of Psychiatry
University of Arizona College of Medicine
Tucson, Arizona

Murray Levine, Ph.D.
Professor and Director, Clinical Community Train-
ing Program, Department of Psychology
State University of New York at Buffalo
Buffalo, New York

Lawrence B. Lurie, M.D.
Director, District V Mental Health Center;
Assistant Clinical Professor
University of California at San Francisco
San Francisco, California

Fortune V. Mannino, Ph.D.
Scientist Director, USPHS, Mental Health Study
Center, National Institute of Mental Health;
Associate Professor, Family and Community
Development
University of Maryland
College Park, Maryland

Joseph L. Massimo, Ed.D.
Chief Psychologist, Newton Public Schools
Newton, Massachusetts

Roger C. Mills
Ph.D. Candidate and Research Associate
University of Michigan
Ann Arbor, Michigan

Lois Barclay Murphy, Ph.D.
Children's Hospital of D.C.
Washington, D.C.

J. R. Newbrough, Ph.D.
Professor of Psychology and
Coordinator, Center for Community Studies
George Peabody College for Teachers
Nashville, Tennessee

David Orme-Johnson, Ph.D.
Director of Research
Drug and Alcohol Abuse Program
Fort Bliss, Texas

Howard J. Parad, D.S.W.
Professor, University of Southern California,
School of Social Work;
Educational consultant, Center for Training in
Community Psychiatry
Los Angeles, California

Stanley Pavey, Ph.D.
Counselor, Counseling Center, and
Assistant Professor, Department of Psychology
University of Maryland
College Park, Maryland

Hildegard E. Peplau, R.N., Ed.D.
Professor and Director, Graduate Program in
Psychiatric-Mental Helath Nursing
College of Nursing and Graduate School
Rutgers, The State University
New Brunswick, New Jersey

Thomas F. A. Plaut, Ph.D., M.P.H.
Associate Director for Program Coordination,
National Institute of Mental Health
Health Services and Mental Health Administration
Department of Health, Education, and Welfare
Rockville, Maryland

Ronald M. Quinlan, Ph.D.
Assistant Professor, Department of Psychology
Yale University
New Haven, Connecticut

Donald C. Ransom, Ph.D.
Assistant Professor and Director, Family Therapy
Training, Division of Ambulatory and Com-
munity Medicine
University of California School of Medicine
San Francisco, California

Lydia Rapoport, M.S.S.*
Professor and Director, Community Mental Health
Training Program, School of Social Welfare
University of California at Berkeley
Berkeley, California

David S. Reynolds, Ph.D.
Deputy Commissioner, Erie County Department
of Mental Health
Buffalo, New York

William C. Rhodes
Professor of Psychology and Professor of Com-
munity Mental Health, School of Public Health
University of Michigan
Ann Arbor, Michigan

Nevitt Sanford, Ph.D.
Scientific Director, The Wright Institute
2728 Durant Avenue
Berkeley, California

Sheldon K. Schiff, M.D.
President, Children's Center for Learning
Capacities
Chicago, Illinois

Saleem A. Shah, Ph.D.
Chief, Center for Studies of Crime and
Delinquency
National Institute of Mental Health
Rockville, Maryland;
Professorial Lecturer
Washington College of Law
American University
Washington, D.C.

Edwin S. Shneidman, Ph.D.
Professor of Medical Psychology, Department of
Psychiatry
University of California at Los Angeles
Los Angeles, California

Milton F. Shore, Ph.D.
Diplomate in Clinical Psychology (ABPP);
Chief, Clinical Research and Program Evaluation
Section

*deceased

Mental Health Study Center, National Institute of Mental Health
Adelphi, Maryland;
Lecturer, University of Maryland Graduate School, and
Graduate School, Catholic University of America

Charles D. Spielberger, Ph.D.
Professor of Psychology and Director, Doctoral Program in Clinical-Community Psychology
University of South Florida
Tampa, Florida

James W. Stockdill
Deputy Director, Office of Program Planning and Evaluation
National Institute of Mental Health
Rockville, Maryland

June Louin Tapp, Ph.D.
Senior Research Social Psychologist, American Bar Foundation;
Associate Professorial Lecturer in Social Science
University of Chicago
Chicago, Illinois

Robert B. Tapp, Ph.D.
Professor of Philosophy of Religion
Meadville Theological School of Lombard College;
Professorial Lecturer in Social Science
University of Chicago
Chicago, Illinois

David M. Todd, Ph.D.
Assistant Professor, Department of Psychology
University of Massachusetts
Amherst, Massachusetts

Edison J. Trickett, Ph.D.
Assistant Professor, Department of Psychology
Yale University
New Haven, Connecticut

Leopold O. Walder, Ph.D.
President, Behavior Service Consultants, Inc.
Greenbelt, Maryland

Frank C. Warman, Ph.D.
Psychologist, Mental Hygiene Consultation Service
U.S. Army Hospital
U.S. Military Academy
West Point, New York

Milton Wittman, D.S.W.
Chief, Social Work Training Branch
Division of Manpower and Training Programs
National Institute of Mental Health
Health Services and Mental Health Administration
U.S. Department of Health, Education, and Welfare
Rockville, Maryland

Foreword

It is questionable whether community mental health can at the present time claim a valid theoretical base or justify a manual of practice. The editors of this volume in their introduction have taken the position that community mental health represents one of several evolutionary phases of mental health ideology. It is an area of enormous diversity, sometimes "revolutionary" concepts, and rapid development. In asking many of the best-known people in the field to write original chapters for the present handbook, the hope of the editors has not been to attempt to define community mental health, community psychiatry, or community psychology, but to help the field move toward greater definition.

The volume is for the behavioral scientist, for the practitioner regardless of discipline, and for the mental health specialist in training. It is designed to provide theoretical and practical bases for action in the context of community mental health. The chapters, each one prepared for this volume by a person or persons intimately involved in the development of community mental health, approach this task from a number of perspectives. Some are designed to facilitate an understanding of community processes and social systems, others focus specifically on community mental health programs, and still others define target populations and high risk groups from specific methodological and project perspectives. The hope of the editors has been for a volume which incorporates a comprehensive and searching analysis of the background issues, targets, and tactics in the field.

Acknowledgments

For their foresight and support for the development of community mental health programs in the United States the editors wish to acknowledge the late Robert Young, M.D., and his associates at Halifax County.

Publication of this volume has depended upon the great patience and cooperation of its contributors throughout the complex process of compiling an extensive collection of original works. The authors wish to thank them.

Dorothy Golann provided help and patience throughout.

Among those who helped in the preparation of this volume were Barbara Minton and Janet Owens. The editors wish to thank them for their help, and in particular to acknowledge the substantial editorial work of Jeffrey Baker and Patricia Walsh.

Contents

V. TRAINING

I

Introduction

In part I the editors provide a framework and historical context for the issues that follow. Community mental health is introduced as the most recent of several phases of mental health ideology. The emergence of community mental health is traced both to mounting dissatisfaction with concepts and strategies derived from earlier ideologies, and to political shifts between states and local communities and between the professions and the persons served by them.

It is pointed out that for each phase of mental health ideology there has existed a system of classification (which tells much about the interests, beliefs, and values of the persons who developed it), a preferred theory of causation, and a sanctioned structure and form of intervention. The authors stress the interrelationships between explanation, classification, and intervention. Each ideology has certain implicit assumptions which can be made explicit, thereby increasing alternative strategies of intervention. A framework for comparing different intervention strategies is introduced which includes administrative, political, and programmatic components.

The authors suggest that the basic issue during the 1960s concerned attempts to break away from fixed approaches to providing mental health services and to develop sufficient helping alternatives to make services available to all who may want them. During the latter part of the 1960s the issues of responsibility, power, and control came to the foreground and the mental health practitioner found himself on unfamiliar ground.

1

Mental Health and the Community: The Development of Issues

Stuart E. Golann and Carl Eisdorfer

In the evolution of mental health ideology, supernatural and demonic explanations of personal torment or unusual behavior gave way to moral-humanistic and next to scientific-physiological orientations. The latter in turn were supplemented or replaced by psychodynamic and interpersonal concepts. Today, clinical interest encompasses the community, and mental health specialists are increasingly involved in the political and social institutions which mediate individual development, adaptation, and satisfaction. With each successive phase in mental health ideology, mental health specialists have expanded their orientation. Attention to a relatively few persons with obvious disorders has grown to include those persons whose development or situation has left them with life styles less effective or satisfying than they desired or judged to be possible.

In assessing the changes in the field, one notes the universality of three related social-clinical processes: (1) *classification* (some acts or behavior patterns are distinguished from others and certain concepts may be grouped together under a single term such as neurosis); (2) *explanation* (a belief system or theory is developed to account for the occurrence of certain acts or patterns of action); (3) *intervention or regulation* (a system of institutions, persons, or practices is built and sanctioned to cope with certain acts of behavior). For each phase of mental health ideology there has existed a system of classification, a preferred theory of causation, and a sanctioned form of response.

Classification represents a technique for the control of disorders and for the systematic understanding of behavior. In earlier periods it appears to have served primarily to identify and isolate deviant behavior so as to achieve some degree of security in the face of frightening events. The choice of what events to classify seems to have been determined more by the fears of men than their aspirations or theories. Today, the separation of certain observations for purposes of classification implies a causative hypothesis, and may reveal much about the assumptions and goals of the scientist or clinician.

Often classification will depart from the observable to seek the explanatory. Tests may be applied to separate two categories of similar behavior from one another on the basis of etiological agents. Organic psychoses may be similar behaviorally but etiological factors such as drugs, toxins, or internal metabolic dysfunctions necessitate a separate classification of such behavioral entities. Response to therapy may also modify classification and our understanding of etiology.

The explanation offered for problem behavior—e.g., demonic possession, biological factors, psychodynamic imbalance, or social stress—is certainly the key concept in any phase of mental health ideology. The causative explanation determines in large part what modes of intervention are to be clinically preferred and politically supported. Like classification, the causative explanation reveals the assumptions and goals of the clinician in that it involves a narrowing of attention to certain events. Decisions implicit in determining mode of intervention include the choice of the providers of mental health services, the selection of patients or client groups, and the specification of psychological, social, geographic, and temporal prerequisites for any given service transaction.

In sum, the community resources that are called upon to influence behavior are closely related to the assumptions of an ideological position. A recognition of this is necessary to an appreciation of community mental health dynamics. What follows now is a brief description of key historical phases of mental health ideology and their implications for community psychology and mental health.

PHASES OF MENTAL HEALTH IDEOLOGY

Deistic and Demonological Theories

Most early cultures invoked gods or demons to explain behavior. Depending upon the person and the social context, possession could have positive or negative connotations. The predominant New Testament view of possession was negative, although in some cultures epilepsy was considered to be a sacred disease.

Various forms of exorcism have existed throughout history for different afflictions and interventions of varying degrees of severity have been called upon to remove the evil believed to have entered the body of the afflicted. In most instances, if the intervention did not help, it did no further harm. But the exorcist who did not effect relief with incantation might attempt more drastic therapies. During the Middle Ages the consequences of demonology were most severe. Witches, most of them women whose behavior today would be classified as mentally disordered, were killed in large numbers. Even during periods when demonic explanations of deviant behavior were predominant, congruence existed between the classification, explanation, and remediation of problem behavior. The lack of validity of these prescientific notions could be masked by the extreme forms of intervention used and by the zealous dedication of their adherents.

When the ambiguous position of the disturbed or deviant persons in society did not lead to such hostile response these persons were often ignored or, as in the case of the Toms O'Bedlam, licensed to beg and left to make their way, but little was done to help them. The relationship between economic status and the mental health field, so apparent during recent years, has much historical precedent. The development of the institutions which preceded the mental hospitals of the 19th century was basically an economic program stimulated by the increased number of beggars and vagrants who had become social problems. The healing techniques of the mental health professions evolved initially from a responsibility for and

concern with institutionalized persons. This may be seen in the successive transitions of mental health institutions from agencies of social control to expressions of moral concern to centers of custodial care.

The Rise and Fall of Moral Treatment and of Psychiatric Morale

According to Rosen (1968), institutions in the 17th and 18th centuries were developed to deal with problems of the poor, dependent, and vagrant. "Within this portmanteau category were included a motley group, the members of which were characterized by the fact that they had overstepped the limits set by the family, social position, religious institutions, the political order, property relations, and the like . . . (p. 167)."

The conception of Pinel that "the mentally sick, far from being guilty people deserving of punishment, are sick people whose miserable state deserves all the consideration that is due to suffering humanity" highlighted the moral approach to the treatment of the mentally ill. Characterized by Bockoven (1963) as "essentially a teaching program in how to make friends and enjoy outside interests," moral treatment was described by Brigham (1847) as the removal of the insane from home and former associations, with respectful and kind treatment and in most cases manual labor, religious worship, establishment of regular habits of self-control, and diversion of the mind from morbid trains of thought.

The relationship of social factors to abnormal behavior and the importance of milieu and social groups and treatment was recognized in this phase of mental health ideology. Butler (1887) described the successful use of group meetings and confidential interviews and insisted that institutions could not care for more than two hundred patients without suffering from a breakdown in appropriate social influences. He also stressed the importance of aesthetics and milieu in the hospital environment.

The results achieved by small institutions run according to such principles by a superintendent who often personally supervised the care of all patients were reported to be very good,[1] thereby sustaining the optimism of the time. During the second half of the 19th century the situation changed markedly from therapeutic optimism to pessimism, from a moral-humanistic philosophy to reliance on scientific classification, from awareness of social factors to somatism. These changes combined with other factors resulted in the transformation of the small asylums into large custodial institutions.

Before the total decline of moral treatment, and largely through the influence of Dorothea Dix, a rapid growth occurred in the number of institutions for the care of the insane. According to one historian of the period (White, 1964), "Miss Dix personally investigated conditions throughout the United States, presenting reports and arguing with state legislators, until she had become the chief moving force in the founding or enlarging of more than thirty state hospitals."

With the number of institutions increasing and the early results of moral treatment so positive, it is difficult to imagine the circumstances that accounted for its abandonment. An increase in persons hospitalized was apparently a basic problem. The effects of moral treatment were soon undermined by a rapidly increased patient load and by socioeconomic and ethnic distance between helpers and their patients. From 1834 to 1853, as Worcester State Hospital grew in size, the doctor-patient ratio moved from 1:58 to 1:140. Physicians' notations became spaced years apart and more superficial.

By the mid-19th century psychiatry was largely limited to hospital management, with patient care and therapy deteriorating progressively. With the Krafft-Ebing studies linking syphillis and general paresis, the new organic approach to psychiatric care was accentuated and the importance of classification reinforced. More remarkable, however, was the continued pessimism and sustained isolation of the state hospital, the primary custodial institution for the mentally ill.

Again economic circumstances played an important part in the shaping of mental health ideology and intervention. With the great immigration of poor Irish to the United States, the commitment to principles of moral treatment was found wanting. It is interesting to note that a new classification category was developed, "foreign insane pauperism" (Bockoven, 1963, p. 25), to apply to increasing numbers of unreachable hospital inmates. According to Grob (1966), "Because psychiatrists were never fully aware of the important part that their own attitudes played

in their professional rationale and ideology, they were unprepared to cope with the heterogeneous patient population that accompanied the new urban and industrialized society. Consequently they were prone to place responsibility for their declining successes elsewhere. . . . Whatever the reasons offered, it was evident that most psychiatrists no longer adhered to the belief that mental disease, irrespective of a patient's background, was a largely curable malady (pp. 521–522)." Furthermore, "When psychiatrists were confronted with the decline in the effectiveness or moral treatment they began to adjust their theoretical approach in the light of their experience. Up to the middle of the 19th century they had accepted the role of psychological factors in etiology and treatment. After this time, however, they began to revert to an outright and explicit somaticism (p. 522)."

Mental institutions continued to grow in size. Appointments to positions became political, the positions themselves had become sinecures, and the care of the mentally ill became increasingly insulated from developments outside the hospital. This insulation was not only from psychological and social developments but also from biological and general medical research, little of which was incorporated into hospital care.

The resulting alienation of psychiatry from the rest of medicine and the extent to which moral treatment had declined are apparent in the admonishments delivered by the neurologist Mitchell (1894) to the members of the medico-psychological society.

What have you taught us of these 91,000 insane whom you see or treat? . . . The thinking general practitioner knows that what he has to deal with is not a disease, but a disease plus a man. This is deeply true of insanity. Nowhere is it more needful to study the human soil in which the disorder exists. . . . The cloistral lives you lead give rise, we think, to certain mental peculiarities. . . . You hold and teach opinions which we have long learned to lose. One is the superstition (almost is it that) to the effect that an asylum is in itself curative. You hear the regret in every report that patients are not sent soon enough, as if you had ways of curing which we have not. Upon my word, I think asylum life is deadly to the insane. Poverty, risk, fear, send you of true need many patients; many more are sent by people quite able to have their friends treated outside. They are placed in asylums because of the wide-spread belief you have so long, and as we think, so unreasonably fostered, to the effect that there is some mysterious therapeutic influence to be found behind your walls and locked doors. We hold the reverse opinion, and think your hospitals are never to be used save as a last resource (pp. 110, 111, 112).

Psychopathology and the Psychology of the Unconscious

The study of hysteria by neurologists, particularly the work of Charcot (1890) and Janet (1920), provided the foundation for the introduction of the next phase of mental health ideology–psychoanalysis. When Breurer and Freud (1895) wrote that "the hysteric suffers mostly from reminiscences,"[2] they broke away from the mainstream of clinical neurology and reintroduced emotional factors to a place of importance in the understanding of behavior disorders.

What followed was a series of insights and concepts that was to change man's image of himself. Hobbs (1964) has written that "Freud was a giant, a companion of Darwin, Marx, and Einstein in shaping our culture, our beliefs about man." It is difficult to summarize the contribution of such men to any field of specialization because their influence is so great and manifest in so many ways.

In general, one might suggest (as has Bellak, 1964) that Freud elucidated the relationship between normal and abnormal behavior, the importance of an individual's early environment, of his unique mode of interaction with the people around him, and the relevance of these factors for his future development.

Approaches to classification changed dramatically from the description of symptoms to the elucidation of mental mechanisms of defense conceptualized by Freud. The psychological dynamics of a person's thinking and the conflicts between different levels of personality became the basis upon which persons were classified. At the same time the symptom-based approach to classification continued to develop in illness-oriented settings.

Just as Freud's concepts changed psychiatric classifications and were important in shaping and influencing the understanding of man and aspects of society, his technical developments were to mold the development and organization of mental health services in America. The development by Freud of the method of free association, the conceptualization of unconscious motivation including repression and resistance, the concepts of the sexual instinct and its importance to personality development, the recognition of transference manifestation during the course of a psychoanalytic investigation, and numerous related concepts all lead to a concentration of professional interests in the psychoanalytic method of treatment. Consequently, the one-to-one treatment modality, demanding of the patient high verbal intelligence, motivation, time, patience, and financial resources and demanding of the therapist extensive training including personal analysis, became the model to which the field aspired. Attempts to apply psychoanalytic methods to the most seriously disordered persons reflected the growing conviction that much of problem behavior could be understood from a historical knowledge of development and defense. Group psychoanalysis received some attention, but individual psychotherapy came to be seen as the treatment of choice for emotional disorders and psychoanalysis the standard by which new therapies were described and compared.

The variations on the psychoanalytic theme proliferated, but all shared the difficulty that patients were those who could afford such treatment and had the verbal capacity and adaptability to deal with a variety of feelings and memories not usually at the level of awareness of the patient when he requests help. This, of course, leads to a variety of alternative styles of verbal interaction with patients, but effective psychotherapy was not available to large numbers of individuals because of financial or logistic constraints, unfamiliarity of socially advantaged mental health professionals with the practical living problems faced by disadvantaged clients, and the impracticality for disadvantaged clients of a method requiring long periods of introspective analysis.

So great has been the influence of psychoanalysis on the thinking and priorities of the mental health fields, that in his presidential address to the American Orthopsychiatric Association, Hobbs (1964) stated that:

A counter-revolution is required to restore balance and common sense. For it has led us to a preoccupation with the intrapsychic life of man. No, I think "obsession" is a better word to suggest the passionate commitment we have to the world inside a man's skull, to the unconscious, the phenomenal, the stuff that dreams are made of. Everyone must become a therapist, probing the argument of insidious intent, stalking ragged claws scuttling over the bottoms of silent seas. The psychiatrist forgets Adolf Myer and can no longer give a physical examination. The psychologist lays down his diagnostic tools, forgets research, and gets behind a desk to listen. The social worker goes inside and waits for the patients to come. The preacher takes to his study and the teacher to the case conference. The most thoroughly trained person of all, the psychiatrist who has completed psychoanalytic training, becomes a monument of Veblenian inutility, able to treat maybe one hundred patients in his entire professional career (p. 823).

A Framework for Comparing Mental Health Programs

Before turning to the "counterrevolution" which Hobbs anticipated, it is well to highlight some of the implications of the developments which have been discussed to this point. To do so requires a framework for the description and comparison of approaches to mental health services and programming. The critical dimensions of mental health programs are the goals, locations, occasions, helpers, and recipients of mental health services and the specific characteristics of these services. These can be grouped into three areas, namely, the organizational process, the mental health transaction, and the ecological placement.

Framework for Program Analysis

I. The Organizational Process
    A. Decision-making system and process
    B. Responsibility interpretation and setting of goals
    C. Resource acquisition and reduction of constraints
II. The Mental Health Transaction
    A. The helper
    B. Nature of the service
    C. The direct recipient
III. The Ecological Placement
    A. Location of the transaction
    B. Occasion or time of receipt of the service

Every program should involve goal setting, and in a community this may involve considerable negotiation between professionals and community members. Resources are deployed to achieve goals, and this process of resource allocation involves a series of choices about *who* will provide *what* service to *whom*, at *what occasion or time*, and *in what location*.

The *Organizational Process* concerns resources, constraints, program responsibility, and goals. The development or bringing together of a decision-making body, the acquisition and administration of resources and the reduction of constraints are part of the planning and of the politics of mental health. An operational framework needs to be established. Fiscal, administrative, and legal responsibilities must be incorporated into a working system and the decision-making process must be codified or implicitly understood. If responsibility is to be shared among several agencies, or if certain prerogatives are to be assigned to one agency or to a community organization, such arrangements should be explicit and workable. Once a program's goals have been specified, the degree to which they are achieved is in large part dependent upon the explicit consideration of the options available and of the priorities and strategies adopted. An efficient and flexible decision-making structure and process facilitates a meaningful weighing of program options.

At any given time resources and constraints are relatively fixed quantities which determine the limits within which choices can be made at that time. During most earlier periods of mental health ideology, goal setting was assumed to be the responsibility of the professional. Currently, community members, the consumers of the services, want to assume power including the responsibility for both goal setting and for resource allocation. The interpretation of program responsibility can lead to a variety of goals. Preventing new cases of personality disorder in children, making psychotherapy available to low income groups, and reducing intrapsychic conflict are three examples of initial goal statements. There are, of course, many different stratagems for obtaining program goals and critical choices must be made (for examples see Golann, 1970). These choices, if not explicitly made, are implicitly determined, thus reducing the options of program planners.

The *Mental Health Transaction* involves three choices—the helper, the nature of the service, and the direct recipient. The question of helper is that of who will provide the service. The specific person is usually chosen as representing a class of individuals who are known to possess certain characteristics, training, skills, or personal attributes. Examples of possible choices include a clergyman, a clinical psychologist, a general practice physician, a mental health counselor, a psychiatrist, a social worker, or a shaman. Indeed, services may be transmitted impersonally, such as information in a pamphlet.

The nature of the service or the service of choice refers to the specific techniques, content, and process made available. Analytic group psychotherapy, exorcism by incantation, individual mental health consultation, rest and moral reeducation, psychoactive drug therapy, psychodiagnostic assessment, vocational counseling, or a comic strip about the needs of infants are examples. The specific individuals who may be the direct recipients of such services constitute the next choice. They, too, may be identified as representative of classes or special groupings of individuals with whom they share certain characteristics. Examples include chronic schizophrenics, female college graduates, anxious college men, individuals thought to be possessed by demons, high school dropouts, industrial foremen, preadolescent boys who are thought by their teachers to be troubled, residents of a given area, or unwed mothers. It is sometimes useful to distinguish between the "direct recipient" and the "target group" and to recognize that a mental health transaction may have primary and secondary targets. In some instances a phasing or sequence of transactions occurs and the "direct recipient" in the first phase may become the "helper" in the second (e.g., consultation with teachers or clergymen).

The *Ecological Placement* involves two important choices: wide variation is possible in the geographic or social setting where a mental health transaction may occur and in the temporal prerequisites or timing of a service. The loci of transactions may include such diverse locations as a community general hospital, an elementary school, a private metropolitan office, a college dormitory, or a storefront near a bus stop. The occasion or time of the delivery and receipt of the service provides another dimension of choice. On a transactional level, examples might include the following: after giving birth to a premature infant; upon application to elementary school; when

self-referred; upon entering college; following loss of a spouse; or when a particular symptom picture is recognized.

Critical Analysis of Earlier Phases of Mental Health Ideology

The three major ideologies which have shaped the development of mental health services today in the United States are those derived from the moral, physiological, and psychodynamic approaches. The more recent impact of public health oriented concepts will be discussed later.

Moral treatment spoke to the importance of social milieu both for its possible etiological contribution to problem behavior and for its role in treatment. The role of milieu in treatment includes such factors as the attitudes and expectations of the helpers, the size of the institutions, the importance given to groups and educational programs. But the techniques were personal and humanistic and limited in the range of persons to whom they could successfully be applied. Moral treatment as a form of mental health ideology has left a rich and often overlooked heritage. But successful application of its techniques has to date been linked to certain helpers, certain recipients, and a sympathetic interrelationship between them.

The scientific-physiological approach to disordered behavior also has a history of some notable success. But this approach depended most heavily upon diagnostic classification and custodial care which in many cases have been thought to have had detrimental effects. Because insufficient treatment alternatives were available, persons who did not require institutional care and their relations were often forced to choose between hospitalization or no services. While certain problems yielded to a biological approach, many hospitalized persons appear not to have been suffering from biological disease. No amount of classification revealed the somatic cause of their behavior, and the numbers of hospitalized persons grew.

Most easily seen in the demonic phases, but true of all approaches, the classification systems developed by men reveal much of their beliefs, values, and aspirations. The categories of classification have important social consequences for those persons to whom they are applied. Society and individuals react differently to persons who have been classified in certain ways and the consequences may be obvious and extreme, such as execution or imprisonment, or more subtle, such as rejection or increased vulnerability to social or institutional sanction. The effect of negative attitudes toward persons classified as suffering from mental disorders has been discussed in numerous publications including the final report of the Joint Commission on Mental Illness and Health (1961). Readjustment following diagnosis may be particularly difficult for lower class patients in part because of the greater stigma of mental illness among persons of lower socioeconomic status (Myers & Bean, 1968; Nunnally, 1961).

Psychoanalysis or dynamic psychology has also made a major contribution to our understanding of problem behavior. The demonstration of the importance of unconscious motivation and its relationship to personality and disorder is of great significance in the controversy over causation. The formulation of a unitary theory of behavior suggesting that the laws which governed the most deviant could be applied to the behavior of all persons was also of great significance. At the same time that this unitary theory appeared to increase the vulnerability of everyone to deviant behavior, it also led to the possibility of disorder prevention. The particular importance of the early phases of development for understanding personality function was of practical as well as theoretical significance.

Perhaps more than any other previous ideological phase, dynamic psychology and psychoanalysis resulted in a broadening of the scope of mental health to range over all aspects of human behavior. An unprecedented impact on literature and the arts made this set of explanations available and relevant to all men.

As did the moral phase, dynamic psychology has had important limitations in applicability, and perhaps for many of the same reasons. Hollingshead and Redlich (1958) studied the distribution of mental health services in New Haven, Connecticut, during the 1950s. Their studies demonstrated a relationship between social class and aspects of diagnosed mental illness including its development, prevalence, form, and treatment. They found that the treatment received from public and private psychiatric sources was unrelated to the diagnosis, age, or sex of the patient. The one thing related to the type of treatment received was the recipient's socioeconomic status. If he were of a higher socioeconomic status he would most probably receive psychotherapy or an extended personal relationship with a helping person. If he were of lower socioeconomic status he would most likely receive a quicker, nonverbal, less personal form of treatment often amounting to nothing more than custodial care.

These findings were extended in a ten-year follow-up study conducted by Myers and Bean (1968) who attempted to determine the current status of 1,563 patients from New Haven who were in hospital or clinic treatment between May 31 and December 1, 1950. Myers and Bean reported that "social class is related to the outcome of psychiatric treatment and adjustment in the community no matter how they are defined or measured (p. 202)." Their results show, moreover, that the chances of hospital discharge were greater for higher status persons not only for first discharge but also for each subsequent discharge following a readmission. Conversely, the chances of readmission were just as high or higher for lower status as for higher status patients.

In addition to the socioeconomic constraints on the distribution of mental health services, there are other constraints in the availability of dynamic psychotherapy which derive from limitations in the number of persons trained to provide psychotherapy and consequently in the number of persons who can receive it. Thus there emerged clear evidence of the failure of this approach to provide equitable care for all persons. Whether the shortcomings were logistical, theoretical, or practical was less clear.

Shortcomings Common to Earlier Approaches

If one shortcoming is common to the three major orientations which have shaped the mental health field in America it has been an overcommitment to the validity of one set of explanatory concepts and methods of intervention coupled with intolerance and suspicion of competing points of view. As each school of thought dominated the field, the result has invariably been an insufficient and artificially limited range of helping alternatives traceable in part to limited public support coupled with exclusive professional concern with one approach to helping. Unnecessary limitations have been imposed on types of helpers or types of clients, or there has been adherence to fixed preconditions in the location or timing of helping services. At any time in the development of mental health ideology there is evidence of a relationship between disordered behavior and low socioeconomic status and of the importance of tolerance or intolerance between different social groups in setting the tone of mental health programs.

The diversity of categories of classification, theories of causation, and techniques of intervention which have been brought forth in past centuries is such as to give pause to the advocate of any particular system. The answer to mental health problems obviously does not lie with any one approach. Yet ideologies are held or abandoned at times when it would appear that the alternative course should have been followed. The problems of determining the validity of intervention are many, not the least of which is a lack of clarity or specificity in goals.

Congruence, a type of face validity which sometimes exists between classification, explanation, and remediation of problem behavior, does not assure validity of results and extreme forms of intervention may mask negative outcomes. The tendency to attribute failure of an intervention not to the limited validity of the explanatory concepts but to special characteristics of the recipients or to the limited power of the techniques used also serves to make the determination of validity more difficult.

It should be noted that when conditions are right, an apparently successful approach toward disordered behavior may be given up even if there is no more successful approach to replace it. The tenacity with which the demonic ideology was held despite its lack of validity and the relative ease with which successful programs of moral treatment gave way to custodial hospitalization presents something of a paradox unless one recognizes that personal factors such as attitudes, pride, and privilege have been powerful determinants of mental health services. As a result, mental health programming has at times been rigid and inflexible and the particular strategies have often been designed to maintain a position of privilege for the helper and not planned for those who needed help.

Dissatisfaction Reaches a Critical Point

Perhaps it was because questions of strategy did not receive sufficient consideration or because institutional and professional prerogatives substituted for or constrained planning of services that dissatisfaction with the mental health enterprise reached a high level during the 1950s and 1960s. The most succinct statement of the problem was that of the Joint Commission on Mental Illness and Health (1961) that "above all the field may be characterized as suffering from two major lacks: verifiable knowledge and competent manpower."

There are many problems. The mental health system is not meeting the needs of troubled people because of manpower limitations, inadequacy and inapplicability of services provided, social class inequities, and constraints on innovative planning. It is reasonably clear that a sizable proportion of the population have had or presently have problems that might be benefited from a helping relationship.[3] The decision to go for help, the type of problem reported, the type of treatment offered, and the outcome of treatment all appear to have educational and socioeconomic correlates which are not adequately taken into account in the planning of mental health programs. Self-referral or sociolegal referral to established treatment agencies is a poor selector of who needs what help at what time. Most people turn to clergymen, family physicians, or other trusted persons when they are troubled, and only a small percentage of troubled persons desiring help with their problems come to the mental health professionals or established mental health agencies.[4] This being the case, one might assume that the mental health professionals help most of the persons who do consult them, but in fact they do not. They treat only a small percentage of those who come to them for aid[5] and, in many instances, the limited range of treatment alternatives still may force placement of troubled people into regressive rather than therapeutic situations.

COMMUNITY MENTAL HEALTH

A change did begin during the early 1960s as mental health workers in all fields experimented with new community-oriented strategies of intervention and new organizations of services in the community such as the Federal Program of Comprehensive Community Mental Health Centers.

Subsequently, the need for new approaches to the problem of balancing patient care and the prevention of disorder has led many professionals to involvement in new roles. The ecosystem in which behavior is transacted has become the arena of concern and the progression from custodian to therapist now takes another move—to agency consultant. The locus of influence has moved from the hospital asylum, to the patient, to the social forces that influence adaptation. Kelly (chapters 9 & 14) has applied concepts from biological ecology to understanding social systems and planning programs of intervention. The focus is thus shifting from intrapsychic to interpersonal, to broader social networks which are presumed to shape behavior.

Approaches to behavior classification have shifted from the classification of internal psychodynamics to concern for social adaptation and the place of the person in a social system. The importance of including social-psychological variables such as power, group status, and socioeconomic status has been recognized (see Glidewell, chapter 10). Various attempts at definition of mental health and illness appear ready to give way to level of competence as a type of conceptual "lowest common denominator" (Erikson, 1950; Menninger, 1959, 1964; White, 1959).

In searching for a theoretical framework within which to understand adaptation there is movement toward concepts such as those of Erikson which focus attention on the coping process, the demands society makes upon persons and the personal consequences of relatively successful or unsuccessful resolution of these demands. The resulting orientation is a more positive one than that based upon a deficit or illness model. Successful resolution of developmental tasks may result in successive increments in ego development. Comparing Erikson to Freud, Maier (1965) writes: "Whereas Freud's mission was to provide the existence and operation of the unconscious, Erikson's mission is to point out the developmental opportunities in the individual to triumph over the psychological hazards of living. Freud's warning of the social doom of man if he is left to his innate strivings is answered in Erikson's optimistic premise that every personal and social crisis furnishes components that are conducent to growth (pp. 17–18)."

For Erikson a crisis is actually a turning point or moment of decision between progress and regression, integration and retardation such as the sense of inferiority or sense of competence which may emerge from experiences with school, learning, production, and attempts to develop skills.

New Approaches and Strategies of Mental Health Services

The several turning points of which Erikson writes are tied to successive phases of development and are less abrupt than those crises described by Lindemann (1944, 1956) and Caplan (1964) in their seminal work in the field of community mental health. An essential similarity is an emphasis on coping with social and cultural demands and the importance of such opportunities for the growth of personality. Caplan (1964) states that "the significance of a crisis is in its temporal telescoping of development." Caplan's basic assumption is that resolution of the crisis state (defined as a time-limited period of psychological disequilibrium) will result in increased psychological ability or increased disability. A difference is that Erikson placed more importance on the psychosocial developmental history in understanding a current situation while Caplan places more importance on contemporary factors.

According to Caplan, the outcome of a crisis in most cases is not determined by antecedent factors, such as the nature of the precipitant or the previous experience of the individual, but on the interplay of forces in the course of the crisis. Antecedent factors are seen as "loading the dice" in one direction or another, but external intervention during the period of psychological disequilibrium may counteract the loading of the dice and lead to unexpected results. During the crisis period it is presumed that the person experiences an increased desire for help and is more susceptible to influence by others. It is apparent how such concepts may lead to different strategies—for example, mental health consultation and education to key community care-givers—for the development of helping resources from those derived from Freud's discoveries and it was these different strategies that Hobbs referred to as "mental health's third revolution."

In what follows it is suggested that the basic struggle during the early 1960s had been an attempt to break away from relatively fixed approaches to providing mental health services and to develop sufficient helping alternatives to make services available to all who may want them. During the latter part of the 1960s the issues of responsibility, power, and control over all community institutions and services came into the foreground and these are likely to continue as problems during the 1970s.

By this point in history, the mental health practitioner had come to another relatively unfamiliar ground. As an individual his professional training had usually been limited to studies of individual psychopathology and psychotherapy, and group therapy. The newly defined requirements of successful functioning are such that the mental health professional is led to a variety of social settings and agencies where his concerns must necessarily be focused upon social and political forces in the community, agency structure and administration, and a host of similar variables. The legitimacy of using clinicians for such activities has long been questioned given the paucity of professionals to care for existing patient needs (Joint Commission, 1961), and a strategy decision must be made. Indeed, much recent discussion has focused on the federally sponsored Comprehensive Community Mental Health Centers and alternative strategies to approach the problem of maximizing program effectiveness.

The Comprehensive Community Mental Health Centers Program

In 1955 a Mental Health Study Act authorized the Joint Commission on Mental Illness and Health and charged the Commission with conducting "an objective, thorough, and nationwide analysis and reevaluation of the human and economic problems of mental illness and of the resources, methods, and practices currently utilized in diagnosing, treating, caring for, and rehabilitation of the mentally ill, both within and outside of institutions, as may lead to the development of comprehensive and realistic recommendations for such better utilization of those resources ... (Public Law 84–182; as reproduced in Joint Commission on Mental Illness and Health, 1961, p. 303)."

Among the recommendations made by the Joint Commission were "a full-time mental health clinic available to each 50,000 of population (pp. 262–263)" the principal functions of which would be "(1) to provide treatment by a basic mental health team ... for persons with acute mental illness, (2) to care for incompletely recovered mental patients either short of admission to a hospital or following discharge from the hospital, and (3) to provide a headquarters base for mental health consultants working with mental health counselors (p. 264)."

The community mental health centers program, when it finally developed, attempted to achieve some balance of priorities between preventive approaches and treatment of major mental illness by aiming toward increased accessibility of service, comprehensiveness of program, and continuity of care. By requiring that each center provide at least five essential services—in-patient care, out-patient care, emergency services, pre- and posthospital care, and mental health consultation and education—it was hoped that these goals could be achieved. The program goal has been set as the establishment of two thousand community mental health centers. (See chapter 29 by Levenson; Brown & Cain, 1964.) As of June 1969 grants had been awarded to 376 centers; as of June 1970 the growth rate had slowed, the total number of centers funded was 420, and future growth was uncertain.

A recent past president of the American Psychiatric Association has expressed doubts that the term "community mental health center" communicates to either professionals or laymen the aims and functions envisioned in the 1963 legislation. In his view (Kolb, 1968) the centers were intended to devote much of their energy to community treatment and rehabilitation of people suffering from psychosis and he notes that "the legislation in defining the structure of a community mental health center is in fact defining a hospital."

While Kolb questions those who see community mental health centers as centers for social and political action, Smith (1968) has argued that the potential of the community is not recognized sufficiently in the hospital-clinic-centered program: "We need to invest more in working on the social contexts in which troubled people are involved, and to count less upon the effectiveness of the isolated therapeutic hour (p. 21)."

In a paper on the *Community and the Community Mental Health Center* (Smith & Hobbs, 1966) later adopted by the American Psychological Association as an official position statement it is argued that

The objective of the center staff should be to help the various social systems of which the community is composed to function in ways that develop and sustain the effectiveness of the individuals who take part in them, and to help the community systems regroup their forces to support the person who runs into trouble. The community is not just a "catchment area" from which patients are drawn; the task of a community mental health center goes far beyond that of purveying professional services to disordered people on a local basis.

The more closely the proposed centers become integrated with the life and institutions of their communities, the less the community can afford to turn over to mental health professionals its responsibility for guiding the center's policies. Professional standards need to be established for the centers by federal and state authorities, and goals and basic policies are matters for local control. A broadly based responsible board of informed leaders would help to insure that the center serves in deed, not just in name, as a focus of the community's varied efforts on behalf of the greater effectiveness and fulfillment of all its residents (pp. 500–501).

Indeed, the Joint Commission on Mental Illness and Health did recommend that a national mental health program should recognize major mental illness as the core problem and that intensive treatment of patients with critical and prolonged mental breakdowns should have first call on fully trained members of the mental health professions. The so-called core problem controversy was thus resolved by the Joint Commission which further recommended that "the risk of false promise (p. xviii)" would be avoided if public education for better mental health focused on disseminating information about mental illness which the public needs and wants in order to recognize psychological forms of sickness and arrive at an informed opinion of its responsibility toward the mentally ill.

The recent manifestations of this core problem controversy have concerned questions of strategy and priorities; consequently, they concern goals and operations to achieve goals. There is no formula to determine what proportion of the nation's resources should be devoted to mental health programs and what proportion of those resources devoted to mental health should be allotted to alternative strategies such as programs oriented toward primary prevention as opposed to the treatment of already identified cases of disorder. Such allocation is not possible because defined and generally accepted goals do not exist and the validity of both preventive and treatment oriented approaches is not determined sufficiently to establish priorities based upon comparative outcomes. Consequently such determinations are made politically (see Brown & Stockdill, chapter 28).

Power and Conflict

During the past few years the core problem issue has become background as the action has moved from concern for what will be done to concern for *who will determine* what will be done. If reorientation in the relationship between the community and the professional is occurring it is presently overshadowed by community group efforts to politicize and to gain power over local institutions.

Everett C. Hughes (1963) has described the role of the professional in society as follows:

Lawyers not only give advice to clients and plead their cases for them; they also develop a philosophy of law—of its nature and its functions, and of the proper way in which to administer justice. Physicians consider it their prerogative to define the nature of disease and of health, and to determine how medical services ought to be distributed and paid for. Social workers are not content to develop a technique of case work; they concern themselves with social legislation. Every profession considers itself the proper body to set the terms in which some aspect of society, life, or nature is to be thought of, and to define the general lines, or even the details, of public policy concerning it (pp. 656–657).

Compare the foregoing with Levin's (1970) recent manifesto for the radical professional and the extent of the questioning of the professional's role becomes clear:

Today, a new tradition for professionals is being molded. We call ourselves radical professionals; that is, we use our skills to help make social change. Thus as advocates for the powerless we assist these groups in gaining a redistribution of power rather than just a redistribution of services.

We have given up our so-called professional neutrality for a partisan role. We believe that there is a conflict of interests between the groups we represent and other groups, and the recognition of this conflict is necessary in guiding our work. Our role has become that of aiding the poor in challenging society's standards rather than meeting them, and our relationship to the poor community and its organizations has been as employees rather than employers.

Since to us community development means a basic redistribution of power rather than a mere redistribution of services, our efforts are focused on initiating and supporting the move for community control of all public institutions and services. Power and conflict are the key concepts with which my staff and I work (p. 122).

Mental health and all health services, education, law enforcement, and welfare have all become increasingly politicized, and both the goals of program planners and the perceived service needs of citizens are now influenced because they are in the front line of civil rights revolutions. All indications are that solution of the problems presented by community control over mental health services will preoccupy the field during the next several years. The major issue of the 1960s has been the achievement of increased flexibility and comprehensiveness of mental health services. The major issue of the 1970s will be that of community control over the mental health field, a process that to date has largely been initiated by professionals and taken over by the urban poor.

If problems of mental health have been so closely interwoven with problems of poverty it might be instructive to look toward social action in the poverty field for increased perspective on the issue of community control over mental health services. It was in the poverty field that the concept "maximum feasible participation" of those persons to be served by programs was developed.

The Economic Opportunity Act of 1964 required that antipoverty programs be carried out with the maximum feasible participation of the residents of the communities involved. In an essay on community action in the war on poverty Moynihan (1969) describes the history of this legislative clause and suggests that the essential problem with community action was that the one term concealed at least four different meanings:

(1) organizing, (2) expanding, (3) confronting, and (4) assisting the power structure.

The poverty legislation was passed in the same era as the Community Mental Health Centers Act but the community action programs which were part of the Economic Opportunity Act affected more cities than the counterpart mental health legislation. By January 1966 all the 50 largest cities in the country had community action programs, and more than 900 grants had been awarded for the establishment or planning of such programs in some one thousand counties. But in the war on poverty, just as in the battle for mental health, a different set of confrontations soon emerged from those which had been planned. Moynihan cites examples of infighting and terrorism which emerged in the poverty program. This type of struggle and confrontation has occurred during recent years in urban mental health programs. Black communities confront white professionals and demand black professional leadership; black paraprofessionals challenge black professionals and demand program control; community members fight among themselves to determine leadership, power, and status. Certainly there are many variations and exceptions but such events are not unusual. Perhaps such conflicts are predictable first phases in social change such as community control over helping services. But the future of mental health services in many communities, particularly large urban communities with concentrations of minority group persons, is uncertain at this time. Concerns over employment, schools, and law enforcement are closer to the daily adaptational needs of the poor than are more abstract mental health services, at least until services are translated into programs which effect employment, education, or delinquency.

The use of indigenous persons to provide helping services and to bridge the gap between psychodynamically oriented socially advantaged mental health professionals and disadvantaged clients concerned with the effects of bigotry, poverty, and powerlessness has grown. A large number of "new careers" programs of an informed citizenry has led to increased conflict over program control.

Conflicts over community control in the area of economic opportunity, education, and crime suggest that as mental health services get more involved in the actual fabric of community life, increased conflict will result. As of this writing, mental health services in many cities are becoming battlegrounds and as in any battle it is hard to see who will be the winner or the loser while the battle is going on.

Earlier in this chapter the importance and interrelationship among classification, explanation, and intervention were stressed. Just as the prayers and rituals of the shamans were expressed in an appropriate idiom and were strategically congruent with the belief that the disturbed person was possessed, so the differential diagnosis and chemical treatment by the physician in a mental hospital were conceptualized within the idiom of medical science and were consistent with his expectation that the person suffered from biological illness. Community mental health is not without theory, although it is certainly less conceptual and more pragmatic than previous ideologies. (See Kluger, 1970, for an example of a pragmatically oriented clinic.) It is recognized that there are multiple causes of disordered behavior—biological, psychological, and sociological. A starting point must be an assessment of the scope of the problem of disordered behavior and the context of its recognition, not a theory of causation. To a considerable extent there has been a recognition of the social relativism of deviance and the need to redefine or indeed to question whether behavior previously identified as a reflection of individual psychopathology is not societally determined. Mental health according to this view is a concern with maximizing the effectiveness of all. The community becomes the source of mental health itself (Klein, 1968) and community organization and processes become the primary level of assessment and intervention.

Whether community approaches to mental health problems will maintain the flexibility of approach which accompanied their development and whether they will receive the support they require is presently uncertain. Whether community control will emerge as a precondition for effective services and whether the use of new mental health workers will finally bring services to persons who heretofore have been deprived of them or whether a new orthodoxy—that of community control—will replace previous orthodoxies, is yet to be seen. Unfortunately, there remains an insufficient commitment to the evaluation of mental health programs and in the past under such conditions the determinants of program survival or abandonment have almost always been particularistic.

A SUMMING-UP

The development of the mental health field has been traced through several key ideological phases. Within each phase of mental health ideology one may discover the interrelationships among the classification system, the preferred theory of causation, and the sanctioned form of response to behavior disorder. In each phase some measure of progress over behavior disorder has been achieved but failure has also been apparent, all too often in the form of narrowness and partisanship resulting in limited and insufficient services.

Dissatisfaction within the mental health field and at the community level culminated in several related forms of innovation which can be loosely termed a community mental health approach. These included flexibility in the location and occasion at which mental health services were made available and incorporated more treatment alternatives and helping stratagems based on varying the timing and location of interventions. The involvement of an increased variety of helpers trained to provide useful services and numerous attempts to reach client groups which had not previously been served also characterized the community approach. New services were also developed, notably mental health consultation and education, and goals oriented toward disorder prevention and optimization of effectiveness revealed the infusion of public health concepts into the mental health field.

But as mental health services are moving into the community they confront a most difficult combination of problems. First, few mental health professionals to date are trained in the community and for the provision of mental health services in community settings. Second, this movement into the community, sometimes termed mental health's third revolution, is occurring at the same time as are civil rights and student revolutions. As a result the community is in a state of active ferment, the definition of mental health in the community is subject to pressures accordingly, and the place of the mental health professional in this process is uncertain and subject to new demands from both agencies and clients.

Notes

The authors wish to acknowledge the contribution of Dr. Sheldon Roen in providing material on the history of community psychology.

1. According to the figures kept by Woodward, the first superintendent of Worcester State Lunatic Hospital (as cited by Grob, 1966), 2,583 cases were admitted to the hospital between 1833 and 1846, during which 2,215 were discharged, of which 1,192 were thought to be recovered. Further data from the records of the same hospital (Bockoven, 1963) indicate recovery rates of newly admitted patients which ranged from 61 percent to 75 percent during the years 1833-1852. Statistical studies by Earle (1887) resulted in much pessimism concerning the curability of mental disorder and this led Eastman and Park, later superintendents at Worcester, to reanalyze Woodward's data employing their own criteria of recovery and not distinguishing between those patients ill for less than one year and those patients ill for longer periods of time at the time of their hospitalization. According to Bockoven (1963), even though Park had hoped to dispute Woodward's findings the results of Park's study with respect to the years when Woodward was superintendent did not differ more than two or three percent from Woodward's own figures, thus lending some reliability to these earlier data.

But even more persuasive were the results of a questionnaire follow-up study of those persons discharged from the hospital as recovered on their only or last admission. This study covered a postdischarge interval which ranged from 36 to 60 years and by the time the study was completed 1,157 had been received of the 1,173 questionnaires sent out! According to Bockoven's (1963) analysis, 48 percent (and according to Grob's analysis, 58 percent) of those discharged by Woodward as recovered had never had a relapse. Either figure would be impressive over such a long follow-up period. In fact, the higher figure is likely the most accurate of the two estimates. Grob (1966) excluded 189 of the 1,173 replies which provided no useable information from his base of 984 while Bockoven used a base of 1,173 which would be the same as assuming relapse had occurred in each of these 189 patients.

2. That Breuer and Freud were themselves surprised by the new direction their work had taken is suggested by the following quotation: "We found, at first to our great surprise, that the *individual hysterical symptoms immediately disappeared without recurring if we succeeded in thoroughly awakening the memories of the causal process with its accompanying affect, and if the patient circumstantially discussed the process in the most detailed manner and gave verbal expression to the affect* (1895, pp. 3–4)."

3. The study of incidence and prevalence of mental health problems is of course compounded by extraordinary lack of clarity and agreement on criteria and definition (see chapter 12). While absolute rates have not been approximated, studies have been sufficient to determine that relative to the numbers of people who are known to be in treatment for mental health problems the number of persons who show similar problems is much higher. For example, it was estimated by Srole et al. (1962), in their household survey of midtown Manhattan residents, that approximately 18 percent of the population were impaired to the point of some disability. Similarly, Leighton et al. (1963), based upon their study in Nova Scotia, estimated that about 33 percent of the study population showed mild impairment from psychiatric disorder and that an additional 15.6 percent showed moderate disorder.

4. Of those adults judged to be "significantly impaired" in the Midtown Manhattan Survey (Srole et al., 1962) only 27 percent had even been patients in any private or public mental health service. Gurin et al. (1960) reported that one of seven persons interviewed in their Joint Commission study reported that he had actually gone for help. Of this group, only 18 percent turned to psychiatrists or psychologists and an additional 10 percent consulted social agencies or marriage clinics. The vast majority of people who went for help (71 percent) consulted either a clergyman or general practice physician.

5. Hunt (1961) reported that only 25 percent of the total number of cases applying for service at an urban child guidance clinic actually entered into psychotherapeutic treatment, and only 7 percent received or remained for a full course of such treatment.

References

Bellak, L. (ed.) *Handbook of community psychiatry.* New York: Grune & Stratton, 1964.

Bockoven, J. S. *Moral treatment in American psychiatry.* New York: Springer, 1963.

Breuer, J., & Freud, S. *Studies in hysteria.* Boston: Beacon Press, 1937. (Translation; original first published in 1895.)

Brigham, A. Moral treatment. *American Journal of Insanity*, 1847, 4, 1–15.

Brown, B. S., & Cain, H. Many meanings of "comprehensive": Key issues in implementing President Kennedy's program. *American Journal of Orthopsychiatry*, 1964, 34, 834–839.

Butler, J. S. *Curability of insanity and the individualized treatment of the insane.* New York: Putnam, 1887.

Caplan, G. *Principles of preventive psychiatry.* New York: Basic Books, 1964.

Charcot, J. M. *Oeuvres complètes.* Paris: Lecrosnier & Babé, 1890.

Cowen, E., & Zax, M. The mental health fields today: Issues and problems. In E. Cowen, E. A. Gardner, & M. Zax (eds.), *Emergent approaches to mental health problems.* New York: Appleton-Century-Crofts, 1967.

Earle, P. *Curability of insanity.* Philadelphia: Lippincott, 1887.

Erikson, E. H. *Childhood and society.* New York: Norton, 1950.

Golann, S. E. Community psychology and mental health: An analysis of strategies and a survey of training. In I. Iscoe & C. D. Spielberger (eds.), *Community psychology: Perspectives in training and research.* New York: Appleton-Century-Crofts, 1970.

Grob, G. N. The state mental hospital in mid-nineteenth century America: A social analysis. *American Psychologist*, 1966, 21, 510–523.

Gurin, G., Veroff, J., & Feld, S. *Americans view their mental health.* New York: Basic Books, 1960.

Hobbs, N. Mental health's third revolution. *American Journal of Orthopsychiatry*, 1964, 34, 1–20.

Hollingshead, A. B., & Redlich, F. C. *Social class and mental illness.* New York: Wiley, 1958.

Hughes, E. C. Professions. *Daedalus*, 1963, 92, 656–657.

Hunt, R. G. Age, sex and service patterns in a child guidance clinic. *Journal of Child Psychology and Psychiatry*, 1961, 2, 185–192.

Janet, P. *The major symptoms of hysteria.* (2nd ed.) New York: Macmillan, 1920.

Joint Commission on Mental Illness and Health. *Action for mental health.* New York: Basic Books, 1961.

Klein, D. C. *Community dynamics and mental health.* New York: Wiley, 1968.

Kluger, J. M. The uninsulated caseload in a neighborhood mental health center. *American Journal of Psychiatry*, 1970, 126, 1430–1435.

Kolb, L. C. The community mental health centers: Some issues in their transition from concept to reality. *Hospital and Community Psychiatry*, 1968, 19(11), 335–340.

Leighton, D. C., Harding, J. S., Macklin, D. B., MacMillan, A. M., & Leighton, A. H. *The character of danger.* New York: Basic Books, 1963.

Levin, H. Psychologist to the powerless. In F. Korten, S. Cook, & J. Lacey (eds.), *Psychology and the problems of society.* Washington, D. C.: American Psychological Association, 1970.

Lindemann, E. Symptomatology and management of acute grief. *American Journal of Psychiatry*, 1944, 101, 141–148.

Lindemann, E. The meaning of crisis in individual and family living. *Teachers College Record*, 1956, 57, 310–315.

Maier, H. W. *Three theories of child development.* New York: Harper & Row, 1965.

Menninger, K. Toward a unitary concept of mental illness. In *A psychiatrist's world: The selected papers of Karl Menninger.* New York: Viking Press, 1959.

Menninger, K. *The vital balance.* New York: Viking, 1964.

Mitchell, S. W. Address before the Fifteenth Annual Meeting of the American Medico-Psychological Association. *Transactions of the American Medico-Psychological Association*, 1894, 1, 102–121.

Moynihan, D. P. *Maximum feasible misunderstanding.* New York: Free Press, 1969.

Myers, J. K., & Bean, L. L. *A decade later.* New York: Wiley, 1968.

Nunnally, J. C., Jr. *Popular conceptions of mental health.* New York: Holt, Rinehart & Winston, 1961.

Public Law 182. 84th Congress. Mental Health Study Act of 1955. (Reprinted in Joint Commission on Mental Illness and Health. *Action for mental health.* New York: Basic Books, 1961.)

Rosen, G. *Madness in society.* New York: Harper & Row, 1968.

Smith, M. B. The revolution in mental-health care—A "bold new approach"? *Trans-action*, 1968, 5, 19–23.

Smith, M. B., & Hobbs, N. *The community and the community mental health center.* Washington, D. C.: American Psychological Association, 1966.

Srole, L., Langer, T. S., Michael, S. T., Opler, M. K., & Rennie, T. A. *Mental health in the metropolis.* New York: McGraw-Hill, 1962.

White, R. W. Motivation reconsidered: The concept of competence. *Psychological Review*, 1959, 66, 297–333.

White, R. W. *The abnormal personality.* (3rd ed.) New York: Ronald Press, 1964.

II

Community Systems and Behavior

The community systems which enhance individual health, shape personal growth, and regulate human behavior reflect in their specific activities the concern of community members. These systems can provide positive and effective action given a community population motivated to seek health and satisfaction for all its members and sufficiently secure to withstand and benefit from varieties of human behavior. This places upon community health, education, and regulatory systems a double responsibility to enhance the mental health of the community, first as part of their assigned functions, and second for the sake of their own effectiveness.

It is not surprising, then, that the systems descriptions presented in part II, written specifically to educate practitioners and students of mental health in community structures, should so fully comprise an invitation as well as an education. At all levels of community systems activity, behavioral scientists are needed to develop mental health resources and interdisciplinary programs, to provide appropriate goal definitions in presently undefined areas, and to provide indicators of system effectiveness. In addition, and ideally, successful application of community mental health programs should further the overall effectiveness of social systems activity simply by enhancing the state of public health upon which society's systems are dependent.

For a rather incoherent network of community systems, community mental health aspirations are an integrating force. For the practitioner and student of community mental health, an under-standing of the structures, functions, and the relationships among the specific community behavior systems is spadework for the growth of a mental health ecology.

William C. Rhodes effectively introduces the discussions of existing systems structures which follow in part II by analyzing their mutual functions and the dynamics of their social interventions, and suggesting the pressures for their integration and change. His encompassing analysis is historical, urgent, and predictive.

Eli M. Bower follows with a quite personal discussion of education as a humanizing process and its relationship to other humanizing processes. He recommends that educators accept as their goal the creation not of satiated students but people in all walks of life with a hunger for new knowledge and growth. He believes that the schools can become humanizing institutions teaching children how to learn by searching out earlier and better partnerships with other essential institutions of health, family, peer grouping, and play.

William L. Kissick, in his chapter on the health system, describes the evolution of a health care system experiencing internal and external pressures for the meeting of new, broader definitions of health for all persons. The health concept itself, always illusive, becomes more illusive as public needs and demands grow to include the as yet undefinable and unmeasurable objectives of total health care and maintenance. A health system already inadequately prepared to measure that which it must now provide is being asked as well to make all-inclusive its services. Progress in the application and effectiveness of health care is significantly dependent on research and scholarship in the behavioral sciences.

Kissick's chapter gathers illuminating statistical data, explores the complex problems encountered in meeting a population's health care needs, and discusses at length methods of systems analysis and their comparative usefulness in enabling us to define and reach relevant objectives.

In his chapter on the criminal justice system, Saleem A. Shah has provided an excellent primer of particular usefulness to persons in the social and behavioral sciences and in mental health roles. His analysis of the interface between the criminal justice system and the field of mental health is sensitive to variations in the definition of deviance, and explores issues of competencies, criminal responsibility and the insanity defense, special statutes relating to specific classes of defenders such as sexual psychopaths, and the issue of dangerousness. The present overreach of the criminal law and the lack of available alternatives to punishment is costly at many levels to the individual and the community.

Robert B. Tapp and June L. Tapp, in their study of religious systems as sources of control and support, foresee a convergence of interests in the fields of religion and mental health toward improving the quality of life in the community. The two fields have strong historical, motivational, and developmental parallels. The authors detail accommodations in both fields which both limit and facilitate acceptance of mental health assumptions, cite test cases, provide a reference guide to works combining the thinking of both fields, draw historical lessons from religious history useful to community mental health developers, and freely predict parallel changes, conflicts, competition, and cooperation between the two fields during the shared, ongoing process of democratization.

Milton Wittman draws a picture of a social welfare system marginally palliative rather than remedial in its overall impact on social problems in the community. He notes, in relation to community mental health, that counseling services for individuals and families are so thinly distributed that many fail to receive them until social problems have become serious pathology for the attention of regulatory agencies. He details the system's mechanisms, development, lacks, and recommends modification, particularly asking for training and operational cooperation with mental health agencies.

Military communities are the subject of a chapter by Earl J. Janda, David S. Reynolds, and Donald S. Carter. Military psychiatry was pressured from its inception by community demands for a social and preventive approach to mental health problems, and mental health practices of a community type were developed in the military at an early date. Resistance to innovation, although not peculiar to the military, is well defined in military communities. The well circumscribed military community with its particular problems and available definitions is a fruitful area for study by those attempting to apply community psychology in the larger population.

Roger C. Mills and James G. Kelly, in the final chapter of part II, consider ecological analogies in community development. The authors emphasize the need to adapt programs for change to the local culture. The ecological approach considers the interrelationships of economic, cultural, and political systems in the host community and attempts to assess the effects of intervention upon the interrelationships of these systems. The ecological analogy provides a view of change that is evolutionary and places the individual community in the broader perspective of its setting.

The authors believe that any knowledge of community psychology should be derived from the study of the development of communities. To illustrate the application of an ecological perspective and to indicate the value of its application in widely differing communities and even across cultures they study in detail the planned development of three communities in Mexico. Their overview of community systems and change is innovative in conception and method.

The comprehensive study of systems in part II is descriptive and critical. In each case the system is intimately related in practice to community mental health roles and responsibilities.

2

Regulation of Community Behavior:
Dynamics and Structure

William C. Rhodes

THE EXCITOR-REACTOR EXCHANGE

In order to move toward an applied science of human behavior in community forms, we must try to gain a better grasp of the primary exchange of a disturbing nature which occurs between the community majority and various forms of individual deviation in the community. We must also study the behavior regulating forces and structures which are moved and mobilized by these critical exchanges and which attempt to alleviate the community turbulence created by them.

The individuals within a community context (either a macrocommunity or a microcommunity) who are detectably different, or who can be categorized as different, are capable of inciting intensive mood transmission and of releasing excited mass reactive behavior in the mainstream masses of the community. This phenomenon is not confined to the human community nor is it a modern human phenomenon. It can be observed in various insect, fish, and animal "communities" and has been recorded across human communities in every part of the globe and in every period of known history.

Animal Ethology

Konrad Lorenz (1967), for instance, reports that in huge communities of social insects such as bees, termites, and ants, the members of the clan recognize each other by a characteristic hive, nest, or anthill smell and that murders occur if a member of a strange colony, deviating from this smell, inadvertently enters the nest. This strange capacity for "community" deviation to release violent responses in surrounding members can also be seen in an underwater ecological unit of fish. This is another example of the excitor-reactor community phenomenon.

If the underwater behavior of a fish is slightly altered by mild drugging or by placing the fish in a floating glass bowl under the sea so that his usual swimming actions are slightly altered, some of the other fish will respond instantly with attack. The rest of the school will immediately flee from his vicinity, as though in panic. Predator fish, aroused by this unaccustomed difference in the individual, will single him out of the school and promptly attack. The altered behavior has an electric effect in releasing excited waves of violent reciprocating behavior in the surrounding area.

Lorenz (1967) also reports in separate ethological studies of the brown rat and the house rat that a stranger whose smell differs from a large colony occupying the same territory will immediately be attacked and killed. If a member of a colony is removed and put in another terrarium for a few days it will lose its "colony" smell and when put back will be attacked by its former neighbors. However, if a rat is put into a clean, empty battery jar, with some soil, nest material, etc., from his clan enclosure, so that the rat takes with it a dowry of objects impregnated with a clan smell, it will be recognized afterwards, even after an absence of weeks.

The excitor-reactor cycle in these rats is instigated by an animal who smells different. The information is transmitted, like an electric shock, through the whole colony. According to Lorenz: "at once the whole colony is alarmed by a process of mood transmission which is communicated in the Brown Rat by expression movements but in the House Rat by a sharp, shrill, satanic cry which is taken up by all members of the tribe within earshot" (p. 155).

In Hebb's study of fear (1949) in chimpanzee colonies, he reports a similar phenomenon in which the presentation of a form or a part of a chimpanzee to a colony released intensive behavior and mood transmission in the colony. The general mood-behavior stimulated by this presentation was fear-flight but some animals reacted with anger and some with strange mixtures of fear and anger. In general, the presentation of a chimpanzee head, an anesthetized chimpanzee, or even separated parts of a chimpanzee was capable of arousing intensive colony excitation. The presentation of an aspect of a fellow species member in an unfamiliar form was disturbing and disruptive.

In each of these evolutionary examples we can witness the impact of unaccustomed differences in a community member upon the mood and behavior of the rest of the community. A wave of excitation is released which reverberates throughout the community and rebounds back upon the incitor. He thereby becomes both the galvanizing force and receptor of violent mood-behavior of the "community."

Human Ecology

In these lower-level forms of the evolutionary community, we are made aware of a phenomenon which is very similar to that which occurs in the human community when an individual member or an identifiable group is perceived to be different or deviant from that with which the community is familiar or to which it has become accustomed. This is a recurrent community upheaval phenomenon which seems to influence much of everyday community life. Whenever a subgroup which has characteristics that are distinctively different from the mainstream enters into or becomes part of a larger community, we can observe turbulent mood-behavioral transmission such as isolation, withdrawal, attack, or fear.

This same reaction occurs within any ecological unit such as a macrocommunity (for example, a village or town) or a microcommunity (for example, a neighborhood or a classroom) when it is presented with individual divergence. We see this excitor-reactor phenomenon in the case of deviant

individual behaviors or life styles such as alcoholism, mental illness, drug addiction, delinquency, mental retardation, etc. The interpretations made by the community of these separate forms of human behavior may be different, but the reaction tendency seems to follow an identical pattern. There is a presentation of the deviant form and then there is reflexive response to this form which seems to be transmitted in waves across the community.

In the summer of 1960, the author, aware of the threat-recoil phenomenon in community life, studied five major cities in the United States to determine how communities were responding to juvenile delinquency. The purpose was to try to see how the array of behavior regulating paraphernalia in the educational system, the legal correction system, the mental health system, and the social welfare system responded to delinquency. The idea was to try to gain a new perspective on delinquency that would be different from the intrapsychic perspective so dominant at that time. Instead of looking at the deviant individual and his response to his own endogenous and exogenous environment, the idea was to assume the perspective of the community and see how it reacted to the excitor or threat signals of the delinquent.

High-problem neighborhoods in five major cities were visited and studied. These neighborhoods harbored impacted rates of delinquency. The various programs and services being brought to bear upon delinquency from the various systems named above were studied to see how they came into being and what types of responses they made to delinquent behavior.

The author found a very familiar pattern in community reactivity to delinquency. In each community studied, current agitation, concern, and turbulence were associated with "delinquency." In each case, new and somewhat frantic efforts were being made to set up delinquency programs. In each case, waves of concern had begun with some dramatic incident (such as the gang killing of a youth on the steps of a school or church, or the mugging of a well-beloved priest or rabbi, etc.), or with some new propaganda input (a delinquency-education campaign) which focused the community's attention upon the threat-quality of delinquents in its midst.

The heightened awareness of this threat led to waves of recoil throughout the community. As the recoil waves circled up the pyramidal track of community power, consensual pressure began to demand that the "authorities" take action. When pressure built up to an intolerable pitch, the "authorities" mobilized a new program of intervention against delinquency.

The same collective reactions occur in the case of any divergent behavior, including alcoholism, drug addiction, mental illness, delinquency, etc. The interpretations made by the community of these forms of human behavior may differ, but the general tendency to respond, as if reflexively, is relatively constant.

The irritant-reactivity currents which are set up between arousers and aroused sectors of the community are likely to continue or to increase until some mediating factor or structure is brought between sectors. The most common institutional response in the community is to introduce behavior-mediating structures at the point of arousal and to channel the provocative individual into these structures.

At the community level, the fixed institutional response patterns mobilized in such an excitant situation are those systems or structures which have been established to influence community behavior through molding, regulating, and controlling the nature of that behavior. Such structures include education, correction, welfare, and mental health.

The Community Mood

Which of these community patterns of behavior mediating structures will be chosen depends upon the general interpretation which the community gives to the behavior and the mood which prevails at the time of provocation. In a democratic society the mood of the community at the time of appearance of the divergent behavior is a deciding factor in the mobilization of institutional forces. Whether the strategic intervention into the behavior is constructive and developmental or reconstructive and remedial, or involves material aid and support or deterrence and constraint, depends as much upon the consensual mood of the general public as it does upon the state or characteristics of the individual or group producing the provocative behavior.

If the prevailing mood of the community is deep disturbance—anger or intense fear, for instance—the institutional response most likely to be called out is deterrence and constraint. Correctional resources such as police, courts, containment facilities, and detention institutions are likely to be maneuvered between the aroused public and the arouser individuals. If the anger or fear is great enough and the size of the provocative population within the society is relatively large, military force and detention camps or detention communities are possible institutional responses.

When the prevailing community mood toward the behavior of concern is benign and sympathetic, the influences of such habitual response systems as education, social welfare aid, and mental health are more likely to be utilized. Under such circumstances, the community is more tolerant and more willing to provide the necessary financial support and intervention sanctions to the professional guilds and the techniques associated with agencies and operational patterns which fall into these categories.

In a sense, then, the utilization of the processes and apparatus of behavior regulation in the community is an extension or psychological expression of the prevailing subjective mood of the general public as much as it is an objective response to an existent condition or state of the individual or individuals responded to. The observable behavior triggers generalized psychological states in the larger community. These create an institutional response from the community and stimulate actions within the regulatory systems which reflect community mood and values. For instance, aggressive behavior which violates social norms or taboos can receive varying interpretations and actions. At one period of time it may be called delinquency and the legal correctional apparatus is brought to bear. At another time it may be called illness and the medical mental health system is called into action. At another time it may be called sin and the religious system is mobilized. It can be the very same aggressive behavior with the very same immediate consequences and still achieve different labels and different community interventions, depending upon the community zeitgeist.

Political and Power Processes

The political and power processes are integrally involved in the dynamics of the community exchange described. When the community is aroused over a deviant group or a deviant individual, it turns toward the community power structure as arbiter of the excitement and controller of the resources and toward agencies of the community which can intervene into the psychologically charged condition.

The political power structures and the informal power structures of the community can activate and deploy these behavior intervention resources in a very direct manner. The basic funding decisions of the systems of education, social welfare, correction, and mental health are directly in the hands of key people within the political and informal power structures. In most cases, these systems and the agencies they operate are units of the executive branch of government at local, county, state, and national levels. They are, therefore, extensions of the governing apparatus and obtain their sanctions and operating funds through this apparatus. At the same time, these agencies are also under the control of informal power structures made up of individuals who are important personages in professional guilds such as the medical societies, etc., and the individuals who control the wealth and the business and industry at national, state, and local levels. Such prestigious personages sit on the boards and councils of the various agencies and thus direct the kinds of interventions they are allowed to make and decide the kinds of problems and populations into which they must intervene.

The coalition between governmental and informal power structures comes under much pressure during periods of intense arousal over a particular human state or behavior. When ripples of apprehension spread throughout the community, the majority population turns to this coalition for protection. Through various political and power processes the community puts pressure upon the power structures to do something about the behavior which has aroused its apprehension and concern.

Since the assimilation and maintenance of power is a major compelling drive in the political and power sectors, individuals within them must be responsive to the mood and opinion of the majority public. When a state of excitation exists in the environment, it is the responsibility of these groups to reduce the excitation level through any available means. Power figures may, in fact, use the opportunity to further arouse the populace in order to stay in positions of power—or to gain

more power. The solutions which can be instigated and guided by the political and power coalition not only depend upon the available array of intervention resources but also on compatibility of the resources chosen with the public mood and public interpretation of the problem.

This patterning of institutional forces makes the power structures and the behavior regulating sources which they can deploy responsive to the current psychological state of the majority population in the society. In this manner the structures of behavior intervention and behavior regulation become extensions of the immediate psychological responses of the community to human divergence.

The divergent individuals themselves, once they have set the process into motion, remain outside this dynamic interaction. They become subjected to the exigencies of community mood, community decision making structures, and behavior regulating resources of the community. Any initial impairment or difference which they may have possessed makes them vulnerable to the psychological forces and processes of the community which their own behavior triggers and mobilizes.

A Summary of the Excitor-Reactor Exchange

In the construction of collective dynamics involved in the excitor-reactor exchange, the excitor was described as any individual or groups of individuals who deviated from the prevailing pattern of the community. The remainder of the collective, the larger mass of individuals who observe this deviation, respond with agitation and excitement which is transmitted in a wave of mood and behavior throughout the collective. The excitor individual then becomes the focus or collective target upon whom the consensual mood is both projected and discharged.

When the waves of collective mood and behavior sweep through the community, the reactors turn toward the authority structure of the community for implementation of action toward the excitor. The authority or power structure then maneuvers certain institutional forms and structures in the community to intervene between the excitor and reactors.

This systematic process of collective dynamics has maintained behavioral stability in the human community over long periods of history. When the system is operating effectively, a simple and clear set of dimensions and standards for normative social conduct facilitates shaping and regulation of behavior through social agencies. The relatively clear-cut tolerance limits of the community for divergence in community behavior are maintained by the cohesive solidarity of political power structures, the public majority, and the domestic regulatory systems. These agencies and forces serve to reinforce the family structures in the adaptation of the individual to the community environment. However, in periods of marked behavioral change the system may be taxed beyond its capacity to maintain behavior regulation.

BEHAVIOR REGULATION SYSTEMS

Let us take a closer look at the current systems of behavior regulation which we are discussing. Just what are these structures of behavior intervention and regulation which become extensions of the immediate psychological responses of the community and are controlled and deployed by the power structures? They are a set of community institutions and agencies which have come into existence over the centuries in the development and evolvement of Western society. In the critical dialectic between the individual and the community which has been conducted primarily through the family, these community agencies serve as supplemental and supportive forces and structures which intervene at the point where the family is expected to share, or ceases to exert, its regulatory function in the life of the individual.

The major family support systems currently operating in our communities can be classified as the legal correctional, social welfare, medical (particularly mental health), educational, and religious systems (Rhodes, 1962). Each of these systems may or may not serve societal functions other than family support. But in their particular family support role for the community, they are responsible for developing, socializing, civilizing, and humanizing the individual member of the community. This psychosocial role brings them into direct contact with individual drives and impulses and it is their function both to educate and control such drives in correspondence with the needs and requirements of the larger community. They are, therefore, the intervention and behavior shaping systems of the community. They intervene in human life to shape its growth and development and to attempt correction and mediation of deviation of individuals in the community.

The major target of these community intervention systems is human behavior. Therefore, they might be thought of as the behavior regulatory systems of the community. They act upon the direction of the growth and expression of individual behavior to give it its community form, and to control it when it creates problems for the individual and the society. With the family, these systems attempt to influence all aspects of the developmental patterning, the quality, the amount, and the deviations from local norms, of those individual behaviors which are expressed into the community.

Structural and Functional Organization of the Behavior Regulation System

Analyses of the structural and functional organizations of behavior regulatory systems suggest common organizational components for all such systems. Each system has been given a particular behavior regulatory mission under governmental legislation. Each has received intervention sanction from the same source. Each reflects a central view of human behavior and its origins and controls. Each reflects a special social philosophy and social policy concerning the relationship of human behavior to the social good. Each has evolved its own intervention methods and technology to implement its mission, and the mission and technology often mirror the underlying philosophy and fundamental assumptions about human behavior.

Therefore, a behavior regulatory system may be defined as a functional community structure composed of (1) a central ideational construct of human behavior in the community; (2) a body of generated knowledge which flows from this central behavioral focus; (3) a professional guild apparatus which is dedicated to this focus and body of knowledge; (4) a set of derivative behavior regulatory techniques which have been developed and perfected by the professional guild; (5) a training and conceptualization apparatus which assures the continuity of the professional guild and its entrusted body of knowledge; (6) a set of community sanctions for operationalizing this constellation to intervene in human lives and human behavior; and (7) a set of hallmark behavior regulating operational patterns through which all of these elements are discharged into the community and brought to bear upon human behavior.

Behavioral Constructs and Body of Knowledge

The human construct is the central and thus most important component of the system. It infuses all other aspects of the system and directly influences the acts which are taken toward human behavior which is of concern to the community. The central human construct of the religious system may be sin; of education it may be learning; of medicine it may be illness; of welfare it may be deprivation; of correction it is crime. Each of these concepts exerts a directional force upon the organization and to a large extent determines all other aspects of the system.

These concepts of the origins and control of human behavior provide the community with a categorization scheme into which it can fit any troubling human behavior which occurs. At the same time, the scheme provides the individual with labels for his own behavior which he may make use of in selecting community structures toward which he can relate. When the community is aroused and becomes unduly concerned about certain behaviors which are being expressed into the environment, these constructs and their derivative structures are mobilized to engage the behaviors of concern.

Each of the regulating systems has developed a body of knowledge about human behavior associated with the focal construct of the system, whether it is sin, crime, learning, illness, or deprivation and poverty. The application of this body of knowledge within the behavior regulatory structures is the primary responsibility of the professional guild which is identified with the particular structure, i.e., educators, social workers, lawyers, correctional specialists, psychiatric physicians, and ministers. In most cases, this guild also has a department or school as part of the university system, and the university becomes the central repository and generating source of the body of knowledge which is applied in the operational patterns of the system.

The Operational Patterns for Behavior Regulation

The operational patterns reflect all of the components and elements of the system. They weld the elements together into an action pattern which makes all of the elements functional. They are the direct intervention vehicles of the systems and regulate the interchange between persons and community. They are the vital organs of the community for shaping and managing behavior. They are commissioned by society to form, direct, and control the human drives of individuals so that they are compatible with life in the community. Like the home, they are structures for channeling and directing behavior into forms which are harmonious with the behavior of others in the community.

These operational patterns are concrete facilities, structures, and agencies. The educational system has the operational pattern of schools. The legal correctional system has the operational patterns of correctional and detention facilities and police departments. The social welfare system has welfare departments, settlement houses, social service agencies, etc. The mental health system has hospitals, clinics, etc. The religious system has churches and religious agencies. All of these operational patterns function at the interface of the community and the individual. Frequently, their functional interventions at this interface are overlapping and replicative. However, they can be distinguished by their operational translation of their central explanatory construct for human behavior.

Intervention Goals and Stratagems

In their behavior regulation functions, these operational patterns might be classified according to their behavioral goals and their intervention stratagems. We might suggest the following kinds of goal classifications into which the operational patterns could be grouped:

1. Construction of Human Behavior

If consensus is reached within the community that the arousal behavior which is concerning it is untutored or undeveloped behavior, an effort will be made to mobilize operational patterns which can educate or construct new patterns of behavior in the individuals singled out for concern. In such a case, the operational patterns of education are most likely to be called upon to intervene. Although systems other than education may also have constructive or developmental goals, education is centrally identified with such outcomes. It is seen as capable of building unique new patterns within human beings and improving their capacity to cope with complexities of the environment.

2. Deterrence and Containment of Behavior

If the behavior is seen as associated with willful infringement upon the society, as a violation of others or an unlawful expression of personal impulses and drives into the environment, then the operational patterns of the legal correctional system are likely to be called upon by the community. Punishment, constraint, correction, deterrence, and containment are employed to bring about the regulation of the behavior. Although this type of intervention is predominantly associated with the operational patterns of the legal correctional system, it is also used to a less dominant extent by other systems. Containment is often a part of the armamentarium of mental hospitals and constraint is frequently found in special schools which cater to the more disruptive among the public school students.

3. Reconstruction or Rehabilitation of Behavior

If the arousal behavior is perceived by the community as being based in an illness or malfunctioning of the individual, the major effort is to mobilize the system and operational patterns dedicated to remediation, reconstruction, or rehabilitation. In this case the medical system and medical or paramedical operational patterns are frequently seen as the first line of defense for the community. In this connection, the mental health structures, with such operational patterns as hospitals, clinics, and centers, are frequently associated with behavioral deviances by the community. Their orientation to reconstruction of the human psyche and restoration of psychic health are seized upon by the community as protective and behavior regulation shields against the troubling behaviors which depart from community norms.

In addition to the classification of operational patterns according to their main behavioral goals, these behavior regulating systems have favored stratagems for intervention. Like the goals, these intervention stratagems are related to the central explanatory constructs and the derived behavioral assumptions of the systems and their operational or functional patterns. Within one system the predominant belief may be that behaviors are manifestations of interpsychic or intrapsychic events. Within another system the behavior itself is defined as the problem with which the community must grapple. The intervention stratagem would then be to bring the operations of the system directly to bear upon the behavior which is arousing concern within the community. Another system might look upon the central problem as residing outside the individual, in his physical and material setting or condition. In such a case the behavior is seen as arising out of the physical context and the stratagem for intervention focuses upon that context. Still another conception of disturbing behavior might be that it is related to the biophysical state or biophysical characteristics of the individual. If this conception predominates, the intervention stratagems are medical in nature. If the major factor associated with the behavior which is of community concern is defined as arising out of material need and deprivation in an individual's life, the intervention employed is usually one of direct support and material aid. This strategy is probably a corollary of interventions into the setting or situation.

Therefore, in classifying operational patterns according to their major stratagem of intervention, we might group them as follows:

1. *Interventions into intrapersonal or interpersonal factors associated with the behavior of concern.* Psychotherapy or education might be considered examples of such interventions.

2. *Behavioral interventions.* Police force, behavior modification, vocational education, and remedial education might be examples of such interventions.

3. *Environmental interventions.* Examples of these intervention stratagems might include urban renewal, community organization and community development, model cities or new towns, and environmental engineering.

4. *Biophysical interventions.* Examples would include psychotherapeutic drugs, psychosurgery, electroconvulsive therapy, and other interventions of physical medicine.

5. *Material aid and direct support.* Examples of this would be family allowances, welfare aid, small business loans, etc.

Recently we have been seeing a blurring of distinctiveness among operational patterns in terms of their major goals, i.e., construction, reconstruction, and containment, and in their intervention strategems, i.e., interpersonal, behavioral, environmental, etc. Many agencies which had formerly been clearly distinctive along these dimensions have begun to develop alternative goals and to adopt a wider range of intervention stratagems so that the time may come when it will be difficult to distinguish among agencies. Furthermore, the legislation of special laws which have sanctioned the use of a particular intervention technique by a particular agency may have to undergo change. Thus, laws which gave exclusive jurisdictional control to an intervention technique such as psychotherapy are already undergoing modification to allow its use by nonmedical agencies and persons of other disciplines.

At a more microscopic level we are beginning to see some interesting blurring and merging. We are seeing systems such as education and welfare or health and welfare beginning to be combined at the operational level. There are interesting multiagency combinations and variations growing up in urban areas across the country. It is interesting that it has taken so long for community structures to be responsive to the nature of the problems as they exist in the human context. Such human problems have never divided themselves into such separate and neat categories as were reflected in the exclusive jurisdictional categories and intervention categories of community agencies and structures.

Other Important Dimensions

There are a number of other important dimensions which distinguish among these community instruments for behavior regulation. A few of the agencies are charged with continuity in the lives of community members and with reinforcing the sense of continuity. Such patterns maintain long-term contact with individuals. Schools and churches discharge such continuous responsibility. Other agencies are charged with emergency responsibility and are designed to assume relatively short-term contact with community members. The emergency intervention patterns usually take custody in time of crisis and subject the person to special patterns of influence. Here we have agencies such as jails, prisons, mental hospitals, etc. They may provide this type of intervention periodically but they are designed to handle the principal crisis which brought the individual under their influence. Their responsibilities and areas of influence are more circumscribed and focused. They usually deal with specific behavioral characteristics of the individual which are of current concern to the community.

Usually, the semipermanent and continuous patterns assume responsibility for nurturing and fostering normal growth and development and for tying the individual into the mainstream of society. The emergency patterns are usually reserved for failures in the socialization process and frequently separate the individual from the mainstream of the community.

The behavior regulating systems and operational patterns differ also in their time orientation with respect to their constituency. The educational system and the school are oriented primarily to the future status of the organism and future behavior in the community. The same is true of the church. The social welfare and legal correctional systems are usually oriented to the present, to the current behavior of the individual. In many ways their operations and influence patterns are time-freezing patterns which take a current pattern of behavior of the individual and establish a pattern of influence which neither considers the past nor acts to bring about a changed future state or condition of the individual. They treat a particular state and particular condition of the individual as though it is unchanging and unchangeable. Welfare departments and prisons seem to operate predominantly in this way. Mental health patterns, on the other hand, seem to put considerable emphasis upon technology oriented to the past history of the organism, with an attempt to redo the past toward a changed present and future. There is usually a concern with a premorbid state and a return of the organism's behavior to this hypothetical state.

Another differential characteristic of the behavior regulatory patterns is the extent to which they are open to, and directly tied to, the pattern of living in the general community. Either because of territorial and proprietary interests or because of the difficulty of maintaining stability and control over the pattern of behavioral influences of the operational pattern, the professional staff and guilds have fostered a definite separation between their operational units and clients and the rest of the community.

Some installations, such as state mental hospitals, state correctional facilities, and institutions for the mentally retarded have been almost completely walled off from any form of life exchange with the outside community. They have been islands of exile and social exclusion for large numbers of troubling individuals who have been extruded from the larger community.

At the other end of this social isolation dimension are the operational patterns of schools, which are much more permeable to community forces and much more integrated into the functional community. Even in this instance, however, there is a tendency for the school to be quite selective in terms of aspects and segments of the functioning society which are allowed free access and influence in the lives of its constituents. Huge sectors of the community, along with their cultural forms and life styles, are barred from entrance into and interaction with the school's life-intervention patterns. This is particularly true when the culture of the surrounding area is different from the mainstream culture. Examples of this are Spanish-American neighborhoods, Negro neighborhoods, and Indian territories.

In the case of correctional and mental health institutions there is a two-way barrier of isolation. The inmates are prevented from having free access to the outside society, and most of the influences and living patterns of the outside society are stopped at the institutional borders. Barriers include geographical separation and distance, architectural barriers, and guards. In the case of the schools, the inhabitants move freely between the community and the facility, but there are selective barriers to the input from the larger community. These can include architecture, guild status requirements for entry, and policing.

Historical Perspective on the Behavior Regulatory Systems

The functions which these systems and their operational patterns serve today have always been an integral part of community life although they have not always assumed their present form. The functions have helped weave the community together into an organic whole and have given this organic whole its special psychological character and tone.

In the history of Western society, these functions have taken on many institutional guises and have passed through a fascinating series of critical philosophical metamorphoses as the warp and woof of community life. In the very earliest states, a group of families formed separate groups or clans which assumed all of the functions now served by these various systems. Later, with the rise of Christianity, many of the functions served by family in the clans were taken over by the institutional forms which grew out of organized Christianity. The monasteries became holding companies for a variety of human regulatory and service functions, including the early versions of hospitals, poor relief, special institutions for orphans, care of widows, etc.

During the 12th century religious orders flourished and much of the land and wealth became concentrated within the monasteries. They were so powerful in economic strength and in the absorption of the moral order of community that they actually weakened family life. In England, with a small population somewhere in the neighborhood of one to two million, the population of professed monks, nuns, and parish priests numbered at least 30,000 to 40,000 (*Encyclopedia Britannica,* 1911). This number of celibates was a protest against the moral sufficiency of the family state of existence. The celibate life-base was looked upon as a higher level of existence than the family institution with its base in a sexual union. Bound together by no common controlling organization, the monasteries were but so many miscellaneous centers of relief, charity, education, medical care, and casual relief.

By the beginning of the 15th century, however, there was a radical shift of these functions away from the ecclesiastical matrix and toward secular life and secular organization. This was the period in which the monasteries were being broken up and economic and governmental control was passing into the hands of the municipalities and the trade guilds. The guilds themselves began to develop a whole range of charitable resources for their members and families. They provided for hospitals, relief, and education of their own. They developed their own strong lay charities and members left estates to these organizations for the support of hospitals, almshouses, and education of the children and widows of "decayed" members.

At the same time, by the close of the Middle Ages, the towns were becoming very strong. The concept of state regulation, which was to control and supervise industry, agriculture, and poor relief, and to repress vagrancy through houses of correction, moved the center of responsibility to the town. Thus the state, rather than the ecclesiastical orders, became the arbiter and regulator of human well-being in the community.

The Reformation also had a profound impact upon the general meaning and theory of charity in community life. Although charity continued to have religious significance, the whole area of religious life had moved from central religious bodies to a property of the whole people. Charity and religion were integrally related and formed the moral base of the human community. This was the significance of the Reformation for charity and for the human regulatory functions.

Thus, during and after the period of the Reformation, charity became the undergirding of society and the moral purpose which bound man to man in the human community. It was tied to the religious order of God, even though the order of God had moved from its seat in religious bodies to the public space occupied by the whole people.

It is interesting to note the historical fate of these critical human service and regulation functions as they moved with major shifts in governmental and economic control. When the state was composed of clans, these community functions resided in the clan. When the ecclesiastical dominance was at its height, these functions resided in the monastery. When the towns themselves took on governing and economic control, these functions moved to the guilds and the municipal bodies.

Through all of these changes religion was the compelling force in charity. However, during the 18th century, when the concepts of humanism were sweeping across Europe and the germinal ideals of Rousseau were profoundly affecting all social institutions, charity took on a new significance. It continued to be the undergirding of society and the moral purpose which bound man to man in the human community but it shifted away from the religious order of God toward a base in the nature of man. Thus the regulation of community behavior became associated with the grand philosophy and purposes of humanism.

Under this recasting of charity, many charity organization societies grew up and flourished in England and throughout all of Europe. It was in this form that it entered the New World.

It was only a short step, then, from the locating of the source and problems of charity in the nature of man to the embracing of science in the regulatory functions. By the early part of the 20th century, science was being included as one of the mainsprings of charity.

The addition of science to the community regulating functions of the special systems, institutions, and public agencies previously lumped together under the umbrella of charity had a profound effect upon the human community. A new set of human service guilds sprang into existence. The functions of education, welfare, correction, etc., moved back from their public spaces in the total community and shifted their residence from the whole people to special, differentiated, scientific bodies. Responsibility and control became located within guild organizations such as social work, medical psychiatry, and education. Each guild developed its identifying operational patterns, its scientific technologies of behavioral regulation and behavioral change, its training programs, etc. The community of the whole turned over its responsibility for, and involvement in, human concerns to these technological segments. The strong professional guild and power coalition thus came into existence.

Increasing Importance for Structuring Human Beings

As the gradual splitting off and separation of the educative, social welfare, and mental health functions became crystallized and solidified in the strong coalition between government and professional guilds, this coalition played on increasingly significant role in forming and controlling the community life of the person. The molding of his drives and character, the regulation of his behavioral intercourse with others in the community, and the containment of his nonnormative behavior were all partially conditioned by this coalition of government and professionals. The operational patterns through which they exert their influence supplemented the influence of the family upon the community member's cognitive development, his affective development, his moral development, and his general community conduct. Schools, religious agencies, social agencies, medical agencies, and correctional and police agencies created a network of influences around the individual which profoundly shaped and influenced his community life and community behavior.

The extent to which these agencies are currently allowed to intervene and supplement, or substitute for, the family in psychosocial development and control of the individual depends upon the way in which the community views the relative competence of the family. The family which either lacks social competence or which is perceived as psychologically and socially incompetent is likely to have its individual members subjected to more interventions from a greater number of these agency sources. When the family does not perform the duties assigned it by society, those duties are relegated by the state to behavior regulatory patterns.

The developmental and regulatory functions which these agencies now serve for the individual and the family are becoming more critical as the social position and the extended structure of the family is changing in our communities. This diminution of family significance as a total regulative force, and the correlated increase in active participation of agencies, is more evident in lower class and lower status groups. These are the groups which produce the so-called multiagency families. However, we can see the same shift in balance of influences occurring in the middle and upper class families. For the middle class family, for instance, the educational system is becoming particularly burdened with shared responsibility for the psychosocial growth and psychosocial learning of the child. Education is beginning to rival family in the basic modeling and developmental functions of society.

Given society's increasing demands upon individual competence in social, skill, and cognitive areas, new types of human structuring institutions, in addition to family, are becoming more and more crucial. Therefore, beside the diminution of the function of the family or of the family's capacity to effectively assume its many existing functions, we are also seeing new demands for human structuring forces coming into existence in the society and community as their complexity increases. This further elevates the importance and significance of the behavior shaping and behavior regulating institutions and their operational patterns.

Even in the emergency, custody-taking patterns, such as prisons and state hospitals, there is a growing need to establish intervention methods which provide the individual inmates with compensatory skills in the social, work, and cognitive areas, as well as in the affective areas.

Résumé of Dynamics and Structure

The dynamics and structure of behavior regulation which revolves around community deviation has been analyzed and discussed in detail. The central collective dynamic presented in this chapter was the excitor-reactor exchange. This exchange was described as the basis for the behavior regulating process and structure of collective forms of life. It was seen as operating in all types of communities—from the lower to the higher forms of the collective.

In the human community, a special collective artifact has grown up to mediate the excitor-reactor exchange. This collective artifact was described as the behavior regulating apparatus of the community. This apparatus has come to be both the shaper and regulator of community behavior. In this chapter the focus has been upon the regulator function of the apparatus.

In community disruptions, occasioned by the excitor-reactor exchange, behavior regulation apparatus is mobilized and maneuvered to intervene in the excited exchange. The mobilization and deployment of the community apparatus of behavior regulation is largely under the control of the power or authority structures of the community. For the behavior regulation apparatus, this power structure was described as coalitions between governmental bodies, informal power groups (such as those who control wealth and industry), and certain professional guild structures.

The behavior regulation apparatus has evolved as the culture of society has evolved. The functions which the apparatus discharges have been lodged in various institutional forms in society at various periods in its history. At the present time, the functions are discharged largely by the apparatus of the educational, legal correctional, social welfare, and medical systems of the community. These systems and their structures support the socializing and regulating task which society has given to the family.

The apparatus of behavior regulation is pictured in this chapter as critical binding elements in community life. However, as we look at the current era, we can see that the whole apparatus is under concerted attack.

THE WINDS OF CHANGE

It is important that the community begin to examine its existing agencies and structures devoted to human care and development. It must make a careful analysis of the function which these structures are supposed to serve, and determine how they can be made more relevant to the current needs of individuals and society. The community must decide also whether it wishes such structures to continue to be vested in the separate guild organizations, or whether or not it wants these functions once again to be lodged in the total community as the substance of a moral force tying man to man in the community.

There is an obvious need for a general overhaul of these systems and a reintegration of their diverse and uncoordinated functions into the life of the human community. In order to accomplish this mammoth task the communities will continue to need the help of those scientific specialists who have studied the psychosocial and behavioral aspects of community and individual functioning. These specialists, in turn, must find ways to increase the relevance of their knowledge and the power of their tools in helping the total community solve its problems in human living.

There is a new urgency for this examination, analysis, and reconstituting. It cannot wait for the usual laissez-faire process of social history because the discontent and disenchantment with the present systems and structures for social order and human regulation have reached the "critical mass" stage and an explosion is likely to occur.

It is important, therefore, that resources and personnel be allocated to this task and that individual behavioral and social scientists who have anything to contribute to the process should begin

to devote their talents and energies toward these critical human solutions.

This urgency is increased by the fact that it appears as though the community response mechanism is beginning to break down under mounting pressures eminating from a variety of axes of community change. These axes include the pressure of population increase and population shifts; the revolt of deviant and minority subcultures from their former social status; the radical recentering of human problems in the ecological context rather than in individuals; and the wide-scale experimentation with new community behaviors and new microcommunities on the part of youth and others in the society.

Population Changes

In the United States, the size of the population increase from 150,697,361, reported in the 1950 census, to 200,294,850, according to the preliminary 1970 census, combined with the rapid population shift from rural disbursion to urban concentration, may be enough in itself to invalidate some of our former solutions to human problems in the community. For instance, the institutional practice of containment facilities such as jails and mental hospitals is no longer as viable a solution as it once was. These facilities cannot accommodate the large number of individuals which could be channeled into them from the open community.

The more gentle socialization and social conformity influences of the schools which operated so effectively upon unadapted or nonconforming individuals in the classroom is no longer working as it once did because of the increase in numbers of such individuals, their subsequent coalescing as a group, and their active resistance to these influences.

The growth and shift of population has also brought about another source of change which is felt with particular keenness in the urban areas. The social barriers around insular, divergent population areas such as slum quarters, Puerto Rican barrios, or Negro ghettos, no longer serve to contain the volume of irritant behaviors which they produce. These behaviors no longer remain sequestered within the invisible boundaries of special neighborhoods. Instead they have overflowed these territories and have broken out into the open community and into the channels of the mainstream culture of that community.

Radical Redefining of Deviance

An even more important result of growth in size and visibleness of these divergent groups and subcultures is the profound psychological changes which are taking place in the relationship between the mainstream sanctioning culture bearers and negatively sanctioned population groups. This relationship, so long stabilized and now very fluid, consisted of a reciprocity between controllers and controlled; between bestowers and bestowed; between definers and defined. In this reciprocal relationship the mainstream culture bearers defined that which is deviant and cared for those who were viewed as the deviant groups. The divergent groups, on their side, performed their ascribed problem status roles and subjected themselves to the ministrations of the community. Now we are seeing this social reciprocity being profoundly upset by the refusal of the target groups to continue in their former social status roles of excitors. The categorical groups are withdrawing from this passive status reciprocity and are pressing for status change and self-definition other than the excitor categories that the community forces upon them. They are insisting upon a new relationship between themselves and the mainstream culture bearers (as seen, for instance, in the Negro population). They are refusing to accept the problem classifications pinned on them by the mainstream culture and are refuting the problem charges leveled against them. They are also vigorously pressing for dramatic changes between themselves and the behavior regulatory structures which functioned under the control of the mainstream culture. For instance, the welfare recipient is redefining his relationship to the welfare giver and the welfare agency. The Puerto Rican barrio parent demands a redefinition of his role vis-à-vis educators and schools. The homosexual associations are pushing for redefinition of themselves and for acceptance into the open society. The drug addict is taking his "cure" into his own hands and is rejecting former patterns of care and care giving which existed prior to Synanon and Daytop Village.

Some of the labeled groups who have been designated as the source of community stress are even reversing the sanctioning process and projecting the stress source into the mainstream culture and standard-setting groups. These labeled groups are saying two things: one, that the supposedly unimplicated culture bearers and culture enforcers are actually deeply implicated in the sources of community stress; and two, that the dominant, culture bearing group deliberately creates, maintains, and supports the conditions which make it possible to label them in negative ways. (This is being said by the militant blacks; it is being said by other minorities such as Mexican-Americans, Indians, etc., and by special devalued target groups such as homosexual societies, youthful drug experimenters, hippies, etc.) All of these groups are accusing the society of projecting its ills upon them. All are demanding action now to change this process of social scapegoating. They are asking that the mainstream culture bearers reexamine their own attitudes and remodel the social conditions which create, support, and maintain the conditions which make it possible to label them in negative ways.

A supporting and very powerful source of challenge to the accepted definition of deviation which undergirds the status relationship between sanctioning and negatively sanctioned populations is coming from behavioral and social science theorists. The critical "individual possession" or "individual property" premise of alarming human states which disturb the social order, such as mental illness, sinfulness, criminality, and delinquency, etc., is being subjected to a radical new interpretation. In this reinterpretation, the individual becomes a symbolic receptacle of a community shared condition. He is no longer pictured as the principle source or the autonomous generator of the problem. Instead, he becomes the visible receptor of shared anguish which ties man to man in the public space of the community. As viewed by the new interpretation, he is being singled out by the community to represent the secret psychological pain—the invisible disorder of the whole. Through his acts the community reflects itself, but denies this reflection and insists that the disorder is his own. Therefore, the atonement or cure must be his own. In this dramatic reanalysis of the problem, fixed categories of deviance move toward obsolescence, and the "community"-process nature of the condition comes to the fore. For instance, Szasz (1963) directly challenges the accepted concept of mental illness: "Let us launch our inquiry by asking, somewhat rhetorically, whether there is such a thing as mental illness. My reply is there is not" (p. 11). He then goes on to compare the concept to earlier historical explanatory conceptions such as deities, witches, and instincts which were offered as self-evident causes of a vast number of calamitous events. Szasz then relocates the problem in the ethical, personal, and social conflicts within society. He says: "I believe that human happiness is possible—not just for a few, but on a scale hitherto unimaginable. But this can be achieved only if many men, not just a few, are willing and able to confront frankly, and tackle courageously, their ethical, personal and social conflicts" (p. 17).

Kvaraceus (1959) seriously questions another prevailing community deviance concept of delinquency. He sees it as norm violating behavior which varies from geographical area to geographical area. Kvaraceus says: "The delinquent serves today to syphon off much of the aggression inevitable in any complex society such as our own."

All societies, he claims, need institutionalized scapegoats to act as hostility targets. The experiences of uncertainty of the modern world, the stresses and strains of recessions, inflations, nuclear race, hot and cold wars, unemployment and labor disputes, lead to frustration and aggression. Accordingly, Kvaraceus says, the irritating adolescent and the annoying "delinquent" afford the adult a handy tool for aggression. In the Kvaraceus interpretation, juvenile delinquency becomes an ambiguous and overused word meaning different things in different places to different writers and readers and being of little use to anyone.

Eveoleen Rexford (1969), reflecting on the American "correctional" facilities for the young, has observed, "It appears sometimes that our society needs its delinquents who act out impulses which the adults do not or cannot and then requires that the youth be viewed with indignation and censure."

In discussing criminality and the criminal, Karl Menninger (1968) says that society secretly wants crime, needs crime, and gains definite satisfaction from the present mishandling of it. He says: "We need crimes to wonder at, to enjoy vicariously, to discuss and speculate about, and to publicly deplore. We need criminals to identify ourselves with, to envy secretly, and to punish stoutly. They do for us the forbidden, illegal things we wish to do and, like scapegoats of old, they bear the burden of our displaced guilt and punishment— 'The iniquities of us all' "(p. 22).

Stark and Glock (1968), taking a look at the changing conception of sin and the sinner, say that the locus of sin has moved from the individual to the human society. They say the theologian no longer concerns himself with the individual's rejection of private vices and the seeking of personal holiness. Instead, he addresses himself to the social situation in which people are embedded and declares the situation to be the determinant of what is ethical and moral.

In all of these restatements and transformations of individual conditions into states or conditions of the human community of the whole, long-established definitions of normative community behavior are being directly challenged; and the complicity of the community in the conditions and states of human distress is made theoretically explicit.

These reexaminations of fixed definitions which equate the community's problem with disturbing individuals, in concert with the new militant rejection of their labels by those who are labeled, are deeply effecting the behavior regulating processes and machinery of the community. Since these processes and machinery are organized around the labels and the implications of the labels, they are bound to feel wide-scale impact of these challenges.

Behavioral Experimentation

At the same time that society is feeling the revolt of labeled groups, and the dramatic reinterpretation of the meaning of the conditions so labeled, another vector of change is coming to bear upon the already overtaxed machinery. This is the wide-scale experimentation either with new behaviors or with behaviors which had not hitherto been made a part of the public marketplace. This applies to the experimental behaviors of militant youth which challenge long-established codes of conduct, self-presentation, dress, and public display. It also applies to violent mob actions, to wide-scale experimentation with new forms of volunteer relationships in therapeutic communities or utopian communities. It applies to public presentation of sexual behaviors which have been long treated as public secrets. It applies to a whole range of behavioral events which may not be unique in the community, but which are being tried on a scale that taxes the established modes of response of the legal correctional, social welfare, medical mental health, and educational systems.

In this time of experimentation, the full burden of responsibility for adaptive effort is being shifted away from the nonaccommodating individuals toward the responsibility of the surrounding environment. In these circumstances, accommodation becomes a bilateral rather than a unilateral function. The environment and the culture is asked to bend and adapt to individual behavior, to increase in flexibility, and to increase its accommodation to wider and wider ranges of individual differences in the community.

As long as the recipients of special community interventions were small in number and relatively acquiescent to the public behavioral standards of the community and to the community definitions of their condition, the existing patterns of behavioral regulation could function smoothly and effectively. It is necessary that the recipient of the intervention of such regulatory apparatus accept such interventions in order that they work.

As the mainstream culture has increased the number of categories of human behavior which it recognizes as deviant, and as the ranks within such negatively sanctioned categories have swelled, the target individuals have begun to challenge the community machinery established to maintain such sanctions.

Net Impact

In sum, all these chance events have a net impact upon those structures and functions which bind man to man in the human community. These structures have not been fluid enough and have not shifted fast enough to realign the relationships existing among the professional sector, political power sectors, and the culture bearing groups of the community as they react and respond to the individuals through whom these changing events are manifesting themselves.

If the forces of conservation within these structures resist the dynamics of change; and if this resistance is bolstered by a supporting coalition of the mainstream culture bearers, political power sectors, and professionals, it may have unfortunate consequences for the integrity and solidarity of the human community.

References

Encyclopedia Britannica. Vol. V (11th ed.). Charity and Charities. New York: Encyclopedia Britannica, Inc., 1911.

Hebb, D. O. *The organization of behavior.* New York: Wiley, 1949.

Kvaraceus, W. C. *Delinquent behavior.* Vol. 1. *Culture and the individual.* Washington, D. C.: Juvenile Delinquency Project, National Education Association, 1959.

Lorenz, K. *On aggression.* (Trans. M. K. Wilson). New York: Bantam Books, 1967.

Menninger, K. The crime of punishment. *Saturday Review of Literature,* September 7, 1968, 21-51.

Rexford, E. N. Children, child psychiatry and our brave new world. *Archives of General Psychiatry,* 1969, 20, 25-37.

Rhodes, W. C. Organization, power and community health. *American Journal of Orthopsychiatry,* 1962, 32, No. 3.

Stark, R., & Glock, C. Will ethics be the death of Christianity? *Trans-action,* June 1968, 7-14.

Szasz, T. *Law, liberty and psychiatry.* New York: Macmillan, 1963.

3

Education as a Humanizing Process
and Its Relationship to Other Humanizing Processes

Eli M. Bower

INTRODUCTION

The American public school system is one of the boldest and most imaginative conceptual jumps in the history of man. In its infancy, in the 17th and 18th centuries, it seemed a pale carbon copy of its European parents. But in its adolescence, around the middle of the 19th century, it moved out and away from its past as few other institutions devised by man have been able to do. Schools became public and common in the elitist sense of those terms. They became free and available to all children. They became secular and under local and state government control. Education and the skills of learning were seen more and more as a basic human commodity available to all. In time, education became an integral concept of the American dream. The gap between the dream and the waking state would still set a hop, skip, and jump record; nevertheless, a direction and philosophy had begun to take shape. It would take two world wars, a depression, engagements in Korea and Vietnam, and wars on poverty, slums, and racism to realize the distance yet to be traveled between the dream and its fulfillment.

In 1967, according to statistics published by The National Educational Association, about 43 million children attended our elementary and secondary schools, taught by approximately 1,759,000 teachers in 23,335 school districts in 50 states. Our current expenditure per child rose to $564 and our total expenditure for education, by federal, state, local, and other sources, rose to close to 28 billion dollars, a sizable sum but somewhat below other national expenditures.

Elementary and secondary public education is only a small part of the educational effort in the United States. There are, of course, 2-year and 4-year colleges, professional schools, church schools, private schools, graduate schools, and schools maintained by the Department of Defense for training service men, for special training, and for elementary and secondary pupils on defense bases in the United States and overseas. There are correspondence schools, home training programs, educational television, and sleep learning programs. An economist, Machlup (1962), estimated the total economic cost of the whole educational effort for the year 1958 to be about 60 billion. He also found that the total expenditure for public schools (elementary and secondary) is somewhere between 3 to 4 percent of our Gross National Product, a pittance when compared to other percentages.

PRESENT STRUCTURE OF PUBLIC SCHOOLS

Schools are supported by local taxes under directives and control of the state legislature. Our public school system is in fact about 23,000 separate systems (districts) operating under the guidance of 50 superboards—state legislatures, superintendents of public instruction, and state boards of education. The costs are usually shared by state and community depending on how much money the state has available to share and its philosophy of support. In many states, support is based on a philosophy of equalization—the less taxable wealth a district can muster to support its schools, the greater the state contribution. States can and do set forth in an education code both mandatory and permissive regulations governing all districts of the state. Such codes are enabling codes in that, unless duties, responsibilities, and privileges are delegated to districts, they cannot be exercised. Often, larger districts in a state are given freedoms and privileges not accorded smaller districts.

As education has become more complex and expensive, state and local resources have been unable to keep up. The federal government has entered the fray with a variety of categorical programs such as assistance for educationally deprived children, school libraries, and supplementary education centers. Federal money has also been used for strengthening state departments of education, higher education, programs for exceptional children, and others. Much of the money has gone into compensatory education programs for disadvantaged children and for schools in the inner city. Nevertheless, neither federal nor state money has been able to stem the rush of the middle class from urban schools, nor to make up for the lack of funds and professional resources needed to cope with the needs and deficiencies of the rural and large city schools.

The Basic Educational Unit—The Classroom

Whereas a home may be divided into a variety of spaces (living room, kitchen, den, bedroom, etc.), a school is in most cases conceptualized as a large eggcrate with halls to get from one cubicle to the next. Students are housed in classrooms. Groups may vary in size from 20 to 40—some larger and some smaller. Teachers are housed in the classrooms with the students and are as much prisoners of the eggcrate as are the students.

In small schools, where students are known and know staff, relationships can be informal and require few formal rules. Large schools tend to develop bureaucratic organizations of a self-serving nature. In large systems, the successful school day is seen as one in which there are no discipline problems, no irate parents, and no threatened teacher strikes. As will be discussed later, the school stands in the midst of swirling eddies of social change and is seen by many as the institution in which most, if not all, social problems will

be solved. For example, the problems of segregation, poor health, and inadequate early development which result from economic, social, and community practices will, it is hoped, be solved by schools. In addition, social injustice, broken homes, crime, and slums will all be coped with and through the public school. It is the one social institution which many citizens feel can be reached—but reached how, and to do what? To many, the school appears to be a self-sufficient, magical institution—ask and it will happen. From the inside, the school appears to be a rather rigid chameleon trying to adjust to a hippie light show.

In reality, the school is highly dependent on other institutions to adequately prepare children to function as effective students. A meaningful look at the school, especially by a psychologist, must include a peek through ecological lenses which highlight the direct and indirect ways the school relates to and depends on other humanizing institutions. In focusing one's ecological lenses on the school, one needs to pay particular attention to the metaphors or concepts which guide and direct institutional behavior, processes, and goals. It is these metaphors which produce the flexibilities and rigidities which make change possible or impossible.

The Metaphor of Education

Man is perhaps the only animal who can reflect on himself and his living experience. While the end of all life in death is a fact of life, the idea of death vitalizes and gives conceptual meaning to living. Metaphorically, living or life has been succinctly characterized as a period of serving time between birth and death by Samuel Beckett, a suck and a sell by Walt Whitman, an empty dream by Longfellow, and an impossible dream by Cervantes. Indeed, man's behavior, goals, and values are spelled out by and with a complex, intertwining combination of explicit and implicit metaphors. Each culture, society, and civilization seems to have its own guiding metaphors. The world has been conceptualized as a vast playground, a jungle, a prison with no exits, and a ship adrift on the high seas. One image that seems most appropriate to the world today is that of a gigantic, open-ward mental hospital.

Each member of a society takes on in his own way and in various strengths those metaphors appropriate to himself. Similarly, the institutions of each society are born and develop via metaphorical maps. Institutions, like people, hold on to their metaphors for dear life. As Schon (1963) points out, the nature of man is such that he finds it easier, safer, and more economical to hold on to old metaphors than to take on new ones. There are times when only a revolution will change concepts, although even in such cases drivers may be replaced without changing the nature of the buggy.

Societies, institutions, and people do not give up basic values and goals without a struggle since it often is quite unclear what the replacement might be. Such an action is much like taking off one's clothes and throwing them away before checking to see if there is a fig leaf or two around to cover the situation. People feel naked without concepts to guide them; having adopted concepts, they are not apt to give them up for a state of uncertainty.

As a prelude to understanding the school as an institution among other institutions, it is important to recognize that while much as changed in the larger society and much has changed in the operations, practices, and technologies of the school, the basic metaphors—the institutional concepts and goals—remain somewhat the same.

One of the critical needs of a rapidly changing society and the psychologists who serve it is to find ways of examining and changing the implicit and explicit metaphors which undergird and give direction to its primary institutions. Despite team teaching, educational TV, programmed instruction, language laboratories, and a host of other "innovative" practices, education is still conceived as (1) a process of cognitive digestion whose goal is (2) the production of ministers and a few physicians. Whatever else is asked of the school, the giving up of these major metaphors is still a difficult task.

HUMANIZING INSTITUTIONS AND THEIR FUNCTIONS

Before expanding and explaining the digestive and ministerial metaphors in education, it might help to understand how these metaphors relate to and are dependent on themes and concepts of other humanizing institutions and their goals. Man is born and develops in and by institutions which he

himself creates, supports, and administers. In order to manage and perhaps understand the ecological schema by which these human and sometimes humanizing institutions are structurally and functionally related, they can be grouped as follows:

Primary Group—The KISS (Key Integrative Social Systems) Institutions

These include institutions which attempt to serve and be served by all members of a society. As a group, the KISS institutions are the organizational matrix or setting in which we all strive to live. They provide the values, the goals, the means, and the rules by which existence is to be gratified, endured, or suffered. The KISS institutions are: the family, informal neighborhood and peer groups, the school, the church, health enhancing agencies, recreation agencies, and economic and governmental institutions. Those most embracing of children and their humanizing are (1) the health enhancing agencies, especially those responsible for the health of pregnant women; (2) the family; (3) informal peer groups including informal and formal recreation and play institutions; and (4) the school. Each of these KISS institutions will vary from community to community in effectiveness and availability to children.

Key integrative institutions contain within their operations and processes the experiences needed by children to grow up into effectively functioning adults. Successful passages through these primary or basic institutions should provide a child with the degrees of freedom to feel, to think, and to act later as an adult human. Looking at the "key" in each of these passages, the health enhancing institutions would provide these services aimed at insuring the birth of a biologically sound organism; the family, the milk of human affection and nutrition plus a few beginning but critical cognitive concepts; neighborhood and peer groups, the opportunity to test oneself socially and physically in play and relationships; and the school, the skills in learning how to manage a variety of symbols and relationships. In all of these institutional passages, there appears to be an epigenetic integrating quality to the overall journey so that difficulties in one KISS initiate added difficulties in the next. Birth injury will induce more than normal stress on child and family which in turn may induce increased difficulties in play, peer groups, and eventually in school. A biologically healthy child who nevertheless finds family life somewhat tedious or terrorizing will not gain the necessary skills to function effectively in play groups or school.

It is possible for one KISS institution to compensate for experiences or learnings missed or misshapen in another but this apparently is most difficult to accomplish by institutions whose functions are narrowed, somewhat exclusive, and specialized. A good obstetrician cannot love all his mothers-to-be nor can teachers make up for lack of affection in mothers-who-are. While there is a program of "compensatory education" (Title I, Elementary and Secondary Education Act), it is still somewhat conjectural who is being compensated and for what. The school is the last in the line of the four relevant KISS institutions, and engages with children and their families for quite a long period of time. While it is not expected that every child will receive adequate prenatal care or live in a happy home, it is expected that the school will be successful with every child.

Secondary Group—The AID (Ailing-in-Difficulty Institutional) Institutions

The primary, or KISS, institutions serve as the basic living environment and structure for society. Some citizens and children, however, find they are temporarily unable or not permitted to live in this setting and are moved to other institutions. Such citizens or children might be ailing physically or in difficulty socially or legally. These are served by specialized personnel and institutions who attempt to help such persons back to effective living in the KISS institutions. Such AID institutions include physicians and hospitals, attorneys and courts of law, varieties of social agencies, clinics, county jails, homes for children, special schools and programs, counselors (including pastoral counselors), and others. Those institutions and persons aim to restore health, economic independence, and social and emotional competence utilizing a variety of resources, processes, and structures. Their general orientation toward their clients is one of temporary care and services focused on moving citizens and children back to physical and social health as soon as possible.

Tertiary Group—ICE (Illness-Correctional Endeavors) Institutions

When the AID institutions cannot restore their clients to physical or social health or when serious social and health problems develop in KISS institutions, persons can be removed or choose to live for a period of time on ICE. ICE institutions are state and federal prisons, state mental hospitals, and other 24-hour-care facilities. Whereas AID institutions reduce to some extent an individual's degrees of freedom, ICE institutions usually do so to a great extent. Such institutions attempt as best they can to restore patients or prisoners to the society at large, with good results in some cases and poor results in many. Usually persons served by such institutions have had a long history of social and emotional problems; ICE institutions in addition are caught on the horns of contradictory metaphors—protect society but restore or cure the patient of his lawlessness or illness. Mental hospitals and prisons often become anxiety ridden communities where both staff and clients find normal living and healthy growth difficult if not impossible.

THE SCHOOL AND THE KISS INSTITUTIONS

The KISS institutions, especially those serving children, have as one of their major tasks the development of human beings who will require no ICE institutions and only a minimum of AID institutions. Of greater importance yet is the possibility that the alliance of the KISS institutions will produce an effectively functioning, compassionate, and creative human being. The school, particularly through its sanction to work with families and health agencies in preschool, early school, and adolescence, develops educational programs which can enhance those emotional and cognitive competencies in children which will give them the skills and robustness to make it in the KISS institutions.

The ecologic and functioning effectiveness of the school is most closely allied to the health enhancing agencies, the peer and play institutions, and the family. Educational institutions must depend on each of these informal and formal arrangements to give prospective students skills and capabilities prerequisite for effective functioning in school. Children who are ill-nourished nutritionally or emotionally, who have not learned the principle of taking turns in play or managing themselves according to rules in games, who have had limited experience with words and concepts, will find the school a tough, irritating experience. To begin with, it helps to have children born hale and hearty.

THE HEALTH ENHANCING INSTITUTION

"A ship under sail," noted Poor Richard, "and a big bellied woman are the handsomest two things that can be seen common." Undoubtedly, pregnancy, like a billowing sail, can be considered beautiful and a state of healthful functioning consistent with nature's purpose and design. But every so often both sail and belly run into rough seas. Studies of prenatal and perinatal difficulties in pregnancy indicate some of the risky shoals of birth. On the basis of past research, the odds for a healthy foetus drop in the very young or those over forty, in young mothers with continuous unspaced pregnancies, in pregnancies conceived in the summer months, in mothers who work in laundries, in short women, and a variety of other conditions. Epidemiologically, the naturalness of childbirth has limited conceptual and practical validity (Maslund, 1961). The significant and overwhelming fact of the services, structure, and processes of this critical stage is the close relationship of complications in pregnancy and socioeconomic level. Indeed, Pasamanick and Knobloch (1961), on the basis of their research, conclude that prematurity and pregnancy rates increase exponentially as one goes down the socioeconomic ladder. All this means is that poor mothers have less of a chance of having healthy babies than do middle class mothers. The major reason which most behavioral scientists, including this one, subscribe to is that the lower class mother has seldom perceived or had access to medical services which were enhancing, preventive, or indeed useful until or unless something hurt bad. This value system can be understood on the basis of lower class experiences with middle class medical practice, with hospitals, and on the basis of a lack of knowledge about pregnancy and its complexities. What it comes down to is that health enhancing institutions as structured around county hospitals, as well as baby clinics, nurses, and relevant community agencies need to reconceptualize their educationaˡ and service impact to lower class pregnant women. A significant and effective program in the reduction of prematurity, birth injury, and mental retardation by health institutions would markedly lighten the load for families and schools doing their key tasks.

THE FAMILY

Once the child is born he goes immediately to a family or some institutional substitute. Since most children are born healthy, most families begin operation in the black. In our society, almost all our joys and triumphs as well as our problems and social ills come to rest on this KISS institution. The family is quite unique in that it spans the sexes, the generations, and the individual with his society. It seems to be an all purpose something-for-everyone kind of arrangement, sanctified by churches, codified by laws, and formally developed in all societies of man.

As an institution, the family qua family has little power but great flexibility. It has no political clout in and of itself; no one pickets the White House or Congress on behalf of aid to normal families. On the other hand, behind its private walls and locked doors it can carry on in any way it wishes other than interfering with the privacy and locked doors of its neighbors or the sensibilities of its community. Indeed it would be difficult to fathom what legislative, financial, or magical procedure could be invoked to strengthen the family as a KISS institution. (An exception might be the recently vetoed Child Development Act which was indeed aimed at helping all families.) Any attempt by government or so-called knowledgeable professionals to help parents be more effective can be seen to have the opposite effect since good parents and good families are known to be self-sufficient. One is not trained to be a parent nor is effective parenting a known quality capable of being communicated to eager spouses.

The family we experienced is not the same family our children experience. Most of us know about family from the few families we have known—the one we were born into, the one we initiated, and the ones our children begat. We are also aware of all the talk about the family outliving its usefulness, of kibbutz children and their families, and other variations and modifications of the so-called nuclear family. Goode (1964) suggests that much of our data about families lacks perspective and accuracy. For example, many primitive societies had high family breakups and much the same kinds of problems with their kids. In the late 19th century, Japan had over 3 divorces for every 10 marriages. In California there is 1 divorce for every 2 marriages. In Napa County, California, particularly, according to Bloom (1969), 7 out of 10 marriages end in divorce.

Despite all the hard data on marriage and divorce (the beginning and end of a family), it is difficult to assess the essential functions provided to children in intact or broken families. Certainly not all children of divorced parents become social or psychiatric casualities nor are all children of intact "happy" families paragons of healthy, effective living. The Goertzels (1962) studied the family backgrounds of 400 eminent (operationally defined) persons and found such things as: about 300 were troubled by family related vicissitudes; 74 out of 85 writers of fiction or drama and 16 of 20 poets came from homes where tense psychological dramas were played out by parents; stepmothers played a helpful role in a great majority of cases. It is also interesting to note that in almost all homes there was a love of learning in one or both parents and an absence of mental disturbances requiring hospitalization of either parent. Another related study (Weisberg & Springer, 1961), compared the families of high-IQed, plodding children with high-IQed creative children and found the creative-producing family to be a nonclinging, not too well adjusted group. In these families there was open and not always controlled expression of strong feelings especially in the case of the father (shades of *Life With Father*).

The Goertzel and Goertzel (1962) and Weisberg and Springer (1961) studies are cited to emphasize that the effective family may not resemble the stereotyped, middle class, controlled, TV-depicted types of parents and children. As Goode (1964) points out, studies of differences between children of broken families and others seldom give you a wide-screen view of the problem. Single-parent families and deaths of parents are highest in poverty areas where delinquency rates are also higher. The problem in other socioeconomic groups is no less serious. If class position is held constant, delinquency is higher in broken homes and higher in families broken by separation or divorce than by death.

There are probably only a few thousand emotionalized fairy tales about what a family is, what it does, and how the roles are effectively played considering the fact that mother and father are the most popular and critical roles played by adult male and female humans. Whatever is right or wrong about a society is tacked onto its family institutions. Every human society must depend on its family institutions to get its kids started right. But the question still remains: what are the specific and unique functions of this institutional structure that make it a mandatory institution in all human societies?

It seems easy enough to toss out a list of survival functions such as nurturance, succorance, love, dry diapers, a sense of belonging, security, protection, play, and sleep—all of which are necessary but probably insufficient functions. What unique and specific function does the family provide which leads the child on to social and individual competence in the subsequent KISS institutions?

Vincent (1967) traces the arguments suggesting that the loss of many of the historical functions of families has doomed the viability of the institution. Sorokin (1937) declared that the family would continue to disintegrate until all that would be left for it would be to provide an overnight parking place for sex relationships. Others have traced the loss of the protective function of the family to the policeman, fireman, nurse, and truant officer; the loss of economic production to agricultural combines, canneries, Safeway, A & P, and laundries; the loss of recreation functions to automobiles, bowling alleys, discotheques, and the Beatles; and the loss of educational functions to TV, schools, and peers. On the other hand, if the family has indeed shucked off many of its traditional functions what is left could be the meat and drink of its existence. Parsons and Bales (1955), for example, suggest that an institution which loses some of its functions is then freer to concentrate on its significant functions. They note: "The family is more specialized than before but not in any general sense less important because the society is dependent *more* exclusively on it for the performance of certain of its various functions (p. 10, 11)."

What remains for the family is the critical task of providing the growing child with the basic mediating skills or processes by which the child can begin to tie sensory data to affective and cognitive concepts. Mediating skills or processes are built on bridges of trust and relationship between adult and child over which notions about the self and the world can be (1) *organized*, i.e., put together into some sort of meaningful *gestalt*; (2) *bound*, i.e., held onto by symbols so that the data can be used, played with, and combined with other organized concepts; (3) *utilized in reality and fantasy testing*, i.e., data which exists in rational modalities such as mathematics, language, science, economics, is connected with nonrational modalities in imaginative thought, daydreaming, sleep dreaming, poetry, music, and art. Mediational or conceptual processes is the name of the game. The children who win are those who experience trust and safety with an adult who can then transmit concepts and ideas with which the child can begin to build a self and world in which to function.

INFORMAL AND FORMAL
PLAY INSTITUTIONS

Children grow through play and games and seek opportunities to do so. In the cities there are playgrounds, streets, parks, and nursery schools. In rural areas there is more room to play but often fewer peers to play with.

One of the crucial outcomes of play and games for the child is gaining competence and confidence in responding to cues, signals, and symbols. It is also a way of testing oneself physically and socially. To play well one needs to be free to imagine. To participate in games one needs to learn to control impulses and adhere to rules. One needs to learn how to step out of the real world into a make-believe one and then step back again. When the external world is overwhelming and there is a daily struggle for survival, the nature and opportunity for play changes. Often children of lower class families are saddled with family and social responsibilities and have little time or chance to play. Their way of life requires that they grow fast to become self-sufficient and fend for themselves as soon as possible. Often such pressures to maintain peace and be a good boy or girl in a family leave little time or interest for normal play. When play is permitted it often emerges as destructive, desultory, or inappropriately comic. Play requires concentration on matters outside of reality; when the grimness of reality is too pervasive such concentration and enjoyment are difficult to find.

The middle class child is often faced with a similar kind of grimness stemming from the anxiety or eagerness of his parents to launch him into the collegiate world as early as possible. This factor coupled with increasing emphasis and research on the significance of preschool learning for school success often makes play a difficult experience to find for young middle class children. In some cases play is seen as taking valuable time away from more important tasks; in other cases the play modality, i.e., the opportunity to be free to imagine, to step out of reality however briefly, is compromised by adults who structure play toward achievement goals and see play activity as a means to other ends.

Undoubtedly one of the hangups of a society desperate for educationally competent citizens on all levels is an educational system which drops sizable chunks of students between the boat and the dock. To many of us it seems axiomatic that all players or teams can't win—be it chase, football, or life. To have winners there must be losers; to have straight-A students, one needs a few failures. After all, the normal curve is normal.

One way to douse Gauss in our thinking is through helping children understand and develop concepts of play as fun. It is possible to help oneself by helping others. In tennis or chess one builds up one's skills and enjoyment as one's opponent becomes more skilled and competent. Where the goal of play is fun the greatest fun is not annihilating or being annihilated but in having a good match. Such matches are good because one is being fully tested. One can win or lose; if the latter, one can try again. To experience this type of relationship one often helps one's opponents to become more effective so that there is more fun in the game.

In the same way it is possible to create communities of people with a variety of styles of living all striving to win but finding their fun in helping the others to do so too. There are few if any experiences within our KISS institutions which provide children with goals, values, and models for this kind of behaving. Such models can be suggested through play and games if made explicit and rewarded. In the game of Equations, a mathematics game developed by Lyman Allen, two teams compete in simultaneous individual matches in developing and solving equations. It is part of the game that the poorest competitors have the highest scoring potential. This means that in order to win a team must help its poorest players to become more competent. As players become more able they advance on the ladder while others may slip a notch or two. It is soon obvious that to win it is more important to communicate strategies and concepts to colleagues than to beat one's opponent.

The institution of education has always had social Darwinism in its historical bones. Learning in a formal sense could be experienced only by the bright and those prepared to deal with education's high level abstractions. Dropout by the noninterested or poor was encouraged and justified on sink-or-swim principles. If education was the royal road to social mobility and was available to all, then the strong of mind and will made it and the weak did not. This value helped to some extent to provide us with a social ethic which was at once democratic and satisfying to the winners.

Our society has reached a point of closeness and dependence in which educational losers cannot be permitted. To grow people who are incompetent, inadequate, insane, or apathetic is everyone's loss.

How we can afford to lose children in a rush of raised hands, large classes, and first-grade failures? In this game, as in life, all must win. As the child moves from home and play institutions we need to devise games and stimulations which will move educational processes and experiences toward positive, helping goals.

Agencies that relate to children's play are housing authorities, toy manufacturers, architects, landscape gardeners, park commissioners, playground developers, administrators of after-school programs, nursery schools, recreation commissions, city governments, and parents. Only a few see play as anything more than a good way to spend leisure time. (It keeps kids out of trouble.) Most recreation agencies see their role as providing space and equipment and the supervision and administration to keep the equipment in good condition. Rarely do recreation or park departments see their role or their duties as more than maintenance. In one case a public school system and a mental health agency developed an effective and quite comprehensive preschool screening program. In the process they identified a significant number of preschool children who lacked adequate play experience. The screening team suggested that the community provide a remedial play program for such children and suggested this be undertaken by the recreation department which had operated a regular program for older children. As a result of the help and encouragement of the screening group, the recreation department developed this new program employing youth workers and volunteers (Newton & Brown, 1967). In the beginning they didn't think they could do it. In the end the parents, the school, the community, and the children found it highly successful.

It is probable that man's unique ability to play, especially with symbols (language, mathematics, visual, and sound symbols), has had much to do with his scientific and social progress. Gregor Mendel was not working to discover genetic laws; he was literally playing around with garden peas. The Wright brothers saw their flying machine as a source of fun and excitement. The adventurous and creative part of man emerges by and large through his capacity to play.

Man's most valuable tool and everlasting glory is his ability to see similarities in things which are different and differences in things which are the

same—in short, to be amused, tickled, and to laugh. If words, concepts, and metaphors have been learned in a healthy and creative manner, the cognitive-affective meanings carried in and by them can be loosened and played with. As Koestler (1964) points out, when there is a sudden switch of ideas, context, intent, or logic, the connative or cognitive aspects of a symbol-concept switch much more readily than the "heavier" emotional loads which continue on course and are discharged in laughter. To accomplish this release one must have had some opportunity to loosen or unfasten cognitive-affective bonds tied by experience. This can only be accomplished in a play modality. "Man's mastery of his environment has not been the product of a grim, relentless struggle for existence. Whenever we trace the origin of a skill or a practice which played a crucial role in the ascent of man, we come to Play (Hoffer, 1967, p. 8)."

THE MEDIATIONAL GOALS
OF THE KISS INSTITUTIONS

Effective play and family experience lead to effective learning or mediational processes. Mediational processes require mediational persons. Most parents have a head start on being mediational persons since the child has usually learned to feel positively toward and trust parents. The child's feeling might be translated thus: "I am of them and must trust them for food, comfort, and shelter. I must also trust them to help me figure out this complex, mixed-up environment I am growing into. Millions upon millions of sense impressions and ideas are beginning to engulf me. Where is the loom to help me weave all these threads into a meaningful fabric?"[1]

The mediational concepts or looms by which a child learns to make sense of the world and himself require two intertwined skeins of experience. One is an emotional experience which allows and encourages the passage of data from adult to child and child to adult; the other, equally important, is the conceptual organizing experience from which maps of the self and the environment are drawn. It is important to recognize that effective mediation requires both the affective and cognitive components. Hess (1964) illustrates part of this notion in experimental studies of mothers

teaching their children a sorting task. Each mother is given an assortment of objects and asked to help her child sort out all the red objects. Here is one mother mediating this task to her child: "Now I'll take them [the objects] all off the board. What is this? A truck? All right, put it there. Now put the other one there and that one over there." It is apparent that as the child sorts objects, little or no organization binding or problem solving is going on. Contrast this with the mother who begins: "All right, Susan, we are going to play a game. This board is the place where we will put the toys. But first of all we are going to place them together by color. This is red but this also is red. Let's place all the red toys over here. Do you think you can do that? Now, remember, we just want to place the red toys here. Would you like to see me do it first?" The child shakes her head and does it. Mother praises the child who is then quite pleased with her own performance.

Children and parents go through thousands of transactions in which symbols and concepts are learned. Such learning makes the learner trust other adults as potential mediators, at least initially. What the learner is searching for in the trusted mediator is some new concept or metaphor which can help the learner be more competent in assessing and interpreting the messages his eyes, ears, nose, tongue, and fingers receive. This interpretation and assessment of sensory data is made by the executive or mediating part of the personality often called the ego. Ego processes are learned patterns of functioning which organize and give meaning to information. Mediation is an active process by an active organism. Stimuli do not pass through neurons to elicit responses; stimuli are selected out of myriads of possibilities, are given shape and meaning, are reflected upon and acted on when necessary or desirable. Effective mediation requires reflection in much the same way that the development of a self-concept requires one to perceive oneself. Jensen (1966) points this out in his emphasis on verbal mediation as a class of behavior of supreme importance to learning. Verbal mediation is simply the learner's skill in talking to himself so that he is cognizant of and interacting with the sensory input. Jensen sees the difference between the nonmediating learner and the mediating learner as a difference in what the learner responds to. *The former will respond directly to sensory input as it is encoded in the sensory areas of the brain while the latter will respond to responses and associations set off by sensory input.* He recalls his observing some so-called culturally deprived children and some middle class children taking the Progressive Matrices Test and watching the lip movements and mutterings of the middle class children and the lack of this type of responding in the deprived group.

It is of great help in all mediating processes to find effective symbols by which objects, events, or feelings can be bound into self. Learning may be in its essential form a process of labeling with enough loose string on the label to tie it to other symbols and concepts. Jensen cites an experiment by Pyles (1932) in which children between two and seven years of age were asked to locate a small toy hidden in a set of five papier-mâché nonsense shapes. The task was presented with (1) the papier mâché shapes unnamed, (2) named with nonsense names, and (3) with animal names. Children given the animal names learned to locate the hidden toy 7 times faster than when given nonsense labeling, 13 times faster than with no labeling.

Ego or mediating processes are not concerned with the bits and pieces; they seek inputs that are perceived to be preserving and enhancing of future mediating processes. They seek to climb the mountain that Dewey described to a young man who persisted in asking him about the purpose of his philosophy: "To climb a mountain/ And when you get to the top/ You'll see another mountain;/ And then/ You'll climb that/ And then/ You'll see another mountain. 'And what will happen when there are no more mountains?' asked the young man. 'When you see no more mountains,' said Dewey, 'it will be time to die'" (Dewey, 1929, p. 110).

MEDIATING AFFECTIVE DATA

Much of what has been presented up to now has dealt with the concept of mediation as a cognitive-affective transaction with the emotional relationship providing the bridge for the passage of conceptual vehicles. There are, however, processes of knowing in which affective concepts pass over affective bridges in one fell swoop. When one sees a well-done performance of Samuel Beckett's *Endgame*, hears Beethoven's Ninth (if you don't

like the Ninth, pick your own), or the Beatles' "Day in the Life," or gazes at a Wyeth, Picasso, or Rembrandt, one is dealing with an experience, or happening, in which the mediation is spontaneous, pleasurable, and "true." Ego processes search for pleasurable acts, sounds, and sights and devour them wholly. What is experienced in enjoyable skiing, tennis playing, music, art, viewing pretty girls, or other vistas is immediate and total.

There are, however, some cognitive-affective access roads to this kind of knowing. Beethoven's Ninth can be better understood and enjoyed after listening to Leonard Bernstein explain how it is put together; Beckett's plays can be experienced more fully if one becomes more aware of the nuances in the dialogue or one has experienced in real life what is being acted out. Esslin (1961) describes the impact of Beckett's *Waiting for Godot* on an audience of men residents of San Quentin Prison. Herbert Blau, the director of the theatre group, was concerned about the audience's reaction to this apparently mystical, no-action play, especially since all exits were blocked and guarded. Blau felt a little warm-up session might help reduce any disruptive expressions via boos, vegetables, or paper airplanes. He admitted to the inmates that while the meaning of the play might be somewhat obscure, it might be best enjoyed as a piece of jazz music "to which one must listen for whatever one may find in it."

Whether this helped or not is conjectural. I think it did. In any case, this captive audience was rocked by the performance. It seemed to them that Beckett had succeeded in communicating an understandable notion of life as waiting and as serving time, a common and heightened affective experience for the whole audience. So where sophisticated San Francisco audiences had puzzled themselves into not liking this play, the San Quentin group spontaneously and pleasurably mediated Godot into their own experience. All human beings "serve time" and are often aware of its vagaries; nevertheless many of us are unable to mediate this critical, life-giving abstraction and to recognize its specific representation.

Attempts to improve spontaneous, affectively loaded knowledge through education can often backfire, much as the centipede knew how to walk until a scientific centipede explained to him how. Communication of affective knowledge must be felt immediately as a warm glow, an all-over tingle, or it's no go. A musician with technical competence can conduct a musical composition in a technically competent manner. Unless he himself is able to mediate the emotional meaning contained in the notes his orchestra will play, his audience will listen, but few will feel. In much the same manner a technically perfect painting can evoke admiration but not much spontaneous gut-level response in viewers.

Experiences which produce spontaneous, warm, pleasurable responses are inherently spontaneous, warm, and pleasurable. Since this kind of knowing comes earlier in development, and is more powerful and enticing than the intellectual-cognitive kind, children expect a certain amount of pleasurable experiencing in all knowing. Some see spontaneous experiencing as the only truthful, worthwhile knowledge. The more traditional cognitive kind is seen as handed down authoritatively from teachers or textbooks; the emotionalized spontaneous combustion is personal, creative, and pleasurable. Such knowing must therefore be superior to a history shot full of distortions, classificatory and taxonomic sciences, biology which describes the structure and function of organs but never puts them together, and English literature made up of "classics," so called by dust-covered scholars and passed on by ritualistic English teachers. As an institution which subscribes to this kind of knowledge, the school can't help but be dull and irrelevant.

So it goes. Students want to feel, to be aware, to extend and expand their senses and thought processes to reach beyond themselves. To some degree this movement and need follow Newton's second law of motion, and can be considered a reaction to a squelching and downgrading of primary or emotional processes as sources of knowing and knowledge. To a great extent it reflects an awareness by younger generations that there is more to knowing and to growing than the rational scientific and descriptive.

Educational institutions have seldom legitimately explored primary process or emotional learning as part of the curriculum. Many university campuses are finding students searching for and demanding experiences in encounter, interpersonal, or T groups. Students seek learning experiences in which strong feelings can be accepted and expressed and in which they can discover more of themselves as people. Yet in all

this it is important that the cognitive-affective bonds in learning and development not be separated. Feelings must affect ideas and ideas feelings. To approach cognition as if it existed pristine and pure can be as disintegrative of human growth as wallowing about in feelings without recourse to cognition. The destiny of man lies in connecting primary and secondary processes of thought so that thinking and action can be enhancing of the self and others. As Freud said, "Education can without further hesitation be described as an incitement to the conquest of the pleasure principle and to its replacement by the reality principle. . . . Actually the substitution of the reality principle for the pleasure principle denotes no dethronement of the pleasure principle but only a safeguarding of it (pp. 18, 19)."

THE SCHOOL

Now we come back to the two metaphors we left hanging earlier: (1) education as a digestive process, the purpose of which is (2) the preparation of ministers and a few physicians.

The earliest educational institutions were universities—guilds or corporations of students and professors who banded together against landlords or booksellers. As Haskins (1923) relates, students often ran the guild; they paid the fees and often made their professors deposit money to guarantee their appearance. What professors did then is to a great extent what they do now—lecture. Derived from the Latin, *legere*, to read, the lecture was exactly that—a reading. Books were few and reading skill a unique competence. Professors were hired to read, especially by those who were serious about knowing—priests and physicians. What was known was in the book. To learn one digested, i.e., listened and remembered what was read or lectured. If chapters were skipped or omitted, the lecturer might or might not escape with his life.

Out of this historical background came the notion of covering the course (getting a full course meal) and the textbook which provided the full course menu. Students preparing for the ministry, medicine, or law filled their empty heads by paying detailed attention to the fonts of knowledge—the teacher and the textbook. Mediation of information was not encouraged. Students were expected to remember the facts and regurgitate on request. Intellectual power was knowing what the teacher and the textbook knew. Fields of study or disciplines came to be closed or circumscribed by great books and scholars. Education was simply the process of swallowing the words of either or both. Those who mastered the material went on; the others were considered to have poor digestive systems and were sent on to other cafeterias.

The metaphor of educational process as digestion needs to be uprooted and replaced by the metaphor of integration or mediation. It is not in the process of filling up students with courses that education goes on but in conceptualizing or mediating meaning and in connecting and binding knowledge within self. The educated person is not a digester but an active processor of information. Further, we need to replace the metaphor of education as preparation for the ministry or medicine with one which provides educational competence for all. This cannot be done by the school alone but by all the KISS institutions carrying out their prerequisite functions.

The school as a humanizing institution can, if given community sanction, reach down to assist and be helped by other agencies. As the last institution in the KISS lineup, it must build pathways from the slum to the university which provide the kinds of health, play, and emotional and intellectual competencies required for human participation in a technological society. Educational goals must be to produce civilized, creative, and competent persons including ministers, physicians, repairmen, taxi drivers, and university professors. To do this we have to take the school out of its eggcrate buildings and develop learning opportunities in buildings containing laboratories, knowledgeable people, interested students, technological aids, films, and books. What will be learned in this setting will be how to learn and will require active participation by the other three KISS agencies described earlier. Symbols (ideas circumscribed by language or mathematics) learned in this manner will not be processed so rigidly or bound so tightly that new ideas cannot be entertained. The process of digestion fills one to satiation; mediational learning makes one hungry for new knowledge and growth. To do this for all children is the Mars shot for the latter part of the 20th century.

SUMMING UP

What is suggested here is that the context of effective learning requires the participation of all KISS institutions. The school is only one agency in an ecological hookup, heavily dependent on other agencies for its own effectiveness and functions. If the school is required to make up health, play, and emotional and cognitive deficiencies for large groups of children before they can learn how to learn, then the institutional processes and goals must change radically. It is suggested as perhaps more economical and preventive that schools search for earlier and better partnerships with the other KISS institutions so that all may profit and grow.

As end man in the KISS constellation of services, the school can ill afford to let any child grow up educationally incompetent. All children need to undergo its demands and processes actively. Just being a good, happy child is not enough. Unless the child picks up the requisite skills of learning he has indeed given hostages to fortune.

Learning how to learn has become the basic business of children. Basic to this skill is the development of mediational or ego processes which give children the ability to use cognitive-affective symbols (concepts) effectively and creatively.

Note

1. Edna St. Vincent Millay said it this way: "Upon this gifted age, in its dark hour,/ Rains from the sky a meteoric shower/ Of facts . . . they lie unquestioned, uncombined./ Wisdom enough to leech us of our ill/ Is daily spun; but there exists no loom/ To weave it into fabric." (From Sonnet CXXXVII, *Collected Poems*, Harper & Row. Copyright 1939, 1967 by Edna St. Vincent Millay and Norma Millay Ellis. By permission of Norma Millay Ellis.)

References

Bloom, M. *The trouble with lawyers.* New York: Simon & Schuster, 1969.

Dewey, J. *Quest for certainty.* New York: Minton, Batch, 1929.

Esslin, M. *The theatre of the absurd.* New York: Anchor Books, 1961.

Freud, S. Formulations regarding the two principles in mental functioning (1911). In *Collected papers*. Vol. 4. (Trans. by J. Riviere) New York: Basic Books, 1959.

Goertzel, V., & Goertzel, M. G. *Cradles of eminence.* Boston: Little, Brown, 1962.

Goode, W. J. *The family.* New Jersey: Prentice-Hall, 1964.

Haskins, R. *The rise of the universities.* New York: Holt, 1923.

Hess, R. Educability and rehabilitation: The future of the welfare class. Paper presented at the 30th Groves Conference on Marriage and the Family, Knoxville, Tenn., April 15, 1964. (Mimeo)

Hoffer, E. Man, play and creativity. *Think Magazine*, 1967, 33(5), 8–10.

Jensen, A. R. Verbal mediation and educational potential. *Psychology in the Schools*, 1966, 3, 99–109.

Koestler, A. *The act of creation.* New York: Macmillan, 1964.

Machlup, F. *The Production and Distribution of Knowledge in the U. S.* Princeton, N. J.: Princeton University Press, 1962.

Maslund, R. Prenatal factors and neuropsychiatric sequalae. In G. Caplan (ed.), *Prevention of mental disorders in children* New York: Basic Books, 1961.

Newton, M. R., & Brown, R. A preventive approach to developmental problems in school children. In E. M. Bower & W. G. Hollister (eds.), *Behavioral science frontiers in education.* New York: Wiley, 1967.

Parsons, T., & Bales, R. *Family socialization and interaction process.* New York: Free Press, 1955.

Pasamanick, B., & Knobloch, H. Epidemiologic studies on the complications of pregnancy and the birth process. In G. Caplan (ed.), *prevention of mental disorders in children.* New York: Basic Books, 1961.

Pyles, M. K. Verbalization as a factor in learning. *Child Development*, 1932, 3, 108–113.

Schon, D. *Displacement of concepts.* London: Tavistock, 1963.

Sorokin, P. as cited in C. Vincent, Mental health and the family. *Journal of Marriage and the Family,* 1967, 29(1), 18–39.

Vincent, C. Mental health and the family. *Journal of Marriage and the Family*, 1967, 29(1), 18–39.

Weisberg, P., & Springer, K. Environmental factors in creative function. *Archives of General Psychiatry*, 1961, 5, 554–564.

4

The Health System

William L. Kissick

The Congress declares that fulfillment of our national purpose depends on promoting and assuring the highest level of health attainable for every person. . . . (Findings and Declaration of Purpose—Public Law 89–749 [*Comprehensive Health Planning*, 1966].)

The Nation must concentrate on the organization of health facilities and other resources into effective, efficient, and economical community systems of comprehensive health care available to all. (National Advisory Commission on Health Facilities [1968, p. 6].)

The above statements of national health policy are indicative of the priority recently assigned to *health* in our society and the necessity to develop *systems* for its realization. Both concepts warrant definition and clarification if one is to discuss meaningfully the health endeavor in the United States and the evolution of a health system.

HEALTH AS A CONCEPT

The word *health* is a deceptively simple, one-syllable noun of Anglo-Saxon derivation meaning "hale" or "whole." It is both a commonplace in our contemporary vernacular and an illusive concept that frustrates description and quantification. In a sense, health is an abstraction that may be viewed as the 20th century equivalent of the Holy Grail—the never-to-be-attained object of a relentless search.

The World Health Organization (undated, p. 5) defines health as "a state of complete physical, mental, and social well-being and not merely the absence of disease or infirmity." Thus, in the preamble to its constitution in 1948, the health agency that speaks for all nations asserts a recognition of the qualitative dimensions of man's existence and endorses a concern for the enhancement of the quality of life as fundamental to an appropriate philosophy of health. An aspiration beyond the mere correction of deficiencies and toward the holistic pursuit of harmony in life is preeminent in the concept.

Rene Dubos (1959) qualifies this definition in his perceptive and engaging essays, *The Mirage of Health*. He notes that, "in reality, complete freedom from disease and from struggle is almost incompatible with the process of living." In his elaboration of this theme, this reknowned medical scientist and philosopher discusses the significant impact man's technological achievements and his behavior as a social animal have had and are having on his state of health and *dis-ease*. The hazards, like the benefits, of our contemporary way of life are everywhere. In a bizarre sense, our society appears to thrive on a precarious balance between health and disease.

Perhaps the balanced perspective is best expressed by Sir Geoffrey Vickers (1958, p. 591) in his characterization of the history of public health as "a record of successive redefinings of the unacceptable." Yesterday's inevitable becomes tomorrow's intolerable. Each achievement presages new expectations. Thus, a single case of a once ubiquitous disease—smallpox—is now considered inexcusable in most parts of the world. In an earlier period of history, a female bore numerous babies in the hopes of having a few survive to

51

adulthood. An infant mortality rate in the United States of 24.8 deaths per 1,000 live births is now considered unacceptable, particularly when contrasted with a rate of 14.2 in Sweden and 19.9 in England and Wales (National Center for Health Statistics, 1967). As medical research continues to advance our knowledge and understanding of human biology, certain types of leukemia may well be found susceptible to a continuous therapeutic regimen much as is diabetes today. In the future, a childhood death of leukemia may be as intolerable as is the death of a childhood diabetic in the 1970s.

Lacking the capacity to identify and measure the positive dimensions of health, we concentrate on the curtailment and elimination of illness—recognizing, however, that an individual can be diseased without being ill and ill without being diseased. At present, the biological dimensions of ill health are better understood than the behavioral aspects. This discrepancy, a reflection of the relative state of advancement of the biological and behavioral sciences, is unfortunate since a comprehensive approach to healing, alleviating, or palliating man's ailments requires an understanding of not only the *soma* but the *psyche* as well. This will become increasingly critical as a consequence of medical progress. The health system of an economically developed and technologically dependent society will have to cope with the problems associated with the inexorable process of aging and the concomitant forms of disability. The medical task will be less the prevention of death through the cure of potentially fatal disease and more the supportive management of the individual's adjustment to his physical condition.

This evolution in the raison d'être of the health system can be appreciated when one reviews a hierarchy of health goals specified by a Committee of the American Public Health Association (Sullivan, 1966, p. 7). The goals have been developed within four stages or levels as follows:
1. Mortality—prevention of death.
2. Serious morbidity—prevention, control, and treatment of disabling, crippling, or chronic illness.
3. Minor morbidity—the treatment of minor illnesses that cause inconvenience, annoyance, or impair social relations.
4. Positive health—the promotion of physical vigor and mental well-being—or, as defined by scientists attempting to conceptualize an index of health, "the individual is capable of fulfilling the requirements of a social role appropriate to his age and sex."

These stages are overlapping; the activities in pursuit of goals at successive stages are considered additive and do not replace activities directed to goals in previous stages. The Committee concluded that the United States in 1960 was ready to initiate an emphasis on stage 3—minor morbidity.

As a society shifts the emphasis from the goal of reducing mortality toward that of promoting positive health, the measurement of progress becomes more difficult. Death is a finite state that can be identified with precision, notwithstanding the recent scientific debates over certification of death prior to the use of the heart or other organs for transplantation. Serious morbidity can also usually be accurately diagnosed, although it may go undetected for a lack of adequate screening programs until years after onset when the disabling sequelae of the disease manifest themselves and are readily recognized. For instance, it is estimated that only one-half of the people in the United States with diabetes mellitus have had the illness diagnosed. A like number have serious morbidity that can be successfully treated—but only if the condition is detected. Nonetheless, in most instances of serious morbidity—as is the case with mortality—its measurement yields data that are indicative of an upswing or a decline in the health status—or more appropriately the status of ill health—of a population.

Definition of "minor morbidity" and "positive health," let alone the measurement rates, trends over time, or other variations in a *General Health Index* (Sullivan, 1966, p. 4) constitute formidable problems. Yet for the children, adolescents, young and middle-aged adults of our society, these will increasingly become the critical measurements if we are to ascertain our relative success and failure in attaining health goals. As is no doubt evident to the reader, advancement in the state of the art vis-à-vis a conceptualization and measurement of a population's health status will be significantly dependent on research and scholarship in the behavioral sciences. Some of the pioneering work on the epidemiology of mental illness (Hollingshead & Redlich, 1958; Myers & Roberts, 1959; Srole, Michael, Largren, Opler, & Rennie, 1962) and survey research addressed to an assessment of happiness (Bradburn & Caplovitz, 1965) suggest the very formidable dimensions and complexities of the inquiry and analyses that lie ahead.

For the present, an increase in life expectancy; reduction in age-specific mortality rates; prevention of epidemics and the outbreak of certain infectious diseases, e.g., polio, tetanus, diphtheria, and typhoid; the early detection and treatment of potentially serious morbidity, e.g., cancer of the cervix and rheumatic fever; and a decrease in disability days experienced in the labor force are the surrogate measures of a population's health status. In the pursuit of "the highest level of health attainable for every person . . ." the population devotes—individually and collectively—an extraordinary level of effort.

The Health Endeavor

The essence of the health endeavor is people giving and receiving services. However, if the encounter between "People Needing Health Services" and "People Providing Health Services" is to be productive, there must be "Organized Arrangements for Performing Medical Care Functions." Each of these components is influenced by a multiplicity of variables—demographic, economic, social, and cultural—as shown in Figure 4–1.

Beginning with "People Needing Health Services" we find a challenging and rapidly changing picture. The population of the United States now exceeds 200 million. Of these, almost one-half (96 million) are 19 years of age and less, or 65 years of age and over. These age groups represent the most frequent consumers of health services. Population is projected to reach 225 million by 1975, 245 million by 1980, and will exceed 300 million before the year 2000 with proportionately greater increases at the youngest and oldest segments of the spectrum. Urbanization and persistent geographic mobility characterize our way of life. Shift of population from rural to urban centers is such that almost three-quarters of the total population are located within the 212 Standard Metropolitan Statistical Areas (SMSA). The economic indicators of gross national product—disposable personal income and median family income—signify a continuously rising standard of living. Educational attainments are also rising. Approximately one-half of persons 25 years of age or older in 1950 had completed high school or college. By 1975 three-quarters of adults 25 years of age and older will have achieved this level of education. These factors in combination with an extraordinary system of communications are features of a sophisticated population which is increasingly

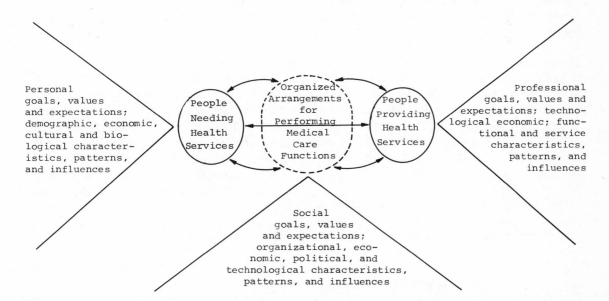

Fig. 4–1. The medical care complex: Boundaries. (Reproduced with permission of the American Journal of Public Health *from* A Guide to Medical Care Administration, *Vol. 1,* Concepts and Principles. *Copyrighted 1969 by the American Public Health Association.)*

articulate in expressing its expectations and demands for health services.

Likewise, in marked contrast to the usual conceptualization of a single physician and his individual patient, the office nurse or bedside nurse with whom the average patient has occasional contact, the dentist we are admonished to visit every six months, or the community hospital not unlike the one in which most of us were born, the health enterprise in our society represents an array of resources and services that are virtually unmatched in their diversity, sophistication, complexity, and organizational challenge. The health enterprise in the United States is a vast and highly complicated social endeavor that accounted in 1971 for expenditures, both public and private, of 75 billion dollars,[1] 7.4 percent of all the goods and services produced, and employs one out of every twenty individuals in the civilian labor force. Thus, as has been noted by one authority on health economics, the "one doctor to one patient mythology" (Somers, 1968, p. 21) must be replaced with a conceptualization consistent with the issues and reality of the day.

An appropriate conceptualization must recognize the sum total of the society's efforts directed toward the mitigation of illness and the realization of health. The limits drawn are arbitrary, especially when viewed in the context suggested by the World Health Organization definition of health. Also, many other secular endeavors—education, agriculture, recreation, and conservation—are obviously relevant to the attainment of health. Nonetheless, those activities directed primarily toward the search for health—the resources both human and material, and the myriad services derived therefrom—can be appreciated and discussed as an interrelated whole. This entity comprises the intangible as well as the tangible, that is programs, people, and facilities. It signifies services, research, and educational activities.

The health endeavor requires the labors of physicians, dentists, nurses, and other professional and technical health personnel. It encompasses hospitals, nursing homes, rehabilitation centers, and health departments. It includes biomedical research programs, the pharmaceutical industry, hospital and medical insurance plans, large national voluntary health agencies, small area-wide planning councils, an interest of the federal, state, and local governments, and the participation of

uncounted individuals from all walks of life. This list is not intended to be more than suggestive of the varied and extensive components. The work of millions of people and expenditures totaling billions of dollars annually constitute the health enterprise. This endeavor represents a significant segment of the energy and fabric of our society.

In more human terms, the health enterprise affects virtually every member of the society. This fact can be readily appreciated when one considers the use of medicines, the prepayment of hospital and medical expense through insurance, efforts to prevent and control communicable disease, and the minor ailments—no matter how inconsequential—for which some health service is sought. Some of the figures are staggering. The National Health Survey (National Center for Health Statistics, 1969) estimates there were 368 million acute illnesses and injuries in the civilian noninstitutional population during 1967. Thus, each member of the population experienced on the average two or three acute illnesses and injuries, causing him to seek medical attention or restrict his usual daily activities. Approximately 830 million visits to physicians occurred in the United States during 1967. During the same year, more than 300 million visits were made to dentists; uncounted millions of prescriptions were filled by pharmacists; approximately 16 million people were admitted to short-term hospitals, accounting for 160 million days of hospitalization; and approximately 3 million people underwent surgical procedures. More than 1.5 million Americans were in a hospital (one-half of these were psychiatric patients) on an average day during 1967.

These are a few of the dimensions of the health endeavor. These efforts constitute a vast societal enterprise that embraces innumerable and varied components. However, do these components taken together constitute a *system* or a seemingly random agglomeration of bits and pieces—parts that elude a whole? This brings us to the second noun in the title of this chapter.

THE SYSTEMS CONCEPT

A system is defined in *Merriam-Webster's Third International Dictionary* as "a regularly interacting or interdependent group of items forming a unified whole." In this definition the key words are *interdependent* and *unified whole*. Although reference to the health enterprise as a system is commonplace, there is still dispute as to the appropriateness of this characterization given the rather tenuous nature of the interdependency among the components and the lack of unity. Commentaries and critiques of "the nonsystem of health services" are frequent. This issue was treated as follows in the recent report of the National Advisory Commission on Health Manpower (1967, p. 2): "The word system is a convenient one for our purposes, but we recognize that it is inaccurate if it implies the existence of an organized, coordinated, planned undertaking . . . medical care in the United States is more a collection of bits and pieces (with overlapping, duplication, great gaps, high costs, and wasted effort), than an integrated system in which needs and efforts are closely related."

Nonetheless, a conceptualization of the health enterprise in systems terms provides an appropriate context within which to analyze health needs, resources, issues, and strategies.

It is helpful to view the health endeavor as would an economist—in terms of its basic resources. Although it is not necessarily the optimal framework for the analysis of the health enterprise, there has been a recent recognition of the importance of health planning, particularly cost/effectiveness and cost/benefit analysis (Kissick, 1967, pp. 201–220). The health enterprise, as is the case in other endeavors, is dependent on four basic resources:

1. Knowledge, or state of the art;
2. Facilities, including equipment and supplies;
3. Manpower—professional, technical, and supportive; and
4. Efficiency in use.

These are discussed briefly below.

The first basic resource, knowledge or state of the art, more than any other determines the fundamental character of the services provided. The rapidly changing nature and rate of growth of the scientific base which medicine utilizes has yielded one of the major challenges to the health enterprise. This rate of growth has been estimated to double every decade, thus assuring each health professional an incredibly rapid rate of obsolescence unless he continues to pursue learning with a compelling dedication. Most of these developments imply changes in both the art and science of professional practice. Some, such as the development of polio and rubella (German measles) vaccines, require us to pursue preventive measures in lieu of the arduous and often painstaking therapeutic and restorative measures of an earlier day needed to manage the serious sequelae of these diseases. Other developments such as chronic renal dialysis (artificial kidneys), kidney transplantation, computerized physiological monitoring, cardiac pacemakers (regulation of heart rate), burn therapy units, and techniques for dealing with cardiac arrest, increase the complexities of health services as well as the need and demand for health care.

The second resource, facilities, including equipment and supplies, comprises more than 7,000 individual hospitals that provide approximately 1,700,000 beds and represent capital assets in excess of $24 billion (Hospital Statistics, 1969). Approximately one-half of these institutions are voluntary, nonprofit hospitals devoted to the care of acute illnesses. The average patient admitted to one of these hospitals is discharged eight days later. The length of hospitalization ranges from one or two days for a tonsillectomy, four or five days for delivery of a baby, ten days to two weeks for major surgical procedures, to one or two months for severe illnesses or injuries. The 3,500 so called short-term general hospitals account for less than one-third of the nation's hospital beds. Only one in ten hospitals have more than 500 beds; one-quarter have 200 or more beds. At the other end of the scale, one-third have less than 50 beds. Further characteristics of these facilities are suggested by the kinds of component resources they represent. Almost all of the hospitals have clinical laboratories and diagnostic X-rays, three out of five include a pharmacy, and more than half have blood banks. Resources for physical therapy are available in one-half and occupational therapy in one-quarter of these institutions.

It must be emphasized that almost 700,000 of the nation's hospital beds are in psychiatric hospitals; 90 percent of these are in some 300 institutions owned and operated by state and local governments. In contrast to the short periods of hospitalization in general hospitals, the average stay by a patient admitted to one of these institutions is more than a year.

In addition to hospitals, more than 12,000 skilled nursing homes account for almost 600,000

TABLE 4–1

Estimated Manpower in Selected Health Occupations: 1950, 1960, and 1962, 1963, or 1964

(Includes only active personnel except as noted)

Health Occupation	1950	1960	1962, 1963, or 1964
All health occupations[1]	1,531,000	2,176,700	–
Medical occupations	608,500	817,200	–
Physicians, M.D. (doctors of medicine)[2]	220,000	260,500	284,300
Physicians, D.O. (doctors of osteopathy)[2]	12,700	14,300	12,900
Administrators, hospital and other	8,600	12,000	12,500
Chiropractors	20,000	25,000	25,000
Dietitians and nutritionists	22,000	26,000	28,000
Educators, health	600	1,000	1,200
Medical secretaries and office assistants	70,000	80,000	–
Medical laboratory technologists-technicians	30,000	68,000	–
Medical record librarians	4,000	8,000	9,000
Medical record technicians	8,000	20,000	23,000
Medical X-ray technologists-technicians	30,800	70,000	–
Opticians and optical laboratory mechanics	19,200	20,300	21,000
Optometrists	17,800	17,300	17,000
Pharmacists	101,100	117,000	117,400
Podiatrists[2]	7,100	7,600	8,000
Psychologists, clinical and other health	3,000	8,000	8,500
Rehabilitation counselors	1,500	3,000	5,000
Social workers, medical and psychiatric	6,200	11,700	15,000
Social scientists, health (anthropologists, economists, sociologists, etc.)	(3)	(3)	500
Statisticians and analysts, health	2,000	5,000	–
Therapists, occupational	2,000	8,000	8,000
Therapists, physical	4,600	9,000	12,000
Therapists, speech and hearing	1,500	5,400	10,200
Veterinarians[2]	15,800	20,100	21,600
Dental occupations	170,400	221,900	–
Dentists[2]	87,200	101,900	107,200
Dental assistants, dentist's office	55,200	82,500	84,000
Dental hygienists	7,000	12,500	14,000
Dental laboratory technicians	21,000	25,000	25,000
Nursing occupations	733,500	1,087,300	–
Professional nurses	375,000	504,000	582,000
Practical nurses	137,000	206,000	225,000
Aides, orderlies, and attendants	221,000	375,000	410,000
Homemakers, home health aides	500	2,300	3,900
Environmental health occupations	11,600	22,300	28,000

Health Occupation	1950	1960	1962, 1963, or 1964
Sanitary and health related engineers	6,000	8,000	9,000
Sanitarians	5,000	11,000	14,000
Radiological health specialists, including health physicists	(^{3})	2,000	3,000
Industrial hygienists	600	1,300	2,000
Health research occupations in the biological sciences, mathematics, physical sciences, and engineering	7,000	^{4}28,000	—

Source: The Facts of Life and Death: Selected Statistics on the Nation's Health and People. National Center for Health Statistics; U. S. Public Health Service; Department of Health, Education, and Welfare; Washington, 1965.

1. Estimates not available for personnel in food and drug protective services, health information and communications, medical engineering and electronics, and orthopedic and prosthetic appliance work.

2. Total personnel, active and inactive.

3. Fewer than 500.

4. Excludes about 11,000 physicians, veterinarians, and dentists engaged in research, who are included in the totals for these professions.

beds. Some 5,000 diagnostic and treatment centers, 3,000 public health centers, and 1,700 medical group practice clinics are further indication of the considerable dimensions of this resource.

The third resource, manpower, has belatedly been acknowledged our most critical resource. Most people tend to think of health manpower in terms of the traditional health professions with physicians occupying the position of both preeminence and predominance. Such a perception was accurate at the turn of the century when three out of five health professionals were physicians (U. S. Department of Health, Education, and Welfare, 1964); at present, however, medical doctors now constitute less than 10 percent of the "health labor force," which totals approximately 4 million—one out of every 20 individuals gainfully employed. The immensity of this figure can be appreciated when it is compared with the work force of General Motors, the largest industrial corporation in the United States, that employed 728,198 people in 1967 (The 500 Largest U. S. Industrial Corporations, 1968). Moreover, the professional, technical, and related manpower in the health labor force range from the highly skilled and extensively educated scientific specialists of many kinds to some of the supportive personnel (maintenance personnel, food handlers, receptionists, etc.) that are not unlike those found in a variety of occupational settings (education, industry, the military, etc.), many of whom have but a minimum of on-the-job training.

The health occupations include those individuals who have required knowledge and skills unique to the health enterprise (Table 4–1). When discrete specialties are considered, more than 200 health careers can be identified within some three dozen occupational categories (National Center for Health Statistics, 1968; United States Department of Labor, 1965). Whereas the population of the United States increased by 29 percent from 1950 to 1966, the number of persons in health occupations increased by 90 percent (United States Department of Health, Education, and Welfare, 1967).

The fourth resource, in terms of economic analysis, is the degree of efficiency in the utilization of basic resources. This includes such factors as allocation of resources among various uses, methods of organization in order to make use of knowledge, and the development of incentives for the production of services. In the health endeavor, degree of efficiency in the use of resources can be subdivided into patterns of organization and financing mechanisms, as these are the principal factors that determine resource utilization. The organizational approaches vary from solo practitioners to comprehensive community health centers and include such items as partnerships, group practices, visiting nurse agencies, hospital-based home care programs, in-plant industrial health services, ambulatory clinics, school health services, or progressive patient care. Financing methods include fee for service, salary and capitation as regards remuneration of professionals, and such concepts as community rating, indemnity insurance service benefits, deductibles, fee schedules, comprehensive prepayment, experience rated premiums, coinsurance, medical indigency, etc.

These resources are inputs into the delivery system. The manner in which these individual components or resources interact and the service configurations that yield health services for the population vary as widely as do the resources. To date there has been greater cognizance of and concern for the resource inputs than the service outputs. As Professor Rashi Fein (1967) has noted, when people can't get medical services they complain of the physician shortage. This is quite natural since the physician usually represents a personification of medical care. For many people, a physician (resource input) is synonymous with a physical examination (service output). In decades past such a perception was valid since a general practitioner provided virtually all of the medical services then available. As a consequence of research discoveries and technological developments, however, it is now acknowledged that a single professional can no longer master the varied knowledge and skills required for the provision of comprehensive health services that incorporate to the fullest our biomedical, scientific capabilities.

The changing character of health services is well illustrated by a recent account of the diagnosis and treatment of phenylketonuria (PKU) in a 28-month-old girl. The medical management of this inborn error of metabolism was effected by the patient's physician and a pediatrician, supported by a team of 14 individuals including other medical specialists, microchemists, psychologists, speech pathologists and social workers, not to mention nurses, aides, and other hospital personnel. The services provided resulted from a mix of the inputs. Thus the delivery of health care was an institutional rather than an individual function and responsibility.

Even a cursory glance at the nation's health enterprise reveals the magnitude and diversity of the services currently being comsumed by the population. Although the dramatic surgical procedures associated with the transplantation of hearts, kidneys, and other organs are most frequently cited as evidence of scientific and technical complexity that requires an organized team effort, the more commonplace experiences can be equally compelling in demonstrating the need for systems of health care. Myocardial infarction is a serious and not infrequent occurrence among middle-aged men. With the introduction of acute coronary care units in general hospitals, the recovery rate among heart attack victims has improved impressively. In these units, nurses and technicians combine forces with electronic equipment to provide continuous, around-the-clock monitoring of a patient's cardiac and circulatory status, searching for any warning signs of impending physiologic changes that can be averted through medical intervention.

A patient history and physical examination are probably the most frequently consumed health services. These are also the most traditional of a physician's services. But when the process is viewed in systems terms it is apparent that there are resource interactions and service configurations that can be substituted for the individual physician. An Automated Multitest Screening Program is currently under development (Collen, 1966). The objective is the annual screening of people with a series of two dozen diagnostic studies requiring a total of approximately two and one-half hours to complete, utilizing self-administered questionnaires, supervision by technicians, and computerized interpretation of results as a substitute for physicians' time.

Turning to the everyday situations experienced by virtually every family, the raising of children is replete with illustrations of the range and diversity of services sought by today's population. Immunizations, nutritional advice, the search for congenital abnormalities, anticipatory guidance, assessment of growth and development, family counselling, treatment of acute illnesses and injury, tests of visual and auditory acuity, preventive dental care, etc., are services that are being shifted from the office of a single physician to a clinic, hospital out-patient department, group practice, or comparable institutional setting. In this instance, it is less the nature of the services that requires a team effort—in contrast to cardiac surgery—but more the recognition that alternative resource interactions are more cost/effective than a single physician.

The growth of institutionalization and specialization is an effort to cope effectively with the requirements for depth and thoroughness in a wide range of tasks. These are essential to adequate provision of many new services. The exponential

TABLE 4-2
Trend in Employment in Health Occupations: 1950, 1960, and 1967 and Projections to 1975 and 1980

Occupation with Group	1950	1960	1967	1975	1980
Total, all health occupations	1,638,800	2,413,400	3,362,000	4,421,500	5,038,300
Other than "allied health"	1,396,200	1,978,200	2,708,500	3,512,500	3,972,300
"Allied health"—at least baccalaureate	64,500	123,400	229,500	350,000	410,000
"Allied health"—less than baccalaureate	177,700	311,800	424,000	559,000	656,000
Medicine and Allied Services, total	522,700	718,700	956,800	1,281,500	1,477,300
Physicians (M.D. and D.O.)	219,900	252,400	305,500	361,500	407,300
Selected practitioners[1]	162,800	180,400	199,800	250,000	275,000
"Allied health"—at least baccalaureate[2]	46,500	92,400	175,000	270,000	320,000
"Allied health"—less than baccalaureate	93,500	186,800	276,500	400,000	475,000
Dentistry and Allied Services, total	161,100	209,200	235,700	248,000	271,000
Dentists	77,900	89,200	98,700	109,000	120,000
"Allied health"—less than baccaluareate[3]	83,200	120,000	137,000	139,000	151,000
Nursing and Allied Services, total	737,000	1,185,000	1,754,000	2,362,000	2,720,000
Registered nurses	375,000	504,000	659,000	816,000	895,000
Licensed practical nurses	137,000	206,000	320,000	546,000	675,000
Nursing aides, orderlies, and attendants[4]	225,000	475,000	775,000	1,000,000	1,150,000
Environmental Health Services, total	19,000	36,000	65,000	100,000	120,000
"Allied health"—at least baccalaureate[5]	18,000	31,000	54,500	80,000	90,000
"Allied health"—less than baccalaureate[6]	1,000	5,000	10,500	20,000	30,000
All Other Services, total[6]	199,000	264,500	350,500	430,000	450,000

Source: Report to the President and the Congress on the Allied Health Professions Personnel Training Act of 1966, as amended. Bureau of Health Professions Education and Manpower Training; National Institutes of Health; U. S. Public Health Service; U. S. Department of Health, Education, and Welfare; Washington, April 1969.

1. Optometrists, pharmacists, podiatrists, clinical psychologists, clinical social workers, chiropractors and naturopaths, and lay midwives.

2. Personnel in administration, biomedical engineering, clinical laboratory services, dietetic and nutritional services, health education, medical record services, occupational therapy, orthotic and prosthetic technology, physical therapy, radiologic technology, specialized rehabilitation services, speech pathology and audiology, vision care (other than ophthalmologists and optometrists), and miscellaneous health services not elsewhere classified.

3. Dental hygienists, dental assistants, and dental laboratory technicians.

4. Includes home health aides.

5. Engineers, scientists, technologists, and technicians in environmental control and food and drug protective services.

6. Personnel in information and communication, library services, mathematical sciences, natural sciences (other than clinical laboratory services and environmental health), social sciences (other than psychology), secretarial and office services, veterinary medicine, and vocational rehabilitation counseling.

Sources: 1967 estimates based on table 1 in "Measuring the Supply of Health Manpower" by M. Y. Pennell. *Health Manpower, United States, 1965–1967.* Public Health Service Publication No. 1000, series 14, No. 1. Washington, Government Printing Office, 1968. 1950 and 1960 estimates based on table 8 in *Health Manpower Source Book 18, Manpower in the 1960's.* Public Health Service Publication No. 263, sec. 18. Washington, Government Printing Office, 1964.

1975 and 1980 projections by the Bureau of Health Professions Education and Manpower Training, Public Health Service.

growth of scientific knowledge has contributed to both this inexorable trend and to a vast potential for improved health care. The greater the diversification among professionals, the more significant the requirement for organization and structure in this human service enterprise. When a solo practitioner could provide all the services, he was de facto the system. Now that specialization is the role among physicians (Table 4–2) and the provision of services requires a shared undertaking, formal mechanisms are needed to assure coordination of effort.

A description of a few health care systems suggests the range, variability, and uncommon quality of the nation's health enterprise. The Hunterdon Medical Center in Flemington, New Jersey, a genuine community health center, brings together the activities of numerous official and voluntary community health agencies with a 160-bed community hospital staffed by two dozen full-time medical specialists working in concert with an equal number of family physicians located throughout the county, all as part of a community effort to realize comprehensive health care for the 70,000 residents of Hunterdon County. The hard-core Appalachian area of eastern Kentucky is the site of a very exciting comprehensive health program involving the energies of the University of Kentucky Medical Center, a chain of seven hospitals built by the United Mine Workers, groups of practicing physicians, the Frontier Nursing Service, state, county, and local health departments, community colleges, and several voluntary health agencies. Not far from there in Greenville, South Carolina, we find a hospital system that brings together one 600-bed general hospital, a 40-bed extended care facility, three small community hospitals (60, 70, and 40 beds), an 80-bed nursing home, a 55-bed mental health center, a 200-bed rehabilitation facility, and a child guidance and education unit, all under unified organizational management. On the opposite coast we find one of the most extensive health care systems, namely the Kaiser Foundation Medical Care Program (National Advisory Commission on Health Manpower, 1967), that provides comprehensive health services to almost 2 million subscribers in California, Washington, Oregon, and Hawaii. The organization includes 19 medical centers for in-patient and out-patient services, 29 medical clinics, and numerous other resources

drawn together in an organization utilizing industrial management capabilities and techniques in the operation of the health care system. Contrasted with the extensive resources of Kaiser and the population density of Oakland, California, a seven-county area in northern New Mexico with a highly dispersed population—50,000 people inhabit an area of some 22,000 square miles—is the setting for the development of a comprehensive health care program attempting to coordinate health resources by linking together seven hospitals, four health centers, and two nursing outposts.

The West Philadelphia Community Mental Health Consortium merges, for the purpose of mental health services delivery, the interests of a city hospital, a university hospital, a university-related hospital, a denominational hospital, a hospital operated and staffed predominantly by black physicians, a specialized psychiatric hospital, and a large, complex, urban university system. These disparate entities, grouped under the umbrella of the West Philadelphia Corporation (a nonprofit enterprise for community development), became an operating community mental health center—"The Consortium"—in July 1967 to serve a catchment area (designate Pennsylvania Region VII–Catchment Area 3), covering 21 square miles and having a population of slightly more than 200,000 representing a mixture of urban elements. Racially, the broad division is about 60 percent white and 40 percent black. The white segment has appreciable numbers of persons of Irish and Italian extraction. In this relatively new urban section for the east coast (about 50 years old), there are many medical facilities, but few social service agencies. More important, although the area has many rather small neighborhood citizens' associations of varying degrees of influence, it has no overall citizens' organization. Thus the geographical boundaries of the area have little meaning to its residents in the sense of demarcating a place where there is any broad community of interest. The neighborhoods themselves vary substantially. For example, there are small, disadvantaged, typically inner-city sections, both black and white; a new middle class black section; an older, largely white, middle class section; and a large, sparsely settled tract, inadequately supplied with municipal and other services, which resembles a "rural slum."

The community's heterogeneity, coupled with the decentralization inherent in the Consortium administrative structure—whereby interests are merged for a common purpose, yet each member agency maintains its own identity—led to an early decision to develop a network of outpatient facilities in the local neighborhoods. Five of these all-purpose neighborhood centers, generically called Counselling Centers, are now in operation. Three of them are attached administratively to member hospitals, but geographically separated from them; one is operated in, but in no way connected with, the municipal district health center that serves the catchment area; and one is attached to, and operated in, premises owned by a civic organization.

Each Counselling Center is responsible for its own intake services and for maintenance of continuity of care. Treatment modalities include crisis intervention, short-term individual psychotherapy, and a variety of group services. In addition to clinical services, each Counselling Center has its own developing program for 1) community organization and community outreach, and 2) consultation and education in the local schools, police force and non-Consortium social service agencies.

The Consortium's other principal components include patient units; a partial hospitalization unit; a 24-hour emergency service (based at Philadelphia General Hospital) which serves the entire catchment area and coordinates its services with all other Consortium clinical units; aftercare and rehabilitation units for chronically ill patients referred both from Philadelphia State Hospital (as well as other state hospitals) and from the Consortium's own system; a large narcotic addict treatment program; a rudimentary service in mental retardation; several small programs offering psychiatric and other services within individual schools; and a research and evaluation program. The Consortium is currently pursuing the development of additional medical services in its delivery system through collaborative planning with the University of Pennsylvania unit of the Greater Delaware Valley Regional Medical Program. The intent is to pursue the effect already initiated through creation of its all-purpose neighborhood centers—of providing entry points to *all* health (and possibly welfare) services for *all* residents of the catchment area.

The Health System in Context

In many respects one of the principal deficiencies among health institutions today is the failure to realize that society and therefore the people, not the authority of science or a supernatural power, is the grantor of prerogatives. There resides the ultimate accountability. Just as constitutional monarchies have replaced the divine right of kings over many centuries in the Western World, so during the recent decades in the history of the health endeavor has society defined, granted, acknowledged, and justified our prerogatives. Most recruits to the health professions, in earning these privileges, fail to recognize to whom they are responsible. The assumptions, expectations, desires, and convictions of many in medicine have served to characterize this endeavor as an estate. Whether or not this was ever true, recent declines in political power, status, and special privilege suggest that such is no longer the circumstance. An exalted origin in Greek mythology and the ecclesiastical character of much of its history notwithstanding, the health endeavor—medicine as it is narrowly perceived—can best be understood as a secular institution. In the 1970s it will no longer be possible to deal with this enterprise as other than an institution in the sociological sense, i.e., "an organized pattern of group behavior, well-established and accepted as a fundamental part of a culture."

Any meaningful discussion, therefore, requires a consideration of the societal fabric encompassing the health endeavor. This fabric, characterized by persistent change, provides a frame of reference that permits a greater understanding of health systems and their dimensions and substance. This perception enables one to appreciate the "dynamic equilibrium" existing between internal developments and external societal forces. The health endeavor is but one among many human enterprises. Moreover, an appreciation of the direction of its probable transition requires an awareness of the forces within society certain to affect its development. It is seldom appreciated that social factors external to the health endeavor can have major and frequently predominant import for the course of health affairs.

Population growth, urbanization, geographic mobility, automation, increased disposable personal income, a rising level of educational attainment, and new technological sophistication all influence our society's health expectations. In many respects, their impact on health systems surpass that of biomedical discoveries, the decisions of individual health professionals, and other components of the health endeavor per se. To date, most of us working within the health system have been so preoccupied with biomedical developments and scientific advances that we have failed to recognize and appreciate the multiplicity of factors influencing the health of individuals, be it the diseases they contract or the medical services they receive.

Chronic diseases and emotional disorders, both major health problems in our society, are known to require the most extensive and complex health services. Accordingly, previous achievements and successes with certain health problems—epidemic disease and nutritional deficiency—and the quickening pace of social interaction are accompanied by the need and demand for even more extensive and elaborate health services. It can be realistically stated that a society with increasing levels of expectation and continued advances in the biomedical sciences has an insatiable need for health services. The degree to which need is translated into demand will be reflected in health policy decisions. These, in turn, will determine the allocation of human and economic resources that will be made to this area of our national life. Thus society has a dual impact on health. It represents resources for attacking health problems, and it manifests an extraordinary proclivity for creating and intensifying man's ills. This is the "process of living" to which René Dubos refers.

The tendency to view health systems in isolation from their societal context provides an incomplete picture. The norms and standards of behavior found in a vast array of statutes, licensure requirements, accreditation procedures, certification mechanisms, stipulated professional ethics, organization policies, insurance regulations, and the like are often overlooked. These and other societal constraints serve to influence the dimensions and character of the health endeavor. The special privileges of practice are granted through licensure by the individual states. The privileged communication of a doctor and patient is recognized and guaranteed by society. The ultimate responsibility is to the people, who, through their elected representatives, define and stipulate the dimensions of professional practice.

Health issues must be approached in their broadest context. This is the only relevant context. Internal forces and those external to the health endeavor react to shape health policy and influence health affairs. There is a dynamic interaction of heretofore unappreciated dimensions and importance that must be recognized and understood. Health systems are now challenged to modify existing activities, services, and programs and to initiate new ones in order to adapt today's social institution to tomorrow's problems. Only thus can optimal health be achieved for the individual and the community.

It has become fashionable to paraphrase Clemenceau's dictum that war is too important to be left to generals. The statement is being made of educators, scientists, and theologians. In health we find decisions too important to be left solely to the professionals.

Enlightened health policy and effective health systems require widespread participation in their formulation by the several and diverse elements of society. Without this balance of perspective, the health endeavor will fail to realize the fullest margin of its potential in terms of measurable human welfare. Indeed, health is everybody's business. To illustrate the implications of the diversity of perspective for each of the components of health systems—"People Needing Health Services," "Organized Arrangement for Performing Medical Care Function," and "People Providing Health Services" (Figure 4—1)—let us examine one aspect of medical care.

The expression "quality of health services" is widely used, discussed, and argued; however, the expression is imprecise and lacks an accepted definition. The expression usually connotes a value judgement as to whether or not the professional is performing his tasks to the best of his ability and in accordance with some generally accepted standards. Actually, standards promulgated by a profession are but one part of a concept of quality of health care. The other basic dimensions to any determination of the quality of health services are the criteria established by the consumer and the society. Admittedly there is some similarity; nevertheless, each set of criteria has distinct features.

The criteria established by the professional are those of peer judgement and are concerned with diagnostic excellence, the scientific validity of one's decisions, and the technical skill manifested in one's provision of service. These are some of the factors toward which record audits and comparable approaches to measuring and evaluating standards are directed. This is also the dimension most severely challenged by the growth in scientific knowledge that has shortened the performance half-life of the practitioner and created an awareness of the need for highly developed and extensively utilized continuing education.

The second dimension of quality health services is that advanced by the consumer. Although he recognizes the importance of the science of medicine, he is also concerned with the art of medicine. The consumer's assessment of quality of health services is subjective and emphasizes the patient's emotional needs. For the consumer, accessibility and compassion are very important elements in determining the quality of health services. This is not to suggest that he is willing to sacrifice scientific quality in order to have accessibility and compassion; but neither is he particularly desirous of sacrificing these in order to receive care of the highest scientific caliber.

The third dimension of the quality of health service is that developed by society. In some respects this dimension is concerned with achieving a balance between the previous two. For a society, efficiency, reasonable costs, and unit productivity are all extremely important variables. A fair statement would be that the societal dimension seeks the most effective utilization, the lowest cost, and the greatest unit productivity without sacrificing the expectations of the professional or the consumer. It is herein that conflicts are destined to be found as those concerned with the formulation of social policy take cognizance of individual and group expectations and seek to achieve satisfactory resolution of incompatibilities.

Analysis in Health Systems

Since a system has relevance and purpose in terms of its outputs and fulfillment of objectives, health systems must be increasingly evaluated in terms of the services they provide and their impact on improving the population's health status. However, in health endeavors, as is the case in other social enterprises, our concern is often with what is commonly felt to be unmeasurable. There is great difficulty in attempting to identify and measure benefits (figure 4–2).

Lacking agreed-upon, numerically commensurable denominators that can be used as the benefit against which to calculate costs, it would appear preferable to specify health program objectives in measurable terms, e.g., services provided, individuals treated, or diseases prevented, and then formulate and analyze alternatives designed to reach the objectives in order to assist the selection of the alternative that can reach the objective at the least cost. The question as to whether disabilities prevented or health care services provided is the greater social benefit must for the present be left to that indefinable mixture of intellectual, professional, and emotional values and preconceptions.

Economists working on health problems support the preference for cost-effectiveness analysis in these areas. They state: "Cost-effectiveness analysis is a special, narrower form of the cost-benefit approach. . . .

"Cost-effectiveness, rather than cost-benefit is employed when various benefits are difficult to measure or when the several benefits that are measured cannot be rendered commensurate." (Klarman, Francis, & Rosenthal, 1968, p. 48).

While cost-effectiveness analyses are being undertaken to assist the selection of the most appropriate programs for achieving specified objectives, the challenge implicit in the concept of cost-benefit analysis must be accepted; definitions and measurements of the benefits of health programs must be sought.

The World Health Organization's definition of health—"complete physical, mental and social well-being. . . ."—suggests formidable intellectual and analytic tasks of description, measurement, and quantification. Nonetheless, formulations of benefits that are as precise but more relevant than "lives saved" and "diseases prevented" are needed as indicators of an individual's capacity to function in "a role appropriate to his age and sex. . . ." At the same time, availability and accessibility of services are appropriate objectives even though the ultimate benefits of many of these services may elude quantification for some time. Thus, regular visits of a mother and her infant to a pediatrician or clinic for guidance and counselling concerning growth and development are assumed to have a beneficial impact through succeeding decades of life. The provision of the service is therefore a priori a valid health objective.

"Cost-benefit" or "cost-effectiveness" analyses are directed toward identifying the program or

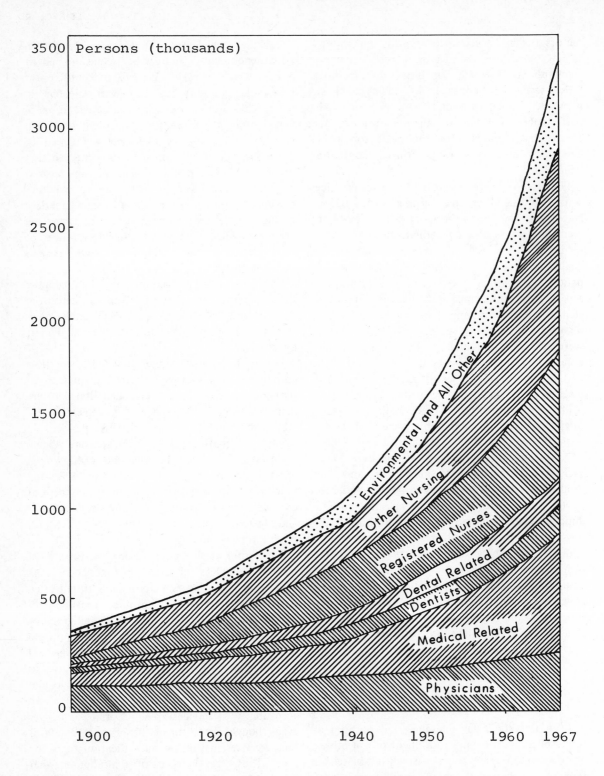

Fig. 4—2. Employment in health occupations: 1900-1967. (Reproduced from "Report to the President and the Congress on the Allied Health Professions Personnel Training Act of 1966," as amended. Washington, D. C.: Bureau of Health Professions Education and Manpower Training, National Institutes of Health, United States Public Health Service, United States Department of Health, Education, and Welfare, April 1969.)

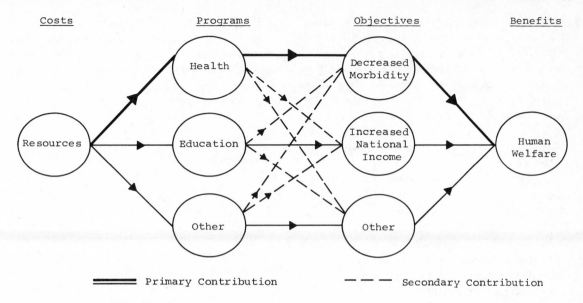

Fig. 4—3. Model of cost-benefit analysis in social endeavors.

service alternatives that will yield the maximum benefits (however defined) for the funds expended or will realize specific objectives at the least cost. The analysis can be subdivided into a few broad elements or extensively into numerous discrete components. Essentially it entails a selection of objectives, the establishment of performance criteria, a formulation of alternatives, and the prospective assessment of as many implications of each alternative as appear relevant. A singular characteristic of the analytic process is a working back and forth through the problem including modification in the objectives; this is called "suboptimumization."

1. Selection of Objectives and Criteria. This is the most critical step. As noted by the two foremost proponents of cost-effectiveness analysis: "Choice of objectives is fundamental; if it is wrongly made, the whole analysis is addressed to the wrong question." (Hitch & McKean, 1960, p. 118)

In some instances, the objective is virtually self-evident, e.g., reduction in the incidence of carcinoma of the cervix. The problem lies in specification of broader objectives that, taken together, sum to the national goal of "the highest level of health attainable for every individual." Lacking a calculus to compute the benefits that would make the greatest contribution to this goal, the policy discussions vis-à-vis the selection of

priorities for health programs become all the more critical. These selections can be called subjective and arbitrary or expressions of community preference. In our society the selection of objectives and priorities is ultimately political in the fullest sense of the word.

A formulation of heirarchies of objectives that are in any sense comprehensive and speak to the totality of the health system, must await the accumulation of a vast body of literature and experience working on the "sub-system" and on the relationships among and between the variables and subobjectives. However, such a level of understanding will be necessary if meaningful cost-benefit analyses among programs are to be attempted.

In some cases criteria for measurement of performance in approximation of objectives is self-evident. If reduction of mortality from tuberculosis is the objective, the ultimate criterion is easily established. Where the objective is the availability of optimal services for the emergency care of acute myocardial infarction, the complexity of the selection of criteria vis-à-vis intensive care beds, nursing services, physician involvement, etc., is extraordinary.

2. Formulation of Alternatives. Most objectives can be achieved via more than one course of action. For example, increasing the availability of nursing services can be pursued by increasing the numbers of graduates, transferring certain nursing tasks to other kinds of health workers with shorter periods of training, or reducing the attrition through marriage and child rearing of nurses from active status (perhaps by converting a significant portion of nursing duties to a job appropriate to a male career). Such analytic efforts afford creativity and imagination in conceiving *feasible* innovations that result in preferred alternatives for realizing an objective.

A recent cost-effectiveness study of health care facilities conducted by the United States Public Health Service (1968) set out to determine an optimal program for the construction and modernization of hospitals and other medical facilities for the next decade. A major concern was the potential for reducing needed construction of acute hospital beds with their subsequent high operating costs. Nine possible alternatives were assessed:

a. Transfer of hospital patients to nursing homes.
b. Transfer of hospital patients to home health services.
c. Expansion of rehabilitation services.
d. Reductions in length of hospital stay.
e. Conversion of unnecessary maternity and pediatric beds to medical-surgical beds.
f. Inter-hospital sharing of facilities.
g. Extended workweek in hospitals.
h. Technological improvements.
i. Increased preventive care.

Although costs tend to be thought of in terms of the investment of dollars required to achieve a benefit, the more thoroughly one examines the problems associated with health care facilities, the more "manpower costs" appear to be the constraining factor. Thus, the transfer of hospital patients to home health services would save on the costs of constructing and operating a hospital bed. The manpower requirements are such that the "cost-effective" solution in many instances may be more beds and longer hospital stays in order to get the best use of a scarce and costly resource, i.e., medical specialists.

3. Model Development and Testing. Analyses increasingly involve the use of mathematical models to test assumptions, hypotheses, and suggested program alternatives, since computer technology permits the use of numerous variables and the simulation of probable outcomes. The quality of the data used and the validity of the assumptions determine the value of the simulations. Accordingly, for many analyses, much time must be spent in the development of accurate data. In many instances longitudinal investigations and demonstrations spanning years may be required.

4. Suboptimumization. The distinguishing feature of these analyses is the recycling of the analysis to modify objectives, criteria, alternatives, and models—frequently several times—before selecting the preferred alternative. This process of "suboptimumization" is referred to as "mini-max" in which one attempts to achieve a maximum approximation of the objective for a minimum unit cost. Objectives as well as program alternatives are subject to modification.

For example, if the program objective is the provision of artificial renal dialysis or kidney transplantation for every individual with end-stage kidney disease who is clinically suitable, the requirements and unit costs can be calculated. However, analysis may reveal that by concentrating the resources in certain geographic regions, 80 percent of the potential beneficiaries can be served at a significantly lower unit cost. Obviously, this is hardly the answer to the problem, since the "mini-max" solution challenges the concept of equity in our society. As noted previously, the decisions are ultimately political. However, further analysis may point the way to a compromise solution that is politically, as well as medically and economically, feasible, i.e., the optimal approximation of the stated objective. Our society—any society—is constantly faced with problems of choice. Agonizing and complex decisions must be made, in some instance determining who shall live and who shall die. Which investments will yield the largest health benefits for the greatest numbers? This is the basic challenge facing the health system now and in the future.

THE DECADE AHEAD

The American population has become increasingly conscious that despite rising costs and per capita expenditures for health and medical care (Table 4–3 and Figure 4–4), the highest of any nation in the world, we enjoy neither the finest health

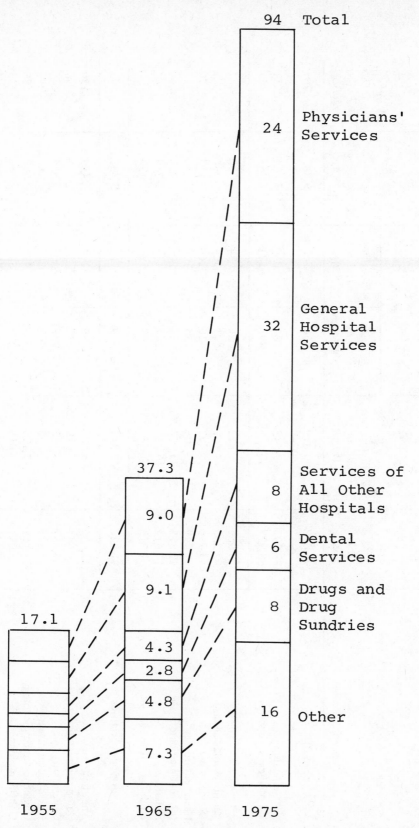

Fig. 4—4. Expenditures for health services and supplies (in billions of dollars). (Reproduced from the Report of the National Advisory Commission on Health Manpower, 1967, Vol 1.)

TABLE 4–3
Type of Practice and Primary Specialty of Physician: 1967

		Number of Physicians (M.D.)				
		Patient Care				
			Hospital-based Practice			
Primary Specialty	Total Active	Solo, Partnership, Group, or Other Practice	Training Programs	Full-time Physician Staff	Other Professional Activity	Number of D.O.'s in Private Practice[1]
All specialties	294,072[2]	190,079	46,856	37,255	19,882	10,067
General practice[3]	83,293	63,543	8,786	7,080	3,884	8,651[4]
Medical specialties	68,927	40,113	12,498	9,571	6,745	354
Allergy	962	872	26	34	30	2
Cardiovascular disease	2,263	1,162	421	324	356	2
Dermatology	3,796	2,807	510	260	219	20
Gastroenterology	749	408	135	106	100	–
Internal medicine	42,325	23,952	8,055	6,205	4,113	266
Pediatrics[5]	17,614	10,466	3,281	2,118	1,749	64
Pulmonary diseases	1,218	446	70	524	178	–
Surgical specialties	91,822	63,317	16,409	8,764	3,332	841
Anesthesiology	9,630	6,681	1,296	1,164	489	180
Colon and rectal surgery	644	610	17	12	5	43
General surgery	29,687	18,365	6,989	3,309	1,024	273
Neurological surgery	2,315	1,390	502	243	180	5
Obstetrics and gynecology	17,964	13,125	2,667	1,499	673	80
Ophthalmology	9,083	7,048	1,247	540	248	133[6]
Orthopedic surgery	8,426	5,853	1,557	807	209	73
Otolaryngology	5,583	4,239	807	382	155	23
Plastic surgery	1,303	948	220	98	37	1
Thoracic surgery	1,725	1,093	228	254	150	5
Urology	5,462	3,965	879	456	162	25

Psychiatry and neurology	23,295	10,809	4,491	5,432	2,563	31
Child psychiatry	1,080	475	255	201	149	—
Neurology	2,466	912	611	444	499	3
Psychiatry	19,749	9,422	3,625	4,787	1,915	28
Other specialties[7]	26,735	12,297	4,672	6,408	3,358	190
Aviation medicine	792	87	64	459	182	—
General preventive medicine	1,007	395	61	171	380	—
Occupational medicine	1,706	1,416	17	100	173	3
Pathology[8]	9,518	2,783	2,222	3,086	1,427	46
Physical medicine and rehabilitation	1,208	386	234	413	175	9
Public health	1,627	984	51	158	434	—
Radiology[9]	10,877	6,246	2,023	2,021	587	132

Source: *Health Resources Statistics.* National Center for Health Statistics; U. S. Department of Health, Education and Welfare, U. S. Public Health Service; Health Services and Mental Health Administration, Washington, 1968.

1. Data not available on specialties for 775 in training programs; 181 in full-time hospital staff positions; and 186 in other professional activities; and 172 Federal D.O.'s. Excludes all inactive D.O.'s and those with status not reported.

2. Includes non-Federal M.D.'s in the 50 States, District of Columbia, Puerto Rico, and other U. S. outlying areas (American Samoa, Canal Zone, Guam, Pacific Islands, and Virgin Islands); and Federal M.D.'s in the U.S. and abroad. Excludes all inactive M.D.'s, those with addresses unknown, and those with temporary foreign addresses.

3. Includes no specialty and other specialties not recognized.

4. Includes 827 with practice limited to manipulative therapy.

5. Includes pediatric allergy and pediatric cardiology.

6. Includes specialty combination of ophthalmology and otolaryngology, and ophthalmology and otorhinolaryngology.

7. In 1966, the American Medical Association eliminated the specialty "Administrative Medicine." Those physicians previously classified in "Administrative Medicine" have been reclassified according to their secondary specialty.

8. Includes forensic pathology.

9. Includes diagnostic radiology and therapeutic radiology.

Sources: AMA Department of Survey Research: *Distribution of Physicians, Hospitals, and Hospital Beds in the U.S., 1967. Regional, State, County, Metropolitan Area.* J. N. Haug and G. A. Roback. Chicago. American Medical Association, 1968. Membership and Statistics Department: *A Statistical Study of the Osteopathic Profession, December 31, 1967.* Chicago. American Osteopathic Association. June 1968.

services nor the highest health status when compared with other developed societies. The death rate has stabilized since 1955 after decades of almost steady decline. Males 20 years of age in 20 other countries enjoy a greater life expectancy than do American men of the same age. We rank almost as unfavorably in terms of our infant mortality rates. The 1960s brought an end to complacency and a demand for solutions to existing health care problems.

The issue was succinctly stated by the Secretary of Health, Education, and Welfare and the Assistant Secretary for Health and Scientific Affairs in their July 10, 1969, report to the President.[2] "What is ultimately at stake is the pluralistic, independent, voluntary nature of our health care system. We will lose it to pressures of monolithic government-dominated medical care unless we can make that system work for everyone in the Nation."

The response to this challenge will pursue two major themes:

1. Removal of the economic barrier to health care.
2. Formulation of optimal organization, structure, and institutions for providing health services.

Titles XVIII and XIX of the Social Security Act of 1965—Medicare and Medicaid—represent the first steps toward the attainment of "universal health insurance" in the United States. Whether a decade or less will be required, one can only guess; however, one can be confident that our society will develop the mechanisms through which virtually all of the population will budget and prepay the costs of health care. Community mental health centers, maternal and infant care projects, OEO neighborhood health centers, regional medical programs, comprehensive health planning (P. L. 89–749), and the National Center for Health Services Research and Development—all new programs initiated by the federal government between 1963 and 1967—are concerned primarily with the search for effective and responsive institutional mechanisms for the provision of human services.

The expression "health system" connotes to some a national health service, i.e., a single governmental agency responsible for the health care of the entire population. This is indeed the character of the health system in some societies of the world. However, if one were to present social action on a scale, with absolute free enterprise at one pole and government domination at the other, health efforts in the United States would fall closer to the former. At present, efforts to develop health systems are forming on attempts to define a middle ground position of community responsibility that merges private initiative and public accountability. We are searching for the appropriate context and structure in which to vest authority—a social instrument short of government that functions adequately in the public interest, perhaps a "social utility" (Burns, 1967), a "quasi-nongovernmental organization" (Pifer, 1967), or a franchised service, not unlike the airlines, with governmental standards and regulation (White, 1967). The organization and financing of health services in the United States in the manner best suited to the aspirations and requirements of both the providers and recipients of medical care are certain to be the ranking concerns of the health system in the 1970s.

Notes

1. *Social Security Bulletin*, January 1972.
2. "The Nation's Health Care System," remarks of the President, HEW Secretary Robert H. Finch, Assistant Secretary Roger O. Egeberg, and Under Secretary John G. Veneman on a Report on Health Care Problems and Programs in *Weekly Compilation of Presidential Documents*, July 14, 1969, p. 969.

References

Bradburn, N. M., & Caplovitz, D. *Reports on happiness.* (National Opinion Research Center Report) Chicago: Aldine, 1965.

Burns, E. The challenge and the potential of the future. In *Community health service for New York City.* New York: Commission on the Delivery of Personal Health Service, 1967.

Collen, M. F. Periodic health examinations using an automated multitest laborator. *Journal of the American Medical Association*, 1966, –, 830–833.

Comprehensive Health Planning and Public Health Service Amendments of 1966. Public Law 89–749. 89th Congress. S. 3008. November 3, 1966. Sec. 2(a.)

Dubos, R. *The mirage of health.* New York: Harper, 1959.

Fein, R. *The doctor shortage: An economic diagnosis.* Washington, D. C.: Brookings Institute, 1967.

Hitch, D. J., & McKean, R. N. *Economics of defense in the nuclear age.* Cambridge: Harvard University Press, 1960.

Hollingshead, A. B., & Redlich, F. C. *Social class and mental illness: A community study*. New York: Wiley, 1958.

Hospital statistics. *Hospitals* (Guide issue), August 1969.

Kissick, W. L. Planning, programming and budgeting in health. *Medical Care*, 1967, 5(4), 201–220.

Klarman, H. E., Francis, U. O., & Rosenthal, G. D. Cost effectiveness analysis applied to the treatment of chronic renal disease. *Medical Care*, 1968, No. 6, 48.

Myers, J. K., & Roberts, B. H. *Family and class dynamics in mental illness*. New York: Wiley, 1959.

National Advisory Commission on Health Facilities. *Report to the President*. Washington, D. C.: United States Government Printing Office, 1968.

National Advisory Commission on Health Manpower. *Report of the National Advisory Commission on Health Manpower*. Washington, D. C.: Author, 1967.

National Center for Health Statistics. *International comparison of perinatal and infant mortality*. (Series 3, No. 6) Washington, D. C.: United States Department of Health, Education, and Welfare, 1967.

National Center for Health Statistics. *Health resources statistics 1968*. Washington, D. C.: United States Department of Health, Education, and Welfare, 1968.

National Center for Health Statistics. *Current estimates from the Health Interview Survey, United States 1967*. (Series 10, No. 52) Washington, D. C.: United States Department of Health, Education, and Welfare, 1969.

Pifer, A. The quasi nongovernmental organization. In *1967 annual report of the Carnegie Corporation of New York*. New York: Carnegie Corporation of New York, 1967.

Somers, A. R. Some basic determinants of medical care and health policy. In, *Dimensions and determinants of health policy*. New York: Milbank Memorial Fund, 1968.

Srole, L., Michael, S. T., Largren, T., Opler, M. K., & Rennie, T. A. C. *Mental health in the metropolis: The Midtown Manhattan Study*. New York: McGraw-Hill, 1962.

Sullivan, D. F. *Conceptual problems in developing an index of health*. (Series 2, No. 17) Washington, D. C.: National Center for Health Statistics, United States Department of Health, Education, and Welfare, 1966.

The 500 largest U. S. industrial corporations. *Fortune*, June 15, 1968.

The Kaiser Foundation medical care program. In *Report of the National Advisory Commission on Health Manpower*. Vol. 2. Appendix IV. Washington, D. C.: National Advisory Commission on Health Manpower, 1967.

United States Department of Health, Education, and Welfare. *Manpower in the 1960's. Health Manpower Source Book*. (Section 18) Washington, D. C.: Author, 1964.

United States Department of Health, Education, and Welfare. *Health manpower. Perspective 1967*. Washington, D. C.: Author, 1967.

United States Department of Labor. *Health careers guidebook*. Washington, D. C.: Author, 1965.

United States Public Health Service. Program analysis of health care facilities. Washington, D. C.: Author, 1968. (Mimeo)

Vickers, G. What sets the goals of public health? *New England Journal of Medicine*, 1958, 258(12), 591.

White, K. Personal incentives, professional standards, and public accountability in the provision of personal health services. Paper presented at the 134th annual meeting of the American Association for the Advancement of Science, New York, December 30, 1967.

World Health Organization. Constitution of the World Health Organization. In *Handbook of basic documents*. New York: Author, undated.

5

The Criminal Justice System

Saleem A. Shah

The legal system is a major institutional complex within society. It is embedded in society and generates a distinctive and more-or-less coherent—even though almost continually changing—set of legal norms, roles, organizations, and practices. There are characteristic patterns of interrelations between the legal system and various other institutional and individual spheres of functioning. In modern industrial societies the systems of law have become very far-reaching and legal rules and procedures permeate almost all realms of behavior. Thus, a man's ownership and use of property, his relations with his wife and children, his relations with his employer and employees and the conditions of his job, his rights and duties in interactions with other individuals and organizations, and many other areas of social functioning are among the aspects of everyday living which are governed by, or subject to, existing or potential rulings of the legal system.

The concern of this chapter will be with the societal system charged with the regulation, control, and sanctioning of behavior which violates norms of conduct established by the criminal law; or, simply stated, with that part of the legal institution which is referred to as the *criminal justice system*. The *criminal sanction* deals with the problem of trying to control antisocial behavior by imposing punishment on people who have been found guilty of violating rules of conduct called criminal statutes. In pointing out that the criminal sanction is the paradigm case of the controlled use of power within a society, Packer (1968) remarks: "It raises legal issues that are too important to be left to the lawyers, philosophic issues that are too important to be left to the philosophers, and behavioral science issues that are too important to be left to the behavioral scientists (page 5)."

The numerous topics and issues encompassed by the criminal justice system are very complex and beyond the scope of this brief discussion. Thus, the topics discussed here will be those which, in the judgment of the author, help to provide an overall description and understanding of the functioning of the aforementioned societal system. These topics will include: law and the social control of behavior; the deviancy-labeling process; some basic characteristics of the criminal law; major components of the criminal justice system; the criminal justice process; specific mental health issues relating to the criminal justice system; and finally, a discussion of some roles and functions of behavioral and social scientists.

LAW AND SOCIAL CONTROL

When certain members violate social norms of the larger group in a society, various means are used to achieve compliance with the norms and to control and regulate the behavior of the offending persons. Some social controls exercised by the group are unintentional, while others are deliberately brought into play through a variety of formal and informal measures. The use of punishment through sanctions of the criminal law is one of the more important formal means of social control. However, such societal sanctions should be seen as only part of the larger picture of making people conform to the rules and mores of the society.

The criminal law is not the only, nor even the primary, method relied upon by society to motivate compliance with its rules. The community depends upon a very broad spectrum of sanctions to regulate and control conduct. Thus, civil liabilities, administrative regulations, licensing, and various noncriminal penalties carry the brunt of the regulatory job in a wide range of fields.

The concept of crime is relative to many other variables. For example, what is officially defined as crime in one city, county, or nation may not be so defined in another. What may be considered crime at a particular period in time may not be so considered at some other period. Moreover, as noted above, criminal laws are but one facet of the regulations imposed on individuals which may vary all the way from ordinary customs and social conventions such as good manners and rules of religious groups, to other sets of norms which relate to public regulations and laws. Indeed, sometimes acts which are not crimes may be punished more severely than if they were—for example, acts leading to the religious penalty of excommunication.

The criminal law, therefore, is only one of a number of devices used by a society to accomplish the goal of social control. The term social control is used to designate those arrangements within a society which have been devised to promote the predictability of certain behaviors and to develop some degree of social regularity in regard to various aspects of social and interpersonal conduct.

A major share of the predictability of human behavior is the result of personal or self-exerted control, rather than external control or coercion. In turn, a major task of the socialization process centers around the development and inculcation of appropriate personal control in keeping with the values and norms of the culture. Quite obviously, personal and social control are not entirely independent phenomena. In a very real sense social controls have been developed and are used to handle instances in which personal controls have broken down or where they are inadequate in regulating behavior. Stated differently, social controls are brought into play when individuals fail to sufficiently control and regulate their own behavior (Clinard, 1958; Gibbons, 1968; Packer, 1968; Sutherland & Cressey, 1966).

Various distinctive features of law as a form of social control have been identified. Laws are a part of the normative structure of a society. That is, they constitute one set of rules regarding obligatory or forbidden actions. Since laws also involve sanctions, they are accompanied by various penalties and punishments in instances where the laws are disobeyed. A third characteristic of laws is that when they conflict with other interests the law must be followed even though there may be a violation of some other set of norms—for example, religious or professional. In other words, the laws of the society are meant to prevail over other injunctions. Finally, laws are part of a larger legal system which includes a relatively explicit underlying rationale or philosophy, a set of procedures for applying and enforcing laws, and a body of recognized officials delegated with the responsibility of carrying out legal procedures. Each of these four characteristics must be present for a normative system to be considered legal (Gibbons, 1968).

Although the *criminal law* exhibits the characteristics identified above, it is only one of a number of legal systems. The criminal law possesses distinctive features which set it off from other systems of law. Broadly speaking, criminal laws are rules which prohibit or compel particular types of conduct held to be important for the welfare of society or the state. The criminal law is separate and distinct from *civil law*, even though the behavior and relationship regulating functions are common to both. The civil law deals with torts (or wrongs committed against the individual), breaches of contract, property rights, inheritance, and so on. In violations of civil laws it is generally the injured person who must set the legal machinery in operation, and he is the recipient of redress from the offender. In contrast, a *crime* is a violation of the criminal law and is viewed as an offense against the state. Thus, the state acts as the plaintiff, initiates the action against the offender, and exacts the punishment which is authorized by law.

THE DEVIANCY-LABELING PROCESS

An analysis of the criminal justice system should logically be preceded by an examination of the societal processes whereby deviant behavior is defined and labeled. It is extremely important to note that deviancy is not a given; nor does it have an absolute and unequivocal meaning within various cultures. It is important to take a careful look at the factors which determine what socially deviant behaviors become the concern of the criminal justice system. What kinds of behaviors are declared to be so objectionable to the larger and more influential segments of the community, so irritating to certain societal groups, or so threatening to social order and stability, that they come to be defined as crimes and are subjected to various social sanctions?

A premise which often seems implicit in the discussions of many mental health professionals concerning various forms of deviant behavior is that such behavior reflects something inherently different about the individual, and that deviant acts occur because of some special characteristic (e.g., psychopathology) of the individual. However, since different groups judge different things to be deviant, it becomes obvious that the determination of deviance very much involves the person or group making the judgment, the particular process by which such a judgment is reached, and the situation and context within which such a determination is made. To ignore this complex and variable character of the deviancy-labeling process would logically tend to limit both the understanding of such behavior as well as the development of adequate theories concerning deviant behavior (Becker, 1963; Shah, 1969a).

Deviancy Defined as Crime

In studying the criminal-labeling process one can start with the presence of various social norms designed to regulate social relations and behavior. Some social norms have considerable force and sanctions to support compliance while others have little such force. Among the more permanent and universal social norms are those associated with social institutions. Institutional norms tend to be supported by high degrees of consensus and usually elicit intense reactions when they are violated. Related to social norms are the central goals of a culture, that is, *social values*. Not only are social values shared widely in the culture but they are regarded as matters of collective welfare and often involve strong emotional beliefs concerning their importance. Social norms often involve some basic goals or values held in high regard in the culture. Thus, murder, manslaughter, rape, robbery, and theft are violations not just of legal norms but also of social norms involving basic values in the protection of human life, sexual and family life, and property, respectively. Criminal laws may therefore be seen as laws regulating behavior which are enforced by coercion of the state (Clinard, 1958).

In complex societies, consensus about discouraging certain kinds of behavior has been embodied in various official rules. While, as noted earlier, the legal system has several means for the regulation of behavior, a most important set of rules and sanctions is contained in the criminal law. Criminal laws are enforced by particular representatives of the state (viz., various personnel within the criminal justice system), as distinguished from other kinds of institutional functionaries. Thus, an act can be a violation of rules for family living or for religious, economic, or educational conduct, and still not stimulate an *official* reaction from society's criminal justice system.

A person may, for example, conduct himself in such a fashion as to violate rules of good etiquette at a wedding or other social situation and as a result lose favor and esteem with other participants and be subjected to varying degrees of social ostracism. However, such a violation is not a crime and is not of concern to the criminal justice system. On the other hand, if a participant at a wedding gets into a fight, behaves in an obscene manner, assaults another person, or steals the wedding presents, he now has engaged in behaviors which constitute crimes. The latter behavior is a violation of rules which go beyond the wedding situation and are of concern to the state as a whole. In such situations, policemen, jailers, attorneys, judges, probation and parole officers, prison wardens, and other functionaries within the criminal justice system will become involved in the various actions which may be directed against the law violator (Clinard, 1958; Sutherland & Cressey, 1966).

THE CRIMINAL LAW

In an earlier period, criminal laws were enacted when almost all the members of a society believed strongly that a particular kind of behavior was so threatening or so repulsive that formal machinery should be set up for dealing with it. Thus, taboos against murder, theft, and incest were considered so important that they became institutionalized. Most criminal laws established in more recent times, however, do not necessarily have such a broad base in society. These are the laws that institutionalize *folkways*. While the same kinds of officials are given authority to enforce the laws once they are enacted, the process of establishing them is different. Rather than a codification of a widespread consensus that certain conduct is morally wrong, these laws are likely to be codifications of the consensus of only a rather small—but powerful or influential—segment of society. In the latter category would be laws against operating a saloon on Sunday and the ban on the sale of contraceptive devices.

Formalized bodies of criminal law, including mechanisms for the implementation of the codes, are a relatively recent human invention. For much of human history behavior has been controlled by personal controls and informal social control devices. However, as societies have grown in size, complexity, and impersonality, the mores and folkways have become inadequate for the task of maintaining social stability. Sutherland and Cressey (1966) note that laws are utilized in America with increasing frequency: the number of statutes in a selected group of states increased approximately 40 percent from 1900 to 1930, and it has been estimated that at least one-half million new state laws have been enacted in the past 50 years. Sutherland and Cressey point out, "Laws have accumulated because the mores have been weak and inconsistent; and because the laws have not had the support of the mores, they have been relatively ineffective as a means of control. When the mores are adequate, laws are unnecessary; when the mores are inadequate, the laws are ineffective (page 11)."

Characteristics of the
Criminal Law

Several essential characteristics of criminal law have been identified by Sutherland and Cressey (1966). These are as follows. The requirement of *politicality* means that in recent times criminal laws typically originate through the actions of the state rather than some private organization or group; only rules promulgated by the law-making bodies of the state and its subdivisions constitute criminal laws. However, as will be discussed later, the *common law* is an important exception to the above characteristic. Another characteristic is *specificity*. Criminal laws have to provide strict and rather precise definitions of the particular acts which constitute crime. In practice, however, specificity is a matter of degree and some laws are relatively broad and general in their language—such as those defining "vagrancy" or "disorderly conduct." *Uniformity* is a characteristic which refers to the effort to specify crimes and invoke sanctions against offenders in an even-handed fashion. Criminal liability is supposed to be uniform for all, irrespective of social background or status. However, in practice this principle appears to break down at several points. Finally, criminal laws provide *penal sanctions* which indicate the penalties specified for violation of statutes.

Requirements for Acts
Considered as Crimes

A number of elements of behavior must occur in order for certain actions properly to become the concern of the criminal law.

The first requirement is that the behavior to be considered a crime must constitute a "harm." That is, the act must result in visible, external consequences which are regarded as detrimental to social interests. To the extent that an act results in injuries only to the parties immediately concerned in the act, that behavior does not qualify as a crime. In this instance the legal system provides various mechanisms for redress through the civil law (cf. page 74).

In order for an act to be identified as a crime, that act must be *legally forbidden*. In other words, antisocial conduct is not criminal until it has specifically been proscribed in the body of the criminal law. A number of other requirements are also identified. The "conduct" must actually occur for a crime to take place. It also has to be shown that there is a "causal" relationship between voluntary misconduct and the legally forbidden harm; that is, the harm has to be shown to be a direct consequence of the misconduct, and not one due to other indirect and antecedent events. There also is required a criminal intent or *mens rea*; that is, it must be shown that the person intended or calculated to behave in the manner defined as criminal. It should be noted, however, that the element of *mens rea* is not involved in certain minor offenses such as traffic violations. In these instances, certain actions and consequences constitute crimes even though the harmful consequences may have been unintended by the offender. Such violations are sometimes referred to as "strict liability" offenses. Statutory rape and "contributing to the delinquency of a minor" are other strict liability offenses.

It should be pointed out that in practice the criminal law shows a number of discrepancies from the aforementioned criteria of crimes. As will be discussed later under the *Criminal Justice Process*, in actual day-to-day functioning the criminal process shows little of the neatness and clear distinctions which this abbreviated description might tend to suggest. Rather, it is a very flexible and elastic societal system. The wide discretion available to and exercised by various criminal justice system functionaries (for example, policemen and prosecutors) makes this a very complex and "living" societal process.

To summarize, as Packer (1968) has noted, three concepts symbolize the basic problems of substance (as opposed to procedures) in the criminal law: 1) what particular conduct should be designated criminal; 2) what determinations must be made before a person can be found to have committed a criminal offense; and 3) what should be done with persons who are found to have committed offenses.

The Development and Classification of Criminal Laws

Most of the present-day crimes in the various states had their origin in the so-called common law of England. The *common law* was the law as developed in the early English case decisions, without the aid of any parliamentary action.

In subsequent years, the common law has been changed or supplemented by the acts of the various state legislatures. Some states have completely abolished the common law and rely solely upon the criminal codes as the source of their criminal law. Most of the conventional crimes, such as burglary and robbery, were crimes under the common law long before the enactment of statutes. Criminal statues, elements of the common law where applicable, and the subsequent interpretation of laws by courts constitute the criminal law (Inbau & Sowle, 1960).

Offenses which were contrary to well-established social mores and values, and which were generally prohibited by the common law, are referred to by lawyers as *mala in se*, that is, as bad or evil in their very nature.

Certain other types of behavior, which constitute a considerable portion of the criminal law, have no such basis in the common law. Lawyers refer to this group of criminal offenses as *mala prohibita*, that is, as bad simply because they have been prohibited by law.

Crimes have generally been classified into three categories: *treason, felonies,* and *misdemeanors. Treason* is generally considered to be a most serious offense because it represents a direct attack upon, or betrayal of, the government itself. *Felonies* are the more serious class of criminal offenses and generally they are punished by a sentence of one year or more in a state prison or reformatory. *Misdemeanors*, on the other hand, are offenses of a relatively minor nature, and typically involve sentences of less than a year in local jails or correctional institutions.

Actually, there are few clear-cut distinctions between felonies and misdemeanors in relation to the acts involved. Often the decision is quite arbitrary, so that the theft of an article worth over $50 is a felony in many states, whereas the theft of an article of less value is considered to be a misdemeanor. Many offenses such as burglary and assault involve varying degrees of seriousness. Some of these offenses arbitrarily constitute felonies and others misdemeanors. Indeed, a felony in one state may well turn out to be a misdemeanor in another state. Likewise, various misdemeanant categories such as "disorderly conduct" can be used to cover a variety of offenses which would otherwise be felonies.

In addition to the categories of crimes noted above (viz., treason, felonies, and misdemeanors), there are a variety of behaviors which are proscribed in city or county ordinances. The violation of such ordinances (for example, traffic violations) is not considered a criminal offense. Although an ordinance violator may be subjected to a fine, such a fine is considered as representing civil damages payable to the city or county.

White-Collar Crime[1]

According to many sociologists the definition of crime solely in terms of the criminal law seems to be too restrictive for understanding and explaining the nature and extent of criminal behavior. Many students of criminal behavior feel that a crime should be defined not only in terms of the criminal law, but in broader terms to include any act punishable by the state regardless of whether the penalty is a criminal one or is administrative or civil in nature. This view maintains that a strict legal definition of crime is too limited and biased and does not include what has been termed "white-collar crime" (Clinard, 1958; Sutherland & Cressey, 1968).

Violations of law by businessmen, politicians and government employees, labor union leaders, physicians, lawyers, and by other professionals in the course of their occupational activity, have come to be known as "white-collar crimes." Such offenses include direct misappropriation of public funds, the illegal acquisition of those funds through padded payrolls or through monetary "kickbacks" from employees, price fixing by business corporations, distribution of fraudulent securities by stock brokers, and many related law-violating activities. Several studies have shown that white-collar crime among business concerns is rather extensive. Sutherland (1949), in a study of 70 large corporations, found that they had a total of 980 decisions rendered against them over a 45 year period for violations of governmental regulations—an average of 14 per corporation.

Quite obviously, the usual crime indices such as arrest, court, and prison statistics furnish very little information about the frequency, distribution, and other characteristics of the aforementioned categories of law-violating behavior by individuals and corporations. As indicated earlier in this chapter, the criminal law is only one of several ways in which the law attempts to regulate, control, and sanction deviant behavior.

During the 19th century the economic life of the country was relatively unregulated. The slow development of legislative action against various types of business offenses appears to have been influenced in part by the philosophy of laissez-faire and *caveat emptor* ("let the buyer beware"), which characterized the general social, political, and economic thinking for a good while. During the 20th century the gradual development of legislation to regulate business has proceeded to a point where, at present, virtually every aspect of business life is regulated in some way. There are, for example, antitrust laws, food-and-drug laws, safety and health laws, licensing provisions for numerous businesses, housing codes, and various other regulatory statutes. Some of these regulations, such as the antitrust laws, are sometimes enforced through criminal sanctions. Violations of housing codes are considered minor offenses, are handled in lower courts, and are punished by small fines. Other regulatory laws, such as some labor laws, are enforced by administrative agencies outside the criminal system (*The challenge of crime in a free society*, 1967).

The report of the President's Commission on Law Enforcement and Administration of Justice provided several estimates concerning the economic impact of business and commercial frauds and related crimes. For example, the cost of unreported commercial theft, business fraud, embezzlement, and tax fraud is estimated to amount to $3 billion. Illegal gambling alone amounts to $7 billion. A single conspiracy in 1964 involving business fraud (the salad oil scandal) is estimated to have cost $125 to $175 million. It has also been estimated that the price fixing by 29 electrical companies, which received much publicity a few years ago, probably cost the utilities (and therefore the public) more money than is reported as stolen by burglars in an entire year! Similarly, in the grocery trade the theft estimates for shoplifting and employee theft appear to almost equal the *total amount of profit (The challenge of crime in a free society*, 1967).

One might note, in conclusion, that both in the legislative process and also in the prosecution and punishment of white-collar crimes there tend to be a number of social class biases.

MAJOR COMPONENTS OF THE CRIMINAL JUSTICE SYSTEM

The system of criminal justice is the societal institution which deals with crimes which have not been prevented and offenders who have not been deterred by the criminal sanctions promised and meted out for law-violating behavior. As noted earlier, the criminal justice system is the societal apparatus used to enforce the standards of conduct necessary to protect and maintain the major values of the culture. The system operates by apprehending, prosecuting, convicting, and sentencing those members of the community who violate the social mores set forth in the criminal law.

The action taken against law breakers is designed to serve at least three major purposes beyond the more immediate punitive one: 1) It removes from the community persons considered to be dangerous to the community; 2) it seeks to deter others from criminal behavior; and 3) it provides an opportunity to attempt to reform and rehabilitate law breakers into law-abiding and constructive members of the community.

The criminal justice system (which has also been referred to as a "nonsystem") has three separately organized parts which have rather distinct although clearly interrelated tasks and functions: 1) police and law enforcement agencies; 2) administration of justice agencies—courts and prosecutors; and 3) correctional agencies. The agencies will briefly be described before discussing details of the criminal justice process.

1. Police and Related Law Enforcement Agencies

These agencies and functionaries are charged with the responsibility for enforcing the law, apprehending persons who have been accused of criminal behavior, and for undertaking the necessary investigative work required to solve crimes. The police are also charged with maintaining peace and order in the community, protecting life and property, and they very frequently are called upon to provide a variety of human services in day-to-day and emergency situations. According to the report of the President's Crime Commission (*The challenge of crime in a free society*, 1967), there are about 420,000 persons involved in police work in about 40,000 separate agencies; these agencies together spend more than $2.5 billion a year. The President's Crime Commission predicted about 50,000 authorized but unfilled vacancies in these departments by 1967, a statistic that relates in large measure to the low salaries and the complexities and hazards of the job.

The policeman has a most difficult and exacting job as the representative of society who has to function on the "front lines" to enforce criminal laws and to maintain peace and order in the community. Considering the responsibilities of the job and the power and authority that society gives to policemen, it is worthy of note that quite generally the educational requirements are no more than a high school education. Written tests, personal interviews, and character investigations are almost invariably conducted. The President's Crime Commission estimated that only about one-quarter of local police departments attempt to screen candidates for emotional fitness, and very few utilize psychological tests in the screening process (*The challenge of crime in a free society*, 1967).

Information gathered by the Crime Commission in 1966 indicated that the median annual salary for patrolmen was $4,600 in small cities and $5,300 in large cities. More recent information compiled by the International Association of Chiefs of Police (Police personnel selection survey, 1968) indicates that starting salaries range between $4,032 and $9,792, with maximum salaries ranging from $4,800 to $12,648. In contrast, special agents of the Federal Bureau of Investigation are required to have at least college degrees, and their starting salary of $10,252 can more than double over the years even without promotion to supervisory positions.

When reference is made to police agencies the concern often appears to be with municipal police systems. However, there are a number of different types of police agencies in the United States. In addition to the municipal police system there is also the sheriff system found in most counties, the sheriff's office being responsible for law enforcement in all of the unincorporated parts of the county. There are various law enforcement agencies at the state level. The most common of these are official groups identified as the state police or the state highway patrol. These organizations are normally restricted to enforcement of motor vehicle laws. In addition, most states also have state narcotic bureaus, tax enforcement organizations, game wardens, liquor inspectors, and other such law enforcement groups. At the federal level also there are a number of law enforcement groups. The most well-known of these, of course, is the Federal Bureau of Investigation in the United States Department of Justice. There are other national police forces such as the Federal Bureau of Narcotics and Dangerous Drugs, the Secret Service, and Post Office Inspectors.

2. Administration of Justice Agencies

These agencies consist of the office of the prosecutor, the courts, and various functionaries such as magistrates, judges, and district attorneys. The criminal court is the central and crucial institution in the criminal justice system. In a very real sense, it is the institution around which the rest of the criminal justice system has developed, and to which the rest of the system is largely responsible. It is the court which regulates the flow of the criminal process under the rules and principles established by the federal and state constitutions, by statute, by practice, and by court decisions. The activities of the police are limited and shaped by the courts, and the work of the correctional system is determined by the sentence passed by the court on the offender.

State courts, which are the central components of the legal operation, are rather diverse in their character throughout the United States. However, the general pattern clearly indicates the two basic forms of the courts—*trial courts* and *appellate courts*. Trial courts in turn are divided into several levels. Some trial courts operate at the local or municipal level and are variously known as justice of the peace courts, magistrate's courts, and municipal courts. More generally, these are referred to as the *lower courts*. The lower courts typically handle the minor or "petty offenses," also known as *misdemeanors*. Misdemeanors are usually punishable by confinement in local jails or prisons for a period of less than one year, or by fines. More serious offenses, called *felonies*, are punishable by confinement in a state prison or reformatory for periods ranging from one year to life. In addition, the death penalty is also provided in some states for very serious crimes such as first-degree murder, kidnapping, and rape.

The higher trial courts, referred to variously as *superior courts, district courts,* or *circuit courts*, are usually organized on a county basis. These courts deal with the more serious offenses (felonies); in some states they have general jurisdiction, with criminal, civil, matrimonial, and probate matters all being handled in the same court. It should be pointed out, however, that the jurisdiction of lower courts and superior courts is not always as exclusive as might be suggested from the above description. These courts can and often do cross the misdemeanor-felony line.

Appellate courts on the state level are usually called supreme courts. The main business of these courts is to hear appeals regarding decisions rendered at the trial courts. The courts of appeal review the proceedings of the trial courts and listen to arguments on legal issues—not on the facts in the case—to determine whether errors have occurred in the trial which might require reversal of the judgment and a new trial. Appellate courts also have the responsibility of scrutinizing the constitutionality of new legislation.

There is also a federal court system which has jurisdiction over offenders who commit ordinary crimes on federal reservations, or who violate federal statutes. The federal system consists of three kinds of courts; district (or trial) courts, courts of appeal, and the United States Supreme Court. The United States Supreme Court takes up all questions which relate to the constitutionality of the issues raised; that is, whenever rights and guarantees provided under the Constitution of the United States are involved.

Since it is the *judge* who tries disputed cases, who supervises and reviews negotiated pleas, passes sentence on convicted offenders, and determines the efficiency, fairness, and effectiveness of the court, quite obviously the quality of the judiciary in very large measure determines the quality of justice. In view of this, judges clearly need to have the highest qualifications and should be fully trained and highly competent persons. In most states judges are elected to office, while in some others they are appointed by the governor or the legislature. In some states, judges are first appointed and then must run for election on their record. While judges generally are experienced lawyers, in some cities lower court judges are not even required to be lawyers (*Task Force Report: The Courts*, 1967).

The *prosecutor* is a key official in the processing of criminal cases and has wide discretionary powers in terms of deciding whether charges should be brought against an accused and what these charges should be, recommending disposition to the court, and influencing police operations. Other than the judge, the prosecutor is the most influential court official. In state criminal systems the chief legal officer is the county prosecuting attorney or the district attorney. This elected official, along with his deputies and assistants, is responsible for representing the state in criminal actions against individuals accused of crime.

Prosecutors generally are elected or selected for office on a partisan political basis and serve for relatively short terms. Traditionally this office is viewed as a stepping stone to higher political office or a judgeship. Despite the very important responsibilities of the office, in many places prosecutors are poorly paid or hold only part-time positions. Thus, they must, and are even expected to, engage in private law practice to supplement their income. This situation tends to create inevitable conflicts between the demands of the office and of private practice (*The challenge of crime in a free society*, 1967).

The prosecutor's adversaries in the criminal justice system are the *defense attorneys*, who assist the accused in defending against the criminal charge brought by the state. In view of the complexities of the legal process and the subtle and complicated ramifications of the criminal laws, their various interpretations, the rules of evidence, and related matters, without the aid of proper legal counsel the accused is not in a very good position to defend himself. Not only does the Constitution of the United States assure the right of the accused to have help of counsel for his defense in federal courts, but recent Supreme Court decisions (e.g., *Gideon v. Wainwright*, 372, U. S. 335, 1963) have stated that all felony defendants must be afforded counsel at trial and on appeal.

In situations where the accused is unable to obtain counsel through his own resources such help is provided in other ways. There are generally two methods for providing legal counsel to indigent defendants. Under a *defender* system indigent persons are represented either by an official known as the public defender or by a legal aid agency. However, the majority of jurisdictions use an *assigned counsel* approach. Under this system, the judge assigns indigent cases to private attorneys on a random (in the general meaning of the word) basis. The President's Crime Commission has recommended that all jurisdictions using the assigned counsel approach should move from random assignment to a carefully coordinated assigned counsel system, or to a defender system.

Public defender or legal aid agencies are becoming more common in urban areas, while the assigned counsel system appears to be more common and also more appropriate for smaller cities and rural areas (*The challenge of crime in a free society*, 1967).

3. Correctional Agencies

These agencies involve the various jails, prisons, reformatories, juvenile training schools, and probation and parole systems. While one might usually think of correctional agencies as coming into play after the person has been convicted and sentenced, and this is generally the case, there are many persons who are housed in jails and prisons while awaiting trial. About one-third of the correctional population is housed in various institutions, while the remaining two-thirds of the population are handled on probation and parole. The report of the President's Crime Commission estimated that on any given day in 1965 the correctional system was responsible for approximately 1.3 million offenders. In the course of a year this system handles nearly 2.5 million admissions, and spends over one billion dollars doing so. Correctional agencies and functionaries are charged with the task of supervising offenders (either in institutions or on probation and parole) in order to safeguard and protect one community, and also to attempt to reform and rehabilitate the offender (*The challenge of crime in a free society*, 1967).

Estimates made in 1965 indicated that the average cost for institutional care of an adult offender was $1,966 per year, while community supervision under probation and parole averaged $198 annually. Annual institutional costs for juveniles were $3,613, and $328 for community supervision. There were more than 121,000 people employed in corrections during 1965. However, only 20 percent of this group (consisting of probation and parole officers and educators, social workers, psychologists, and psychiatrists working in institutions) were primarily engaged in treatment and rehabilitative functions. The remaining 80 percent of correctional manpower were primarily engaged in custodial and maintenance functions (*The challenge of crime in a free society*, 1967).

The President's Crime Commission found very serious staff problems in the corrections field. For adult felons the Commission felt that the manpower needed to be tripled. Where misdemeanants were concerned, the Commission termed the need for staff "staggering." About 2,000 were employed in 1965, only a small proportion of the 15,400 needed. The 1975 requirement was estimated as 22,000. It was estimated that a total of 23,000 probation and parole officers would be needed by 1975 for the community supervision of juvenile delinquents (*The challenge of crime in a free society*, 1967).

The Joint Commission on Correctional Manpower and Training[2] has conducted numerous studies over the past four years. Based on one of its surveys, the Joint Commission found that the line staffs in correctional institutions have no more than a high school education. Starting and maximum salaries for line officers fluctuate widely across the country; the entrance salaries range from a low of $2,400 to a high of $6,924 annually, with maximum salaries ranging from $2,700 to $10,836. Almost 80 percent of the administrators, 70 percent of supervisors, and 83 percent of specialists (educational and treatment professionals) had bachelor's degrees or better. The fields of major study, both for bachelor's and master's degrees, in order of frequency were: sociology, social work, education, and psychology. Those with master's degrees most frequently were from the field of social work. When questioned about the field of study viewed as most desirable for concentration, correctional staff with college degrees first mentioned psychology, followed by sociology, social work, criminology, and corrections (*Corrections 1968: A climate for change*, 1968; *A time to act*, 1969).

Protection of the Rights of the Accused[3]

Among the fundamental features which serve to distinguish criminal justice systems in various countries are the extent and the forms of the protections the societies offer to individuals who have been accused of criminal behavior. The American system of criminal justice quite deliberately sacrifices much in efficiency and in overall effectiveness in order to protect certain Constitutional rights of the individual from the power of the federal and state governments.

The first 10 amendments to the Constitution of the United States were adopted shortly after the Constitution had been ratified by the necessary number of states. There was some fear at the time that in the absence of specific limitations on its powers the federal government might infringe upon the liberties of the people. These original amendments were designed to eliminate this hazard and they are referred to as the Bill of Rights. However, it was only in 1925, in the case of *Gitlow v. New York* (268 U. S. 652, 1925), that the Supreme Court began to apply the Bill of Rights to state actions.

Among the various protections provided by the Constitution of the United States, and the several later amendments, are the following: a confined person has the right to petition a federal court for a writ of *habeas corpus* to test whether his confinement violates the Constitution or laws of the United States; protection is provided against unreasonable searches and seizures unless there has first been obtained a court order (warrant) based upon "probable cause," or there is good reason to believe that the individual involved has committed a crime or that he has in his possession the fruits of the crime (Fourth Amendment); protection is provided against double jeopardy and self-incrimination, and the deprivation of life, liberty, or property without due process of law (Fifth Amendment); and, among other things, the Sixth Amendment provides that in all criminal prosecutions the accused has the right to a speedy and public trial by an impartial jury.

While there are many other Constitutional and legal protections, we might consider very briefly the meaning and implications of the phrase "due process of law."

A *due process* clause is found in both the Fifth and Fourteenth Amendments to the Constitution as a restraint upon the federal and state governments, respectively. This clause provides procedural protection by preventing federal and state governments from using unfair methods in law enforcement. Thus, a forced confession from an accused, the failure to make the presumption of innocence, or the denial to the accused of proper notice of a judicial proceeding and an opportunity to present evidence on his own behalf, would all clearly be in violation of the due process protections afforded by the Constitution of the United States.

More recently, in the *Escobedo* case[4], the Supreme Court voided a murder confession because the accused had been prevented from seeing his lawyer, who was present in the police station. Later, in the *Miranda* case[5], the Supreme Court prohibited, by a five-to-four decision, the questioning of a suspect in custody unless his legal counsel is present or the suspect expressly waives the right to counsel.

THE CRIMINAL JUSTICE PROCESS

The procedure by which persons are accused of crime, officially labeled as criminals, and then subjected to the sanctions of the criminal law, is referred to as the criminal justice process or the criminal process. These procedures are very complex, necessitate a great number of critical decisions, and require consideration of many factors at various stages of the process. The criminal process is determined by the Constitution of the United States and by state constitutions, by statute, by practice, and by the various court decisions.

Earlier discussion has indicated that deviant behaviors defined as delinquency and crime, and the reactions to them, are social products and are socially defined. That is, it is society (or its representatives) which establishes rules, labels those who violate the rules, and prescribes ways for dealing with those who have been given the criminal label.

Thus various deviant acts have to be defined, graded as to their perceived severity, and penalties have to be fixed in some relation to the judged seriousness of the deviant behavior. In addition, the adjudicated offender has to be handled in such a fashion as to safeguard the interests of the community while also considering the offender's rehabilitative needs.

The criminal justice system has to distinguish among the many offenders who come to its attention. While adhering broadly to the notion of equal justice, there also has to be consideration for the real differences among various offenders, for example, the habitual, dangerous, and hardened criminal charged with a particular offense, and also the marginal first offender who has been charged with the same offense. In order to make the above distinctions and to attempt to individualize justice, much latitude and discretion are provided at various points in the criminal justice process.

Contrary to the impression laymen may sometimes have that the courts are clogged with dangerous offenders such as robbers, rapists, and persons charged with serious assaults, in terms of actual volume most of the cases in the criminal courts consist of annoying, indecent, and other behaviors which essentially offend moral norms of the community. For example, *almost half of all arrests* are on charges of drunkenness, disorderly conduct, vagrancy, and gambling (*The challenge of crime in a free society*, 1967).

This section provides a fairly detailed description and analysis of the criminal justice process, and of the various points at which critical decisions have to be made regarding individuals who come into the System. The "Flow Chart" (Figure 5–1) is designed to facilitate this description and to provide an overall view of the movement of persons through the various stages of the criminal justice process.

1. Police and Law Enforcement

In a very real sense the community's efforts to deal with deviant and law-violating behavior begin long before the police enter the picture to enforce criminal laws. Whether or not a particular type of behavior is to be considered a crime and so defined by law is a matter which relates to the overall values and mores of the community—or, at least, the values of a significant or influential segment of the community. As Becker (1963) has pointed out, in a sense deviance is *created* by society, in that society establishes various rules whose infraction constitutes deviance. It becomes apparent, therefore, that deviance or criminality is not simply a quality of the act a person commits, but is also a consequence of the application by others of rules and sanctions to the offender.

Police Discretion. Involving as it does a number of interacting variables, the criminal labeling process is certainly not infallible. It cannot at all be assumed that the category of criminals includes all who have violated criminal laws. Indeed there are numerous studies which indicate that only a very small proportion of all law-violating behavior in the community comes to official attention (see, e.g., *The challenge of crime in a free society*, 1967).

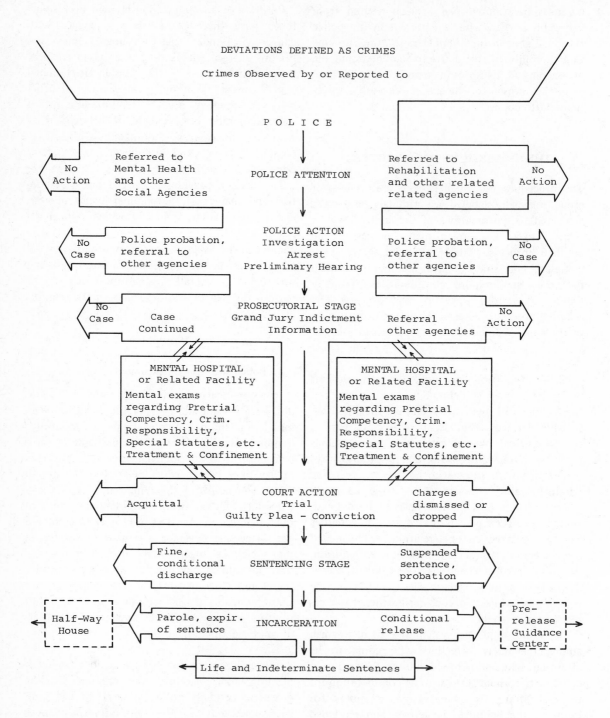

Fig. 5—1. Flow chart showing the criminal justice process and related mental health issues.

Although many law violations are committed, the offender may suffer no official sanction unless his violation comes to official attention and the individual is processed through the criminal justice system. Moreover, persons believed to have committed criminal acts may at certain times and in certain situations be handled more leniently, or more severely, than at other times. For example, during festive occasions drunkenness in public and disorderly behavior may receive a rather tolerant response. Such behavior in middle and upper class neighborhoods may be handled more permissively than in lower class neighborhoods. In contrast, during periods of "all-out attack" by law enforcement agencies on particular types of crimes, for example homosexuality, narcotics addiction, and gambling, many persons previously ignored or tolerated may now be given official attention and related sanctions.

What should be evident from the above discussion is that in a very real sense law enforcement policy is made by the policeman. To be sure, social norms and various pressures from the community influence and often direct the kind of policy which the policeman is able to exercise. Furthermore, the criminal code, in practice, is not a set of specific instructions to policemen. Rather, it provides rough guidelines and lays down broad principles on the basis of which the policeman has to work. Obviously, crime does not look the same on the street as it does in a legislative chamber or a courtroom. The police officer has to decide whether the noise or profanity is sufficient to constitute "disorderly conduct" within the meaning of the law. He also has to determine, and often rather quickly and in the middle of much confusion and opposing pressures, whether a quarrel should simply be broken up and the matter dropped or whether at a certain point the behavior should be handled as a criminal assault.

Thus, in a very real sense, every policeman is an interpreter of the law. Similarly, every policeman is also the arbiter of social values, for he meets numerous situations in which the invocation of criminal sanctions is a questionable line of action. The manner in which a policeman works is influenced by a number of practical considerations: the legal strength of the available evidence, the willingness of the victims to press charges and

of witnesses to testify, the attitude and general sentiments of the community in regard to the particular offense, and the time and information available to the policeman in that particular situation.

In any event, the point at which the law-violating behavior is brought to the attention of the police is the first "gate" into the criminal justice process (see Figure 5—1). The policeman is, therefore, in the critical role of being the first official "gate keeper" to the criminal justice system. It is his judgment and action in many cases which will determine whether the law-violating individual will be ignored, let off with a warning, referred to other community agencies, or whether he will receive official action and be processed through the criminal justice system. Obviously, the more serious the law-violating behavior and the more concerned the victims are to take official action, the less is the discretion which the policeman generally can exercise.

Procedures Between Arrest and Trial. After an individual has been apprehended by the police and placed under arrest, he has to be taken without unnecessary delay before a magistrate or judge. In the case of minor offenses (misdemeanors), a formal accusation called a *complaint* is made against the person by the police officer or private citizen who was a victim in the offense. In such cases, the judge or magistrate will often have the authority to hear the case himself and he will usually proceed with the trial unless the accused demands a trial by jury, wishes to consult with an attorney, or requests a continuance for some other reason.

If the charge involves a felony, the initial appearance before the magistrate or judge is for the purpose of setting bail and arranging for a preliminary hearing. A *preliminary hearing* is a relatively informal proceeding which determines whether there are sufficient grounds for believing that the accused committed the offense, in which case he is required to stand trial. If the judge or magistrate decides that the accusation is without probable cause, the accused is discharged. This discharge, however, does not bar a grand jury indictment if evidence satisfies a grand jury that the accusation is well founded.

Bail. The judge or magistrate conducting the preliminary hearing is empowered to decide whether or not defendants who have been "bound over" for the grand jury, or those who must await further action (e.g., trial), can be released pending such disposition. Such a decision is an extremely important one. A defendant who is released pending grand jury action or trial can continue to live in the community, maintain his employment, support his family, and also can work to develop his own defense, search for witnesses, and be able more readily to consult with his attorney. The defendant who is held in custody during this period is denied the above advantages.

On the other side of the picture, the community appears to rely on the preliminary hearing officer for protection when the decision about releasing a defendant is being considered. If a released defendant fails to appear for the trial the law appears to have been flouted. Furthermore, if the released defendant commits new crimes while awaiting grand jury action or trial, the community is endangered.

The device that is used in most instances to resolve some of the aforementioned issues is money bail in amounts that are fixed by the judge or magistrate. The defendant may be released when a certain amount of money (bond) has been posted to ensure his presence at the trial. The defendant can either raise the money for bail from his own resources or, more often, he may try to obtain it from a bail bondsman for a fee. The fee generally ranges from 10 to 25 percent of the full amount of the bail. The bail bondsman then posts a bond for the full amount with the court; if the defendant fails to appear for the trial, the bond may be forfeited.

Except in the case of capital offenses (i.e., offenses punishable by death), defendants accused of criminal offenses are generally entitled to release on bail. It is important to note here that the basic purpose of the bail is to ensure the defendant's appearance for the trial. Bail is not meant to be used for the purpose of keeping off the street those judged by the preliminary hearing officer to constitute a danger or a menace to the community. In fact, the Constitution of the United States specifically prohibits excessive bail (Eighth Amendment). In practice, however, the magistrate or judge can prevent release on bail by setting the amount of the bail at such a high figure that release may be very difficult to obtain.

By and large, money bail appears to be an unfair device since it clearly discriminates against poor defendants. Moreover, persons who are detained while awaiting trial may suffer a considerable disadvantage when compared to those who are not incarcerated. Empey (1967) cites a number of studies which clearly indicate that persons who are detained in jail because of their inability to raise bail are more likely to be convicted and are more likely to receive later jail sentences. This finding does not relate simply to the variables of prior criminal record and seriousness of the offense. Even when the type of offense and prior record were held constant, the disadvantage of the jailed defendant continued to appear (Empey, 1967, pages 14–17; see also, Freed & Wald, 1964).

On the basis of such data, and also in view of the wide-ranging criticism of the money bail practice, in recent years a number of jurisdictions have implemented programs whereby persons who are screened and judged to be good risks can be released by the court on their own recognizance. Furthermore, the Federal Bail Reform Act of 1966 has attempted to allow greater flexibility in the release on bail, and allows judges to place nonmonetary conditions for release of the defendants, for example assigning the person to the custody of a person or organization for supervision, restricting travel, and other such requirements (see *The challenge of crime in a free society*, 1967, page 132).

The Habeas Corpus Writ. In the event an arrested person is not formally charged with an offense and is not taken before a judge or magistrate "without unnecessary delay" he, or some one acting on his behalf, may petition the judge for a "writ of habeas corpus." This writ provides a means to secure the person's release or at least compels the police or other detaining authorities to file a specific charge or provide other reasons for the person's detention. If the court issues the writ, the police or other custodians of the arrested individual are required at an early designated date to bring the person into court to explain the reasons for holding him in custody.

Coroner's Inquest. This very old legal proceeding, still used in certain jurisdictions, is peculiar to homicide cases or other situations in which death has resulted. Its function is to determine the "cause of death." The coroner's jury in most states is made up of six laymen selected by the coroner; the verdict of this jury is not binding on the prosecuting attorney, grand jury, or court. In effect, it is merely an advisory finding which can be either accepted or completely ignored. Thus, even in instances where a coroner's jury returns a verdict of "accidental death," a grand jury may later find that death resulted because of someone's criminal act and may charge the suspected person with the offense (Inbau & Sowle, 1960).

It will be noted that even though many of the foregoing details have not been shown in Figure 1, the discussion has reached the point at which police action has in large measure been completed.

2. The Prosecutorial Stage

A key administrative official in the processing of criminal cases is the prosecutor, whose general role within the criminal justice system has been described earlier.

In theory, the examination of the evidence against the defendant, by the judge or magistrate at the preliminary hearing and later by a grand jury in felony cases, is very important because it allows the evidence to be weighed carefully before proceeding to the next stage of the criminal justice process. In practice, however, the prosecutor wields almost undisputed sway over the pretrial progress of most cases. During these initial stages it is the prosecutor who introduces evidence to indicate reasonable cause to require the defendant to stand trial. That is, the prosecutor has to make a *prima facie* case against the defendant to support movement of the defendant to the next stage of the criminal process—grand jury indictment and/or trial.

Earlier it was noted that policemen make frequent use of the discretion not to arrest or officially process certain offenders. Prosecutors also exercise rather wide discretion in their handling of criminal cases—they do not charge all arrested persons, they typically have wide choices in regard to the particular offense with which the person will be charged, and they may even move to dismiss charges which have already been made.

Much of the criminal process, it should be remembered, is administrative rather than judicial. The number of cases which come into the criminal justice system, particularly in urban and metropolitan areas, is very large. The circumstances of the particular cases, the evidence to support the charges initially placed against the accused, and other factors, vary considerably. If a substantial percentage of these cases were not dropped or carried to negotiated conclusions on an administrative basis the machinery of the criminal justice system would almost grind to a halt. More importantly, the essential facts in many cases are not in dispute; therefore, an expensive and prolonged trial to develop and determine such facts is not needed.

The Grand Jury. It was noted earlier that minor violations of the criminal law (misdemeanors) are usually prosecuted on the basis of information and sworn complaints which the prosecutor has received from the victims or other persons (cf. page 85). Such action is said to be based upon an "information." When the criminal charge involves a felony, many states require that the accusations first be heard by a grand jury.

The grand jury is usually composed of 23 citizen-voters, 16 of whom constitute a quorum. The votes of at least 12 members are necessary in order to return an "indictment" against the accused. This indictment is also referred to as a "true bill."

The consideration of a felony charge by a grand jury is in no sense of the word a trial. At the grand jury hearing the prosecutor is required only to show that there is reasonable evidence to indicate that the accusations warrant a trial. Grand jury consideration of felony charges is designed essentially to provide another safeguard to the accused against arbitrary action by the prosecutor (Inbau & Sowle, 1960).

The Arraignment and Plea. Following an indictment, the person accused of a felony is sent before a judge empowered to try felony cases. The indictment, or the facts stated in the "information," is read to the defendant; in other words, the accused is advised of the criminal charges made against him. At this time the accused indicates whether he wishes to plead guilty or not guilty to the charges. If the defendant enters a plea of guilty, the judge can pass sentence immediately or take the matter under advisement, obtain a presentence report from the probation office, and make his decision regarding the sentence at a later date. If the accused enters a plea of not guilty, a date is then set for his actual trial.

In some states, and in federal courts, the defendant may also enter a plea of *nolo contendere*. This plea has the same effect or meaning as a plea of guilty, except that the admission thus made cannot be used against the individual in any other action, such as a civil suit to recover damages (Inbau & Sowle, 1960).

Plea Bargaining. The prosecutor exercises a rather wide range of discretion referred to commonly as "prosecutorial discretion." Thus, the prosecutor decides whether to press a case or to let it drop. He also determines the specific charges to be placed against the individual and, more importantly, he has the discretion to reduce charges. This latter process—referred to as *plea bargaining*—involves discussions between the prosecutor and the defense attorney.

The basic issue at stake in the plea bargaining process is the degree to which the prosecutor will reduce his original charge or how lenient a sentence he will recommend to the judge in return for a plea of guilty. In their plea bargaining activity the prosecutor and defense counsel are generally searching for a reduced charge which will meet the ends of justice while also providing an incentive to the accused to plead guilty. It is therefore extremely difficult to assess the degree to which the plea bargaining process reflects an element of flexibility to mitigate the rigidities of the system and to individualize justice, or the extent to which such bargaining is an inevitable consequence of crowded court calendars and acute shortages of necessary personnel in the existing system of administering criminal justice.

Newman (1956) conducted a rather detailed study of felony cases in a Wisconsin county and found that over 90 percent of the offenders had been sentenced on guilty pleas. That is, they had entered guilty pleas and had not contested their guilt in a trial. He also found that a third of this group had originally entered pleas of not guilty.

The incentive to the prosecutor for accepting a guilty plea is readily apparent since it allows the state to avoid a rather costly and lengthy court trial. One might wonder, however, about the incentives for the accused to "cop a plea." Newman (1956) found that there were four kinds of bargains offered the defendant: 1) some had reduced charges placed against them; 2) about a half had received a "deal" in the form of a

reduction of sentence for pleading guilty; 3) other defendants received concurrent sentences rather than consecutive ones for the several offenses, or several counts of the same offense, which they were alleged to have committed; and 4) some defendants who pleaded guilty for consideration had some of the charges against them dropped in return for their guilty plea.

Blumberg (1967) provides an excellent picture of the various practical considerations and constraints which influence the actual operation of the criminal process. In a court studied over a 15-year period he found that less than five percent of all indictments ended in adversary trials and 75 to 90 percent of the adversary trials ended in convictions. Blumberg (1967) describes the defense lawyer as a key person in arranging guilty pleas, and comments: As members of a bureaucratic system the defense lawyers become committed to rational, impersonal goals based on saving time, labor, and expense and on attaining maximum output for the system. For the defense lawyer this means choosing strategies which will lead to working out a plea of guilty, assuring a fee, and shrouding these acts with legitimacy (page 18).

In discussing the diversion of cases as a function of prosecutorial discretion, the report of the President's Crime Commission noted that approximately one-half of those arrested are dismissed by the police, a prosecutor, or a magistrate at an early stage of the case. For example, some persons are released because it is determined that they did not commit the acts they were earlier suspected of having committed, while others are released because there is lacking adequate and sufficient evidence to support the charges. It is also important to remember that the police can arrest on the basis of "probable cause," while conviction of the criminal charge requires proof "beyond a reasonable doubt." It is quite clear, therefore, that some justified arrests cannot lead to prosecution and conviction (*The challenge of crime in a free society*, 1967).

As Figure 5–1 indicates, there are various formal and informal dispositional choices open to the prosecutor within the scope of the wide discretion available to him; this is particularly true in regard to misdemeanors. The prosecutor may decide not to take formal action but may assure that damages are paid and appropriate restitution made to satisfy the grievance of the victim. The issuance of a warrant and other formal action may be withheld on condition that the person will seek appropriate help through family, private, or public sources. The prosecutor may also decide to "continue the case" for a period of a few months contingent upon the efforts to the accused to seek appropriate help for emotional or related problems.

In the interests of screening out of the criminal process persons whose problems might more effectively and appropriately be handled by other social agencies, various recommendations have been made for the development of mechanisms to assist in initial screening and diversion of persons away from the criminal justice process. For example, persons believed to be suffering from various forms of mental disorders and related problems could be identified and diverted to other appropriate social agencies (see, e.g., Shah, 1968).

3. Court Action

Persons charged with criminal offenses who do not leave the criminal justice process at the prosecutorial stage, advance to the court action stage (see Figure 5–1). It has been noted, however, that court officials such as magistrates and judges have already been involved in some of the earlier proceedings, for example preliminary hearings and arraignment. The actions to be discussed in this particular section involve the trial, the passing of sentence, and appeals which can be made following the trial.

The criminal court is the central and crucial institution in the criminal justice system. It is the part that is the most venerable, the most formally organized, and the most elaborately circumscribed by law and tradition. The criminal court regulates the flow of the criminal process under the constraints of the law. Thus, the activities of the police are limited and shaped by the rules and procedures of the court, and the work of the correctional system is also very much determined by the sentences which the court hands down to convicted offenders.

These various roles, responsibilities, and social functions of criminal courts have very well been summarized by the report of the Crime Commission (*The challenge of crime in a free society*, 1967):

Society asks much of the criminal court. The court is expected to meet society's demand that serious offenders be convicted and punished, and at the same time it is expected to insure that the innocent and the unfortunate are not oppressed. It is expected to control the application of force against the individual by the State, and it is expected to find which of two conflicting versions of events is the truth. And so the court is not merely an operating agency, but one that has a vital educational and symbolic significance (page 125).

The criminal courts operate under a number of constitutional limitations. For example, criminal courts can act only against specific criminal acts which already have taken place; they cannot act against persons out of a fear that *they may* commit crimes at some future time. That is, under the system of criminal justice used in the United States, there are restraints against the use of *preventive detention.* (Some interesting exceptions to this limitation will be discussed later under *The Criminal Justice System and Mental Health Issues.*) The system imposes clear limitations on how the prosecution may prove its case against the person accused of crime. Guilt of the accused must be established *beyond a reasonable doubt* and this must be done without compelling the accused to produce evidence or to testify. That is, the defendant can refuse to take the witness stand and may refuse to explain his actions.

Very clearly, then, the basic decision rule in criminal law proceedings is reflected in the clearly stated maxim: "A man is innocent until proven guilty." The rule takes the further form that, when in doubt, the defendant must be acquitted. That is, the judge and jury must *not* be equally wary of erroneously convicting or acquitting. The error that is most important to avoid is to erroneously convict the accused (Scheff, 1963; Shah, 1969a).

The aforementioned and many additional procedural, due process, and other Constitutional protections for persons accused of crime are designed to provide a balance between the rights of the accused and those of society. These safeguards also protect the accused against the improper use of the collective power of the state.

The Trial. It will be remembered that persons accused of crimes go to trial in only a small percentage of cases. As noted earlier, in about 90 percent of the cases where persons are convicted the case does not go to trial.

In all states and also in the federal system the accused is entitled to a "speedy trial." The right to an early trial is guaranteed by the Constitution of the United States and by various state constitutions, as well as the right to trial by an impartial jury, as specifically stated in the Sixth Amendment.

Although the accused is entitled to trial by jury as a matter of constitutional right, he may choose to waive this right and be tried by a judge alone. In a jury trial, it is the jury which has responsibility for determination of the facts, with the judge serving more or less as a referee who makes sure that the evidence is presented, or withheld, in accordance with certain procedural rules. The ultimate decision as to the guilt or innocence of the defendant in a jury trial is one to be made by the jury alone (Inbau & Sowle, 1960).

Twelve registered voters have to be selected to serve on a trial jury. Some states, and the federal system, select more than 12 jurors so that the required number of jurors will still be available in the event a particular juror is later disqualified or becomes ill.

The prosecuting attorney and the defense attorney are entitled to make "opening statements" in which each outlines what he intends to prove. The prosecutor then produces the testimony and evidence which the state (or government) has developed against the defendant. The defense then presents its evidence, which attempts to refute the prosecution's case and is designed to show the defendant's innocence. After closing arguments by both sides, the judge in most jurisdictions reads and gives to the jury certain written instructions as to the legal principles which should be applied to the facts of the case as they have been determined by the jury. The jury is also provided various forms of the possible verdicts which may be reached. The jury then retires to deliberate upon the matter.

If the defendant is found "not guilty," he is acquitted, goes free, and is immune from further prosecution for the same offense. In the event the jurors are unable to agree upon a verdict (the verdict must be unanimous in most states), the jury—commonly referred to as a "hung jury"—is discharged and a new trial date may be set for a retrial of the case before another jury. The judge may in some situations rule that a "mistrial" has

taken place; for example, when some essential rule governing the presentation of evidence has been violated. In these instances, too, a new trial will take place.

Even after the trial and a verdict of "guilty," certain opportunities are provided for the defendant to obtain his freedom. Motions may be filed for a new trial alleging certain legal "errors" in the course of the previous trial. If the appellate judges agree with the allegations of "errors" which may have affected the verdict, the conviction may be set aside and a new trial ordered for the defendant. Such a new trial does not in any way violate the Constitutional protection against double jeopardy since it is the defendant himself who seeks the trial by virtue of his appeal. The effect of the setting aside of the original verdict is to wipe the slate clean and, as requested by the defendant, an opportunity is provided for a new trial. Where the motion for a new trial is overruled or denied by the court, the judge then proceeds to sentence the convicted offender.

4. The Sentencing Stage

In cases tried without a jury the judge typically determines the sentence to be imposed. In jury cases the practice varies among the states, with most following the practice of confining the jury function to a determination of guilt or innocence and then permitting the judge to fix the penalty. However, in the case of capital offenses most of the states place the responsibility for recommending the sentence also upon the jury; the jury decides whether the penalty is to be death (where this is still allowed by statute) or imprisonment.

In some states there are statutory provisions which clearly prescribe that upon conviction of a felony the offender must be sentenced for a specified minimum-maximum term (i.e., lower and upper limits of the sentence). For example, the statutory sentence for a particular felony may be for a minimum of one year to a maximum of ten years. Such a statute leaves it up to the parole board to determine the appropriate time for release based upon factors such as the offender's indicated rehabilitation, the risk involved, and other such considerations. In many states a judge is permitted to set a minimum-maximum period for the convicted offender anywhere within the term prescribed by statute. For example, if the sentence to be given for aggravated assault is one to ten years, the judge may set any combination within that range such as one to two or two to six years. This minimum-maximum term means that the offender cannot be released before serving the minimum period (less "time off for good behavior"), nor can he be kept in the prison longer than the maximum term (less "time off for good behavior"). In between this minimum-maximum period the offender is eligible for *parole*.

Prior to the passing of sentence, most higher courts (viz., those dealing with felonies) have an opportunity to obtain presentence reports prepared by the probation departments attached to the courts. The purpose of the presentence report is to provide the sentencing judge with relevant background information about the offender—family background, educational and vocational adjustment, previous trouble with the law, and other such information. The presentence report may, where possible, include the findings of psychiatric or psychological examinations conducted on the offender to assist in recommending appropriate disposition. Even though the presentence report is only advisory, it does provide an opportunity for the judge to individualize his disposition.

Sentencing Alternatives. It goes without saying that the individualization of the disposition by the court relates in very large measure to the particular choices available to the sentencing judge. By and large, available facilities and resources for appropriate rehabilitation, treatment, and related assistance to offenders, are remarkably limited. Thus, while theoretically having wide discretion in regard to disposition, in practice the judge may be faced simply with giving varying lengths of confinement in the only available correctional institution. Or, if he wished to withhold imposition or execution of the sentence in lieu of a period of probation, he is again aware of the very limited supervision and services available.

In choosing among the various sentencing alternatives the judge is generally influenced by three kinds of considerations. First, there are the specific statutory constraints regarding the sentence. Second, the decision of the court is influenced by the conflicting pressures or recommendations from the police, the probation department and its supporting services, the prosecutor's office, public opinion, the victim or his family, and the defendant's counsel and his family. Obviously, these groups feel differently about the offender and about the kind of sentence and disposition which are seen to be deserved and appropriate. Finally, the court's decision is limited by the facilities to which it has access.

5. Corrections

The correctional system, consisting of the various jails, prisons, and probation and parole agencies, is the part of the criminal justice system which the public is typically least aware of and seldom sees in its day to day operations. Correctional institutions often are located in remote rural areas, and visits by members of the community—and even by the judges who send people there—are infrequent events. Other than the limited knowledge obtained by visitors to incarcerated offenders, the public often becomes aware of correctional institutions mainly when these facilities get into the news because of a prison break, a riot, or other sensational incident. As discussed earlier (cf. *Administration of Justice Agencies*), approximately one-third of the correctional population is housed in various institutions, the other two-thirds being on probation and parole in the community.

A quick look at historical developments in corrections indicates that the societal approach to the handling of criminals can conveniently be summarized as a succession of three R's: revenge, restraint, and reformation. Revenge was the primary response prior to the first correctional revolution in the 18th and 19th centuries. Until about the middle of the 18th century, execution and corporal punishment such as flogging and pillorying were the principal means for dealing with offenders. With the growing movement toward humanitarianism which accompanied the "Enlightenment" in Western Europe, the emphasis shifted from revenge to restraint. With the occurrence of what is considered to have been the second revolution in corrections in the late 19th and early 20th centuries, reformation increasingly became a more important objective of the correctional system. Attention increasingly was placed upon understanding the psychological and emotional functioning of the offender in order to change the offender (Empey, 1967).

In more recent years two additional R's appear to have been added: rehabilitation and reintegration. It has been stated in some correctional writings that reformation and rehabilitation actually have to lead to a basic focus on reintegrating the offender into the community from which he is removed either physically or through the stigma of the criminal label (Empey, 1967; Glaser, 1964; Gibbons, 1968; *The challenge of crime in a free society*, 1967). It should be noted, however, that actual shifts or changes in correctional programs, resources, and objectives have *not* been as clear as the aforementioned progression might suggest. Thus, even though discussion of correctional objectives increasingly refers to rehabilitation and reintegration, it is quite evident that elements of revenge and restraint continue to be in evidence. In the opinion of this writer, it would be fair to say that there has been more progress in correctional *rhetoric* and in the *conceptualization* of correctional goals and objectives than is reflected concretely in existing programs. While many new and promising approaches and models have come into existence, it would be fair to say that, by and large, the correctional system has neither the resources nor the community support which would enable it to do the kind of rehabilitation or reintegration of the offender that seems to be expected of it.

Over the past several decades there have been numerous attempts by national correctional organizations such as the National Council on Crime and Delinquency and the American Corrections Association, and their state and local affiliates and counterparts, to draw greater public and legislative attention to the critical needs for improving the juvenile and adult correctional systems. While reacting to periodic news media reports of prison escapes, homosexual assaults within such institutions, and related incidents, the general public and legislative bodies have not seriously addressed the needs of the correctional system. Indeed, it is noteworthy that increased funds have more readily been available for building new institutions, rather than for major improvement of existing facilities and the development of a variety of community-based alternatives to incarceration.

Most recently, the President's Commission on Law Enforcement and Administration of Justice undertook a massive and landmark study of the problems of crime and delinquency, published its findings in several volumes, and made wide-ranging recommendations (see, e.g., *The challenge of crime in a free society*, 1967). Several pieces of federal legislation have resulted from the work of the Crime Commission and increased federal assistance to the states in these areas has been made available.

Correctional Alternatives. Reference has already been made to the fact that while the sentencing judge typically has rather wide discretion as to the correctional disposition to be used, in reality he is very much constrained by the actual availability of programs and facilities.

The four most common sentencing alternatives within the correctional system are: 1) institutionalization, 2) suspended sentence, 3) fines, and 4) probation.

1. *Institutionalization* remains a disposition frequently used by the courts. The length of confinement is usually determined by statute and further specified in terms of the minimum-maximum term imposed by the court. The report of the Crime Commission indicated that on an average day in 1965 there were some 426,000 persons confined in correctional institutions (*The challenge of crime in a free society*, 1967). These institutions range from huge maximum-security prisons complete with high fences, walls, and watchtowers, to open forestry camps without guards or fences. Similarly, these facilities range from jails and detention centers where persons may spend relatively short sentences ranging from a month up to a year, to reformatories and penitentiaries where some prisoners may well spend their entire lives. While some of these institutions have a variety of educational, vocational, and other rehabilitative and treatment programs, there are many others where the main concern is with secure custody and where treatment and rehabilitative programs are negligible.

The Crime Commission found that 62 percent of personnel in correctional institutions were involved with custodial duties, 29 percent with service and maintenance functions, and only nine percent were involved in educational, counseling, and other treatment functions (*Task force report: Corrections*, 1967). Thus, despite the talk about the need for "treatment and rehabilitation" in correctional institutions, the great majority of such programs have neither the staff, facilities, nor funds to develop programs which could give real meaning to the frequently mentioned treatment and rehabilitative objectives of correctional institutions. Quite clearly, therefore, correctional institutions generally are used primarily and essentially to confine offenders for the protection of society.

Correctional institutions typically require a variety of educational, clinical, vocational, and related services. Thus, while medical personnel are used to assist in some classification and placement functions, they primarily provide basic medical, dental, and related services. An important element in the screening, classification, and placement functions is psychological testing and assessment. Most correctional institutions make some use of such testing and assessment; however, there is a paucity of evaluative research pointing to the actual relevance and utilization of such assessment to specific placement and treatment decisions. It would appear desirable that such testing and related activities be markedly refined and streamlined in order that available clinical staff be able to give much greater emphasis to various treatment, training, and consultative roles within such total institutions.

The bulk of therapeutic efforts in correctional institutions has increasingly and understandably moved toward various group approaches. Group counseling, guided group interaction, cottage groups, and related programs are increasingly being utilized. While some research has demonstrated the usefulness of group counseling, especially when used in conjunction with graduated release and aftercare programs, the bulk of correctional programs remains relatively untested by careful evaluative research (*Task force report: Corrections*, 1967). Wilkins & Gottfredson (1969) have provided a very comprehensive description and analysis of a large number of research and demonstration projects in the field of crime and delinquency.

Correctional institutions also provide educational programs for inmates. While the bulk of institutions are seriously limited in what they can offer, through the utilization of various federal grants' programs a number of innovative and promising projects have achieved fairly impressive results. Among these programs is that conducted by Clements & McKee (1968) at the Draper Prison in Alabama using programmed instruction, and Cohen's work (1968) at the National Training School in Washington, D. C., using operant procedures, including programmed instruction.

While vocational and industrial programs are to be found in many adult prisons, it is notable that a number of serious impediments have prevented the development of meaningful and useful correctional industries. The amount and type of work available for prison inmates and the products they can produce have very much been influenced by the labor market in the free community, a variety of restrictive laws including those which prohibit interstate transportation of prison-made goods, and, of course, political pressures brought to bear by private industry and labor organizations (*Task force report: Corrections*, 1967).

2. *Suspended sentences* generally take two main forms which the court can use: suspension of the *imposition* of sentence, and suspension of the *execution* of sentence. Under suspension of the *imposition* of sentence the court withholds a decision on the length of the prison term at the time of conviction so that if it is later necessary to revoke the suspended sentence, the court can then fix the period of imprisonment. In suspending the *execution* of sentence the court fixes a sentence of imprisonment but suspends execution of that sentence subject to the satisfactory adjustment of the offender in the community. If the court subsequently finds it necessary to revoke the suspension it must ordinarily impose the term originally fixed.

3. *Fines* are another distinct form of sanctions which appear to be based on the notion that the offender does not require imprisonment, or that he will be deterred through the imposition of monetary sanctions. Fines are frequently used in association with probation sentences, the payment of the fine often being an explicit condition of probation. While the money received from fines generally goes to the state, the court may sometimes make provision for the offender to pay restitution to the victim of his crime.

4. *Probation* is the most frequently used alternative to incarceration. As noted earlier, the cost of such supervision of the offender in the community is about one-tenth that of institutionalization. This form of disposition is available to the courts in virtually every jurisdiction. While in the case of juveniles the probation term can be indeterminate up to the age of 21, in the case of adult offenders the length of probation is clearly specified. For misdemeanors the period of probation is often one year—the maximum jail

sentence generally allowed for such offenses. However, the period of probation may in certain instances be longer, or it may also be increased if the offender's adjustment is believed to warrant a longer period of supervision. While the period of probation for felons typically is five years, in many cases the court may decide to terminate probation earlier if the probation officer makes such a recommendation based on the offender's progress and adjustment in the community. During the period of probation the offender is required to report on a regular basis to his supervising probation officer. The probation officer also attempts to assist the person in regard to employment, family, psychological and other problems and needs. While most courts dealing with felonies have some kind of probation service available to them, the bulk of misdemeanor courts lacks such services.

In recent years a variety of new and promising models of correctional treatment and rehabilitation have been tried. One example is the Community Treatment Project conducted within the California Youth Authority as part of a research project supported by the National Institute of Mental Health (Palmer, 1969). Using a typological approach to treatment this action-research program is attempting to find answers to the question: what kinds of treatment programs, in what kinds of settings, mediated by what kinds of treatment agents, are most effective with what kinds of delinquents? The results thus far indicate that the experimental group, handled in small caseloads in the community, had a significantly lower failure rate (new offenses and parole revocations) compared to the control group receiving regular parole supervision. While some methodological problems remain and the relative contribution of a number of independent variables to outcome results has still to be determined, this project provides an example of developments designed to facilitate and increase community alternatives for the treatment of offenders (*The challenge of crime in a free society*, 1967).

Work Release Programs. The concept of work release, or work furlough as it is also called, dates back to the Huber law enacted in Wisconsin in 1913. Under such work release programs offenders judged to be suitable are allowed to leave the correctional institution to go to jobs in the community during the day, and then return to the institution for overnight and weekend confinement. This law sought to accomplish two main objectives; to provide for reformation and rehabilitation of prisoners, and to provide means of financial support other than public relief for the prisoner's dependents. Despite their early beginnings, programs allowing for work release were not employed to any extensive degree until World War II, when workers were sorely needed. Many additional work release programs have been developed within the last ten years; it has been estimated that at least 25 states (as well as the Federal Bureau of Prisons) presently provide some form of work release programs (Moeller 1969).

6. Exit from the Process

The last step in the criminal justice process is the point at which the individual leaves the system and returns to the community. While the person may be released from confinement within correctional institutions under a variety of programs (e.g., parole, prerelease guidance centers, and half way houses), he may often continue under some form of parole supervision for a period of time. *Parole* is very similar to probation in that it is a casework type of operation, much like aftercare, in which a variety of services and supervision are supposed to be provided to the offender released from confinement. In actuality, because of serious staff shortages and excessive demands for service, a parole officer's caseloads tend to be very high and few services may be available. While the President's Crime Commission recommended that parole and probation caseloads should average 35 per officer, a national survey conducted by the Commission revealed that adults released on parole are supervised in caseloads averaging 68 (*Task force report: Corrections*, 1967).

There are two broad types of sentences which might briefly be discussed at this point, *determinate* and *indeterminate*. Determinate sentences are specifically limited to certain periods of time by statute and by the precise term imposed by the sentencing judge. For example, a sentence of one to three years is a determinate one; it means that the offender has to serve at least one year in prison after which time he is eligible for parole. However, even if not accepted for parole the offender may not be confined any longer than a maximum of three years, less whatever time he has earned for good behavior.

There are some special statutes (for example, Dangerous Offender and Sexual Psychopath laws) under which the term of confinement is indeterminate. Under most indeterminate sentences the individual can theoretically spend his entire life in an institution if it is felt that he is not safe enough to be released.

Unlike sentencing, which has traditionally been a judicial function, the parole decision is administrative. Such decisions are made by correctional authorities or by special parole boards, usually consisting of laymen. There are, however, many questions concerning the value of the information and criteria used in making parole decisions and the actual validity of such decisions. Understandably, there are many social policy considerations also involved in such decisions. Thus, parole boards and correctional authorities tend to be apprehensive about unfavorable publicity resulting from new offenses committed by parolees. In view of this, there is a tendency to be more concerned with avoiding errors which could lead to release of persons likely to commit new offenses. Decisions which may lead to the other type of error, namely, confinement of persons who may actually be capable of satisfactory community adjustment, do not arouse negative community reactions and thus appear to be more frequent.

Graduated Release Programs. Reference has already been made to programs of work release which allow selected offenders to hold gainful employment in the community while continuing to serve their sentences through nighttime and weekend incarceration. Other recent programs which attempt to address the important task of assisting the offender to make a more graduated return to the community are *Prerelease Guidance Centers* and *Half Way Houses.* Under these and several related programs, offenders are released from the institution and placed in small residential facilities. While being in these community-based facilities, the persons continue to receive guidance and assistance in regard to vocational, employment, educational, familial, and related problems, and are prepared for independent adjustment in the community.

The Effectiveness of Corrections. As the President's Crime Commission (*Task force report: Corrections*, 1967) pointed out, "The ultimate goals of corrections under any theory is to make the community safer by reducing the incidence of crime. Rehabilitation of offenders to prevent their return to crime is in general the most promising way to achieve this end (page 16)."

The most frequently employed measure of rehabilitation has been the recidivism rate or a rate of return to crime. As Martin and Barry (1969) have recently noted in a fairly comprehensive review of recidivism studies, the definitions and criteria for determining recidivism show rather large variations. Thus, effectiveness of probation (measured in terms of those who complete their period of probation supervision without revocations) shows a success rate of from 60 to 90 percent. Effectiveness of parole, similarly measured, is much poorer. About half of all parolees generally commit violations within the first six months after release from prisons, and over 60 percent within the first year (*Task force report: Corrections*, 1967).

In regard to criminal recidivism rates generally, on the basis of the study by Glaser (1964), estimates made by the President's Crime Commission, and the review by Martin and Barry (1969), it appears that reimprisonment rates tend to be within the range of 35 to 55 percent.

Quite clearly, then, the kind of correctional system which society has developed and seems willing to support does not do a very good job of correcting. Indeed, there appears to be increasing concern that the conditions under which many offenders are handled, especially those confined in prisons, are too often a distinct detriment to rehabilitiation. Given their rather meager facilities and resources, correctional agencies are expected to accomplish a great deal. Conrad (1969) notes the many and even conflicting objectives which correctional agencies are intended to serve: "They are to control the offender while changing him into a better man. They are to punish while they resocialize. They are to exact retribution while instilling in the offender a firm adherence to the principles of law and order (page xi)."

THE CRIMINAL JUSTICE SYSTEM AND SOME MENTAL HEALTH ISSUES

Early in this chapter there was discussion of the deviancy labeling process as it pertains to the definition and handling of norm-violating behavior which is considered to constitute crime. The discussion regarding the labeling process whereby deviant behaviors are defined as crimes is equally relevant in considering deviant behaviors which come to be defined as *mental illness*. Many problems inherent in the concept of mental illness have been discussed in chapter 11 by Newbrough, and in chapters 1 and 2, and elsewhere in this volume. Suffice it to say that deviant behavior which may in some instances be considered by some persons as crime, may be viewed by others as indicative of mental illness. Indeed, as Wootton (1959) has pointed out, while at one point in history those considered to be mentally ill were placed in chains and put in dungeons like criminals, the societal reactions appear almost to have come full circle. At the present time an increasingly wide range of social deviants viewed as criminals are being regarded by many as suffering from mental disease or illness.

The concept of mental disease has long been used in the legal process for dealing with social deviants who not only were law violators but who in addition displayed characteristics which were viewed as "strange," "bizarre," and "odd." There are a variety of situations where mental health concepts, definitions, and even social value judgments expressed as "expert" opinions, interact with the legal process. A number of rather serious and perplexing problems arise when the differing concepts, labels, and philosophical and ideological orientations of law and mental health interact. These problems often seem to involve a confusing and confounding of the "social control" or deterrent functions and objectives of the criminal law with the "therapeutic" and remedial objectives of mental health (Shah, 1970). This section will touch briefly on some of the more outstanding issues pertaining to mental health and the criminal justice system. (For a more detailed discussion of these issues see: Dershowitz, 1969; Goldstein, 1967; Hess & Thomas, 1963; Hunt & Wiley, 1968; Kutner, 1962; Lindman & McIntyre, 1961; McGarry, 1965; Morris, 1968; Rubin, 1963; Shah, 1968b; Szasz, 1963).

Competency to Stand Trial. Rather early in the criminal process it may appear that the accused is so mentally disturbed that he does not appear able to either understand the nature of the proceedings against him nor to assist his attorney in preparing the defense. Thus, in keeping with the common

law tenet that an accused may not be tried or sentenced while "insane," the court has to determine whether the accused is mentally competent to stand trial. The underlying rationale appears to be that an accused cannot have a fair trial unless he is able to participate adequately in the proceedings and is able to assist in his own defense.

The following statement is illustrative of the definition and meaning of the legal test of pretrial competency; an accused is considered competent to stand trial if he is capable of understanding the nature and object of the proceedings going on against him; if he rightly comprehends his own condition with reference to such proceedings and can conduct his defense in a rational manner, . . . although on some other subject his mind must be deranged or unsound."[6]

As clearly indicated from the language and general criteria noted above, the issue is legal in nature, the criteria are legal, the question requires a judicial determination, and this determination pertains specifically to a particular legal proceeding, namely the trial.

A problem which often arises is that mental health professionals involved in such examinations often confuse the legal criteria with various mental health criteria. Several studies have indicated that a large number of mental health professionals (more commonly psychiatrists) conducting pretrial competency examinations and testifying on this issue do *not* properly understand the legal questions and considerations involved. Not infrequently the question of pretrial competency tends to be confused with the later and separate issue of criminal responsibility and exculpatory insanity. Further, even though the particular question or the criteria involved are legal in nature, mental health professionals often translate the issue into mental health terms. Thus, a common rule of thumb appears to be to associate a finding of psychosis with pretrial incompetence, and lack of psychosis with competence to stand trial (Hess & Thomas, 1963; Lindman & McIntyre, 1961; McGarry, 1965; Shah, 1968).

Criminal Responsibility and the Insanity Defense. The subject of criminal responsibility and exculpatory insanity has been discussed at considerable length in the literature. However, since about 90 percent of defendants enter guilty pleas, and of those who stand trial less than five percent raise the defense of insanity, it can quite accurately be said that the issue of criminal responsibility has been given attention and emphasis far in excess of its actual importance in the overall administration of justice. It might further be noted that the aforementioned issue of pretrial competency is raised more often, occurs much earlier in the legal proceedings, and often terminates the criminal justice involvement in the case (Lindman & McIntyre, 1961; Rubin, 1963).

This chapter is not the place to discuss in detail the historical roots, rationale, and the various legal tests currently in use to determine whether or not a defendant is to be held criminally responsible for his actions. (For a good recent discussion of this topic see Goldstein, 1967.) It may be noted that the doctrine of *mens rea* and criminal responsibility is fundamentally and inextricably tied to the traditional punitive philosophy of the criminal law. The basic concern is with "blameworthiness" and "punishability" of the individual who has been accused of crime. As a consequence, a considerable amount of time, effort, and expense is devoted to the preoccupation with attaching the legally appropriate label on the accused. The courtroom "battle of expert witnesses," and almost the entire trial in such cases, revolves around the determination of whether the accused is legally to be considered *responsible*, that is, as blameworthy, "bad," and therefore deserving the punitive sanctions of the criminal law; or whether he is to be considered *not responsible*, that is, as not blameworthy but rather as "mad," and hence deserving "treatment" rather than "punishment."

As stated above some rather complex issues have indeed been simplified. Nevertheless, the fundamental determination facing the court in such situations is essentially one of making a social, ethical, and moral judgment. It is not very clear how one set of societal processes for defining and dealing with deviant behavior (the concept of mental disease and mental health handling) are to be related to another set of societal processes for dealing with social deviance (the concept of crime and the criminal justice system). The making of complex moral judgments is a most difficult matter. In the views of this writer, the difficulty is not one which can be resolved by changes in the wording of the insanity tests used in making such determinations.

Here again, as in the matter of pretrial competency, legal, moral, and mental health concepts tend to become intertwined and confounded. Once again legal rules and questions become translated into mental health issues. For example, it is difficult to understand why in many jurisdictions, once a defendant has been acquitted by reason of insanity—a moral and legal judgment—, involuntary and indeterminate confinement to a mental hospital automatically follows. The legal issues suddenly become mental health ones and the person who is removed from the punitive sanctions of the criminal law is then placed into a situation of involuntary and indeterminate confinement—even though no finding of current need for psychiatric hospitalization may have been made. Moreover, even though the person acquitted by reason of insanity is removed from the criminal process because he is found not to be "blameworthy" and hence is not to be punished, the criteria for release from indeterminate confinement in mental hospitals and the burden and standard of proof requirements generally are far *stricter* than those which even a convicted murderer faces after he has served his term in prison.

Special Statutes. A number of special statutes are now in existence in roughly half the states and in the District of Columbia, aimed at persons legally defined as "sexual psychopaths," "sexually dangerous persons," "sex offenders," "mentally abnormal sex offenders," "criminal sexual psychopaths," "psychopathic personalities," and "defective delinquents."

A study of the history and enactment of such statutes indicates that these laws stemmed neither from any sudden or sharp increase in sex crimes, nor certainly from any dramatic advances in knowledge concerning the treatment of sex offenders. Rather typically such legislation was enacted in response to public outcries and concern following some particularly heinous sex crimes which were accompanied by much publicity in the news media. It is interesting to note that some of these early statutes were judged to be unconstitutional by appellate courts, and had to be redrafted and reenacted (Lindman & McIntyre, 1961; Rubin 1963).

The constitutionality of such statutes has generally been upheld by appellate courts on the grounds that the proceedings are "civil," that is, nonpunitive in nature, and hence the customary safeguards of the "criminal" trial need not apply. The purpose of such "civil" proceedings has been stated to be "remedial," "curative," and "regulatory." As such, even though the "sexual psychopath" may in some states later be liable for criminal prosecution for the very behavior which led to his involuntarily "civil" confinement for "treatment" in a mental hospital or similar "treatment" facility, the subsequent criminal sanctions are not considered to constitute double jeopardy. The basic reason for such rulings has been that since the first proceeding was "civil" in nature the person was not twice exposed to "criminal" proceedings.

The above legal arguments notwithstanding, it does seem quite evident that the Constitutional safeguards against preventive detention and involuntary and indeterminate confinement do not apply in situations where the deviant behavior comes to be defined as "mental illness," where the intent of the actions is said to be "remedial and therapeutic" in nature, and where such proceedings can be labeled as "civil."

The Issue of "Dangerousness." Concern about the dangerousness of an individual is often raised in cases where involuntary commitment to a mental hospital is being considered. Such questions are also raised in the adjudication of "sexual psychopaths" and "defective delinquents." While these concerns about an individual's dangerousness to the community are quite reasonable, it is important to note two critical factors involved in such determinations. *Firstly*, the issue of dangerousness as involved in such legal proceedings involves essentially *matters of social policy. Secondly*, it should be evident from the earlier discussion in this chapter that the definition of deviancy and the official labeling process involve not only the deviant, but also the groups in the community responsible for such definitions and labels.

It has been noted that what constitutes "dangerousness" is frequently left unspecified by the law—except for rather broad and general statements. This situation allows for various administrative decisions by lawyers, psychiatrists, and others (Szasz, 1963). The fact that often mental health professionals view "dangerousness"

as a sort of clinical entity, namely, as a quality which resides entirely or largely in the individual, can also be a source of problems. What often seems not adequately to be appreciated is that when the law addresses itself to the question of "dangerousness" the concern is *not* with medical, psychiatric, psychological, or other criteria, but rather with the making of a public policy determination. Furthermore, although it is common to find mental health professionals making predictions and recommendations as to the future dangerousness of an individual, it is very hard to find careful evaluative studies to determine the accuracy—or even the reliability—of predictions which can lead to incarceration. The follow-up study by Hunt and Wiley (1968) of persons released from involuntary confinement following the *Baxstrom* decision,[7] revealed that clinicians typically tend to overpredict the likelihood of dangerousness. Other writers on this subject (see, e.g., Dershowitz, 1969; Livermore et al., 1968) have noted the limited accuracy of the aforementioned predictions and the many related social policy considerations.

Thus, while the law wishes to know whether the individual has a propensity for engaging in behavior which can threaten the safety and welfare of others, the basic question to be decided goes beyond this issue. The court has to determine whether the particular form of "dangerous" behavior is so threatening to the welfare and safety of the community that involuntary confinement, usually of an indeterminate nature, is to be invoked. Whether or not a society wishes to control and sanction "dangerousness" in the above fashion is, therefore, fundamentally a matter of public policy and has to be based on broad societal values (Dershowitz, 1969; Shah, 1970). For example, many persons are allowed by the community to be dangerous; others are allowed to be dangerous in some ways but not in others; and some forms of dangerous behavior may legally be permissible, for example, automobile track racing, sky diving, and the various "death-defying" circus acts. It could very readily be shown that drunken drivers are both dangerous to themselves and to others, and that the number of persons killed (about 25,000 a year; see *Alcohol and traffic safety*, 1968) as well as those seriously injured by drunken drivers is *many times more* than persons harmed by schizophrenics and various sex offenders. Nevertheless, persons labeled as schizo-phrenics and many types of sex offenders may involuntarily be committed for indeterminate periods of time because of their possible "dangerousness" to themselves or to others, but drunken drivers—even those with several such convictions—cannot be committed in this fashion.

THE CRIMINAL JUSTICE SYSTEM AND BEHAVIORAL AND SOCIAL SCIENTISTS

This section will touch on just a few of the many areas in the criminal justice system where important contributions can be made by behav-ioral and social scientists and mental health professionals. An examination of Figure 1 will readily indicate a number of areas where the knowledge and interventions of behavioral and social scientists can be of value. Such functions go well beyond the usual clinical involvement of mental health professionals in regard to diagnostic, treatment, training, and consultative roles. Of course, the research opportunities and needs pertaining to this complex social system are almost endless, and considerable work has been done by social scientists (particularly sociologists) in this field (see e.g., Becker, 1963; Chambliss, 1969; Cressey & Ward, 1969; Glaser, 1964; Lemert, 1967; Lindman & McIntyre, 1961; Quay, 1965; Schur, 1965; Warren, 1970). Another recent development has been the increasing application of systems analysis and other scientific and techno-logical tools to the criminal justice system. For example, mathematical models and computer simulation techniques have been used to obtain information concerning the relative effectiveness and consequences of complex decisional alterna-tives and intervention strategies (see, e.g., *Task force report: Science and technology*, 1967; Blumstein, 1967).

1. The first point of study and intervention pertains to the very beginning of the societal process whereby deviant behavior is defined and labeled. It has been noted earlier that social norms which are used to regulate behavior through the coercive authority of the state (i.e., criminal laws) provide the starting point for the juvenile and criminal justice systems. Our society defines a very large range of deviant behaviors as the concerns of the criminal justice system. Yet, in terms of sheer volume, most of the cases in the criminal courts involve, essentially, violations of moral norms or instances of annoying behavior rather than dangerous crimes. Almost half of all arrests are on the charges of drunkenness, disorderly conduct vagrancy, gambling, and minor sexual violations (*The challenge of crime in a free society*, 1967). The President's Crime Commission also pointed out that a major factor in the predicament faced by the criminal system involves the too ready acceptance of the notion that the way to deal with almost any kind of reprehensible conduct is to label and handle it as a crime.

Aside from the obvious primary penalties involving loss of freedom which are administered by the criminal-correctional process, there are generally also a number of other and less tangible secondary penalities. Among these are the stigma resulting from the criminal conviction, with this stigma often transferring to the family of the offender, loss of employment, reduced job opportunities, loss of voting rights and the right to hold public office, exposure to dangerous criminal and sexual deviates in prisons, social ostracism, and increased probabilities of arrest after release (see, e.g., Crowther, 1969; *Task force report: Corrections*, 1967).

The criminal law in the United States has a rather long tradition of being used as an instrument for sanctioning sin, validating virtue, maintaining morality, coercing good conduct, and upholding uprightness. It has been pointed out by many legal thinkers and social scientists (see, e.g., Allen, 1964; Hart, 1963; Kadish, 1967; Morris & Hawkins, 1969; Packer, 1968), as well as by the President's Crime Commission (*The challenge of crime in a free society*, 1967), that the "overreach" of the criminal law is extremely costly—in terms both of the harm that is done to people subjected to penal sanctions and the secondary deviance that is generated when the criminal law attempts to regulate morality, and also in terms of the neglect of the more important tasks of law enforcement and the criminal process to deal with more serious threats to social order.

In view of the above, major efforts are needed to decrease the number of persons who are funneled into the juvenile and criminal justice systems. These endeavors should include efforts directed at increasing societal understanding of and tolerance for nondysfunctional deviance, in order that the range of behaviors defined as delinquency and crime be reduced and alternate community resources be developed to address such social problems.

One can be sure that the aforementioned attempts to change societal handling of deviancy will not be easy to accomplish. Such endeavors will require careful understanding of community values and ideologies, sociopolitical factors, legislative processes, and related factors influencing social policy and programs.

2. Even in the absence of legislative and social policy changes or court decisions eliminating "marginal" crimes, much can be done to divert persons from the juvenile and criminal justice systems to alternate community facilities. For example, the police are key "gate keepers" to the juvenile and criminal justice systems; they control the initial intake to a very large extent. The policeman typically has to determine whether to take official action, whether certain behavior comes within the definition of crime as stated in the criminal statutes, whether the matter might appropriately be ignored, excused, referred to other societal resources, or whether formal police action should be initiated.

There is rather obvious need to develop and make available to such "gate keepers" useful guidelines and criteria for screening and also to provide related consultation and training which could result in more appropriate decisions. Clearly, however, vague clinical hunches and speculations will not suffice. Careful research is needed to develop an adequate information base and to test and evaluate the aforementioned criteria. As part of the aforementioned endeavors, it will be necessary to develop new community resources and to further improve existing community facilities such as community mental health clinics, vocational rehabilitation and guidance agencies, child and family services, youth service bureaus, and related programs.

Similarly, in view of the very critical responsibilities given by society to policemen, and the "life-and-death" decisions they often are called upon to make, psychologists and other behavioral scientists need to devise tests and other screening instruments to aid in the selection and training of law enforcement officers.

It has been estimated that a good portion of a policeman's time and effort does not relate strictly to law enforcement activities, but involves dealing with a variety of human problem situations and indeed to the provision of social services. In addition to answering calls to assist in locating runaway pets and runaway children, policemen also assist deserted mothers, help persons locked out of their cars and houses in the middle of the night, and assist helpless drunks. Other relatively common problem situations can be most delicate and fraught with danger. Police work frequently involves answering calls regarding family disputes and related crises. These crises often occur late at night, involve inebriated and very angry persons, and they can lead to serious crimes. In fact, fights among married couples, family members, and intimates are the greatest cause of homicides. It is not infrequent that serious injuries and occasional fatalities also involve the police officers responding to such calls.

Given the above situations which commonly confront policemen, various training and consultative contributions by behavioral scientists and mental health professionals are clearly indicated. The demonstration project by Bard and Berkowitz (1967) provides an excellent example of mental health related training to improve police functioning. These two psychologists have trained police officers in the West Harlem section of New York to function as family crisis intervention specialists. This project is important also in illustrating the manner in which mental health training was used to improve and enhance skills very much needed by policemen in their usual roles! The training did not make them mental health aides, nor did it attempt to shift them from their primary and appropriate roles.

Another very good example of applying social science principles to assist policemen has been reported by Shellow and Roemer (1966). These social scientists provided consultative services to a county police department to better understand a mob situation and to prevent a potential riot involving members of various motorcycle groups.

3. As described earlier, prosecutors exercise considerable discretion in determining who shall be processed by the criminal justice system, what particular charges will be placed, and what further actions will be taken or recommended. Various guidelines and criteria and other consultative services could be provided to assist prosecutors to exercise their discretion in a more informed and

meaningful fashion. A mechanism which has been suggested as a means for more rationally diverting mentally disturbed and other persons away from the criminal process is the "pretrial conference" (Shah, 1968). These conferences could provide an opportunity to the two attorneys—representing the interests of the community and of the accused—to discuss dispositional alternatives with the addition of appropriate mental health information and consultation. The above process is frequently used in the "plea bargaining" situation—although without mental health or related consultation and without clear guidelines. The additional information could provide a very useful means for increasing diversion from the criminal justice process and improving the utilization of dispositional alternatives at the "plea bargaining" stage.

4. There are a number of decision-points in the criminal justice process where reliable, efficient, and accurate assessment and predictive instruments are sorely needed. At the present time a variety of traditional clinical procedures are often used for making sentencing evaluations, for determinating "dangerousness" and readiness for parole, and for other related situations. Unfortunately, as a general rule, mental health professionals making such assessments do *not* have information about the reliability of their statements and recommendations, nor even about the reliability of their data. Further, since systematic follow-up and evaluation are conspicuous by their absence, the predictive accuracy of the recommendations remains largely unknown.

Fairly objective, easily administered, scored, and interpreted measures are very much needed. A good deal of work already has been done in regard to the development of parole prediction tables based upon actuarial data (see, e.g., Gottfredson, 1967).

5. There is great need to test the validity of many assumptions made in the criminal process. For example, a common assumption is that longer penal sentences provide greater deterrence, more rehabilitation, and more protection for the community. At the same time, however, correctional experts have estimated that at least a third of adult and juvenile offenders confined in institutions could safely be released to intensive community supervision (*Task force report: Corrections*, 1967; Burdman, 1969).

The state of California recently undertook a very comprehensive study of its criminal and correctional system and obtained some very significant information. The data did *not* support the common implicit assumption that longer penal sentences provide greater deterrence, rehabilitation, and community protection. Indeed, there was substantive evidence that such an assumption was wrong. The cost of maintaining a single adult prisoner in California in 1966-1967 was $2,628 (excluding capital outlay), while the average parole cost during the same period was $572 per parolee. Since longer prison terms did *not* lead to lower recidivism rates, for every five less serious offenders released to parole a year earlier than the median time (30 months), the savings could be used to add one policeman to local law enforcement or several could be trained to higher levels of competence (Crowther, 1969).

6. As emphasized earlier, there is a rather common tendency among clinicians to over-predict psychopathology as well as the presumed "dangerousness" of individuals (see, e.g., Dershowitz, 1969; Morris, 1968). A glaring example of such overprediction of "dangerousness" was revealed following the decision of the U. S. Supreme Court in the *Baxstrom* case.[7] In this landmark decision the Supreme Court ruled that several hundred persons who had been civilly committed to security hospitals under provisions of the New York State Corrections Law had been committed without proper judicial determination. As a result, compliance with the decision required prompt action either to make a proper determination of "dangerousness," or to transfer almost a thousand (969) "insane criminals" and "criminally insane" persons to various civil mental hospitals within the state (Hunt & Wiley, 1968). On the basis of this experience and the subsequent adjustment of these supposedly "dangerous" persons in civil hospitals, and some on release, it became obvious that rather unrealistic and unnecessarily strict criteria had been used. As Hunt and Wiley (1968) note, most of these patients had been examined at least once—often several times—by experienced psychiatrists and had been denied transfer to civil hospitals on the grounds that they were too disturbed or potentially dangerous. Yet, *over 99 percent* of these patients did quite well when the move was compelled by the court decision.

It should be obvious that much more reliable and valid assessment and predictive criteria and instruments are needed when the decisions to be made can and do have serious implications for the liberty and welfare of the people involved.

7. The Probation Subsidy Program developed in California provides an excellent example of promoting and facilitating state-wide utilization of a community-based approach to the treatment and rehabilitation of offenders. Based in large measure on the results of the Community Treatment Project (Palmer, 1969; Warren, 1969), in 1966 California launched the Probation Subsidy Program. Simply stated, the plan encourages counties to reduce their *rates* of commitment to state correctional institutions in return for a subsidy (up to $4,000 for each uncommitted case) which is commensurate with the overall degree of reduction achieved. Consistent with a state-approved treatment plan, the subsidy (which is derived from savings by the state for cases previously institutionalized in state facilities) is used by the counties to improve and expand probation supervision and other community treatment and rehabilitation resources. In addition to monetary savings, for the first time in its history the California Youth Authority has a substantial number of empty beds in its institutions and a few youth institutions have been closed (Smith, 1967; Warren, 1969).

8. Recent developments pertaining to various behavior modification approaches, the growth of community mental health, and other promising trends in the field, have many implications for the improved handling of social deviants (see, e.g., Clements & McKee, 1968; Cohen, 1968; Hobbs 1966; Phillips, 1968). In view of the rather acute manpower shortages in the mental health and related fields and the immensity of the crime and delinquency problems in society, continued reliance on traditional "clinical" models of treatment is clearly inefficient. It is essential to develop a whole range of new service and manpower models as well as innovative treatment facilities which can provide constructive alternatives to the correctional institutions which have traditionally been used.

Furthermore, in order to better understand and also to influence the handling of social deviance, it is essential to devise conceptual schemes and intervention strategies which can be directed at the larger social systems rather than at individual cases.

The aforementioned Probation Subsidy Program in California provides an excellent example of a strategy designed to influence the entire state correctional system. Similarly, it should be noted that key appellate and Supreme Court decisions are also excellent ways of bringing about rather wide ranging and relatively prompt changes in institutional practices. Thus, as compared to the relatively limited range of treatment endeavors aimed at particular individuals in an institution, or even at the entire institution, landmark decisions such as *Kent v. United States, In re Gault*, and *Baxtrom v. Herold*[8] can influence the handling of literally thousands of persons across the entire country and bring about significant changes in the future handling of such persons.

One can view the entire legal system and the criminal justice process as providing a rather unique setting or laboratory for the study of a wide range of social behaviors and interactions. The research possibilities cover almost the entire range of the behavioral and social sciences and other related fields. For example, while psychologists frequently are involved in the study of behavior changes in small and tightly controlled laboratory situations, the criminal justice system provides numerous examples of society-wide and rather macroscopic efforts to control, change, and regulate human behavior.

Behavioral and social scientists also need to undertake studies to translate various legal concepts and doctrines into more operational and testable hypotheses in order that the actual relevance and utility of such hypotheses may be more precisely evaluated in reference to the purposes for which they are used.

CONCLUSION

This discussion has provided a general description of the outstanding and essential features of the criminal justice system and of its operation in the handling of socially deviant behaviors. Various stages in the definition, labeling, and sanctioning of criminal behaviors have been indicated, as well as the major roles of the various functionaries operating within this important social system. There are, of course, a number of very important issues which have barely been touched upon and others which have not been dealt with at all. Some of the references can provide more detailed information about a number of other important issues pertaining to the criminal justice system.

Like other social systems and institutions the criminal justice process has some outstanding weaknesses. Thus, despite its worthy aspirations and ideals, and the lofty tone of its rhetoric, the actual operation of the system of administering criminal justice leaves a great deal to be desired. The various problems and needs of the American criminal justice system have very succinctly been summarized in the following comment by the President's Commission on Law Enforcement and Administration of Justice (*The challenge of crime in a free society*, 1967):

"In sum, America's system of criminal justice is overcrowded and overworked, undermanned, underfinanced, and very often misunderstood. It needs more information and more knowledge. It needs more technical resources. It needs more coordination among its many parts. It needs more public support. It needs the help of the community programs and institutions in dealing with offenders and potential offenders. It needs, above all, the willingness to reexamine old ways of doing things, to reform itself, to experiment, to run risks, to dare. It needs vision (page 12)."

Notes

The author would like to acknowledge the assistance received from the following who read and commented on an earlier draft of this chapter: Beatric M. Cowen, LL.B., Paul D. Lipsitt, LL.B., Ph.D., and Ecford S. Voit, Jr., M.S.W.

1. See Quinney (1964) for a discussion of this concept and related issues pertaining to criminological theory and research.

2. The several reports of the Joint Commission on Correctional Manpower and Training were published in 1969.

3. Source: *Layman's guide to individual rights under the United States Constitution.* Prepared by the Subcommittee on Constitutional Rights, of the Committee on the Judiciary, United States Senate, U. S. Government Printing Office, Washington, D. C. 1966.

4. *Escobedo v. Illinois*, 378 U. S. 478 (1964)

5. *Miranda v. Arizona*, 384 U. S. 436 (1966)

6. *State v. Severn*, 184 Kan. 213, 336 P.2d 447, 452 (1959)

7. *Baxstrom v. Herold*, 383 U. S. 107 (1966)

8. *Kent v. United States,* 383 U. S. 541 (1966); *In re Gault,* 387 U. S. 1 (1967); *Baxstrom v. Herold,* 383 U.S. 107 (1966)

References

A time to act. Final report of Joint Commission of Correctional Manpower and Training. Published by the Joint Commission. Washington, D. C. October 1969.

Alcohol and traffic safety. (A report to the Congress from the Secretary of Transportation) Washington, D. C.: United States Department of Transportation, August 1968.

Allen, F. *The borderland of criminal justice.* Chicago: University of Chicago Press, 1964.

Aubert, V. Legal justice and mental health. *Psychiatry*, 1958, 21, 101–113.

Bard, M., & Berkowitz, B. Training police as specialists in family crisis intervention: A community psychology action program. *Community Mental Health Journal*, 1967, 3, 315–317.

Becker, H. S. *Outsiders: Studies in the sociology of deviance.* New York: Free Press, 1963.

Blumberg, A. S. Lawyers with convictions. *Trans-action*, 1967, 4, 18–24.

Blumstein, A. Systems analysis and the criminal justice system. *Annals of the American Academy of Political and Social Science*, 1967, 374, 92–100.

Burdman, M. Realism in community-based correctional services. *Annals of the American Academy of Political and Social Science*, 1969, 381, 71–80.

Chambliss, W. J. (ed.) *Crime and the legal process.* New York: McGraw-Hill, 1969.

Clements, C., & McKee, J. M. Programmed instruction for institutionalized offenders: Contingency management and performance contracts. *Psychological Reports*, 1968, 22, 956–964.

Clinard, M. B. *Sociology of deviant behavior.* New York: Rinehart, 1958.

Cohen, H. L. Educational therapy: The design of learning environments. In J. Shlien (ed.), *Research in psychotherapy.* Vol. III. Washington D. C.: American Psychological Association, 1968.

Conrad, J. P. Introduction to the future of corrections. *Annals of the American Academy of Political and Social Science*, 1969, 381, xi–xiii.

Corrections 1968: A climate for change. Washington, D. C.: Joint Commission on Correctional Manpower and Training, 1968.

Cressey, D. R., & Ward, D. A. *Delinquency, crime, and social process.* New York: Harper & Row, 1969.

Crowther, C. Crimes, penalties, and legislatures. *Annals of the American Academy of Political and Social Science*, 1969, 381, 147–158.

Dershowitz, A. M. The psychiatrist's power in civil commitment: A knife that cuts both ways. *Psychology Today*, 1969, 2, 42–47.

Empey, L. T. *Alternatives to incarceration.* (United States Department of Health, Education, and Welfare) Washington, D. C.: United States Government Printing Office, 1967.

Frank, J. *Law and the modern mind.* Garden City, N. Y.: Anchor Books, 1963.

Freed, D. J., & Wald, P. M. *Bail in the United States: 1964.* (A report to the National Conference on Bail and

Criminal Justice) Washington, D. C.: National Conference on Bail and Criminal Justice, May 1964.

Gibbons, D. C. *Society, crime, and criminal careers.* Englewood Cliffs, N. J.: Prentice-Hall, 1968.

Glaser, D. *The effectiveness of a prison and parole system.* Indianapolis: Bobbs-Merrill, 1964.

Goldstein, A. S. *The insanity defense.* New Haven: Yale University Press, 1967.

Gottfredson, D. M. Assessment and prediction methods in crime and delinquency. In *Task force report: Juvenile delinquency and youth crime.* (The President's Commission on Law Enforcement and Administration of Justice) Washington, D. C.: United States Government Printing Office, 1967.

Hart, H.L.A. *Law, liberty, and morality.* Stanford: Stanford University Press, 1963.

Hess, J. A., & Thomas, T. E. Incompetence to stand trial: Procedures, results and problems. *American Journal of Psychiatry*, 1963, 119, 715–720.

Hobbs, N. Helping disturbed children: Psychological and ecological strategies. *American Psychologist*, 1966, 21, 1105–1115.

Hunt, R. C., & Wiley, E. D. Operation Baxstrom after one year. *American Journal of Psychiatry*, 1968, 124, 974–978.

Inbau, F. E., & Sowle, C. R. *Criminal justice: Cases and comments.* Brooklyn: Foundation Press, 1960.

Kadish, S. H. The crisis of overcriminalization. *Annals of the American Academy of Political and Social Science*, 1967, 374, 157–170.

Kitsuse, J. I. Societal reaction to deviant behavior: Problems of theory and method. *Social Problems*, 1962, 9, 247–256.

Kutner, L. The illusion of due process in commitment proceedings. *Northwestern University Law Review*, 1962, 57, 383–399.

Layman's guide to individual rights under the United States Constitution. (Prepared by the Subcommittee on Constitutional Rights, United States Senate) Washington, D. C.: United States Government Printing Office, 1966.

Leibenson, H. A., & Wepmen, J. M. *The psychologist as a witness.* Mundelein, Ill.: Callaghan, 1964.

Lemert, E. M. *Human deviance, social problems and social controls.* Englewood Cliffs, N. J.: Prentice-Hall, 1967.

Lindman, F. T., & McIntyre, D. M. (eds.) *The mentally disabled and the law.* Chicago: University of Chicago Press, 1961.

Livermore, J. M., Malmquist, C. P., & Meehl, P. E. On the justifications for civil commitment. *University of Pennsylvania Law Review*, 1968, 117, 75–96.

Martin, P. L., Barry, J. R. A prediction of recidivism. *Correctional Psychologist*, 1969, 3, 6–13.

McGarry, A. L. Competency for trial and due process via the mental hospital. *American Journal of Psychiatry*, 1965, 122, 623–630.

McGarry, A. L. Demonstration and research in competency for trial and mental illness: review and preview. *Boston University Law Review*, 1969, 49, 46–61.

Moeller, H. G. The Continuum of corrections. *The Annals of the American Academy of Political and Social Science*. 1969, 381, 81–88.

Morris, N. Psychiatry and the dangerous criminal. *Southern California Law Review*, 1968, 41, 514–547.

Morris, N., & Hawkins, G. The overreach of the criminal law. *Midway*, 1969, 9, 71–90.

Newman, D. J. Pleading guilty for considerations: A study of bargain justice. *Journal of Criminal Law, Criminology and Police Science*, 1956, 780–790.

Packer, H. L. *The limits of the criminal sanction.* Stanford: Stanford University Press. 1968.

Palmer, T. California's community treatment project in 1969: An assessment of its relevance and utility to the field of corrections. Washington D. C.: Joint Commission on Correctional Manpower and Training, March 1969. (Mimeo)

Phillips, E. L. Achievement Place: token reinforcement procedures in a home-style rehabilitation setting for predelinquent boys. *Journal of Applied Behavior Analysis*, 1968, 1, 213–223.

Quay, H. C. *Juvenile delinquency: research and theory.* Princeton N. J.: Van Nostrand Company, 1965.

Quinney, E. R. The study of white collar crime: Toward a reorientation in theory and research. *Journal of Criminal Law, Criminology and Police Science*, 1964, 55, 208–214.

Rubin, S. *The law of criminal corrections.* St. Paul, Minn.: West Publishing Co., 1963.

Scheff, T. J. Decision rules, types of error, and their consequences in medical diagnosis. *Behavioral Science*, 1963, 8, 97–107.

Schur, E. M. *Crimes without victims.* Englewood Cliffs, N. J.: Prentice-Hall, 1965.

Schur, E. M. *Law and society: A sociological view.* New York: Random House, 1968.

Shah, S. A. The mentally disordered offender. (Paper prepared for the President's Commission on Law Enforcement and Administration of Justice, August 1966.) Excerpted in R. Allen, E. Z. Ferster, & J. Rubin (eds.), *Readings in law and psychiatry.* Baltimore: Johns Hopkins University Press, 1968.

Shah, S. A. Crime and mental illness: Some problems regarding the conceptualization and labeling of deviant behavior. *Mental Hygiene*, 1969, 53, 21–33. (a)

Shah, S. A. Community mental health and the criminal justice system: Some issues and problems. *Mental Hygiene*, 1970, 54, 1–12.

Shellow, R., & Roemer, D. No heaven for hell's angels. *Trans-action*, 1966, 3, 12–19.

Smith, R. L. Probation subsidy: Success story. *California Youth Authority Quarterly*, Winter 1967.

Sutherland, E. H. *White collar crime.* New York: Dryden Press, 1949.

Sutherland, E. H., & Cressey, D. R. *Principles of criminology.* (7th ed.) New York: Lippincott, 1966.

Sykes, G. M. *Crime and society.* New York: Random House, 1967.

Szasz, T. S. The myth of mental illness. *American Psychologist*, 1969, 15, 113–118.

Szasz, T. S. *Law, liberty and psychiatry.* New York: Macmillan, 1963.

Tapp, J. L. Psychology and the law: The dilemma. *Psychology Today*, 1969, 2, 16–22.

Task force report: Corrections. (The President's Commission on Law Enforcement and Administration of Justice) Washington, D. C.: United States Government Printing Office, 1967.

Task force report: Drunkenness. (The President's Commission on Law Enforcement and Administration of Justice) Washington, D. C.: United States Government Printing Office, 1967.

Task force report: Juvenile delinquency and youth crime. (The President's Commission on Law Enforcement and Administration of Justice) Washington, D. C.: United States Government Printing Office, 1967.

Task force report: Science and technology. (The President's Commission on Law Enforcement and Administration of Justice) Washington D. C.: United States Government Printing Office, 1967.

Task force report: The courts. (The President's Commission on Law Enforcement and Administration of Justice) Washington, D. C.: United States Government Printing Office, 1967.

Task force report: The police. (The President's Commission on Law Enforcement and Administration of Justice) Washington, D. C.: United States Government Printing Office, 1967.

The challenge of crime in a free society. (The President's Commission on Law Enforcement and Administration of Justice) Washington, D. C: United States Government Printing Office, 1967.

Toch, H. (ed.) *Legal and criminal psychology.* New York: Holt, Rinehart & Winston, 1961.

Warren, M. Q. The case for differential treatment of delinquents. *Annals of the American Academy of Political and Social Science*, 1969, 381, 47–59.

Warren, M. Q. Correctional treatment in community settings: a report of current research. Paper prepared for the Sixth International Congress on Criminology, Madrid, Spain. September 1970. (Mimeo)

Wilkins, L. T., & Gottfredson, D. M. *Research, demonstration and social action.* Davis, Calif.: National Council on Crime and Delinquency, 1969.

Wootton, B. *Social science and social pathology.* London: Allen & Unwin, 1959.

6

Religious Systems as Sources of Control and Support

Robert B. Tapp and June L. Tapp

"Religion" and "community mental health" share conceptual ambiguity, but for different reasons. Western religions are ancient, varied, and in great flux. Empirical studies of religion, whether individually or institutionally focused, are surprisingly scarce (cf. Berkowitz & Johnson, 1967). The concept of community mental health, on the other hand, is too new and broad to be plagued with serious or disruptive divisions. Nevertheless, its status in relation to earlier mental health and psychotherapeutic movements is a matter of contention. Any discussion of present and potential relationships between religion and community mental health starts with these ambiguities and proceeds by analytic and historical means.

Social movements as pervasive as mental health or religion are bound to produce coexisting partisans reflecting many historical changes and developments. When we find many "true believers," each with conflicting claims, the best way to proceed is by a careful ground mapping. We will then at least know who belongs where, and where we are ourselves. While this in itself will not give us any sense of direction, it will nevertheless prove essential to anyone who has decided where he wants to go.

Traditional Western religion and traditional interpretations of mental health afford a number of intriguing structural similarities. Both have been highly individualistic, focusing upon the person. Each begins with diagnosis (sin/neurosis), proffers a therapy, and promises a remisssion (salvation/mental health). Each has its experts, its texts, its institutions, its devoted laity. Each has its enemies.

Each has a clearly discernible past and a likely future.

The thesis here is that this future will be one of increasing convergence. For quite different reasons, the role of expertise in the two areas is lessening. A mixture of democratization and secularization affects both, fostered in part by growing doubts about the efficacies of their respective diagnoses, therapies and remissions. If religion has been strong on goals, it has been weak in techniques. And if mental health has been strong in techniques, it has been vague on goals—better able to define "illness" than "health." The present shared mood of uneasiness and lost dogmatisms is reminiscent of "actors in search of a play."

In what follows, we will generally use the broader term "psychology" as including psychotherapy and psychiatry, and "community mental health" as synonymous with community psychology or community psychiatry. When the more specific terms are used, the reasons will be obvious. In speaking of "mental health," we have in mind the various movements aimed at promoting "mental hygiene," or "psychotherapeutic orientation"—movements which have given rise to the relatively recent efforts toward "community mental health." Our references to religion will concentrate on the American scene but will make occasional reference to comparative religious phenomena.

RELIGION AND MENTAL HEALTH

Parallels. Focusing on the last half-century, religion and mental health can be viewed as distinct *weltanschauungen*, exhibiting parallels and differences. Both are *totalistic* rather than adjunct. They presume to cover the whole range of human life, from basic needs to highest satisfactions. In this totalism they differ from, for instance, medicine, which typically has been concerned with physical health and not the more philosophical issue of "health for what." Put another way, the physician does not follow his client out of the consulting room and into his job, family life, recreation, creativity or solitude. Such pervasive human activities only concern an adjunct orientation when they produce painful symptomology. No human activity, however, can be alien to a totalistic orientation. This parallelism of concern has brought religion and mental health into both confrontation and accommodation.

Both orientations are also *expertistic*. Western religions especially have relied heavily on prophets, priests, theologians, and teachers who have "correctly" interpreted their beliefs. In the West, this has been an ongoing interpretation of some "revelation"—an intrusion upon the human scene from a supernatural realm of divine person whose basic authority cannot be questioned. The religious expert or theologian has been seen as a guardian, interpreter, and channel of the supernaturals. In certain non-Western religions and some modernized versions of Western religions, the functional supernaturals have been "highly unusual" persons or events (the *man* Buddha or Confucius, a *human* Jesus, creations, holocausts) but the function of the expert has remained. A similar expertism can be found in the mental health movement in relation to the issues of who is competent to make a diagnosis or evaluate a therapy. Illustrative of this would be Heinz Hartmann's contention that only another psychoanalyst could correctly interpret or evaluate the transcript of a psychoanalysis (1959).

Differences. If totalism and expertism are the main parallels between religion and mental health, there are also differences which must be noted. In both these parallels and differences, there are often gaps between pretense and practice—between what a field would like to do and what it in fact does. At this point, we are primarily concerned with the pretenses, and necessary qualifiers will be added as we proceed.

The mental health movement has been typically naturalistic in the philosophical sense of that term. It has concerned itself with events and processes in the ordinary world of human experience. While there are assuredly difficult problems surrounding the concept of "mental event" or allegations concerning "other minds," these problem areas are in the ordinary, natural world and not in the supernatural time and space which occupy part of religions' concern. The "time" in which psychological processes unfold is ordinary time, or what philosophers would call "public time." This naturalism makes the mental health orientation both scientistic and temporalistic—stances that have never characterized religion. Religious events, and subsequent human experiences recapturing and recapitulating those events, occur in what Mircea Eliade calls "sacred space" and "sacred time" (1958). These terms are a helpful explication of a supernaturalistic orientation.

Flowing from this naturalism of the mental health orientation is a kind of pragmatism which differs from the religious orientation. The results of psychotherapy transpire in some foreseeable future, some point in time at which verification procedures become appropriate. Indefinite or endless psychotherapy is conceptually impossible. The verification of religious assertions turns out to be quite another matter. Recent attempts to clarify religious language have led one religious philosopher to speak of "eschatological verification"—a verification that takes place only in some end-of-time or after-history (Hick, 1957). Quite apart from the logical difficulties in conceiving of "time" when there is no more "time," such a category illustrates well the nonpragmatic nature of religious thinking.

The third major difference we see between the religions and a mental health orientation is in the universalism of *outlook* (in psychological terminology, generality of construct). Because of its scientistic stance, mental health speaks typically of "the human condition" and describes particular behaviors within the context of assumptions about general behavior. Recent concerns with genetic determinants of behavior may qualify this somewhat, but the basic proposition still seems to be valid. Religion, on the other hand, is primarily concerned with particular groups. While it may generalize about "the human condition," its focus is on the "true believers," the "members of the church," the "born Jews" (or Hindus, or Shintos, or Navahos). As we will argue later, this religious nonuniversalism (particularism) poses serious barriers to the assimilation of mental health values.

ACCOMMODATIONS OF CONTEMPORARY AMERICAN RELIGION TO MENTAL HEALTH

We have thus far been regarding religion as a set of orientations occurring within all human cultures. In order to assess the reciprocal relationships of religion and community mental health, we must now examine American forms of religion since 1900. One dominant process, highly significant for our purposes, has been that of accommodation—the religious adoption of the mental health orientation without basic modification or critique. This has, in religious circles, been a selective situation. Along with accommodation, there has been intransigeant rejection as well as critical assimilation. All three processes must be borne in mind, but we will first look at accommodation.

Determining the valence of religious institutions and ideas in American life is a complex matter. Religious statistics are notoriously uneven in reliability. Nevertheless, they give some picture of the institutional structuring of religion. The most recent *Yearbook of American Churches* (1968) lists a total membership of 105,000,000. This total probably reflects 80–90 percent of church membership, and includes Roman Catholics (45 percent) and Jews (5 percent). The clergy total is 264,000, of whom 138,000 have "charges" (meaning they are related to a parish or congregation). Granting that many of those listed are not engaged in full-time religious professions, the community mental health movement can still count on a sizable personnel reservoir from the allied helping-field of religion.

If we try to understand American religions in less denominational terms, we must distinguish Catholics, Jews, "cooperative" Protestants, and "other" Protestants. This distinction between Protestants notes that the members of the National Council of Churches as well as most state and local councils are drawn from those Protestant groups committed to cooperative or common action despite ideological diversity. The fact remains, however, that the "other" Protestants are increasingly cooperating in their own common causes. Furthermore, National Council membership does not have the same ideological implica-

tions as does nonmembership. We can safely assert that most of the 27 million nonmembers share a common "evangelical" ideology. If one-third of the 39 million National Council members are also conservative-fundamentalist in outlook (cf. *Time*, 1969), this gives the right wing of Protestantism a 60 percent plurality. This membership base inflates the totals of the *Yearbook*, but the proportions are probably correct.

Americans are more "religious" than other Western nations on a number of indices—frequency of church membership and attendance, frequency of financial support, and donated time. Between 60 and 70 percent belong to churches and synagogues (this is very near an all-time historical high). An unknown additional percentage are nonmember attenders. Polls consistently find that 97 percent "believe in God." Clergymen are ranked high on occupational scales and as sources of help in crisis. What this all means is that any assessment of the role of religion in community mental health must necessarily come to terms with the "meaning" of religion for a very large segment of the population.

Even if we had more accurate institutional data, however, this kind of analysis would become complex. For instance, one must distinguish between institution, bureaucracy, and value structure. In the case of Roman Catholicism, the institution and the bureaucracy are most readily visible, but this should not allow us to overlook the nominal member who is barely touched by the institution or bureaucracy and yet has assumed no other affiliation. We should not stop short of asking people which church they "stay away from," since this will help define the meaning of religion for them and help us discover the various noninstitutional, nonbureaucratic modulations of religious values and aspirations.

In the case of American Jews, the complications stem from whether Jewishness is an ethnicity or a community, largely of birth, which must somehow be voluntarily affirmed and maintained. The traditional position is that one is Jewish if he had a Jewish mother. Among some Reform spokesmen one finds the polar position that Judaism should be a voluntary faith (like Methodism) and that unless one chooses to be Jewish he is not. Further confusion is fostered by the fact that most non-Jews probably concur with the Orthodox position that persons from "Jewish" families remain "Jewish" unless they convert. Some fundamentalist Protestant groups and their converts even refer to "Hebrew Christians." In any event, some sizable number of Americans regard Judaism as the religion they "stay away from." They differ from the nominal Catholics in that the label of their birth is urged upon them not only by their former coreligionists but by many in the community at large.

When we turn to the majority Protestant group, the situation is highly ambiguous. Recently, historians have argued that the Weber-Troeltsch typology of church/sect has little relevance to the American scene where the key institution is the "denomination"—characterized by relative openness of membership and diffuseness of belief (Mead, 1963). Denominations are far more significantly correlated to social class than to specific beliefs or behaviors.

The least diffusion, institutionally, occurs at the conservative right end of the Protestant spectrum. This is, perhaps, the unique American aspect of Protestant development and will be, we contend, of great significance as the community mental health movement expands. Professionalized groups have tended to overlook this fundamentalism since it lies outside their class experience, but it is a major religious phenomenon. Fundamentalism is characterized by two features: a simple, direct approach to the Bible (rather than a concern for some historical tradition of interpretation) and a stress upon "spiritual experience" rather than intellectualized belief. For these reasons, the bureaucracy of fundamentalism reflects a nonuniversity, nonseminary type of training. Six out of ten American Protestant ministers have had neither college nor seminary education (Nichols, 1952). This represents a very real departure from the mainstream European Protestant tradition of a "learned ministry." It also explains why more Americans would view Billy Graham and Oral Roberts as great theologians than they would so regard Reinhold Niebuhr or Paul Tillich. And it points up the difficulties that community mental health personnel will experience when involving the clergy. Since this dichotomy in class, education, and outlook pervades the Protestant ministry, it is hard to find a city where clergy are able to effect serious cooperation with one another, let alone with other professional groups.

Since acceptance, status, and power are interrelated, present processes of democratization seem likely to increase the influence of fundamentalism and fundamentalist leadership. One of the real effects of court decisions and social policies aimed at "separation of church and state" is to weaken the "established" religions and therefore increase the relative strength of the less-known religions. Perhaps this will also be the net outcome of the various ecumenical movements aimed at bringing religious groups into closer cooperation. If so, the present hegemony of university and seminary trained religious professionals will attenuate.

Religious accommodation to a mental health orientation is most readily observed on bureaucratic rather than institutional levels. That is to say, we must look to the behavior of individual clergymen and the seminaries that train them. The roster of the American Academy of Religion and Mental Health, founded in 1954, provides illustrative data, as do the affiliations of those who write for its organ, the *Journal of Religion and Mental Health.* A number of overlaps will be found here and in the Council for Clinical Training, founded in 1930. In the main, such clergymen, professors, and hospital chaplains come from those denominations serving the middle class, educated, white American Protestant and Jew (Klausner, 1964). In other words, there has been a close relationship between bureaucratic concern for a mental health orientation and parishioners open to, and able to afford, psychotherapy. Most of the mainstream Protestant seminaries now offer instruction in "pastoral psychology" or "pastoral counseling." Two journals reflect this development and are valuable as descriptions of ideology and practice: *Pastoral Psychology* and the *Journal of Pastoral Care.* Many seminaries—Protestant, Catholic, and Jewish—now require a supervised hospital internship (usually lasting for one summer).

One cannot, however, explain the rapid spread of mental health ideas among the mainstream Protestant bureaucracy simply in terms of the acceptability of these values to the general membership. Unpopular social values (antiwar, prointegration) have spread as rapidly without similar lay acceptance. We must, therefore, examine some of the factors within the bureaucracy—especially if we are concerned to estimate the continuance of support for the mental health movement.

The mainstream Protestant bureaucracy is today characterized by an urge to "relevance." This is seen in the considerable clerical involvement in various phases of civil rights activity and in opposition to the Vietnam war. In these cases, as we have suggested, clerics have often paid a high price in being ahead of their members. Yet this very increase in marginality creates its own kind of opennesses. In earlier decades psychotherapeutic themes were more dominant in intellectual circles and this same urge to relevance impelled clergymen into mental hygiene, mental health orientations, and organizations.

This very salience of the mental health movement affected the members of many mainstream Protestant churches, and some of the bureaucratic accommodation may be attributed to a "normal" motivation of holding members. O. Hobart Mowrer has in fact argued that some clergymen were too zealous in referring parishioners to psychotherapists (1961). A parallel response was the creation of church sponsored and housed counseling centers (e.g., Fritz Kunkel in Los Angeles, Smiley Blanton in New York). Certainly there has been a reciprocal relationship between Protestant acceptance of psychotherapy and the increase in "Protestant" psychotherapists. More recently, Roman Catholic openness has led to an increase of "Catholic" psychotherapists. We take it for granted that the hostility of classical psychoanalysis toward religion needs no documentation here. Interested readers may find an historical explication of this in the semipublic discussions of Sigmund Freud and Oskar Pfister, a Swiss pastor (Freud, 1964).

A more ideological factor helping accommodation was the popularity of "neoorthodox" theology during the 1930s and '40s, reviving an Augustinian view of man which stressed the limitations of rationality in personal and social life (cf. especially Reinhold Niebuhr). Man was instead to be viewed as "sinner," prone to self-deception, pride, and continuing distortion of outlook. Mowrer (1961) has tellingly delineated the parallels of this stance to an orthodox Freudian position. Libido provides a kind of biological determinism just as sin provides it religiously. Faith relaxes anxiety just as insight relaxes

superego. Perhaps less apparent outside theological circles is the devastating critique the neoorthodox position leveled against "pietism" and "Christian liberalism" which had stressed inward growth and human self-perfectability.

More recently, the ideas of Paul Tillich have promoted accommodation. Tillich fused German romanticism and existentialism with a number of psychoanalytic concepts. Tillich's memorial sermon for Karen Horney is an interesting example of this ideological blend (1953). Perhaps more importantly, his own dialectical treatment of such key theological problems as the God-concept (equating it with "the ground of being") not only made religious thought palatable to many skeptical outsiders but led some followers to proclaim "Christian atheism" or assert that "God is dead." Insofar as a naturalistic outlook is troubled by theistic allegations and God-talk, this new climate of opinion reduces many barriers to accommodation.

As a final factor, we must note the ecumenical movement. The Protestant ecumenical movement, beginning in the early twentieth century, brought together spokesmen from different traditions in an atmosphere of mutual respect to discuss theological as well as social concerns. Such cooperative experiences have fostered a kind of federationism, coupled with a will to compromise. Since Vatican II, Roman Catholicism has fostered its own ecumenism, reflecting an eagerness to enter into dialogue with other positions. In differing ways, both ecumenical movements have fostered an increasing openness to accommodation. Interestingly, most clinical pastoral training programs in hospitals have been ecumenical in the sense of being interfaith. There the focus upon the problems of patients inevitably creates an awareness of the relativity of particular and traditional theological solutions.

BARRIERS AND LIMITATIONS TO ACCOMMODATION

Accommodation, as used here, describes those who have essentially incorporated mental health ideas into their overall religious framework. If our initial characterization of the contrasts and parallels of religion and mental health is correct, accommodation can only occur when certain religious ideas are either lacking or abandoned. This is another way of stating Samuel Klausner's conclusion, after analyzing years of religion and psychology literature, that the "marginals" on either side are most likely to adopt the terminology and ideas of the other camp (1964). This is an instance of the openness we have described.

Theologically, psychotherapeutic ideas have most directly challenged certain "doctrines of man." (We would favor "humankind" as a less gender-biased term, but classical and contemporary theological formulations not only use "man" but often treat "woman" as a separate "order.") At the risk of oversimplification, we will characterize these as the "pilgrim" doctrine and the "citizen of two worlds" doctrine. The monastic system obviously embodies the pilgrim doctrine, but modified versions of it are found throughout Christian history, especially in what has been called "ascetic Protestantism." Man is understood as a kind of horizontal duality, with upper and lower parts. The upper, spiritual part is higher and its needs and demands should be heeded, whereas the needs of the lower part must be suppressed. Plato had described the body as "the prison of the soul" and this theme is the basis of the pilgrim doctrine. Man's real home is not on earth but in some postmortem, heavenly abode and this life should be treated only as a journey. A Muslim version of this runs, "This world is a bridge; build not a house thereon." Any human activity must be legitimated by its contribution to the welfare of the soul; and the "soul" is viewed as nonmaterial and therefore not subject to empirical description or assessment. Clearly, the pilgrim doctrine leads to excessive denial and suppression from a mental health standpoint. Equally clearly, the pilgrim doctrine must view mental health ideology as naturalistic and unspiritual.

The "citizen of two worlds" doctrine, on the other hand, views man as a kind of vertical duality. One "side" is religious allegiance and responsibility; the other side is responsible to the world. The "world" is necessary, real, and not inherently bad (although, of course, it cannot rival or reach the "heavenly city"). This doctrine of man has the advantage of granting a quasi-legitimacy to many human activities. Sex, for example, is to the pilgrim doctrine an unfortunate necessity at best,

and a thing to be shunned at worst. For the citizen of two worlds, however, it can be seen as a legitimate activity of pleasure and fulfillment insofar as it is always subordinated to a spiritual doctrine of cosmic love. In most versions of this doctrine, there are many dimensions on the "secular" side that have no spiritual counterparts and therefore no ecclesiastical inhibitors. For most modern treatments of this kind of dualism, this would apply to areas of power, pleasure, politics justice, and the like. Here there is no overarching spiritual wisdom, and secular wisdom is neither inhibited nor challenged.

In other words, if we view various religious doctrines of man from the mental health *weltanschauung*, they can be arranged along a continuum. The pilgrim doctrine at the far right demands rejection of all "secular" wisdom, including psychotherapy. The citizen of two worlds doctrine would fall somewhat right of center. On the far left, we hypothesize a naturalistic doctrine of man, indistinguishable from the mental health, naturalistic position. This represents complete accommodation. Between the extreme and the center of our spectrum is space for a number of stances that we shall call "critical assimilation" doctrines.

Earlier, we outlined a number of cultural and historical presses that had encouraged doctrines of accommodation. Now we will suggest three types of theological press that limit accommodation and therefore result in some sort of critical assimilation. One is the result of viewing psychotherapy as a "method" rather than a *weltanschauung*. Albert Outler suggests that the Freudian "wisdom about life" can be rejected while the "wisdom about therapy" is adopted (1954). While this approach leads into philosophical problems such as the actual independence of alleged ends and methodologies, it clearly recognizes that full accommodation would indeed involve crucial ideological shifts.

The second type of theological limitation is somewhat harder to state but represents the most prevalent and serious form of reservation held by theologians. Cyprian, a 2nd century church father, contended: *Extra ecclesiam nulla salus* ("Outside the church there is no salvation"). That doctrine has always been troublesome in its arrogance and has typically been hedged with footnotes about an "invisible" or "latent" church. The initial dilemma that forced these qualifications was the need to ascribe postmortem status to pre- or extra-Christian worthies such as Plato and Moses. To consign them to Hell might have made "logical-theological" sense, but it grated upon common human decencies and left the Deity who wrote such a script in the position of being more arbitrary and less humane than ordinary humans. Thus the footnotes.

This same dilemma persists in relation to modern mental health. If we regard this as the highest human good, it approximates what religion has called "salvation." Can it exist *extra-ecclesiam*; is it possible for non-Christians? If so, what becomes of the basic rationale for the church? Those theologians who grant extra-ecclesiastical salvation have one set of problems while those who deny it must either rely upon some arbitrary definitional basis, or show, by some empirical procedures, that non-Christian mental health still leaves something to be desired.

A third theological limitation upon accommodation stems from the conflict between certain modern values and what could be termed "historical integrity." This can be illustrated by reference to anti-Semitism. Men of good will, Christian and otherwise, are now agreed that anti-Semitism is a disvalue. Nevertheless, early Christianity was shaped in an anti-Jewish environment. Its literature both reflects this and also sustains a more broad-gauged and complicated anti-Semitism. While there may well be a number of causal determinants for anti-Semitism, recent empirical studies consistently show its close relationship to mainstream forms of Christian and New Testament instruction. Should modern Christians therefore purge their basic book? Liberal democratic ideology might argue "Yes," while historical integrity might demur. Numerous American communities have been torn apart by arguments over the "Passion Play," which focuses on this issue. Such controversies are better indicators of conflicted feelings than are discussions of the evils of prejudice or the inevitably desirable results of religiousness.

In assessing the degree to which American religion has accommodated to, or assimilated, mental health concepts, we must not be misled by trends and tendencies which, although widely publicized, have actually a very limited and stratified appeal. For the great majority of American Protestants and Catholics, there has been little exposure to mental health ideology through religious channels—due to the concomitance of limited educational exposure of both parishioners and clergy. Milton Rokeach observed (1968) that religious persons do not seem to be significantly freer from anxiety or prejudice than their non-church-going neighbors. In part, this may simply indicate that these mental health values have not been effectively assimilated. More likely, it points to the confounding of such values with inhibiting values—"double messages." In many religions, for instance, teachings about the brotherhood of man exist along with exhortation to convert others to one's own faith. Such confounding of values is probably the explanation of numerous findings on the correlation of orthodoxy and prejudice.

A further explanation of the ideological nonaccommodation of religion to mental health is semantic. Similar words often carry dissimilar meanings in religious and psychological contexts. The controversial papal encyclical on contraception *Humanae vitae* speaks continually of "love" and "duty" but uses these words with connotations strange to most non-Catholics. The controversy created by this pronouncement indicates that these older connotations are also unfamiliar or no longer acceptable to many Catholics as well.

Sexuality as a Test Case of Accommodation

It will be clear that we have been regarding the mental health movement and the several religious traditions of our culture as embodying different, and often conflicting, outlooks. A number of terms could be used to describe the interaction processes at work here: accommodation, assimilation, rejection, rapprochement, competition, conflict. The traditional religious term for the desirable outcome in such confrontations is "conversion"—a fundamental shift in basic outlook which makes the erstwhile outsider an insider. There is no reason to think that this is a one-way process. In fact, one of the most intriguing conversions of the present century has occurred in relation to Western religions and sexuality. The history of this conversion is worth reviewing as an extreme illustration of religious accommodation to the mental health movement.

One of Freud's greatest contributions was a delineation of psychosexual development, culminating in mature genital sexuality. Freud's focus was upon the price paid for "civilization" in terms of repression and pain. To recognize and alleviate repression became a major goal of mental health, along with the minimization of pain. This pain-pleasure balance is acutely centered in man's attitude toward his sexuality. More precisely, the problem is one of human sexuality, since Freud's vision insisted upon the sexuality of children and women.

A gross, but nonetheless significant, measure of attitudes toward sexuality is found in attitudes toward birth control and family planning. Here the ecclesiastical record is both available and instructive. At the turn of the century, religious groups were almost unanimous in condemning contraception as a negation of the fundamentally "procreative" function of sexuality. One by one, the churches have come to accept and then endorse birth control. It would, of course, be too simple to regard this as the ready acceptance of a mental health movement value. We have to reckon with urbanization, education, democratization, feminism, class mobility, and a number of other cultural forces. But the acceptance was essentially completed even before the advent of "the Pill" and the women's liberation movement. Even more significant than the endorsement of contraception was the religious reformulation of values toward human sexuality. *Towards a Quaker View of Sex* (1964) is perhaps the most revolutionary restatement, but the search for new values may also be seen in the more moderate treatments of Seward Hiltner (1953) and Joseph Fletcher (1954). Also instructive is the historical reconstructionism of William Cole (1955). Sex, for these modern Christians, becomes recreation as well as procreation, and the emphasis broadens toward almost total theories of human fulfillment through sexuality (Bailey, 1952).

What this sexuality paradigm shows is the inevitability of religious-cultural rapprochement. We have chosen it not because it is isolated but precisely because we regard it as prototypical of accommodation. If this assumption is correct, similar processes will become patent in regard to pleasure generally, to leisure, to social freedom, and other preoccupations of postindustrial society.

CRITICAL ASSIMILATORS AND INTRANSIGEANT REJECTORS

The almost uncritical religious adoption of a mental health attitude of sexuality, just described, represents a nearly unparalleled situation. Almost no other aspect of mental helath emphasis has been as freely adopted. The much more normal religious reaction, where there is not total rejection, is one of "critical assimilation." By this we mean a reassessment of present religious practices and traditional ideas in the light of mental health ideology, guided by the basic assumption that there is something sound in these practices and that the critical assimilation of the challenging ideology will build upon and improve existing religious practices. A great majority of theologically trained writers who have confronted the mental health movement have fallen in this camp, as has been the case with psychotherapeutically trained workers with personal religious involvement. What follows is simply a pointing to a few of the major contemporary figures in this area. It is illustrative rather than exhaustive.

Jesse McNeill's *History of the Cure of Souls* (1951) is a useful survey of religious traditions, including some materials from the non-Western world, and provides a helpful context in which to assess contemporary efforts at critical assimilation. Where parallels of theory or practice between existing religions and particular aspects of the mental health movement can be found, a reenforcing assimilation can occur. Some specific instances of this occur in the treatment of alcoholism as described by Howard Clinebell (1966), Richard McCann's treatment of religious leadership (1962), and Hans Hofmann's discussion of attitudes toward sexuality (1967). Useful examples from the standpoint of counseling practice are Paul Tournier (1957) and O. Pfister (1923). From the psychological side, the personality theories of Gordon Allport (1950) and of Rollo May (1953) have explicit religious components.

Somewhat further removed from the religious mainstream, a number of Jungians have explored religious and mental health parallelisms. Ira Progoff (1959) and F. Kunkel (1943) are representative of this orientation.

Mowrer's writings (1961, 1964), while sharply critical of the Freudian component in mental health, are very concerned to find prototypical religious theories. Erich Fromm's interests, while well to the left of the religious mainstream, reflect a continuing reassessment of past religious contributions (1950, 1966). Operating from a somewhat similar humanist orientation, Rudolf Dreikurs reflects a parallelism in the Adlerian tradition (1968). Henry Murray's later writings also blend a humanist orientation with a concern for preparallelisms in the religious traditions (1960). Gardner Murphy also shares a similar orientation (1958). "Peak experiences," according to Abraham Maslow's typology, are a widespread human phenomenon, and some of them occur in religious contexts (1964).

There has also been an interest in discovering parallelisms between mental health and non-Western religions. These parallels are, of course, more useful in building critical models than in assimilating social structures, but they reflect yet another approach to the problem of the inner relations of religion and psychotherapy. Alan Watts (1961) and Gerald Heard (1964) are good introductions to this interest. We can also note Charles Morris' assumption that the personality structures typically associated with varied religions are quite universally distributed, and his several attempts to build empirical models to assess this (1942, 1956).

Consistent rejection of a mental health orientation by religious persons has been a somewhat different process than accommodation or critical assimilation. For one thing, persons may not know or care to know a different ideological position if they are sufficiently satisfied with their present one. In a culture where the mental health orientation is widespread, ignorance of it becomes de facto rejection. But this is a process without a rationale.

In some cases this rejection becomes conscious and takes on polemical qualities. Most of these polemics, however, have been addressed to the faithful and have not been intended primarily as academic treatments. A brief survey of some of these positions may be found in Klausner (1964).

Since it is the thesis here that religious perspectives will have an increasing voice in policy determination regarding community mental health, and since a sizable proportion of American religious affiliation is sympathetic to intransigeant rejection, it is important to sketch certain recurring themes found along the religious "right." Academic psychology and psychotherapy have been faulted for their naturalistic view of man which ignores his spiritual, transcendent dimensions. Without such a dualistic perspective, it is held, sin and evil lose their cosmic definition and succumb to cultural relativism. The most serious issue for conservative religions, however, has already been noted—the prospect of salvation apart from "Christ and/or the Church" (for conservative Judaism, substitute "the People"). While critical assimilators might be willing to view psychotherapy as a preface or restorative to "religious" living, the intransigeant rejectors view it as a subversive competitor.

WHEN MODELS FAIL

An abundant literature has grown, from within and without, detailing the "failures" of the mental health movement. This is relevant in explaining the emergence of the community mental health movement and also because of its significance in assessing religious reactions to mental health in its various forms. It was inevitable that the slow and lengthy processes of psychoanalytic therapy would be criticized as economically discriminatory and class bound. It was probably equally inevitable that various forms of group therapy would emerge, whereby individual therapists could carry larger loads. It was probably also predictable that as psychotherapy came to be defined as a "helping" process, the necessity for having highly trained helpers would be questioned. Part of this same process may be seen in the rise of client-centered therapies where the diagnostic skill of the therapist is less important than the potentials for self-cure of the patient so far as this can be properly facilitated.

An interesting challenge to the traditional model of "illness" came from the studies of Hans Eysenck and his followers (1965). Logically, of course, there must be something like a "spontaneous remission rate." Insofar as it can be estimated, this provides a base rate for assessing the effectiveness of various psychotherapies. Thus far, empirical research in this area has not provided a decisive verdict in favor of various therapies.

The central aspect of the mental health crisis, however, has been the direct attack upon the "illness model" itself. If "mental illness" is essentially a euphemism for behavior that some particular culture or subculture does not like (Szasz, 1961), then of course the mental health practitioner is in no sense analogous to the medical practitioner who has a reasonably specific cure for a reasonably specific malady. Mental illness is not so much a "real" thing as a form of behaving that is "labeled" as undesirable by the society. The psychotherapist has lost that authority that was his when his role was viewed as analogous to the medical therapist.

It may be reassuring to know from the history of science that the breakdown of a model is typically the symptom that some larger, more effective synthesis is on the horizon. Nevertheless, as workers lose faith in the old model a clear demoralization results until its better replacement is in being.

This breakdown of model has intriguing parallels with a similar breakdown of the religious model of "sin" and its "cure." The mainstream of Western religiousness has also diagnosed the human ailment and prescribed a cure for that illness. The same secular mentality, however, that has insisted that psychotherapy produce its "results" has done the same thing for religion, with the same disquieting outcome. In the past, religion has been able to deal with the call for verification by suggesting that it may not occur "in this world" but rather may only appear in some *eschaton*, some "other world" or some "new epoch." As the metaphysical basis for such dualism attenuates, the attractiveness of the solution disappears. Similarly, religion has often argued that the cure will be more evident to God than to man or that even if it is apparent to man, it is apparent to man in his individual subjectivity and is not a matter for public appraisal or verification.

These solutions, needless to say, have lost much of their attractiveness in the current critical climate. Thus the background for our discussion of the emergence of community mental health and the relationship of religious institutions and ideas to this emerging movement is set by the somewhat parallel breakdown in the traditional patterns of dealing with mental illness on the one hand and

religious illness on the other. When traditional models break down, it is both easier and more necessary to try new solutions. The old ways may or may not "work"—whatever that means. The patent fact is that they are surrounded by a large-scale loss of confidence and an intense impatience.

COMMUNITY MENTAL HEALTH AS A RESPONSE TO THE CRISIS

The community mental health movement is a major response to this internal crisis within psychotherapeutic circles. The history of the community psychology movement is detailed elsewhere within this volume, and our purpose here is simply to highlight certain aspects of the development that are relevant in the assessment of the interactions with religious institutions and ideas. The development is intriguing in that funds have preceded theories, perhaps more so than in any other aspect of psychotherapy. As a result, those who controlled the funding were in a position to give some clear direction to development of the field; at the present time, however, there is little evidence that such direction has occurred. M. Brewster Smith has openly voiced the fear that this "third revolution in mental health" may have misfired into an urbanized version of the state mental hospital (1968).

Certainly there is a built-in conflict between those who see the greatest mental health needs among the poor and those who are willing to fund a kind of necessary activity and let geographical allocations be determined by normal political processes. Whatever their needs, the poor do not lobby effectively in city councils and state legislatures. Since the enabling legislation and funding for community mental health centers preceded any serious national concern for "the poor," it is not surprising that the outcomes have proved less than ideal or that middle class areas have found these centers a way to augment their own supply of mental health services.

If we view traditional psychotherapy as a response to the demand for services in a middle class market, then the community mental health center is a potential experiment in mass-marketing of a comparable product. The outcome may well hinge upon the social power that those now deprived of treatment are able to bring to bear. Insofar as education, health, and police services as presently distributed are examples of what will be achieved by democratic political mechanisms, it seems unlikely that major benefits of community mental health will be directed to the poor.

Equally interesting will be the response to various community powers within local community mental health centers. Given the traditional tensions between psychiatric and psychological professionals, the addition of religious and other professionals may lead to some interesting alliances. Quite possibly, persons who pose the least threat to existing interests may be drawn into this balance of power. The threat posed by clergymen may well be a function of their own psychological sophistication and the amount of community power they represent. In theory, their interests will ultimately be harnessed and balanced by a board drawn from the community.

Most interesting of all will be the situation when it is realized that the center's "catchment area" and the clergymen's "parish" are coterminous, and that this single space inadvertently is now served by de facto co-"ministers." Neither profession has a notable record of willingness to share power.

Since the early stages of the community mental health movement, attempts have been made to explore the epidemiological model developed in public health. This model is considerably more sophisticated than the earlier illness or sin models, and may prove quite fruitful. For one thing, it shifts attention to prevention rather than cure. It also posits an ecology of pathogens rather than simply the breakdown of individual defenses.

Notwithstanding, this alternative model carries some of the same disabilities as the earlier illness model. The very construct is much more feasible if the patient is a subsection of society and not society itself. This would also seem to be true with the concept of a "catchment area." The original illness model provided a rationale and a legitimation of the intervention by one group of people in the lives of other groups. With the loss of this model, however, such intervention becomes a more politically sensitive thing and is more likely to succeed when an upper class intervenes in the lives of an under class. The poor represent such an under class group and, to a very large extent, the same can be said of intervention with children. There may be perfectly valid theoretical reasons for intervention on these levels of society, but the fact remains that such intervention is also considerably easier and more expedient. This is a basic polarity between need and demand that characterizes any allocation of social resources. Very often those who most need some particular service are not those who actually have the means to command that service. The literature of community mental health reflects this polarity which in turn reflects basic philosophical issues about obligations and rights within the social order.

If we are really to speak of *community* mental health, our referent must be not just the poor, some manageable group, or even some particular city. It is even doubtful if we can settle for a particular country or society. In the final analysis, nothing less than the whole community of humankind will do. The logic of such an extension of the concept is flawless. But it brings into immediate relief the crucial need to redefine both the meaning of "community" and of "health."

Some sharp redefinitions of normalcy and deviancy will emerge as the connotation of community expands: "*ours* is the desirable pattern" to "the desirable pattern is either *ours* or *theirs*" to "the desired patterns include *ours* and *theirs* and *theirs*. . . ." At the present time, most of our mental health criteria revolve around adequacy, coping, mastery, control, identity. Imagine the shift in scoring standardizations when Hindus, for instance, are given "the franchise." How acceptable to Westerners will be their acceptance, contemplativity, aestheticism, familialism?

As an illustration of the controversies that may lie ahead, Brock Chisholm may be regarded as one of the significant public pioneers of community mental health on a global scale. His writings concerned the application of psychiatric wisdom to the role of illusory systems in human life, such as religion or belief in Santa Claus (1947), and also explorations along the lines of a nonmedically-derived model for community well-being. The latter he termed a "people's psychiatry" (1955). The controversial reception of many of Chisholm's ideas affords an indication of what lies in store for the community mental health movement as it broadens its focus to include more diverse as well as larger and larger communities.

A serious problem of authority will inevitably emerge. As the community psychotherapist views himself less as an expert and more as a catalyst, and as calls for community definition of well-being are heeded, we can foresee the rehabilitation and relegitimation of a number of alternative religious (and, for that matter, political) alternatives in defining community well-being. On a global scale, the possibilities are almost endless. With the democratization of authority, a "white Southern way of life," a "Muslim way of life," a "Maoist way of life " a "liberal, scientist, democratic way of life" will compete with a variety of other options for public acceptance. Note that each of these ways of life fulfills our initial definition of both religious and psychotherapeutic systems as being "totalistic."

It should also be noted that despite the loss of the illness model, the behavioral sciences will enrich this process of democratization of standards of well-being. For any totalistic perspective, the selection of ends is only the beginning of the problem. The evaluation of alternative means to these ends, the training of persons who can facilitate these means, the supply of a continuing flow of research and feedback, and the continuing determination of unexpected results are all part of the psychological armamentum. Since neither the tradition nor the techniques of this kind of hard-headed analysis have been part of religious practice in the past, it would seem that psychology and psychiatry will continue to play a dominant role in the determination of the means of community well-being, even though the determination of ends comes to be more widely shared.

THE INTERVENTION DILEMMA

With the loss of the medical model, the problem of intervention has become intensified. In the traditional practice of psychotherapy, the functions of diagnosis and therapy were separated. Persons might be diagnosed as ill but until they somehow adopted a patient role, therapy was not possible. In the ideal circumstance, this patient role was voluntarily adopted. In more extreme cases it was involuntary as a result of a commitment to institutionalization by third parties. Outside of these circumstances, however

clear the diagnosis might have been, it would have been unethical to intervene into the life of another person.

For purposes of analysis, let us pursue somewhat in more detail this problem of intervention, using the traditional model of pathology and considering the case of an individual. The most obvious level is that of "felt pathology." In this case, the patient comes to the doctor, showing his symptom and asking relief. The doctor, in turn, shows his expertise in the ways of diagnosis and therapy. The situation became more complicated even in the traditional situation, when "unfelt pathology" was present. Incipient alcoholism or unknown cancer would be examples of this. In this case, the therapist had to make a decision concerning his right to answer questions that had not been asked. A yet more ambiguous level appeared in the case of what might be called "unacknowledged pathology." From the standpoint of traditional mental health values, this would occur in the case of the well-adjusted "authoritarian," whether of the right or of the left. Here, above all, the diagnosis might be quite clear but the possibility or procedures of therapy received little illumination from the traditional wisdom.

The diagnosis, on which intervention might be based, was itself grounded in a consensus of an elite. This would seem to have been true even on the first level of felt pathology, where in certain extreme cases the therapist, on the basis of this consensus, might proceed to alleviate the symptom by altering the pain threshold of a hypersensitive patient. On the unfelt and unacknowledged levels of pathology, the role of this elite consensus becomes increasingly clearer.

Applying the traditional pathological model to the diagnosis of illness in a social group, the therapist had even more difficulty justifying both his diagnosis and his possible application of therapy. The epidemiological model improved the situation only insofar as it could be shown that some pathogen in an individual or subgroup had a demonstrably deleterious effect upon the surrounding group. It was considerably easier to show this in the case of smallpox than it has been in the case of, for instance, racism. Yet any realistic use of epidemiology must consider carriers as well as pathogens.

What we have been saying about the dilemmas of social intervention clearly points up the problems that will face the mental health movement as it both gives up its original medical model and shifts its focus from the individual to society as a whole. As it makes this shift, the mental health movement will come to resemble the religious movements within our culture. That is to say, its authority and legitimacy will no longer stem from an external guarantor ("science") but will have to be societally based and democratically determined. If "illness" is defined by the community, it follows that the community is willing to support therapeutic interventions to correct such deviances and probably unwilling to tolerate unrequested interventions. This process has interesting parallels to the earlier development of religious toleration where impermissible heresies became fewer in number as experience with freedom expanded.

We might also note the precedents from religious history where differing derivations have been made from a common term. "God" has been the authoritative term to denote a set of perceptions and evaluations taken to be true by a particular community. In 1914, for instance, most Germans and English were agreed that their nations should follow "the will of God." In practice, the derivations each side made from this "will" were in obvious conflict, but few on either side seriously argued that both derivations could not be simultaneously correct. Is it reasonable to expect "mental health" to fare any better?

THE RELIGIOUS RESPONSE TO COMMUNITY MENTAL HEALTH

In terms of our description of the significant religious accommodation to the traditional mental health movement, 1968 is surely too early to assess any response to the nascent community health movement. Religious institutions had incorporated many aspects of the earlier mental health movement into their practice of counseling and pastoral psychology. Granger Westberg and Edgar Draper's *Community Psychiatry and the Clergyman* (1966) is really the first book in the field, and it is worth noting that its actual concern, despite its title, is the traditional one: How can clergymen more effectively enter a cooperative role with physicians and psychiatrists in a hospital setting? Their study is also highly significant in that it shows the degree to which clergymen have a sense of playing a secondary role in matters of health. We predict that the religious response to community mental health will primarily be the loss of this inferiority complex.

As the community mental health professional loses his definitive expertise (by his loss of the medical model), he will simply become one professional among the many concerned with the problems of community and society. The contemporary university-trained clergyman and the community health worker will play complementary roles in the diagnosis and therapy of society, each having moved away from the traditional concerns of his own past. On the other hand, those clergymen whose concerns have not basically been with the direct rebuilding of society, but who have nevertheless yielded to some forms of accommodation to mental health, will lose their own inferiority complexes in relation to the new community mental health professional. They will also much more vocally reassert the alternative life styles of their particular religious traditions.

Putting this another way, we are predicting that there will be a rapid drop in the accommodation rate of religious professionals and institutions to a traditional psychotherapeutic orientation when the current rethinking in relation to community mental health becomes more widely known. Not only will accommodation, which primarily affected the religious professional's dealings with individual members of his congregation, decline, but an actual competitive situation regarding alternative life styles will come into being.

Historically, the variety of Western religions have been deeply concerned for the quality of the community. After the breakdown of the medieval Christendom, where to a considerable degree the church was able to set the style for the total society, religious values were effected by a pervasive moralism. From certain religious perspectives modern history can be read as the struggle of this moralism with an encroaching secularization process which successively removed from religious control the economic, educational, and sexual sectors. In those religious perspectives usually labeled "modernist," secularization has been encouraged on the assumption that it could be informed by religious values. This was the real meaning of the "social gospel" movement. Only in very recent times have religious thinkers argued that secularization, as such, might be a good thing. There is a sense, then, in which the psychotherapeutic workers' retreating from the quasi-absolutism afforded them by a now-difficult illness model will cross paths with religious thinkers retreating from the hyperindividualism of either a traditional, pietistic orientation which is concerned only with the private and spiritual side of man or retreating from a highly psychotherapeutically accommodated version of religion which legitimated primarily a counseling function.

We predict that this crossing of paths will occur epicentric to the urban trouble spots of American cities. Specifically, the problems of long-range community mental health will be faced neither in ghetto nor suburb but in "interurbia"—where the basic deprivations have been reduced and where psychic escapism is less. Assuming that effective coping is central to the mental health of individuals and that the coping arena cannot be geographically confined, the place where concerned cosmopolitan man lives can be termed interurbia. There the unsolved problems will be both the by-products and the opportunities of an advanced technological society—and how persons in the community come to define and improve the quality of their lives.

Putting this another way, a major push for both community mental health professionals and for many religious professionals is to be "relevant." As they explore together the issues of "relevant to whom" and "relevant for when," we are suggesting that they will find a common challenge in the problem of "tomorrow." They may also discover a common lack of ready, assured, or dogmatic solutions.

THE CONTRIBUTIONS OF RELIGION TO COMMUNITY MENTAL HEALTH

The overall contention here is that we can expect a greater confluence of the psychotherapeutic pioneers of community mental health and those whose primary base is within religious institutions. If an increasing sense of equality and partnership emerges in this situation, a number of specific contributions can be made by religion to community mental health. The most obvious has to do with personnel. Recently, it has become quite clear that many professional clergymen serving local churches have been able to bring their professional skills and to devote a considerable portion of their work time to community concerns which traditionally have fallen outside the justifiable scope of pastoral activity. In the past few years, the civil rights and peace arenas have been illustrative of this. Somewhat less visible are the increasing numbers of ex-ministers and members of religious orders who have been able to transfer their professional skills to community causes. In some cases this has been funded by religious denominations, but in a large number of cases it has been funded by private and governmental agencies. While no figures are available, it is clear from the number of defections from the ministry that many are now engaged in education, the Peace Corps, Vista, poverty programs, and social work. While this vocational shifting no doubt indicates an alienation from religion in some cases, it is more likely to reflect a disenchantment with the particular possibilities of the parish ministry and traditional religious structures (e.g., parochial schools, monastic orders). We make this reference because of the increasing discussions going on within religious institutions of the viability of the present form of the local church and because of the increasing number of ex-ministers who are shifting into the college teaching of religion. In this latter case, it would seem clear that there is not a total disenchantment with the religious enterprise but only with the forms of a traditional parish ministry.

In addition to this supply of fully professional contributors to community mental health, religious institutions have provided a supply of semi- and paraprofessionals in a number of community activities and have also stimulated a flow of volunteers into organizations. Beyond this, religious institutions have provided both physical facilities and often sources of funds to the work of the larger community.

On an ideological level, religion has been a source and transmission belt of what might be called "transcultural" concerns. The most dramatic illustration of this in recent years has been the religious opposition to the war in Vietnam. Almost every denomination has gone on record against this war, and polls have indicated a significant opposition of clergymen to the war.

The degree to which this concern reflects or is communicated to the ordinary church member is more problematic, but the concern is nevertheless indicative of the potential of religion to generate an outlook that transcends nationalism or chauvinism.

A somewhat less obvious contribution of religion may be its experience and experiments with what could be called "transgenerational" community. The survival of a religious institution almost inevitably depends upon the degree to which it can communicate its values to the children who are born to its members. At an early age, the children are initiated into a symbolic community that attempts to comprehend persons of all age levels. While it would be difficult to generate criteria for success in transgenerational communication, it is clear that it is a basic value for both religion and the community mental health movement.

Within local congregations, there often emerge genuine examples of the helping network, where sensitivity to human need draws persons to hospitals, families, and persons in crises. The traditions of giving to "charity" reflect a less personal version of this same religious commitment.

Finally, there have been a number of experiments throughout religious history with small group techniques. These have occurred in religious orders, in "intentional communities," and in a number of sectarian and utopian community experiments. They are also seen historically in pietistic-lay movements and in such lay groups as the Franciscan Tertiaries. A number of contemporary "underground churches" are reviving these traditions of a small, close, sharing community, and religious communes have been multiplying. As the community mental health movement transcends a one-to-one conception of psychotherapy, these experiences will become increasingly valuable.

THE PROBLEM OF RELIGIOUS SURVIVAL

While an analysis of human history thus far would seem to indicate the persistence of religious institutions of some form in every culture, it is less clear that there is any kind of inevitability to the centrality of influence within a culture. It is conceivable that religion might become the kind of quaint, vestigial survival that we see in astrology today.

Nothing is clearer than that Western religion in its traditional forms is threatened by the major trends of modern society. If religion is defined as fidelity to some set of beliefs, as has been done in most empirical studies, then loss of faith correlates positively with increasing education, increasing urbanization, and increasing affluence. It seems more likely, however, that just such trends will generate their own correctives. Such a process seems to us the most obvious explanation for the intellectual ferment found within churches today. Assertions that "God is dead" are not new, but it is a novelty to have such assertions made by any significant number of ministers and theologians. Such rethinking is indeed eroding the traditional dualism and supernaturalism of past religious traditions. But the new naturalism, if successful, will have the effect of providing an intellectual survival-base for future religions.

In this process, the focus of religious attention will shift sharply from metaphysical assertions to concerns with human values and their achievement. That shift will provide a basis for rapprochement between many forms of religious thinking and the more positivistic scientific thinking characteristic of university-educated persons. It will also shift the focus of religious thought from traditional beliefs to matters of life style and concern with the general quality of life.

Philosophically, there is great concern among religious thinkers with the problems of "religious language." Increasingly, one is told that it has a symbolic rather than literal function. This shift provides not only openness to a functional analysis of religion, bringing religion and the behavioral sciences closer together, but it also may lead to a general rehabilitation of religious symbolism within the culture. In the past, such symbols have proved to be both communicatively powerful and widely understood. If the present intellectual dilemmas can be overcome, we may again see religious language play such a community function.

Finally, it would seem that the survival of Western religion depends upon a rapid attenuation of its missionary complex. The orientation of the psychotherapeutic movement is clearly pluralistic, and the philosophical situation we have been describing has eroded the certainties and absolutism that are essential to a conversionist-missionary stance. If religion is increasingly a matter of human values, it is patently impossible to contend that any particular religion has a monopoly upon desirable values. Its beliefs might be unique, but values are a much more generalized product of human creativity.

If our analysis is correct, there are intellectual as well as sociological reasons for expecting an increase in the influence of religious institutions within Western communities. Religious ideas and personnel will therefore play an increasing role in the future of the community mental health movement, precisely because the two will have converged.

LESSONS FROM RELIGIOUS HISTORY FOR COMMUNITY MENTAL HEALTH

We have been arguing that both the psychotherapeutic and the religious orientations are totalistic. When the parallelism between the two is further extended by the development of an institutional structure around the psychotherapeutic, as is the case in the community mental health movement, the parallelism becomes quite striking. This is the case today. For quite different reasons, we have argued, both movements are in transitional stages reflecting considerable lack of clarity regarding methods, directions, and evaluative criteria. While institutional parallelism might serve to generate two competing movements, this inner condition makes it much more likely that the next few years will see cooperation rather than competition. In either case, however, an examination of religious history would prove quite valuable. To the extent that the institutional structures and ideological thrusts of religion and of community mental health are parallel, one could expect to find similar problems and patterns emerging.

Sometimes religious history is read as the resultant created by innovative "heresies" against an orthodox establishment. From the point of view of orthodoxy, heresy is always a partial, limited position. This latter position is probably correct, but various heresies have nevertheless probably provided the necessary dynamism to remind establishments of their implicit possibilities. The usefulness of dialectical interpretation should not, however, screen out the high psychic price often paid by the heretics and innovators.

One of the oldest polarities in Western religious history has been that of priest versus prophet—of the man who attempts to preserve the established order as against him who would transform it. On balance, even the most partisan historian of religion tends to recognize that there is an appropriate degree of ambivalence in viewing this polarity. Certainly this is the situation with psychotherapy, where the dilemma is whether to support the ego in its present functioning or find ways of strengthening motivation toward change. Certainly this dilemma appears on the social level, where decisions are continually required between the need for stability and the need for innovation and renewal.

At the moment, the community mental health movement is clearly on the side of innovation. Kenneth Keniston's chilling satire (1968), in which the mental health workers of the future become the enforcers of social order, suggests the ease with which innovation can shift into stabilization. If religious institutions, in their thus-far successful evolution of survival techniques, have any lessons to offer, it is precisely at this point of institutionalizing both the prophet and the priest into some kind of competitive coexistence. This is a problem of building in dissent without ever permitting it to dominate and of building in stability without permitting it to suffocate; a delicate balance, but one perhaps more easily achieved when its necessity is recognized. Parenthetically, the last two centuries of history afford a distressing series of secular revolutionary regimes that have become repressive and reactionary when in power.

A second instructive phase of religious history would be the development of the social gospel movement from the latter decades of the 19th century into our time. Here is a clear example of certain religious thinkers developing a rationale for social intervention. Early spokesmen for this movement tended to find direct religious authority for certain social stances. One could find arguments that Jesus was really a socialist, that Christianity demanded a clear commitment to the working classes rather than the owning classes. As the movement developed, it generated its own quite intense opposition. In the polemic period that ensued, the rationale for the intervention evolved. Rather than debating the issue of whether religion was concerned with the individual or with the society, contemporary defenders of intervention argue that certain social situations (e.g., poverty, racism, or sexism) so corrupt certain individuals that they are unable to hear the basic religious message. Since presumably all believers have a concern to have their message heard by unbelievers, it appears somewhat easier to defend social intervention on the grounds of its furtherance of the traditional individual religious goals of the institution. This argument would seem to have its parallels in the defense of community mental health as a way of bringing nonparticipants into fuller social participation. This might prove more successful than basing intervention upon appeal to some moral imperative that the successful ought to feel in relation to the less successful. Opponents of intervention have found it considerably harder to argue against this basically instrumentalist version of ethics.

The process of democratization provides yet another instructive model. Within religious institutions, it has inevitably meant a dilution of the initial purity of the structure when it had been controlled by an elite. The experience of the Calvinist congregations of colonial New England illustrate this. Initially, voting membership was restricted to those who not only were baptized and believing Christians, but who also had personally had the experience of "regeneration." From the outset, of course, there was a certain problem relating to the membership status of the children of such persons. But the real pressures came when a majority of those who lived in the parish were viewed, and viewed themselves, as believers but nevertheless had not had the intense personal experience required for membership. This led to the development of a "half-way covenant" providing status for such persons. Quite obviously, the direction that an institution will take is a function of the size of its power base, and the ease with which consensus can be reached is similarly a function of the size of the group. In the development of Protestantism, where development of democratization has typically been found, each extension of the franchise has led to a blurring of the distinctiveness between the group and general culture surrounding it.

The other side of this coin, however, is that the extension of democratization is an extension of participation and thereby of morale. As members become involved in decisions, they become willing to commit more of their time and money. It would be hard to find a sharper contrast

illustrating this than the participation levels of American and European Christians. The percentage of church attenders in America is near an all-time high, whereas European churches tend to be quite empty. In this connection it is also worth noting that the frequent prediction that democratization and high participation will lead to trivialization is not borne out. Churchgoers continue to resemble their cultural neighbors in most respects, whether they are living in churchgoing America or in non-church-going Europe. Apart from the smaller sects, church participation supports neither trivialization nor salience.

It would also be instructive to range outside of Western culture for examples from religious history which will illuminate some of the future problems of community mental health. Hinduism probably reflects the most pluralistic religion ever evolved. Intellectual atheism and intellectual theism coexist, sometimes even praying together. This variety on the level of intellectual formulation has not, however, reduced in any visible way the intensity of the religious affect and experience for the individual believer. Most interestingly, the roots of the basic ideology of toleration that has emerged in India go back into early times and are in no small measure the product of Buddhist as well as Muslim influence. It may well be that the actual encouragement of a variety of life styles, providing some kind of self-acceptance for a wide range of personality types, is most likely to flower in a culture where a variety of countervailing ideological powers exist. Pluralism in regard to religion can provide this, and probably democratization in terms of the criteria and goals of community mental health will do the same.

It may also be noted that the real impact of democratization will emerge only when genuine cultural and psychological freedom emerge. American society is only beginning to transcend its Puritan work-ethos. As alternative life styles become real options, that is, as they acquire followers and "votes," real democratization will appear. It will then become much more difficult to define deviant or aberrant behavior, and much less possible to defend restraints upon it.

It may also be that in a more direct way the development of a community mental health orientation will encourage persons of our society to scan other societies in terms of their traditionally fulfilling ways of life. One can imagine an intensification of current interest in Japanese religion to a full-blown assessment and assimilation of the aestheticism associated with Shinto and with Japanese Buddhism. One can also imagine a reassessment of the pragmatism associated with Chinese Confucianism and the building of a society on basically nontheistic grounds. And certainly one can expect a reassessment of the ability of Hinduism to preserve a good deal of the religious tradition of its past without violation of intellect.

This kind of scrutiny of "ways of being healthily human" that have been tested in the evolutionary survival arena of the major world's religions will have a slow and indirect effect upon the pluralization of community norms. Much more intense and direct will be the impact of what could be termed religious "sector-imports." When parts of some exotic tradition are taken over (rather than full conversion) and when these parts are differentiated from their traditionally intrinsic goals, sector importation occurs. Yoga is a good example. Differentiated from the total context of Hinduism, it is being advocated as a means to physical improvement, mental focus, and even sexual prowess. Books have been published on "Christian Yoga." Certain features of Zen Buddhism lend themselves to sector import, and the same has been true of Vedantic Hinduism. The point here is that sector importation, because of existentialism involvement, facilitates an intensive pluralization.

Finally we must note the role of Western parareligions in this process of expanding the spectrum of life styles. Among the communal experiments, many consciously derive from religious "intentional communities." Certain aspects of the hippie-youth-drug subculture have adopted an explicitly religious stance. Esalenlike small group techniques are used more widely, and again the parareligious element is present. If one element of those experiences termed religious in the past is idiosyncrasy, we are well into a religious revival. Nor is the literature of psychedelic experimentation devoid of religious referents and claims.

IN SUM

This chapter has delineated a variety of religious responses to the traditional ideas and values of the mental health movement, and has suggested a number of parallel aspects in both movements which have created the uncertainties and fluidities of the present. Both the rise of community psychology and the current democratization of Western religions have been interpreted as reflecting a pluralization of life styles. As a result, an increasing convergence of religious and community mental health workers is foreseen, partly as the result of the abandonment of sharply antagonistic goals firmly held by each side.

EPILOGUE—1972

During the Dalmatian summer of 1968 when we wrote this chapter, religious identifications seemed less vital, and therefore less potentially divisive, than political identifications. Soviet tanks were rolling into Prague and the Arab-Israeli war had only been tangentially religious. Since then, we have witnessed the explosiveness of religious allegiances in northern Ireland and East Pakistan-Bangladesh. Most recently, the China doors have begun to open on the world's largest project in religious transformation. To what extent can Maoism carry out its commitment to replace the traditional faiths (which include Confucianism, Taoism, Buddhism, Islam, Christianity)?

Our description of the American religious scene had focused mainly upon institutions and their visible elites, while noting a scattered individual interest in adaptation of Oriental religions. Not only has this latter development burgeoned but a more domesticated version of religious individualism has appeared within Christian circles. Among the young, "Jesus freaks" have lifted fingers. A number of their elders, especially surprising in the Roman Catholic circles, have been cultivating glossolalic experiences ("speaking in tongues"). While neither of these are new phenomena, their emergence in unexpected places reflects growing dissatisfaction with elite-defined patterns of establishment religiosities. This democratization of religious institutions has been called a rise of "demotheology" (R. Tapp, 1971).

The surfacing of demotheology is also concomitant with the liberation movements among both women and blacks. In quite different ways, it has been made manifest that American religious establishments, and much of their ideologies, have been consistently, if covertly, "white" and "male." For the foreseeable future, this pluralization and democratization seems both necessary and desirable, although some will experience it as painful and disruptive. If anyone is sanguine that ideological intergration will appear soon, we again revert to examples from religious history. In the early decades of this century, a kind of children's liberation occurred in some Protestant circles— although it was accomplished *for* children and not *by* them—and the resultant religious education movement brought deep fissures into doctrines of "original sin" and "human nature." Somewhat similarly, one could interpret the rise of the social gospel in late 19th century Protestantism as a consequence of workers' liberation. A strong insistence that religion should deal with more than "souls" or "spiritual matters" was in large part the result of consciousness raising within lower class denominations and individuals. A third historical example would be the family liberation that took place in 16th century Europe. Protestants raised the banner against a monastic Catholicism, and counterattacking Catholicism made explicit place for "Christian family life."

The significant point of these historical examples is not that liberation movements have appeared before, but that their predictable long-range impact is ideological pluralization. Catholicism can hardly be said to have surmounted the cloister/hearth tensions. Nor have Protestants moved beyond recurrent cleavages over social activism. Nor have either Protestants or Catholics ceased to debate whether children are "naturally" good or evil. The liberation, within religious circles, of the consciousnesses of blacks and women may produce an even wider and longer lasting pluralization—given the percentages involved, the extent of the historical oppression, and the combined contemporary catalysts of education and communication.

Turning from religious circles to psychological circles, the implications of the medical model breakdown that we noted have also become more patent. Whatever consensus might have existed in the mid-'60s regarding mental health or illth has dissipated. As with religious ideologies, the defections and innovations have come via insiders as well as outsiders. The proliferation of models and therapies is perhaps now sufficiently widespread to be labeled "demopsychology." How else should we characterize the gravitation to such phrases as humanistic psychology, self-actualiza-

tion, human potential, consciousness expansion? The common element is the continuing assertion of individually validated life styles and values.

In short, it now seems clearer that the predicted convergence of religious and psychological forces into the community mental health movement is occurring. On the religious side, an increasing diversity of practices will also be coupled with a more self-conscious and less apologetic stance. The psychological side will be marked by great openness and experimentation. As a result, the chief characteristic of community mental health centers will be a new fluidity in generating, supporting, and evaluating life styles. More difficult to foresee is how critical canons will emerge or gain acceptance. A grim religious reminder comes to mind: Enthusiasm has always destroyed both criteria and its devotees (Dionysus needs Apollo).

References

Allport, G. *The individual and his religion*. New York: Macmillan, 1950.

Bailey, D. S. *The mystery of love and marriage: A study in the theology of sexual relation*. New York: Harper, 1952.

Berkowitz, M. I., & Johnson, J. E. *Social scientific studies of religion*. Pittsburgh: University of Pittsburgh Press, 1967.

Chisholm, B. Changing sources of security. *Etc.*, 1947, 5(1), 107.

Chisholm, B. Mental health in our new kind of world. *Mental Health*, 1955, 4, 529–532.

Clinebell, H. J. *Basic types of pastoral counseling*. Nashville: Abingdon Press, 1966.

Cole, W. G. *Sex in Christianity and psychoanalysis*. New York: Oxford University Press, 1955.

Dreikurs, R. *Psychology in the class room*. (2nd ed.) New York: Harper & Row, 1968.

Eliade, M. *Patterns in comparative religion*. New York: Sheed & Ward, 1958.

Eysenck, H. J. *Fact and fiction in psychology*. London: Penguin Books, 1965.

Fletcher, J. *Morals and medicine*. Princeton, N. J.: Princeton University Press, 1954.

Freud, S. *Psychoanalysis and faith: The letters of Sigmund Freud and Oskar Pfister*. New York: Basic Books, 1964.

Friends Home Service Committee. *Towards a Quaker view of sex*. London: Friends House, 1964.

Fromm, E. *Psychoanalysis and religion*. New Haven: Yale University Press, 1950.

Fromm, E. *You shall be as gods*. New York: Holt, Rinehart & Winston, 1966.

Hartmann, H. Psychoanalysis as a scientific theory. In S. Hook (ed.), *Psychoanalysis, scientific method, and philosophy.* New York: New York University Press, 1959.

Heard, G. *The five ages of man.* New York: Julian Press, 1964

Hick, J. *Faith and knowledge.* Ithaca, N. Y.: Cornell University Press, 1957.

Hiltner, S. *Sex ethics and the Kinsey Report.* New York: Association Press, 1953.

Hofmann, H. F. *Sex incorporated.* Boston: Beacon Press, 1967.

Keniston, K. How community mental health stamped out the riots (1968–78). *Trans-action,* 1968, 5(8), 21–29.

Klausner, S. Z. *Psychiatry and religion.* Glencoe, Ill.: Free Press, 1964.

Kunkel, F. *In search of maturity.* New York: Scribner's, 1943

McCann, R. *The churches and mental health.* New York: Basic Books, 1962.

McNeill, J. T. *The history of the cure of souls.* New York: Harper, 1951.

Maslow, A. H. *Religions, values and peak-experiences.* Columbus: Ohio State University Press, 1964.

May, R. *Man's search for himself.* New York: Norton, 1953.

Mead, S. *The lively experiment: The shaping of Christianity in America.* New York: Harper & Row, 1963.

Morris, C. *Paths of life.* New York: Harper, 1942.

Morris, C. *Varieties of human value.* Chicago: University of Chicago Press, 1956.

Mowrer, O. H. *The crisis in psychiatry and religion.* Princeton. N. J.: Van Nostrand, 1961.

Mowrer, O. H. *The new group therapy.* Princeton, N. J.: Van Nostrand, 1964.

Murphy, C. *Human potentialities.* New York: Basic Books, 1958.

Murray, H. A. (ed.) *Myths and mythmaking.* New York: Braziller, 1960.

Nichols, J. H. Protestantism and theological education. *Bulletin of American Association of Theological Schools,* 1952, 20, 109–117.

Outler, A. *Psychotherapy and the Christian message.* New York: Harper, 1954.

Pfister, O. *Some applications of psychoanalysis.* London: Allen, 1923.

Progoff, I. *Depth psychology and modern man.* New York: Julian Press, 1959.

Rokeach, M. *Beliefs, attitudes and values.* San Francisco: Jossey-Bass, 1968.

Smith, M. B. A revolution in mental-health care—A "bold new approach"? *Trans-action,* 1968, 5(5), 19–23.

Szasz, T. S. *The myth of mental illness.* New York: Harper, 1961.

Tapp, R. B. On the rise of demotheology. Christian Century, 1971, (LXXXVIII), 153–156.

Tillich, P. Karen Horney. *Pastoral psychology,* 1953, 66, 11–13.

Tournier, P. *The meaning of persons.* New York: Harper, 1957.

U. S. Evangelicals: Moving again. *Time,* September 19, 1969, 58–60.

Watts, A. *Psychotherapy east and west.* New York: Pantheon, 1961.

Westberg, G. E., & Draper, E. *Community psychiatry and the clergyman.* Springfield, Ill.: Charles C Thomas, 1966.

Yearbook of American churches. New York: Round Table, 1968.

7

The Social Welfare System:
Its Relation to Community Mental Health

Milton Wittman

The American social welfare system is a congeries of interlocking structures aimed at maintaining and restoring the physical, mental, and social well-being of individuals and families. It is based on two main threads of humanitarianism, which, over the centuries, have indicated that part of society needs help and the rest of society provides it. The two threads have discernible sources which will be examined in their respective contexts. The first derives from the Biblical injunction (Deuteronomy 14:29) to tithe for the succor of the stranger, the fatherless, and the widow. The second is found in the Elizabethan Poor Law of 1601 which established public responsibility for relief and care of those without means. These are the two main antecedents of the American social welfare system, a system comprising the network of voluntary and tax-supported social services which covers the nation today. After a brief historical introduction, this chapter will outline the scope and nature of American social services, will review significant trends and developments, and will relate the welfare system to community mental health in the United States.

AN OUTLINE OF THE SYSTEM

The social welfare system is a network of interlinked public and voluntary services to people. It supplies basic economic needs for the dependent segment of the population, for people with no income or limited income. It provides rehabilitation for those with physical, mental, and social limitations. Within the scope of its concern

would fall every conceivable variation of social pathology which appears on the American scene. Illustrative of the most pressing problems which challenge and burden the social welfare system are those of poverty, family breakdown, divorce, desertion, illegitimacy, interpersonal conflict, delinquency, crime, mental disorders, racial strife, and urban decay. There is an aspect of universality in this system that is little understood or accepted. The notion of care and service "from the cradle to the grave" perhaps best defines the intent of the system. The care and service are at present being provided unevenly because the network, or system, does not yet meet the humanitarian goals implied in the intentions to eradicate poverty or to intervene if personal or community health and welfare are threatened by deviant behavior. The uneven development of the welfare services has resulted in imperfections in the structure of the system and in its ability adequately to meet social and health needs (Titmuss, 1968). The imperfections are illustrated by an incredibly wide variation, state by state, in welfare policies as they apply to individuals and families in need of social and financial assistance. Another painful reminder of the defects in the system is the highly uneven distribution of trained manpower in the helping professions when the rich states are compared with the poor.

The historical evolution of the social welfare system to its present imperfect and fragmented state derives from the birth of this nation in the 18th century, when the legal and social institutions of the British system formed the basis for the pattern of social and economic organization. The colonial system for care of the poor and the deviant was based on programs of miserably funded outdoor relief and on the almshouse or workhouse (Coll, 1969). The grim days of the punitive approach to welfare have not entirely disappeared, but the situation has much improved since the time when starvation levels of support and inadequate institutional care were the principal resource for those in poverty, or in need of rehabilitation and social services. During the 19th century, which saw the transition from an agrarian to an industrial economy, the modes for provision of care and service underwent substantive changes (Wilensky & Lebeaux, 1967). From what had been in the main a religious enterprise, the voluntary social services expanded to include a strong nonsectarian philanthropic establishment under the title of charity organization. This continues today in the privately funded social agency network which serves most larger municipalities and some rural areas (Cohen, 1958). In the public sector there was a significant shift from local to state welfare administration. This was the century when the federal government confined its efforts to assistance only to specific categories of persons needing social and health services (e.g., United States Marine Hospital Service for sick and disabled seamen, and war veterans institutions). Public social policy fell far short of recognizing any sweeping obligation on the part of the national government to help the dependent and neglected classes of the population. Social insurance was just beginning to appear in some European nations and, at the turn of the 20th century, the scene was being set for the concatenation of events leading to the establishment of federal involvement in social planning and in the legislation that has evolved since the historic date of August 14, 1935, when the Social Security Act came into being. From this date forward, there have occurred intermittent amendments to the legislation and new related legislation which have persistently increased the range of coverage of beneficiaries and the quality of benefits available. The numerous volumes which describe the evolution of the Social Security Act point to the conditions of destitution and deprivation under which large segments of the population lived.[1]

The present system reflects the current stage of public concern for meeting economic needs of people who are past their earning capacity or who, for various reasons, cannot maintain economic sufficiency for themselves or their families. The fact remains, however, that the system still functions imperfectly because it does not yet meet *all* of the economic needs of the population groups it was intended to serve (Burns, 1968). Similarly, the social needs are still unmet for vast numbers of people who have no resources for counseling and guidance in their communities or who do not make use of them when they are there. It is sadly true that poverty and social pathology exist in distressing degree in rural and urban areas alike and will exist until the nation allocates a far greater amount of its fiscal and manpower resources to overcome them (Ferman, Kornbluh, & Haber, 1968).

The Gross National Product exceeded 800 billion dollars in 1968 and will probably reach one trillion before 1980. In 1968, the proportion of this Gross National Product allocated to social welfare expenditures was 13.7 percent. This is compared to 11.8 percent in 1965 (Cohen, 1968). Expenditures from public funds in 1967 amounted to over 100 billion dollars for income-maintenance programs, health and medical care, education, housing, relevant military expenditures (for medical care and education), veterans' benefits, and other social services (Merriam & Skolnick, 1968). With all this investment of public funds, the number estimated to be living in poverty in January 1969 was still about 22 million of 200 million in the population. The efforts of the federal government could be said to have brought about a startling reduction from an estimated 40 million in 1960 (Cohen 1968). Even the reduced proportion represents an inordinately high number of people, considering the economic potential of the nation.

INSTITUTIONAL AND RESIDUAL MECHANISMS

A leading theory suggests that two main types of welfare organizations prevail in the structure of service as it is known today. These are the *institutional* and *residual* patterns of structure (Wilensky & Lebeauz, 1967). The incorporation of a service or benefit in an established and accepted organizational system describes the *institutional* form of provision. The old age insurance program has been institutionalized, and it provides assistance to all covered persons. Payments for unemployment compensation or for permanent and total disability also fall into this category. The system is planned to meet the costs of certain risks to vulnerable members of the community. However, the amount of welfare payments may be (and frequently are) insufficient to meet the income needs of recipients of such benefits, and the residual system must then supply the deficit, if indeed it is met at all. The basic adequacy of the welfare system in its capacity to meet apparent economic needs in the United States is subject to serious question (Schorr, 1966).

The nature of poverty in the United States is such that it is pervasive in both industrial and agricultural communities. There are pockets of poverty in every major city in the United States. The blight rests particularly heavily on the black and Spanish-speaking populations. Migrant workers and American Indians are two additional groups among whom poverty is found in large measure. With the advance of technology, the premium is increasingly on the better educated worker in the labor market. Therefore, those who have completed education at the high school or college level are in a better position to compete for available openings in the industrial market. The new poverty programs have been intended to remedy the deficiency in education which occurs when young people leave high school without completing the basic 12 years of education. Welfare payments and survivors' benefits are continued beyond the age of 18 for children and families receiving such payments, on condition that they remain in school to complete the necessary preparation for life work. In recent years, the development of "new careers" as a means of advancing the employability of welfare recipients has gained currency and new programs are in operation in most parts of the country (Grosser, Henry, & Kelly, 1969; Pruger & Specht, 1968).

The foregoing descriptive statements portray a dismal picture of the capacity of an open society to meet its historical social problems. The fact remains that the nation is far from achieving a pattern of social organization which will assure an income for each individual or family sufficient to maintain standards of health and decency (see Merriam, in Jenkins, 1969). A vastly changed physical environment is urgently needed. The decay of the inner city has outsped all efforts to improve living space for low-income groups. City planning has displaced low-income groups to even more restricted space than they inhabited before deteriorated housing was destroyed to make way for the high rise developments of the present. This situation calls for much improved federal, state, and local planning buttressed by federal subsidy to permit long range and comprehensive planning by even the poorest states (Riessman, 1968).

TRENDS AND SIGNIFICANT DEVELOPMENTS IN WELFARE SERVICES

The welfare system in the United States has been subject to continuous expansion and development in the decades since the end of World War II. Each in the series of amendments to the Social Security Act has tended to broaden the scope of coverage and the types of benefits available through public funding. The latest substantive additions to the Act were the Medicare and Medicaid programs embodied in Titles XVIII and XIX of the Social Security Act. These titles have permitted Federal matching to expand the volume of health care available for aged persons in the first instance and medically indigenous persons in the second (see Somers, in Jenkins, 1969). The comprehensive mental health legislation of 1963 and 1965 have together produced a revolution in the care and treatment of the mentally ill individual and his family in the United States. The comprehensive health legislation of Public Law 89–749, which mandated a broad comprehensive health program for the United States, is not without its impact on the demands placed on the normal network of health and manpower resources. Nearly every known social problem in the United States is now matched by federal and state legislation aimed at providing remedies through expanded services. Moreover, there is increased interest in and evidence of more systematic study and exploration of basic problems of causation and duration of social and mental health problems (Kahn, 1969).

Studies of the delivery of social and health services indicate that these services do not by any means provide as yet a satisfactory level of service in any community in the country. The cities lack welfare resources (Stein, 1969). Some counties in the United States have no general physicians; others are woefully short of nursing and social work personnel. The study completed by Robinson, DeMarche, and Wagle (1960) shows quite conclusively how unevenly social and health services are distributed throughout the various regions of the United States. The supply of professional manpower has barely, if at all, kept pace with the population growth since this study was completed.

One prominent means of redistributing services so that they more adequately meet the needs of people closer to their own homes has been the invention of the multipurpose neighborhood service center. This center is a direct outgrowth of the old social settlement houses of the 19th century which in effect did have a multiple function in the community. They tended to provide educational, recreational, and counseling services in the community in which they were lodged. Many were indeed focal points for institutional change in their respective communities. The seedbed of the more advanced social legislation of the times was found in the social settlement houses in the major cities of the United States. The introduction of the neighborhood service center as the prime service delivery unit of the poverty program has placed services in closer proximity to large numbers of low-income population in the major cities. The spread of neighborhood service centers throughout the United States has considerably outsped the availability of qualified staff to man these centers. A similar experience has resulted from the widespread introduction of comprehensive community mental health centers. These, too, are very much in need of highly qualified professionals and nonprofessionals capable of delivering adequate social and health services at the local level. The deficit in personnel is particularly felt in the field of social work where an estimated 12,000 to 14,000 positions are unfilled every year. One source (Lecht, 1969) suggests that the annual growth requirement for social workers projected to 1975 is 20,000 a year. It would appear that the number of social workers in training would need to be tripled in order to meet the estimated need for treatment and service personnel in social and health agencies throughout the country.

MODIFICATION OF THE WELFARE SYSTEM

From the point of view of the recipient of services, of the professional personnel responsible for operation of social welfare programs, and of those whose contributions support these services, the present system is marginally palliative rather than remedial in its overall impact on social problems in the community. The provision of financial assistance for those in need is so scanty and discontinuous that in some parts of the country the amount of food necessary to prevent hunger and malnutrition is seriously lacking. Similarly, the dispersion of services for individuals and families needing skillful counseling finds these so thinly distributed that many fail to receive them until social problems have become so acute that serious social pathology such as family breakdown, divorce, desertion, suicide, alcoholism, and drug addiction occurs with serious and disastrous results. These facts have been brought home more clearly as national manpower issues during time of national emergency. It was found, for example, during World War II, that large numbers of personnel were lost to the military services because of serious physical and mental disabilities. The result was the launching of broad-based programs in health, mental health, welfare, and education in order to remedy some of the deficiencies that resulted in such a serious loss in manpower resources for the nation.

One of the primary problems in the welfare system is that good models for welfare structure do not exist. There is a general reluctance to make effective use of those models presented by foreign nations, many of which have made great strides toward the elimination of poverty as a national indicator of social disorganization. A combination of social insurance and employment services in several European nations virtually guarantees an income to every citizen, regardless of his social condition. If he is not able to work for physical or mental reasons, health and retraining services are available to help meet his special needs (Furman, 1965; Timms, 1964). The income guarantees and the social and health services are legislated into the system so that these benefits become a right to which he is entitled by virtue of his citizenship in that nation (Goldberg, 1965; Jefferys, 1965; Jenkins, 1969; Titmuss, 1968). While deficiencies still exist in terms of total coverage, the benefit of social and health service has been mandated by public legislation.

In the United States the public welfare system is recognized to have specific deficiencies that can be remedied only by the development of a quite different approach to provision of economic aid for people who are without income. The two most popular proposals at this point are the guaranteed annual income and the family allowance program. The guaranteed annual income presupposes an economic survival level of income which would insure the capacity of a family to meet its minimum economic needs. If, because of unemployment, illness, or catastrophe, a family should be without income at the prescribed level, the federal government would provide this as a social security benefit available as a natural consequence of the situation in which the family might find itself. This welfare approach has been introduced as a Family Assistance Plan (Proposals, 1969). The family allowance system sets a specific monthly payment for each child which is paid regardless of the income level of the parents. For those families who have adequate or ample financial means, the additional income would be collected in taxes. The income would be particularly beneficial to large families with low income (Schorr, 1966). Implementation of these alternatives to the present system depends a great deal on the level of public understanding and governmental support for sweeping changes which would radically modify the present delivery system for welfare grants and welfare services (Burns, 1968; Green, 1966).

An important barrier to change is the inevitable contrast between welfare payments and wages in low-income employment. When these coincide, or when welfare payments exceed the wages at the lowest level, serious objection arises on the part of taxpayers and employees with low incomes. While it would appear to be inevitable that eventually some form of guaranteed income will evolve as a solution to the problem of poverty in the United States, the various steps to its initiation and operation are seriously hampered by negative public attitudes and by objections related to the cost of this program. The revision of the welfare system to eliminate state variations and inade-

quacies is a highly regarded goal on the part of welfare planners (Ball, 1968). This goal cannot be achieved unless a federally-operated system is evolved (Proposals, 1969). The success of the present Federal Social Security Program, which includes systematic benefits for retired persons, for permanently and totally disabled individuals, and for the blind, suggests that a similar pattern can be developed eventually to provide a more complete system for meeting basic economic need. Any projected overhaul of the social welfare system must invariably take into account the fundamental objectives of the welfare system. *If the intention is to eliminate poverty*, then *sufficient funds* must be provided so that *all families and individuals without sufficient income* are assured that this will be provided. Action to raise minimum wages for industrial and other types of work that currently provide substandard incomes for individuals who are employed full time is another important step related to the elimination of poverty. An intermediate step has been suggested to provide supplemental welfare benefits for all individuals whose full-time income is below the poverty line. This would do much to relieve the situation of those who, though fully employed, must struggle with insufficient economic means to provide the essentials of life (Proposals, 1969).

The existing network of service is in urgent need of consolidation and reorganization. The delivery of social services at the local level is being provided by a patchwork system which has yet to make full use of what is now known about community planning. The problem of achieving adequate coordination between health and welfare services for the aged is a good example of how people are served imperfectly by the present system. The United States is quite capable of producing a blueprint for the local delivery of services adequately funded and staffed with qualified professionals and other related personnel to assure that *all* persons receive a minimum of economic aid or social and health services aimed at the roots of social pathology (Ginzberg, 1968; Lecht, 1969). The preconditions for success in achieving a revised system are: improved public understanding of the role of welfare in maintaining family and individual stability; legislative and fiscal adequacy; and an articulated public service structure with sufficient staff at all levels to accomplish an effective delivery of services (Kahn, 1969).

RELATION BETWEEN THE WELFARE AND MENTAL HEALTH SYSTEMS

The concluding section of the chapter will deal with the relationship between the welfare and community mental health systems. Both function in American society with the objective of alleviation of human deprivation and suffering. Both fall short of achieving this objective because the scope of service intended to reach every individual and family under stress is as yet insufficient for this purpose. The client and patient populations served by these two systems constitute those persons who, at some point in their life span, require help from society beyond the resources of natural endowment or the immediate family. It is quite possible that in a general sense, the welfare and mental health systems influence the lives of every citizen directly or indirectly at some point in the life cycle. Most commonly recognized are interventions around personal and family crises. Less visible but equally important are the increasing number of preventive services being institutionalized in the welfare and mental health systems (Geismar, 1969). These include a wide range of activities from family planning and family life education to anticipatory counseling and retirement advising.

The history of the mental health movement records the great strides that have been made in the past decade in reconceptualizing the organization and structure of community mental health services. During the early part of the present century, the common conception of the ideal focal point for the delivery of public mental health services moved successively from the mental hospital to the outpatient mental health clinic to the community mental health center. In each of these stages of development, different types of delivery systems emerged (Yolles, 1969).

Most states have yet to achieve adequate coordination between community mental health and welfare services. This is partly a function of the lack of sufficient personnel, but it can also be attributed to structural inadequacies in the organization of the delivery of local services (Riessman, Cohen, & Pearl, 1964). The relatively

high cost of long-term psychiatric service would normally place this beyond the means of the family with an average income (Hollingshead & Redlich, 1957; Langner & Michael, 1963; Srole, Langner, Michael, Opler, & Rennie, 1962). The availability of excellent services in teaching centers and the expansion of public subsidies have induced a wider dispersion and distribution of mental health services but, as yet, insufficient to the demonstrated need. The comprehensive community mental health service operating from a center in a catchment area of a feasible size for geographic coverage is aimed at serving all socioeconomic levels of the population with an adequate quality of service. A large volume of social treatment services are delivered by a wide variety of social and health agencies. These include services in most communities, but may serve as primary treatment resources where the mental health services are in short supply (Robinson, DeMarche, & Wagle, 1960).

It would be interesting to speculate about the existing caseloads in public welfare, private welfare, and in community mental health, and to explore how they tend to overlap. The patients served in the community mental health system tend to consist of those who have serious psychiatric illnesses and therefore need some form of care away from home, and those who are less seriously ill who can be served while living in their own homes. In a comprehensive system, provision can be made for short-term institutional care or for a follow-up service in the patient's own home where this is needed to meet the psychosocial situation. The welfare system is also directly involved where psychosocial problems create individual or family behavioral conflict. Many of these individuals and families are served by social work practitioners. These services are frequently provided in collaboration with mental health units. There are several examples where the need for close collaboration between mental hospitals and welfare departments has been convincingly demonstrated (Auman, Ellis, Hedgepeth, Murray, & Pemberton, 1969; Herrick, 1967).

With the maturation of social and public health policy, it becomes possible to envision a level of service coverage which would assure that each individual or family would have available a complete spectrum of social and health services intended to maintain family health (Titmuss,

1968). This postulates the existence of social and health services in sufficient quality and quantity so that children in the early years of life can have adequate nurture and sufficient economic support to assure that deprivation does not exist (Schorr, 1966). The traditional course of social and health program development does not yet permit adequate service coverage for each family in any given geographic area (Langner & Michael, 1963; Srole et al., 1962). It should be expected that every family, whether in an urban or rural location, will have access to a neighborhood service center or other service unit where personal or family counseling services would be available and where skilled diagnostic help could be provided on an emergency basis whenever needed. It is also implied from this that all of the helping or related professions including law, medicine, the ministry, public health, social work, nursing, teaching, and others would have available adequately prepared consultant personnel to provide guidance and information regarding incipient or full-blown mental health problems. These services would be adapted to the needs of industry, business, and the public school system. Public housing projects would have "built-in" service systems intended to provide for social, health, and recreational activities adapted to the needs of the tenant population. The public welfare services would be adequately housed in establishments which would command respect and which would be seen as service institutions on a parallel with highly regarded, efficiently operated hospitals or medical clinics.

The interlinking of the health and welfare systems implied in the foregoing comments is long overdue. The establishment of service in the community is so frequently rigidly structured into historic institutional patterns that the achievement of a blend of services is very difficult to bring about (Riessman, 1968). The professional education of staff serving the welfare and community mental health systems should include collaborative experiences working on identical case material and on program development which would draw on the respective skills of the staffs in each of the organizations. It can be predicted that the scope of service will be considerably wider when the use of volunteers and nonprofessional personnel is multiplied beyond the present token use in many installations (Grosser et al., 1969).

CONCLUSIONS

This chapter has set forth a brief outline of the welfare system and its relation to community mental health. There has been emphasis here on the uneven and generally ineffective structure of welfare services in terms of fully meeting social and economic needs of the population. It has been stated that the development of these services is far below the fiscal and strategic capacity of the American community in terms of dealing with problems of economic need and personal and family problems of social adjustment. It has been suggested that a radical revision of the system to provide for an assured income for those in economic need is an imperative that must be met in the near future. There are important mental health implications in the assurance that each child in each family will be adequately clothed, housed, and fed during its early years (Schorr, 1966). While the mental health system is seen as providing for the care, treatment, and rehabilitation of the mentally ill, it also is seen as having a major responsibility for the prevention of mental illness and social breakdown. It is inconceivable that any form of mental illness would be without its social implications, and these must receive careful consideration during the period that mental health care is needed and after (Riessman et al., 1964). The resolution of long standing social and health problems cannot be achieved until an adequate distribution of services has been obtained throughout the United States. A much improved communication between the health and welfare systems and more particularly between mental health and welfare personnel is much needed (Wittman, 1963).

What is suggested here is a considerable increase in content on issues around collaboration in the pre-service preparation of all the professional and paraprofessional personnel concerned with the delivery of health and social services. In addition to theoretical knowledge, it would be important that relevant content be included in the practicum experiences undertaken during the period of all professional preparation for practice in welfare and mental health. It can be expected that experimental modes of practice will point the way toward improved local delivery of service. A leader in mental health has reaffirmed very clearly the close relationship between mental health and social welfare:

Social agencies and social workers have specialized skills and special responsibilities for doing mental health work. The term 'mental health' itself covers social as well as psychological health. The field of mental health, therefore, depends heavily upon social welfare to see to it that psychological services are made available to everyone in the community at crisis and pre-crisis points in their lives; that the total community environment is conducive to mental health; that there is a continuum of service covering prevention of mental illness, promotion of mental health, and care, treatment, and rehabilitation of the mentally ill; that the network of mental health services in the community reaches the total population as well as special risk groups. (Felix, 1961, p. 19)

It is apparent that the comprehensive mental health center and the welfare service center would need to be placed in a proper juxtaposition to assure good communication between the two institutions and to assure that adequate coverage is provided for catchment area populations. In addition to the training objectives suggested, it is also important that joint research activities should be established as a means of producing new knowledge regarding the causes of psychosocial breakdown, the endemic nature of its patterns in the community, and improved ways of resolving or preventing social and psychological pathology. The success of these two systems in meeting the massive human needs for service is greatly dependent on the quality of manpower recruited and trained to staff these programs and on the support of the consumer population who make use of their services.

Notes

The opinions expressed herein are those of the author and do not necessarily reflect policy of the Department of Health, Education, and Welfare.

1. See the following: Altmeyer (1966); Ball (1968); Breckinridge (1938); Burns (1968); Cohen (1958); Klein (1968); Lubove (1968); Pumphrey (1965); Pumphrey and Pumphrey (1961); Schottland (1963); and Witte (1962).

References

Altmeyer, A. J. *The formative years of Social Security.* Madison: University of Wisconsin Press, 1966.

Arnhoff, F. N., Rubinstein, E. A., Shriver, B. M., & Jones, D. R. The mental health fields: An overview of manpower growth and development. In F. N. Arnhoff, E. A. Rubinstein, & J. C. Speisman (eds.), *Manpower for mental health.* Chicago: Aldine, 1969.

Auman, C., Ellis, C. M., Hedgepeth, B. W., Murray, Q. D., & Pemberton, A. M. A state mental hospital and public welfare team up. *Public Welfare*, 1969, 27, No. 1.

Ball, R. M. Social Security perspectives. In *Social Security Bulletin.* Washington, D. C.: Social Security Administration, United States Department of Health, Education, and Welfare, August 1968.

Breckinridge, S. P. *Public welfare administration in the United States.* (2nd ed.) Chicago: University of Chicago Press, 1938.

Burns, E. M. Where welfare falls short. In B. J. Frieden & R. Morris (eds.), *Urban planning and social policy.* New York: Basic Books, 1968.

Cohen, N. E. *Social work in the American tradition.* New York: Dryden, 1958.

Cohen, W. J. A ten point program to abolish poverty. *Social Security Bulletin*, 1968, 31(12), 3–13.

Coll, B. D. *Perspectives in public welfare.* (United States Department of Health, Education, and Welfare) Washington, D. C.: United States Government Printing Office, 1969.

Felix, R. H. A comprehensive community mental health program. In *Mental health and social welfare.* New York: Columbia University Press, 1961.

Ferman, L. A., Kornbluh, J. L., & Haber, A. *Poverty in America.* Ann Arbor: University of Michigan Press, 1968.

Furman S. S. *Community mental health services in Northern Europe.* Washington, D. C.: United States Department of Health, Education, and Welfare, 1965.

Geismar, L. L. *Preventive intervention in social work.* Metuchen, N. J.: Scarecrow Press, 1969.

Ginzberg, E. *Manpower agenda for America.* New York: McGraw-Hill, 1968.

Goldberg, E. M. Working in the community: What kind of help do people need? *Social Work* (British), 1965, 22(2–3), 6–18.

Green, C. *Negative taxes and the poverty problem.* Washington, D. C.: Brookings Institute, 1966.

Grosser, C., Henry, W. E., & Kelly, J. G. (eds.) *Nonprofessionals in the human services.* San Francisco: Jossey-Bass, 1969.

Herrick, H. *Mental health problems of public assistance clients.* Sacramento, Calif.: California Department of Mental Hygiene, 1967.

Hollingshead, A. B., & Redlich, F. C. *Social class and mental illness: A community study.* New York: Wiley, 1957.

Jefferys, M. *An anatomy of social welfare services.* London: Michael Joseph, 1965.

Jenkins, S. (ed.) *Social security in international perspective: Essays in honor of Eveline M. Burns.* New York: Columbia University Press, 1969.

Kahn, A. J. *Theory and practice of social planning.* New York: Russell Sage Foundation, 1969.

Klein, P. *From philanthropy to social welfare.* San Francisco: Jossey-Bass, 1968.

Langner, T. S., & Michael, S. T. *Life stress and mental health: The Midtown Manhattan Study.* Vol. II. London: Free Press of Glencoe, Collier-Macmillan, 1963.

Lecht, L. A. *Manpower needs for national goals in the 1970's.* New York: Praeger, 1969.

Lubove, R. *The struggle for social security: 1900–1935.* Cambridge: Harvard University Press, 1968.

Merriam, I. C. Young adults and social security. *Social Security Bulletin*, 1968, 31, No. 8.

Merriam, I. C., & Skolnick, A. M. *Social welfare expenditures under public programs in the United States, 1929–66.* (Social Security Administration Research Report No. 25) Washington, D. C.: United States Government Printing Office, 1968.

Merriam, I. C., Skolnick, A. M., & Dales, S. R. Social welfare expenditures, 1967–68. *Social Security Bulletin*, 1968, 31, 14–27.

Meyer, H. J., Litwak, E., Thomas, E. J., & Vinter, R. D. Social work and social welfare. In P. F. Lazarsfeld, W. H. Sewell, & H. L. Wilensky (eds.), *The uses of sociology.* New York: Basic Books, 1967.

Proposals for welfare reform. (message from the President of the United States, House Document 91–146, House of Representatives, August 11, 1969) Washington, D. C.: United States Government Printing Office, 1969.

Pruger, R., & Specht, H. Establishing new careers programs: Organizational barriers and strategies. *Social Work*, 1968, 13(4), 21–32.

Pumphrey, R. E. Social welfare in the United States. In *Encyclopedia of social work.* New York: National Association of Social Work, 1965.

Pumphrey, R. E., & Pumphrey, M. W. *The heritage of American social work.* New York: Columbia University Press, 1961.

Riessman, F. *Strategies against poverty.* New York: Random House, 1968.

Riessman, F., Cohen, J., & Pearl, A. (eds.) *Mental health of the poor.* London: Free Press of Glencoe, Collier-Macmillan, 1964.

Robinson, R., DeMarche, D. E., & Wagle, M. K. *Community resources in mental health.* New York: Basic Books, 1960.

Schorr, A. L. *Poor kids.* New York: Basic Books, 1966.

Schottland, C. I. *The Social Security Program in the United States.* New York: Appleton-Century-Crofts, 1963.

Srole, L., Langner, T. S., Michael, S. T., Opler, M. K., & Rennie, T. A. C. *Mental health in the metropolis: The Midtown Manhattan Study.* Vol. 1. New York: McGraw-Hill, 1962.

Stein, H. D. *The welfare crisis in Cleveland.* Cleveland: Case Western Reserve University Press, 1969.

Timms, N. *Psychiatric social work in Great Britain (1939–1962).* London: Routledge & Kegan Paul, 1964.

Titmuss, R. M. Social policy and economic progress. In *Commitment to welfare.* London: Allen & Unwin, 1968.

Wilensky, H. L., & Lebeaux, C. N. *Industrial society and social welfare.* New York: Free Press, 1967.

Witte, E. E. *The development of the Social Security Act.* Madison: University of Wisconsin Press, 1962.

Wittman, M. Some problems in the development of cooperation between mental health and community welfare programs. *Mental Hygiene*, 1963, 47(4), 641–648.

Yolles, S. F. From witchcraft and sorcery to head-shrinking—Society's concern about mental health. In *What's going on in HEW: The HEW forum papers, 1967–68.* Washington, D. C.: United States Government Printing Office, 1969.

8

Military Communities

Earl J. Janda, David S. Reynolds, and Donald S. Carter

CHARACTERISTICS OF MILITARY COMMUNITIES

Over the past 25 years, the military establishment has become a highly visible, permanent part of American society. From the rather simple, self-contained, and essentially closed pre-World War II military society there has developed an increasingly complex subculture which both reflects and influences social institutions and the larger society of which it is a part. Military communities include more than the primary military members, the uniformed active duty members of military organizations. They also include the many persons whose roles and relationships are intertwined with the primary military members. Civilian employees of military organizations, retired military personnel, part-time or inactive military personnel, as well as dependents of military personnel living with or apart from their sponsor, are all part of the broader military community.

Coates and Pellegrin (1965) have reviewed the concept of "community" in relation to the military. While many definitions exist, the military community is most generally seen as a territorial grouping within which all or nearly all of the goods and services necessary for the maintenance of life can be found. Such a community would be composed of a relatively large number of people concentrated in one area who carry out their day-to-day activities within the context of community groups, organizations, and institutions. The military-based community is the most representative example of this functional approach to definition of the military community.

It is difficult to speak of a typical military community because of the great differences which exist. Factors such as location, size, and mission contribute to these differences. The host environment may be familiar or foreign, friendly or hostile, depending upon such factors as stateside or overseas location. The military mission, whether combat, support, or training, directly defines the unique characteristics of any particular military community. The shipboard military community in a combat situation is obviously different from a stateside logistical support base with its many military families. Such factors as the availability of on-base family housing lead to differences. In some situations, military families must find housing within the civilian community with frequent result that military families are more identifed with the civilian host community than with the military base.

The military community can also be defined as a psychosocial grouping that shares a feeling of social solidarity. Thus a military base can be considered a community in the psychological sense, as well as in terms of the functions it performs. Janowitz (1960) has contrasted the feeling of community which was possible in earlier years because of territorial isolation and the changed present day military community with its weakened social cohesion. Many factors, including a sheer increase in numbers, tend to interfere with the development of psychosocial solidarity. One ever present inhibiting factor is the relative impermanence of assignment of military members. The increased use of civilian personnel in varied capacities has contributed to a military-civilian schism, yet the more permanently assigned civilian gives continuity to operations and sustains the feeling of community. The changing and dynamic military society produces psychosocial influences which are common to many military communities but the uniqueness of each military community requires individualized appraisal and understanding. The characteristic social structures and systems of expectation in military communities have profound effects on behavior and therefore set the stage for the interventions of the community psychologist.

ROLE EXPECTATIONS IN MILITARY LIFE

The primary military member of the military social system becomes very aware of distinguishing features of the military environment. These include:

1. Entry into and continued membership in the social system are based upon fairly rigorous personal requirements (e.g., age, health, intelligence, adjustment).

2. Members are expected to conform to a highly structured set of role behaviors, which in turn signify acceptance of membership (e.g., wearing the uniform, following the customs of the service).

3. Power is hierarchically distributed among superiors who are expected to follow an explicit system of consequences for deviant behavior and role taking (i.e., the Uniform Code of Military Justice).

4. Apart from the social recognition accorded by society to military members there are explicit material benefits and rewards (e.g., active duty pay, commissary and PX privileges, medical benefits).

5. With membership goes a position in a status hierarchy and the opportunity for a fairly well defined pattern of personal development and career progression.

6. With membership goes the possibility of personal danger and hardship for the primary military member, and attendant consequences for members of his family (e.g., father absence, family mobility and dislocation).

7. With membership goes the security of work in a highly structured environment, but in this environment decisions about individuals can be impersonal and "for the good of the service" rather than on the basis of personal preference or need (e.g., regulations directing and limiting activities, assignment by computer).

8. Membership includes support from the military community whose announced ethic is "to take care of its own."

These requirements and rewards of the military social system become accepted and often valued by the careerist. While subject to criticism and change in regard to particulars, these distinguishing features form the outline of a way of life for the primary military member and his family.

THE MILITARY COMMAND SYSTEM

The emphasis upon discipline and control in the hierarchical structure of military organizations is well known. Feld (1959) in his review identifies these basic characteristics:

1. The military chain of command postulates a downward flow of directive.

2. Discretionary authority of commanders at every echelon is progressively limited and circumscribed.

3. Strict compliance with the commands of superiors is expected.

4. Maintenance of discipline is based on the assumption that superiors have access to a more relevant and comprehensive order of information.

5. The hierarchical structure produces a multiplicity of channels of communication and organizational forms.

6. Superiors are dependent upon the upward flow of information and the technical knowledge of staff officers, who gain a considerable degree of de facto authority.

The increasing size and complexity of military organizations and the increasing awareness of the interdependent relationships between superior and subordinate have generated changes in traditionally rigid expectations. Janowitz (1959) has pointed out the trend toward modification from direct to more indirect patterns of control in military organizations. Attendant strains upon role definition and organizational effectiveness are being recognized (Karcher, 1962).

PROGRAM LEADERS AND
HUMAN RELATIONS AGENTS

The term "program leader" can be applied to that diverse group of essential persons entrusted with the responsibility for planning, organizing, directing, and evaluating activities which relate to the military mission. Program leaders constitute the recognized leadership of the military community. The program leader, typically, is in charge of a work group, which is hierarchically organized, and he is supported by key subordinates with whom he shares authority for program development and execution. The best known example of a program leader in the military is the unit commander who is charged with the development and direction of a combat force. However, there are many other positions within the military community which confer program leadership. Program leaders may hold either civilian or military status but they have in common formalized leadership responsibilities.

As program leaders operate within the military command structure, they are accorded a delimited yet centralized amount of power and control. They are expected to accomplish their objectives, to be task oriented. Among the generic functions of all program leaders are:

1. To be a responsible follower (to follow the orders of superiors, to adapt within assigned limits, to accept responsibility for decisions, to communicate upward).

2. To serve as program director (to provide structure, to assign responsibilities to others, to allocate resources, to prescribe procedures, to define communication channels, to coordinate activities of subordinates).

3. To serve as program evaluator (to set standards of performance, to maintain conformity to prescribed roles, to conduct critical reviews, to give approval and rewards, to enforce discipline).

4. To be a problem solver (to aid in program development, suggest improvements to superiors, to consult on subordinates' work problems, to provide for technical assistance, to maximize resource utilization).

5. To be a team developer (to serve as group symbol and representative, to build espirit de corps, to support and defend subordinates, to establish personal relationships with work group members, to assist with human relations problems, to promote full communication).

There is another group of influential persons in the military community whose function is principally to support program leaders through activities related to people. These human relations agents typically differ from program leaders in that they function as staff advisors; however, they may be given responsibilities of such a scope that they may also function as program leaders. Typically, their programs are seen as integral and supportive but secondary to primary military objectives. Thus the roles of personnel officer, military policeman, chaplain, or Red Cross worker, among others, all serve to maintain the military community in order to allow the primary military mission to be accomplished. Medical Service leaders, for example, may function as program leaders but their people-related programs are designed "to conserve the fighting strength" rather than to actually do the fighting. The community psychologist functions as a human relations agent in the military community. He may also serve as consultant to other human relations agents.

ADJUSTMENT TO MILITARY LIFE

The classic psychosoical problem in the military is the problem of adjustment to military life (Hollingshead, 1946). Strains occur when new members bring to the military value-attitude systems which are incompatible with the expectations and requirements of the military social system. Spindler (1948), for example, has noted that group solidarity is valued positively in the American national character but other elements of military life, such as hierarchy and status, impersonal authority and rigid discipline, and orderliness and calculability are negatively valued. The impact of involuntary membership, the felt meaninglessness of peacetime military life, and the break with one's civilian vocational identity have been reviewed (Bidwell, 1961). The subject of adjustment to military life has been accorded increasing attention since World War II (Stouffer, 1949; Ginsberg, 1959; Janowitz, 1960; Merton & Lazarsfeld, 1950).

Transition from civilian to military status in the first few months of active duty has been seen as a crisis period analogous to other crises in personal development. The new recruit may find his abrupt initiation into military culture a traumatic experience which has been described as "culture shock" (Hilmar, 1965). Entry means dealing with a new set of social demands and assimilation into a new subculture. It leads to adjustive behavior patterns which are often new or more frequently encountered in the military (Janis, 1945). Problems of adaptation to status deprivation are encountered as one is relegated to recruit status, assigned menial tasks, and subjected to censure by superiors. Goffman (1957) speaks of the "mortification of the self" which "total institutions," such as the military, inflict upon new members. Outward expressions of aggression toward superiors are suppressed because of the threat of very real consequences. Reactions to authority and powerlessness may take the form of "gold-bricking," griping, derogatory gossip, and mimicry of superiors. New forms of behavior which emerge may have greater social sanction in military than in civilian life. Subsequent anxieties may be masked through overcompensatory demonstrations of masculinity such as "kidding around," joking about sex, and using taboo words.

While not all experiences in the military are negative, coping skills are severely tested. For those who are successful, adjustment means passing the test of adulthood, independence, and masculinity in the sense of toughness and virility. The military becomes a reference group which is accorded prestige value, and a demonstrable public identity offering status satisfactions (Merton & Kitt, 1950). The obscuring of identity which occurs in basic training by means of highly structured activities, uniformity in appearance and action, and even by according a recruit a serial number appears to constitute a "rite de passage" toward a new identity as part of the military. Marlowe (1959) and Bourne (1967) have described the shifts in perceptual and evaluate behavior which occur during immersion in the basic training process. Each phase of the training cycle seems marked by characteristic attitudes toward military life, the training cadre, other trainees, and the self. Even more demanding upon adjustment skills than basic training are the four-year courses of instruction at the service academies where increasing emphasis is being placed upon the study of the adaptative process (Dornbush, 1955).

The residential group life of military members poses special problems of adjustment. Most common is the situation of the youthful, unmarried barracks resident living in close proximity to large numbers of individuals similarly dependent upon military base facilities and services. Many associates are also work partners and friendships are typically limited to those living within the barracks. A common reality is the stress of being unable to fully avoid those toward whom one feels enmity. The idiosyncrasies of individuals test self-control, and privacy for individuals is very limited or completely lacking. Group life may result in individuals' feeling submerged by the close, continuous, and enforced relationship with others. Individuals are subject to very real social pressures and the threat of rejection and isolation. The strains of group life are matched by the central problem of loneliness, stemming from separation from family, friends, familiar scenes, and previous interpersonal satisfactions (Maskin & Altman, 1943). The central importance of new friendships and feelings of belonging which emerge to meet primary social needs has been frequently reaffirmed (Mandelbaum, 1952). The presence of a "buddy" who listens, provides support, has common experiences, and assists in the process of self-validation often compensates for the disorganizing and esteem-reducing aspects of military life.

The deviant individual quickly becomes identified as the military system and residential group make demands for conformity and appropriate interaction. Erickson and Marlowe (1959) describe three patterns of group response to the schizophrenic in basic training who demonstrates his "singularity" vis-à-vis the group. One group of schizophrenics characterized by others as not caring was baited continuously, taken advantage of, and not provided excuses for behavior. Another group characterized by ineffective and odd behavior was seen as trying rather than uncaring, but also as frightening, with the result that aid and support were withdrawn. Another group was seen as likable but odd, inept, and overly friendly, like puppies and therefore deserving of some interpersonal support. Consideration of the dynamics of the group response earned by deviant individuals in a military situation must include the labeling behavior on the part of military and medical authorities. For example, the development, differentiation, and focus on varieties of "character and behavior disorders," particularly since World War II, have had profound effect upon concepts of administrative disposition, treatability, and rehabilitation.

The stress of combat poses the ultimate task of adaptation. The "normal battle reaction" has been described by Ranson (1949). Both the tested and untested experience anticipatory anxiety prior to combat. Normal combat fear may relate to fear of death, pain, injury, mutilation, or gross incapacitation by fear itself, with resultant inability to guard oneself or discharge duties, and fear of exhibiting fear and ineffectiveness, and thereby losing caste with the combat group. Attendant symptoms of overresponse of the autonomic nervous system are expected and judged abnormal only in terms of their excessive degree and duration. Deprivation of food and water, deprivation of sleep, and being subject to fatigue and the oppressive stimuli of combat have profound effects. Psychodynamic factors produce differential responses to combat-induced anxiety.

In reports of the effects of combat stress, emphasis has been placed upon individual patterns of handling hostility and guilt (Weinstein & Drayer, 1949), use of defense mechanisms and the importance of group identification (Glass, 1953), interpersonal transactions and communication patterns (Spiegel, 1953), and group or mass phenomena and morale (Lidz, 1953). The crucial effects of group solidarity upon personal commitment and behavior in combat have been extensively reported (Stouffer, Vol. 2, 1949; Little, 1955). The stress of becoming a prisoner of war subject to "brainwashing" and "thought reform" has received a great deal of attention in recent years (Eiderman, 1963).

Developing understanding of the many facets of adaptation in common combat and noncombat situations poses an enormous undertaking and requires multidisciplinary involvement. Those who assume community psychology roles in the military are confronted with the formidable task of seeking to integrate accumulated knowledge and differing points of view. Needless to say this comprehensive integration is a future goal rather than a present reality. Still the program leaders in the military may call upon the community psychologist for his analysis of problems of adjustment to military life. Any analysis requires consideration of situational and system demands, individual and group adaptation processes, the effectiveness of adjustment and performance, and patterns of dysfunction. In turn, the program leader can be helped to meet his organizational goals, promote positive adaptation, and manage the individual and group dysfunction which occurs.

PROBLEMS OF MILITARY FAMILIES

Military families are like other families in terms of their being subject to the common range of family problems and crises; yet unique strains are encountered. Hill (1949), in his pioneering study of the impact of war upon the family, speaks of family crises which involve dismemberment (loss of a family member), accession (addition of an unprepared—for member), demoralization (loss of family unity and morale), or some combination of these. The death of the father in war and the occasions of father absence because of military need, in this framework, would constitute a dismemberment crisis for the military family. The reentry of the father into the family group after a period of extended absence could contribute to a crisis based on reaccession. A crisis of demoralization could be the result of a strong identification with the military by the primary military member which conflicts with negative attitudes toward the military by other family members. Other methods of classifying family crises exist (Hansen & Hill, 1964) and the crises experienced by military families may parallel those present in other segments of the civilian community. The military father can produce the equivalent of dismemberment by becoming overinvolved with military duties, which can be readily rationalized as being expected given his military role. Family unity may be strained by the inability of a military wife to adjust to social protocol and the society of military wives. The disruptive effects of family problems on the primary military person and his effectiveness at times contribute to the family-military schism (Waldrop, 1962), but the need for career military members generally leads to official concern about the welfare of the military family.

Just as in civilian life, military family patterns of adjustment are, in part, determined by solutions to the economic problems of the family. Although there is a relatively high degree of economic security for the career military man, economic pressures are very real, particularly for enlisted men. Recent years have seen an increase in the percentage of enlisted men who are married. The typical career enlisted man and his family are beset with a limited income and limited prospect for accumulating savings. As a result, military families tend to live financially from month to month. In stateside assignments, a large number of enlisted men with families secure second jobs ("moonlighting") in the civilian community. Ryan and Bevilacqua (1964), in their limited sample, found 56 percent of the married enlisted men had a source of income exclusive of military pay. They found that in those families reporting extra income, 41 percent of the enlisted men had second jobs, 40 percent of the wives worked, and in 17 percent both husband and wife worked. It is not known how this sample compares with civilian families, but it is clear that such working patterns have a significant effect on the military family. The adequacy of family housing varies with the region, the character of the host community, and the availability of on-base family quarters. Typically, base family quarters are seen as adequate, if not highly desirable, but their numbers are limited. Trailer and apartment communities are a prominent feature adjacent to stateside military bases since home ownership is frequently impractical. The cost of housing becomes a significant factor leading to the need for added income. Apart from periodic surveys conducted for special administrative purposes by the Department of Defense and reported in military publications, relatively little is known about the economic status and problems of the military family and still less is known about their psychosocial impact.

Family mobility, while a prominent feature of our mobile society, is more frequent in military than in civilian life. Programmed and unscheduled reassignments are predictable occurrences for the military family. The family must struggle with the logistics of relocation, the withdrawal of personal community ties, and reintegration into a new community. While certain similarities exist from one to another military community and old acquaintances are encountered upon reassignment, the adaptive capacity of the family unit is taxed. The experience of father absence is frequent and expected for the military family. Most military families are called upon to adapt during the father's unaccompanied or "hardship" tour of duty, in which he is absent for 12 or more months. In addition, the military father is subject to periods of temporary duty for several weeks or even months, as he serves in training or other assignments away from his home base. Lindquist (1952), for example, has reported upon marriage and family life of men in the Strategic Air Command. Their highly significant work demands, and the prospect of irregular departures on short notice, make the monthly allotment check in some families the one important contribution by the

husband on which the wife can count. Only in recent years have the factors of mobility and father absence in military families been accorded study (Pedersen & Sullivan, 1964; Dickerson & Arthur, 1965; Baker, 1967, 1968; Lyon, 1967). The presumed negative impact of these factors upon community ties and social participation of family members, family solidarity, and marital happiness, the individual adjustment and development of family members, and identification with the military is very plausible yet not adequately documented. Fagen (1967) indicates that the ego-strengthening impact of father absence and mobility upon adaptation should also be considered.

The impact of mobility and father absence on the education of children of military families is still another area that has not been adequately studied. No doubt sudden and rapid displacements of families result in irregular and disrupted educational programming. Since facilities, requirements, and grade levels vary so widely, educational gaps, discrepancies, overlapping, and inconsistencies occur. In some instances of displacement, programming for special educational problems cannot be developed in coordination with other base systems. A frequent problem, too, has to do with staffing. Since many on-base dependent schools are staffed almost wholly by the wives of servicemen, the turnover within any given school term becomes unusually high and unpredictable. In overseas areas there are even more limitations in that the educational programs must of necessity be less varied, and educational discrepancies with stateside standards are bound to exist.

PROBLEMS OF LEADERSHIP AND ORGANIZATIONAL EFFECTIVENESS

Stereotypes about the military leader and the impact of military life are very prevalent. It is often asserted that military careers are more attractive to persons with authoritarian tendencies and that military life fosters development and maintenance of authoritarian values. Certainly military training and ideology and the military command system call for acceptance of status-oriented, strongly directive leadership. Several studies (French & Ernest 1955; Campbell & McCormack, 1967; Firestone, 1959) have sought to relate military experience to authoritarianism, as measured by the F scale. It appears that military trainees express greater agreement with authoritarian thinking under conditions which encourage making a good showing, but there is no evidence to indicate that attitudes become more authoritarian following military experience. Campbell and McCormack conclude from their work that if military experience has any effect on general attitudes toward authority it is to make them less authoritarian. Hollander (1954) found a negative relationship between authoritarianism and peer nominations for leadership. These studies suggest a need for clarification of the multiple uses of the term authoritarian (Sanford, 1950).

The military social system has been seen as promoting and institutionalizing certain leadership styles. It is commonly believed that military leaders tend to focus on "task leader" functions and attaining productivity, in contrast to "social-emotional leader" functions centered about interpersonal relationships. Military customs do tend to formalize patterns of social distance between leaders and followers. Fiedler (1957) has pointed up the possible interference with decision-making in military leaders with insufficient social distance. He argues in effect that military leaders need the defense of social distance to remain effective rather than be too influenced by personal feelings about followers. Halpin (1954) found that leadership ratings by superiors tended to correlate negatively with ratings of consideration shown followers, but consideration was associated with an increase in group satisfaction with the leader. Such opposing evaluations by superiors and subordinates reflect the conflicting role demands inherent in the position of the military leader. Phrased in military terms, the primary responsibilities of the military leader are accomplishment of mission and duty to subordinates (Carter, 1962). The military leader's dilemma is somewhat resolved within the military community as a whole by the presence of differentiated and institutionalized socioemotional leader roles. Still a creative integration of the apparently contradictory orientations to be task- or person-oriented can be a goal in leadership development (Blake & Mouton, 1964; Fiedler, 1967).

The military command system provides a formal social organization and system of control to be implemented by two leadership classes, the commissioned officers and the noncommissioned officers. The commanding officer (CO) is assisted by the noncommissioned officer in charge (NCOIC) in passing orders and directives to enlisted men and enforcing compliance with these orders. The CO's formal position endows him with the ability to provide rewards and to mediate punishments. This power is shared with the NCOIC who has far greater contact with subordinates. Typically the position of the NCOIC allows a highly personal, informal leadership, in contrast to the more impersonal, formal leadership of the CO. These "leader-keymen" patterns have been seen to have profound effects on group effectiveness (Fiedler, 1955). A frequent dilemma of the NCOIC is that while responsibility appears to be proportional to the position in the overall status system, authority appears to be discretely and disproportionately associated with the officers and the NCOIC feels himself frequently bypassed (Borgatta, 1955).

Despite the formal organizational powers accorded formal military leaders, many areas of activity are controlled and carried on by informal social groups (Anonymous, 1946). Noncommissioned officers may become part of the informal group and even serve in leadership roles. Studies of the American soldier (Stouffer, Vol. 1, 1949) indicated that enlisted men are more likely to approve of noncom behavior when it is characterized by more intimate social relationships with men, more indulgent and sympathetic supervision, and a lack of emphasis upon status differences in social and work relationships. Noncoms are in the difficult position of the middleman, subject to pressures from the informal group and the CO. Rose (1946) has described the informal social structures which occur in the enlisted ranks in terms of mechanisms of defense against the formal organization. Informal group pressures may also be brought to bear upon members in the form of social ostracism, name calling, and withholding of privileges. The threat to formally designated leaders posed by informal group processes and pressures therefore can be very real and present the classic challenge to military leadership and its system of social control.

Despite the advances toward a comprehensive theory of leadership and organizational behavior, and the accumulation of empirical and experimental data, really satisfactory solutions to everyday problems have not yet been found. Nevertheless, the concept of the military leader as a manager of men receives much attention (West Point, 1959). The shifting bases of authority and discipline in the military and the influence of human relations concepts has led to a shift in emphasis from "command" to "leadership." Manipulative, persuasive, educational, and group techniques are being more widely used. As always, the development of desirable leadership attributes is advocated for the military leader as a self ideal as well as an inspirational model for subordinates. The military command system places the responsibility for outcome upon the military leader despite the character of the group led or the influence of the total situation. Military leaders become both managers of weapons systems and social systems. It is the burden of these responsibilities of leadership that prompts a willingness, sometimes clouded with ambivalence, to seek the aid of the human relations expert.

PROBLEMS OF COMMUNITY INTEGRATION

The very purpose and structure of the military establishment dictates that certain special problems of subgroup integration would inevitably occur. Such relationships as officer and enlisted (Lewis, 1947), military and civilian, problems of racial minorities (Mandelbaum, 1952), as well as servicewomen minority groupings create sensitive problem areas. Even beyond this, consideration needs to be given to the problem of the reservist in his relationship to the career member, as well as that of the closed military community and the surrounding host civilian milieu.

With regard to officer and enlisted relationships, the findings of the Doolittle Board following World War II now have an established place in the literature. This Board concluded that defects in leadership and inadequacies of the stratification system were present, and recommended certain improvements in leadership and the establishment of various policies for reducing the social gap between officers and enlisted men. It recommended that all military personnel be permitted to pursue normal social patterns comparable to our democratic way of life when off duty, that there be equality of treatment of officers and enlisted men in the administration of military justice, and that regulations and instructions be established to

prohibit or minimize abuses of privilege and authority. These recommendations were subsequently implemented to a limited extent and have resulted in improved leadership training, the revision of the Manual of Courts Martial, and certain other procedures such as the removal of discriminatory references to enlisted men in army regulations. The great lesson of the Doolittle Report lies in its implications for morale and efficiency. The fact remains, however, that the stratification system encourages poor officer-enlisted man relations, low morale, and inefficiency at any time when the armed forces contain large numbers of nonregulars (Coates & Pellegrin, 1965).

This may indicate that attention should be given to the manner in which nonregulars are absorbed. Identification with the military takes time and preparation and commanders are all too frequently unable to adequately effect a health integration either because of a personal bias toward the nonregular or because insufficient attention is given to the problem.

In today's modern military operation, one so demanding of special technical skills, the employment of large numbers of civilians working side by side with the military has now become a "way of life," and to a large extent, the rule rather than the exception. Civilian employees of the Department of Defense deserve special mention in considering the military professional and nonprofessional. Civilian employees vary in their commitment to the values and goals of the armed forces. However, many career civilian employees develop a very close identification with the particular service for which they work (Coates & Pellegrin, 1965).

As to racial minorities (the principal one being the Negro serviceman), there is no question but that integration is an established fact in the armed forces. Notable efficiences and economics as well as other tangible values have resulted from integration. Predictions that integration would be followed by a deterioration of race relations and lower morale and efficiency have been nowhere substantiated. The morale of the black serviceman has been greatly improved in that he now has opportunities previously unavailable to him and no longer does he serve in a segregated and subordinated capacity. It is now possible to promote Negroes on the basis of merit, the determining factor being individual capability rather than race. At the Department of Defense level, firm and decisive support for integrated housing in the host community has given added impetus to the declared policy of racial equality. There are still, however, some manifest gaps and inconsistencies pointing toward the need for professional consultants to assist commanders with problems of integration. Although this is less perceptible at the higher social strata, at all levels there are competitive factors, distrust, suspicion, and at best only toleration.

Women in uniform also constitute a minority group. In general, the servicemen of World War II shared the sentiment of their fellow Americans with regard to women in uniform. In addition to the usual negative predispositions, the situation was aggravated by the threat posed by service-women to some servicemen. That is, much publicity was given to the plan to use women as replacements for men in noncombat capacities. Understandably, little enthusiasm was shown for this idea by some men in chairborne positions. It was discovered that servicemen who did not work with servicewomen and lacked opportunities to observe their behavior and job performance at first hand were most critical of them. The attitudes of men toward servicewomen have been gradually modified in the direction of acceptance and the presence of women in the armed forces is now taken for granted much as it is taken for granted by Congress and the American public. The servicewoman is still, however, often neglected and uneconomically deployed. This is another relationship where increased professional consultation is greatly needed.

Since the size of the military establishment varies with the vicissitudes of international relations, reserve officers and enlisted men are used to make up the difference between the strength of the hard-core regulars and the overall strength required at any given time. Reserve personnel are therefore called to active duty in periods of military expansion involuntarily and are sometimes also released involuntarily during a reduction in force (RIF) imposed by law or by budgetary considerations. There is a special category of reserve officers who remain on active duty for a major portion of their adult careers. These officers form an integral part of the professional officer corps. They attend military service schools, are assigned to varied positions to broaden their experiences and competence, and presumably receive the same considerations as do the regular officers for temporary promotion and other emoluments of military careers (Coates & Pellegrin, 1965). In recent years, concerted efforts have been made by the services to stabilize the active duty reservist's career situation by such devices as contracted periods of obligated duty binding on both the reservist and the military. Nevertheless, the fact that the active duty career officer corps is composed of both regulars and reserve officers tends to create a strain on the corporate fabric of the corps, to engender invidious distinctions between the two groups, and sometimes to encourage mutual suspicions and recriminations between them regarding the equitability of rewards for merit and devotion.

The contact and coordination between the military community and its host civilian community has been generally regarded as a public relations problem since it is related to how the civilian community views the military base. If they see it favorably they will be inclined to cooperate. Most frequently there is generally limited understanding by the host community and all too often civilian resources are not available to the military base.

In certain compact areas, large numbers of retired as well as active duty servicemen reside within the host community. Some civilian schools may have as many as 50 to 75 percent military dependents. Military personnel engaged in moonlighting operations are many times actively involved in every aspect of community functioning. Civilian communities are pitifully unprepared to handle the large number of military families that so often descend upon them. All of this points toward increasing need for improved education and consultation between the primary and host communities.

REPRESENTATIVE HUMAN RELATIONS AGENCIES AND ROLES

Within all military establishments there are a number of agencies through which the community psychologist may work. It might be said that all agencies in one sense are human relations agencies since their very existence is in support of the military membership. There are some agencies, however, that are clearly so designated, by regulation and by custom.

The military member's immediate commanding officer, for example, is the first echelon human relations agent with responsibility for the total welfare of the serviceman and his family members.

The legal assistance officer provides the service of protecting the individual and his rights. He is also available for marital, financial, and personal counseling. In this connection, he may render assistance in filing taxes and the preparation of wills.

The chaplain has, as his primary mission, responsibility for providing religious and moral guidance to military personnel and their families. In accomplishing this mission, the chaplain seeks to develop a relationship of trust and mutual respect between himself and all members of the command.

The personal affairs officer deals with the many things affecting the welfare and personal and private lives of people, present and future. Important among the things affecting the personal affairs of military personnel are the rights, benefits, and privileges afforded in the military service.

The inspector general is immediately available for grievances, complaints, or investigation of problems confronting the serviceman and his family.

The education and training officer offers courses, guidance, and counseling to the military member along the lines of general educational and career development. This agency attempts to broaden and strengthen the opportunities provided military personnel to continue their education while in service. Increasing attention is being given to counseling those about to retire and those physically or emotionally impaired as a result of military service.

More recently there have been developed within the services community and family service agencies (Marine Corps Family Assistance, Naval Family Service Center, Army Community Services, and Air Force Family Services) designed to assist the serviceman and his family in resolving personal and family problems beyond their ability. The complexities of modern living are such as to sometimes overwhelm the average serviceman—particularly when he is in crisis. Although clearly structured agencies exist for the purpose of helping the military member, many cases "fall between the cracks" and require special consideration.

The American Red Cross, chartered by the United States Congress, is committed to provide a wide variety of services to members of the armed forces, their dependents, and the military community as a whole.

The dependent school liaison officer is uniquely positioned between the command and the school system to render assistance to dependent children where command support is necessary.

APPROACHES TO COMMUNITY MENTAL HEALTH

Problems related to the mental health of the military community have traditionally been viewed as the special province of military psychiatry. In fact, it was not until the latter stages of World War II that psychology and social work as professions became involved directly in mental health problems. It may be more than coincidental that this broadening of the professional base corresponds to the period when major efforts were being made to formalize a preventive approach.

The early efforts of psychiatry in the military community were directed toward the problems of the individual combat soldier. It soon became apparent, however, that responding to every psychologically disrupted soldier as though he were an independent, self-contained problem was a limitless and futile task. As one observer during World War II noted, in an oblique reference to the interface between individual problems and their environmental substratum, "Neurosis is as contagious as a virulent infection" (Eisendorfer, 1944). Of equal importance in the history of military psychiatry is the fact that protracted treatment of individual problems, as had gained support in civilian communities, found little favor in military environments oriented to a full and immediate utilization of all its members at all times.

Subsequently, military psychiatry was pressured from its early development by community demands, and the nature of the problems with which it dealt, toward a social and preventive approach to mental health problems. This pattern of development has led Perkins (1964) to conclude that military psychiatry has been in the "mainstream" of what is now called community psychiatry.

Problems of Combat

Most of what is now fundamental to military community mental health programs had its inception during periods of combat. In the course of World War I attempts were made to provide psychiatric treatment as close to the front as possible. Psychiatrists were assigned for the first time in American military history at division levels. These efforts were made in order to reduce "secondary gain" associated with evacuation to rear hospitals and to treat cases of so-called combat exhaustion or war neurosis in their early stages. At the same time first attempts were made to screen recruits at induction centers in order to eliminate those whom it was felt would become psychiatric casualties. The results of this program were mixed. Finally, army hospitals undertook, for the first time, definitive treatment of mental illness. (For reviews of developments during World War I the reader is referred to Anderson, circa 1960; United States War Department, 1929.)

After a slow start in World War II efforts were made to expand on earlier programs and move toward preventive measures in the field of mental health. Division psychiatrists were instructed and encouraged to advise commanders on problems affecting morale as well as treat psychiatric casualties. During this same period massive attempts were also made to screen out the "unfit" at induction centers. Predicting reactions to the stress of military life on the basis of personality variables failed dismally, however, and the program was finally dropped. Ironically, this failure fostered what has been considered by some to be the most constructive effort of World War II on military psychiatry—the introduction of mental hygiene consultation services. (For a review of mental health activities during World War II the reader is referred to Anderson, 1960).

Community Mental Health

The problems of the selection and induction of military personnel have received heavy emphasis as reflected in studies by Brill and Gilbert (1952), Fry (1951), and more recently Perry (1967). The stress inherent in combat situations has also been given special attention through such reports as those by Glass (1949, 1951, 1952), Klein (1948), Ludwig and Ranson (1947), and Weinstein (1947).

The elimination of psychiatric screening at induction centers was an admission of the inability to predict gross stress reactions on the basis of personality variables. The development of mental hygiene consultation service was at least tacit acknowledgment of the role played by the community in development of individual psychological disturbances. Beginning with the introduction of such a service to 13 replacement training centers in World War II, the program has evolved to the point that now over 50 percent of the army psychiatrists are assigned to Mental Hygiene Consultation Services (MHCS) (Tiffany & Allerton, 1967).

The original design of MHCS programs focused on the immediate handling of referrals from any of the military program leaders including chaplains, troop commanders, and provost marshals. More importantly, however, an advisory service was to be provided to each of the essential program leaders in the military community. This advisory service was to focus on the impact of training programs and leadership techniques on the adjustment of the individual soldier. Unfortunately, the advisory role has tended to be slighted throughout the history of MHCS programs for a multitude of reasons including some resistance from commanders (Maillet, 1966) and shortages of MHCS personnel. As a result, the consultative aspects of mental hygiene facilities in military communities have received only passing attention in much of the literature. Notable exceptions include Datel's (1962, 1966) work with basic trainee groups and Spencer and Gray's (1965) formulations.

Otherwise, the impact of interweaving mental health facilities with the larger military community appears to have been a compromise between the practice of clinical psychiatry, per se, and large scale planning of community mental health consultation. This compromise has consisted of a heightened interest in the effects of different sociotemporal stages of military life on individual behavior and in the communicative nature of behavioral dysfunction.

The disciplinary barracks, stockades, and the delinquent soldier are other aspects of military life which have been studied extensively. Tiffany and Allerton (1967) have tied a leveling off of military offender populations over the past few years to increased screening program activity by mental hygiene personnel. At the same time efforts toward increased sophistication in the rehabilitation of military offenders have been highlighted by reports such as that of Robbins (1967). The terminal stage of military life, retirement, has also provoked considerable psychological inquiry as evidenced in reports by Greenberg (1965), McNeil and Griffen (1965, 1967), and Milowe (1964). There is continued interest in the social meaning and communication inherent in a variety of specific behavioral symptoms. Included in this category would be indebtedness, alcoholism, malingering (Ludwig, 1949), and suicide gestures (Tucker & Gorman, 1967).

An overview of military psychiatry and community mental hygiene efforts during the last two decades suggests that a comprehensive preventive approach to mental health problems is yet to be formulated. Instead, it appears that the field has been undergoing a crucial preliminary information-gathering phase.

TARGET SYSTEM LEVELS
AND EFFECTIVENESS

Structurally, any military community can be viewed as a social system which is part of a larger societal system. In turn, it is composed of a number of interrelated subsystems. These subsystems may be formal or informal and classified as being on an individual (P), small group (G), organizational group (O), or community (C) level. The term "target system" can be applied to any

system chosen as the object of analysis and change. Goals for change are set in response to the effectiveness status of the target system. It is the concern for effectiveness of a target system which prompts the need for intervention even though criteria for effectiveness may be arbitrarily or poorly defined and vary with changing situational requirements. Any target system can be generally assigned to one of four stages of effectiveness. These are:

1. Stage I   Effectiveness Development
2. Stage II   Effectiveness Maintenance
3. Stage III Emergent Ineffectiveness
4. Stage IV   Established Ineffectiveness

The effectiveness status of an individual in relation to a combat situation can illustrate these stages. At Stage I, an individual while in basic training acquires skill and confidence in relation to role requirements in combat. At Stage II an individual can maintain and consolidate his effectiveness, upon joining a new unit, by seeking new friendships, and developing a group loyalty. At Stage III, while in combat, signs of ineffectiveness may become evident in the emotional overreaction to the loss of a buddy. At Stage IV, pronounced ineffectiveness, as a result of a dissociative reaction, might require hospitalization. Similarly, other target systems at small group, organizational system, and community levels can be described in terms of their effectiveness status. Modes of intervention must be considered in relation to the target system level and stage (see Table 8–1).

TABLE 8–1
Target System Levels and Effectiveness Status

Target System Levels	Stages of Effectiveness			
	I Effectiveness Development	II Effectiveness Maintenance	III Emergent Ineffectiveness	IV Established Ineffectiveness
(C) Community				
(O) Organizational System				
(G) Small Group				
(P) Individual Person				

REPRESENTATIVE PROBLEMS:
ORGANIZATIONAL LEVEL

The social embeddedness of military life dictates that the central focus for intervention by the community psychologist must be at the organizational or group level. The military group provides the principal source of identity and the primary access to physical and psychological support for individual military members. Without it, the entire military system would collapse.

Because every military group has sharply defined but permiable boundaries, it is imperative that a community psychologist have a working knowledge of both its internal structure and its external relatedness. Just as an individual must fulfill a specific role function within his basic group, so the group must establish certain external relationships to other groups in the military community. Information concerning the form and stability of these external relationships is particularly necessary where power-centered intervention is involved. Otherwise, the human relations agent, working with program leaders of any one group, runs the risk of reducing his own effectiveness by inadvertently and adversely altering the balance of relationships in the larger community.

In contrast to civilian organizations, military groups seldom evolve over a period of time in any one community. Typically they are formed in a short time span or arrive already organized in the midst of an ongoing, larger community system. The interdependence of a group and the larger community is perhaps never more visible than when a new unit is established on a post. For a period of time, until relationships with the community become structured and formalized, the lines of relatedness tend to be abrasive and disruptive.

The establishment of a unit of regimental strength (approximately 3,500 members), for example, presents a military community with demands for a complete reordering of established patterns. The capability of community housing, schools, commissaries, medical, and recreational facilities to support the active military and dependent members of the regiment must be examined. Augmentation of existing services to accommodate the new demands could entail abrupt changes in the lives of already established community members. Schools may become crowded, housing scarce, shopping hours changed, recreational opportunities limited, and medical facilities less accessible.

At the same time, the military community must accommodate to increased demands for logistical support because of the new unit. A group of regimental size requires support including the special skills of carpenters, plumbers, and electricians. Food ration warehouses must be expanded; unit supply stores which handle such basic items as cooking utensils, paint, and office equipment must increase their available stock.

Human relations agents in the military community are no less affected by a sudden increase in population. Such changes typically generate a high percentage of family disruptions requiring the assistance of the Red Cross, community and family service agencies and mental hygiene personnel. The police systems, stockade facilities, and legal sections of the community must be bolstered to allow for the greater service demand.

While all of these obvious, foreseeable changes are occurring, many other, less predictable, more subtle, and perhaps more far-reaching accommodations are being made. A unit of regimental size brings with it to a military community a new set of program leaders, and this threatens the existing hierarchy of power. Channels of communication and the direction of information flow must subsequently be altered. Changes in relative seniority, among both officers and noncommissioned officers in the community, are likely. Subsequently, previous power positions may be threatened. Based on the prestige and relative power of the new members and the organization itself, subgroup alliances within the community must be altered.

While adjustment to the larger community is being accomplished, a new unit must also look to its own internal goals. Training schedules must be developed and plans for meeting both organizational and individual training needs formulated. Such plans must allow for a variety of experience levels among the group members. A military unit of today, for example, contains an admixture of seasoned careerists, experienced noncareer personnel, inexperienced neophytes encountering their first unit assignment, individuals with only a short period of obligated service remaining, and personnel who are being retrained for new skills.

Furthermore, any unit expects a rapid turnover of members. For this reason, training programs must be not only encompassing but repetitive as well.

All of the above factors must be considered by the community psychologist entering into a consultation program with a new unit on a military post. He must be aware of whether the basic needs of the unit are being met by the community, what positions of relative power the program leaders in the organization play in the community, and what the objectives and training plans of the organization are. Only within the context of such information can he begin to assess any problems of organizatonal dysfunction.

In any military organization, new or established, there are a variety of indices of dysfunction which can be measured. These range from the more typical AWOL rate, sick call rate, excessive drinking and drug abuse rate, volume of courts martial, numbers of administrative discharge, and accident rates to the less often noted indices such as requests for transfer, leave and pass requests, referrals to mental hygiene, incidents of minor crimes such as petty theft, amount of indebtedness among unit members, failure of subgroups within the organization to pass training tests, and letters from parents or Congressmen to unit commanders expressing concern about individual members of the unit. Any of these indices might reflect problems among either the program leaders or the followers in the organization. This determination becomes the first challenge to the consultant. Typically, his only initial guideline is that the greater any one index becomes or the greater the number of indices that become prominent, the more do the program leaders become implicated.

PROBLEMS IN HUMAN
RELATIONS CONSULTATION

As noted above, military program leaders are task oriented and focus upon the variety of activities which constitute the military mission. They are imbedded in a precisely defined hierarchical system of leaders and subordinates with tasks accorded on the basis of officially delegated responsibility. Since World War II the Army Mental Hygiene Consultation Service (MHCS) has been idealized by these program leaders. The results of this effort are illuminating.

Over the past 15 years there have been few, if any, reports of successful MHCS programs. Schulman and Myers (1954) and Sousa (1963) report that program leaders feel the most appropriate role for mental hygiene personnel is in the area of individual treatment. The usual explanation for the failure of the consultation function is that the MHCS workers have not really tried to move away from the clinical treatment role in their practice. Maillet (1966) has suggested an alternative explanation for the difficulty. He advanced the idea that the MHCS workers' attempts to become broadly defined command consultants could be conceptualized as an attempt to enter into the command system in a role relatively alien to that system. After carefully interviewing over 100 commanders he concluded that when adjustment problems were not defined as related to mental illness per se, organizational norms were no longer supportive of MHCS involvement. Expertise in such cases was viewed as possessed by the experienced commanding officer and the norms of the organization supported seeking guidance within the chain of command.

From all these indicators it would appear that consultation with military program leaders involves a critical entry problem. Military leaders have sharply defined, narrow expectations with respect to the services of mental hygiene personnel. In order to protect their own leadership positions they feel it necessary to maintain MHCS functions within a circumscribed medical model. Until means are found to modify these expectations while simultaneously preserving the leadership integrity of the military commander, only modest gains can be anticipated from human relations consultation in the military community. A solution to this entry problem will, no doubt, have to involve educational efforts at critical points in the career development of military program leaders. Such efforts might be made, for example, in Officers Candidate Schools or career courses which every career officer must attend.

In addition to resistance from commanders, a human relations consultation program must face problems among those individuals providing the service. The latter occur because consultation programs currently must be developed by individuals with a history of participation in medically oriented psychiatric outpatient services and all the attendant staff hierarchies. As these professionals begin to approximate a consultation effort their former roles become blurred. It becomes imperative either to structure new roles or fall back on the traditional "psychiatric team" hierarchy thereby compromising and perhaps precluding the implementation of a consultation program.

Unfortunately, attempts to conceptualize the role relationships among psychologists, psychiatrists, and social workers in consultation programs have been practically nonexistent. An exception might be the role proposed for psychologists in MHCS programs by Reynolds (1967). Reynolds elaborated an idea suggested by Turner (1966) for using psychology classes as "dithering devices" on college campuses. "Dithering device" is a term used for electrical vibrators which British scientists frequently attach to laboratory equipment in order to keep all the parts articulating well together. As Turner (1966) remarked, "anyone who has successfully resorted to kicking a piece of machinery to get it going can quickly see the value of a dithering device."

Reynolds has suggested that psychologists may function most appropriately in MHCS programs if they view their role as that of a "professional ditherer." Operationally the art of skillful dithering would include raising issues, asking questions, gathering information about and suggesting modifications of: (a) the internal operation of the consultation program and (b) the relation of the program to the community itself. It may be that psychologists are uniquely qualified for this role because of their academic background of questioning, research, theory building, conceptualizing, and calculated testing of the so-called "tried and true" approaches to problems.

In MHCS programs professional dithering is, no doubt, only one of many possible roles that could be assumed by personnel with backgrounds in psychology. It is one, however, which might suggest complimentary role development for other professionals since a dithering device, by definition, functions within an interrelated system. Certainly, it avoids any involvement with medical models.

The military rank structure and the interest of command in maintaining mental hygiene activities within a medical mold create special problems when attempting to utilize nonprofessionals in consultation programs. For the past 20 years the army has utilized such nonprofessionals—"specialists," as they are termed—in the MHCS activities. It was hoped that these specialists, being enlisted men, working under the supervision of qualified psychiatrists and social workers, could more effectively communicate with enlisted men who were having adjustment problems. Moreover, they were to maintain contact with army units so as to provide information on the problems within those groups and act as liaison between the units and mental health professionals. Monahan (1968) studied the utilization of specialists in these programs. His findings indicated that, generally, they were of low military rank. Subsequently, their effectiveness seemed to depend on their being viewed by command in a dual role of specialist and soldier. The lower the rank they held the more they had to depend on the prestige of being a member of the mental hygiene facility for status. In addition, they tended to identify with the more prestigious members of the mental hygiene staff—the psychiatrist or medical officer. Although not discussed by Monahan, this identification is possibly a natural outgrowth of their need to gain status in a command system which views mental hygiene as primarily medical in character. Given this orientation on the part of command and providing that enlisted specialists are a basic link between command and mental hygiene consultation programs, the entry problem is compounded. Solutions suggested by the nature of the problem would include using only high-ranking specialists for command consultation and, as indicated above, altering the perception by command of the ways in which the MHCS can be utilized.

THE FUTURE OF MILITARY COMMUNITY PSYCHOLOGY

Several reviews of the history of psychology in the military since World War I are available (Hedlund, 1966; Seidenfeld, 1966; Zehrer, 1954). Since World War II the psychologist in uniform, in all military services, has been predominantly a clinical psychologist functioning in a medical-psychiatric setting. The traditional roles of psychodiagnosis, psychotherapy, and research have been emphasized. Approved programs of psychology internship training have been developed, and despite difficulties in retention (Military Psychology, 1968) a core group of career psychologists has been maintained. Many clinical psychologists have preferred to serve in medical settings in traditional ways. However, for the past decade, psychologists in the military have stressed the importance of developing nontraditional roles. Supported by the evolving focus upon preventive psychiatry and mental health consultation, a broader range of psychological services is being provided. Greater effort has been placed in internship training upon family, group, organizational, and community problems and consultation methods.

Prospects for the formal recognition of the community psychology function in the military are constantly improving. For example, a number of significant proposals were made at the 1966 conference, Current Trends in Army Medical Service Psychology. It was proposed that recognition of the considerable "nonclinical" services presently being undertaken and in need of further expansion would be substantially enhanced by formal creation of the occupational designation consulting psychologist, as different from that of clinical psychologist. Hardison (1966) and Nichols (1966) effectively presented the case for the establishment of Psychological Service Centers in the military. Created as a personnel support function, such a center would circumvent some of the burdensome restraints presently encountered when military psychologists work in medical settings. As envisioned, the internal organizaton of a Psychological Service Center would include a Community Consultation Service and a Community Survey and Research Service. It was also proposed that selected centers provide training in community and consulting psychology.

We may expect that the present relatively undeveloped status of military community psychology will be even more painfully apparent in future years. The core of present day community psychology efforts, consultation with program leaders, will undoubtedly remain, and hopefully the current preoccupation with the entry problem of the consultant will be reduced as activities expand and gain greater acceptance. Education of leaders about the place of the human relations consultant will continue to be crucial. Focus upon problems of effectiveness development and effectiveness maintenance at organizational and com-

munity levels should aid in recasting the too frequently encountered expectation that the consultant takes a clinical approach concerned with established ineffectiveness and individual pathology. Fostering the distinction between community and clinical approaches can perhaps best be accomplished by delineating the variety of consultation programs that could be established at organizational and community levels. Much remains to be done toward organizing the military for effective management of human relations problems and providing institutionalized approaches and supports. Military communities have not mobilized the talent that is presently available for the serious and systematic study of human relations problems. Greater awareness of community problems should result in establishment of human relations study groups or human relations councils at the base community level or higher. The community psychologist should serve as catalyst and "ditherer" in community organization efforts and be prepared to serve as a study group member, one of several interested human relations agents.

The manifold opportunities for positive contributions by community psychologists in the military seem matched by the barriers and challenges. In some ways the opportunities to demonstrate the scope of community problems and their impact upon organizational objectives is far greater in the military than in the civilian community. The reality of a single benevolent employer and a highly centralized structure of community authority for some may cast the negative image of the military community as a "company town." However, an enlightened leadership can help enhance community awareness and make intervention more effective. The military society has been a unique testing ground for innovation in human relations areas. Because it is a publicly supported enterprise, which personally may touch almost every American family, there is the opportunity for a variety of models of community psychology service to emerge and be evaluated by public and professional criteria. Just as today, the military community psychologist of the future will be confronted with the task of developing and maintaining a professional identity while adapting to a special social system that he seeks to change. The neutralization of the threats to leadership inherent in the change agent role and the development of methods of serving as a resource person to military leaders will remain.

References

American Psychiatric Association. *Diagnostic and statistical manual of mental disorders.* Washington, D. C.: Author, 1952.

American Psychological Association. Military psychology: A comparative image. (Summary report of the Ad Hoc Committee to Study Career Status of Military Psychologists, Division 19) *American Psychologist,* 1968, 23, 112–122.

Anderson, W. H. *An abbreviated history of military psychiatry in the United States Army.* Washington, D. C.: Department of Neuropsychiatry, Walter Reed General Hospital, 1960.

Anonymous. Informal social organization in the Army. *American Journal of Sociology,* 1946, 51, 365–370.

Baker, S. L., Cove, L. A., Fagen, S. A., Fischer, E. G., & Janda, E. J. Impact of father absence: III. Problems of family reintegration following prolonged father absence. Presented at the 45th annual meeting of the American Orthopsychiatric Association, Chicago, March 23, 1968.

Baker, S. L., Fagen, S. A., Janda, E. J., Fischer, E. G., & Cove, L. A. Impact of father absence in military families: I. An evaluation of the military family's adjustment. Presented at the 44th annual meeting of the American Orthopsychiatric Association, Washington, D. C., March 21, 1967.

Bavelas, A. Leadership: Man and function. *Administrative Science Quarterly,* March 1960.

Bidwell, C. E. The young professional in the Army: A study of occupational identity. *American Sociological Review,* 1961, 26, 360–372.

Borgatta, E. F. Attitudinal concomitants to military statuses. *Social Forces,* 1955, 33, 342–347.

Bourne, P. G. Some observations on the psychosocial phenomena seen in basic training. *Psychiatry,* 1967, 30, 187–196.

Brill, N. W., & Gilbert, W. B. Some applications of a follow-up study to psychiatric standards for mobilization. *American Journal of Psychiatry,* 1952, 109, 401–410.

Campbell, D. J., & McCormack, T. H. Military experience and attitude toward authority. *American Journal of Sociology,* 1957, 62, 482–490.

Carter, J. H. Military leadership. *Military Review,* 1952, 32, 14–18.

Committee on Classification of Personnel in the Army. *The personnel system of the United States Army.* Vol. 1. *History of the personnel system.* Washington, D. C.: Author, 1919.

Coates, C. H., & Pellegrin, R. J. *Military sociology.* University Park, Md.: Social Science Press, 1965.

Datel, W. E. The caretaker group and its effect upon transient ineffectiveness. In *Current trends in psychology in the Army Medical Service.* Washington, D. C.:

Headquarters, Office of the Surgeon General, Department of the Army, 1962.

Dickerson, W. J., & Arthur, R. J. Navy families in distress. *Military Medicine,* 1965, 130, 894–898.

Dornbush, S. M. The military academy as an assimilating institution. *Social Forces,* 1955, 33, 316–321.

Eiderman, A. D. *March to columny.* New York: Macmillan, 1963.

Erickson, K., & Marlowe, D. H. The schizophrenic in the basic training process. In K. L. Artiss (ed.), *The symptom as communication in schizophrenia.* New York: Grune & Stratton, 1959.

Fagen, S. A., Janda, E. J., Baker, S. L., Fischer, E. G., & Cove, L. A. Impact of father absence in military families: II. Factors relating to success of coping with crisis. Presented at the annual meeting of the American Psychological Association, Washington, D. C., September 1967.

Feld, M. D. Information, authority and military organization. *American Sociological Review,* 1959, 24, 15–22.

Fiedler, F. E. Non-fraternization between leaders and followers and its effects on group productivity and psychological adjustment. In *Symposium on preventive and social psychology.* Washington, D. C.: Walter Reed Army Institute of Research, 1957.

Fiedler, F. E. The influence of leader-keyman relations on combat crew effectiveness. *Journal of Abnormal and Social Psychology,* 1955, 51, 227–235.

Fiedler, F. E. *A theory of leadership effectiveness.* New York: McGraw-Hill, 1967.

Firestone, R. W. Social conformity and authoritarianism in the Marine Corps. *Dissertation Abstracts,* 1959.

French, E. G., & Ernest, R. R. The relationship between authoritarianism and acceptance of military ideology. *Journal of Personality,* 1955, 24, 181–191.

Fry, C. C. A study of the rejection causes, successes, and subsequent performance of special groups. *Military Medicine Notes* (Army Medical Service Graduate School), 1951, 1, Sec. B.

Gibb, C. A. Leadership. In C. Lindzey (ed.), *Handbook of social psychology.* Cambridge, Mass.: Addison-Wesley, 1954.

Ginzberg, E., et al. *The ineffective soldier.* New York: Columbia University Press, 1959. 3 vols.

Glass, A. J. An attempt to predict probable combat effectiveness by brief psychiatric examination. *American Journal of Psychiatry,* 1949, 106, 81–90.

Glass, A. J. Combat exhaustion in U. S. Army. Far East Command medical section. In *Symposium on military medicine in the Far East Command,* 1951.

Glass, A. J. Combat psychiatry. In *Transactions at symposium on military medicine.* Waltham, Mass.: Murphy Army Hospital, 1952.

Glass, A. J. The problem of stress in the combat zone. In *Symposium on stress.* Washington, D. C.: Walter Reed Army Institute of Research, 1953.

Goffman, E. Characteristics of total institutions. In *Symposium on preventive and social psychiatry.* (Walter Reed Army Institute of Research) Washington, D. C.: United States Government Printing Office, 1957.

Greenberg, H. R. Depressive equivalents in the pre-retirement years: The old sergeant syndrome. *Military Medicine*, 1965, 130, 251–255.

Halpin, A. W. The leadership behavior and combat performance of airplane commanders. *Journal of Abnormal and Social Psychology*, 1954, 49, 19–22.

Hansen, D. A., & Hill, R. Families under stress. In H. T. Christensen (ed.), *Handbook of marriage and the family.* Chicago: Rand McNally, 1964.

Hardison, J. L. A psychological center in the U. S. Army. In *Current trends in Army Medical Service psychology.* Washington, D. C.: Walter Reed Army Institute of Research, 1966.

Hare, A. P. *Handbook of small group research.* New York: Free Press, 1962.

Hedlund, J. L. Traditional roles of Army Medical Service psychologists. In *Current trends in Army Medical Service psychology.* Washington, D. C.: Walter Reed Army Institute of Research, 1966.

Hill, R: *families under stress.* New York: Harper, 1949.

Hilmar, N. A. The transition from civilian to military life. In C. H. Coates & R. J. Pellegrin (eds.), *Military sociology.* University Park, Md.: Social Science Press, 1965.

Hollander, E. P. Authoritarianism and leadership choice in a military setting. *Journal of Abnormal and Social Psychology*, 1954, 49, 365–370.

Hollingshead, A. B. Adjustment to military life. *American Journal of Sociology*, 1946, 51, 439–450.

Hovland, C. The order of presentation in persuasion. In *Yale studies in attitude and communication.* New Haven, Conn.: Yale University Press, 1957.

Janis, I. L. Psychodynamic aspects of adjustment to army life. *Psychiatry*, 1945, 8, 159–176.

Janowitz, M. Changing patterns of organizational authority: The military establishment. *Administrative Science Quarterly*, 1959, 3, 473–793.

Janowitz, M. *The professional soldier.* Glencoe, Ill.: Free Press, 1960.

Jenkins, W. O. A review of leadership studies with particular reference to military problems. *Psychological Bulletin*, 1947, 44, 54–79.

Karcher, E. K., Jr. Role ambiguity as a factor in organizational effectiveness. In R. V. Bowers (ed.), *Studies in organizational effectiveness.* Washington, D. C.: Air Force Office of Scientific Research, 1962.

Klein, E. Acute psychiatric war casualties. *Journal of Nervous and Mental Disease*, 1948, 107, 25–42.

Leadership in the service. West Point, N. Y.: Department of Tactics, Office of Military Psychology and Leadership, United States Military Academy, 1959.

Lewis, R. Officer-enlisted men's relationships. *American Journal of Sociology*, 1947, 52, 410–419.

Lidz, T. Chronic situations evoking psychological stress and the common signs of resulting strain. In *Symposium on stress.* Washington, D. C.: Walter Reed Army Institute of Research, 1953.

Lindquist, R. *Marriage and family life of officers and airmen in a strategic air command wing.* (Technical Report No. 5) Chapel Hill, N. C.: Air Force Base Project, Institute for Research in Social Science, University of North Carolina, 1952.

Little, R. W. A study of the relationship between collective solidarity and combat role performance. Unpublished doctoral dissertation, Michigan State University, 1955.

Ludwig, A. O. Malingering in combat soldiers. *Bulletin of the U. S. Army Medical Department*, 1949, 9, 26–32.

Ludwig, A. O., & Ranson, S. W. A statistical follow-up of effectiveness of treatment of combat-induced psychiatric casualties; returns to full combat duty. *Military Surgeon*, 1947, 100, 51–62.

Lyon, W. B., & Oldaker, L. L. The child, the school and the military family. Paper presented at the 44th annual meeting of the American Orthopsychiatric Association, Washington, D. C., March 21, 1967.

Maillet, E. *A study of the readiness of troop commanders to use the services of the Army Mental Hygiene Consultation Service.* Ann Arbor, Mich.: University Microfilms, Inc., 1960.

Maillet, E. The readiness of commanders to use the services of the MHCS. Paper presented at the Current Trends in Army Psychology course, Walter Reed Army Institute of Research, Washington, D. C., 1966.

Mandelbaum, D. C. *Soldier groups and Negro soldiers.* Berkeley, Calif.: University of California Press, 1952.

Marlowe, D. H. The basic training process. In K. L. Artiss (ed.), *The symptom as communication in schizophrenia.* New York: Grune & Stratton, 1959.

Maskin, M. M., & Altman, I. L. Military psychodynamics: Psychological factors in the transition from civilian to soldier. *Psychiatry*, 1943, 6, 263–269.

McNeil, J. S., & Griffen, M. B. The social impact of military retirement. *Social Casework*, 1965, 46, 203–207.

Merton, R. K., & Kitt, A. D. Contributions to the theory of reference group behavior. In R. K. Merton & P. F. Lazarsfeld (eds.), *Continuities in social research: Studies in the scope and method of "the American soldier."* Glencoe, Ill.: Free Press, 1950.

Merton, R. K., & Lazarsfeld, P. F. (eds.) *Continuities in social research: Studies in the scope and method of "the American soldier."* Glencoe, Ill.: Free Press, 1950.

Milowe, I. D. A study in role diffusion. The chief and the sergeant face retirement. *Mental Hygiene*, 1964, 48, 101–107.

Monahan, F. *A study of nonprofessional personnel in social work—The army social work specialist.* Washington, D. C.: Catholic University of America Press, 1960.

Nichols, R. S. Psychological services in the army. In *Current trends in Army Medical Service psychology.* Washington, D. C.: Walter Reed Army Institute of Research, 1966.

Office of the Surgeon General. Neuropsychiatry. In *The Medical Department of the United States Army in the World War.* Vol. 10. Washington, D. C.: United States Government Printing Office, 1929.

Office of the Surgeon General. Neuropsychiatry in World War II. In *Medical Department of the United States Army in World War II.* Vol. 1. Washington, D. C.: United States Government Printing Office, 1966.

Pedersen, F. A., & Sullivan, E. J. Relationships among geographical mobility, parental attitudes and emotional disturbance in children. *American Journal of Orthopsychiatry*, 1964, 34, 575–580.

Perkins, M. E. The concept of community psychiatry. Paper presented at the biennial course on social and preventive psychiatry, Walter Reed Army Institute of Research, Washington, D. C., 1964.

Perry, C. J. A pyshciatric "back-up" system for selection of space crews. *American Journal of Psychiatry*, 1967, 123, 821–828.

Ranson, S. W. The normal battle reaction: Its relation to the pathologic battle reaction. *Bulletin of the U. S. Army Medical Department*, 1949, 9, Supple. 3–11.

Redlich, F. C., & Freedman, D. X. *The theory and practice of psychiatry.* New York: Basic Books, 1966.

Reynolds, D. Army mental hygiene consultation—A role for psychologists. Paper presented at the annual meeting of the American Psychological Association, Washington, D. C., September 1967.

Rioch, D. McK. Psychiatry as a biological science. *Psychiatry*, 1955, 18, 313,

Robbins, D. B. Innovations in military correction. *American Journal of Psychiatry*, 1967, 123, 828–835.

Rose, A. The social structure of the army. *American Journal of Sociology*, 1946, 51, 361–364.

Ruch, F. L., & Reveal, R., Jr. *Incidents of leadership in combat.* Colorado Springs, Colo.: Department of Behavioral Sciences, United States Air Force Academy, 1962.

Ryan, F. J., & Bevilacqua, J. J. The military family: An asset or a liability. *Military Medicine*, 1964, 129, 956–959.

Sanford, F. H. *Authoritarianism and leadership.* Philadelphia: Institute for Research in Human Relations, 1950.

Sanford, F. H. Research on military leadership. In *Current trends, psychology and the world emergency.* Pittsburgh: University of Pittsburgh, 1952.

Seidenfeld, M. A. Clinical psychology. In *Neuropsychiatry in World War II.* Vol 1. Washington, D. C.: Office of the Surgeon General, Department of the Army, 1966.

Shulman, B., & Myers, N. Reaction of troop commanders to a mental hygiene consultation service. *U. S. Armed Forces Medical Journal*, November 1954, 1657-1662.

Silber, E. Adjustment to army life: The soldier's identification with the group. *U. S. Armed Forces Medical Journal*, 1954, 5, 1340–1348.

Sousa, J. Command and staff viewpoints about mental hygiene consultation service in a European Armored Division. Unpublished report, November 1963.

Spencer, C. D., & Gray, B. An approach to mental health consultation within the military. *Military Medicine*, 1965, 130, 691.

Spiegel, J. P. Psychological transactions in situations of acute stress. In *Symposium on stress.* Washington, D. C.: Walter Reed Army Institute of Research, 1953.

Spindler, G. D. American character as revealed by the military. *Psychiatry*, 1948, 11, 275–281.

Stouffer, S. A., et al. *The American soldier.* Vol. 1. *Adjustment during army life.* Princeton, N. J.: Princeton University Press, 1949.

Stouffer, S. A., et al. *The American Soldier.* Vol. 2. *Combat and its aftermath.* Princeton, N. J.: Princeton University Press, 1949.

Tiffany, W. J., & Allerton, W. S. Army psychiatry in the mid-60's. *American Journal of Psychiatry*, 1967, 123, 810–819.

Tucker, M. D., & Gorman, E. R. The significance of the suicide gesture in the military. *American Journal of Psychiatry*, 1967, 123, 854–861.

Turner, R. Dithering devices in the classroom: How to succeed in shaking up a campus without really trying. *American Psychologist*, 1966, 21, 957-963.

Uyeki, E. Draftee behavior in the cold war army. *Social Problems*, 1960, 8, 151–158.

Waldrop, G. A. Let's stop subsidizing non-rated men who marry. *U. S. Naval Institute Proceedings*, 1962, 88, 11.

Weinstein, E. A., & Drayer, C. S. A dynamic approach to the problems of combat-induced anxiety. *Bulletin of the U. S. Army Medical Department*, 1949, 9, Supple. 12–26.

Weinstein, E. A. The function of interpersonal relations in the neurosis of combat. *Psychiatry*, 1947, 10, 307–314.

Williams, S. D., & Leavitt, H. J. Group opinion as a predictor of military leadership. *Journal of Consulting Psychology*, 1947, 11, 283–291.

Zehrer, F, A. Clinical psychology in the United States Army. In B. D. Rubenstein & M. Lorr (eds.), *Survey of clinical practice in psychology.* New York: International Universities Press, 1954.

9

Cultural Adaptation and Ecological Analogies: Analysis of Three Mexican Villages

Roger C. Mills and James G. Kelly

This chapter presents ecological concepts for the design of therapeutic interventions. Case studies of community development outside the United States are presented to highlight individual and group adaptations in varied settings. It is the premise of this chapter that knowledge of community psychology should be derived from the study of the development of communities. The relevance of community development projects in areas of the world undergoing rapid change to developed countries such as the United States is not always apparent. Although recent sociological and anthropological work has implied such relevance, the authors of this chapter feel that it is imperative that conceptions of community development be based upon case examples from divergent cultures to design interventions that have the widest application (see Geertz, 1966; Goldschmidt, 1966; Levy, 1952; Parsons, 1967; Steward, Introduction to Vol. 1, 1967).

Much energy and many interdisciplinary resources have been allocated to community development in countries caught up in what many authors refer to as a "modernization" process. It is a rare event to see the subject of social change in the United States as a legitimate topic for interdisciplinary studies. The use of the term "modernization" when applied to such developing countries points out the bias inherent in such work, that a "modernized" country will have political systems like the United States, and economic and social systems that at least are very similar. The only expected alternative for such a country is to emerge as a "communist" country, a condition which United States foreign aid funds have been designed to avoid.

ECOLOGY: A PERSPECTIVE FOR CASE STUDIES OF COMMUNITY DEVELOPMENT

The above point of view has been criticized by scholars of developing nations. These criticisms however are often replaced by approaches which overemphasize the uniqueness and unrelatedness of other cultures to the West. Ecology, on the other hand, provides an analytic context in which to deal with what Cohen has described as the most basic demographic or reproducing unit in any particular setting, the "adaptive" unit (Cohen, 1968). For the analysis of most human ecosystems this unit can be defined as the social group. In the United States the social group most often referred to is the nuclear family; in other settings it may be a larger kinship unit or an age-graded society. An ecological perspective offers an analysis of the interrelationships of these units with one another and with the larger environment. These interrelationships, in fact, constitute the essence of the term "ecosystem" as used in natural ecology: "The significance of the term ecosystem affirms that a community of plants and animals depends on the specific and local events that surround the organism, and that the organism's response to this environment continually redefines the properties of the ecosystem" (Smith, 1966).

Thus, the ecological perspective provides an approach to dealing with social systems that focuses on interrelationships among the members of significant social groups, and provides long-term predictions for the effects of social change on a particular system by noting the manner in which these relationships change in the light of functions introduced as a result of interventions or alterations in environmental parameters. Cohen, in focusing on the long-range determinants of cultural change, writes that:

While anthropologists are still some way from understanding the reasons for [differing] lags and accelerations in the rate of cultural change, the axiom that every technology is also a particular kind of social system . . . can serve as a starting point. Cultural evolution involves not only changes in sources of energy but also alterations in social institutions, and the evolutionary record suggests that more time is required to effect the latter than the former. The transition from one level of adaptation to another requires the harnessing of new energy sources *plus* changes in settlement patterns, household and family organization, political institutions, religion, education and the like (Cohen, 1968, pp. 59–60).

In turn, the ecological approach asserts that those changes which are "acceptable" responses in a particular setting will be determined by the interrelationships among modes of adaptation of social groups already legitimized in the culture of that particular setting. An "ecological perspective" provides a dynamic frame of reference which analyzes changes in terms of the particular setting in which they occur, and generates dimensions along which change can be evaluated for cross-cultural comparisons. An ecological perspective looks at the local setting in terms of dimensions that are related to the organic functions of the environment. Dimensions such as interdependence, resource cycling, adaptation, and succession are concepts for evaluating the entire social system in terms of linkages between the larger environment and the local setting.

The Case Studies: Illustrations of Contrasting Responses to Development

The ecological perspective advocated by the authors of this chapter will be presented via case studies. Three case studies drawn from rural and village development projects in three distinct regions of Mexico are used to provide specific illustrations of development and how it affects styles of sustenance, social adaptation, and political functioning of contrasting communities.

The case studies illustrate the complex set of interlocking factors influencing the direction, magnitude, and styles of adaptation involved in community development. They also illustrate differences in methods of intervention and relationships of development programs to host communities. These differing styles in turn result in differing reactions to change which are comparable across communities. In two case studies presented by Erasmus of the Yaqui tribal region and the rural Mayo Indians, the development has been sponsored primarily by the national government (Erasmus, 1967a). Secondary resources and interventions were generated from agencies from other countries (mainly the United States) and provided additional development projects. Both governments have presumably been motivated by the same types of goals which involve rapid economic development and industrialization as attempts to strengthen their countrys' positions among the nations of the world. Mexico is now experiencing rapid population growth and is attempting to move away from an agrarian society. The urbanization rate is high, yet a significant proportion of the population still lives in the countryside and most persons are dependent on some form of agriculture for their means of livelihood. A self-styled "revolutionary" government has been the dominant power since the last major change in political regimes and each successive government has rationalized its continued rule in terms of being the protector of revolutionary goals such as economic development or social equality. While Mexico has had experience with colonial powers, the government party has not won its position of leadership by fighting and defeating a foreign army. It claims, however, to have delivered the country from the hands of reactionary or feudal elements.

The problem that is brought out among the three rural development cases is the varying success the government has had in intervening and spurring development and change among the majority of peasant communities which have been less affected by "modernization" than Mexico's urban population. Despite a long history of development efforts and higher levels of living than most developing nations, Mexico, until recently, made less progress in relative terms than many in inducing changes in the rural sector. Lately this situation seems to be changing and the potential for making much progress toward such policy goals with respect to the Indian subpopulation in the near future has increased, due largely to the combination of the indigenous people's efforts and the provision of rural social structure within the local community.

Premises

The authors have reviewed the extensive literature on community development. One finding from the review of the literature is that many workers have attempted to treat communities in isolation. It is often the case that the major constraints on a community's development are its relationships to the larger environment, such as the number of relationships between the social groupings within the community and those larger social organizations of which the local community is a subsystem. In selecting case studies for the present chapter, very few reports were identified in the literature which present a context for evaluating a particular community and its relationship to a larger ecological system. The implication of this idea is that it is equally incomplete to discuss or plan for the inner cities of America's large metropolitan regions without talking about the suburbs, and federal policies, or national corporate structures, etc. Consequently, the boundaries of this chapter are sufficiently wide so as to include examples of patterns of cultural adaptations. In addition to issues of interdependence between the individual community and the larger environment, a compelling reason for providing background material describing national/ local issues is that development workers often enter communities to initiate a change program that may be secondarily important to the concerns of the local community. They thereby disregard those effects operative at the local level, because their reference group is other than the local community.

The present authors have attempted to deal with these issues by documenting the appraisals of others in sufficient detail so as to represent the natural complexities of the ecological system. The authors believe that a presentation of these three case studies has relevance for deriving community development principles and guidelines for intervention in varied social settings. In presenting each of the cases, we have referred to anthropological studies that describe local reactions to change efforts, and have presented a summary of reactions at the national level.

The premise of the authors is that presentation of these individual cases of the development process provides a starting point to build a theory of community development that is rigorous, interdisciplinary, and cogent for varied communities.

The presentation of case materials in this chapter is intended to accomplish several goals: (1) To illustrate the value of ecological concepts in describing important change processes and life patterns in a social setting; (2) to present examples of how these same ecological concepts are useful in the design of change programs for these settings; and (3) in carrying out the above two goals, to provide examples of the types of data that are essential for the development of knowledge for a psychology of the community.

There are few examples for viewing communities and community development as an ecological enterprise. The authors in fact made an exhaustive search of the vast literature on economic, social, and community development and found only a sparse number of writers who see the community as an ecological process. One of the authors has worked abroad in a development planning context and has written up that experience as an example of community processes related to urban planning (see Mills, 1968). Those few workers who have done field work on culture change as an ecological task have done some of their work in Mexico. Writings about culture change in Mexico provide, then, a unique concentration of ecological perspective. Consequently, the authors of this chapter have relied heavily on the observations and studies of Charles Erasmus (1961) (1967a) 1967b) (1968), George Foster (1967), supplemented by comments by Scott (1964), Vernon (1964) (1965), and others.

The analysis of culture change secondhand, via the reports of others, is not a preferred mode of work. It was elected as a way of illustrating how an ecological analysis of culture change can suggest new relationships to study, new criteria to observe, and new topics to ponder. The desired end result of this chapter is to suggest a point of view for the development of communities, and to stimulate the reader to take these ideas and work with them in planning the development of his own community. It is hoped that by talking about the pitfalls of change in rural Mexico, we can see opportunities for doing the job better in local communities in the United States. The fact that the authors of this chapter have not carried out the field work in Mexico themselves means that direct appraisal of the culture and its changing styles of adaptation is lacking. In order to partially compensate for this inadequacy, the authors have been in personal communication with Charles Erasmus and George Foster whose exhaustive field work in Mexico provided the bulk of the empirical material on the local communities that are contrasted below. It is essential to affirm that only the present authors are accountable for the interpretation of the work of Erasmus and Foster and the implications drawn for designing change programs. In addition, it should be kept in mind that the material utilized for this chapter is material that was collected approximately ten years ago. Much has changed in rural Mexico since that time; primarily, the rural sector has become much more dynamic and more integrated into the commercial economy.

THE BASIS FOR AN
ECOLOGICAL APPROACH

The Need for a New Approach
to Development

In developed countries such as the United States, there has been little interest in formulating interdisciplinary approaches for such topics as analysis of economic growth, political "modernization," or economic and social development. At the same time there has been almost universal frustration among development workers who have worked with and studied "development" outside the United States, who have come up against the inadequacies of univariate approaches, or who have worried about the general ineffectiveness of

their work (see Arensburg & Niehoff, 1964; Bohannan, 1964; Furnivall, 1948; Hagen, 1964; Myrdal, 1968). Although such examples are plentiful in the developmental literature, there have been few attempts to go beyond disciplinary boundaries and to create a cross-cultural analysis of these failures. A second problem is the attempts made by Western specialists in public administration to "reform" often corrupt and confusing bureaucracies of developing nations, and to "rationalize" them according to Western bureaucratic models. Complicating the problem are the unique value sets, interpersonal styles, and coping mechanisms within a culture that may be adaptive within an environment that is not Western or rational and which requires unique styles of organizational structure and functioning (LaPalombara, 1963; Riggs, 1964).

Recent studies of anthropologists of primitive societies at the community level have noted unanticipated reactions to changes induced by outside "change agents." As a result, they have made requests for an interdisciplinary view of the development process in emerging nations (Erasmus, 1961; Goldschmidt, 1966; Nair, 1961; Steward, 1967). There has also been a demand from scholars such as Gunnar Myrdal to look more closely at the change agent/client relationship and to analyze it more objectively from both sides, whether it is a political scientist attempting to reform the national bureaucracy or a community development worker entering a rural village to heighten "community action" for economic development (see Erasmus, 1961, pp. 3–17; Foster, 1967, pp. 348 ff; Myrdal, 1968, Vol. I, Prologue).

Yet in the face of such criticism the majority of development economists and planners tend to exclude other social scientists from any role in constructing development objectives. What synthesis that has been presented consists largely of piecemeal graftings of two or three approaches, with no overall cohesive theoretical framework. Still fewer approaches are relevant for planners and international agencies working in an ongoing environment.

The purpose of this chapter is to review the development process in the light of various approaches, particularly in terms of the development worker/client relationship and the relationships of particular social systems to each other.

The authors' approach to the change process links economic, political, and social variables of the environment in a context for designing interventions to facilitate individual and societal adaptations. Since the planner or community development worker is often less interested in individual differences than in group reactions to development plans, the focus of this chapter is to identify the significant social groups within a natural setting and their relationships with one another.

Review of Traditional Approaches to Development

Prior to presenting the case for an ecological perspective for the development process, a brief review of contributions of other approaches will be presented. A selection of the major premises of these various approaches follows.

The Sociocultural Approach

The assumption here is that neither economic development nor political "sophistication" is achieved unless new instrumental values are internalized and predispositions to action are included in the "subjective culture" of a population.[1] For example, to facilitate economic growth the value system should include goals which can be promoted by increased production and/or increased consumption along with the felt need to learn the technical skills necessary for industrial development (see Hoselitz, 1960; Triandis, 1968a, 1968b).

Goals. Given this perspective, evaluations for specific interventions may conclude that the goals of previous development workers have been too limited in nature and scope and are usually exploitive, for example, bringing the host community under stricter political or economic control in order to achieve either a more viable power base or a more profitable exploitation of the local environment. This vision of the typical development worker is of someone limited by his own cultural goals and perceptions. The result is that his methods of inducing change are either singularly unsuccessful or create a crisis. The goals of development workers, if not explicitly exploitive, are seen as erroneous, in that they perceive interventions as attempts to lead backward people out of the dark ages. Advocates of a sociocultural approach tend to denigrate other approaches as too concerned with merely creating a higher economic status. At the same time the host population is pictured as perceiving the primary goals of the intervention going to the development team. The attitudes are typified, for example, by the differences between the way that Africans and missionaries view demands for higher pay and greater welfare benefits for those natives in the service of missionary groups. The Africans perceive the missionaries living in relative affluence, while the missionaries perceive their own role as one of self-abnegation and sacrifice leading to the "salvation" of the pagan native who desires only more material goods (see Bohannon, 1964 and Steward, 1967, Vol. I, p. 166 ff). Goals of sociocultural development agents on the other hand involve appreciating the local culture, its value systems and social norms, and then working directly on changing cultural norms, values, and status symbols in the community to bring them more in line with the requirements of "modernization." Thus many researchers have described the movement of tribal Africans, for example, into urban areas or the commercial economy as "detribalization."

Methods of Change. The methodology usually asserts that development workers become more sensitive and responsive to the desires of local people and the protective mechanisms within a culture which provide a particular orientation toward the world, a way of dealing with it that rationalizes their historical experience and legitimizes their traditional role in the larger system. This approach assumes that the interrelationships among relevant policy variables emanate from the goal of recognizing and changing local norms, values, and aspirations.

The process used to accomplish the necessary interactions is most often seen as involving (1) mass media exposure; (2) high status people in the community acting as early innovators; (3) identification of the masses with early innovators; (4) long-term educational efforts; (5) positive reaction of elites to "felt needs" of local communities whereby (6) communities will begin to organize for change. A demonstration effect is assumed to relate to the status of the early innovator in the community as well as the availability of other "models" of modernization such as those found in urban areas or pilot project communities. As changes are adopted incrementally by the host population, values, aspirations, social norms, and eventually the relevant social institutions will change over time. It may take one or two generations for the process of social change to become self-sustaining, but this will occur as the younger generations are exposed to modernizing sectors of the socioeconomic structure.

Explanations for Failures. Researchers have recorded failures in interventions where development workers err in operating under the assumption that their own perceptions of the advantages of change will be immediately appreciated by the host community. In some cases this results in large capital outlays for the creation of infrastructures (schools, an irrigation network, power stations, roads, development banks) that are not utilized (Ingersoll, 1968). Other unanticipated consequences have been a stronger identification by the host population with traditional norms and institutions (Steward, 1967, Vol. III, pp. 20 ff) and a retreat from the more modernized sector. A reaction reported in case studies of communities near large urban areas has entailed a breakdown of the social order and the failure of new norms and institutions to replace the old. In many cases where there is resistance to change on the part of the community, it was found that the development workers' perceptions of the role of the host population in the larger socioeconomic condition was distorted to the extent that those people who did not adopt the proposed changes were actually better off economically with respect to group acceptance than those members of the host community that accepted the change methods for one reason or another (Gallin, 1966; Steward, 1967, Vol. III, p. 53).

Other unanticipated reactions include increased incidence of lawbreaking in culturally heterogeneous areas and in regions where pressure for change is strong (Ingersoll, 1968). In some cases those groups that do conform to new norms and methods tend to be the least innovative, becoming excessively dependent upon the development agents or institutions introduced by them (Steward, 1967, Vol. III, p. 85).

The Economic Approach

In contrast to the above set of assumptions regarding the change process, developmental economists stress the economic "level" of development achieved at any one point in time. Sociocultural indicators are seen as dependent variables and employed as measures of "modernity" in a univariate sense. The existence of a certain category of values (e.g., those associated with a "feudal" type of economy) are taken as an indication of which type of economic interventions need be applied (Vernon, 1965).

Goals. The primary goals of the development worker are usually a rising Gross National Product and a rising per capita income for the local population. This is seen as necessarily accompanied by a rising middle class orientation and the evolution of a market economy. Social goals often include income redistributive mechanisms and such welfare policies as public housing, as well as agricultural credit, market and production incentives, and business advisory groups (Meier, 1965).

The primary assumptions regarding the change process are that definite causal relations exist between economic factors so that they can be manipulated in sequences with the result that development can be initiated and achieve a state of forward momentum. The economic factors are derived primarily from macroeconomic and price system theories which have been found applicable to Western capitalist economies and have been constructed from the workings of these economies. It is largely assumed that these parameters are valid cross-culturally and that their application in a specific setting depends more on the missing links and level of development than on sociocultural features of the indigenous group. The premises of the researcher are that the unsuccessful development worker is one who has not utilized the correct economic tools. Thus, he is primarily concerned with evaluating the tools used by the change agent; with the wisdom of hindsight, he picks out those that were neglected, or unavailable, which were crucial to project success. The economic planner is presented as a key figure in the change process, who must not only have a grasp of the subtle interactions of economic factors but must be in a position to prevent outside powers from exploiting a region's economic resources and leaving the area in question depleted or unprepared to accomplish an indigenous economic "take-off."

Methods of Change. The necessary economic resources to sustain forward momentum in the transitional stage are capital availability, physical infrastructure, market accessibility, adequate de-

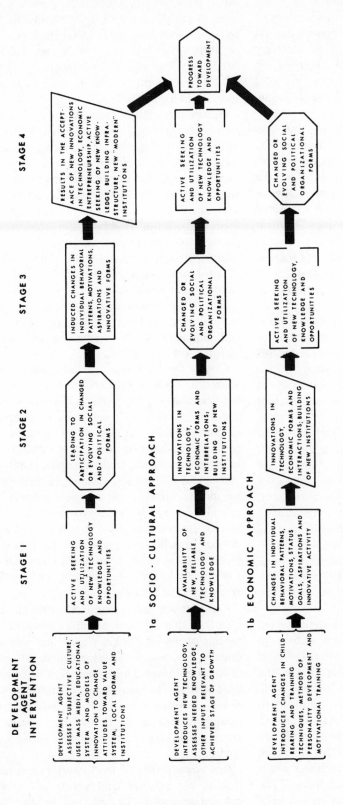

DEVELOPMENT AGENT INTERVENTION   **STAGE 1**   **STAGE 2**   **STAGE 3**   **STAGE 4**

1a SOCIO-CULTURAL APPROACH

DEVELOPMENT AGENT ASSESSES "SUBJECTIVE CULTURE," USES MASS MEDIA, EDUCATIONAL SYSTEM AND MODELS OF INNOVATION TO CHANGE ATTITUDES TOWARD VALUE SYSTEM, LOCAL NORMS AND INSTITUTIONS

ACTIVE SEEKING AND UTILIZATION OF NEW TECHNOLOGY KNOWLEDGE AND OPPORTUNITIES

LEADING TO PARTICIPATION IN CHANGED OR EVOLVING SOCIAL AND POLITICAL FORMS

INDUCED CHANGES IN INDIVIDUAL BEHAVIORAL PATTERNS, MOTIVATIONS, ASPIRATIONS AND INNOVATIVE FORMS

RESULTS IN THE ACCEPTANCE OF NEW INNOVATIONS IN TECHNOLOGY, ECONOMIC ENTREPRENEURSHIP, ACTIVE SEEKING OF NEW KNOWLEDGE, BUILDING INFRASTRUCTURE, NEW "MODERN" INSTITUTIONS

1b ECONOMIC APPROACH

DEVELOPMENT AGENT INTRODUCES NEW TECHNOLOGY, ASSESSES NEEDED KNOWLEDGE, OTHER INPUTS RELEVANT TO ACHIEVED STAGE OF GROWTH

AVAILABILITY OF NEW, RELIABLE TECHNOLOGY AND KNOWLEDGE

INNOVATIONS IN TECHNOLOGY, ECONOMIC FORMS AND INTERRELATIONS; BUILDING OF NEW INSTITUTIONS

CHANGED OR EVOLVING SOCIAL AND POLITICAL ORGANIZATIONAL FORMS

ACTIVE SEEKING AND UTILIZATION OF NEW TECHNOLOGY KNOWLEDGE AND OPPORTUNITIES

1c PSYCHO-GENERATIONAL APPROACH

DEVELOPMENT AGENT INTRODUCES CHANGES IN CHILD-REARING AND TRAINING TECHNIQUES, METHODS OF PERSONALITY DEVELOPMENT AND MOTIVATIONAL TRAINING

CHANGES IN INDIVIDUAL BEHAVIORAL PATTERNS, MOTIVATIONS, STATUS GOALS, ASPIRATIONS AND INNOVATIVE ACTIVITY

INNOVATIONS IN TECHNOLOGY, ECONOMIC FORMS AND INTERACTIONS; BUILDING OF NEW INSTITUTIONS

ACTIVE SEEKING AND UTILIZATION OF NEW TECHNOLOGY, KNOWLEDGE AND OPPORTUNITIES

CHANGED OR EVOLVING SOCIAL AND POLITICAL ORGANIZATIONAL FORMS

PROGRESS TOWARD DEVELOPMENT

FOR A RAPID COMPARISON OF THE CAUSAL MECHANISMS IMPLIED IN VARIOUS APPROACHES NOTE DIFFERENT LOCATIONS OF VARIOUS BOX TYPES REPRESENTING SIMILAR STAGES IN PROCESS OF CHANGE

Fig. 9-1. Traditional approaches to development.

mand, raw materials, sound government fiscal and monetary policy including taxation, import/export control, and credit regulation. Government control of outside investors and awareness of necessary forward and backward industrial programs are required so that the planner can steer the local entrepreneur into open areas of the economy (Hirschman, 1958; Vernon, 1964).

To accomplish this, a modernizing entrepreneurial class is needed, and, in addition, "technocrats" who have the technical expertise to guide public investment and policy in the economic sphere are highly valuable human resources. An adequately trained and motivated labor force is recognized as the most difficult "modernizing" group to create in a developing nation or region. This presumes adequate training facilities and the existence of adequate wage incentives to discontinue traditional forms of employment.

Evaluation of the development process is made on the basis of measurement of various types of growth rates and output statistics. Other indicators are the percent of population in "modern" sectors of the economy, and rough indicators such as amount of fertilizers used and other input/output statistics.

In many cases evaluation of project success at the local level is presented in terms of amount of participation in change programs, degree of orientation toward a market economy, amount of credit and capital utilized, rise in the standard of living, and intensity of use of new machinery, tools, and infrastructure made available by the change agent (Ingersoll, 1968). The main differences between this approach and the sociocultural approach regarding the causal mechanisms involved in development are presented in Figure 9–1, Sections a & b.

For the economic approach the development agent attempts to use economic incentives to motivate a population. At the same time, advocates of a sociocultural approach characterize the community as organized around noneconomic goals. The economist uses economic indicators to evaluate the success or failure of the intervention. Researchers of a sociocultural bent who are convinced of the inadequacy of this approach argue that "indeterminancy of the exchange rate is the characteristic fact of primitive exchange." The organizing principles of the economy are not to be

found in economizing (maximizing profit) because rates of exchange are set by noneconomic factors such as kinship distance, relative rank, relative wealth, and urgency of goods (see Halpern & Brode, 1967, p. 40). This perspective presupposes a different form of intervention strategy as outlined in Figure 9–1.

On the other hand, investigators advocating the economic approach have concluded that "the overwhelming majority of societies are achievement oriented, even where roles are heavily ascribed, and the maximization principle is at work in all of them . . . the entrepreneurial function is omnipresent and a condition of any form of social life" (Belshaw, 1965; Moore, 1968). Barriers to growth are seen as the result of technological limitations, factor immobility, lack of information about markets, credit and production or sales opportunities, and coercion by elite groups. The need for supplying the relevant technologies, marketing knowledge, credit sources, and economic incentives is seen as paramount, as pictured in Figure 9–1.

Given the assumptions of the economic approach, supplying the above inputs in a correct balance creates an "investment climate" within the community, which can induce local entrepreneurs to emerge to exploit opportunities and seek help from the relevant agencies. Government may be required to provide credit agencies, development banks, and training and research facilities in order to direct certain areas of the economy which provide the necessary infrastructure so that the private sector has the resources available to develop a self-sustaining stage. As this stage is reached, social and political institutions will evolve toward "modern" forms and entrepreneurial activity will be institutionalized.

Explanations of Failures. Unanticipated side effects of this approach are dislocations in various regions or among certain classes that may not be directly involved in developmental efforts. The disruptions noted range from local resistance to open warfare. In many cases it is difficult for the economic planner to predict which groups will create disruptions, as they are not always social groupings at the bottom of the socioeconomic ladder.

One consequence of most development schemes that is not planned—and yet is not very well guarded against—is the tendency for the "rich to get richer while the poor get poorer." People with greater wealth and status before development are usually in an advantageous position and take fuller advantage of project benefits in addition to already being more "innovative."

Especially when a Western model of development is used, the gap between the rich and the poor tends to widen rather than narrow during the growth process. This has proved true to the point that many investigators and planners feel that the uplifting of the lower classes occurs only after modernity is reached, or a certain plateau in the growth process is attained near complete modernization. Yet in many non-Western settings, traditional elite groups that gain through development become more and more rigid with regard to changes in project goals and methods of implementation (Vernon, 1964).

Marginal groups to the economic development process also tend to create obstacles to change. These are mainly groups that are situated in relatively economically autonomous regions, and those ethnic groups that have not played roles in the mainstream of the culture of the region. The first type of group is usually also politically autonomous and resists any type of incursions into its territory while demanding greater benefits from the growth process. Alien ethnic groups may have played key economic roles in the community prior to development and resist project implementation as threatening to their position and security. These tendencies are in many cases as much a result of the exclusive identification of the change agent with the dominant cultural and political systems, and the resulting marginal inclusion of these groups in the planning process (Steward, 1967, Vol. III, pp. 1–100).

In many development projects, planners encounter unanticipated problems of "overurbanization." This is partially a result of overemphasis on heavy industry and a neglect of the rural sector, and partially a result of the higher standards of living in urban areas. Cities tend to become congested with excess labor, creating a motley collection of socially dislocated, economically marginal groupings that are usually inadequately provided for by welfare measures and public services. Contrary to the expectations of economic planners, growth has slowed or stopped in many overpopulated urban areas because of stagnation in the rural sector. The result is an inability to provide food to the urban population and enough exports to maintain foreign exchange balances.

Even in those cases where the planner has attempted to modernize the rural sector, often farmers who had previously reacted positively to foreign market incentives, when subject to the exploitation of rural money lenders and middlemen, react more negatively when these are replaced by more "efficient" marketing cooperatives or government marketing agencies. In southeast Asia many rural groups refused to join cooperatives and stopped marketing their goods altogether (Gallin, 1966; Hagen, 1964).

The Psychogenerational Approach

This approach has attempted to explain deviant reactions to development by the host population from results relating to changes in the economic achievements of individuals or groups of individuals. Examples of this approach include the motivational ideas popularized by Hagen (1964) and McClelland (1961, 1969) and applied by other writers on development. Hagen has attempted to utilize traditional psychological concepts regarding child rearing and personality characteristics, applying them at the community level. While he provides some useful insights into attitudinal change as communities are confronted with a changing political and social environment, his presentation does not explain the processes by which new social organizations are formed or how the economy changes over time.

Goals. The primary assumptions of Hagen's theory are that when the society changes over time, specific groups in society lose their traditional standing in the social structure; consequently, specific occupations within the local population cease to function as essential roles for the larger system. Alienation and resentment toward the larger civilization are expected to develop in such groups of the community who then begin to adopt more authoritarian child rearing practices. This process continues over two or three generations to the point where particular members of the community become apathetic, then react by changing their personality characteristics to become "innovators" and entrepreneurs.

Methods of Change. The psychogenerational approach to development as proposed by Hagen does not include operational requirements for implementing change programs. Rather, it is a thesis about the selection of certain types of individuals into new positions of influence as a result of externally generated social changes. Brief comments are presented here about this point of view in order to illustrate the range of constructs used by development workers to view the goals and processes of community change. Hagen's explanations for the presence of specific individuals performing newly created social positions in a society relate largely to a view of changes in social position resulting as a consequence of shifts in the social order, making it possible for new "personalities" to appear.

A divergent example of a psychogenerational approach is the work of McClelland (1969). McClelland's theory of achievement and its correlation with economic development is perhaps the most well-known psychological explanation for economic development. No brief review of this theory could do justice to the extensive number of studies and critiques published on this work. McClelland in 1969 responded to much of the criticism of his earlier work and moved away from his initial presentation of intrinsic motivational factors as the primary determinants of entrepreneurial activity leading to economic growth (McClelland, 1969). The point of view of the sociocultural and economic perspectives mentioned in this chapter is now included in his revision which moves toward a more balanced view of social and economic change. The preliminary conclusions to be drawn from his work are that this achievement methodology, which induces motivational pressures, is related to economic development in communities but under very specific conditions. In a community where economic opportunities are emerging, where a sociocultural pattern is evolving to an urban condition, and where political constraints make upward mobility a possibility, McClelland's strategy for development can be very effective. In communities where these conditions are not present, this approach is equally nonapplicable. The causal mechanisms for change implied in the psychogenerational approach are shown in Figure 9–1c.

Explanations of Failure. Researchers working from these approaches would conclude that development projects based on the sociocultural or economic approaches failed because the agents of change did not adequately account for the individual motivational factors involved. Advocates of the McClelland approach see the need to design motivational training for change programs to help would-be entrepreneurs internalize achievement needs and achievement motivations in areas that relate to the goals of the change program. Hagen's view, on the other hand, would be interpreted as calling for the change agent to seek out as targets for development projects those subcultures where pervasive political and social forces over three to four generations have created an incipient entrepreneurial class motivated to take advantage of economic opportunities. In McClelland's program the need would be for economic training programs to be carried out as part of a change effort in the selected setting. For Hagen's thesis the choice of the target population is the critical factor. In both cases those change programs that ignore group or individual data about achievement motivation would have minimal success, e.g., changing the economic structure of the community.

In studies of actual entrepreneurial groups in developing countries, slight evidence has been found to substantiate these approaches. Mexico's entrepreneurial group studied by Vernon gives little support to Hagen's thesis (Vernon, 1964). In Pakistan, studies have shown that farming communities, which are relatively well-off, as well as the traditional Muslim elite, are reluctant to abandon entrenched positions regarding value orientations and social norms. Still they react positively to economic incentives to modernize agricultural and industrial spheres (Papenak, 1965). Geertz (1966) found in the outer islands of Indonesia that those social groups lending the most support to modernization of the economy were primarily traditional elites while the peasantry and lower class urbanites were reluctant to abandon outmoded attitudes and norms regarding the importance of traditional occupations.

The results to date indicate that such approaches are too narrow. While the work generated from the psychogenerational approach supplements the range of variables included within the sociocultural and economic approaches, the psychogenerational approach does not focus specifically on those processes in a local community that help to explain the context for change. The approach implicitly assumes either that the individual is without opportunities to change his social or economic status or that the efficacy of community development work can be achieved by training of individual motivation and competence without attending to the complex array of social structures in any community.

Conclusion

While the above review of existing approaches to development has been brief, it is hoped that sufficient background material has been presented in order to set the stage for an ecological perspective. What emerges thus far is that the term "development" and the set of concepts associated with it in each of the above approaches are inadequate to deal with the complexities of development. With the help of analogies from natural ecology, the authors will suggest guidelines for community development that are both developmental and can generate interventions that are valid for particular cultures.

Analogies from Natural Ecology

At the present time there is much debate over the term "development." Its exact meaning varies not only in terms of the goals of planners and "nation building" governments but also in terms of persons uplifted by the development process. Given the considerations mentioned above and the issues presented by the following case studies, the authors feel that the concept of development fits most meaningfully as an ecological construct. The definition of development, in this context, appears relevant to the avowed goals of most development workers: the process by which a system evolves from one level to a higher level so that more groups within the society are able to share in the growth process. Viewing development as an evolutionary process can be made more explicit by drawing analogies from biological ecology and by highlighting the important aspects of development requirements. Four of these principles have been cited in other papers by Kelly (1966, 1968) and by Trickett, Kelly, and Todd in a companion chapter in this Handbook (see chapter 14). In this presentation the authors are interested in explicating the relevance of such ideas for developmental problems.

The goal of this chapter is to combine the ecological and developmental perspectives and attempt to account for the outcomes of development. The following principles outline an approach for examining the links between physical settings and social and political subsystems.

Principle of Interdependence

As in biology, this principle affirms that attaining new resources will depend upon creating functional relationships among various groups in the society and between the structures and functions of societal institutions. The basic assumption is that in any system in equilibrium, a certain interdependence is maintained within the system and between the system and other systems.

Thus, members of any population depend either directly or indirectly upon one another for their well-being and existence, as well as upon the environment (see Smith, 1966, pp. 12–13). Goldschmidt (1966) has stated the case for the use of this perspective in studying human environments. He notes that: "While it is not quite accurate to say that a society is merely constructed of social groups . . . it is proper to say (1) that all societies involve a multiplicty of groups; (2) these groups are structured so as to interrelate, and (3) group structures and group interrelations are essential for the operation of all social systems" (p. 64).

There exists, moreover, a high degree of similarity in styles of functional interrelatedness between the workings of social institutions in any particular setting and those in other settings. Frequently there are environmental limitations on institutional possibilities, illustrating that there is often an advantage to certain solutions to problems of social organization under given situations and that "the forms which institutions take will not merely be the product of the needs of the individuals in society, but will be situationally relevant" (Goldschmidt, 1966, p. 84).

The requirement that institutions are ecologically or environmentally relevant points out the problem, noted by Riggs, that is involved in transplanting Western institutions, such as bureaucratic or financial agencies, into non-Western environments. While most development workers would agree that new interrelationships are needed for development, it must also be recognized that they should evolve from interrelationships that are already existing and legitimized in that setting, and with which the local population strongly identifies.[2]

Cycling of Resources

This principle, as used in the ecological context, refers to "resource-imbalance." In ecological studies, the reproducing group is regarded as the primary adaptive unit. In the study of cultural adaptation, the basic units are social groups, particularly those that fulfill similar roles or utilize similar resources in the economic and political systems (Cohen, 1968, p. 7). Growth and economic development then proceed in an optimal manner when these groups enter into symbiotic relationships with regard to resource cycling. "Unbalanced resource structures" refers to situations where groups have access to resources in an incongruous manner or where resources are not optimally allocated among groups relevant to the developmental process. An extreme example of this imbalance is a society in which traditional economic units that are almost self-sufficient persist. The result is that there is a lack of constraining economic interdependence between such units and the urban sectors. In such cases, the result is cohesion by coercion, rather than a central organization coordinating or fostering exchanges that are inside and outside traditional markets via incentives for traders and merchants.

Another unbalanced situation is the presence of a traditional elite closely allied with a national power structure that depends upon more traditional methods of resource cycling and is threatened by development pressures. Groups that are oriented toward modernization may not have the proper training. In addition, communication for training such resources may be lacking or controlled by small elite groups. Groups peripheral to economic activity in the developed countries may, in underdeveloped nations, have a major amount of resource control. In some societies, the army, for example, may be the most competent and modern organization with respect to technical training and literacy (Millikan & Blackner, 1961, p. 32). The army may also aid in balancing resources among different social groups as it tends to recruit from all sectors and socioeconomic classes. In other countries religious elites may have the same function, as they often control the largest amounts of communication for social control.

One of the axioms of community development workers is that prestructured methods for introducing new resources into a community do exist and that these methods are applicable for any place at any time. The ecological thesis in contrast argues that development groups operate within a natural setting and with unique organizational forms as well as unbalanced resource structures. How these organizations have evolved and how they interact provides a basis for defining resource cycling. In order to expand the resources available to a community, it is necessary to understand and work to correct resource imbalance and incongruity. It must be understood that sectors tend to develop as units rather than as nations, and as a result unbalanced growth between regions, cities, different sectors of the economy, and different social groups produce conflict and resistance between competing groups in the society (Horowitz, 1966, p. 337).

While many researchers assert that conflict and resistance to development is mitigated by intergroup contact, empirical studies show that often it is intensified rather than mitigated by increasing mobility and contact among groups from different areas or sectors of society in situations of resource imbalance (Erasmus, 1967a, pp. 123–129; Skinner, 1967). In addition, such reactions as "anomie" and other forms of maladaptiveness seem to emerge in the course of economic and social change with unbalanced resource cycling. These manifestations of the effects of development are also relevant for the next two principles.

Adaptation

As noted by Kelly (1968), empirical research on this principle suggests that an organism exhibiting a wide range of tolerance for all environmental influences will be widely distributed in multiple and contrasting settings (Ardrey, 1966; Smith, 1966). This phenomenon, known as *niche breadth*, is related to environmental uncertainty.[3] There is evidence that unchanging environments lead to specialization of members with the likelihood that for such species, adaptation to different settings will be more difficult (Levins, 1966, pp. 426–427). This perspective is close to that offered by Parsons (1967) and McClelland (1961) in contrasting traditional and modern societies.[4] They assert that in a modern society an individual is exposed to varying organizations and institutions and as a result: "great disparities of behavior are permitted for different roles and associational contexts, and individuals move freely from one context and role to another" (Riggs, 1964, p. 91).

This implies that an ability to adapt to the varying requirements of different groups is developed in most individuals in the "modern" society. In the traditional society, individual differences that are not relevant to the prevailing system of environmental exploitation will be suppressed. Thus, in an environmental setting that is static, certain individual potentialities are allowed expression, while others are not. Parsons, Riggs, and McClelland tend to equate "static" with "traditional" environments and "diverse" with "modern" environments. The assumption that individuals are more likely to be exposed to a variety of emerging groups in a transitional society where norms and expectations may be mutually exclusive and identified by members of each group as "total ways of life" is highlighted in the case studies of development presented in this chapter.[5] The authors of this chapter also assert that what the modern/traditional dichotomy does not bring out is that communities in transition also can be found in advanced societies.

Whether one is attempting to work with primitive cultures or more advanced groups, critical areas for inducing change are in the role structure of the community vis-à-vis desired developmental goals and the interactions of local institutions with the larger system. A primary method of inducing change in the direction of development is to provide the community with a greater variety of niches, or functional roles, while not directly threatening the status of those roles already legitimized in the community. New roles should be made compatible with the existing system in the sense that they are amenable to legitimization in the existing culture. These new roles should be meaningful to the population in such a way that they can interact with existing roles and institutions without causing excessive competition, and yet create linkages with institutions and roles in more "modernized" sectors. This discussion of methods of changing roles and legitimizing new roles in a society leads to consideration of the final principal, the succession principle.

Succession

Odum (1966) defines the biological concept of succession in terms of three parameters: "1) It is the orderly process of community changes; these are directional, and, therefore, predictable. 2) It results from the modification of the physical environments by the community. 3) It culminates in the establishment of as stable an ecosystem as is biologically possible on the site in question."

Two primary criteria in this process are (1) that the unique environment involved determines the pattern of succession, but does not cause it (Odum, 1966, p. 78) and (2) as Kelly has noted, the resulting members of the community are more differentiated, form more complex structures, and have a higher probability of adaptation (Kelly, 1968, p. 28). While this process is analogous to the increasing division of labor in modernizing economies, with increasing diversity of life styles accompanying this division, the major implication for community development is that it emphasizes that this process in different social settings will vary from community to community depending on: (1) the social groupings and institutions present at the start of the process and (2) the unique set of environmental constraints on, and resources available to, a particular community.

The late Julian Steward (1967) proposed a model that deals with levels of organization in a society defined by changing functional relationships that lead to a particular path of succession. His approach emphasizes (1) the relevance of social institutions as a response to the primary form of environmental (economic) exploitation in a unique setting; (2) the consequences of such institutions upon the behavior of members of social groups; (3) the power of the historical evolution of a particular social group on the formation and maintenance of political, cultural, and economic relationships among social groupings; (4) the relationship of (1), (2), and (3) to the surrounding environment, and (5) the impact of exogenous changes in the environment or the social, economic, and political patterns of group behavior.

This perspective coincides with the conclusions of Arensburg and Niehoff (1964) regarding their cross-cultural studies of social change. They found that cultures which have developed particular forms of local adaptation, including social institutions, economic forms, and technical lore, will not only resist change but there will emerge an evolutionary process that is unique to that community which preserves many of its historical cultural forms (Arensburg & Niehoff, 1964, pp. 50–100). Steward neatly summarizes this perspective by concluding that the process of community change can be referred to as a

TABLE 9–1
Ecological Criteria for Development

Traditional Criteria	Ecological Criteria			
	Interdependence	Cycling-of Resources	Adaptation	Succession
Position of Local Community in Economic Structure	Linkage of Local Economy to National Economy	Similarity of Resource Cycling at Local and National Levels	National Policies for Training, Technical and Financial Opportunities	Long-Term Effects of Interventions for the Functioning of the Local Community
Positions of Local Community in Political Structure	Role of Local Political Leadership at National Level	Access by Local Persons to Resources for Public Policy	Opportunities for Local Persons for Upward Mobility in Decision Making	Goals of Development Programs and Perceptions of These Goals by Host Community
Position of Local Community in Sociocultural Pattern of Dominant Civilization	Historical Relationships with Cultural, Religious Elites at National Level	Fit between Human Resource Programs and Needs for Local Development	Educational Opportunities for Achieving New Status Positions	External Limits of Change Process vs. Indigenous Goals and Drives
Ethnology at the Local Level	Level of Internal Group Cohesion and Stability	Division of Labor, and Patterns of Help Giving	Relationship of New Cultural Roles to Traditional System of Identification	Balance between Needs for Security and Uncertainty for Local Persons
Interregional Interactions	Development of Symbiotic Relationships with Other Communities	Distribution of Resources over Geographic Areas	Amount of Interregional Interaction and Interdependence	Amount of Mobility and Receptivity to New Cultural Form between Regions
Response to Development Programs	Legitimization of Development Agent and His Role in Socioeconomic System	Control of Meaningful Resources and Balances Use of Inputs by Host Community	Congruity of Community Goals with Methods of Developmental Agent	Goals of Development Agents Identical with Goals for Cumulative Change

sociological and economic transformation that "is evolutionary in that basic structures and patterns are altered. The use of evolution, however, does not imply general world stages of transformations. To the contrary, it refers to specific alterations in particular societies that must be determined empirically in each case and may or may not be cross-culturally similar" (Steward, 1967, Vol. I, p. 4). This use of the term appears most analogous to the biological meaning of succession and the manner in which succession is relevant for human or cultural ecology. While communities cannot be compared in terms of general stages of growth, the comparison across cultures is relevant to an understanding of the dynamics of change. This is explored in the next section.

Dimensions of Cross-Cultural Studies and the Developmental Process

An ecological approach can provide dimensions for assessing social change that can generate predictions about the community process. Policy goals and interventions can then be based on these ecological principles rather than the biases of the researcher. For example, as a societal group adapts to changes in the environment, a good measure of adaptability is documenting how the "help-giving" function evolves in that community relative to other communities. A change program that creates a modified form of resource sharing similar to the traditional form is more likely to enhance the chances for survival and healthy coping of citizens with the change program.

Table 9–1 is an attempt to identify factors relevant to an evaluation of the change process that emerges from an evaluation of the case studies and the accompanying review of the literature on development. The vertical columns present the four ecological principles. The horizontal rows show other concepts involved in studies of development and economic change. Within the blocks are examples of variables that could be derived from mixing the two approaches. The chart represents criteria for generating new dimensions for critical topics.

Table 9–1 may be useful in highlighting the factors found to be relevant for a cross-cultural appraisal of the change process. The interrelationships of these factors with one another and their relationships to the different sectors of analysis for social change are usually broken down according to categories such as sociocultural change, educational programs, economic systems, and political socialization. These are seldom linked together in any systematic way.

Figure 9–2 has been adapted from Himmelstrand and Okediji (1968) to show the assumptions inherent in an ecological approach regarding the relationship of relevant variables in the developmental process. This presentation invites comparison with Figures 9–1a through 9–1c which highlight the perspectives of the three approaches outlined earlier.

The arrows identifying the various dimensions presented in the above figure point toward the direction of primary causality in creating cumulative forces for development. It becomes more difficult to portray the circular causality within the system. The main point is that development is viewed as an iterative process. The arrows recycling from development to changes in environmental and social variables represent the circular causality of the entire system. Progress in development creates changes which in turn are processed through the system. The basic unit of analysis is the "social group" (introduced in the section on the "Principle of Interdependence") while the categories in the first column, social and institutional structures, are usually broken down into the separate disciplines of economics (productive units), political science (dynamics of power distribution), and sociology (individual status and socioeconomic position). The determinants of the functions of social groups and the other two dimensions represented in the column labeled "Community Structures Relevant to Development" are the basic sustenance patterns related to the natural and technological environment and the exogenous political and economic constraints on the system. All of these represent the environmental determinants of the particular social setting or "ecosystem" under study. The arrows moving from the first column to the right represent secondary interaction effects which are shaped by the primary forces within the system and act to formulate acceptable responses to pressures for change within the system. In turn such responses as noted above act iteratively to redetermine a path to reformulate sustenance patterns.

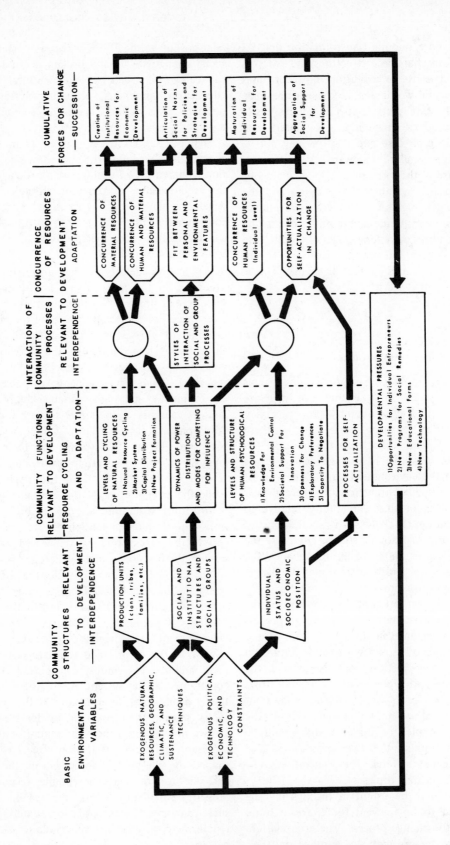

Fig. 9-2. Ecological perspective of community development.

Effects as they are recycled into the social system create a process that causes changes in the cultural patterns, economic and political institutions, and their styles of interaction. These then in turn create further changes in the locus of acceptable responses to change pressures altering the evolutionary path of development.

While a chart such as this can illustrate the impact of development pressures as they are processed through a new system, the time dimension cannot be easily portrayed. The effects of the rate of change, as well as the direction of change, should be taken into account in this illustration, for changes that occur too quickly may cause as much dislocation, frustration, and divergence from goals as can changes occurring too slowly. (For explication of these reactions, see Myrdal, 1968, pp. 1871–1877.)

While the use of diagrams and charts can help to orient the reader to the basic assumptions and perspective of the ecological approach, a more detailed presentation of the factors involved and the causal relationships implied by use of an ecological perspective are as academic and abstract as those of other approaches without the background provided by case studies and empirical findings. Thus, prior to enlarging on the factors presented in the cells of the matrix of Table 9–1 or attempting to further assess the implications of the interdependencies shown in Figure 9–2, the three case studies will be presented.

In the presentation of these examples an attempt will be made to highlight the most influential economic, political, and social forces, and the resulting institutions and attitudes that act to channel the change process in each setting. A description of interactions of these forces within a particular culture which affect certain types of alterations in the system will be particularly noted. These examples have been chosen because these cases illustrate varying reactions to change pressures introduced by different types of external development efforts.

MEXICO—THE PROBLEM OF
CHANGE IN THREE COMMUNITIES

The location of two of the communities is in northwest Mexico along the Mayo River in Sonora, an area which is the primary habitat of Mayo Indian families and the Yaqui Indian tribe. These two groups, Yaquis and Mayos, are located near one another in northwest Mexico, mainly south of the Yaqui River. The third community is a village in central Mexico not too far from Mexico City, Tzintzuntzan, studied by Foster. The Yaquis and Mayos are outside of the Yaqui River irrigation district and until the late 1950s neither tribe had much irrigation available. Their use of the natural environment has been restricted to subsistence farming and exploitation of the thorn forest. The *Masiaca communidad indigena*, the indigenous community or reservation of the Mayos, lies just south of the Mayo River irrigation district where the Mayo Indian population is dispersed among many small communities in which white Mexicans (Yoris) live alongside the Mayo families. The Yaqui Ejido, north of the Yaqui irrigation district, is more similar to a "pure" tribal reservation, with only Yaqui families allowed to live on the reservation and few venturing to live permanently outside the tribal area (Erasmus, 1967b, p. 374). The Yaquis occupy marginal land located north of the fertile river valley at the foot of high mountain ranges, known as the Yaqui River valley.

Both the Yaqui and Mayo tribes are minority groups in this region. The bulk of the population of this area is white Mexicans, known locally as Yoris, and mixed Mexican-Indian farmers and townspeople, known as Mestizos. These two groups have been much more attuned to the dominant Spanish-American culture of the towns and cities and are regarded as generally higher on the socioeconomic status ladder of Mexican society.

The Tzintzuntzan village is located along the shores of Lake Pátzcuaro at an elevation of 6,700 feet. The volcanic soil in the area around the village is not too fertile, yet a temperate climate and good rainfall make possible good crops of maize, wheat beans, squash, garden vegetables, and fruits. The village once was the capital of the vast pre-Conquest Tarascan Indian Empire and Tzintzuntzan's rulers including priests exercised at least religious hegemony over vast areas. Now most villagers eke out an existence as potters, farmers, day laborers, fishermen, or pottery wholesalers and retailers. In recent years the pottery market has come to serve kitchens of Mexicans with only a small part entering into the tourist trade in and around Mexico City. The national government has

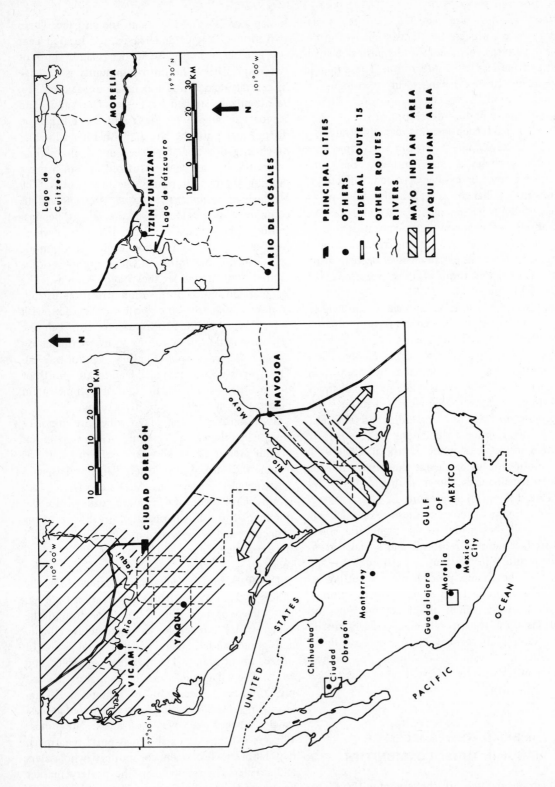

Fig. 9-3. Village location.

been somewhat embarrassed by the poverty of this area, as it has been of historical interest and attracts a large group of tourists. Thus, there have been some special development efforts aimed at this area which will be discussed in addition to the more general thrust of rural development in Mexico.

The main development efforts that will be analyzed are the Ejido Land Reform Associations, which were instituted following the revolution of 1910 and expanded through the 1930s when the last of the large land redistribution schemes were carried out under the land reform program. In addition to these programs, which have affected almost all of rural Mexico, attention will be focused on the workings of the Ejido banks, the institutions through which most of the changes introduced by the rural credit system have been channeled. The majority of Mexican Indian groups have felt the effects of such institutions and have been forced to deal with government-sponsored development programs.

As a result of government development activity and local economic growth, the region of Sonora where the Yaquis and Mayos are located has become a very dynamic, rapidly changing area. Erasmus, on a recent visit to this area ten years after the original anthropological work, observed that most of the problems he documented in earlier books and articles have evaporated, as the Indian population has begun to utilize the rural infrastructure of roads, markets, and irrigation projects and educational and other facilities for their own benefit. The role that this infrastructure has played with regard to the Yaquis and Mayos specifically is touched on below.

In Tzintzuntzan, a village of mostly non-agriculture-related occupations, infrastructural inputs have also played a large role while the Ejido bank is of less concern. The main development scheme directed specifically at this village has been a United Nations and United States sponsored community development project known as CREFAL (Centro Regional de Educación Fundamental para la América Latina) consisting of professors and students from national universities, government development agency personnel, and a few foreign community development workers coming to the village to organize professional cooperatives and to upgrade skills and technology in the major occupations of the villagers. Erasmus

and Foster, the two anthropologists most cited, have spent a great deal of time in Mexican villages collecting material for longitudinal observations and historical accounts covering the 15-year period of 1940–1955 and provide the primary source documents. Other background material has been taken from observers of Mexico's national political and economic scenes, Scott (1964), Glade and Anderson (1968), and Vernon (1965). A review of this material is presented in the following section in order to develop a context for evaluating specific development programs in rural Mexico.

Mexico—Leaving Behind the Indians

A pivotal historical event is the Mexican Revolution of 1910. Peasant participation in this revolution ensured its success, while its culmination resulted in sweeping changes in the social structure of all of Mexico. While these changes have affected all classes and social groups, some have benefited more than others. Some groups have emerged with their place in the society not changed as much as the revolutionary rhetoric proclaims.

The national party that achieved control of the revolution, and of the central government after the revolution, has based its claim for mass support on its continued allegiance to the goals of the revolution, which have included a stress on development in both rural and urban sectors. Various agencies have been set up and have achieved powerful positions within the government to control and allocate development funds and initiate and supervise projects. The two most important are the National Financiera and the Bank of Mexico. These titles reflect the emphasis of the bulk of government sponsored development, namely financing or extending credit to private groups or local agencies. Thus, developmental resources from the government have been primarily monetary, with the control highly decentralized and each Ejido bank highly independent of central administration.

The present analysis will focus on problems that have emerged in this indirect system related to the Indian populations. While each of the three groups, the Mayos, the Yaqui tribe, and the Tzintzuntzeños, has been similarly affected by the linguistic and cultural difficulties of dealing with

TABLE 9–2

Relation of Communities and Groups Studied to Developmental Criteria

Dimensions Relevant to Development Goals	Local Agency Personnel, CREFAL Worker	Mayo Tzintzuntzeños	Yaqui Indians	Indians
(1) Degree of Urbanization (economic)	High	Medium	Low	Very Low
(2) Degree of Acculturation (sociocultural)	Medium to High	Low	Low	Very Low
(3) Differential Accessibility (political)	Medium	Low	Very Low	Medium
(4) Relationship to Development Agents	Identification	Patron/Client	Tentative	Hostile

the Mexican bureaucracy and economic elite in the towns and cities, development projects and policies directed at specific areas have affected these groups differentially. Each group's reactions to the rural development process are the primary interest of this chapter and will be explored further. Before a review of the government's efforts in rural development, an orientation of the communities studied vis-à-vis developmental goals will be presented. A summary of this presentation appears in Table 9–2.

Dealing with the services and demands of an urban, market economy is a general prerequisite for economic modernization. This requirement is indicated by the dimension labeled "Urbanization" in Table 9–2. Secondly, in the case of the Indian groups in Mexico, a measure of familiarity with and knowledge of how to operate in the urban-oriented, semimodernized Mexican culture is necessary; this is noted as "acculturation." In the political sphere a sense of political efficacy and a feeling that a group can change a system through its actions as a partisan interest group is important to that group's chances for success along developmental lines; this is labeled "Differential Accessibility" in Table 9–2. The entries in the boxes of Table 9–2 show approximately how each of the groups studied in this chapter varies along

these dimensions with respect to the other groups. The development personnel working directly with the Indian communities in rural Mexico are also included for reference.

The dimension "Relationship to Development Agents" has been included to point to the problems encountered with the developmental agents. The urbanization and acculturation dimensions are recognized by the Indians themselves, often by the more traditional Indians in deprecatory terms as "wanting to become a Yori" (Erasmus, 1961, 1967a). The differences between the three communities noted in Table 9–2 could also be discussed along a continuum of alienation vs. aspirations toward the modernizing system. As suggested in Table 9–2, the Yaqui tribe is more alienated politically and culturally from the urban elites, while Mestizo (Mexican Indian) and other change agents are most highly identified, in an aspirational sense, with the urban leadership. The Mayo Indians fall in between these two extremes as indicated by Table 9–3. The "ecological" factors that have produced these differences in the qualitative nature of the change process are explored in the remainder of this chapter.

The factors indicated in Table 9–3 also can be partially explained by an understanding of how the government and the ruling party, the PRI

TABLE 9–3
Relative Aspirational Orientations of Three Different Villages

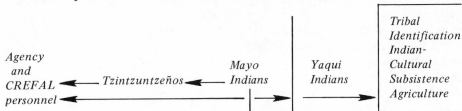

(Partido Revolucioncerio Institucional), have handled rural development and their orientation toward the rural Indian sector.

The ruling party historically is related to the citizens via revolution, with few links to the Indian rural sector. Rural development is relegated to white Mexicans who are themselves identified with urban areas. As a result of this, an exploitive type of relationship emerged in the agencies responsible for development.[6] Even among those agencies which have in general been responsive to the Indian population's needs, there has been an incapacity to differentiate between different rural groups. Therefore, the strategies used in dealing with each of the groups have been more uniform than would be dictated by a more realistic appraisal of the "ecosystem" of each group. The problem of controls and accountability along with this lack of sensitivity has contributed to an exploitive type of relationship, especially in the rural Indian sector.

Because of the predominance of short-term goals in planning that shift with each administration, and because there are no criteria by which each agency can monitor progress for long-term development, not much has been done to improve this situation. Lack of human resource development programs at the local level, reinforced by cultural differences between urban Yoris and rural Indians, have resulted in a lack of new leadership and there is little upward mobility within the host population in terms of the agency structure or in other areas which might replace the existing structure. This has reinforced the cultural distance between the host population and the governmental agencies. In addition to the general problems of cultural distance between the citizens and the development agents, the groups studied vary differently along historical dimensions in ways that affect their amenability to various intervention strategies, and their reactions to technological, social, and economic change. The historical background of rural development and of each of these groups will now be discussed.

General Background:
Aftermath of the Revolution

The revolution of 1910 has been described as a "middle class" revolution which wrested power from the traditional Spanish descended aristocracy and large landholders, or Latifunda. The leaders of the revolution identified themselves with the Mexican Revolutionary Party, PRI, which has managed to consolidate its hold on political power to the point that at the present time there are few serious opposition groups, and Mexico is essentially a one-party state (Scott, 1964, chapters 1 and 5).

The PRI retained its leadership through a period of almost complete breakdown in the social structure and a return to regionalism and rule by local governors and strong men immediately following the revolutionary period. It managed to do this by retaining a monopoly on the goals of the revolution and by a strategy of consolidation of interest groups, many of which were formed by the party and immediately given a formal role in the party structure. Successive governments since the revolution have formed alliances with local leaders and gained control over states by centralizing revenue collection, handpicking congressional representatives at the center, and creating more nationally oriented interest groups so that no one sector would dominate. At the same time that the Revolutionary Party was ensuring the loyalty of the majority of significant interest groups, it maintained policy goals which proclaimed the revolutionary aims and the party aims to be one and the same. This established a party "charisma" by legitimizing the PRI as the one party capable of carrying out the meaning of the revolution in practice (Vernon, 1965, pp. 60–74).

Agrarian policy goals since the revolution have consistently been dominated by such shibboleths as land reform, cooperative movements, and the uplifting of the peasant. Land reform was extensive and has been an instrument for change (Vernon, 1965, p. 73). Glade asserts that much rural incentive and changes in mobility and sociocultural patterns were released when the Latifunda system was overthrown (Glade & Anderson, 1968, p. 68). During the Cardenas period, in the late 1930s, private and government banks were forced by the government to move into rural areas and extend credit, primarily to Ejido cooperatives on land that had been redistributed to peasants on the provision that they join the government cooperatives (Blair, 1964, p. 144).

Yet while these steps were taken on a massive scale with much attendant fanfare, the increasing urban orientation of the middle class leadership of the PRI resulted in the emphasis in development being focused more consistently on the industrial sector (Scott, 1964, pp. 79–81). This is reflected in the primary goals of government planning which have been expressed as (1) keeping a favorable balance of payments position, (2) price stability, and (3) industrial growth and growth in agricultural output to feed the urban population and to maintain exports in order to insure an influx of foreign exchange (Shafer, 1966, pp. 65–69). Writers on economic development in Mexico have described the Ejido system of cooperative farming as having had as its primary function the absorption of rural unemployment (Glade & Anderson, 1968, p. 57), while the focus of government investment and expertise has been in the industrial sector. What government investment has been channeled into the rural sector most effectively has gone to promote export crops such as cotton and coffee, produced primarily on large estates. This has been reflected in government investment figures which show that 17.8

percent of all public investment has gone into the agricultural sector for about the last ten-year period. Of this, 92 percent has been in large irrigation schemes, which, it has been claimed by many writers, have benefited primarily large-scale farmers[7] (Schafer, 1966, p. 143; Urquidi, 1966, pp. 181–182).

Historical Perspective of the Indian Populations

Mayos

The peasant community is less aware of, or involved in, newer development projects such as the construction of large dams or highways, which at present use up most of the development funds earmarked for the rural areas of Mexico, than it is of the ongoing operations of the Ejido banks. Thus most peasants perceive the development work of the government most directly through the Ejidos, and the most direct contact with government development personnel is with the officials of the development banks. While the Ejido system was operating as a collective, or cooperative system in the 1920s, by the 1930s most of the banks had been changed, through peasant demand, to individual credit associations whereby each farmer owned his own plot.

Peasants complained that they did not know the state of Ejido finances nor the size of harvests nor the prices at which they were sold. As the bank officials were responsible for collecting and selling produce, farmers tended to assume (sometimes correctly) that profits were being taken from them by bank officials (Erasmus, 1961, pp. 263–268). Erasmus describes the Mayos as representative of the majority of Mexicanizing Indians, who have been caught up in the change process in the countryside and rural villages. They are: "an increasing number of discontented persons, among whom can be found some symptoms of anomie. Many of these are nominally Mayo Indians, but they have lost interest in Indian ceremonies ... yet they do not feel adequate to enter the Yori [Mexican] world, where both business and consumption are conducted largely on credit, and depend so much on friends and influence" (Erasmus, 1961, p. 253).

These reactions illustrate the position of the Mayo Indians along the urbanization and the acculturation dimension of Table 9–2. They are moving away from traditional ceremonial and resource sharing patterns of local interdependence and would like to take part more fully in the consumption patterns of commercialized areas. They are dispersed throughout the countryside, and there is some "demonstration effect" from the towns and Mexican commercial farmers.

Erasmus notes that local markets for most crops planted by the Mayos in the Mayo reserve area are limited and that "the export market is beyond the business and financial abilities of most of the inhabitants" (Erasmus, 1967a, p. 49). While the largest industry of the area is woodcutting and making furniture, bags, saddle cinches, hammocks, and saddle pads for sale, this is becoming less profitable as mass produced products in urban areas replace these handmade goods. Many Mayos still dislike the idea of going out to find wage labor and working for Yoris as "Yori's dogs." Erasmus reports that they would rather work at unproductive jobs in the reservation than become dependent on Mexican civilization and lose their cultural independence.

Ironically, it appears that the poorest Mayo families are the ones trying the hardest to maintain their traditional life style and cultural system. Erasmus writes: "among the Mayos fiesta sponsorship was no longer a means by which more affluent individuals sought social esteem through redistribution. Out of a sample of 100 Mayo Indian fiesteros interviewed in 1958, half were field laborers with no lands at all, and of the other half—made up of small landowners and ejidatarios—only seven had farming operations large enough that they did not have to hire out as field hands during part of the year to support their families" (Erasmus, 1967b, p. 375).

Thus, it appears that those Mayos who do not feel capable of achieving in terms of the Mexican "status ladder of economic enterprise and rising standards of consumption" cling to older status forms for security and confidence. Among the Mayos there appears to be a range of acculturation and urbanization, with those near the upper end having greater confidence in their ability to win rewards in the urbanizing system. While the Mayos range from the lower to the upper end of this spectrum, it appears that the Yaquis anchor the lower end, while the villagers of Tzintzuntzan anchor the top end. Thus, Erasmus found that about 90 percent of the Yaqui households were affiliated with ceremonial societies and traditional associations, whereas 18 percent was the highest figure found for any Mayo village (Erasmus, 1967b, p. 375).

Tzintzuntzan Villagers

In describing Tzintzuntzan, Foster writes that the village is not, and has not been for centuries, an Indian village. He classifies people as Indian or non-Indian by language. If people speak Tarascan, the local Indian dialect, they are Indian; if not, they are Mestizo or Indian-Mexican. On this basis approximately 11 percent of the population is Indian. Still he concludes: "Whether Tarascan or Mestizo the average villager has a precarious existence. For Tzintzuntzan is a poor community, and its resources and productive techniques are inadequate to provide a level of living that its inhabitants increasingly will demand. Land particularly is in short supply . . . and soils are thin. A 1960 agrarian census lists only ten men and two women with more than five hectares of agricultural land, and the largest holding is only fourteen acres" (Foster, 1967, p. 37).

Foster refers to the villagers of Tzintzuntzan as "marginal" people, as they are moving out of subsistence agriculture and into commerce or production in cottage industries of pottery, weaving, and other simple products. Still they don't really understand the "modernizing" part of Mexico and "the rules of the game of living that prevail in cities, to which they are bound, and for this ignorance they are at the mercy of personal and impersonal urban controls" (Foster, 1967, p. 10). In spite of these constraints, they have introduced some new, innovative techniques into production and stand at the top of our scale on the "urbanization" continuum.

Along the acculturation dimension, the position of Tzintzuntzan can be measured by the degree to which the villagers cling to and participate in more traditional ceremonies and festivals. In all Indian and Mestizo communities, these require a large outlay of time and resources, and compete with their adoption of more urban, consumption-oriented, individualistic types of activities. In Tzintzuntzan, Foster noted that the "cargo" system[8] has been the most prevalent form of traditional ceremonial and civil obligation imposed on villagers, but that it has withered significantly since the 1920s. Foster asserts that the cargo system and other similar forms of ceremonial service were the major way to win prestige and status in the relatively closed peasant villages of the 1920s. "Until the 1920's there was only one major way for an individual . . . to acquire prestige, spending large sums of money in ritual fashion for 'community service.' [In the 1930s] of the seven sets of cargueros [cargo holdings] five disappeared. . . ." (Foster, 1967, p. 313).

Foster notes that only one of the remaining two ceremonial services functioned "full blown" in 1945. In contrast to earlier days, "today prestige is beginning to accrue to those people who have the wealth necessary, and the will to use it, to acquire the material symbols that villagers believe characterize city people" (Foster, 1967, p. 313).

For the dimension of political accessibility, it is difficult to distinguish between the Mayo Indians and the Tzintzuntzeños, except that as a village population with their own elected officials the villagers of Tzintzuntzan would be expected to exert more upward influence than the scattered, rural Mayo Indians. While most people vote for mayor, Foster asserts that the mechanics of local political elections are difficult to understand for the villagers. Even for those who participate and are elected to office, there remains something of the quality of the unknowable that characterizes the supernatural and the city. This is in large part due to the methods the PRI (Partido Revolucion-cerio Institucional) uses to select candidates. After each ward selects its slate, it is sent to the city of Morelia, the capital of the state, where the PRI either approves it, modifies the list, or throws it out and names new men to compete. Even after electing candidates to positions, the people don't look to them to represent their interests to the larger society but expect these people to "move and manipulate" for their own advantage. Foster concludes that Tzintzuntzan elections are little more than stylized rituals affording the villagers an opportunity to express and reinforce loyalty to the Mexican nation (Foster, 1967, pp. 175–177).

The Yaqui Tribe

In the Yaqui reservation area, however, the political strength of the tribal governors is in contrast to the low degree of urbanization and acculturation of the Yaqui people generally. The Yaquis elect their own governors. Attempts to manipulate these elections by outsiders have failed. The Yaquis have been extremely militant

until recent times and fought control by the Mexican government successfully until 1927. Their political representatives deal less with the local officials of the Mexican government than they do directly with the central government offices in Mexico City. In 1958 after a successful battle with the government's development agencies, they were granted financial and technical aid to irrigate most of their land north of the Yaqui River. Their irrigation had previously been cut off by the creation of the Yaqui River irrigation district to the south, diverting the water away from their reservation. The Yaquis won this battle as a group, something few other Indian groups have even attempted. They were awarded their land as a group and have dealt with the government's development agencies, especially the Ejido banks, with more unity than the Mayos or even the Tzintzuntzeños (Erasmus, 1967a, pp. 115–118).

Summary

Comparing the three populations, one would have to rank the Yaquis at the top in political accessibility, due to their success in mobilizing leadership to push for the development schemes they desire. At the same time they are the lowest on dimensions of urbanization and acculturation. They most adamantly reaffirm the validity of their own cultural heritage as opposed to that emerging in urbanizing Mexico. Geographically they have isolated themselves, while the Mayos live interspersed among Yori rural families, and the Tzintzuntzeños have most access to larger urban centers. The Yaquis have been the most reluctant to work outside the reservation and have faced increasing poverty rather than do so. Mayo tribe members are increasingly taking menial day labor jobs outside their farming community, while the villagers of Tzintzuntzan are functionally linked to urban markets through sales of pottery, weaving, and carpentry and purchases of consumer goods. Ironically the accessibility of the Tzintzuntzeños to urban areas has resulted in an even higher degree of centralized political control, as the governmental political unit seems to be more dominant over the Tzintzuntzan than the other two areas studied. The above perspective on the relative positions of the three tribes along dimensions of acculturation, urbanization, and political accessibility provides initial background. The following section will explore how each of the three populations evolved to its various levels of organization. Before doing that a few comments will be made describing the types of development programs that have been operating with these populations.

Development Programs in the Three Areas

The Ejido Banks

The Ejido credit associations have been most directly involved with intervention strategies among the farm population of the rural Indian sector and are the major representatives of the government's development efforts in the Mayo and Yaqui tribal regions of Sonora. Under the Cardenas regime in the 1930s, albeit reluctantly, agricultural banks were moved into the rural sector and have largely been responsible for the running of Ejido credit systems and other types of credit societies, even in the Yaqui tribal areas (Blair, 1964, p. 144). Largely unconvinced of the security or profit opportunities involved, they have set stiff regulations for credit applications. They are reluctant to advance more than short-term credit to small holders and will not give credit to farmers who will not mechanize or invest in new types of seed and fertilizer. The people who run the banks are Yoris who do not want to have too much to do with the rural Indian and relate more to the urban centers.

Early in the history of the Ejido system, when the peasants were forced to join cooperatives in order to get bank credit, practically everything the Indian did with respect to his farm was under control of the bank. Farmers were forced to buy machinery they felt they could not afford and subsequently found they could not use. There were, and still are, constant charges of corruption aimed at the banks by ejidatarios. While the collective system has been modified to one of individual holdings in the vast majority of Ejidos, peasants who want credit still must meet stringent requirements, and any peasant who obtained land under the Ejido land reform system is not allowed to sell or rent it. As landowners become more and more in debt to the bank, they attempt to get out by sharecropping, a way to get around the illegality of renting out land. Erasmus found in Sonora that more than half the plots of many Ejidos were being rented or sharecropped in 1959. Erasmus asserts that these tendencies toward a reconsolidation of plots into larger, more eco-nomic parcels, are a way to get out from under the system.

Under the thumb of the Ejidos, whose officials often worked in collusion with government officials to their own benefit, the peasants are "readily taken advantage of by the employees of welfare agencies established to help them, and even by their own local leaders." While the government has been attempting to curtail such graft, it appears that little progress has been made in alleviating Indian suspicion of the banks or the officials' feelings of cultural superiority. The officials order the peasants around with little knowledge of or sensitivity to local environmental conditions (Erasmus, 1967b, p. 373). The same general situation can be said to hold among the Tzintzuntzeños.

The CREFAL Project

In Tzintzuntzan, as well as in Sonora, most development personnel are Yoris who reside in, and identify with, urban areas (Scott, 1964, p. 73). The situation has been somewhat different in Tzintzuntzan, however, where CREFAL personnel attempted a number of community development projects during the 1950s. These were based on the prevailing community development ideology emphasizing cooperative groups and self-help. They attempted to teach each group a special skill or trade, infuse them with a development ideology, provide resources for initial efforts, and then let the villagers pull themselves up and continue on their own (Foster, 1967, pp. 328–330). Work on projects had started in 1953. By 1960 the Community Development workers had left, considering their efforts as largely unsuccessful. In Tzintzuntzan the CREFAL workers started several pottery projects to improve methods and techniques and for the introduction of cooperative working methods. Other projects included a weaving cooperative, using modern hand-operated looms, the establishment of a furniture factory, the introduction of chicken ranching, and bringing women who did embroidery together in a cooperative, teaching them new techniques. A community store was reorganized to serve as a "consumer's cooperative" where people could purchase goods at lower prices. By 1960 only one of the projects was still in operation, the embroidery cooperative, while all others had ceased to operate entirely (Foster, 1967, pp. 330–340).

Outcomes and
Resistance to Change

It is clearer why resistance had remained strong in Northwest Mexico's rural areas in spite of government pressure to join credit Ejidos and to mechanize. The government planners hoped that such efforts would induce farmers to adopt more advanced methods of production and increase overall productivity. This has resulted instead in increased strivings by all Indian groups to avoid what they consider "Mexican exploitation" and to strive to remain independent of the larger economic system in terms of production, even of cash crops.

That the CREFAL projects should have failed seems less obvious. The CREFAL cooperative workers to some degree attempted to emphasize "self-help" methods along the lines of McClelland's motivational training techniques. It was hoped that subsequently production techniques would change and cooperative efforts would be induced. While there hasn't been as much overt resistance to this approach, Tzintzuntzeños backed out of the cooperative groups formed by CREFAL workers and abandoned many "improved techniques" as soon as pressure by CREFAL personnel was lifted (Foster, 1967, p. 334). Foster writes of the expectations of CREFAL workers: "Successful community development work is ... seen as embracing a combination of 'community organization,' building new forms of organizations suited to action—and simultaneously improving production methods and techniques to raise the general standard of living" (Foster, p. 332). While the expected outcomes did not emerge, at least to the extent the CREFAL workers had hoped, it is instructive in understanding the dynamics of the change process to look at what changes did occur as a result of development efforts. As will be discussed below, the failure of the CREFAL projects was largely a failure of the development agents. Not only Tzintzuntzan, but also the other two areas were affected to different degrees by development efforts with mixed results. With the CREFAL project, the effects have been direct; with the Ejido banks, results often were more indirect, resulting often from large-scale infrastructural projects, such as the example of the Yaquis whose irrigation was cut off by dam building and who subsequently had to fight to get it restored.

Known Effects

In discussing the desirable and undesirable effects of change efforts in rural Mexico, the three Indian groups can be placed in a continuum from most changed to least affected by the goals of the change agent groups. In the case of the villagers of Tzintzuntzan, who were introduced to community development by the CREFAL projects, it can be said that they were most exposed to attempts at directed change of all the peasant groups. In addition to government development in terms of rural infrastructure, to which all groups were exposed, plus schools, hospitals, and other institutions, they were directly approached by field workers who introduced modern techniques and attempted to organize them for change. The second group is composed of peasants such as the Mayo Indian Tribes who, by living among Yoris (Spanish-Mexicans), took part in the cash economy, and found it more and more difficult to retain economic independence. They began to emulate middle class Mexicans rather than continue traditional patterns of interpersonal and ceremonial behavior (Erasmus, 1967a, pp. 120–123). The Yaquis, on the other hand, have been successful in not accomodating to the National government's conception of rural development.

CAUSAL LINKS TO
ECOLOGICAL PRINCIPLES

The varying positions of each of the three groups discussed above along the dimensions presented in Table 9–2 will now be related to the ecological principles presented in Table 9–1.

Interdependence

Looking at each of the groups in terms of the interdependence principle, it appears that the Tzintzuntzeños have had their economic and political activities linked most tightly to the nearby urban economies. As a village of poor Mestizos and Indians, they are dependent on the larger society, while not having learned how to operate in it. Foster asserts that they realize the extent of their dependence and recognize their humble position and lack of power and influence.

This makes them continually alert to the possibility of obligating a person of superior wealth, position, or influence, thereby initiating a patron/client relationship which will buttress security in a variety of life crises (Foster, 1967, p. 229).

While the relations of the villagers of Tzintzuntzan through the CREFAL project and government efforts have helped them to feel a desire for greater interdependence, the same situation cannot be said to prevail with regard to the Mayo and Yaqui experience with the Ejido banks. These are the main thrust of government development efforts in the Yaqui and Mayo tribal areas of Sonora.

Apparently the perceptions of the Indians of these areas of their experience with the Ejido banks has not fostered a desire for a greater amount of interdependence, but rather the opposite: "To most ejidatarios the Bank seems like a very cold and impersonal sort of patron. 'The bank does not care if we starve' is a common complaint. A man fairly regularly employed by a rich landowner can always get a loan of money or food. . . . In contrast, the Bank's practice of taking an entire wheat harvest [seemed] unwarranted and heartless. . . . 'They are just employees. They get paid no matter what happens, so why should they care about us?' " (Erasmus, 1961, p. 217).

The Yaquis have rejected increasing interdependence with the larger system more completely than either the Mayos or the Tzintzuntzeños. They have done this by remaining physically isolated on the reservation, by maintaining traditional social and ceremonial forms, and by a strong sense of tribal identity. Erasmus notes that even in the late 1950s after the irrigation project had started operating in the reservation, "new farm collectives were still so tightly under the administration of the Ejido Bank that the Yaquis who so 'benefited' were more angry than pleased" (Erasmus, 1967b, p. 374). Yet in order to maintain their isolation, the Yaquis were increasingly forced to accept a lower standard of living rather than go to work for Yoris outside the reservation. A typical reaction to this alternative was reported by Erasmus as "I am not a peon; there are no peons in this house: we Yaquis work only for ourselves" (Erasmus, 1967a, p. 36).

This militant independence on the part of the Yaquis may be contrasted to the situation of the Mayos who are not as physically isolated and have to live among Yoris and Mestizos who are benefiting more from Mexico's overall development. They seem ambivalent as to the orientation they should take as they are drawn more into the economy of the urbanizing areas, but don't share the political or cultural rewards and identification. Most Mayos seem well described by Scott who writes of rural Indians in general: "The vast majority . . . are poor, isolated and easily manipulated by their farm leaders in the CNC (National Farmers Federation); so are many of the small farmers who own their own land. Despite efforts to integrate many of these small landholders into the national economy by supplying credit facilities (Ejido banks) and technical advisors, the program is neither so systematic nor so successful as to offer immediate inclusion of most of these people in effective national life" (Scott, 1964, p. 69).

Summary

If one views the results of development programs from the perspective of interdependence, each of the communities varies in its expression of its relationship to the surrounding environment. The Yaquis, reinforced by their tribal cohesion and geographical isolation, have rejected increasing interdependence with the outside world socially, economically, and politically. Instead they increased their own internal cohesion and interdependence upon one another. The Mayos have moved reluctantly, forced almost by the train of events outside of their own control, into increasing political and social interdependence with the Yoris. It is in the social area that resistance is still highest. Among the Tzintzuntzeños, political interdependence is enforced by the PRI. They are moving quickly into increasing economic interdependence and the social emulation of Yori life styles.

Cycling of Resources

The situation of these groups in the light of attempts to alter their ecological interdependence must also be seen relative to the resource cycling patterns of each of the communities. Foster and Erasmus both view the modal type of peasant society similarly and compare the changing resource cycling pattern in Tzintzuntzan and the Mayo populations with this modal type. They feel that in a traditional peasant community, in which consumer goods are scarce and productivity is limited by traditional methods and where social patterns are reflected in conspicuous giving, such as fiestas and ceremonial donations, there are sanctions to ensure that no one in the closed community monopolizes wealth. As technological growth and modernization intrude to create more prosperity and opportunity, these patterns of resource sharing give way to conspicuous ownership and prestige seeking which look like "keeping up with the Joneses." Yet this replacement will not occur as quickly or as smoothly if there is continued insecurity in changing statuses due to inadequate knowledge of how to grasp new opportunities (see Erasmus, 1961, pp. 13–16 and 80–83; Foster, 1967, chapters 6 and 16).

Foster describes the resistance to change in Tzintzuntzan in terms of a particular cognitive orientation to the world which he labels the "Image of Limited Good." He asserts that in a world of limited resources, the community developed and maintained a viable system of resource cycling which insured some economic security to all. This entailed development of a "world view" that until recently represented the world with fair accuracy:

The accumulation and reinvestment of wealth by one man, (Wolf) argues, threatens to take from others the instruments of their livelihood, and it leads to power, which if unchecked, corrupts . . . the community must abolish wealth and redistribute power continually to maintain the social and economic equality that spells security and constitutes a defense against the outside world. It (the cargo system) was the visible evidence that "here we are all equal," that no one, for long, had more than his share of limited economic goods. Prestige and status were the only commodities the community could permit a man to accumulate in large amounts (Foster, 1967, p. 205).

While Erasmus disagrees with the idea of an overriding cognitive map of the world that makes it difficult for Indians to cope in the modernizing sector, he agrees that lack of knowledge concerning new opportunities, technology, and social relations in urban areas creates a high level of insecurity and thus a dependence effect which reinforces the existing class structure. Erasmus talks more specifically about what options and opportunities Indians do have for dealing with their insecurity. One of these, available to the lower class Indian, is to become more dependent on urban people, through entering into wage labor contracts, emulating urban customs, and striving for urban status. Becoming literate in Spanish, for example, through gaining only three years of primary education, is now a high status producing skill. It shows the native how he can be like the Yori, and very lucrative jobs are available in the countryside teaching Spanish to others. Another status position is that of a government or Ejido official. In these positions one is expected to wheel and deal and become adept at corruption, a sign of becoming a Yori; for this, one is admired.

Among the Mayos, Erasmus has observed that while the bulk of the Indian population still preserves ceremonial practices of the type that traditionally included conspicuous giving and a considerable investment of effort, these practices have changed to minimize the sharing aspects yet still include opportunities for conspicuous production. He concluded that "the stress that existed was most intense among peasants who were losing their old prestige system but who did not have the confidence, the background or the opportunity to take part in the new one" (Erasmus, 1961, p. 185).

Foster documents a similar reaction on the part of the villagers of Tzintzuntzan, and asserts that the background, confidence, and opportunities necessary to allow the villagers to operate within the larger system can come only through the provision of "culture capital." Parts of this "culture capital" are extravillage resources that are needed to train villagers and support them in innovative efforts. One of many examples Foster presents is that of a young potter who invented a new glazing technique. Because he had no materials available that could withstand the heat of the hotter flame he produced and because he did not understand the mechanisms needed to regulate the size of the flame, he gave up, discouraged. Foster asserts that the outcome would have been different: "had he lived where he could have access to mechanical and engineering advice that would have solved the relatively minor design problems [and] proper tools, places to purchase very heat-resisting materials. An innovative mentality . . . was defeated because it was not supported by the infrastructure, we, in industrialized countries take for granted" (Foster, 1967, p. 254).

The young inventor was also opposed by most of the other potters and thus received very little social support. This is also part of the "culture capital" that must be provided to break through the closed resource cycling system whereby the "guild" of potters in Tzintzuntzan all help one another in maintaining traditional techniques and feel that any change or innovation by one would threaten the entire group with failure.

Other aspects of the skills needed to break out of traditional resource cycling are the need for learning how to deal with city people, bank officials, and government personnel, and the security of knowing that by one's efforts there is a good chance of being accepted and of surviving in a new status or social system. In addition there is a need to feel either that city people are not out to exploit the peasant or that there are people around who can help one to deal with this situation. Foster states that in spite of massive improvements in physical infrastructure, until culture capital is provided in adequate amounts, the process of change will be erratic and halting (Foster, 1967, pp. 255–264). While there has been progress made in gross, large-scale infrastructural inputs related to resource cycling, the role that the public sector in Mexico has assigned itself has not had much relevance to private "felt needs" at the community level. The division of rewards and elite relationships to the masses has not changed extensively, as noted above by Scott and Vernon. Partially as a result of these imbalances, as well as the government's emphasis on industrialization, development agents, such as the CREFAL workers, have either not had adequate control of meaningful resources at the levels needed or have been unable to balance inputs in such a way as to insure that all facets of any one project were provided.

The above comments on the cycling of resources are most meaningfully interpreted with respect to the Mayo Indians and Tzintzuntzeños. The Yaquis differ along this dimension in that the tribal orientation continues to be most heavily toward maintenance of traditional resource cycling forms within the reservation. Erasmus observed that: "Yaquis are very conscious of each other's financial condition. Most of them are very impoverished and they soon notice when others are eating well or have purchased new wearing apparel. A rise in affluence makes a man in a target for ceremonial demands . . ." (Erasmus, 1967a, p. 29).

Thus, among the Yaquis there has been little pressure for changing resource cycling patterns, and this group seems to represent most "purely" the modal "peasant" type of social system.

Summary

The Tzintzuntzeños, then, have moved farthest from traditional resource cycling forms and are entering slowly into those predominating in urban Yori culture. Again the unfamiliarity and lack of culture capital and social support sustain resistances and uncertainty. The Mayos would like to move more in the direction of modernizing their resources, yet have fewer skills or opportunities than the Tzintzuntzeños. Thus there is a wider variance among the Mayo population and less internal consistency than for either of the other two groups.

While the Yaqui group remains at the traditional end of the spectrum in terms of patterns of resource cycling, this has resulted in less dependence between this tribe and the urban culture. It appears that this dependence is strongest among the Tzintzuntzeños given the manner in which they have linked into the urban system. Again the widest variance seems to be among the Mayos.

Adaptation

The varying levels of resource cycling and interdependencies within the ecosystem of each of the three groups, when combined with their heritage and physical ecology, have interesting consequences for adaptation, the third of the ecological dimensions. The Yaquis have not only moved little in the direction of adapting to the life styles and demands of the outside system, but through their autonomy and cohesion have in some areas reversed the trend. Erasmus found that they had become quite adept at manipulating outsiders for the benefit of their own group. He offers the examples of the governor of one of the Yaqui pueblos who in 1967 was able to manipulate the Mexican ranchers who wished to graze their cattle within the boundaries of the reservation. By "continually holding out the threat of expulsion from the reserve, he kept them sufficiently intimidated so that they were willing to make frequent gifts of cattle . . . requested for individual Yaquis who needed an animal to butcher for a household or public religious festival." Within the reservation the Yaquis have adapted by continuing and reinforcing traditional social patterns which maintain group identity and cohesion. One such case is the traditional courtship and marriage forms. Erasmus found that within the Yaqui reservation, marriages are still most often arranged by parents, whereas among the Mayos this practice has almost been eliminated. In addition the Yaquis still prefer to depend on extended family ties; often married sons will live with parents even after having several children (Erasmus, 1967a, pp. 41–45).

In the face of an outside environment perceived as hostile and exploitive, with rapid change occurring in the larger environment, the Yaquis have chosen an adaptation pattern that reemphasizes their own cultural identity and provides strong intragroup support within a somewhat isolated environment. Given the types of interventions that have been experienced by this group, costs of other modes of adaptation are perceived as quite high: "Many reservation Yaquis would find few rewards in attempting to join lower class Yori society. With little education, often unable to speak Spanish well, they would be forced to perform the most menial of day labor jobs without much security or social position. They would undoubtedly have to work for, and take orders from, a hated Yori which would put them in the category of 'White Man's Dog' " (Erasmus, 1967a, p. 119).

On the other hand, the Mayo Indians, who live in a more dispersed fashion with less latitude of political action and more direct interdependencies with the larger system, appear to be moving more and more toward styles of adaptation that could prove more functional in a changing, urbanized world. Erasmus found that although the Mayos appear to depend on others for direction and are slower than Yoris in expanding their wants and expectations, given sufficient opportunities they seem to be able to overcome these constraints. Many have acquired a desire to send their children to school to compete with Yoris for educational rewards. Another interesting aspect of their adaptation is the recent tendency for Mayos to convert to Protestant sects. This seems to help them to dissociate themselves from hardships of fiesta expenses at the same time that they can maintain an identification with a socioreligious group (Erasmus, 1967a, p. 88).

Another group within the Mayo community, mostly older and poorer, tend toward the Yaqui end of the acculturation continuum. They feel insecure and have lost a sense of control in the midst of rapid changes. They see too many people "losing the faith," violating religious vows and refusing to sponsor fiestas. It appears that fears such as these led to a religious reform movement in the Mayo community stemming from the appearance of "God" to a young Mayo Indian. Stories were spread by the more traditional families that "God" would punish all that refused to sponsor fiestas. One story that developed said "God was displeased with the administration of water resources because the rich were being favored through illegal means" (Erasmus, 1967a, pp. 100–102).

The villagers of Tzintzuntzan seem to be making changes in adaptation styles similar to those Mayos who denounce the ceremonial traditions and "want to be Yori." The majority of Tzintzuntzeños are purchasing city goods as fast as they can save their money. Most villagers show a rudimentary understanding of modern market-economy processes and a few are beginning to learn what is involved in mass merchandising and dealing with wholesalers from the city in order to try to sell their products. Yet the primary form of changed adaptation appears, according to Foster, to entail attempts to form patron/client relationships with city personnel. These take a form similar to the old Latifunda or landlord/tenant, superior/subordinate relationships that characterized the rural areas of Mexico before the revolution. Erasmus has labeled this coping style the "Encogido Syndrome," the name implying obsequiousness, currying favor, humility, and dependency (Erasmus, 1968).

Thus a range of adaptive styles and coping preferences can be observed among the three communities. These range from a kind of reverse exploitation attempted by the Yaquis to expressions of humility and servitude in order to gain special favors from the Yoris. Erasmus notes that the Yaqui Indians whom he interviewed on his second visit seemed more "Encogido" than many Mayos who were learning to cope with the urban world. It is not clear whether this behavior is expressed only when the Yaquis are dealing with outsiders in an unfamiliar context or is expressed in familiar settings as well. Given the higher degree of environmental control of the Yaquis within their reservation, it would be surprising if outsiders dealing with the Yaquis on Yaqui grounds within their culture were not themselves highly "Encogido." Such a condition would be less true when dealing with the Mayo tribe, and least of all when in Tzintzuntzan where the villagers' orientation toward urban values could only lead to a feeling of superiority on the development agent's part. Predictions of how these styles of mutual adaptation can be expected to change over time will be introduced in the following section.

Succession

The fourth ecological principle, the succession principle, deals with the effects an environment has in its interactions with local communities over time. From the point of view of "modernizers," those who believe that the rural Indian must abandon traditional ceremonial and resource sharing before he can become a productive member of the more modern sector of society, one of the desirable effects of change has been the erosion among both the Tzintzuntzeños and the Mayo Indians of the "cargo" system of sponsoring fiestas (Foster, 1967, p. 155).

Those persons at the highest status positions in the community typically made up the wealthier families. Being at the top, however, required heavy expenditures in terms of sponsoring costly fiestas and providing food, entertainment, and religious decorations for local events (Foster, 1967, pp. 196–202). Both Foster and Erasmus, as well as other anthropologists such as Wolf (1966) who have studied peasant societies, seem to agree that the resource cycling process, which ties local economic gains into traditional sociocultural resource sharing, needs to change before sustained development can emerge. They also feel that it will change naturally with incursions of urban consumption goods and opportunities for taking part in the modern market-oriented production system. Yet these opportunities cannot merely be economic. The most basic insight provided by the ecological perspective is that the economic system, political system, cultural identifications, and the institutions and structure of the social system are all interlocked and mutually interdependent. Given the presence or absence of different conditions such as those in Table 9–1, adaptation and succession will follow different courses depending upon the balance of these factors in

creating new interdependencies and resource cycling opportunities. From this perspective, it is instructive to observe how things did change in Tzintzuntzan and in Sonora as a result of government interventions described above.

According to Foster the opportunities needed to push the Indian groups in the direction of successful emulation of the urban middle class are not merely economic, but are often educational, in terms of attaining a better understanding of how to operate successfully in the changed system. They are also "linkage" opportunities, in terms of being linked up to groups, operating in the more modern sector in a way that provides economic and status security. In this respect the Tzintzuntzeños, partially as a result of the CREFAL community development efforts, are better off than the Mayos. Foster writes that each CREFAL program left something of value: "In pottery a number of men learned that there are new ways of producing vessels, and that there are many ways to combine colors and glazes. With the tourist market's growth, and the demand for interesting pieces, an experimental mood now prevails that, without the CREFAL stimulus, would be lacking" (Foster, 1967, p. 340).

In a more general sense, Foster claims that beneficial results were obtained that had little to do with the specific goals of the program. Foster cites an increasing awareness of and interest in the outside world through contacts with CREFAL staff and urban students. There is a growing feeling that city people are not necessarily out to exploit peasants. One native of Tzintzuntzan remarked that he had learned "how to deal with the government, how to meet people, what his constitutional rights were–in short he gained the knowledge and self-confidence which have made him one of the very few individuals who have effectively represented the community in its dealings with the state and national governments" (Foster, 1967, pp. 340–341).

In the Mayo area there appears to be less of a sense of efficacy in dealing with the system. It appears that some Mayos, at least, have exploited the government's development bureaucracy through graft on the local level. If kept within certain bounds, this can be beneficial for some natives and can facilitate the succession process. If the Ejido land reform has failed to introduce new opportunities for individual entrepreneurship on the local level, then the lack of sanctions against corruption functioned to create new opportunities. "The objective of most grafters—particularly those who get away with it—is not to graft and run but to graft and invest. Although most improve their living conditions fairly rapidly, it is usually the ones who are too greedy and who consume their fraudulent gains too conspicuously who provoke legal sanctions. The objective of most successful grafters is to accumulate enough capital to become independent of their government jobs. [Those] who stay in this region buy farm land and become independent farmers" (Erasmus, 1961, p. 227).

An argument for increasing rural initiative and investment among the few innovative and progressive persons could be made by allowing increased opportunities for graft or by increasing exposure to outside experts and people who understand and operate well in the system. For the majority, however, frustration and increasing discontent appear to be the modal responses.

The insecurity that the bulk of the peasant population feels toward the system does not preclude the fact that there is a felt need to get something done. It also reflects an increasing interdependence between the social systems at the community level and the urban areas. Modernizing communications, mass transportation, and extension of control by the urban center can be cited as critical factors. The most significant factor is that in the economic sphere the ability to retain independent patterns of production is decreasing as industrialization in the cities affects the countryside. Household manufacture of fiber products, furniture, and farm tools is declining due to the abundance of cheap factory goods. Erasmus notes that for both Mayos and Yaquis who are dependent upon a more independent way of life, "the ease with which a man can shift from work to leisure as it suits his own convenience is still strongly prized." The increasing dependence on wage labor away from the village is resisted, but seems an irreversible trend (Erasmus, 1967a, p. 59). While wage laborers feel boxed in by daily work hours, there is a feeling that collective members are boxed in by the bank's regulations among those Mayos who are still members of Ejido collectives.

The illegality of renting land adds to the feeling that there is no way out and introduces more graft into the system, for there is pressure to reconsolidate land into larger and more efficient farming units. The pressures such a system makes upon the Indian groups in rural Mexico have obvious implications for succession and preferred modes of adaptation.

From the point of view of a dedicated change agent within this system, it is difficult to be optimistic that the Indian groups as a whole will eagerly embrace the larger system and work diligently through the legitimate channels to take advantage of the rewards of urban Mexico. The Yaquis represent the polar case of hostility toward the larger system, lack of change in the direction of espoused developmental goals, and inability, or unwillingness, to adopt new techniques. Foster concurs with Scott that: "Commercial farming and urban social development probably are unequalled in the free world among countries starting at a similar level of development. On the other hand, thousands of villages like Tzintzuntzan have shared only modestly in this progress, so that the gap between traditional villages and modern urban areas is greater than before the war" (Foster, 1967, p. 248).

Foster illustrates this with the anomaly of the CREFAL projects in Tzintzuntzan, where the population seemed more amenable to change in terms of being more positively oriented, more highly acculturated and urbanized than the other Indian groups. Yet the design and implementation of the interventions did not address themselves to a situation in which villagers were extremely sensitive to "real and imagined slights and insults, derived from generations of unhappy dealings with city people." The CREFAL workers asked the villagers to change their production methods radically, assume heavy debts for new equipment, experiment with untried and imperfect techniques without adequate technical supervision, and then left them to try to market their own products. Given the conservative nature of the community, Foster asserts that even with more aid there might not have been successful project achievement. To more fully understand the roots of this conservatism as it shapes the succession process, it is necessary to explore further the relationships of villagers and country people in Mexico to the government and development agencies, and how the internal structure of village life has been affected by these relations.

In evaluating the relationships of development agencies with the host community, Erasmus emphasizes how involvement with *local* officials affects the chances for success or failure of development projects at the local level. He notes that a health program which failed in Tepoztlan in 1944 was resisted by local officials as it threatened their status and prestige in the eyes of the villagers (Erasmus, 1961, p. 93). Foster notes that one of the obstacles to cooperation between the CREFAL workers and the villagers of Tzintzuntzan was the patronizing and controlling attitude of the CREFAL staff (Foster, 1967, p. 298). Foster emphasizes that "members of such a bureaucratic 'society' share common values . . . engage in professional rituals, and . . . operate on the basis of implicit assumptions about themselves and their goals that normally are not questioned" (Foster, 1967, p. 343). This appears especially true in Mexico where members of the government bureaucracy are, more often than not, Yoris who feel themselves culturally and intellectually superior to the "backward" Indian tribes. They are also usually from urban areas and look down on the relative naiveté and inexperience of rural people (Foster, 1967, p. 344).

Where in the case of the Tzintzuntzeños, the predominant response of the outside world appears to be one of exploitation, the host community is more likely to feel that relying on traditional ways and relationships is much more secure (Foster, 1967, pp. 352–361). In reviewing the causes for failure of the CREFAL projects in Tzintzuntzan, Foster notes that:

Many difficulties that were encountered stemmed from CREFAL planning operations and from the psychological problems of some of the personnel, rather than from deficiencies in the local people themselves . . . people in Tzintzuntzan felt that some of the students and teaching personnel were very patronizing in their attitudes, and that they ordered villagers about in an arbitrary and sometimes humiliating fashion. . . . A second major error . . . also noted in CREFAL itself . . . was the failure to develop a comprehensive, broad plan in which all factors that might bear on success or failure were taken into consideration (Foster, 1967, pp. 344–346).

Foster attributes many of these mistakes to the assumption on the part of CREFAL workers that peasants would be highly cooperative if given a chance, and that a spirit of cooperative work could easily be induced (Foster, 1967, p. 345). Yet peasants apparently found that combining into work cooperatives gave them no more insights into marketing problems or other unresolved questions than they had previously had, while at the same time, these new methods of organization seemed to be less compelling in terms of providing a sense of personal psychological and economic security than had old, sanctioned styles of group interaction. Because of the historical relationships between the Yoris as a ruling class and the Indians as a "peon" class, middle class Yoris tend to identify more strongly with the old landholding families. Scott notes that even today: "There is an overlap in outlook and political ability between those town dwellers and the larger landowners of today . . . they also overlap with the metropolitan middle class . . . both share an adherence to nationally oriented, relatively moderate viewpoints on politics, as well as the traditional Latin middle class-upper class lack of respect for manual or menial labor" (Scott, 1964, p. 72). This problem is added to and reinforced by the continuation of what Mexicans call "personalismo" in political relations, the tendency to identify with an individual leader and follow his directions with blind loyalty (Scott, 1964, p. 94). Opportunities for the operation of this type of relationship have been aggravated by the use of decentralized organizations of the central government. The national leadership had originally hoped such organizations would create effective government agencies at the local level, and at the same time weaken the power of the local "bossism" type of politics. The proliferation of decentralized offices has outpaced the ability of the central government to control them and each has built up an autonomous power base within its operating region (Shafer, 1966, pp. 1–11).

In rural areas, this "every man for himself" attitude has been reinforced by the fact that the central government has historically been more responsive to urban business groups and large commercial farmers. This has left much leeway for local development agencies to operate on their own, while at the same time it has provided them with few resources to help them survive. For example, as rural development banks were forced to give credit to Ejido cooperatives, they moved with little enthusiasm into an area that they felt was unprofitable, and in which they were leery of getting much support from the central government (Vernon, 1964, p. 14). Shafer notes that while there are over ten ministries responsible for agricultural extension work and other aspects of farm production, most are weak ministries with control over few resources and all operate in an uncoordinated, unsystematic fashion (Shafer, 1966, pp. 85–86). At the same time, it is not so much the quantity of resources as it is a matter of controlling organizational improvements and balancing factors of production in the right proportions. An International Bank of Reconstruction and Development Study of Mexico's rural problems emphasized that relatively small expenditures in organizational improvements could produce substantial gains in the use of fertilizer, improved seeds, crop rotation, credit use, and market facilities (Shafer, 1966, p. 189). This assessment is essentially the same as that of other economists studying the rural sector of Mexico. Vernon comments on the lack of sensitivity to resource balance in allocation to small-scale farmers and the persistence of the Ejido system "despite the well advertised weaknesses of that form of land tenure and lack of progress in correcting those weaknesses" (Vernon, 1964, p. 15). While the villagers of Tzintzuntzan were given more personalized attention and were host to a more dedicated corps of change agents, the difficulties that sprang up there seemed similar in nature in some respects to those encountered by other Indian groups in dealing with Ejido staff. One such difficulty noted by Foster was the patronizing attitude of the CREFAL staff, hindering the emergence of self-confidence on the villagers' side.

Other factors that bear on the succession problem that are cited by Foster include: the relating of social goals to the economic reality of the villagers' conditions; the development of skills not directly related to, but necessary for, the effective use of new production techniques such as sound marketing, bookkeeping, and financial skills; and the integration of technical goals with the social reality of the local community ecosystem (Foster, 1967, p. 362). Thus, in Tzintzuntzan, while there is more of a desire to move away from traditional resource cycling patterns, this movement is hindered by a lack of new forms of social interdependency, resulting in a need to rely on intravillage, familiar relationships; consequently, forms of the social structure have not changed markedly. As a result of this and the manner in which change agents dealt with the villagers, the range of skills needed to deal with

urban people and the urban economy are not yet available within the village. This absence again acts as a block to transformation of the economy to a more dynamic phase. The Mayos, on the other hand, are beginning to feel more at home dealing in a Yori world, and feel more constrained by their environment to do so perhaps than do the villagers of Tzintzuntzan. Thus they are adopting some new references and desires. Yet they are even less technically skilled than the Tzintzuntzeños and the successful entrepreneur is still the exception rather than the rule. The succession process has also been shaped by the fact that changes in life styles and interdependencies offer less cultural and psychological security than the older status forms which are seen as more and more inadequate.

Contrasting these two areas with the Yaqui tribal reservation, the succession process has moved this tribe the least distance away from the traditional peasant pattern. Traditional status and resource cycling forms are still perceived as adequate and preferable due to the combination of factors. These included a history of hostile relations, negative interactions with development agents, physical isolation, strong group support for unchanging life styles and interdependencies, and the success the Yaqui leadership has had in resisting manipulation. The most pressing question is not whether slow and halting evolution can be speeded up as in the case of the other two groups, but how long this resistance can be contained within the reservation. Answering these questions in the context of ecologically designed interventions is the subject of the next section.

Summary

The principle of succession deals with the effects external interventions have on shaping long-term responses to change. As such it is the most difficult to neatly summarize. The Tzintzuntzeños have become most linked to the urban economy, but in a socially inferior manner and with inadequate individual opportunity. Stagnation in this culture could perhaps be predicted to continue the longest despite economic development efforts. The dependency effect and the lack of channels for individual initiative appeared most fixed at the time field studies were done. The Yaqui group, given the right inputs, could conceivably become the most dynamic and rapidly changing without community development if the political constraints of the Ejidos were lifted. Within the Mayo tribe there seems to be the most potential for diversity, individual expression entrepreneurship for moving into the "Yori World." It could be predicted that for the Mayos, strict economic development projects could be most successful.

In conclusion, the principle of succession is useful, for it provides a basis for comparing not only stages but also varying dynamic modes by which communities adapt over time to their larger environments. Without reference to such a principle, persons involved in community development can restrict their interpretations to more blatant, pathological forces; problems can be defined and understood with greater opportunity for resolution if they are seen as unique phases of development which are predictable by-products of natural events. The use of this principle forces the development worker to broaden the time period under consideration and apply a different view of each community, given the stage that particular population is at at that particular time.

This principle, along with the other three ecological principles reviewed above, is advocated as a useful and convincing concept for understanding the complex, chaotic processes of community change. The manner in which different groups manage adaptation, interdependence, and resource cycling enables the planner to gain critical insights into how the population relates to its locale, how resources are used and misused, and how changes in styles of coping emerge. Thus one can plan how to best utilize local and outside talent, and can create mechanisms that lead to more optimal methods for development. Utilization of the insights of the ecological perspective, reviewed for the three Indian groups in Mexico in the previous section, enables us to begin to understand some of the basic meanings and implications of the words "community development."

INTEGRATION OF PLANNED CHANGE
WITH THE LOCAL ECOLOGY

Most rural villages in Mexico are now inextricably bound up, politically and economically, with the larger culture. Ecological principles suggest that for planning goals to be effective an intervention must define how new interdependencies will be affected. A case in point is the evolving relationship of the Ejido bank to the population within the Yaqui reservation. Because of the greater sense of control the Yaquis have in the community, the management of the Ejido bank has moved more in line with the internal political structure of the reservation (Erasmus, 1967a, p. 26).

Although the bank is still in tight control of financing, one result has been that the incidence of corruption by local leadership also seems to be much less in the Yaqui area, as the Socio Delagados, leaders of the credit societies, are more integrated into the local community structure. An intervention designed for this system would have to differ greatly from one designed for Tzintzuntzan where the peasants drawn initially into the CREFAL cooperative became dependent on outside resources but acquired few new insights that helped them to deal more effectively with the outside world. The cooperative system, as set up by the CREFAL staff, seemed to be less compelling in terms of providing a sense of personal psychological and economic security than were older, more traditionally sanctioned styles of group interaction.

In assessing the succession process in the Yaqui area, Erasmus introduces the concept of the "peasant" ecotype and asserts that changing this ecotype, which includes creation of new technology, transportation, and market availability, is the determining condition for the evolution to a more developed ecotype. He concludes that: "Removing economic exploitation (funds of rent) without radically changing the ecotype will result in new forms of exploitation and little change in the level and quality of living . . . redistribution of land in small 'decommoditized' plots [will effect] a subsistence level of 'security' [which] will help rural peoples retain such peasant characteristics as ceremonial service, multiple interest coalitions, and the primitive technology of a minimal replacement fund" (Erasmus, 1967b, p. 379).

When this type of change is combined with ethnic differences and low social status, then social isolation and a low degree of social mobility and adaptation can be predicted to persist in spite of available alternatives in production and consumption patterns. Erasmus also predicts that Indians perceiving the changes in the ecosystem around them will view achievements of peers as a measure of their own inadequacy and may act together "in bringing sanctions against the mobile individual as a means of protecting their own self-image" (Erasmus, 1967b, p. 379).

Assessing these issues in terms of the ecological principles presented in Table 9–1, it is possible to evaluate their relevance for the developmental process. Starting with the interdependence principle, the problems the peasant groups have had in operating in the larger economic system and the irrelevance of local forms of help-giving to the urban oriented economy are dealt with. In the political sphere, each of the three groups is to some degree isolated from the national political process, including the Tzintzuntzeños who are most linked into the system. In terms of the development of agent/client relationships, conflicting forms of legitimization of the development agents' role in the local socioeconomic system on the part of the host community in Tzintzuntzan, as well as within the regular government bureaucracy, have prevented movement toward development goals.

With reference to the adaptation dimension, provision of manpower training to the local populations of Mexico's villages has been minimal, with the exception of areas such as Tzintzuntzan, where it was inadequate in several respects. In Tzintzuntzan, new resources made available were not always relevant to local needs, and they were often presented in ways that conflicted with local norms concerning organizational styles and individual efforts. The villages of Tzintzuntzan are just beginning to feel that the locus of decision making is accessible to some degree, while the situation is worse in the other areas studied. Opportunities for new status positions are still extremely limited and the same is true of educational opportunities beyond primary school. The new role opportunities that have emerged are either not socially legitimized in the village or haven't the linkages needed to ensure the successful emergence of a new status level. While the CREFAL workers attempted to introduce cooperative working arrangements, the villages neither identified with them nor felt they could be effective in gaining leverage on the larger system by organizing.

While business groups were allowed to organize themselves into formal business organizations, and there has been a history of give and take between government agencies and entrepreneurial groups, in the rural sector the Ejido programs have been much less responsive or flexible. The government and rural banks seem to have operated with a paternal and patronizing attitude, with little accountability to the peasants (Shafer, 1966, pp. xxi–xxiv). Anderson writes that: "There is little evidence to suggest that policy making in the development banks is dominated by their clientele groups. Rather the more general pattern is for the development banks to be used to encourage performance by their clientele deemed desirable in terms of general economic policy considerations. The relationship of the banks to their clientele is more apt to be tutelary or directive than responsive" (Anderson & Glade, 1968, pp. 168–169).

Anderson claims in consequence that the sources of influence for credit sources "fell into the hands of the better prepared, upwardly mobile farmers ... which viewed from below, seemed to represent the arbitrary power based on the imperative need for credit" (Anderson & Glade, 1968, p. 171). A Mexican social scientist, Dr. Lucis Mandiete y Nuñez, claims that "the Ejidal cooperatives are a farce. There are no cooperatives of this type. The Bank decides how much [the peasants] can make" (Nuñez, 1968).

In the case of Yaqui groups, the fight to retain their tribal land seems to have accentuated their sensitivity to this type of exploitation, and they resent very much Ejido control over the use of their land exercised through dispensation of credit. Erasmus writes that "jealousy over their land is still the Yaquis' major concern and the major inspiration of their continued tribal identity" (Erasmus, 1961, p. 204). The "emotional satisfaction derived from ceremonial service and the social approval and support of self-esteem which it involves" are more rewarding to Yaqui Indians than attempting to join lower class Yori society (Erasmus, 1967a, p. 119).

Designing Ecological Interventions

A change program designed as an ecological intervention considers the relationship of the economic, cultural, and political systems of the host community and attempts to assess the effects of any change upon the interrelationships of these systems. The principle of interdependence focuses upon how the various processes of the society are related. The adaptation principle helps in determining how persons or groups of persons are responding to the society in dominant activities. The cycling-of-resources principle specifies how persons in and outside of the society are involved in carrying out the work of the society. The succession principle focuses on the society's future level of development.

Each of these principles provides guidelines for designing interventions which take into account the properties of the total ecosystem, and thereby can help to create a change program which increases the probability of the society to initiate and accommodate to interventions which are truly developmental. The authors believe that the utility of ecological concepts affirms the types of resources to be combined in specific ways to assist local communities to adapt to change. The authors' thesis is that therapeutic interventions designed to produce social change can be planned and implemented to increase the level of development of a community, producing both short-term and long-term effects for the functions of the society and future generations who live there.

In the previous sections, ecological principles were presented to assess the three cultures. It was intended that these ideas could provide an assessment of those groups, particularly regarding their adaptation to internal changes as well as responses to external events. It is hoped that the previous sections have achieved this purpose and have illuminated new facets of the social structure of these populations.

Ecological principles, because they derive from organic processes of social environments, focus upon critical events affecting the culture and have therefore particular value for designing preventive interventions. The following sections of the chapter will present specific guidelines for development programs derived from this preceding analysis. Each of these ecological principles can generate guidelines for programs which are relevant for each of the three groups. What follows are such designs proposed for each group in order

to illustrate how ecology can be useful in designing programs that are true to the culture and effective for program goals.

Elements of Contrasting Interventions

Table 9–4 presents five elements to assess interventions designed for different cultural settings. The formulation of the interventions has derived from an analysis of the needs of the three cultures rather than any one specific method of community development. All of the five elements are viewed as interrelated.

The Yaquis

The first element, source of the intervention, refers to the background and locale for the change program. For example, with the Yaquis, the geographical location for the intervention program is considered critical. Here, specific reference is made to land adjacent to the Yaqui tribe as the site for the change program. It is here that a group of community development workers could locate. Their program for development could be to take advantage of every opportunity to establish effective communication with the Yaquis. The second element, direction of the intervention process, is presented in order to specify the type of interactions between the client and the development program. In this case the direction of the development program flows from the host environment to the Yaqui tribe since the first phase of the intervention process will not involve direct responses from the Yaqui tribe. The informal reconnaissance for the intervention program is expected to reach the perimeter of the Yaqui culture. Its purpose is to establish contacts at the periphery of the Yaqui community. Given the hostile Yaqui mode of relating to the larger environment, there is no attempt proposed in the change program to forge a major intervention into the nucleus of the Yaqui social structure. The next element, the media for the intervention, refers to the specific content of the intervention. In the case of the Yaquis, the media refers to the presence of community development workers close to the Yaqui tribe. Here the aim is to offer relevant services to the tribe when opportunities arise. The rationale for this type of intervention is the expected lack of positive responses of the Yaquis to the host environment. In this case,

TABLE 9–4

Ecological Interventions for Three Mexican Villages

Dimensions of the Intervention	Yaqui	Mayo	Tzintzuntzeños
Locale for the Intervention:	Adjacent area to the tribe	A few social settings close to family units	Selected multiple and clearly marked sites
Direction of the Intervention Process:	Unidirectional and incomplete	Unidirectional and focused	Reciprocal between village and host environment
Media for Intervention:	Community development workers create opportunities for social interaction (work at the boundaries of the community)	Improving *economic* solvency of tribe when in host environment (work with the family)	Improving *Political* effectiveness of tribe when in host environment (work on the community social structure)
Focus upon Local Culture:	Help tribe to interact with host environment	Expand and diversify local culture	Create new political leadership in local and host culture
Criteria for Evaluating Intervention:	Increased reciprocal communication between Yaqui and host environment	Strengthening family structure and generating *new* primary groups	Increase economic solvency of the population in host environment

rather than attempting to change the culture of the Yaqui Indians, the ecological intervention is to assist the Yaqui tribe to tolerate the neighboring host environment. If the change program is effective, subsequent interventions then can expand and focus upon more important aspects of the dominant culture of the host environment as well as the Yaqui culture.

Another element of the intervention process is the criteria for evaluating the intervention. This important element defines how the other four elements are brought together and how they are related to the outcome of the intervention. For the Yaquis, an ecological intervention derived according to the above ideas is expected to increase the communication between the tribe and the host environment. This modest and tenuous goal is suggested as the method of choice, given the level of nonacculturation and primitive response to non-Yaqui.

An elaboration of the elements for the two other populations illustrates contrasting interventions. The presentation of interventions for the Yaquis, Mayos, and Tzintzuntzeños represents a continuum of interventions, ranging from an attempt to initiate a dialogue for social interactions between the host environment and the Yaqui tribe to programs for increasing the economic solvency of the Mayos or improving the political effectiveness of the Tzintzuntzeños. The assumption is that the three cultures are sufficiently different and require varied interventions. Economic development programs are viewed as viable after the establishment of functional ties between the host community and the surrounding community. It is also suggested that interventions focusing upon political development can thrive if there is first an adequate economic base.

The Mayos

With reference to the Mayo village, it is expected that this particular tribe could tolerate the introduction of community development agents from the major culture and that their presence would be accepted and utilized. Opportunities for the Mayo natives to develop and merchandise their goods for purchase by the native culture is an expected outcome. The development workers would be prepared to operate in a number of technical roles and could utilize these economic opportunities to teach the Mayos significant aspects about their own culture. The preferred attitude of the development workers toward the local culture is to accept the core culture and expand and diversify the local culture via economic programs. This type of program is based upon the assumption that the Mayo culture, in contrast to the Yaqui culture, is ready to increase its economic base and can accommodate to the larger culture. The broadening of the Mayo culture is expected to follow as the new products of the culture are created and thereby increase the communication between the two cultures. In order for this side benefit to be realized, the community development workers will need to expend a great deal of effort in order to train the Mayos in successful coping of the dominant cultures. The criterion for this type of program is to utilize the success of the marketplace as a source for systemic change in the culture. An ecological criterion proposed for the evaluation of the intervention is an analysis of new patternings in the family structure of the tribes. The desired effects of a bountiful economy are not to replace the ways of the native culture with a new culture, but instead to create new expressions, new morphologies for the family and primary groups. If the Mayos are unable to develop economically so as to take advantage of resources located in the urban area, then needed or desired changes in the Mayo family are expected to be slow in emerging. This may in turn hinder cultural, social, and economic adaptations to the larger culture.

One example of how economic change has proceeded without adequate intervention strategies is cited by Erasmus. It refers to a Mayo who opened a store and achieved more status in the community by becoming a "man of business." Yet his interpersonal relationships with the community were such that he was forced to extend unlimited credit to fellow villagers. The probability that debts will be repaid by members of the community lessens as debts grow. The store-owning family then had to think of ways to use local labor in order to realize at least some form of repayment. While Mayos increasingly are interested in taking part in the larger economy and want to reap its long- as well as short-term benefits, that is, sending their children to high school and college or building new homes, they have trouble altering their reference group or understanding how to establish and maintain ties with the economy of the urban areas.

With the right mix of economic resources relevant to the entrepreneurial opportunities of the Mayo environment, the conditions under which rapid economic change can proceed could be made evident to the more energetic and innovative members of the tribe. Opportunities in retail trade, setting up processing factories, obtaining credit from urban sources, taking advantage of a wider range of urban financial, capital, and business resources, and dealing with urban buyers and commercial people in general could become more relevant to the incipient Mayo entrepreneur. In so doing the Mayos could be open to changing their life styles in order to cope with new· demands. As the energies of the Mayos are transferred to new economic forms, such as setting up retail stores, or wholesale dealerships, or even working in and/or forming factories, the demands for resource sharing and ceremonial forms of status seeking will need to be replaced systematically with other ways of contributing to the welfare of the community. The status of the individual could be defined in terms of their moving the system toward higher levels of development. A new way to seek status is via the acquisition of manufactured goods. Another, which has come to dominate many ex-colonial countries, is getting as much education for children as possible. These trends can prove as dysfunctional as older ceremonial forms if they are not linked in to a dynamic economy. If this is not developed then new family structures will not emerge, and the educated son will either return and live with the extended family and do nothing or he will be forced to use the bulk of his earnings to support an extended family back in Sonora no matter where he works. New forms of economic activities, such as food processing or furniture factories, plastics industries, etc., can prove more conducive to the evolution of a nuclear family system toward which the Mayos are already moving. If economic growth is rapid, the development agent, to prevent dislocations in the social structure, must provide attachments to businessmen and others in urban areas and provide opportunities for the Mayo to emulate successfully some Yori life-styles.

The storekeeper mentioned above has done this to some extent by putting a brick veneer on his home, paving his floors with cement, and purchasing a truck for 50,000 pesos. Although the truck is worth ten times his store inventories, it is a good status symbol for his dealings with urban Yori wholesalers. Still, he is accused by his relatives of being stingy and not sharing his wealth with them (Erasmus, 1967a, p. 64).

This storekeeper, and the few others like him who have attempted to move into the more modern economy, is sacrificing much to attempt to live in two worlds to the extent that he can survive in both. Erasmus concludes this example with the observation that were it not for the herds of cattle this man owns, his store would collapse. When he gets too far in debt, he can recoup with sales of cattle (Erasmus, 1967a, p. 64). In order to loosen these types of constraints on this storekeeper, not only must his perspective change, but also new opportunities must be brought to other families who continue to pressure the storekeepers for support.

Mayos and Yaquis—Some Contrasts

In the instance of the Yaqui tribe, the ecological interventions were designed to support an increase in reciprocal communication between the two tribes and the larger community. For the Yaqui program there is proposed to be a looseness, an undefined effort upon the part of the development program that includes positive responses to all opportunities for maximizing communication. In the case of the Mayo tribe, the style of the development program is more clearly defined and is purposely focused on a narrow sector of the Mayo culture, that which is already moving in the direction of modernization. At the same time the program is sensitive to the total culture of the Mayos. The ecology for the development program is to feed its successes back into the family structure. The opportunistic aspect of this program is that it draws upon the activities of the economic program to increase the interaction between the development agents and the indigenous and primary group leaders. Such occasions including new ceremonial occasions can function as critical social settings for the evolution of the culture.

Some advantage can be made of some of the new ceremonial forms already emerging in the Mayo areas such as public dances and performances of dance troupes. Such events are already moving away from an identification with religious festivals to more secular affairs where males are charged an admission fee and females allowed in free. In other developing countries, such as Taiwan, it is customary for local businesses and factories to sponsor festivals, feasts, and even parades and athletic contexts. The development team could initially take on the role of initiating new ceremonial forms such as athletic contests, dances, or cooperative group meetings spanning the range from more ceremonial dinners to seminars on how to finance a business or utilize technological inputs to agriculture. The sponsorship of such activities increasingly could be transferred to emerging institutions such as farmer or business cooperatives and local business leader and factory owner associations and clubs.

That this type of strategy is inappropriate for the Yaqui tribe is made obvious by observations of their reactions not only to changed ceremonial forms such as public dancing, which is considered by the vast majority unsuitable for Yaqui girls, but also by their negative reaction to the control or sponsorship of anything by outside change agents. In 1948 a Mexican general, General Guerrero, attempted to gain control over the finances of the reservation by substituting puppet governors of his choosing in each pueblo. By 1959 all of these governors had been thrown out of power and traditional Yaqui governors reinstated (Erasmus, 1967a, p. 26). This reaction reinforces the negative attitude toward outside control of the Ejido banks. Erasmus concludes that there is no reason to believe recent changes in the form of the Ejido collectives are creating any divisive effects within the tribe which would tend to weaken their solidarity: "Most of the animosity is directed against the Ejido bank, in other words, against the Yori and the outsider as usual. At harvest time, when members of the credit societies steal wheat that is supposed to go to the Ejido bank to pay operation costs and other debts as well as member's 'profits'—for their own household consumption, the socio delegado and the vigilante look the other way" (Erasmus, 1967a, p. 28).

The Yaquis apparently have not had much reason to change their image of the larger culture since the days when they carried on guerrilla warfare against the Mexican government. They see their continued distrust and hatred of Mexican officials in charge of development and credit agencies as justified by the exploitive nature of the relationship and their observations of the increasing wealth of these officials, gained through officials' positions relative to the economic stagnation within the Yaqui population.

Thus it appears that increased communication may not initially take place around development goals per se, but must emerge in the context of showing that a community of development workers can live contiguously with the Yaqui reservation without exploiting the resources of the tribe or denigrating its culture and historical role in the immediate area. Given the tribal orientation of the Yaquis, communication would be difficult, and a challenge to the most dedicated. Yet perhaps initiative taken by the development group *not* to attempt to change Yaqui economic or ceremonial forms but to reinforce their ecological validity and dignity could create a sense of mutual respect. Waiting for Yaqui leaders to perceive opportunities for fruitful contacts and initiate them themselves may require Herculean patience within a development community, but could prove more productive for later and more rapid and positive orientations and interchanges.

One aspect of the wait-and-see orientation that would be taken toward the Yaquis is the possibility that they would themselves begin to take advantage of and use the infrastructure and facilities that would be made available. This point was strongly made by Erasmus in a recent communication to the authors about a visit there in 1969. He observed the rapid urbanization process that had taken place within the Yaqui area in the last ten years due to the building of the Pan American Highway in that region. As a result of the construction effort, the Vicam Station, built within the reservation, has become a bustling commercial center. This has been a side effect of the building of the highway and not a direct economic development gain in itself. Yet it has resulted in a dynamic change process.

Now that the Yaquis have obtained irrigation and more control over their land, one example would be to locate an agricultural experimental station and a food processing plant in a region contiguous to the Yaqui reservation. Such a site could take advantage of modern packaging and/or freezing techniques to process food grown on and around the experimental farm. If this should prove productive and profitable as an innovation, interest might be aroused and Yaqui leaders might come forward and take advantage of opportunities to learn how to mix new technological inputs or can and package their own cash crops for sale in urban markets. The experimental farms could also raise cattle and other livestock to experiment with the best breeds for that particular natural setting. This could provide the rationale for the setting up of experimental farms since the region already supports a large number of cattle ranches run by commercial Yori farmers.

One of the most important functions that could develop out of such a center is the employment and training opportunities that could be offered to young Yaqui Indians, whose families' farms within the reservation are not large or productive enough to give them full-time employment or a cultivatable land of their own. Higher wages and job training could lure a large portion of younger Yaquis out of the reservation to work on experimental farms or within the laboratory and food processing plants.

This opportunity for younger members of the tribe could be the most critical aspect of the intervention strategy. Implications for the viability of the urbanization and modernization of the larger culture as well as the future of the Yaqui tribe are contained in the problem of Yaqui youth. With little economic opportunity within the reservation and the decreasing ability of the tribal elders to hold the extended family together, the uneducated and unacculturated youth of the Yaqui tribe, and tribes similar in ecological heritage, will migrate to urban areas to look for higher paying jobs. They will arrive in urbanizing areas with a low social status, a background of hostility to the dominant culture, and will undoubtedly be forced into menial jobs; it is difficult to be optimistic about their assimilation into the urban society.

An additional factor to consider is the toughness developed as a by-product emerging from the subsistence level environment of the tribal reservation, namely the self-selection by those who are strong enough to break away from the tribal culture. These young Yaquis could develop a socially deviant orientation along the lines of rural southerners in the United States who migrated to the large urban areas during rapid growth periods here. Alienating themselves from the values of the larger society because of an inability to achieve in

it and/or a history of hostile relations inculcated through early socialization, they could emerge as a distinct subculture. If such a process did occur, young militants could in all probability act as foci of leadership around which disaffected young Indians of many tribal origins could organize, including those similar in background to the Mayo tribe.

A primary factor reducing this consequence of inadequate development could be the reaction Erasmus writes of when describing the dealings of members of all tribal groups with members of the larger society. They tend to show an obsequiousness and humility which he labels the "Encogido Syndrome," mentioned above in the discussion of the principle of adaptation. This response could continue as a coping style in urban areas. Yet the ecology of the city in the United States has led to a gradual weakening of this type of response on the part of southern blacks in urban areas over time; a similar trend could probably be predicted in Mexico's cities as well. Another mitigating factor could be a more rapid acceptance of the validity and status of Indian culture in Mexico's urban areas.

Erasmus writes that the rural Indian tends to denigrate Yori culture and aggrandize traditional Indian society in order to rationalize his failure to achieve status and material success in the larger culture (Erasmus, 1967b). This outlet would be almost impossible in an urban setting where the society functions largely within the context of the dominant Yori culture. Thus, more extreme forms of deviance and organized hostility seem predictable as responses to low status, nonacceptance, and an economically marginal "niche." The remaining factor which would act to prevent the formation of such an alienated subculture in the cities could be the emergence of an ability by the Yaqui tribe as a whole to exploit their tribal environment much more rapidly than they are presently. Economic growth could accelerate at a rapid pace to retain the younger, more dynamic members on the reservation and absorb the labor produced by population growth at rising standards of living. Given the historical account provided by Erasmus, this does not seem too probable without an intervention designed similarly to the one suggested here.

Given the initial hostility of the Yaqui tribe and the unwillingness of many to work outside the reservation, it is possible that greater incentives and inducements would have to be provided for the entire tribe in order to induce the tribe to release a significant number of its younger members to work in a development project. Such incentives could include offers to share the productivity of experimental farms with the Yaquis, focused primarily on providing cattle and other produce for the Yaqui ceremonial feasts, and enabling the Yaquis to reinvigorate their festival schedule. Other incentives could be the offer of supplies of fertilizer and other needed technical inputs to Yaqui agriculture, or supplying cattle to enable the Yaquis to build tribal herds. With time, if Yaqui leaders show an interest, seminars could be offered to improve agricultural techniques or to organize credit cooperatives.

The development group should let it be known to the tribal leaders that by employing and training younger tribal members they are preparing them for two choices: to go into the larger culture better equipped to survive and even prosper or to return to the tribe as development agents themselves, working with their own people to improve the development of the reservation and pass on to others improved economic and social opportunities. As the program gathers some momentum, the development agent group could sit down with the group's leaders and explore how the group as a whole can best utilize these better equipped members and how they can accommodate them as they return to the culture. This is, of course, a difficult task, as shown by the experience in the village of Tzintzuntzan, where after many villagers had the opportunity to spend two to six months in California as migrant laborers they became the disaffected villagers after their return to Tzintzuntzan (Foster, 1967, pp. 30, 275–277). With this social support, such a program may succeed.

While the possibility remains that the Yaqui youth migrating to urban areas will marry into Mestizo families and become Mexicanized and accommodate to the larger culture, the fact is that not many Mayo Indian youth do this. The impact of the Yaqui heritage suggests that this type of adaptation to a hostile urban environment may prove the exception rather than the rule. Provision of some kind of mediating and equilibrating resources, such as suggested above, may provide social functions that were lacking during periods of urbanization in the United States. The fundamental aim is to provide immigrants with better preparation for widening the choice of their niches and coping styles within the larger environment and to develop opportunities for the Yaqui tribe to participate more fully in the development process.

The Tzintzuntzeños

The intervention program for the Tzintzuntzeños can be more comprehensive in view of the fact that the direction of the Tzintzuntzeños' development is already toward the level of the more dominant culture. The villagers' urbanization and their motivation to move further already have been demonstrated. The development program in this case could draw upon a wide array of talent from the larger culture and would attempt to maximize the reciprocity between the host culture and the Tzintzuntzeños, not only via an increase in patterns of communication but in a wide variety of activities. It is expected that there could exist a mutual cultural exchange program providing a continuous basis for interaction between the two cultures. One premise is that the major limitations in the development of this culture is the small number of occasions in which the members of the village have been able to develop political constituencies. One possible medium for the political solvency of the Tzintzuntzeños is a series of community development programs, where emphasis is placed upon training a wide representation of citizens to receive training in methods and skills in political development. The critical features of this development program are that the host environment must be able to tolerate the rapid development of the Tzintzuntzeños in their demands for greater involvement in advocating self-determination for their village members. The program with its multiple programs for helping the citizen to organize politically and for developing resources for political influence at all segments of the society will place demands upon the established political order. An essential aspect of the intervention is to forge linkages between the training programs and those decision-making groups which are likely to be recipients of the training program. Several supplementary effects of the design may be required to loosen the dominant social structure of the host environment in order to facilitate achieving the purpose of the design. For example, simultaneously with efforts to provide political training for members of the village, opportunities for members of the dominant culture to accommodate to the increased effective demands of the Tzintzuntzeños will also be needed. The assumption is made that an adequate design for the political development of the Tzintzuntzeños must require the effective absorption and utilization of the new political constituency. Without a readiness upon the part of the host culture to respond to a new political awareness, the training program will not be able to realize any benefits for its intended good works. The aim of the training program is to create new leadership for the local culture. Without explicit signs of the effectiveness of such programs both for the local culture and the dominant culture, it is unlikely that the intervention will be valid. The interrelationships between the local group and the dominant culture are then critical for the adaptation of the larger culture and the evolution of the smaller culture.

There is another type of interdependence that is ecological, namely the criteria for evaluating the various types of training programs. For each local group the intervention can be evaluated in terms of increased economic development for that local area. This is mentioned for two reasons. One is that such a point defines how two kinds of ecological subsystems can be related. Secondly, the basis for an ecologically designed change program is the extent to which the positive gains of a political intervention are expressed in terms that are beyond those critieria normally employed to assess political gains. It is not enough to link the accomplishment of an intervention to an increase in the number of registered voters or to increased participation in political affairs. The ecological criteria are whether the effects of political training do result in more jobs, more high level careers for the members of the group, and the appearance of new careers. The measure of increased political influence is seen in increased economic benefits. This type of design is considered relevant for the Tzintzuntzeños, for it relates to the momentum of the Tzintzuntzeños' urbanization.

The interventions proposed for each of the three Mexican communities differed from each other. The program designed for the Mayo population utilized the strengths of the family unit as the host for economic development. Since economic development is progressing in the Tzintzuntzeños community, the design for this population emphasized an increase in political efficacy in order to insure that any benefits from new economic resources can be returned for the cultural development of the Tzintzuntzeños population. As the assessment illustrated, the proper initial ecological intervention with the Yaquis is to create resources near the Yaqui population without intruding on or exploiting their community. Such a design for the Yaquis may seem like no design, but it is a plan which provides the possibility of help while appreciating the ecological validity of Yaqui autonomy.

These analyses have been proposed for a specific local community at a particular point in time and fit a design for change to the unique local conditions. Analyses generated by the more traditional approaches reviewed earlier in the chapter represent universal treatments for most all occasions without generally focusing on the community's unique ecology. The intervention plans derived in this chapter emerge from analyses of historic events and social processes at the local level so as to predict dynamic and long-term change in multiple sectors (e.g., family units, larger social structures, economic bases, and political structures). It is assumed that an appreciation of these interrelationships allows for the design of a development program that can aid personal and social adaptations and make it possible for new kinds of resources to be generated within each community.

SUMMARY

The brief outline of designs for interventions for the three Mexican villages has been presented to provide examples of how ecological ideas can be useful for stimulating intervention programs as well as for assessing the local culture.

The most salient illustration from the literature upon which this chapter draws is that presented by Foster of. the CREFAL development agents. Some of the difficulties they had dealing with the villagers of Tzintzuntzan have been mentioned earlier. One explanation of their inability to motivate the peasant population they were dealing with is that they entered the village with a very narrow view of what community development is, and a narrow idea of what resources needed to be employed. When their preconception failed them, they defended their own sense of inadequacy by falling back on their cultural superiority, concepts of the inherent laziness and stupidity of rural Indians, and similar notions. Manifestations of this attitude in dealing with the peasants made their relationships deteriorate even further. Apparently no attempt was made to go beyond this vicious circle to look for unanticipated causes or alternate resources.

As far as the Ejido banks are concerned, these were controlled by a distant and unsympathetic bureaucracy which failed to differentiate among unique localities in terms of needs and constraints. At the same time the cultural norms of the rural bureaucratic society sanctioned corruption and personal aggrandizement, but did not foster or allow empathic concern for the client to lend to a broader range of attempted solutions or even new conceptualizations. The ecological ideas, in their proposed validity, are presented in this chapter to provide a theoretical perspective to stimulate programs for change that work, and to assist the evolution of communities. The axiom has been: concepts from biological ecology provide a significantly different view of the environment, a view which emphasizes the natural processes of adaptation, interdependence, resource cycling, and succession intrinsic to local communities. The power of the ecological analogy provides a point of view for the design of interventions that takes into account the varied properties of contrasting environments. An ecological design for therapeutic interventions includes concepts for reducing the limitations when programs for change are derived from the local culture. The local culture and the design of the change program are coupled within an ecological design. While the designs for ecological interventions may not be revolutionary in the eyes of the citizens, they are most often radical in the demands they make upon the professional development workers.

As the above examples have portrayed, serious and meaningful change in cultures that are foreign to the development program requires programs that go beyond the technical and substantive competencies of the development agent. If such programs are truly developmental, they demand at least two types of shifts in professional training. One is that the professional can no longer be just an economist or a political scientist, he must see the benefits and limitations of his work for a particular host environment. Secondly, professionals must recognize that meaningful change comes as a result of putting together know-how from varied sources and creating interdisciplinary programs. Since no single profession provides this synthesis, ecological concepts are suggested as a baseline for developing new conceptions for social change. It is hoped that the illustrations from these three Mexican populations do offer a frame of reference that is useful and thereby valid for further explorations.

CONCLUSION

The case material presented in this chapter is an example of the use of ecological concepts for assessing and changing local communities. The purpose of the chapter has been to illustrate how an ecological view, a view derived from a dynamic conception of the locale and its interrelationships with the surrounding environment, can generate a new model of the change process. From the ecological view, change is not considered as the sole result of the interventions of the professional practitioner and is not restricted to the specification of short-term goals stimulated by a single development program. Community development as an ecological enterprise is not conceived to be related to the participation of a small group of clients. In contrast, the ideas presented in this chapter view change as an ongoing and evolutionary process. The power of an ecological perspective is that it helps to guide the development of long-range planning and helps assess the effects of interventions upon the functioning of the various segments of a community. The premises of ecology are that an externally imposed intervention alters the entire ecosystem. The ethic of ecology assumes that a development program anticipates the effects of the intervention upon the ecosystem before the program is developed.

The symmetry of the ecological perspective affirms that the same concepts used for assessment can provide a basis for designing change. Within the helping professions, traditional concepts, often useful for understanding the plights of people and communities, are not the same concepts that help us design our change programs or help us make sense of our aspirations. Very often there is no relationship between our finely chiseled clarifications of what is wrong and our awkward gropings and vague stirrings for what to do. The ecological analogy is offered as sets of ideas which can help us clear our heads and focus our efforts on activities that are of consequence. It is hoped that the case materials of the three Mexican villages and the proposed change programs for these varied communities have suggested ideas that are valid for the development of a psychology of the community.

Community psychology has largely been restricted by concepts that have come from a psychology of sick individuals. Community psychology has not yet been able to develop a framework for relationships of effective individuals to varied environments. The ecological perspective can bring clarity to both of these topics, for the community is perceived to have an organic quality. The assessment of the community includes knowledge of processes and functions of the locale as well as knowledge of various groupings of persons assembled according to their particular place in that locale. For the ecological perspective, the person is a part of the environment, and the behavior of persons is seen as interdependent with the environment and vice versa. The second author has remarked elsewhere that community psychology is beyond psychology and requires a new set of premises and a new set of methods to design preventive interventions (Kelly, 1970, 1971). The ecological viewpoint is proposed to get us moving in these new ways.

By focusing upon the three Mexican villages the authors have presented a framework for beginning the mandatory and exciting tasks of changing our local communities here in the United States. As the three Mexican villages varied in their development, a sample of communities in the United States would also be expected to vary. The task of the community psychologist is to define the psychological functions and resources that can assist our locales to achieve constructive, long-term change. The authors offer these ideas as a stimulus to generate new ways of thinking about change in our local communities.

Notes

The authors of this work are deeply indebted to those who carried out the field work and provided background material and critical comments for this chapter. We would like especially to thank Charles Erasmus whose field work in northwestern Mexico and whose publications enabled us to understand much about Sonoran Indian society and its adaptation to the changing rural scene. We are also appreciative of the comments and suggestions of Professor Erasmus to both early and final versions of this chapter. Similarly we would like to acknowledge Eric Wolf for his very helpful critical comments concerning both the theoretical and descriptive sections of the chapter. The work of George Foster and his students, in their detailed analysis of development projects in Tzintzuntzan, enabled us to broaden our comparative framework. We also acknowledge Dr. Foster's careful and constructive review of final chapters. For much of our theoretical orientation, we are indebted to the insights provided by Clifford Geertz through his studies of peasant societies in southeast Asia, to Walter Goldschmidt for his cross-cultural insights, and to the late Julian Steward for his theoretical contributions to the area of social change and development. Roy Rappaport also aided us in viewing development problems in the context of cultural ecology.

We would also like to thank Merikay Bryan for her untiring work on the technical aspects of the paper and for her patience with us. Our appreciation also goes to Leonard Bryan, who provided us with the maps and figures. Gayl Ness of the University of Michigan acquainted the authors with significant literature presenting various perspectives in the field of social change and cultural adaptation. The research for this chapter was supported by National Institute of Mental Health grant R01—MH15606—02, Adaptive Behavior in Varied High School Environments, and by National Institute of Mental Health Pre-Doctoral Research Fellowship F01—MH46006—01—BEHA.

1. A term coined by Triandis defined as the system of beliefs a person carries within him concerning how the world is structured, "the kinds of goals or outcomes that are highly desirable, or less desirable, and the kinds of actions that he should undertake in order to reach his more desirable goals" (Triandis, 1968b, p. 2).

2. An interesting example of a change process in which the introduction of Western institutions, trade unions, aided in creating new interdependencies that were functional for a social group in a new setting is presented by Miller (1967). His example illustrates the point that "modern" institutions, corporate management of a highlands Peruvian Hacienda, introduced into a traditional culture proved dysfunctional and disorganizing for the

population in one setting. In a new setting with changed requirements for adaptation, another "modern" institution provided a necessary linkage for new interdependencies and new coping styles to aid in the adaptation of Indian groups migrating from the highlands to the urbanizing coastal region of Peru. The point is effectively made by Miller that new interdependencies can prove dysfunctional in one setting, while they may be a requirement for successful coping in another. (See Miller, Solomon in Steward (ed.), Vol. III, 1967, pp. 133–211.)

3. In a recent study by Edgerton of ecological relationships among ethnic groups in North Pakistan, it was found that the distribution of ethnic groups was related to the distribution of specific ecological niches. Different ethnic groups evolved unique economic and political organizations in order to exploit particular environmental niches. Edgerton found that if two groups attempted to occupy the same niche, the most powerful won out and weaker groups survived as they were able to adapt their economic and social organization to utilize marginal environments (Edgerton, 1968, p. 330).

4. While Riggs utilizes the "tradition-modern" dichotomy of Parsons and Levy (see Levy, 1952; Parsons, 1967), with "transitional" describing a range between these two, the authors of this chapter feel that the concept "transitional" should be generalized to mean all societies, or subcultures within a society, where environmental and ecological changes are creating a need for changed responses on the part of the population, as communities, groups, and individuals, in order to successfully cope with new ecological demands and environmental pressures.

5. Riggs defines the term "Polycommunalism" to describe a situation where several communities exist simultaneously in a society with differing norms, life styles, and socioeconomic systems. Riggs asserts that the polycommunal nature of the society leads to unanticipated results of interventions or even attempts to unify the society. For example, promoting nationalism as a value: "If the society is polycommunal, it uses the symbols of the dominant elite, causing alarm and fear on the part of deviant communities and their counter elites" (Riggs, 1964, p. 160).

6. Erasmus, in a recent communication with the authors, disagrees with this conclusion. He cites a forthcoming study by Manuel Carlos, an Assistant Professor of Anthropology at the University of California in Santa Barbara, which concludes that in general, government irrigation projects, financial institutions, and other development inputs have helped the rural population a great deal. Whether this includes the rural Indian subpopulation to any great extent is not clear, however.

7. In a recent communication with the authors, Erasmus observed that recently the bureaucracy in the rural areas has improved markedly and the problems he documented ten years ago have correspondingly diminished.

8. Foster describes the cargo system as it operated traditionally in the village of Tzintzuntzan: "According to this system, an aspiring young man began community service at the bottom of the 'ladder' whose two sides corresponded to the religious and civil hierarchies of his community. First he served a lowly religious (or civil) function and then a correspondingly lowly civil (or religious) function. Next he advanced a step up the ladder, in turn filling slightly higher religious and civil positions until, little by little, skipping back and forth from one hierarchy to the other, he reached the top and became a principal, a respected village elder" (Foster, 1967, p. 187).

References

Anderson, C. W., & Glade, W. P. *The political economy of Mexico*. Milwaukee, Wisc.: University of Wisconsin Press, 1968.

Ardrey, R. *The territorial imperative*. New York: Atheneum, 1966.

Arensberg, C. M., & Niehoff, A. H. *Introducing social change: A manual for Americans overseas*. Chicago: Aldine, 1964.

Belshaw, C. S. *Traditional exchange and modern markets*. Englewood Cliffs, N. J.: Prentice-Hall, 1965.

Bohannan, P. *Africa and Africans*. Garden City, N. Y.: National History Press, 1964.

Blair, C. P. National financiera: Entrepreneurship in a mixed economy. In R. Vernon (ed.), *Public policy and private enterprise in Mexico*. Cambridge: Harvard University Press, 1964.

Cohen, Y. A. *Man in adaptation: The cultural present*. Chicago: Aldine, 1968.

Duesenberry, J. S. *Money and credit: Impact and control*. Englewood Cliffs, N. J.: Prentice-Hall, 1964.

Edgerton, R. B. Cultural or ecological factors in the expression of values, attitudes and personality characteristics. In Y. A. Cohen (ed.), *Man in adaptation: The cultural present*. Chicago: Aldine, 1968.

Erasmus, C. J. *Man takes control: Cultural development and American aid*. Minneapolis: University of Minnesota Press, 1961.

Erasmus, C. J. Culture change in northwest Mexico. In J. H. Steward (ed.), *Contemporary change in traditional societies, Vol. III: Mexico and Peruvian communities*. Urbana, Ill.: University of Illinois Press, 1967, pp. 3–131. (a)

Erasmus, C. J. Upper limits of peasantry and agrarian reform: Bolivia, Venezuela and Mexico compared. *Ethnology*, 1967, 6(4), 349–380. (b)

Erasmus, C. J. Community development and the encogido syndrome. *Human Organization*, 1968, 27(1), 65–94.

Foster, G. M. *Tzintzuntzan: Mexican peasants in a changing world*. Boston: Little, Brown, 1967.

Furnivall, J. S. *Colonial policy and practice: A comparative study of Burma and the Netherlands Indies*. Cambridge: Cambridge University Press, 1948.

Gallin, B. *Hsin Hsing, Taiwan: A Chinese village in change.* Berkeley: University of California Press, 1966.

Geertz, C. *Agricultural involution: The process of ecological change in Indonesia.* Berkeley: University of California Press, 1966.

Glade, W. P., & Anderson, C. W. *The political economy of Mexico.* Milwaukee, Wis.: University of Wisconsin Press, 1968.

Goldschmidt, W. *Comparative functionalism.* Berkeley: University of California Press, 1966.

Hagen, E. E. *On the theory of social change: How economic growth begins.* Homewood, Ill.: Dorsey Press, 1964.

Halpern, J. M., & Brode, J. Studies in peasant society—Historical background, economic change and revolutionary transformation. In *Biennial review of anthropology.* Stanford, Calif.: Stanford University Press, 1967. Pp. 46–139.

Himmelstrand, U., & Okediji, F. O. Social structure and motivational tuning in social and economic development. *Journal of Social Issues*, 1968, 24(2), 25–42.

Hirschman, L. *Strategy of economic development.* New Haven, Conn.: Yale University Press, 1958.

Horowitz, I. L. *Three worlds of development.* New York: Oxford University Press, 1966.

Hoselitz, B. F. *Sociological aspects of economic growth.* London: Free Press of Glencoe, Collier-MacMillan, 1960.

Ingersoll, J. *Human factors in Mekong River basin development.* Second Progress Report to A.I.D., 1968.

Kelly, J. G. Ecological constraints on mental health services. *American Psychologist*, 1966, 21, 535–539.

Kelly, J. G. Towards an ecological conception of preventive interventions. In J. W. Carter (ed.), *Research contributions from psychology to community mental health.* New York: Behavioral Publications, 1968.

Kelly, J. G. Antidotes for arrogance: Training for community psychology. *American Psychologist*, 1970, 25, 524–531.

Kelly, J. G. Qualities For The Community Psychologist. *American Psychologist*, 1971, 26, 897–903.

LaPalombara (ed.) *Bureaucracy and political development.* Princeton, N. J.: Princeton University Press, 1963.

Levins, R. The strategy of model building in population biology. *American Scientist*, 1966, 54, 421–431.

Levy, M. J. Some sources of the vulnerability of the structure of relatively non-industrialized societies to those of highly industrialized societies. In B. Hoselitz (ed.), *The progress of underdeveloped areas.* Chicago: University of Chicago Press, 1952. Pp. 113–125.

Levy, M. J. *The structure of society.* Princeton, N. J.: Princeton University Press, 1952.

McClelland, D. C. *The achieving society.* New York: Van Nostrand, 1961.

McClelland, D. C., & Winter, D. G. *Motivating economic development.* New York: Free Press, 1969.

Meier, R. L. *Developmental planning.* New York: McGraw-Hill, 1965.

Mezirow, J. D. *Dynamics of community development.* New York: Scarecrow Press, 1963.

Miller, S. Hacienda to plantation in northern Peru: The processes of proletarianization of a tenant farmer society. In J. H. Steward (ed.), *Contemporary change in traditional societies, Vol. III: Mexican and Peruvian communities.* Urbana, Ill.: University of Illinois Press, 1967. Pp. 134–225.

Millikan, M. F., & Blackner, D. L. M. (eds.) *The emerging nations.* Boston: Little, Brown, 1961.

Mills, R. *Findings on the industries of the Taichung area.* Washington, D. C.: Urban and Housing Development Committee, Council for International Economic Cooperation and Development, Republic of China, 1968.

Moore, C. Simulation of organizational decision making: A survey. In W. Coplin (ed.), *Simulation in the study of politics.* Chicago: Markham, 1968.

Myrdal, G., et al. *Asian drama: An inquiry into the poverty of nations.* Vols. 1, 2, & 3. New York: Random House, 1968.

Nair, K. *Blossoms in the dust: The human factor in Indian development.* New York: Frederick A. Praeger, 1961.

Nuñez, L. M. Quoted from Glade, W. P., & Anderson, C. W. *The political economy of Mexico.* Milwaukee, Wis.: University of Wisconsin Press, 1968, P. 171.

Odum, F. P. *Fundamentals of ecology.* Philadelphia: W. B. Saunders, 1966.

Papanek, G. F. *Pakistan's development: Social goals and private incentives.* Cambridge: Harvard University Press, 1967.

Parsons, T. *Societies: Evolutioning and comparative perspectives.* Englewood Cliffs, N. J.: Prentice-Hall, 1967.

Riggs, F. *Administration in developing societies.* Boston: Houghton Mifflin, 1964.

Scott, R. E. *Mexican government in transition.* Urbana, Ill.: University of Illinois Press, 1964.

Shafer, R. J. *Mexico: A mutual adjustment planning.* Syracuse: Syracuse University Press, 1966.

Skinner, G. W. The nature of loyalties in rural Indonesia. In I. M. Wallerstein (ed.), *Social change: The colonial situation.* New York: Wiley, 1966.

Smith, R. L. *Ecology and field biology.* New York: Harper & Row, 1966.

Steward, Julian H. Perspectives on modernization: Introduction to the studies. In J. H. Steward (ed.), *Contemporary change in traditional societies, Vol. I: Introduction and African tribes.* Urbana, Ill.: University of Illinois Press, 1967.

Steward, J. H. (ed.) *Contemporary change in traditional societies.* Vols. 1, 2, & 3. Urbana, Ill.: University of Illinois Press, 1967.

Triandis, H. C. *Nation building: A psychologist's viewpoint.* Paper presented to Center for Research in Social Systems, American University, Washington, D. C., April 1968. (a)

Triandis, H. C. *Concepts of social psychology and strategy implications for behavioral change.* Paper presented at the Conference on Strategies for Behavior Change in International Agricultural Development, Cornell University, Ithaca, New York, January 1968. (b)

Urquidi, V. L. *Fundamental problems of the Mexican economy: Mexico's recent economic growth.* Houston, Tex.: Texas University Press, 1966.

Vernon, R. *Public policy and private enterprise in Mexico.* Cambridge, Mass.: Harvard University Press, 1964.

Vernon, R. *The dilemma of Mexico's development.* Cambridge, Mass.: Harvard University Press, 1965.

Wolf, Eric. *Peasants.* Englewood Cliffs, N. J.: Prentice-Hall, 1966.

III

The Prevention of Disorder and
the Promotion of Effectiveness

Part I was historical and developmental, part II has been concerned with community systems dynamics, and parts IV and V will focus respectively on intervention and training practices in community mental health. Part III, which appears now, is addressed directly to the conceptual issues that arise in attempting to define community science, and in this sense is a pivotal section for all that has come before and will follow.

The early chapters of part III are devoted to clarifying the role of social influences in individual mental health, the very concept of mental health, and the measurement of personality and behavior disorder. Later chapters single out dominant areas for preventive intervention and stress promotion of personal effectiveness. Interventive action is discussed for the stages of preschool development, the high school years, and later life; further chapters consider the prevention of intermediate problems of mental health significance. All of the presentations contain widely applicable concepts; the authors are community oriented, and are attentive to ecological integrity and the promotion of mental health as broadly defined.

John C. Glidewell, in "A Social Psychology of Mental Health," defines those aspects of social systems that are of mental health significance, citing dimensions which distinguish among social systems and those dimensions which distinguish positions of individuals within social systems. He analyzes the mental health significance of each dimension, drawing extensively on empirical evidence. Then, directing his focus to society's specialized helping subsystems, he examines the functioning of the helping dyad and the helping triad, and their extensions, from a social-psychological, systems-analytical, viewpoint. He feels the attempts of community mental health to create a helping system with extended social linkages can do much to facilitate social accommodation of varieties of behavior. He suggests that the great promise of community mental health may be its potential to break up the static, social order maintenance function of the traditional helping triad.

In "Concepts of Behavior Disorder," J. R. Newbrough cites the need for an approach to behavior classification which will provide a standard frame of reference to account for multiple perspectives, and will define appropriate methodological approaches to behavioral problems. He surveys closely the diversity of classification approaches in the mental health field, and presents a model approach to behavior classification that would treat deviancy labeling as verbal behavior subject to relativistic measurement, in hopes of providing greater reliability in categorization.

Both Newbrough, and Bruce P. and Barbara Snell Dohrenwend in their chapter "Psychiatric Epidemiology: Analysis of the 'True Prevalence'

Studies" are concerned with the definition of a "case." The Dohrenwends survey the overall problems encountered in attempting to conceptualize and measure the prevalence of emotional disorders in the community, and provide analysis of existing studies toward determining what facts are available. In the process of summarizing the state of the art of psychiatric epidemiology, the authors effectively redefine key problems and issues. Problems in epidemiology, such as coming to grips with the relationship between socioeconomic status and psychiatric disorder (social causation versus social selection), in many cases parallel problems in definition faced in attempting to develop a theoretical base for community mental health.

Lois B. Murphy and Caroline A. Chandler, in "Building Foundations for Strength in the Preschool Years: Preventing Developmental Disturbances," emphasize the need for more earnest application of our extensive and varied cultural knowledge to the healthy development of all children in relation to their individual needs and characters. The authors believe that building strength in children requires multidisciplinary child-oriented and family-oriented thinking and planning, and provision of developmental care beginning in the prenatal period. The authors introduce their discussion with theoretical and predictive background, evaluate existing child development research and clinical studies, and provide new perspectives and working hypotheses derived in part from their own research. The chapter concludes with a detailed summary outline of physical and mental health factors of prime consideration in the year-by-year development of each infant and preschool child.

Earlier, in part II, Eli M. Bower wrote about school systems, with emphasis on the earlier levels of education. The high schools are the focus of the next chapter in part III, from the viewpoint of intervention and change. Although the high schools represent a controllable socialization force for all persons at the adolescent level, they suffer from a paucity of mental health services, and where mental health services exist they seldom direct themselves toward understanding the high school environment for purposes of well planned, long-term intervention. Edison J. Trickett, James G. Kelly, and David M. Todd, in "The Social Environment of the High School: Guidelines for Individual Change and Organizational Redevelopment," stress interactional intervention and ecological understanding of the high school as an environment for adolescent socialization. They explore the range and scope of existing mental

health services for adolescents within the schools and their surrounding communities, evaluate the status of research on the high school, and analyze the social organization of the high school particularly in regard to specific roles and requirements. The authors have also provided consideration of directions for naturalistic observation and case reporting on high schools in crisis. A highlight of the chapter in the context of this volume is its presentation of ecological concepts, derived from biology, as they apply directly to the high school setting and are applicable by the behavioral sciences in general.

Carl Eisdorfer, in "Mental Health in Later Life," shows that the aged have profited little from innovation in the mental health field. From his study of the target population, the special problems in planning for the needs of the aged, and his analysis of cultural and professional attitudes toward older persons, it is clear that the aged population constitutes an immediate challenge for the mental health profession in the community. Eisdorfer cites the need for an open reappraisal for the role of the aged in our culture, and for specific community mental health strategies to meet the often clearly predictable needs of this group with its heightened risk for mental illness.

In "Prevention of Alcoholism," Thomas F. A. Plaut concentrates his attention on the need to modify American drinking attitudes and practices, which currently are obscured and confounded by emotionalism, rigid pro-and-con stances, and failure to discriminate among different kinds of drinking behaviors. He cites a need for study, open discussion, and education in this major area of social behavior, and suggests that the virtual revolution required in American attitudes toward drinking is intimately related to societal attitudes toward drug dependency.

Arnold Bernstein, Leon J. Epstein, Henry L. Lennard, and Donald C. Ransom, writing on "The Prevention of Drug Abuse," have adopted a conceptual, socially focused framework applicable to the abuse of both legal and illegal drugs. They specify societal forces, whether institutional or interactional, generating increased drug abuse and point to the social context of psychoactive drug abuse as the target for intervention.

Suicide prevention programs dramatically illustrate the necessity for community program developers to establish strong community-program ties. In "Prevention of Suicide: A Challenge for Community Science," Edwin S. Shneidman provides a conceptual blueprint for comprehensive community suicide prevention. For this purpose he proposes a temporal conceptualization focusing on prevention, intervention, and postvention (the latter including close attention to the health of the survivor-victims of a suicide). The temporal scheme encourages utilization of a wide variety of professionals and other community members in helping roles.

Nevitt Sanford concludes this part with his provocatively titled chapter "Is the Concept of Prevention Necessary or Useful." His emphasis is the necessity for professional and social efforts to promote positive personality development, where at present our resources are spent primarily on efforts to prevent particular personality problems. Sanford integrates the themes of earlier chapters on the importance of growth-sustaining education and cultural identity, while providing a specific developmental model for a shift toward concern with healthful individual growth and action for a more enlightened and humane society.

10

A Social Psychology of Mental Health

John C. Glidewell

A fundamental proposition of social psychology is that there are powerful connections between variations in social organization and variations in individual behavior. On the surface of the thing, the proposition seems valid. It is clear enough that the people in Samoa behave differently from the people in Las Vegas. The traditional methods of science—the quest for truth—in the Western world are, in part, attempts to control nature, but in the Eastern world they are more clearly attempts to reach a harmony with nature. Suicide attempts in the Arctic are quiet, unceremonial, and successful. Suicide attempts in Japan are dramatic, ceremonial, and also successful. Suicide attempts in the United States are dramatic, unceremonial, and often unsuccessful. The differences in individual behavior are clearly not random. There must be some connection with the differences in the forms and functions of the social organizations. To specify the chain of events which make up the connecting links is the task of social psychology. To the extent that the chain of events has mental health significance, the specification is the task of a social psychology of mental health.

It is necessary to set some limits on those aspects of individual behavior which are significant in mental health. It is proposed that these are the phenomena of significance: motivational strength and direction, emotional state and expression, intellectual potential and efficiency, interpersonal skills and enjoyments. The limits are too broad, but they are a beginning of a specification.

It is also necessary to define which aspects of social organization are relevant. I propose that two kinds of social dimensions are relevant: dimensions which distinguish among social systems and those which distinguish positions of individuals within social systems. The principal dimensions of mental health significance which distinguish systems are size, density, complexity, and rate of change. The principal dimensions distinguishing positions are interpersonal attraction, perceived competence, social power, and vulnerability to sanction.

The view of a social psychology of mental health to be presented includes two sorts of connections between social organization and individual behavior. One sort of connection includes those processes by which a social organization influences, and is influenced by, the mental health or illnesses of the individuals in it—for example, the processes by which the lower classes develop schizophrenia while the upper classes develop depressions. A second sort of connection includes those processes by which social organizations develop special roles and institutions to prevent or correct individual behaviors perceived as manifestations of mental illnesses—for example, specialized helping roles.

The first of the sections which follow will contain an examination of some social forces which may be antecedents of mental illnesses in individuals: (a) social order and change, (b) interpersonal attraction and aversion, (c) perceived competence, (d) social power, and (e) vulnerability to sanction.

The second of the sections which follow will contain an examination of helping subsystems: (a) the helping dyad, (b) the helping triad, and (c) extensions of the helping subsystems.

General

The following assertions are presented as a conceptual structure to organize the empirical findings to follow.

In simple terms, a social system may be defined as an arrangement of people engaged in the interchange and modification of resources in accord with a discernible set of shared expectations. Social order lies in the shared expectations—the prediction of valued outcomes. It provides an important basis of foresight. It is a necessary condition to predicting the consequences of one's action, to a personal sense of security, and to ego development. It is also a necessary condition to large-scale, sustained production of standard items needed by social systems. Social change occurs when expectations are violated. It is disruptive of predictability and security and production. Social change of some sort may be among the forces producing psychoses in individuals; it certainly is one of the forces producing distress in individuals. Intervention to prevent either psychosis or distress is probably most effective if it focuses upon small decision making groups of people with social power in large suprasystems. Support for these assertions follows.

Social Order

There are many social theories with many divergencies, but there is discernible convergence upon the following aspects of social order (Parsons, 1951; Merton, 1957; Homans, 1961; Loomis & Loomis, 1961).

The prime requisite of order is predictability. Order doesn't mean that things stay the same all the time. It means that one can predict what is going to happen next. Sustained social order has a second requisite: that one can predict that what happens next will be just. Sometimes, in fact, in social systems justice is more important than predictability. It is more interesting *not to know* exactly what is going to happen as long as one is confident that whatever happens will be a thing which is interesting and just—or as just as can be.

Social order is also the result of an accommodation between the individual and the system, between freedom and constraint—the freedom of the individual to pursue his interests, and the constraints necessary to allow others to pursue their interests. Superimposed on all of these processes of accommodation are symbolic abstractions about what are the ultimate ends of the society—what are the good outcomes.

One of the things that social order makes possible is resource development and refinement. It can lead to widespread distribution of resources but the distribution depends on more than order. Systems can be very orderly and very productive and permit a very limited distribution of resources. I have previously proposed in a number of places (e.g., Glidewell, 1966, 1969) that as long as members of a society wish to maintain a steady development of resources—human and material—they must develop specialization, organization, and discipline.

Specialization is necessary because no one person, however brilliant, can hope to acquire and use all the knowledge and skills he wishes to have available. If the available resources are to be fully developed, each person must concentrate on the development for which he has the greatest aptitude and inclination. He must depend upon others to supply the resources he does not develop. Independence is available only to those who have limited needs.

Organization is necessary because each person needs to know the time, the place, and the manner in which the specialized resources of others will be made available to him. Discipline is necessary because, if one is to be so dependent upon others, he wants to be sure that they are dependable.

Dependability is the key connection between social order and personal security. Security comes from experience—experience showing that others are committed to the agreements they have made, to the goals of the system. Commitment is shown by doing the things one is expected to do at the time, in the place, and in the manner expected; in a word, by conformity.

Commitment which is nothing more than conformity results in a very rigid system, and security has a high cost in dependency. Commitment also means doing unexpected things that one believes will turn out to be good—to improve the accommodation between the individual and the system—to move the system further toward its ultimate goals. Confidence that psychosocial experiments will yield valued returns, and willingness to participate in such experiments, is a form of commitment. It is, however, a less rigid basis for social commitment and security and its costs are different.

It is at times of conformity—times when mutual expectations are dependably met—that regular, sustained, and repetitive production has been possible. Resources are interchanged at high rates. Raw resources are transformed into more refined ones, more suited to the uses for which current demands are great. It is also true that such regularity becomes boring to people and they feel like cogs in machines. Under such conditions people sometimes do unexpected things which disrupt production. When they do, they find themselves subject to great social pressures to return to conformity and maintain production. Often, when asked why they did the unexpected thing, they say, "I just wanted to see what would happen."

Many social scientists (such as Argyris, 1962, and Likert, 1961) have produced data showing that some highly organized social systems debilitate human resources and induce distress. Others (such as Durkheim, 1951) have produced data indicating that lack of social order has produced great human distress and behavior aberrations. The following sections contain a sample of empirical findings about the social forces generated by social order and social change and their implications for mental health.

Social Change

It took two million years to generate the first billion persons simultaneously alive on this planet. That was accomplished by about 1825. It took but 100 years to generate the second billion. That level was reached about 1930. It took only 30 years to produce the third billion—from 1930 to 1960. It will not take 30 years to produce the fourth billion (Hauser, 1968, 1969).

People have not only become more numerous, they have crowded themselves into smaller and smaller spaces, generally, seeking access to concentrated resources. It took two million years—perhaps a little less—to develop a culture which could sustain the first primitive community, the Neolithic settlements of eight thousand years ago. It took almost all the eight thousand years (and numerous inventions like money economy and wheeled transport) for the Western world to learn to sustain a city of 100,000—the Greek and

Roman cities. By 1800, the Western world had developed the know-how to develop a city of a million. By far, most of the gain in urbanization has occurred in but a single century, but it is not clear that we really have the know-how to manage urbanization in the human interest. Today, two-thirds of the population of the United States live in cities—cities which are becoming more physically poisoned, socially unjust, and psychologically explosive. Many people have access to many resources and conform to many expectations quite well, but the whole thing produces a sense of danger, not security.

All the time that mankind has been multiplying his numbers and crowding them into smaller spaces, he has also rapidly become physically much more mobile, technically much more able to communicate, motivationally more driven to control socioeconomic resources, and emotionally more estranged from his fellows. Such increased interaction should, according to many social theorists (e.g., Loomis, 1967; Homans, 1961), lead to greater interpersonal attraction and greater linkage between systems. The fact is that this mobility and crowding have led to social instability and personal insecurity.

Man is the only culture-building animal on the globe. He not only adapts to environment, he creates environment to which to adapt, and he is still trying to learn to live in the world that he himself has created—a world of large populations, great densities, and great population diversification subject to rapid technological and social change. It is within this perspective that we can better understand the physical problems of the United States—air and water pollution, traffic congestion, parking problems and the commuter crisis; the personal and social problems of juvenile delinquency, crime and drug addiction, the revolt of the younger generation . . . ; the problems of intergroup relations climaxed by the Negro Revolt; and the problems of governance on the Federal, state, and local levels. (Hauser, 1968, pp. 5—6.)

Given this background of fast and fundamental social changes, one may consider with perspective the data available about the nature of the processes of accommodation of individuals to changing social systems.

Changes in Size, Density, and Complexity

As size increases, density increases. People in social systems apparently increase their numbers faster than they increase the space they occupy. As systems increase in size and density, they have greater and more varied human resources available to them, but they have more trouble using the resources. They also develop more complex organizations, form a more centralized power structure, evolve more highly specialized roles, and demand greater conformity (Simmel, 1950; Asch, 1951; Herbst, 1957; Slater, 1958; Thomas & Fink, 1963; Barker & Gump, 1964; Gerard, Wilhelmy, & Conolley, 1968). Generalizing from small systems which increase in size, larger systems provide a reduced range of opportunity to participate, provide central roles in fewer activities, and less satisfaction with decisions made (Hare, 1952; Bales & Borgatta, 1965; Indik, 1964; Barker & Gump, 1964). In the larger system there is a greater resource input—a larger number of suggestions made—but a smaller demand for resources—fewer opinions requested or given (Bales & Borgatta, 1965). In the larger group, time limits usually do not permit consideration of all the opinions available, and many members feel that their views have not been considered, that their influence has been quite limited, or that their demands have not been met (Newcomb, Turner, & Converse, 1965). Smaller groups provide a constricted range of opinions and abilities, a simpler organization, a greater intimacy, a closer identification, and a stronger reference group (Thomas & Fink, 1963).

Complexity of social organization is a concomitant of both increased size and complexity of tasks. The advantages of both large and small size might be obtained if the larger system were organized into subsystems of small groups with active linkages. Social forces within small groups provide both the demand and the opportunity for the internal participation, influence, intimacy, and identification required for strong loyalties. The larger suprasystem provides the wealth of resources, the demand and the opportunity for specialization, and the *possibility* for a wide availability of specialized resources. The key, however, lies in the linkage function. Fundamentally, linkages are forms of resource interchange. Systems of groups tend to develop intergroup suspicions, reduce communication between groups, and reduce the rate of interaction and interchange of resources—objects, ideas, skills—between groups (Sherif, et al., 1961; Blake, 1959; Loomis, 1967; Deutsch, 1969). Unless there is

some mutual attraction between groups (based upon needs for consensual validation, social comparison, or mutual aid), and a reciprocity of interchange (Gouldner, 1960), linkages tend to deteriorate (Loomis, 1967). The individual and the small group in large complex suprasystems come to feel—and to be—impotent, insignificant, and apathetic, especially if they are seen as marginal in the resources they offer.

When size is small and the system is undermanned, each person must supply more resources, and there are more demands upon each person to participate actively. Persons who are seen as marginal in the resources they represent—marginal in motives, feelings, ideas, or skills—will more often be invited and encouraged to participate in the work and the maintenance of the system. This view of the undermanned system has been put forth by Barker (1968), but little specific data are available to support the view, except in the study of the size of schools (Barker & Gump, 1964). The view is, however, consistent with previous findings about system size and density, and it has important mental health implications. As size and density increase—as systems become overmanned—one may expect fewer persons who are seen as marginal in resources to be invited to participate and more persons becoming isolated.

The question of antecedent and consequence remains unanswered in the study of isolation and psychoses. For example, Kohn and Clausen (1955) studied quite carefully the social isolation experienced by hospitalized patients with psychoses and isolation experienced by a nonhospitalized group of people matched on age, sex, and occupation. The hospitalized patients had been clearly socially isolated between ages 13 and 14, while the nonhospitalized persons had not. The data indicated, however, that the isolation might well have been the consequence of the beginning of the illness, not the antecedent of it. There were no differences in number of available peers, extent of mobility, parental restrictions, or other possible causes of isolation—other than the illness.

On the other hand, as is to be reviewed in the section on interpersonal attraction, there is no question about the personal distress, defensiveness, and anxiousness induced by social isolation.

Similar questions exist concerning the relationship between social change in general and psychoses. Fast or extensive social changes have often been cited as a cause both of psychoses and of a variety of forms of personal distress. Durkheim (1951) set out such an explanation for variations in suicide rates. Goldhamer and Marshall (1953) searched for *long-term* increases in hospital admissions for psychoses in Massachusetts during the century from 1840 to 1940, a century during which there was major social change. They found that "admission data do show short-term changes that coincide with marked social changes such as those incidental to wars and depressions," (p. 92–93), but they found no long-term increases—19th and 20th century rates were remarkably homogeneous. Dunham (1959) could find no long-term increase in the rate of hospital admissions of persons aged 20 to 60 between 1910 and 1950, another time of great social change. In general, studies of hospital admissions of psychotics (or persons so diagnosed) from the middle of the age range (20–60) have shown changes more closely related to changes in hospital beds available than to other forms of social change. Changes in beds available are, indeed, a form of social change, often connected with other social changes in the allocation of resources. It is, however, the effects on the incidence of psychoses of the changes in norms and allocations of significant resources which are of importance to the issue.

The studies cited do indicate increases in rates of admissions for adolescent and older (above 60) persons during the last 50 years. The increases in admission rates for adolescents (Kramer, 1967) may reflect a true increase in incidence. The reduction in the perception of the adolescent as an economic and social resource to families may have induced new stress, but the interpretation is not supported by specific data.

Social changes *may* have influenced the increased admission rates for older persons. During the last 100 years in the United States extended family life has become much less prevalent. In modern nuclear families older persons have less significant roles. Their economic value has decreased or become negative; their wisdom has become less respected. Whether they are ill or not, confinement to state hospitals effectively excludes aging persons from the nuclear family.

One could also argue that the change to nuclear families may have increased the true incidence of illness. The loss of family social power of older adults, who by tradition expected to exercise much power, could have induced a stress which contributed to a true increase in the incidence of mental health problems in older adults. Data specifically relevant to these social change influences on illness were not found.

Studies of social and spatial mobility have been somewhat more productive. Murphy's (1965) review of the data available on adult mobility and mental illnesses (especially psychoses) indicated that the crucial mental health problem came not from spatial mobility, but from the change in social setting—changes (in my conception) in the individual's confidence that he knew what to expect from others with whom he was in direct interaction. Fried (1965) found widespread grief among those residents who were *forced* to move from slum housing. Fried concluded that "prerelocation evidences of preparedness for change are the most important factors determining postrelocation adjustment adaptation," (p. 59). Scotch (1963) studied Zulus who moved into cities and those who did not. He found the move to cities to be clearly stressful, evidenced by increased incidence of hypertension. The main core of a series of findings of studies involving spatial and social mobility—each with and without the other—was that it was not the move in space, but the change in social norms and roles that was associated with distress (Kantor, 1965). A review of studies by Joy (1933), Sackett (1935), Tetreau and Fuller (1942), and Gilliland (1959), concluded that mobile school children from middle and upper class backgrounds, of high self-esteem, and with moderately high intelligence learned significantly from the varied experiences accompanying their mobility (as indicated by higher achievement rates) than did matched nonmobile children (Glidewell, et al., 1965, 1966).

The foregoing findings are not without their unanswered questions, particularly about the connections between social change and psychoses, but they do agree that the processes of social change—with or without spatial mobility—temporarily disrupt the psychosocial functioning of the individual and that repeated involvement in rapid social change can lead to more permanent mental health problems.

A Focus for Induced Social Change

If the violations of expectations are at the core of the effects of social change, then the social organizations which have the greatest immediate impact upon the individual are small, face-to-face groups which go about trying to interchange and transform their resources—motives, feelings, ideas, skills—in ways which meet their expectations of themselves and of each other. Such small groups are often so limited in resources available or so limited by sanctions from suprasystems that, however strong their influence on their members, their general social power remains a potential unrealized.

Research on *rates* of school achievement (Bredemeier, 1968) has indicated that, however resourceful and stimulating a particular innovative slum school may turn out to be, it is still limited by the social forces generated in the larger community—forces identified here as perceived incompetence, interpersonal aversion, felt impotence, and vulnerability to sanction. Further, no matter how privileged a school, unless the resources are used, rates of achievement are little affected. The action of these community forces is not directly from the larger community; it acts through the resources interchanged among small face-to-face groups—dyads, triads, families, neighborhood groups, and work groups. Special linking structures are often small but potent: teacher-pupil, policeman-citizen, doctor-patient, lawyer-client, clergyman-parishioner, supervisor-worker.

Indeed, if the limitations of the larger community—a suprasystem of component systems—are to be lifted, the changes must originate in, or be sanctioned by, small, face-to-face groups of powerful people who must make the decisions about how community resources are to be allocated, who is to implement the allocation, and how he is to be accountable to the community. Such decisions are not sufficient, however, unless they are reinforced by the actions of many of the small, face-to-face systems which are the basic implementing social components of the community—families, neighborhoods, classrooms, work groups, church groups, recreational groups, and criminal syndicates.

An early study indicating the power of small groups to resist change in individual behavior was that of Shils and Janowitz (1948). They studied the behavior of German soldiers who perceived their situation to be hopeless at the end of World War II. They found that the greatest restraining force against a soldier's accepting offers of safety in return for surrender was his loyalty to his basic unit, the face-to-face group with which he served.

American soldiers, when asked what induced them to face great dangers, expressed similar loyalties to their basic units (Shils, 1950). During the Korean War, United Nations prisoners of war resisted "brainwashing" much more effectively when they remained in interaction with small groups of fellow prisoners than when isolated (Schein, Schneier, & Barker, 1961). A number of studies have shown that group members resist communications which are at odds with the values and norms of the groups (e.g., Kelley & Volkart, 1952).

Newly formed groups or groups in the process of breaking up do not exert such strong resistances to changes in members' behavior and, in fact, may encourage some changes (Gilchrist, 1952). When the basic units of the German army in World War II were broken up and could not supply food, ammunition, or direction, the soldiers surrendered readily (Shils & Janowitz, 1948). Similar findings have been reported by Herz (1954), Riley, Schramm, and Williams (1951), and Kelley and Woodruff (1956).

Lewin (1952) and his associates developed a well-known series of experiments using ad hoc groups as support for changes in individual behavior. Generally, the new behavior was one which had been previously avoided by the members of the group but for which some acceptable rationale could be presented (like eating glandular meats). A wide range of work was done on this line of investigation, but the outcomes can be summarized as follows: (1) group discussions of controversial proposals usually make explicit some latent conflicts about existing norms of behavior (Katz & Lazarsfeld, 1955; Klapper, 1961); (2) group support of changed behavior is increased by the explicit individual decision (public or private) to try the new behavior (Bennett, 1955; Schachter & Hall, 1952); (3) the change is supported by the perception that a large number of other group members are committed to try the new behavior (Bennett, 1955); and (4) the change is supported by group leadership which exercises only reward power or exercises no sanctions at all (Kipnis, 1958; Coch & French, 1948).

As new individual behaviors develop in small groups, some new demands for conformity develop (Asch, 1956). There is the phenomenon of "refreezing" of behavior, in Lewin's sense of the term. If individual behaviors are widely discrepant in the group, the attention of the members will turn to reducing the discrepancy (Schachter, 1951, 1959).

The postulate is that it is the position of the individual in a social organization, usually a relatively small, face-to-face group, which is the source of the most potent forces for social change and, accordingly, the most potent focus for research and practice in community mental health.

Summary

The findings available are not really satisfactory, because the very social changes which may be the antecedents of new mental health problems are also changes which are the antecedents of new resources for recognizing and treating mental health problems. The data are consistent with one conception of the impact of social forces. (The trouble is that they probably are consistent with other conceptions, also.) Social organization and social change always represent some accommodation of social support and social control of the individuals in it. The conception is that social order and social change, in themselves, do not induce mental health problems. Given that the system continues at a constant density and becomes neither more nor less undermanned, problems are generated when a social order maintains a continuing perceived inequity. The individual believes that his returns from the system (in motives, emotions, ideas, skills, or objects) are not equitable to his investment in the system. Problems are generated temporarily when a social change makes even the inequity unpredictable, but if the change is toward greater equity, after a time for stabilization problems are reduced. If a social change increases the inequity, the unpredictability is added, the inequity compounded, and the incidence of problems rises—whether or not they are recognized and treated. These interpretations are consistent with the idea that there may be a very pervasive norm of reciprocity (Gouldner, 1960), which when violated, creates mental health problems.

One may consider that the current state of knowledge only suggests the nature of the influences of social order and social change on individual mental health—that is, motivational strength and direction, emotional state and expression, intellectual potential and efficiency, interpersonal skills and enjoyments. One may also

support the idea that it is important to examine in more detail the particular position of an individual within a social system. If changes in size, density, and complexity influence the individual, such changes must be exerted through inducing changes in the position of the individual within the systems in which he must live. Four variables have been specified in the introduction to this work as particularly significant in distinguishing positions of individuals in social systems: interpersonal attraction, perceived competence, social power, and vulnerability to sanction. The next section will examine the nature and mental health significance of interpersonal attraction and its opposite, interpersonal aversion.

INTERPERSONAL ATTRACTION AND AVERSION

One of the most powerful social forces is generated by the fact that each of us likes some people better than he likes others. To be attractive to others enhances one's self-esteem; to be unattractive reduces it. To be unacceptable to others injures one's self-esteem; to be actively rejected cripples it. "You are nobody till somebody loves you."

The basic nature of the phenomenon of interpersonal attraction has been the subject of a variety of analyses. It seems clear that propinquity is the first factor leading to attraction. Both theorists and empiricists have confirmed its effects: Lunberg and Beazley (1948) on a college campus; Festinger, Schachter, and Back (1950) in a housing unit; Gullahorn (1952) in a corporation office; Newcomb (1956) in a student rooming house; and Kendall (1960) in a medical school. The data come from diverse sources, but the effects are consistent. Spatial proximity, however, is not a sufficient condition for lasting attraction, and, if other forces are strong enough, not even a necessary condition.

Newcomb (1961) has demonstrated that much interpersonal attraction is determined by perceived similarity of attitudes of common importance and relevance to the individuals involved. He does, however, point out a dilemma. While initial attraction is largely a matter of perceived personal characteristics, as acquaintance develops a circular process appears, and one finds it difficult to separate antecedent from consequence. Nonetheless, in Newcomb's (1961) study of college men living in the same house, attitudinal data taken prior to the first meeting of the men accounted for a significant part of the variation in the mutual attractions in effect late in a 16-week period.

Rokeach (1961) and Stein, Hardyck, and Smith (1965) have shown that while both group membership (such as race) and belief influence attraction, belief is the more powerful. Smith, Williams, and Willis (1967) found relationships supporting this position.

Thibaut and Kelley (1959), Homans (1961), and Blau (1964) have proposed that in voluntary associations, in order for attraction to occur, the expectations of the participants developed during initial exploratory contacts must be that the cost-benefit comparison will exceed that of the alternatives available to each participant. These conceptions allow for the attraction of persons with dissimilar attitudes, if the comparative cost-benefit analysis is favorable. The experienced expectation of "favorableness" is often implicit and not based upon conscious deliberation.

The question of complementarity pervades the analyses of attraction and aversion. Is it necessarily true that each attracted participant supplies for the other some resource which the other cannot supply so well for himself? When complementary motives are involved (e.g., nurturance and dependence), such a formulation clearly applies. When similar attitudes are involved, it does not seem to fit, except that each actor may supply the other with a validating agreement. When complementary abilities are involved (e.g., analysis and synthesis), the formulation applies again, but when similar abilities are involved, the application becomes unclear. Gross (1956), for example, found that those small groups (in a military organization) which were most long-lived and cohesive were those in which the members were different, their resources complementary. Persons with similar abilities are, however, often attracted to one another, although neither can supply an important relevant ability the other doesn't have. To explain such findings, Festinger (1954) suggested that individuals are attracted by the opportunity to compare their abilities with those of someone about equally competent. The interchange in such a case would almost necessarily take some competitive form. A

professional golfer learns but little about his ability when playing against a beginner, and the beginner is not attracted by a hopelessly unfavorable comparison.

Under other conditions, the attraction of people with similar abilities occurs in a mutual dependency relationship in which each requires some increment of ability (help) from another of similar ability. One scientist seeks help from another scientist in the same specialty in order to solve a particularly knotty problem, offering his help in return. Each can take turns helping the other or receiving help from the other in solving either mutual or individual problems (e.g., the Manhattan Project of World War II).

The theories have not often been applied to interpersonal aversion or isolation, but they were clearly intended to apply to both ends of the continuum. Schachter (1959) described the beginnings of an attempt to study social isolation. His preliminary work showed such wide individual variations in reactions to isolation (both social and sensory) that he abandoned the project. His only conclusion was that some degree of anxiety was commonly a consequence of social isolation.

In order to understand the effects of both interpersonal attraction and interpersonal aversion, some more nearly integrated theory is required. Such a theory must take account of the processes involved in perceived similarities, perceived complementarities, and perceived social comparisons. In addition such a theory should specify some reasonable connections between these processes and individual motivation, emotionality, intellect, and skill development. Following is an attempt at a theory of both attraction and aversion, taking account of existing data and extrapolating to findings yet to be produced empirically.

One may consider that *all* interpersonal attraction has at least three social forces in action: (1) consensual validation, (2) social comparison, and (3) mutual aid. Some attractions involve one force primarily and other forces secondarily. For example, the members of a golfing foursome may be attracted to each other primarily by the opportunity for social comparison of golfing prowess, but the particular foursome may also be preferred to another group because of the opportunity for consensual validation of political attitudes. In addition, each participant may provide new information to the others and acquire

TABLE 10–1
Consensual Validation

	Attraction	*Aversion*
Input from the Society	Issues about Values, Beliefs, Attitudes	Issues about Values, Beliefs, Attitudes
Input fron Actors	Similar Values, Beliefs, Attitudes	Different Values, Beliefs, Attitudes
Processes of Interchange and Transformation	Request, Express, Approve	Request, Express, Disapprove
Systemic Incorporation into Actors	Attraction, Confidence, Sense of Worth	Aversion, Doubt, Mistrust, Isolation
Output to the Society	Group Identity, Predictability of Group Attitude, Exclusiveness	Individual Alienation, Disillusionment, Rebellion or Apathy

new information from the others. Indeed, under some conditions, golfing foursomes may be more attracted to each other by the prospect of mutual aid in business than by needs for social comparison of golfing skills. Denial of membership may be more a deprivation of mutual aid and consensual validation than a denial of an opportunity to compare prowess at golf.

One may also consider that all interpersonal attraction involves some input from the larger society (or suprasystem) and some output to the society. In between, there is also input from the actors themselves, a process of interchange and transformation of resources, and some incorporation of transformed resources into the system.

Considering first the attraction due to consensual validation, the inputs from society are issues: the alternative values, beliefs, and attitudes tolerated in the society. (Some say brown-shell eggs are more nutritious, some say white.) The actors, however, prefer one position. (It is really the brown-shell ones that have the most food value.) They are attracted to others with similar positions (see Table 10–1). The process of interchange, refinement, and transformation takes the form of request for opinion, expression of opinion, approval of opinion. Each actor takes his turn, sometimes requesting, sometimes expressing, sometimes approving. Where individual needs for dominance are involved or where differences in

power positions are involved, power-based specialization develops. Some actors request most often, some express most often, some approve most often. The outcomes to the actors are reversible; one *may* change his opinions. One would expect, however, both some form of regular reaffirmation of beliefs and some attempts to set up penalties for reversing an opinion.

Incorporated into each of the actors is an increase in confidence in his values, beliefs, and attitudes. The social forces inhibit the development of new values, beliefs, or attitudes. Incorporated into the members of the system is an increased interpersonal attraction and value on membership. The output to the society is clarity of group identity, predictability and dependability of group attitude, and exclusiveness of membership in the group. Consensual validation provides a basis for social foresight.

Attraction resulting from consensual validation develops in stages as the actors explore the opinions of others in close proximity. From the same exploratory process, aversion may also develop. The inputs from the actors may be different or conflicting values, beliefs, or attitudes. The process is request-express-disapprove, and there can be—depending on the saliency of the attitudes—a high-cost disconfirmation. The incorporation into the system is aversion, doubt, and distrust. For the individual, repeated costly

TABLE 10–2

Social Comparison

	Attraction	Aversion
Input from Society	Rewards for Specific Competencies	Rewards for Specific Competencies
Input from Actors	Similar Competencies	Different Competencies
Processes of Interchange and Transformation	Competitive Activity, Comparison	Competitive Activity, Humiliation
Systemic Incorporation	Winner: Confidence Loser: Resolve, Mistrust	Winner: Guilt, Doubt Loser: Hostility, Mistrust
Output to the Society	Gratification from Identification with Competitors, Production Incidential to Competition, Intergroup Tension	Resentment from Identification, Domination, Illegitimate Victory

disconfirmations, from many alternative others, of his values, beliefs, or attitudes lead either to a change in his views or an increasing doubt of his competence or worth. If he finds isolation too costly for him, he changes his views. Isolation is often used as a corrective measure for deviancy. If, however, he finds the interaction with others too costly for him, he prefers isolation, rebellion, or apathy. He experiences an alienation and a deterioration in his capacity for enjoyment, his interpersonal skills, and those cognitive processes dependent upon consensual validation.

Turning to social comparison as a social force toward attraction, the inputs from the society are (a) rewards for unusual talents or (b) special statuses based on specific competencies (as for surgeons and baseball pitchers) (see Table 10–2). The inputs from the actors are specific competencies (skill, knowledge, ability) and motivation to demonstrate the superiority of the competencies (Hoffman, Festinger, & Lawrence, 1954). The interaction process is some form of competitive activity involving challenge, demonstration, and comparison (Festinger, 1954; Dreyer, 1953, 1954). Transformation of the knowledge, skill, or ability involved may be at a minimum, but the stress of the competition may stimulate new ideas or skills—largely for incorporation by the actor developing the new resource. Additional incorporation into the system includes confidence by the winner and despair and resolve by the loser (Blake, 1959). A possible by-product of a hostile competition is distrust of each other by the actors (Sherif, et al., 1961). The outputs to the society are: (a) the production incidental to the demonstration; (b) the gratification from identification with the competitors by the spectators—in both business and sports; and (c) intergroup tensions.

Repeated experiences of losing in social comparisons leave the individual in general doubt about his competence and worth (Festinger, Torrey, & Willerman, 1954) and move him to seek social comparisons with others less competent—more like him. He may come to avoid social comparisons of abilities—if that is possible in his society (Hoffman, Festinger, & Lawrence, 1954). If realignment or avoidance is not possible, repeated losses lead to apathy or to illegitimate victories or acquisitions. Winners of one-sided contests evidence guilt and doubt; losers evidence mistrust and hostility, either expressed or suppressed, depending on the vulnerability to sanction (Pettigrew, 1967). (Merton has developed a theory of crime and delinquency based on relative deprivation and availability of legitimate means to reach goals. See Merton, 1957.)

The third force operating—attraction generated by expectations of mutual aid—involves the most complex of inputs, transformations, and outputs

TABLE 10—3
Mutual Aid

	Attraction	Aversion
Input from the Society	Demand for Products, Norms of Reciprocity	Demand for Products, Norms of Reciprocity
Input from Actors	Different Feelings, Ideas, Motives, Skills	Different Feelings, Ideas, Motives, Skills
Processes of Interchange and Transformation	Offer A—Get B Offer B—Get A	Offer A—Get X Offer B—Get X
Systemic Incorporation	New Motives, Ideas, Skills Trust	Resource Deterioration, Mistrust
Output to the Society	New Products or Services in more Usable Forms Social Integration	Confusion, Apathy

(see Table 10—3). From the society the inputs are offered rewards for (demand for) desired products in forms not currently available (like electric power from the sun's rays). From the actors the inputs are diverse resources—objects, motives, feelings, ideas, skills—perceived to be amenable to transformation into desired forms—capital and labor, machines and materials, soil and seeds, metals and heat. Thus the new product development group in industry attracts persons with a variety of resources: imagination, analytic abilities, synthesizing skills, market knowledge, and the like.

The process of interaction involves interchange, refinement, and transformation of the motives, ideas, feelings, and skills into products for output to the society—steel, professional services, food, entertainment, thermocouples. Other new resources—such as new motives, ideas, or skills—are incorporated into the actors.

If, however, the interchange produces no transformation, if the diverse resources are not in fact complementary, the outcomes to the individuals are frustrations, deterioration of motives and skills, confusion, and disintegration of the system. ("Wait for me here in the lobby and I'll bring my etchings down.")

For persons interested in mental health, it is instructive to review the negative outcomes to the actors who find disconfirmation of beliefs,

unfavorable social comparisons, and frustrated mutual aid—and find them repeatedly in many alternative situations. They incorporate into their personality systems (self-concept?) repeated doubt, mistrust, confusion, apathy, frustration, and a sense of injustice. They come to expect negative outcomes, defend themselves in advance, and produce a self-fulfilling prophecy: aversion by others.

Although the etiology of most functional psychiatric disorders remains indeterminate, there is one deficiency common to most disorders. From the schizophrenias to the depressions, from the hysterias to the obsessions, the deprivation of simple human acceptance is found in nearly every history. To be regularly—and individually—friendless, discounted, degraded, and humiliated is a psychosocial experience with which few humans can cope for a prolonged time.

The effects of isolation in young children are well-known. At the extreme of deprivation, the child undertakes walking or talking only very late or not at all (e.g., K. Davis, 1947). In the social structure of elementary school classrooms, lack of friendly interaction is associated with a variety of emotional handicaps. Moreno's (1934) classroom sociometric studies of the '30s showed such negative effects in New York. Jennings (1943) replicated that work, and, in spite of the fact that her data came from a school for delinquent girls, she produced findings which have influenced most of the work on interpersonal attraction since then. Bonney (1942, 1943) found similar phenomena in Texas, Stendler (1949) in the Middle West, Potashin (1946) in Canada, and Bower and his colleagues (1958) in California. Trent (1957) also showed connections between anxiety and popularity and rejection.

Friendlessness among adults is an equally crippling social force. It exerts its most damaging influence in the slums of cities and along skid row (Pittman & Gordon, 1958). In less dramatic forms, lack of acceptance experienced by workers in industry is associated with interpersonal tensions and somatic complaints (Kasl & French, 1962). In school faculties, the isolation of teachers influenced their interpersonal skills and reduced their teaching effectiveness (Singer, 1954).

The deprivation of acceptance is a central social force in the "depersonalization process" so common in institutions—called "total institutions" by Goffman (1961)—which take responsibility for the total life of their members. The use of social power to deny personal acceptance is an effective way both to cripple interpersonal trust, to deflate achievement motivation (Solomon, 1957, cited by Thibaut & Kelley, 1959, pp. 177–178), and to induce apathy (Brown, et al., 1968). In even more extreme situations such as the Nazi prison camps described by Bettelheim (1943), one finds aggression turned toward the self.

The rejection of minorities by majorities produces severe disruption of motivation, emotional expression, intellectual efficiency, and interpersonal skills. Festinger (1954) proposed that members of minority groups, when unable to avoid social comparisons, should be less secure in their self-evaluations, favorable or unfavorable. He also reasoned, from his theory of social comparison, that minority groups would tolerate fewer differences in opinion or abilities seen as relevant by the group. With respect to opinions, the findings of Gerard (1953) support these propositions.

Evidence of related effects is contained in the work of Simpson and Yinger (1953), and in Allport's studies of Jewish college students (e.g. Allport & Kramer, 1946), proportionately more of whom felt victimized and were inclined to return prejudice with prejudice. Lewin's observations of the experiences of the Jews (1948) also confirmed the effects of social aversion. The early work of Landreth and Johnson (1953) and of the Clarks on the self-conceptions of Negroes revealed the same effects. Especially striking was the one finding that a majority of Negro children rejected Negro dolls (Clark & Clark, 1958). Currently (1970), the interest in these effects is at a peak and a wide variety of investigations is under way.

While histories of mental illnesses show rather consistent effects of interpersonal aversion, it is not true that such aversion regularly induces mental illnesses. The repeated lack of consensual validation of beliefs in many alternative groups may just impair one's social skills, reduce one's self-esteem, confound one's affiliation motives, and make one still more unattractive to others—without producing illnesses. The same is true of repeated unfavorable social comparisons and frustrated attempts at coordinated production. While the victim is not ill, he is caught in a vicious cycle and his mental health is far from what he would like it to be.

At the other extreme, the experience of repeated attraction produces a sense of competence, confidence, trust, and self-esteem which leads to further attractiveness. The resources thus developed represent the stability under stress, the tolerance for frustration, and the skill in reality testing often associated with vigorous mental health.

Following is a summary of the findings concerning interpersonal attraction and mental health. People are attracted toward one another by motivation toward consensual validation of opinions and ideas, toward social comparison of skills and abilities, and toward mutual aid. The inputs from the environment and from the actors, the processes of interchange and development of resources, and the outputs to the environment vary with bases for attraction. Among adults and children, repeated experiences of attracting others in interaction lead to increased self-esteem, increased affiliation motivation, enhanced interpersonal skills, and further attractiveness in a self-sustaining circular process. In the opposite direction, repeated experiences of repelling others lead to reduced self-esteem, decreased affiliation motivation, disruption of interpersonal skills, and further unattractiveness in a self-sustaining circular process of increasing distress and a sense of unworthiness, but not necessarily mental illness.

PERCEIVED COMPETENCE

Perceived competence is conceptually distinct from interpersonal attraction and social power, but it is empirically related to both. Competence is a basis for both power and attractiveness, but it is only one of several bases for both. As conceived here, competence is also something more than a basis for attraction or power. One's competence, as perceived by one's fellows, is a basic dimension distinguishing between positions in a social system. The competence dimension contributes a distinction *in addition to* those contributed by attraction and power.

Perceived competence has a general aspect. Some people are perceived to be more competent *at most tasks*, others less competent *at most tasks.* Perceived competence is, however, most often task specific. Competence at specific tasks which vary in importance in the social situation is the aspect of competence most clearly distinct from attraction and power. The sifting out of the specific contributions of task-specific competence to social distinction, separately from its contribution to attraction and power, remains an important but rarely studied problem.

R. W. White has been most interested in conceptualizing competence. He defines it in very broad terms: "an organism's capacity to interact effectively with its environment" (White, 1959, p. 297). Erikson is almost as broad: "*the free exercise of dexterity and intelligence in the completion of tasks, unimpaired by infantile inferiority*" (Erikson, 1964, p. 124). Foote and Cottrell (1955) include a consideration of task specificity: "ability for performing certain implied kinds of tasks" (p. 36).

Foote and Cottrell also add a distinction between task competence and interpersonal competence, separating "rational and efficient manipulations of objects of the environment" and "relationships of selves and others, not as objects, but as human subjects with whom each person is engaged in the plots of the human drama" (p. 59). It is especially interesting to note that task competence is usually less a function of some social comparison process than interpersonal competence, because often task competence can be judged directly by nonsocial criteria, whereas interpersonal competence is almost necessarily judged from some consensual validation. In self-evaluations, Combs and Snygg (1959) propose that both task competence and positive experiences in interaction with others are highly valued. The task-specificity of task competence influences its social value—the more central and important the task to the life of the system, the greater is the value assigned to the competence. In spite of its wide generality, interpersonal competence can be seen as peripheral and unimportant in some systems and thus assigned small value in those systems. For example, interpersonal competence is central and highly regarded in psychiatry but peripheral and neutrally regarded in surgery.

In a review of work on socialization in the classroom (Glidewell, et al., 1965, 1966), the reviewers interpreted the empirical work to show a distinction between perceived competence and other variables of social structure. They emphasized the importance of distinguishing between specific competencies and their relevance to the social situation. Other studies of school children indicate the importance of perceived competence in classrom tasks as a dimension of the social structure of the classroom (Gold, 1958; Gordon, 1959, 1966; Sears & Sherman, 1964; Stringer & Glidewell, 1967).

That competence is a prime basis of self-esteem is widely assumed. The idea that competence as perceived by others is a basis of self-esteem implies that both social comparison and consensual validation are involved. Conceptions vary. White tends to emphasize internal experiences of competence as bases for self-esteem, but he elaborates:

There are two points to be made. The first is that the flow of esteem from others is not regulated entirely by their character structure or their whims. It is to some extent a reply to our own behavior, a response elicited by our doing something that commands esteem, and what commands esteem is very often a display of some sort of competence. The second point is that the exercise of such competence yields experiences of efficacy that are satisfying in their own right, though added satisfaction may be obtained if the accomplishments are recognized by others. (White, 1965, p. 9.)

Combs and Snygg (1959) describe the "adequate person" as one who perceives himself to be able, contributing, capable, and effective as well as liked, wanted, acceptable, and belonging. Diggory (1966) maintains that goal accomplishment is the prime connection between competence and self-esteem. He assigns social criteria (consensual validation) a secondary significance, but he does allow that one type of self-evaluation is "based solely on social approval and acceptance" (p. ix). D. R. Miller (1963) asserts that an individual's perceptions of how he is evaluated by other members of his group make up one element of influence on his self-esteem. He goes further to say that if an individual is deeply involved with a group, the group's evaluation of him can become the main basis of his self-esteem.

Havighurst, in his Edward L. Thorndike Award Address (1969) interpreted available data to indicate that perceived competence was the outcome of a sociocultural reward structure, developmental in nature. Beginning with satisfactions of physiological appetites, the development continued through approval and disapproval from parents, teachers, and peers, internal approval and disapproval based on the superego, and finally internal approval or disapproval based upon the ego. In his view, ego development depended upon a reward system based on social regularity, and perceived competence was based on the individual foresight produced by social regularity.

These conceptions make clear that there are two bases producing two kinds of self-esteem. One—unsocialized self-esteem—is based upon the internal experience of accomplishment, the sense of mastery or effectance which comes from nonsocial information. The other—socialized self-esteem—is based on social comparison and consensual validation, the individual's perceptions of the responses and opinions of others about his acts.

C. R. Smith (1967) confirmed this distinction empirically. She used a self-report scale including two kinds of items. One kind of item measured self-esteem and was positively related to social desirability. The other items measured self-esteem also, but were negatively related to social desirability. Factor analysis from five samples showed two orthogonal factors. All the items reflecting socialized self-esteem were highly loaded on one factor; all those reflecting unsocialized self-esteem were highly loaded on the second factor.

The distinction, however, was not very readily made by persons who were making general ratings of self-esteem, their own and others'. In C. R. Smith's work, the two scales showed little of the changes one would expect concomitant with other data (interpersonal perceptions) which did show changes in perceived competence and self-esteem. K. E. Smith (1968) sought to instruct elementary school teachers to distinguish between socialized and unsocialized self-esteem in rating themselves and their colleagues, and he found that they had difficulty making the distinction.

It seems reasonable to conclude that the conceptual distinction between socialized and unsocialized self-esteem is a valid one and can be shown expirically by inference from factor analysis. It also seems reasonable to suggest that the distinction may not be very clear to the subjects themselves. In Bruyn's terms (1966), the distinction is a concept useful in science, but it may not be useful in the thinking of culture studied.

The connections between competence, social status, and self-esteem grow out of the fact that valued competencies give one both social status and self-esteem. The connections between competence and status have been described and supported by Foote and Cottrell (1955), Homans (1961), and Blau (1955). The relationship between competence, status, and self-esteem has received some support from the findings of de Charms and Rosenbaum (1960). The most specific support came from the experimental findings of C. R. Smith (1967). She was able to vary an actual and specific task competence experimentally and to show that increases in competence were followed by deference from partners in dyads, and that, *in sequence*, self-esteem also increased.

K. E. Smith (1968), in a pilot correlational study, found high positive relationships between competence (as seen by colleagues), status (also as seen by colleagues), and self-esteem (as seen by oneself). When the perceived status was partialled out, the correlation between competence and self-esteem dropped from .51 to zero (.03). When all three ratings were self-perceptions, the correlations between competence, status, and self-esteem remained high. When status was partialled out, however, there was almost no reduction in the correlation between competence and self-esteem (from .80 to .64). There appeared to be a direct connection between self-perceived competence and self-esteem, but only an indirect connection (through status) between peer-perceived competence and self-esteem. It would appear—based on these pilot data—that one's own view of one's self-esteem is closer to unsocialized self-esteem, whereas the views of one's colleagues are closer to socialized self-esteem. In any case, the empirical data available support the idea that perceived competence is an important basis for self-esteem, and that socialized self-esteem is closely connected with competence as perceived by others.

The most nearly clear connections between perceived competence, self-esteem, and mental health have been demonstrated in school children. For example, Coopersmith (1959), Fink (1962), Williams and Cole (1968), Campbell (1965), and Torshen (1969) have reported positive correlations between positive student self-evaluations and measures of achievement. Brandt (1958) added accuracy of self-evaluation and showed that performance is related to accuracy. Brookover, Thomas, and Paterson (1964) found positive correlations between pupils' self-evaluations and grades. Dyson (1967) found a positive relationship between pupils' academic self-concept and grades. Stringer and Glidewell (1967) assessed competence, enjoyments, achievement, self-esteem, and mental health and found a pattern of correlations which revealed self-esteem as the central variable. The correlation between global self-esteem and mental health status was .84 (p. 42). Brownfain (1952) and Engel (1959) reported positive relationships between positive self-evaluation and psychological adjustment. Feldhusen and Thurston (1964) reported relationships between anxiety and (a) achievement in relation to capacity, (b) emotional adjustment, and (c) integration of self-concept.

Tagiuri (1952) found connections between peer acceptance (not specifically competence), self-esteem, and mental health, in a small sample (35) of adolescent boys. Bower's (1958) findings indicated that, in a sample of 4,400 elementary school children, emotionally handicapped children were often selected for hostile or inadequate roles in casting a class play. The emotionally handicapped boys, but not the girls, felt greater dissatisfaction with self and school behavior; both boys and girls, who were emotionally handicapped were less competent in academic tasks. Bruce (1958) showed negative relationships between

self-acceptance and measures of insecurity and anxiety. Coopersmith (1959, 1967) and Horowitz (1962) found significant relationships between self-esteem, anxiety, and evaluations by others. McCandless, Castaneda, and Palermo (1956) showed negative relationships between sociometric choices and anxiety. Roth's (1959) results were equivocal. Dyson's (1967) work included the finding that a measure of *nonacademic* self-evaluation was *not* related to grades and Torshen's (1969) findings tended to confirm the specificity of the relationship between *academic* self-evaluation and grades. Both Coopersmith (1967) and Torshen (1969) showed that it was not actual achievement that was connected with self-esteem and mental health, but perceived success as compared to the immediate peer group. A child with low achievement may show high self-esteem if his perceived successes compare favorably with those of his peers.

In summary, perceived competence is a dimension of social organization adding a differentiation to individual position in a social system not made by attraction or power. Task competence can be distinguished from interpersonal competence, but both are significant in social evaluations. Competence in central and important tasks, as perceived by others in immediate peer groups, provides a significant basis for status in such groups, and through status produces socialized self-esteem. There is, however, an unsocialized self-esteem (possibly orthogonal to socialized self-esteem) which is based upon one's own inner experiences of competence. Both competence and self-esteem are closely related to aspects of motivational strength and direction, feelings of anxiety, and interpersonal enjoyments.

SOCIAL POWER

Some conception of social power is central to most analyses of psychosocial systems, large or small. Such conceptions have been the bases for analyses of international relationships, intranational developments, industrial achievements and failures, neighborhood integration and disintegration, and family interaction. Analytically, power is a secondary concept. It can be derived from more simple concepts of boundaries, resources, and reciprocity of interchange. In a general sense, power is the control of needed resources (see Berrien, 1968). Two of the general bases of social power (two generally needed resources) are interpersonal attraction and perceived competence. Power is thus related to both; but it is not the same thing. The relationships between power and attraction and power and competence vary from one system to the next, with the nature of the needed resources.

The relative social power of individuals in a social system is usually accurately perceived by the members of the system. Most research findings indicate that even young children hold an accurate perception of the power structure of a group and of their own position in the structure. Potashin (1946) demonstrated this accuracy in an economically privileged community; Goslin (1962) obtained similar findings in middle-class adolescents in a suburban community; Lippitt, Polansky, and Rosen (1952) reported congruent findings from a boys' camp; and Gold (1958) produced similar data from interviews with elementary school children. Among adults, the generally accurate perception of power has been noted by French and Snyder (1959) and Hunter (1953), among others.

Public discussion and analysis of the power relationships among discussants is probably rare. In human relations training, where the training often involves public discussion of power relationships, the discussants typically are embarrassed by participating in a public discussion by which they are assigned power positions. Apparently high power individuals are embarrassed for two reasons. There is the view that power corrupts and he who holds it must be corrupt. There is also the value on "equality" of participants which implies that any form of superiority is bad. At the other end of the power structure, participants are embarrassed by a public assignment to a low power position, seemingly because of the implication of inferiority. When power is explicitly based upon some specific competency, public discussion usually includes the agreement that the power applies only to the current situation, which situation demands that specific competency.

Social power has its basis in the capacity of the individual to control resources, especially valued resources which are complementary to the resources being offered by others in the system (see, for example, Wilensky's observations of staff experts, 1956). French and Raven (1959), in a well-known paper, set out a theory differentiating five bases of social power: (1) reward power, the control of others' rewards; (2) coercive power, the control of punishment to others; (3) legitimate power, the control of salient institutional sanctions; (4) referent power, the control of a desired identification or approval; and (5) expert power, the control of needed special knowledge or skill. The bases are not mutually exclusive, and often the position of an individual has many bases. Running through all bases of power are interpersonal attraction (a source of identification which can be rewarding and punishing), perceived competence (a source of expertness which can also be both a reward and, by deprivation, a punishment), and institutional assignment to a position on the basis of something other than attractiveness or competence, such as birthright, age, or sex.

Power is allocated by a social system in return for valued resources, risk-taking, conformity to norms and values, and personal attraction—"competence, capital, courage, and charisma." Popular conceptions of social power often do not take account of the fact that social power, even when acquired as an institutional gift, as in inheritances, is exercised at a cost as well as a profit. The powerful person must provide to the others in the system some motives, feelings, ideas, skills, or objects in exchange for the power he exercises (see, for example, Thibaut & Kelley, 1959; Homans, 1961; Blau, 1964).

Social theorists have commonly taken two positions: (a) that most persons will allow an actor to exercise power over them only when there is no alternative, and (b) that power—personal and political—is allocated in return for some form of competence, attraction, or institutional legitimation. Given those two positions, the general conditions required for an actor to establish power can be taken from Emerson (1962) and Blau (1964). The "social contract" by which an actor acquires power over others in exchange for resources supplied to others can be established and maintained under the following conditions. First, the low-power others must not be able to supply equally valuable resources to the high power actor. The power "takes up the slack" in an exchange of resources which would otherwise be inequitable. Second, the others must not be able to obtain the resources (competence, attraction, or legitimation) more readily (in exchange for less power) from another available source. Third, the others must not be able to coerce the actor (physically or morally) to supply the resources, thus making the award of power unnecessary to the acquisition of the resources. Fourth, the others cannot adapt themselves to do without the resources.

The issue about the asymmetrical interchange of resources has been analyzed by both Homans (1961) (on social esteem) and Blau (1964). The position taken here is that the total interchange is symmetrical. The exercise of power over others is a right which continues only as long as the exercise is accompanied by performing the duties of supplying valued resources to others. A person may use his power to gain control over new resources to perpetuate his power, but the base is still in resource control. Usually this sort of conception excludes coercive power, but even coercive power can be seen as exchanged for comfort. If the other is willing to undergo the pain of coercive punishment, the actor can exercise no power to influence any behavior but being punished. Deliberate civil disobedience deprives the state of most of its legal coercive power. Its power is limited to the power to imprison—an impractical power when applied to large numbers of persons.

Not very much attention has been given to the mental health effects of holding high power positions in social systems. Kasl and French (1962) studied the personnel of two companies and found that—*status being constant*—greater supervisory repsonsibility led to increased frequency of visits to the company dispensary. The implication was that when supervisory responsibility (a cost of power) was relatively high for a given status or public esteem (a reward of power), the individuals felt a stress from the system which affected their health. When some of those same individuals (in positions where responsibility was higher than status) were promoted so that their public esteem (reward) was in balance with their responsibility (cost), their visits to the dispensary decreased. Tentatively, one may conclude that high power positions have negative effects on individual mental health when the costs of exercising power (e.g., time, risk-taking, skill development) are not seen as reciprocal with the rewards from it (public esteem, resource control, prestige, etc.).

More attention has been given to the effects of being in a low power position. In the many studies

following Malzberg (1940), Lemkau, Tietze, and Cooper (1941), and Hollingshead and Redlich (1958), a major explanation for the high incidence and prevalence of mental illnesses in the lower classes was the inability of the lower class persons to influence others in the system to supply the resources they needed to cope with social and economic emergencies. Srole and his colleagues (1962) have clearly developed such a position. Crisis intervention, the idea that maladaptive behavior can be prevented by supplying needed resources at times of crisis is, in a major way, an approach to providing the individual with a temporary relatively high power position in the community. Eric Lindemann (1960) produced some of the findings on which the idea was based. Parad (1965) has provided a recent compilation of the current applications.

There is a real question about whether the low power position, in itself, is an illness-inducing condition. The higher incidence of schizophrenia in the lower classes could have been found due to failure to identify cases not seen by professionals, as the work of Kaplan, Reed, and Richardson (1956) would indicate. Many investigations have made it clear that low socioeconomic status determines commitment to (Rose and Stub, 1955) and delay in discharge from (Meyers, Bean, & Pepper, 1964) state hospitals as well as the kind of helping structure one becomes involved in (Hollingshead & Redlich, 1958; Hardt & Feinhandler, 1959; Brill & Storrow, 1960).

Freeman (1968), citing especially Kornhauser's (1965) studies of automobile workers, interprets the work on social class and mental illness this way: "There apparently is a relationship between mental health and what a person wants, what he would like to be as a person, and what he sees himself being and becoming" (pp. 89–90). Following Freeman (and others), one may propose that the most likely influence of social power—high or low—on the development of psychoses is generated by a perceived discrepancy between power actually exercised, the cost of exercising it, and the rewards from exercising it. Holding a low power position means, by definition, having access to fewer resources. If exercising power requires the expenditure of resources, as is proposed here, the exercise will always be relatively more costly to the person in a low power position than to a person in a high power position. What a low power person wants—and, in fact, needs—and what he sees himself able to acquire comes into balance only when his needs are limited. When he is confronted by a crisis requiring more resources than he can supply based on his current power, he must either (1) seek resources from others at the cost of a further reduction in power and greater vulnerability to the next crisis, or (2) seek relief by some break with reality.

The data concerning the relationship between the power position of an individual—its costs and rewards—and less drastic aspects of mental health are more compelling. That relatively low power increases tendencies to conform to social pressures has been often demonstrated (for a review, see Hollander & Willis, 1967). The induction of such defensive behavior as denial or projection has been found by Douglas (1959) and Lippitt and Gold (1959). The reduction in the authenticity of self-presentation has been noted by Goffman (1958), F. Davis (1961) in the struggles of the visibly handicapped, and Cohen (1958) in studying upward communications in experimental social hierarchies. Satisfaction with one's position has been shown to increase with the increase in power (centrality) and possibilities for independent action (Leavitt, 1951; Shaw, 1954; Gilchrist, Shaw & Walker, 1954; Barker & Gump, 1964).

Studies of the influence of the low power position of the lower classes have reflected some sense of powerlessness and defenselessness (Smith & Geoffrey, 1968, Dean, 1961) presumably associated with experiences of being unable to cope with crises. It is also clear, however, that there is, from a psychosocial point of view, no homogeneous lower class group. A number of students have distinguished clear variations in motivational and emotional life styles among lower class individuals and families. Rainwater (1966) distinguished three developmental phases in life cycles: (1) *expressive*, in which one copes by making oneself as attractive as possible (2) *violent*, in which, finding the expressive style ineffective, one tries to influence others by force, and (3) *depressive*, in which influence attempts are abandoned and one's needs are reduced to simple necessities. Miller and Riessman (1961) have distinguished the stable working class—"regular members of the nonagricultural labor force in manual occupations" (p. 88)—from the more unstable workers leading irregular lives. The stable

workers find that "coping with the instability threats becomes a dominant activity within the working class family" (p. 91). Hollingshead and Redlich (1958) found that socially nonmobile, skilled workers in New Haven took fewer personal risks, manifested more positive self-concepts, and showed a greater sense of personal dignity than did their upward mobile counterparts. Assuming that upward mobility involved taking greater risk of being unsuccessful in some achievement attempt, one again finds vulnerability to coping failures erodes positive self-concepts and presumably mental health. It seems clear that being a member of the lower classes does not necessarily impart a sense of powerlessness. It is also clear that, when it does appear, a sense of powerlessness in the face of crises has negative mental health consequences.

In summary, social power is a concept widely used in the analyses of relationships between individuals and social systems. The relative social power of individuals is generally accurately perceived by the self and others but is not typically publicly discussed. Social power has its prime basis in the capacity of an individual to control complementary resources including motives, feelings, ideas, and skills, as well as objects. Power is allocated by a social system in return for valued resources; it has both costs and rewards. The primary effects of power on individual mental health are generated by the degree of inequity between the costs and rewards of exercising power. When the costs are perceived to be too high for the rewards, the individual is subject to intrapersonal tensions which increase the likelihood of disturbances in the development of motivational strength and direction, emotional state and expression, intellectual potential and utilization, and interpersonal enjoyments and skills. Persons in low power positions, having relatively few resources under control, are less able to cope with repeated crises and more likely to develop some break with reality—if not psychosis, then denial and projection, reduced authenticity of self-presentation, or just apathy and a sense of impotence and defenselessness.

Defenselessness has been regarded as synonomous with low power and vulnerability to sanction, but a number of considerations make it appropriate to consider vulnerability to sanction as a conceptually distinct dimension of the position of an individual in a social system. These considerations are developed in the following section.

VULNERABILITY TO SANCTION

A fourth dimension which differentiates positions of individuals in social systems has received little attention and study, but it might be of particular importance to mental health. Vulnerability to sanction refers to the likelihood that any deviation from norms will be responded to with some constraint or punishment. It can be applied to individual behavior, to roles, and to subsystems to differentiate one from the other with respect to the likelihood that any deviation from norms will evoke restraint or punishment.

Most typically, high vulnerability to sanction has been associated with low power positions, but it may also be associated with high power positions, if risk-taking is a significant part of the basis for power. Corporation presidents, when required to risk large investments in new undertakings, find themselves particularly vulnerable to sanction from the board of directors or from the stockholders directly. In spite of his very powerful position, the President of the United States, who commits troops to war, is particularly vulnerable to sanction from public opinion and from voters.

Vulnerability to sanction is closely associated with visibility. Some roles, such as traffic policeman, professional athlete, trial lawyer, and politician, require frequent actions which are widely visible. Some roles, such as vice-squad policeman, coach in professional sports, tax attorney, and physician are usually performed in private and are even subject to privileged communication to insure that privacy. It might be noted that as television news cameras are turned on more activities, more role performances become widely visible and vulnerable to sanction —"The whole world is watching."

Individuals seem also to be subject to variations in visibility, sometimes due to physical characteristics or to some aspect of temperament. Very tall and very short persons, persons with unusual skin color, persons with unusual hair color, persons with limbs missing or other unusual physical characteristics are generally more visible. Especially visible people are noticed first, and when it is not clear who has performed some deviant act, especially visible people may find themselves suspected simply because they were noticed very soon after the act was performed.

At the other extreme are the "invisible" persons. Some empirical data are available about the "invisible" child in the classroom. Hudgins and Loftis (1966) have given considerable attention to the invisible child who (a) had high competencies which were not recognized by other children, (b) was not rejected by other children and was not an isolate in the usual sense, (c) seemed not to be noticed by other children even though he was often in interaction with the teacher, and (d) did not seem to need to be noticed. Stringer and Glidewell (1965) noted that trained observers in the classroom had great difficulties because a few children simply went unnoticed during the observation period. Gronlund (1959) and Northway (1944) observed that there were some healthy, self-sufficient, or socially uninterested children who seemed to be unaware of the classroom social structure or their positions in it. Paul Painter (personal communication, 1962) reported that in the practice of child psychiatry, some quite healthy children were referred to him as emotionally ill when their only symptom seemed to be that they were "loners"—often unaware of and not interested in the social expectations of them held by other children. The nature of the personality and social adaptation of such "invisible children" is not clear from the data, but it is clear that these children cannot be assumed to be in psychological distress.

Logically, it would seem that if reinforcement conditions are important to learning and if threat is important to defensiveness, then vulnerability of one's role to social sanction must influence the development of motivational, emotional, and intellectual aspects of human behavior. In particular, vulnerability must disrupt the development of such behavior by defensiveness. At present, however, empirical data showing specific connections between vulnerability to sanction and mental health are hard to come by.

A RECAPITULATION

Looking back at the foregoing sections, one may draw some conclusions about the mental health significance of social order and change, inter-personal attraction, perceived competence, social power, and vulnerability to sanction. It is unlikely that either social order or social change, in themselves, induce mental health problems. Problems are generated, however, when (a) a social order maintains a continuing perceived inequity, (b) a social change makes equity unpredictable, or (c) a social change increases inequities more than it reduces them.

Repeated experiences of attracting others in interaction lead to increased self-esteem, increased affiliation motivation, enhanced interpersonal skills, and further attractiveness in a self-sustaining circular process. In the opposite direction, repeated experiences of repelling others lead to reduced self-esteem, decreased affiliation motivation, disruption of interpersonal skills and further unattractiveness—again in a self-sustaining circular process. Repeated rejection or social aversion appears to be regularly accompanied by increasing distress, distrust, and a sense of unworthiness—but not necessarily by mental illness of clinical severity.

Competence in central and important tasks, as perceived by others in immediate peer groups, provides a significant basis for status in such groups, and, through status, induces a socialized self-esteem. There is, however, an unsocialized self-esteem (possibly independent of socialized self-esteem) which is based upon one's own inner experiences of competence. Both competence and self-esteem are closely related to aspects of motivational strength and direction, feelings of anxiety, productivity, and interpersonal enjoyments.

The primary effects of social power on individual mental health are generated by the degree of inequity between the costs and rewards of exercising or not exercising power. When the costs are perceived as too high for the rewards, the individual is subject to intrapersonal tensions which increase the likelihood of disturbances in motivational strength and direction, emotional state and expression, intellectual potential and utilization, and interpersonal enjoyments and skills. Persons in low power positions, having relatively few resources under their control, are less able to cope with repeated crises and more likely to develop some break with reality—if not psychosis, then denial and projection, reduced authenticity of self-presentation, or just apathy.

Vulnerability to sanction is a dimension of social organization cutting across the other dimensions. While logically it should produce concomitant vulnerability to mental health problems, little empirical information is available to support that position.

One theme runs through all the foregoing analyses: equity of social resource interchange. There may indeed be a universal norm of reciprocity, the violation of which not only makes a system more unstable but also deprives the individual of the balance of social support and control which is his basis for foresight.

With the foregoing generalizations as background, the focus of the discussion is to be changed. In the following sections the concepts of social order and change and the concepts of social forces acting on individual positions in social systems will be applied to smaller units. The focus will be upon the specialized subsystems which have evolved to prevent or correct individual behaviors perceived as manifestations of mental illnesses—the helping subsystems.

THE HELPING SUBSYSTEMS

The Helping Dyad

In all sorts of societies and cultures there is an old, honorable, and traditional method for dealing with an individual (child or adult) who responds to the demands of the society by acting so badly or strangely that he upsets the system: isolation. As indicated in the section on interpersonal attraction, continued social isolation is an experience with which few persons can cope. If *simple* isolation doesn't work, the difficult individual is subjected to a more *complex* detachment. He is temporarily relieved of his usual responsibilities and assigned to a helping dyad—a temporary relationship with a person of special status who is to help him. Sometimes the one-to-one interaction in the dyad is training, sometimes tutoring, sometimes consultation, sometimes treatment, sometimes rehabilitation, sometimes confession, sometimes exorcizing evil spirits, and sometimes it is therapy.

A dyad is the simplest of social systems. In a dyad the nature of the interaction can be most clear and explicit to the two actors. Consider the socialization process in a dyad. Socialization may be defined as a process which begins with learning the likelihood of receiving rewards and punishments from others in response to alternative ways of behaving in a social system. Nowhere are such likelihoods more clear and explicit than in the one-to-one interaction of a dyad.

The helper in the dyad is some person of special status and power based upon age, knowledge, skill, or magic. The high power helper is almost always constrained by social sanction not to abuse his power over his client, to act in his client's best interests, and to try to restore him quickly to his usual responsibilities in the larger system. The deviant client, often in distress, is constrained to cooperate, which constraint usually means trying hard to follow the instructions of the helper.

Characteristic of the helping dyad is some form of privileged communication. The deviant client is expected to expose his personal problems—or personal devils—in his interaction with the helper, but he is protected from a more general exposure and thereby from the social sanctions which would accompany a more general exposure. The privileged communication reduces the costs of errors in behavioral experiments. Connected with this privilege are very close limits on system linkage by interaction—limits on the interchange of ideas and feelings between the subsystem unit and the suprasystem. Even with all the bureaucratic supervision in complex societies, the professional practitioner in the helping professions is very rarely directly observed in the process of interaction with his client or patient. System linkage is confined to overlapping roles (see Merton's conception of the social mechanisms for the articulation of roles in the "role set," 1957).

Under such freedom from observation and limitations on linkage with the larger system, the helper is given license to decide just what the best interests of his client really are (see, for example the work of Blau and Scott, 1962, on professional bureaucracies). This license gives the helper a considerable power over the client and creates a power imbalance. Such power imbalances have at least a slight tendency to change in the direction of balance. This social force interacts with the system constraints on the amount of time available for the helping process. An extended time may, on the one hand, keep the client subservient to the helper to the point of exploitation. It may, on the other hand, limit the power of the helper and increase the power of the client in ways which

have been subjected to analysis by several investigators.

Homans has put forth the proposition (1950) that continued interaction between any two persons will increase the dependency of each of the persons on the rewards supplied by the other. The trend of such increased dependencies is toward a balance of power. The helping dyad is a *temporary* system, limiting the balance of power which would accrue from continued interaction. The limitation of the time available is one of the safeguards the larger system places upon the tendency for such subsystems to stabilize and become rigid. The doctor must not extend his patient's illness; the lawyer must not prolong litigation indefinitely; the welfare worker must not perpetuate his client's poverty—such rules are made to counteract the tendency for a powerful person to maintain his power.

The opposite social force is not so widely recognized. The continuation may limit rather than increase the power of the helper. If the welfare worker becomes dependent upon his client's continued poverty, the client may develop as much power over the worker as the worker has over the client. Thibaut and Kelley (1959) have proposed that if the client (in the low power position) can lengthen his time perspective far enough into the future, he can devaluate the assistance of the helper (in the high power position), reflect question upon the skill of the helper, and thereby make the helper dependent upon him for the demonstration of his competence. Sometimes children discover how their achievement reflects credit or discredit on a teacher and begin to act on the power that this discovery gives them. (Personal communication, 1968, from Dan Lortie suggests that his interviews with teachers show that children are the primary source of reward for teachers.) Such a dependency creates a balance of power.

Given the limitations on power equalization placed by the larger system on the life of the dyad, one might expect other power-balancing forces to be generated. Following Emerson (1962) and Secord and Backman (1964), one would expect that a prime effort of the deviant client toward a power balance would be an assignment of increasing value to the assistance of the helper. Such increasing value would tend to justify the power the client awards to the helper. He is "getting" valuable help in return for the power he "gives" the helper. Two findings are related to this phenomenon. Thibaut and Kelley (1959) found that the more powerful person in a dyad is better able to keep the values with which he enters the relationship; the less powerful is more likely to change them. If, in addition, the client entered the dyad by choice—and many deviants do ask for help in their distress—he often tries to decrease the tension generated by perceiving the chosen alternative (the help received) to be increasingly more valuable. Brehm's (1956) experiment demonstrated this tendency to increase the value assigned to a chosen alternative. A prime norm of almost all systems is that power is obtained in exchange for instrumental help (Blau, 1954). Under such an arrangement, a common sequence of events ensues. The client receives valuable help, he becomes more acceptable to the larger system, he is relieved of his assignment to the helping dyad, and he is returned to his usual responsibilities in the larger system. The cause of the change in the behavior would be attributed to the acts of the more powerful helper, as had been shown by Thibaut and Riecken (1955 a & b). The operation of such social forces probably accounts for much of the long and honorable tradition—and effectiveness—of the helping dyad in so many societies.

There are conditions, however, under which the client does not assign much value to the assistance of the helper, and the failure of reciprocity persists. Following Emerson again, one would expect the client to attempt to withdraw from the dyad—against the helper's professional advice. It is from just such forces that many helping dyads are terminated while they are still in process.

Withdrawal is often difficult. Sanctions from the larger system often make withdrawal more costly to the client than continued interaction in the helping dyad, as costly as it may be. Under such conditions, one might expect the client to begin to ration his positive responses to the helper—gratitude, approval, conformity, esteem—and thereby achieve some control over the rewards available to the helper. A number of students have observed this phenomenon (Newcomb, 1961; Thibaut & Kelley, 1959; Emerson, 1962). To the extent that the helper becomes more dependent upon his client for such status-reinforcing rewards, the client will have achieved greater power in the dyad. In order to limit the dependency of the

helper on his client for positive evaluation, most systems are designed to provide primary status-reinforcing rewards to the helper from the larger system.

Within the time and reward-control limits set by the larger system, there are still other psychosocial forces which act to bring the power in the helping dyad into balance. The client may extend the power network as described by Emerson (1962). If he can establish relationships with other legitimate helpers, he has options about whose instructions to follow. Inherent in the helping dyad there is one set of forces which generates a very common extension of the power network. Helpers, being persons of special status committed to the best interests of the client, find themselves identifying with the client. His costs and benefits become their costs and benefits. Such expressive ties often come into conflict with the instrumental requirements of the helper's role. To confront the client with his distortions of reality is to cause him pain and distress. To cause the client pain and distress is also to cause the helper pain and distress. The helper finds himself in the typical conflict of the person who undertakes to perform both instrumental and expressive roles in the same interaction. This conflict motivates both members of the dyad to seek a third role. These are the forces which lead to the formation of a helping *triad*.

The Helping Triad

It may be that if one examined the informal as well as the formal helping systems, the helping functions are always performed by a triad. Even where the dyad is the formally established structure, one may well find a third person functioning informally in a high-status expressive role, complementing the high-status instrumental role of the formally designated helper. Roethlisberger and Dickson (1939) noted such triads in the Hawthorne Plant; Homans (1950) observed them in Firth's (1936) reports of socialization among the Tikopia; Blau (1955) found such triads in the informal organization of a government bureau. Freilich (1964) has made a discerning analysis of natural triads in both simple kinship systems and more complex social systems. Although Freilich was interested in a more general phenomenon, by following his lead one may explicate some powerful psychosocial forces influencing helping functions in social systems. Following is an attempt at such an explication.

The proposition is that the upsetting tensions which are often induced by the social forces discussed previously are often managed by a natural triad. The triad always includes a high-status instrumental figure responsible for the success of the socialization or rehabilitation process, a high-status expressive figure responsible for expressive support and tension relief, and a low-status subordinate (the deviant client) whose behavior is not satisfactory—his bad or strange behavior is upsetting the people in the system. Freilich was interested in the typical tensions induced by the usual socialization process and the use of the triad to manage those tensions. Here the interest is in the more intense tensions, induced by inequities of social control or support, producing bad or strange behavior. The functions of the triad should become even more clear and explicit under such conditions.

The roots of the social forces leading to the formation of helping triads may be found in the wide prevalence of this basic form. Benne and Sheats (1948), Carter (1954), Bales and Slater (1955), Slater (1965), and others have observed that in the development of small groups, the "task" leadership role, supplying instrumental inputs, is regularly complemented by a second central role supplying expressive inputs. The functions of this very common role differentiation have been described as (a) reduction of conflict in the instrumental leader by relieving him of demands for expressive inputs, (b) management of the tensions induced in the group by the necessary demands for control from the instrumental, task-oriented role, and (c) modifying and extending the power structure of the group.

Studies of more primitive societies have also revealed the wide prevalence of the basic form of the helping triad. In patrilineal societies the triad is formed by the father, the mother's brother, and the son. In an analysis of the reports of Firth (1936), Homans clearly described the expressive input and the tension management connected with the role of the mother's brother in Tikopia. "In all the great occasions of life . . . the mother's brother acts as an older friend . . . and helps him [the son]

over the rough places . . . Emotionally the relationship between them is friendly, free, and easy . . ."

It should be clear by now that the mother's brother is a practical and emotional necessity to a Tikopia man (Homans, 1950, p. 218). Freilich (1964) describes the general form of the triad in patrilineal societies as follows:

The father has jural authority over ego: he has the right to give orders and ego has the obligation to obey them. This relation, between a superior and an inferior, is often marked by formality and considerable restraint, while relations between ego and his mother's brother are characterized by ease and freedom. The mother's brother, though superior in status to ego, frequently plays the role of intimate friend, adviser, and helper. The . . . triad . . . exists in many societies including Batak, Gilyak, Karadjeri, Lakher, Lhota, Lovedu, Mbundu, Mende, Murngin, Sema, Venda, Wik-Munkan and Tikopia (p. 530).

The triad also appears in matrilineal societies but there it is the mother's brother who has jural authority over the child while the father performs the expressive role of friend, confidant, and supporter. Such matrilineal triads are found, according to Freilich, among the Trobriand Islanders, the Haida, the Tlinget and the Pende.

Zelditch (1955) studied the family structures of 56 societies and found that in 46 of them a clear differentiation between instrumental and expressive role occurred. Bernard (1942), Parsons and Bales (1955), and Bronfenbrenner (1961) differ about whether the mother or the father is more likely to perform the instrumental or expressive role in the American family, but all agree that this particular differentiation in parent-parent-child triads is widely prevalent. Where the differentiation is absent, role conflict and incompatibility are more common.

A triad of the same structure can be found in most bureaucracies. There is a high status figure who insures compliance to rules, but the low status worker confronted with a knotty problem will consult a friendly colleague—high in the informal power structure—before he takes the risk of exposing his difficulties to the person in the high-status instrumental role. Such triads have been found in government agencies (Blau, 1955); in prisons where the warden, the chaplain, and the prisoner form the triad; it is indicated in hospitals where the physician, the nurse, and the patient take the three roles; in high schools where the principal, the counselor, and the student are the actors (Stringer, 1959); and in mental health centers where the psychiatrist, the social worker, and the patient form the triad.

It seems reasonable to conclude that any consideration of the helping functions of a social system should take account of the triadic structures within the system, even if it is necessary to look closely into the informal interactions within the system.

Given that the helping triad has evolved as a psychosocial structure for coping with the tensions of inequities between social support and social control, one may turn to an analysis of the nature of the psychosocial forces which are generated to produce the helping function in the triad.

The helping triad aids in mitigating the power problems of the dyad. Extending the network to the high status supporter offers alternative benefits to the client, but, because the supporter is expressive and supportive only, he does not offer a competitive substitute for the instrumental helper. It becomes harder to withdraw from the triad than the dyad, because it is harder to find more attractive and equally supportive alternative arrangements. It is particularly effective in providing positive affection and friendship while avoiding the undermining of the helper's power by making him subject to demands from the client based upon duties to supply friendship or affectional support.

The triad is particularly adaptable to power balancing based upon coalition formation. Beginning with the observations of Simmel (1950), a long line of research has substantiated the tendency of triads to form into coalitions of two persons exerting influence on the third (Mills, 1954; Caplow, 1956; Vinacke & Arkoff, 1957; Gamson, 1961).

If one assumes a norm of reciprocity (Gouldner, 1960) which maintains the change in output from an actor equal to the changes in input, one may deduce the impact of the social forces generated when a helping triad is created as an open system.

The environment isolates the deviant and thereby the environment reduces both instrumental and expressive output to the deviant. The other aspect of the isolation lies in the fact that the deviant reduces both instrumental and expressive output to the environment. The deviant and the environment, thus, create a vacuous reciprocity; or, as is more often the case, any existing violations of reciprocity are temporarily suspended by the cessation of interchanges.

The instrumental helper must increase his instrumental output to the deviant. This increased output of instrumental resources by the helper must be balanced by a reduced instrumental output to either the supporter or the environment. Because the system does not relieve the helper of his usual responsibilities, he cannot reduce his output to the environment without failing in those responsibilities. The reduction must be in his instrumental output to the supporter.

The expressive supporter must increase his expressive output to the deviant. He, too, must maintain his responsibilities in the suprasystem. The increased output of expressive resources by the supporter is counterbalanced by a reduction in expressive acts toward the helper. The changes discussed thus far leave the helper relatively deprived of expressive resources; the supporter relatively deprived of instrumental resources; and the deviant relatively well supplied with both instrumental and expressive resources. Forces thus exist to reduce the "privileged" position of the deviant and reduce the costs to the helper and supporter. If rehabilitation of the deviant is rapid, the triad can tolerate such a violation of reciprocity, concentrating its resources on the "treatment" of the deviant, and no further changes may appear until the triad and system are rewarded by conformity from the deviant—and the triad is dissolved. The added responsibilities (outputs) of the helper and supporter and the lack of linkage with the suprasystem are compensated for by the rewards from the system for quick return of the deviant to the system.

If, however, the rehabilitation requires a more extended time, the helper and supporter are motivated to improve the equity of their positions in the triad, and the suprasystem seeks linkages to maintain surveillance and to prevent prolongation of the isolation of the triad. Typically, interchange with the deviant is avoided, and the system seeks some additional interchange with the helper and the supporter. Considering that the instrumental resources of the helper are already taxed, he tends to add an expressive output usually by entering into an expressive, supportive role with a person outside the triad. This additional output must be compensated for, and the tendency is to reduce the privileged position of the deviant by decreasing the helper's expressive output to him. In a similar manner the expressive supporter is constrained to enter an instrumental role with a person outside the triad and reduce his instrumental output to the deviant. These actions also (a) make both the instrumental and expressive roles more nearly "pure," and (b) establish a linking extension of the network of power and sentiment.

To review the analysis in quantitative form, assuming an open system, the changes occuring in the triad of helper, supporter, and deviant are as follows: (1) En (environment) decreases both I (instrumental) and E (expressive) output to D (deviant). (2) D reduces both I and E output to En. (3) H (helper) increases I output to D. (4) H reduced I output to S (supporter). (5) S increases E output to D. (6) S reduces E output to H. If rehabilitation takes more times, these additional steps occur. (7) H increased E output to En. (8) H reduces E output to D. (9) S increases I output to En. (10) S reduces I output to D.

Restating this process in algebraic terms (subscripts designate steps in the sequence above):

$$-H(+I_3-I_4+E_7-E_8)+S(-I_4 \qquad)+D(+I_3-E_8)+En(+E_7 \quad)=0.$$
$$+H(-E_6 \qquad)-S(+E_5-E_6+I_9-I_{10})+D(+E_5-I_{10})+En(+I_9 \quad)=0.$$
$$+H(\qquad)+S(\qquad)-D(-I_2-E_2)+En(-I_2-E_2)=0.$$
$$+H(\qquad)+S(\qquad)+D(-I_1-E_1)-En(-I_1-E_1)=0.$$

These equations are identities. Each shows that the total change in output from the actors (H, S, D, and En) is equal to the total change in input from each actor to the others. The algebraic additions, although not included here, can by performed for each column of this set of equations and represent the reciprocity existing after the changes are induced by creation of the helping triad.

These changes leave the deviant in balance, but the helper and the supporter are not (see Figure 10–1). The helper is still deprived of expressive resources, and the supporter is still deprived of instrumental resources because of the uncompensated reduced output from each other. The same resources are over supplied to the environment. If such resources are forthcoming from any source—deviant, environment, or each other—the triad will reach a balanced state within itself and with its environment and it will continue beyond its appointed time. Such balanced states occur when the suprasystem is rewarded by the continued isolation of the deviant, as with psychotic persons and retardates. For the triad to serve its purposes as a temporary system, the reduced interaction and deprivation of the helper and the supporter must be tolerated until the triad is terminated, with or without successfully inducing an accommodation between the deviant and the system. (This analysis has been greatly influenced by the quantitative formulations of Herbst, 1954, 1957. The reader may want to compare these with Herbst's algebraic forms.) The following sections contain further elaborations of the actions of these social forces.

The usual constraints obtain in the triad. The high status figures, instrumental or expressive, are not to abuse their power. They are to act in the client's best interests, according to their judgments of his best interests; and they are to try hard to restore him quickly to his usual responsibilities or duties in the larger system. The client is constrained to seek the instructions of the instrumental figure and to seek support and understanding from the expressive figure. The privileged communication is extended to the third role, and in fact, some communications between the client and the expressive supporter are not available to the instrumental helper. Most typically, the client may express his hostility toward the instrumental helper only in communication with the expressive supporter—and in confidence—to avoid the sanctions which the larger system expects its agent, the instrumental helper, to invoke. Conversely, communication with the instrumental helper may be repeated to the expressive supporter without concern, because the original communication was usually carefully selected by the client, and because the expressive helper is not under constraint from the larger system to invoke sanctions.

As has been proposed by a number of students (e.g., Homans, 1950), the high status expressive role acts as a check on the possible exploitation of the power of the high status instrumental role. Should the actor in the high status instrumental role become corrupt and use his power to extract resources (objects, ideas, or sentiments) from his client, the high-status expressive actor would become aware of the corruption. Through his linkage to the larger system and his status in it, the supporter could invoke sanctions against the instrumental actor to end his exploitation.

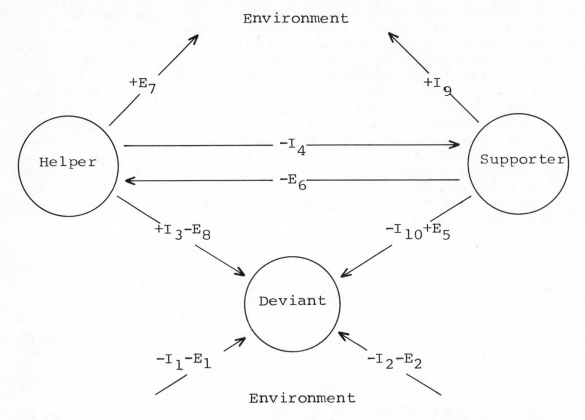

Fig. 10–1. A graphic representation of the changes generated by establishing a helpful triad. ("I" represents instrumental outputs. "E" represents expressive outputs. Subscripts designate steps in the sequence of creating the subsystem.)

A second psychosocial force induced in the triad is generated by the tension incident to the demands made by the instrumental helper. If the instrumental helper is to correct the bad or strange behavior of his client, he must necessarily place his client in positions in which the client must suppress his urges to act in socially disapproved ways. Accordingly, he must induce tensions in his client. In Freilich's terms, he feeds tensions into the system. Ordinarily, the tensions are generated in the helper when the low status person experiments with new or unusual modes of behavior in seeking an adaptation between himself and the system. The client, feeling his urges frustrated by the demands of the helper, experiences negative feelings toward the helper. No matter how carefully the helper is trained to accept and work with such negative feelings from clients, the larger system, of which the helper is an agent, disapproves of them. The client, like all low power persons, screens his communications to the high power helper. The client finds it easier and less guilt-producing to express his negative feelings about the helper to the supporter, who is not a control agent of the larger system and need not invoke sanctions. Thus, the tensions in the individuals, induced by the system, are relieved.

The analysis of tension reduction thus far has not included the interaction between the high status helper and the high status supporter. The helper is acting as an agent of the larger system to help in the socialization of a client who behaves badly or strangely. His role requires that the helper restrain some of the urges which come naturally to him—to seek gratitude from the client, or to coerce compliance from the client, to moderate unusual experiments, or to temper demands upon the client. He must absorb some of the tension his actions generate. Coordinately, the supporter also must restrain some of his natural urges—to criticize the instrumental helper, to express negative feelings toward the client, or to invoke sanctions on the client. He, too, absorbs some of the tensions generated in the system. The internal tension management acts mainly to change the deviant to fit the system. There is potential, however, to change the system to accomodate to the deviant.

In the basic analysis the point was made that the relief of the deviant's usual responsibilities to the system means a reduction of output from the triad to the system. As was indicated, such reduction is often compensated for by an increase in the output of expressive resources from the instrumental helper and an increase in the output of instrumental resources from the expressive helper. These forces lead to tension management by system linkage. To the extent that the helper feels some tension due to his interchange with his client, his tensions can be relieved by performing the expressive supporter role vis-à-vis another client. Similarly the supporter may perform the instrumental helper vis-à-vis another client. The tension management network is thus extended into the larger system, and the possibilities for complementary and reciprocal interchanges of tension induction and tension relief are multiplied.

It is the extension of the network—the subsystem linkages—which gives the helping triad its major potential as an agency for social change induction in the suprasystem. First, extension of the network manages tensions induced in both helper and supporter by any markedly unusual or innovative experiments mounted by the deviant client in trying to find an accommodation to the suprasystem. For example, a former member of an illicit gang may substitute social service to the deprived for open rebellion. Such a substitution may make the helper nervous about his client's good intentions. If, however, he is offering expressive support to another client's experiments, he must resolve the dissonance between withholding trust from the first client's experiment while supporting that of another client. *One possible* resolution is a change of perception about what sorts of experimental behavior are acceptable and trustworthy—the beginning of a change of expectation and eventually a change of norms. The linkage also provides a channel for diffusion for successful accommodation-producing experiments.

The helping triad also generates forces in the direction of what Heider (1958) and his students have called "congruence of sentiment" (see especially the summary in Berger, et al., 1962).

Considering first the internal exchange (Heider analyzes a closed system), where socialization has not been effective and the individual behaves badly or strangely, the relationship between him and the instrumental helper to whom he is assigned is expected to be negative. Further, the relationship between the client and the expressive supporter is expected to be positive. According to Heider's theory, the relationship between the helper and the supporter should be negative—unless the two high status figures remain out of contact with one another and thus achieve a vacuous balance. Under conditions of regular contact, the helper and supporter would experience a negative relationship. The helper would resent the positive expressions to the supporter by the deviant client, and the supporter would resent the demands made on the client by the instrumental helper.

To reduce the negative feelings, the supporter is constrained to advise the client of the wisdom and competence of the instrumental helper. While he expresses sympathy for and understanding of the distress of the client, he also reaffirms the value that the distress is a necessary condition to achieve the accommodation of the deviant to the system. Within itself, the helping triad is not an instrument of social change. It evolved to change the individual to fit the society, not the society to accommodate the individual.

When mothers have taken on the role of supporter of a child in psychotherapy, the outcome frequently is that the mother resents the therapist and the therapist resents the mother. Under some conditions, social workers in clinics have taken on the supporter role in complementation to the psychiatrist's instrumental role, and the negative relationship emerging between the two has presented a problem in staff relationships, often resulting in reduced or overly formal interactions to achieve a vacuous balance.

On the other hand, returning to the position that the triad is an open system, interaction between the helper and the supporter in other subsystems often leads to positive relationships between them. Again, according to Heider's theory, if the positive relationship is to continue, some change in the relationship of each with the client must take place. Either the helper-client relationship must become positive, yielding the balance of all positive relationships, or the supporter-client relationship must become negative.

The first case occurs when the deviant's behavior changes to conform to the norms of the total system, at which point the deviant resumes his usual responsibilities and the triad is dissolved. The second case occurs when the client's deviancy becomes so great that there is a cessation of interaction with him (as in the observations of Festinger, Schachter, & Back, 1950). Again, the triad is dissolved as a helping subsystem.

The foregoing analysis indicates a balance of forces in the helping triad which tends to keep the deviant (1) isolated from the larger system, (2) under stress to modify his behavior to fit the norms of the larger system, in a position to experiment with new accommodations with the two high status figures, and (3) supported in the distress due to the tensions he feels. The two high status figures are induced to (1) reduce the rate of interaction with each other, (2) tolerate negative sentiments between them, and (3) seek to reduce those negative sentiments by achieving an accommodation between the deviant and the instrumental helper and thus return the deviant to his usual responsibilities in the larger system.

Helping Subsystems and Social Change

Increasing size, complexity, and density of modern societies has engendered forces of social change and has provided a setting highly conducive to the extension of the helping networks of the natural triad. It became more necessary to return the deviant to the society in some condition more adaptive than the *status quo ante*. There appeared in all sorts of creeds and movements a call for prevention of new deviancies and for contributing to "growth." Nowhere was the call more strong and clear than in the child guidance movement.

The child guidance clinic: An expansion of the triad. The early orthopsychiatric interest in children was developed in the context of urbanization, increasing size and complexity, but decreasing facility of subsystem linkage, especially the linkage between the health institution, the educational institution, and the neighborhood. It began in the 1920s and grew fastest in the post World War II 1940s and 1950s. (The growth of ideology and practice can be traced in the collection of papers published in the *American Journal of Orthopsychiatry* between 1930 and 1957, edited by Tulchin, 1964.) The child guidance clinic was developed as an innovation within the health institution, perhaps as much to induce social change in child rearing practices as to treat disorders of children. It called itself "orthopsychiatric" because it proposed to straighten the bent twig so that the tree might grow straight. While it concentrated upon the treatment of children, such treatment was believed to prevent mental illnesses in adults. Furthermore, the leaders of the movement thought the family was the most appropriate treatment unit and took the position that family treatment could prevent illnesses in the healthy children belonging to the same family as the treated ill children (Stevenson & Smith, 1934; Lowrey, 1957). The extension of the traditional doctor-patient dyad to a team-patient-family network had all the potential linkages for an extended, social-change-inducing network—but the linkages were potential only.

The child guidance clinic was manned by a team of both medical and nonmedical specialists, but the codes of medical practice were carefully followed—codes for helping *dyads*. In the eyes of the community, medical practice was clearly the legitimized practice. Psychologists and social workers—explicitly or implicitly—found it easier to establish the legitimacy of their professional services when they associated themselves with "the doctor" and followed his dyadic codes and customs in "taking care of the patient." During the 1930s, to the patient who was ill and in distress, the doctor's codes and customs were appropriate. The practice of medicine had an excellent reputation for relieving distress and curing illnesses (Stevenson & Smith, 1934; Ackerman, 1945).

However, there were complications. The social role of the child who had the measles was quite clear to the family and the neighborhood. He was relieved of his usual responsibilities at school and at home. He was kept in bed, and he was expected to do the best he could to get well and resume his responsibilities as soon as possible. Getting well as soon as possible meant following the doctor's orders, and his parents were the agents of the doctor. They sympathized with the child's distress at having to stay in bed and take the foul-tasting medicine, but they assured the child of the doctor's wisdom and saw to it that the doctor's orders were followed. (This view of the social role of the ill person was much influenced by the conceptions of Parsons, 1951, 1958.) In helping a child recover from an infectious disease, the classical helping triad was altogether effective and rewarding for both the actors and the suprasystem. No extensions were mounted. Social change was unnecessary.

When a child had a phobia, however, his social role was not so clear as it was when he had the measles. He was rarely taken out of school, and when he was, the act was often considered to be illegitimate. He had to stay out of bed and discharge his usual responsibilities, no matter how crippling his phobic distress might be.

When a child had the measles, he had done enough when he followed the doctor's orders, but in the child guidance clinic, the child was often told that relief from his distress depended as much on his own efforts as upon the doctor's—but there were very few clear-cut doctor's orders (Allen, 1934). The instrumental nature of the doctor's role was blurred. To complicate matters further, his parents were by no means the doctor's expressive agents. They were patients, too. The traditional helping triad was disrupted. The roles were confused, and the expected relationships were denied by the doctor.

Parents, however, often insisted on continuing what had worked so well in the past. They did not accept the role of the patient. They did not perceive themselves to be ill—nor did the family or neighborhood. In an effort to meet their responsibilities in the traditional triadic subsystem, they took the role of the doctor's expressive agents, in spite of the clinic's advice, and tried sympathetically to implement what they inferred to be the doctor's advice—and added more confusion. Sometimes, in a traditional attempt to extend the power network, the parents told the teacher of the doctor's advice, and often found that the teacher confirmed their view that the doctor's advice was rather hard to understand and difficult to follow (see, for example, the report of Lowrey, 1934).

The role of the parent in the helping triad, altogether complementary and reciprocal in the traditional helping triad treating a child for an acute infectious disease, was vague, overlapping, inequitable, and confused when used in treating a family for a chronic, noninfectious distress which might not be a disease at all. As the contact of the clinic with the family grew, so did the tensions.

At the point at which the school referred a child to the clinic, still further complications arose. In addition to the parents, the teacher was involved. It was not often explicit whether the teacher, too, was a patient, but it was often implied, in the interchange between the teacher and the clinic team (such as it was), that the teacher's behavior in the classroom probably aggravated, if it did not induce, the child's distress. Furthermore, it was often explicitly stated that the teacher *could* become a therapeutic agent—an agent of the doctor—if only she could develop the proper relationship with the child—and the proper "therapeutic skills"—if she could just be more like a clinician (Tri-state Conference, 1962).

Analyses of the sources of tension in these attempts at system linkage have been widely reported from Crestwood Heights (Seeley, Sim, & Loosley, 1956), from the Wellesley group (Elizabeth Lindemann, 1957), from New York City (New York City Board of Education, 1955), from St. Louis County (Glidewell & Stringer, 1967), from Sumter County, South Carolina (Newton & Brown, 1967), and from various reports of school psychologists (Tri-state Conference, 1962; Cutts, 1955).

The interdisciplinary child guidance clinic, however, had enough staff to provide a differentiated expressive, supporting role—often through a social worker. The tensions inherent in the helping triad, however, could not be readily managed. The production of negative sentiments between doctor and social worker became apparent. It was not as easy to reduce the rate of interaction between doctor and social worker on the same staff as between doctor and mother. (The reduction did sometimes occur, however, and the isolation was often attributed to personality conflicts.) Roles were rather fixed, and it was not as easy to reverse roles in extended relationships with other deviants in the larger systems.

Enter community mental health. It is not surprising that a more extensive system linkage began to develop in other directions. Community mental health, as conceived in the 1950s, required of the practitioner more role flexibility in the interchanges between the clinic and the community. Much has been written of the demands of community mental health, but for the purposes of this analysis, the relevant demands were (a) that instrumental roles be differentiated from expressive roles, (b) that the instrumental practitioner add some expressive roles to his repertoire when he entered the community, and (c) that the professional practitioner share some of his instrumental and expressive roles with nonprofessional community agents—both policy making and policy implementing.

Community boards, first formed to be expressive and supportive adjuncts to the doctors, became instrumental in influencing intake policies, fees for services, and even professional roles. Alternation of instrumental and expressive roles with respect to patients, parents, and teachers evolved.

The voluntary mental health association was often formed to support the clinic and reduce the tension between the clinic, the family, and the school. It was, however, expected to take minimum initiative, to support "the professionals," and develop community goodwill largely through mass media—all in all, to take the expressive supporting role. Community opinion leaders were often sought as leaders of the association in an effort to extend the power network upward—to link to powerful, high-status supportive roles—but to support doctors as well as, or even more than, to support patients. Such support directly opposed the social forces "naturally" generated in the helping triad.

The later development of the indigenous mental health worker was another attempt to extend the power network, but downward. The indigenous worker could speak the language of the family and provide for a successful interchange in what had been a blocked one. Whether the role is to remain only expressive and supportive is in question, but it represents the nearest parallel to the former parental supportive role in the triad subsystem—and it provides extensive linkages to many families in a neighborhood. Accordingly, indigenous workers may introduce a social change potential not before available, especially if they develop both instrumental and expressive roles—instrumental with one family, expressive with another.

In summary, perhaps the great promise of community mental health is that it is breaking up the static, social order maintenance function of the traditional helping triad. It is experimenting with a variety of extensions and linkages of helping subsystems and community institutions. The evolution is still in progress, but if the foregoing analysis has validity, it is through just such extensions—both upward into powerful resource-allocating groups and downward into resource-utilizing groups—that helping subsystems can give appropriate attention to modifying expectations, norms, and roles, in both subsystems and suprasystems, so that they may accommodate to wider variations in individual behavior.

A SUMMARY STATEMENT

The critical aspect of social order and social change as an influence on individual mental health lies in its effect on the accommodation between the individual and the systems of which he is a member. If, in the perception of the individual, the equity of the interchange of resources (motives, emotions, ideas, skills, objects) between him and the system is enhanced, mental health is enhanced; if the perceived equity is reduced, mental health is reduced.

Four of the dimensions of an individual's position in a social system which are related to the equity of his accommodation to the system are: interpersonal attraction, perceived competence, social power, and vulnerability to sanction. Repeated experiences of attracting others into interaction leads to increased self-esteem and enhanced mental health. Repeated experiences of repelling others leads to reduced self-esteem and some form of break with reality. Similar enhancements are seen from repeated growth in perceived competence and balance between the rewards and cost of social power; similar debilitations are seen from repeated limitations on perceived competence and inequities between the rewards and costs of social power.

There has evolved a powerful structure—the helping triad—for facilitating the "correction" or "treatment" of individuals whose behavior is so strange or bad or sick that they upset the system. The triad has a considerable effectiveness in managing the tensions of the helping process. It does not have, however, such effectiveness as an agent of social change except when the unit is linked with other such units in the suprasystem. Current innovations in helping structures developing in community mental health may be seen as attempts to create a helping system with extended linkages which will do as much to modify the system to accommodate to the individual as to modify the individual to accommodate to the system.

Note

The author most gratefully acknowledges the excellent assistance of Carolyn S. Swallow in developing the work and of Kenneth E. Smith and Susan Lourenço in reviewing the manuscript.

References

Ackerman, N. W. What constitutes intensive psychotherapy in a child guidance clinic. *American Journal of Orthopsychiatry*, 1945, 15, 711–720.

Allen, F. H. Therapeutic work with children. *American Journal of Orthopsychiatry*, 1934, 4, 193–202.

Allport, G. W., & Kramer, B. M. Some roots of prejudice. *Journal of Psychology*, 1946, 22, 9–39.

Argyris, C. *Interpersonal competence and organizational effectiveness.* Homewood, Ill.: Dorsey Press, 1962.

Asch, S. E. Effects of group pressure upon the modification and distortion of judgments. In H. Guertzkow (ed.), *Groups, leadership, and men.* Pittsburgh: Carnegie Press, 1951.

Asch, S. E. Studies of independence and conformity: A minority of one against a unanimous majority. *Psychological Monographs*, 1956, 70, No. 9.

Bales, R. F., & Borgatta, E. F. Size of group as a factor in the interaction profile. In A. Hare, E. Borgatta, & R. Bales (eds.), *Small groups: Studies in social interaction.* (Rev. ed.) New York: Knopf, 1965.

Bales, R. F., & Slater, P. E. Role differentiation in small decision-making groups. In T. Parsons & R. Bales (eds.), *Family, socialization, and interaction process.* Glencoe, Ill.: Free Press, 1955.

Barker, R. G. *Ecological psychology.* Stanford, Calif.: Stanford University Press, 1968.

Barker, R. G., & Gump, P. V. *Big school, small school.* Stanford, Calif.: Stanford University Press, 1964.

Benne, K. D., & Sheats, P. Functional roles of group members. *Journal of Social Issues*, 1948, 4(2), 41–49.

Bennett, E. B. Discussion, decision, commitment, and consensus in "group decision." *Human Relations*, 1955, 8, 251–274.

Berger, J., Cohen, B. P., Snell, J. L., & Zelditch, M. *Types of formalization in small group research.* Boston: Houghton Mifflin, 1962.

Bernard, J. *American family behavior.* New York: Harper, 1942.

Berrien, F. K. *General and social systems.* New Brunswick, N. J.: Rutgers University Press, 1968.

Bettelheim, B. Individual and mass behavior in extreme situations. *Journals of Abnormal and Social Psychology*, 1943, 38, 417–452.

Blake, R. R. Psychology and the crisis of statesmanship. *American Psychologist*, 1959, 14, 87–94.

Blau, P. M. *The dynamics of bureaucracy.* Chicago: University of Chicago Press, 1955.

Blau, P. M. *Exchange and power in social life.* New York: Wiley, 1964.

Blau, P. M. Patterns of interaction among a group of officials in a government agency. *Human Relations*, 1954, 7, 337–348.

Blau, P. M., & Scott, W. R. *Formal organizations: A comparative approach.* San Francisco: Chandler, 1962.

Bonney, M. E. The relative stability of social, intellectual, and academic status in grades II to IV, and the inter-relationships between these various forms of growth. *Journal of Educational Psychology*, 1943, 34, 88–102.

Bonney, M. E. A study of social status on the second grade level. *Journal of Genetic Psychology*, 1942, 60, 271–305.

Bower, E. M., Tashnovian, P. J., & Larson, C. A. A process for early identification of emotionally disturbed children. *Bulletin of the California State Department of Education*, 1958, 27, No. 6.

Brandt, R. M. The accuracy of self-estimate: A measure of self-concept reality. *Genetic Psychology Monographs*, 1958, 58, 55–99.

Bredemeier, H. C. Schools and student growth. *Urban Review*, 1968, 2, 21–27.

Brehm, J. Postdecision changes in the desirability of alternatives. *Journal of Abnormal and Social Psychology*, 1956, 52, 384–389.

Brill, N. Q., & Storrow, W. A. Social class and psychiatric treatment. *Archives of General Psychiatry*, 1960, 3, 340–344.

Bronfenbrenner, U. Toward a theoretical model for the analysis of parent-child relationships in a social context. In J. Glidewell (ed.), *Parental attitudes and child behavior.* Springfield, Ill.: Charles C Thomas, 1961.

Brookover, W. B., Thomas, S., & Paterson, A. Self-concept of ability and school achievement. *Journal of Educational Sociology*, 1964, 37, 271–278.

Brown, M. M., Brown, P. R., Glidewell, J. C., Hunt, R. G., & Weiss, J. M. A. *Nurses, patients, and social systems.* Columbia, Mo.: University of Missouri Press, 1968.

Brownfain, J. J. Stability of the self-concept as a dimension of personality. *Journal of Abnormal and Social Psychology*, 1952, 47, 597–606.

Bruce, P. Relationship of self-acceptance to other variables with sixth grade children oriented in self-understanding. *Journal of Educational Psychology*, 1958, 49, 229–238.

Bruyn, S. T. *The human perspective in sociology.* Englewood Cliffs, N. J.: Prentice-Hall, 1966.

Campbell, P. B. Self-concept and academic achievement in middle grade public school children. Unpublished doctoral dissertation, Wayne State University, 1965.

Caplow, T. A theory of coalitions in the triad. *American Sociological Review*, 1956, 21, 489–493.

Carter, L. Evaluating the performance of individuals as members of small groups. *Personnel Psychology*, 1954, 7, 477–484.

Clark, K. B., & Clark, M. P. Racial identification and preference in Negro children. In E. Maccoby, T. Newcomb, & E. Hartley (eds.), *Readings in social psychology.* New York: Holt, Rinehart & Winston, 1958.

Coch, L., & French, J. R. P. Overcoming resistance to change. *Human Relations,* 1948, 1, 512–532.

Cohen, A. R. Situational structure, self-esteem, and threat-oriented reactions to power. In D. Cartwright (ed.), *Studies in social power.* Ann Arbor, Mich.: Institute for Social Research, University of Michigan, 1959.

Cohen, A. R. Upward communication in experimentally created hierarchies. *Human Relations,* 1958, 11, 41–53.

Combs, A. W., & Snygg, D. *Individual behavior: A perceptual approach to behavior.* New York: Harper & Row, 1959.

Coopersmith, S. A method for determining types of self-esteem. *Journal of Abnormal and Social Psychology,* 1959, 59, 87–94.

Coopersmith, S. *The antecedents of self-esteem.* San Francisco: W. H. Freeman, 1967.

Cutts, N. E. (ed.) *School psychologists at mid-century.* Washington, D. C.: American Psychological Association, 1955.

Davis, F. Deviance disavowal: The management of strained interaction by the visibly handicapped. *Social Problems,* 1961, 9, 120–132.

Davis, K. Final note on a case of extreme isolation. *American Journal of Sociology,* 1947, 52, 432–437.

Dean, D. G. Alienation: Its meaning and measurement. *American Sociological Review,* 1961, 26, 753–758.

de Charms, R., & Rosenbaum, M. E. Status variables and matching behavior. *Journal of Personality,* 1960, 28, 492–502.

Deutsch, M. Conflicts: Productive and destructive. *Journal of Social Issues,* 1969, 25, 7–41.

Diggory, J. C. *Self-evaluation.* New York: Wiley, 1966.

Douglas, V. I. B. The development of two families of defense. *Dissertation Abstracts,* 1959, 20, 1438.

Dreyer, A. S. Behavior in a level of aspiration situation as affected by group comparison. Unpublished doctoral dissertation, University of Minnesota, 1953.

Dreyer, A. S. Aspiration behavior as influenced by expectation and group comparison. *Human Relations,* 1954, 7, 175–190.

Dunham, H. W. *Sociological theory and mental disorder.* Detroit: Wayne State University Press, 1959.

Durkheim, E. *Suicide.* (Trans. by J. A. Spaulding & G. Simpson) Glencoe, Ill.: Free Press, 1951.

Dyson, E. Study of ability grouping and the self-concept. *Journal of Educational Research,* 1967, 60, 403–405.

Emerson, R. M. Deviation and rejection: An experimental replication. *American Sociological Review,* 1954, 19, 688–693.

Emerson, R. M. Power-dependence relations. *American Sociological Review,* 1962, 27, 31–41.

Engel, M. The stability of the self-concept in adolescence. *Journal of Abnormal and Social Psychology,* 1959, 58, 211–215.

Erikson, E. H. *Insight and responsibility.* New York: Norton, 1964.

Feldhusen, J. F., & Thurston, J. R. Personality and adjustment of high and low anxious children. *Journal of Educational Research,* 1964, 57, 265–267.

Festinger, L. A theory of social comparison processes. *Human Relations,* 1954, 7, 117–140.

Festinger, L., Schachter, S., & Back, K. *Social pressures in informal groups.* New York: Harper, 1950.

Festinger, L., Torrey, J., & Willerman, B. Self-evaluation as a function of attraction to the group. *Human Relations,* 1954, 7, 161–174.

Fink, M. B. Self-concept as it relates to academic achievement. *California Journal of Educational Research,* 1962, 13, 57–62.

Firth, R. *We, the Tikopia.* London: George Allen & Unwin, 1936.

Foote, N. N., & Cottrell, L. S. *Identity and interpersonal competence.* Chicago: University of Chicago Press, 1955.

Freeman, H. E. Evaluation research and the explanatory power of social factors. In L. Roberts, N. Greenfield, & M. Miller (eds.), *Comprehensive mental health: The challenge of evaluation.* Madison, Wisc.: University of Wisconsin Press, 1968.

Freilich, M. The natural triad in kinship and complex systems. *American Sociological Review,* 1964, 29, 529–540.

French, J. R. P., & Raven, B. The bases of social power. In D. Cartwright (ed.), *Studies in social power.* Ann Arbor, Mich.: University of Michigan Press, 1959.

French, J. R. P., & Snyder, R. Leadership and interpersonal power. In D. Cartwright (ed.), *Studies in social power.* Ann Arbor, Mich.: University of Michigan Press, 1959.

Fried, M. Transitional functions of working class communities: Implications for forces relocation. In M. B. Kantor (ed.), *Mobility and mental health.* Springfield, Ill.: Charles C Thomas, 1965.

Gamson, W. A. A theory of coalition formation. *American Sociological Review,* 1961, 26, 373–382.

Gerard, H. B. The effect of different dimensions of disagreement on the communication process in small groups. *Human Relations,* 1953, 6, 249–271.

Gerard, H. B., Wilhelmy, R. A., & Conolley, E. S. Conformity and group size. *Journal of Personality and Social Psychology,* 1968, 8, 79–82.

Gilchrist, J. C. The formation of social groups under conditions of success and failure. *Journal of Abnormal and Social Psychology,* 1952, 47, 174–187.

Gilchrist, J. C., Shaw, M. E., & Walker, L. C. Some effects of unequal distribution of information in a wheel group structure. *Journal of Abnormal and Social Psychology,* 1954, 49, 554–556.

Gilliland, C. H. *The relationships of pupil mobility to achievement in the elementary school.* University Microfilms, Inc. Ann Arbor, Michigan, 1959.

Glidewell, J. C. The child at school. In J. Howells (ed.), *Modern perspectives in international child psychiatry.* Edinburgh: Oliver & Boyd, 1969.

Glidewell, J. C. Perspectives in community mental health. In *Community psychology.* (The report from the conference on the education of psychologists for community mental health) Boston: Boston University Press, 1966.

Glidewell, J. C., Kantor, M. B., Smith, L. M., & Stringer, L. A. Socialization and social structure in the classroom. In L. Hoffman & M. Hoffman (eds.), *Review of child development research.* Vol. II. New York: Russell Sage Foundation, 1966.

Glidewell, J. C., Kantor, M. B., Smith, L. M., & Stringer, L. A. *Social structure and socialization in the elementary school classroom.* (Social Science Research Council. Committee on Social Structure and Socialization) Clayton, Mo.: St. Louis County Health Department, 1965.

Glidewell, J. C., & Stringer, L. A. The educational institution and the health institution. In E. M. Bower & W. G. Hollister (eds.), *Behavioral science frontiers in education.* New York: Wiley, 1967.

Goffman, E. *Asylums.* New York: Doubleday, 1961.

Goffman, E. *The presentation of self in everyday life.* Edinburgh: University of Edinburgh Social Science Research Center, 1958.

Gold, M. Power in the classroom. *Sociometry,* 1958, 25, 50–60.

Goldhamer, H., & Marshall, A. W. *Psychosis and civilization.* Glencoe, Ill.: Free Press, 1953.

Gordon, I. J. *Children's views of themselves.* Washington, D. C.: Association for Childhood Education International, 1959.

Gordon, I. J. *Studying the child in school.* New York: Wiley, 1966.

Goslin, D. A. Accuracy of self perception and social acceptance. *Sociometry,* 1962, 25, 283–296.

Gouldner, A. W. The norm of reciprocity: A preliminary statement. *American Sociological Review,* 1960, 25, 161–178.

Gronlund, N. E. *Sociometry in the classroom.* New York: Harper, 1959.

Gross, E. Symbiosis and consensus as integrative factors in small groups. *American Sociological Review,* 1956, 21, 174–179.

Gullahorn, J. T. Distance and friendship as factors in the gross interaction matrix. *Sociometry,* 1952, 15, 123–134.

Hardt, R. H., & Feinhandler, S. J. Social class and mental hospitalization prognosis. *American Sociological Review,* 1959, 24, 815–821.

Hare, A. P. A study of interaction and consensus in different sized groups. *American Sociological Review,* 1952, 17, 261–267.

Hauser, P. M. After the riots, what? *University of Chicago Magazine,* 1968, 60, 4–10.

Hauser, P. M. The chaotic society. *American Sociological Review,* 1969, 34, 1–19.

Havighurst, R. J. Minority sub-cultures and the laws of learning. Annual Edward L. Thorndike Award Address presented at the annual meeting of the American Psychologic Association, Washington, D. C., August 31, 1969.

Heider, F. *The psychology of interpersonal relations.* New York: Wiley, 1958.

Herbst, P. G. An analysis of social flow systems. *Human Relations,* 1954, 7, 327–336.

Herbst, P. G. Measurement of behavior structures by means of input-output data. *Human Relations,* 1957, 10, 335–346.

Herz, M. F. Some psychological lessons from leaflet propaganda in World War II. In D. Katz, D. Cartwright, S. Eldersfeld, & A. M. Lee (eds.), *Public opinion and propaganda.* New York: Dryden Press, 1954.

Hoffman, P. J., Festinger, L., & Lawrence, D. H. Tendencies toward comparability in competitive bargaining. *Human Relations,* 1954, 7, 141–159.

Hollander, E. P., & Willis, R. H. Some current issues in the psychology of conformity and nonconformity. *Psychological Bulletin,* 1967, 68, 62–76.

Hollingshead, A. B., & Redlich, F. C. *Social class and mental illness.* New York: Wiley, 1958.

Homans, G. C. *The human group.* New York: Harcourt, Brace, & World, 1950.

Homans, G. C. *Social behavior: Its elementary forms.* New York: Harcourt, Brace, & World, 1961.

Horowitz, F. D. The relationship of anxiety, self-concept, and sociometric status among fourth, fifth, and sixth grade children. *Journal of Abnormal and Social Psychology,* 1962, 65, 212–214.

Hudgins, B. B., & Loftis, L. The invisible child in the arithmetic class. *Journal of Genetic Psychology,* 1966, 108, 143–152.

Hunter, F. *Community power structure.* Chapel Hill, N. C.: University of North Carolina Press, 1953.

Indik, B. P. The relationship between organization size and supervision ratio. *Administrative Science Quarterly,* 1964, 9, 301–312.

Jennings, H. H. *Leadership and isolation.* New York: Longmans, Green, 1943.

Joy, G. E. Some aspects of a moving population–A comparative study of transient children in the Panama Canal Zone schools. Unpublished master's thesis, University of Michigan, 1933.

Kantor, M. B. (ed.) *Mobility and mental health.* Springfield, Ill.: Charles C Thomas, 1965.

Kaplan, B., Reed, R. B., & Richardson, W. A. A comparison of the incidence of hospitalized and non-hospitalized cases of psychosis in two communities. *American Sociological Review,* 1956, 21, 472–479.

Kasl, S. V., & French, J. R. P. The effects of occupational status on physical and mental health. *Journal of Social Issues,* 1962, 18(3), 67–89.

Katz, E., & Lazarsfeld, P. *Personal influence.* Glencoe, Ill.: Free Press, 1955.

Kelley, H. H., & Volkart, E. H. The resistance to change of group anchored attitudes. *American Sociological Review,* 1952, 17, 453–465.

Kelley, H. H., & Woodruff, C. L. Members' reactions to apparent group approval of a counter-norm communication. *Journal of Abnormal and Social Psychology,* 1956, 52, 67–74.

Kendall, P. Medical education as social process. Paper presented at the annual meeting of the American Sociological Association, New York, August 1960.

Kipnis, D. The effects of leadership style and leadership power upon the inducement of an attitude change. *Journal of Abnormal and Social Psychology,* 1958, 57, 173–180.

Klapper, J. T. *The effects of mass media.* Glencoe, Ill.: Free Press, 1961.

Kohn, M. L., & Clausen, J. A. Social isolation and schizophrenia. *American Sociological Review*, 1955, 20, 265–273.

Kornhauser, A. *Mental health of the industrial worker.* New York: Wiley, 1965.

Kramer, M. *Some implications of trends in the usage of psychiatric facilities for community mental health programs and related research.* Bethesda, Md.: United States Public Health Service, NIMH, 1967.

Landreth, C., & Johnson, B. C. Young children's responses to a picture and in-set test designed to reveal reactions to persons of different skin color. *Child Development*, 1953, 24, 63–80.

Leavitt, H. J. Some effects of certain communication patterns on group performance. *Journal of Abnormal and Social Psychology*, 1951, 46, 38–50.

Lemkau, P., Tietze, C., & Cooper, M. Mental-hygiene problems in an urban district. *Mental Hygiene*, 1941, 25, 624–646.

Levinger, G. The development of perceptions and behavior in newly formed social power relationships. In D. Cartwright (ed.), *Studies in social power.* Ann Arbor, Mich.: University of Michigan Press, 1959.

Lewin, K. Self-hatred among Jews. In G. Lewin (ed.), *Resolving social conflicts.* New York: Harper, 1948.

Lewin, K. Group decision and social change. In G. E. Swanson, T. M. Newcomb, & E. L. Hartley (eds.), *Readings in social psychology.* New York: Holt, 1952.

Likert, R. A. *Organization theory.* New York: McGraw-Hill, 1961.

Lindemann, E. Mental health in the classroom: The Wellesley experience. Paper presented at the annual meeting of the American Psychological Association, New York, September 1957.

Lindemann, E. Psycho-social factors as stressor agents. In J. M. Tanner (ed.), *Stress and psychiatric disorder.* Oxford: Blackwell Scientific Publications, 1960.

Lippitt, R. and Gold, M. Classroom social structure as a mental health problem. *Journal of Social Issues*, 1959, 15(1), 40–49.

Lippitt, R., Polansky, N., & Rosen, S. The dynamics of power. *Human Relations*, 1952, 5, 37–64.

Loomis, C. P. In praise of conflict and its resolution. *American Sociological Review*, 1967, 32, 875–890.

Loomis, C. P., & Loomis, Z. K. *Modern social theories.* New York: Van Nostrand, 1961.

Lowrey, L. G. Orthopsychiatry and prevention: Historical perspective. *American Journal of Orthopsychiatry*, 1957, 27, 223–225.

Lowrey, L. G. Treatment of behavior problems. *American Journal of Orthopsychiatry*, 1934, 4, 120–137.

Lundberg, G. A., & Beazley, V. "Consciousness of kind" in a college population. *Sociometry*, 1948, 11, 59–74.

Malzberg, B. *Social and biological aspects of mental disease.* Utica, N. Y.: State Hospitals Press, 1940.

McCandless, B. R., Castaneda, A., & Palermo, D. S. Anxiety in children and social status. *Child Development*, 1956, 27, 385–391.

Merton, R. K. *Social theory and social structure.* Glencoe, Ill.: Free Press, 1957.

Meyers, J. K., Bean, L. L., & Pepper, M. P. Social class and mental illness: A ten-year follow-up of psychiatric patients. *Connecticut Journal of Medicine*, 1964, 28, 355–362.

Miller, D. R. The study of social relationships: Situation, identity, and social interaction. In S. Koch (ed.), *Psychology: A study of a science*, Vol. 5. New York: McGraw-Hill, 1963.

Miller, S. M., & Riessman, F. The working class subculture: A new view. *Social Problems*, 1961, 9, 86–97.

Mills, T. M. The coalition pattern in three-person groups. *American Sociological Review*, 1954, 19, 657–667.

Moreno, J. L. *Who shall survive?* (Nervous and Mental Disease Monograph Series No. 58) Washington, D. C.: Nervous and Mental Disease Publishing Company, 1934.

Murphy, H. B. M. Migration and the major mental disorders: A reappraisal. In M. B. Kantor (ed.), *Mobility and mental health.* Springfield, Ill.: Charles C Thomas, 1965.

Newcomb, T. M. *The acquaintance process.* New York: Holt, Rinehart & Winston, 1961.

Newcomb, T. M. The prediction of interpersonal attraction. *American Psychologist*, 1956, 11, 575–586.

Newcomb, T. M., Turner, R. H., & Converse, P. E. *Social psychology.* New York: Holt, Rinehart & Winston, 1965.

Newton, R., & Brown, R. A preventive approach to developmental problems in children. In E. M. Bower & W. G. Hollister (eds.), *Behavioral science frontiers in education.* New York: Wiley, 1967.

New York City Board of Education. *The bureau of child guidance in the New York City Schools.* New York: Board of Education, 1955.

Northway, M. L. Outsiders: A study of the personality patterns of children least acceptable to their age-mates. *Sociometry*, 1944, 7, 10–15.

Parad, H. J. (ed.) *Crisis intervention.* New York: Family Service Association of America, 1965.

Parsons, T. Definition of health and illness in the light of American values and social structure. In E. G. Jaco (ed.), *Patients, physicians, and illnesses.* Glencoe, Ill.: Free Press, 1958.

Parsons, T. *The social system.* Glencoe, Ill.: Free Press, 1951.

Parsons, T., & Bales, R. F. *Family socialization and interaction process.* Glencoe, Ill.: Free Press, 1955.

Pettigrew, T. F. Social evaluation theory: Convergences and applications. In D. Levine (ed.), *Nebraska symposium on motivation.* Lincoln, Neb.: University of Nebraska Press, 1967.

Pittman, D. J., & Gordon, C. W. *The revolving door.* Glencoe, Ill.: Free Press, 1958.

Potashin, R. Sociometric study of children's friendships. *Sociometry*, 1946, 9, 48–70.

Rainwater, L. Crucible of identity: The Negro lower-class family. *Daedalus*, 1966, 95, 172–216.

Riley, J. W., Schramm, W., & Williams, F. W. Flight from communism: A report on Korean refugees. *Public Opinion Quarterly*, 1951, 15, 274–286.

Roethlisberger, F. J., & Dickson, W. J. *Management and the worker.* Cambridge, Mass.: Harvard University Press, 1939.

Rokeach, M. Belief versus race as determinants of social distance: Comment on Triandis' paper. *Journal of Abnormal and Social Psychology*, 1961, 62, 187–188.

Rose, A. M., & Stub, H. R. Summary of studies in the incidence of mental disorders. In A. M. Rose (ed.), *Mental health and mental disorder.* New York: Norton, 1955.

Roth, R. M. Role of self-concept in achievement. *Journal of Experimental Education*, 1959, 27, 265–281.

Sackett, E. B. The effect of moving on the educational status of the child. *Elementary School Journal*, 1935, 35, 517–526.

Schachter, S. Deviation, rejection and communication. *Journal of Abnormal and Social Psychology*, 1951, 46, 190–207.

Schachter, S. *The psychology of affiliation.* Stanford, Calif.: Stanford University Press, 1959.

Schachter, S., & Hall, R. Group derived restraints and audience persuasion. *Human Relations*, 1952, 5, 397–406.

Schein, E. H., Schneier, I., & Barker, C. H. *Coercive persuasion.* New York: Norton, 1961.

Scotch, N. A. Sociocultural factors in the epidemiology of Zulu hypertension. *American Journal of Public Health*, 1963, 53, 1205–1213.

Sears, P., & Sherman, V. S. *In pursuit of self-esteem.* Belmont, Calif.: Wadsworth Publishing Company, 1964.

Secord, P. F., & Backman, C. W. *Social psychology.* New York: McGraw-Hill, 1964.

Seeley, J., Sim, R., & Loosely, E. *Crestwood Heights.* New York: Basic Books, 1956.

Shaw, M. E. Some effects of inequal distribution of information upon group performance in various communication nets. *Journal of Abnormal and Social Psychology*, 1954, 49, 547–553.

Sherif, M., Harvey, O. J., White, B. J., Hood, W. R., & Sherif, C. W. *Intergroup conflict and cooperation.* Norman, Okla.: Institute of Group Relations, University of Oklahoma, 1961.

Shils, E. A. Primary groups in the American Army. In R. K. Merton & P. F. Lazarsfeld (eds.), *Continuities in social research.* Glencoe, Ill.: Free Press, 1950.

Shils, E. A., & Janowitz, M. Cohesion and disintegration in the Wehrmacht in World War II. *Public Opinion Quarterly*, 1948, 12, 280–315.

Simmel, G. *The sociology of Georg Simmel.* (Trans. & ed. by K. H. Wolff) Glencoe, Ill.: Free Press, 1950.

Simpson, G. E., & Yinger, J. M. *Racial and cultural minorities.* New York: Harper, 1953.

Singer, A. Social competence and success in teaching. *Journal of Experimental Education*, 1954, 23, 99–131.

Slater, P. E. Contrasting correlates of group size. *Sociometry*, 1958, 21, 129–139.

Slater, P. E. Role differentiation in small groups. In A. Hare, E. Borgatta, & R. Bales (eds.), *Small groups: Studies in social interaction.* New York: Knopf, 1965.

Smith, C. R. An experimental study of status and self-esteem. Unpublished doctoral dissertation, Washington University, St. Louis, Missouri, 1967.

Smith, C. R., Williams, L., & Willis, R. H. Race, sex, and belief as determinants of friendship acceptance. *Journal of Personality and Social Psychology*, 1967, 5, 127–137.

Smith, K. E. The relationship of perceived competence and status to the self-esteem of teachers: A pilot study. Unpublished manuscript, University of Chicago, 1968. (Mimeo)

Smith, L. M., & Geoffrey. W. *The complexities of an urban classroom.* New York: Holt, Rinehart & Winston, 1968.

Solomon, L. The influence of some types of power relationships and motivational treatments upon the development of inter-personal trust. New York: Research Center for Human Relations, New York University, 1957. (As cited in J. W. Thibaut & H. H. Kelley, *The social psychology of groups.* New York: Wiley, 1959.)

Srole, L., Langner, T. S., Michael, S. T., Opler, M. K., & Rennie, T. A. C. *Mental health in the metropolis.* New York: McGraw-Hill, 1962.

Stein, D. S., Hardyck, J., & Smith, M. B. Race and belief: An open and shut case. *Journal of personality and social Psychology*, 1965, 1, 281–289.

Stendler, C. B. *Children of Brasstown.* Urbana, Ill.: Bureau of Research and Service of the College of Education, University of Illinois, 1949.

Stevenson, G. S., & Smith, G. *Child guidance clinics.* New York: Commonwealth Fund, 1934.

Stringer, L. A. Problems in the administration of school mental health programs. In *Proceedings of the regional conference on the health of school age children, Chapel Hill, North Carolina.* Washington, D. C.: Children's Bureau, United States Department of Health, Education, and Welfare, 1959.

Stringer, L. A., & Glidewell, J. C. *Early detection of emotional illnesses in school children, Final report.* Clayton, Mo.: St. Louis County Health Department, 1967.

Stringer, L. A., Glidewell, J. C., & Taylor, R. M. *Mothers as colleagues in school mental health work.* Clayton, Mo.: St. Louis County Health Department, 1965.

Tagiuri, R. Relational analysis: An extension of sociometric method with emphasis upon social perception. *Sociometry*, 1952, 15, 91–104.

Tetreau, E. D., & Fuller, V. Some factors associated with the school achievement of children in migrant families. *Elementary School Journal*, 1942, 42, 423–431.

Thibaut, J. W., & Kelley, H. H. *The social psychology of groups.* New York: Wiley, 1959.

Thibaut, J. W., & Riecken, H. W. Authoritarianism, status, and the communication of aggression. *Human Relations*, 1955, 8, 95–120. (a)

Thibaut, J. W., & Riecken, H. W. Some determinants and consequences of the perception of social causality. *Journal of Personality*, 1955, 24, 113–133. (b)

Thomas, E. J., & Fink, C. F. Effects of group size. *Psychological Bulletin*, 1963, 60, 371–384.

Torshen, K. The relation of evaluation in classrooms to students' self-concepts and mental health. Unpublished doctoral dissertation, University of Chicago, 1969.

Trent, R. D. The relationship of anxiety to popularity and rejection among institutionalized delinquent boys. *Child Development*, 1957, 28, 379–384.

Tri-state Conference on School Psychology, *Proceedings*, 1962.

Tulchin, S. H. (ed.) *Child guidance.* New York: American Orthopsychiatric Association, 1964.

Vinacke, W. E., & Arkoff, A. An experimental study of coalitions in the triad. *American Sociological Review*, 1957, 22, 406–414.

White, R. W. Motivation reconsidered: The concept of competence. *Psychological Review*, 1959, 66, 297–333.

White, R. W. Competence as a basic concept in the growth of personality. Paper presented at the Social Science Research Council's Conference on the Socialization and Evocation of Competence, San Juan, Puerto Rico, April 29–May 2, 1965.

Wilensky, H. L. *Intellectuals in labor unions.* Glencoe, Ill.: Free Press, 1956.

Williams, R. L., & Cole, S. Self-concept and school adjustment. *Personnel and Guidance Journal*, 1968, 46, 478–481.

Zelditch, M. Role differentiation in the nuclear family: A comparative study. In T. Parsons & R. F. Bales (eds.), *Family socialization and interaction process.* Glencoe, 'll.: Free Press, 1955.

11

Concepts of Behavior Disorder

J. R. Newbrough

Mental health as an area of service is directed toward forms of behavior which generally trouble someone. This is generally reflected in what is presented to the practitioner or agency when help is sought. The specific forms of the behavior are highly variable, due to combinations of the behavior, the behaver, the viewer, and the particular helping agent. In order to consider the troublesome behaviors all together, they were grouped under the title "Behavior Disorders" and approached at a relatively abstract level. The decision to consider behavior disorders globally and conceptually was taken in light of the existence of an array of writings on the subject and the fact that there were already several specialized reviews (for example, Stengel, 1959; Lorr, 1961, 1966; Eron, 1966, Rubenfeld, 1967; Zubin, 1967; Katz, Cole, and Barton, 1968). This chapter was specifically designed to serve three purposes: (1) to introduce the reader to several frames of reference for considering behavior disorders, with particular reference to the process of classification and the current status of such efforts, (2) to relate developments in the sociology of deviance to the psychology of behavior disorders, and (3) to consider behavior disorder as a relativistic matter from the perspective of psychophysics. This last purpose was chosen to illustrate an approach to the problem which draws from both psychology and sociology and may therefore stimulate new integrations of current knowledge.

PART I: BEHAVIOR DISORDERS

Disordered behavior is the primary focus of interest in community mental health and for all helping professions. It is explained and interpreted in a variety of ways, each way providing the basis for the help given. Since the definition of the problem is usually the first step in the process of both service and science, it was thought that an analysis of this aspect of behavior disorders might be most illuminating—particularly for those attempting to devise new approaches to case definition.

Disordered behavior may be described as that which deviates from expected sociocultural norms and which is deleterious either to the person or to the society or both (Zubin, 1967). Within this definition:

(1) There is a set of expectations or normative standards which provide the context within which to judge behavior,
(2) there is an observer to judge the behavior and classify or label it,
(3) there is a set of values operating which suggest that some behaviors are desired and that others are not.

This is to say that the definition for the disorder is dependent both upon the behavior and its setting. The label Behavior Disorder seems to function as a kind of residual category for disorders of unknown origins; as soon as the cause becomes defined as something else (e.g., biological), the condition is redefined and removed from this category (Zubin, 1967).

Two issues are typically encountered by the student of behavior disorders, which seem to be primarily philosophical. The first issue is whether there are disorders which are entirely *relative* to the culture setting, or whether disorder as an entity or process can exist independent of setting and thus be studied cross-culturally.[1] Zubin

(1966, 1967, 1968) discussed this issue in detail and approached the problem as if it could be settled clearly and empirically. There are, however, empirical findings on both sides and this seems more likely to be related to the theoretical orientation of the writer. The second issue is whether one system of classification can serve to describe all disordered behavior (such as the *Diagnostic and Statistical Manual of the American Psychiatric Association*), or whether it is necessary to have a number of systems to serve very specific purposes (Katz, Cole, & Barton, 1968).[2] Katz and Cole (1968) describe this second issue as having two bodies of opinion about the purpose of classification. One is a need to predict specific outcomes from a particular intervention; the other is to investigate and to validate the existence of natural groupings. They refer to these as *dimensional* and *typological* approaches respectively. The dimensional approach is mostly associated with applied research; the typological approach with theory and practice in psychopathology (Katz & Cole, 1968).

Classification of Behavior Disorders

In approaching a consideration of behavior disorders, one first must ask "What are they?" before proceeding on to such interesting matters as how many there are, what they lead to, what causes them, and how could they be prevented. Classification provides a way of answering this first question, and it is the basis of systematization.[3] Storage, retrieval, and utilization of information is impossible without it. The foundation and method of classification depends upon the purposes for which information is required.

Simplest classification can be regarded as little more than an arrangement for recognizing, handling, and disposing of the disorder. It is based on an hypothesis as to the nature of things subject to classifying, and utilizes categories which denote certain common qualities. This can be fairly simple if the phenomena to be classified do not change or if the purpose is merely one of describing the phenomena (Miller, 1968). In those cases where the behavior is highly variable and the purposes range from understanding the behavior to its control and change, the situation is much more complex. Scientifically the approach would be one of differentiation and specificity. This could be

expected to lead, at early stages of the process, to differences in approaches and results. Zubin (1967) noted that there were at least 50 different types of classification systems in use throughout the world, and he described the situation as "chaotic."

This has yielded a situation in which there is much confusion about "what is a case?"[4] It has implications for the provision of service since one is not sure how the phenomena behave, and for the conduct of research since one does not know how to group individuals. Thus the matter of classification deserves high priority since it seems to keep progress in abeyance.

Classification of Classifications

In considering the contemporary problems noted above, the author arrived at the conclusion that the difficulties with classification of behavior disorders derive in part from lack of clarity about the *nature* and *purpose* of classification itself. In order to better understand classifications, it was decided to examine some of the current approaches and to classify them with regard to their *nature* and *purpose*.

Classifications can be divided into two broad types—descriptive and explanatory—though in the health field, classifications are rarely pure. Figure 11–1 illustrates the types and purposes of classification as developed for this analysis. The simple, if rudimentary, typology of classifications provides a framework for consideration of some of the approaches to behavior disorders.

Descriptive Classification

Descriptive classifications are representations of groups of similar phenomena and imply no causal or etiological explanation. Descriptions may be divided into those which depict structure or morphology based on a static set of observations, and those which portray function, using dynamic sets of observations over time. These may be based on single units or entities, such as diseases, or they may refer to complex units or systems of relationships between units, such as groups or communities.[5]

Explanatory Classification

Explanatory classification attempts to group phenomena according to etiological or causative

CLASSIFICATION OF CLASSIFICATIONS
BY TYPES AND PURPOSES

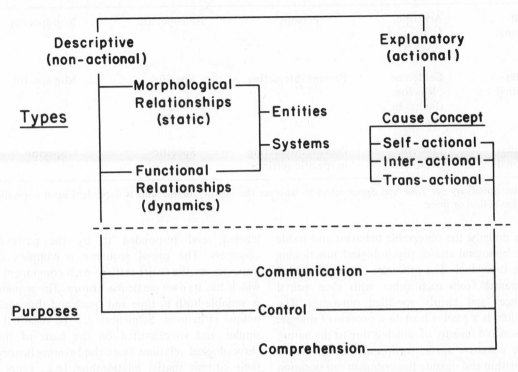

Fig. 11—1. Classification of classifications by types and purposes. (Reprinted with permission from Spitzer and Wilson, 1968. Copyrighted by the American Psychiatric Association, 1968.)

features (the descriptive element being based on the observed consequences of causal groups). However, the causal basis of explanatory classifications is often itself complex, since the concept of cause has undergone development in the health and social science fields just as it has in the physical sciences.

Classification of cause. Dewey and Bentley (1949), in their discussion of the philosophical development of the concept of cause, described three ways of considering the causal relation according to the postulated origin of causal action.

1. *Self-actional causality*; a prescientific presentation in terms of presumptively independent "actors," souls," "minds," "selves," "powers," or "forces" taken as activating events (Dewey & Bentley, 1949, p. 72).

2. *Interactional causality*; a presentation of particles or other objects organized as

operating upon one another (Dewey & Bentley, 1949, p. 73).

3. *Transactional causality*; systems of description and naming which are employed to deal with aspects and phases of action without final attribution to "elements" or other presumptively detachable or independent "entities," "essences," or "realities," (self-action) and without isolation of presumptively detachable "elements" (Dewey & Bentley, 1949, p. 108).

The characteristics and differences of these three types of causality are summarized in Table 11—1 to illustrate the ways in which phenomena are typically considered. Behavior disorder viewed from the perspective of these three types of causality would have rather different characteristics as illustrated by the following examples.

Behavior disorder as self-actional. Disordered behavior would be regarded as due to processes

TABLE 11–1
Classifications of Causality Derived from Dewey and Bentley (1949)

Causal Type	Theorist	Unit of Analysis	Time Orientation	Space Orientation
Self-actional	Aristotle, (activating events)	Persons	Non-specific	Non-specific
Inter-actional	Galileo or Newton, (bodies in motion)	Persons interacting	Specific	Non-specific
Trans-actional	Einstein, (relativism)	Persons interacting in specific settings	Specific	Specific

Note: Specificity for *Time* and *Space* refers to whether the identity of the unit is dependent upon a specific location in time or space.

which underly the observable behavior and reside in the biological and/or psychological functioning of the individual. The processes can be identified as separate from each other with clear causal sequences and clearly specified outcomes. The individual is a passive host to a process of disease, the form and severity of which is due to the nature of the causative agent. Environmental influences both within and outside the organism can occasion the onset and speed of the disorder, but do not affect the basic process which unfolds.

Behavior disorder as interactional. Within the interactional framework, disordered behavior would be regarded as resulting from a sequence of experiences of the individual. The causal sequence is a complex of variables impinging upon or affecting the individual; it may vary from time to time, but the disorder will be characterized by a particular causal sequence (or set of sequences). It is possible to understand the current behavior by the sequence and not its particular setting. Conditions are to be understood as interactions between the stress (or invader) and the organism. Severity is influenced by the biological, psychological, and social state of the host (Robbins, 1966). The process of interaction (or nature of relationships) can be influenced by environmental forces.

Behavior disorder as transactional. Disordered behavior as transactional is viewed as the result of the person in his particular setting perceived, labeled, and responded to by the particular observers. The causal sequence is complex and impinges on the entire setting—each component of which has its own particular history. The sequence is variable both in time and space and thus yields unique situations. Sequences can be regarded as similar and so classified on the basis of their chronological relations (e.g., child-rearing history), their current spatial relationships (e.g., types of interpersonal communication patterns), or a combination of the two. Events are transactions of all parts of a situation with everything interrelated; change in any part should yield a different transaction. The individual is an active participant in the disorder.[6]

In the field of social science and health generally, and in the field of behavior disorders specifically, the chief purposes of classification may best be described as *communication, control,* and *comprehension.* Efficient *communication* is essential to effective functioning of all agencies concerned with the control of disease and social behavior. Efficiency in communication is a function of parsimony in the use of words or other symbols used in the communication system—the language of the system. By placing complex phenomena into categories which are in general use, a single symbol or word may be used to convey the whole complex and so simplify value judgments. It is difficult, perhaps impossible, to control disordered behavior without classifying it in some way so that the necessarily limited range of alternative actions can be used to best advantage.[7] *Comprehension* is usually a desired, if not essential, objective of classification. While it is always possible to communicate about phenomena that are not fully understood and it is often possible to control them, it is usually assumed that better understanding facilitates better communication and control. Comprehension as used here is synonymous with explanation, which in turn includes a theory of causality.

The analytic approach to considering classifications (by classifying their *purpose* and *type*) is offered as a way of describing the several attempts at behavior classification in the literature. The three actional systems as illustrated above in Table 11—1 were chosen as the frame of reference (Dewey & Bentley, 1949). It describes them as having developed in a chronological sequence. It might be said that each evolved from the other as knowledge and philosophy changed. It would be tempting to assert that the latest (transactionalism) is the *best*, since it represents the last stage of evolution. It may be that each serves its purpose. If so, one might expect that some classification systems now in use would be found at each level.[8]

Current opinions about the state of behavioral classification suggest that the old systems are regarded as not particularly useful and that a considerable search is being undertaken to find new directions (Opler, 1963; Zubin & Fleiss, 1964; Zubin, 1967, 1968). This is a situation which might be likened to the state of physics during the latter part of the 19th century. The common themes running through the review articles on classification were:

1. Classification systems are generally unreliable due to low relationships between diagnoses and symptoms (Zubin, 1967).
2. The phenomena are generally influenced by their settings; are culturally dependent (Zubin & Fleiss, 1964; Zubin, 1967; Miller, 1968).
3. Specific approaches to particular problems seem more useful than generalized systems like the American Psychiatric Association Standard Nomenclature (Katz, Cole, & Barton, 1968).

The concepts and the data are not compatible; prediction is imprecise. Zubin (1967) believes this to be due in part to the increase in the variety of treatment procedures available and of kinds of behavior desired. Perhaps the development of many classification approaches and the use of systematic rating scales (along with sophisticated statistical procedures) is producing a situation where new ways of thought are in conflict with the old and established approaches.

A classification procedure for classification systems was devised based on the concepts of their relationships in Figure 11—1 and Table 11—1. It is shown in Table 11—2 where a number of representative approaches are summarized. The categories used are:

1. *Purpose.* Comprehension, communication, and/or control are noted in their presumed order of importance.
2. *Unit of analysis.* Entities, relationships, and/or events are stated as the unit of action.
3. *Norms.* The frame of reference provides the standards against which the behavior is to be judged as congruent or discrepant.
4. *Type of system.* Descriptive or explanatory as described in Table 11—1.
5. *Causality.* Within the explanatory system (as noted in Table 11—1), the three actional systems will be used. For the descriptive system, causality will also be described in these terms but will be qualified as only "implied."
6. *Behavioral data.* The kinds of behavior observed and the methods for obtaining it are noted. This will indicate what the system is classifying.

These six points provide a structure within which to compare and contrast the following approaches to behavioral classification.

CLASSIFICATION OF ADULT BEHAVIOR

The behavior disorders of primary interest and importance in the mental health field have been those of adults. This is due, in large part, to the effects of World War II and its aftermath, where the adjustment problems of returning veterans became a major social problem. This section will include the major approaches to disordered adult behavior, even though some (e.g., *Diagnostic and Statistical Manual*, American Psychiatric Association) provide a few categories to include behavior of children.

TABLE 11–2
Classification of Classification Systems for Behavioral Disorder

Name of System	Purpose	Unit of Analysis	Norms	Type	Causality	Behavior Data
American Psychiatric Association and International Statistical Classification	1. Communication 2. Control 3. Comprehension	Person whether organic or functional disorder	1. Health 2. Social behavior 3. Personality adjustment	1. Explanatory for Organic 2. Descriptive for Functional Disorders (Mixed types)	Interaction	1. Interview typically
Inpatient Multidimensional Psychiatric Scale (Lorr)	1. Control 2. Comprehension 3. Communication	Person	1. Social behavior 2. Personality adjustment	1. Descriptive a. functional	Interaction (implied)	1. Interview
Katz Adjustment Scales	1. Control 2. Communication 3. Comprehension	Person	1. Social behavior 2. Personality adjustment	1. Descriptive a. functional	Interaction (implied)	1. Community behavior
Dreger: Behavioral Classification Project	1. Control 2. Communication 3. Comprehension	Person	1. Mental health 2. Social behavior	1. Descriptive a. functional	Interaction (implied)	Outside of clinic behavior

TABLE 11–2 (Continued)

Classification of Classification Systems for Behavioral Disorder

Name of System	Purpose	Unit of Analysis	Norms	Type	Causality	Behavior Data
Cromwell: Behavior Dimensions for Emotionally Disturbed Children	1. Control 2. Communication 3. Comprehension	Person	1. Social Behavior 2. Mental Health	1. Descriptive functional	Interaction Implied (Transactional Implied)	Observations
Operant Approach to Behavior Modification	1. Control 2. Communication	Person in relationship to environment	1. Expectations of significant others	1. Descriptive functional	Transaction Implied	Behavior observed in relevant settings
Ackerman's Family Diagnosis	1. Control 2. Communication	The family unit; the individuals and their interrelationships	1. Social Behavior 2. Mental Health	1. Descriptive functional	Interaction	Interview and observation
Review of Delinquency Classification (Rubenfeld)	1. Comprehension 2. Control 3. Communication	Person as entity; some focus on behavioral characteristics	1. Legal 2. Social 3. Mental Health	1. Descriptive a. functional, or 2. Explanatory	Interaction	Interview, test data, history and offense

American Psychiatric Association System

The *Diagnostic and Statistical Manual: Mental Disorders* was published in 1952 and was used extensively by mental health professionals working in mental hospitals and psychiatric clinics (American Psychiatric Association, 1952). It served as the standard reference until 1968 when the second revision, designated *DSM–II*, was published (American Psychiatric Association, 1968). The revision, while representing a number of specific changes in classification categories, does not seem to represent a substantive change in philosophy or structure and is more appropriately viewed as an updating which incorporated new labels.

Historically these two publications derive from a standard system for uniform statistics in hospitals developed by the Committee on Statistics of the American Psychiatric Association and introduced by the National Committee for Mental Hygiene in 1917. It was entitled, *Statistical Manual for the Use of Hospitals for Mental Diseases.* The system was revised between 1928–1934 when the New York Academy of Medicine led a drive to devise a nationally accepted standard nomenclature of disease. The American Psychiatric Association provided the leadership for the revision of the part on mental disorders.

The 1934 system was used until World War II. Application by the armed forces showed that only 10 percent of the cases were being classified into the categories of the system—categories which were developed for use in public mental hospitals. As a consequence several new classification systems were developed. The army, the navy, and the Veterans Administration each developed one, with the army system being the one most widely used.

By 1948 the American Psychiatric Association regarded the situation with classification as having "deteriorated to the point of confusion." Most psychiatrists were using the army system. The apparent problem with the army system was that it did not provide for conditions accompanying organic brain damage, conditions frequently encountered by psychiatrists in civilian practice. This led to the first edition of the diagnostic and statistical manual which was published in 1952.

There has been considerable interest over the years, both within the United States and at international levels, to achieve a single system of classification. The 1952 *Diagnostic and Statistical Manual (DSM–I)* presented a number of new categories not found in the section dealing with mental disorder of the *International Classification of Diseases*, sixth revision (*ICD–6*).[9] Accordingly, the United States Public Health Service established a committee to develop a series of categories to adapt the *ICD–6* for use in the United States. Stengel (1959) noted that the *ICD–6* presented problems for use in the United States and in a number of other countries as well. A revision was adopted by an International Revision Conference in 1965 and by the 19th World Health Assembly in 1966. The eighth *ICD* revision (*ICD–8*), published in 1968, included this new section on mental disorders.

In 1965 the Committee on Nomenclature and Statistics (of the American Psychiatric Association) published a supplement to the 18th printing of *DSM–I*.in which the *ICD–8* section on mental disorders was published and the *DSM–II* revision was announced. It was drafted and reviewed in 1966 and 1967 and published as *DSM–II* in 1968.

In the new revision there was a change in the order of presentation and some change in the categories used. Table 11–3[10] summarizes the changes in the organization of the system. The specific changes to the classification categories, as described in detail by Spitzer and Wilson (1968), do not obscure the distinction between organic and functional disorders made so explicitly in *DSM–I*.

Brain Syndromes

The disorders classified as brain syndromes are those associated with organic conditions which are presumed to be causal. The conditions include prenatal influences, infection, intoxication, trauma, circulatory disturbances, convulsions, metabolism, neoplasm, and diseases of unknown origin. In both *DSM–I* and *DSM–II* the causal logic can be seen as:

$$\text{organic condition} \longrightarrow \text{brain syndrome} \longrightarrow \text{observed behavior}$$

Functional Disorders

Behaviors classified as functionally disordered are those patterns which are not associated with organic disorders and cannot therefore be explained by a structural difficulty. As described

TABLE 11–3
Organization of Nomenclature in DSM-1 and DSM-II

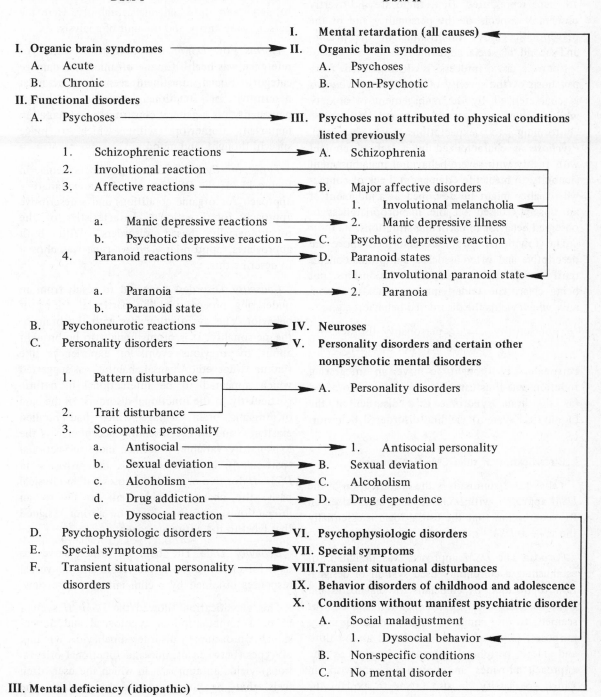

DSM-I

DSM-II

I. Mental retardation (all causes)

I. Organic brain syndromes → II. Organic brain syndromes
  A. Acute   A. Psychoses
  B. Chronic   B. Non-Psychotic

II. Functional disorders
  A. Psychoses → III. Psychoses not attributed to physical conditions listed previously

    1. Schizophrenic reactions → A. Schizophrenia
    2. Involutional reaction
    3. Affective reactions → B. Major affective disorders
                                          1. Involutional melancholia
      a. Manic depressive reactions → 2. Manic depressive illness
      b. Psychotic depressive reaction → C. Psychotic depressive reaction
    4. Paranoid reactions → D. Paranoid states
                                          1. Involutional paranoid state
      a. Paranoia → 2. Paranoia
      b. Paranoid state
  B. Psychoneurotic reactions → IV. Neuroses
  C. Personality disorders → V. Personality disorders and certain other nonpsychotic mental disorders

    1. Pattern disturbance
                              → A. Personality disorders
    2. Trait disturbance
    3. Sociopathic personality
      a. Antisocial → 1. Antisocial personality
      b. Sexual deviation → B. Sexual deviation
      c. Alcoholism → C. Alcoholism
      d. Drug addiction → D. Drug dependence
      e. Dyssocial reaction
  D. Psychophysiologic disorders → VI. Psychophysiologic disorders
  E. Special symptoms → VII. Special symptoms
  F. Transient situational personality disorders → VIII. Transient situational disturbances
                                IX. Behavior disorders of childhood and adolescence
                                X. Conditions without manifest psychiatric disorder
                                A. Social maladjustment
                                        1. Dyssocial behavior
                                B. Non-specific conditions
                                C. No mental disorder

III. Mental deficiency (idiopathic)

in *DSM–I*, functional disorders show (1) varying degrees of personality disintegration, (2) failure to test and evaluate correctly external reality in various spheres, and (3) failure in ability to relate self effectively to other people. Two perspectives are here represented; first, there are the overtly observable aspects of the personality and of the perceptual/cognitive functioning of the person, and second, his social adjustment.

Neurosis as a process is distinguished from psychosis by the severity of the disorder. *Neurosis* is characterized by the management of anxiety while keeping contact with external reality (i.e., conforming to expectations of observers). *Psychosis* is characterized by a lack of contact with reality with severe behavioral maladjustment (inability to meet life's demands). Lack of contact with reality might be described as a judgment of an observer based on the inappropriateness of observed behavior to particular situations.

The functional diagnoses described above are descriptive and often associate symptoms concurrently with their causal interrelationships not being clear. The underlying construct is personality which yields the disordered behavior, e.g.:

personality ⟶ personality disorder
⟶ observed behavior disorder

Personality is thought to have an integrating function and thus can be conceived as disordered (as the brain syndrome is a disorder of the biophysical system) yielding disordered behavior.

Classification of the DSM–II Approach

Table 11–2 summarizes the classification of the *DSM* approach, with *DSM–II* being categorized on the assumption that the causal logic is essentially the same as *DSM–I*.

Purpose. The *DSM* approach was designed for establishing a commonly used system of designation to be used by clinicians for diagnostic and treatment purposes. *Communication* and *control* seemed to be similarly important as primary purposes. *Comprehension* was listed as the third and more peripheral purpose. Insofar as the approach provides an etiological framework in which to classify, it also serves to explain the disorder. This is most clear with organic brain damage. With the functional disorders, there was only an associational orientation, so the author regarded it as only descriptive.

Unit of Analysis. The disorder is described by *DSM* as residing with an individual—either in his brain or in his personality—and is expressed in his behavior and its social unacceptability. Here the person is the entity and the unit of analysis.

Norms. For *DSM*, the normative frame of reference was health for the organic brain damage category. Social adjustment seemed to be most descriptive of functional disorders, although personality (as a general construct) was seen as an important framework within which to judge speech, thought, and mood.

Type of System. Following the schema in Figure 11–1, the *DSM* seems to be an explanatory approach for organic conditions and a descriptive approach for functional characteristics of the psychologically based disorders. With both approaches, appropriate, *mixed type* was chosen to describe this.

Causality. Disorders appeared to result from an underlying process yielding particular forms of behavior. The dysfunction was with the brain or the personality. It is often thought to be brought about by previous events or experiences like trauma, drugs, etc. A causal chaining was suggested which appeared to be interactional in nature, particularly in the functional disorders. In the case of organic brain damage which had implied existence, and an overwhelming acceptance as the explanatory variable, it seemed more self-actional (particularly in *DSM–I*). With the provision in *DSM–II* for two or more diagnoses with a physical basis, the change would seem to be to an interactionist position—thus, the author assigned that label to the entire approach.

Behavior Data. The behavior which serves as data for classification is the verbal and nonverbal responses obtained by a clinician in an interview.

This classification showed the *DSM–II* system to be a combination of typological and dimensional approaches to disordered behavior. The mix of types (between organic and functional orientations) yields an approach in which the user often feels that he more adequately explains the behavior when an organic component can be found.

International Classification of Diseases

The *International Statistical Classification of Diseases (ICD)* is a system of classification, sponsored by the World Health Organization (WHO), which is in the eighth revision published in 1968. This revision contained a section on mental disorders, which was the latest attempt to make that section maximally useful in several countries and which was stimulated by the lack of utility of the sixth revision (*ICD–6*) as reported by Stengel (1959) and by the American Psychiatric Association (1968).[11]

The problems with the *ICD–6* were seen to be the variety of nosological approaches and conceptions of etiology at an international level (Stengel, 1959). From the United States perspective, it was seen to have the following specific faults:

1. No coding for chronic brain syndrome with neurotic reaction, behavioral reaction, or without qualifying phrase.
2. No coding for acute brain syndrome within the psychotic conditions except alcoholic delirium and exhaustion delirium (American Psychiatric Association, 1952).

The seventh revision was only a minor change from *ICD–6* and thus represented no major improvement so far as most writers were concerned. *ICD–8* was the next major revision and was accomplished by coordination of effort between WHO experts and the American committee. Thus it was possible to make *ICD–8* and *DSM–II* essentially identical. For that reason, *ICD–8* was not differentiated from *DSM–II* in Table 11–2 and was considered to have the same characteristics.[12]

Behavior Rating Scales

Shortly after World War II there arose a strong interest in being more objective than the traditional diagnostic approach in psychiatry. Based in a psychometric tradition, rating scales for mentally disordered behavior were devised (Lyerly & Abbott, 1966).[13] The scales yield quantitative scores along one or more specific dimensions. These were thought to be a more detailed and systematic way of describing a disorder than the assignment to a nosological category on the basis of a qualitative judgment. The typical approach was to rate the behavior observed by the rater or rate the self-reports of the patient on a scale. Most of the scales were designed for hospitalized patients, often developed on criterion groups selected by means of the usual psychiatric classification (Lyerly & Abbott, 1966).

The Multidimensional Scale for Rating Psychiatric Patients (MSRPP) was one of the early postwar scales and was developed by Maurice Lorr and colleagues in the Veterans Administration (Lorr, 1953). It provided the basis for five of the 19 scales reviewed by Lyerly and Abbott (1966), and has apparently had more influence upon the field than any other single work.[14] Lorr and colleagues have revised it (Lorr, Klatt, McNair, & Lasky, 1963), and have devised a companion scale to measure ward behavior (Lorr & Vestre, 1968).

The Inpatient Multidimensional Psychiatric Scale (IMPS)

The IMPS is a complete revision of the MSRPP and was completed in 1963. It was designed to measure (with 75 questions) ten psychotic syndromes based on a clinician's observations of a patient and his verbal reports on beliefs, attitudes, and feelings. The ten syndromes are:

1. *Excitement.* Characterized by an excess and acceleration of the individual's speech and motor activities and also by lack of restraint in the expression of emotions and feelings. Mood level and self-esteem are usually high.
2. *Hostile Belligerence.* A complaining, griping attitude, manifest hostility, and an inclination to express resentment toward others and to feel suspicious of others' intentions.
3. *Paranoid Projection.* Beliefs that attribute a hostile and controlling intent to the world around the patient.
4. *Grandiose Expansiveness.* The syndrome appears to represent a stage beyond paranoid projections. The individual characterized has found an explanation for his persecution. He is really an important personage with a divine mission and unusual powers.
5. *Perceptual Distortion.* Hallucinations that threaten, accuse, and demand. The underlying mechanism is one of distortion

of sensory and perceptual stimuli. Voices say "bad" things about the patient.

6. *Anxious Intropunitiveness.* Three elements appear to characterize this syndrome: anxiety, turning against the self, and lowered mood level. The individual experiences guilt and remorse and holds himself to blame for real or imagined faults.

7. *Retardation and Apathy.* A slowing down and reduction of ideation, speech, and motor behavior. At the extreme there is apathy and disinterest.

8. *Disorientation.* The syndrome measures varying degrees of disorientation. Here it probably is not due to brain injury but is indicative of autism or intense self-directed attention.

9. *Motor Disturbances.* Rigid and bizarre postures, grimacing, and repetitive movements are the principal behaviors defining this syndrome.

10. *Conceptual Disorganization.* Disturbances in the stream of thought evidenced in irrelevant answers and incoherent or rambling speech. These suggest disorganization of thinking processes.

The rater is provided two frameworks in which to judge the behavior: first, to compare it with the normal person, and second, to note the presence of certain specific characteristics or behaviors. Scores are the ten individual syndrome measures and three derived morbidity scores. The latter are (1) an excitement vs. hostility pattern, (2) the tendency toward distortion of thinking and perception, and (3) schizophrenic disorganization. The interrater reliability ranges from .82 to .91 for the syndrome scores and .61 to .92 on individual items. It has been found useful in discriminating between patients on open and closed wards, and in agreeing with psychiatric classifications of paranoid schizophrenia and catatonia. The scale has also been used extensively in measuring the effects of various treatment approaches and chemotherapy agents.

As classified in Table 11—2, the characteristics of the scale are described below.

Purpose. The scale was designed to yield reliable scores which will be descriptive of cognitive and emotional behavior on the ward and which will show changes in that behavior with treatment. The primary purpose was seen to be *control*; that is, change of behavior. Second, the scale is extensively used for research—for the purpose of understanding the behavior: thus, *comprehension.* *Communication* with others about the results of work with the scale seems to hold the third level of importance.

Unit of Analysis. The person (patient) is the focus of interest but his several behaviors are the phenomena rated and scored. The measures are all treated as equal in importance.

Norms. The frame of reference is the cognitive, emotional, and interpersonal responses of normal individuals. These were classified from social behavior and personality perspectives.

Type. The type of classification system seems best described as a descriptive orientation concerned with functional aspects of a personality system.

Causality. The action seems to be interactional where the multiple characteristics measured are presumed to reflect an underlying process of disorder.[15]

Behavior Data. The behavior used as data are the answers of the subjects to specific questions on an inventory as rated by an interviewer/observer.

Psychotic Inpatient Profile (PIP)

The PIP is a revision and expansion of the Psychotic Reaction Profile (Lorr, O'Connor, & Stafford, 1961). The PRP was a rating scale for use by hospital personnel to measure ward behavior of psychiatric patients. The PIP is designed to measure both manifest ward behavior (with 74 statements) and patients' self-reports (22 items). Ratings are made by a nurse or aide following three days of observation of an interaction with the patient (Lorr & Vestre, 1968). Whereas the PRP had eight factors, research with the PIP has yielded twelve psychotic syndromes; ten of these are essentially identical with the IMPS and two are unique to PIP (Seclusiveness and Need for Care). The PIP was not classified in Table 11—2 since it is identical with the IMPS classification except for Behavior Data which was ward behavior and self-reports.

These two scales represent the two general approaches in the use of rating scales: (1) to describe characteristics of thinking and feelings of individuals and (2) to describe behavior of individuals in various settings. Several are broader in scope than ward behavior and take in such areas as family life, job, friends, community, etc. These are the Social Ineffectiveness Scale (Parloff, Kelman, & Frank, 1955), Symptom and Adjustment Index (Gross, *et al.*, 1961), the Katz Adjustment Scales (Katz & Lyerly, 1963), and Community Adjustment Scale (Ellsworth, *et al.*, 1968). The Katz Scales are perhaps the most developed and, therefore, the most useful to community mental health workers. They will be considered below since they seem to represent an important trend in this research, the move to collect behavioral adjustment measures in other settings than the hospital.

Katz Adjustment Scales

The Katz Adjustment Scales were developed by Martin M. Katz at the National Institute of Mental Health (Katz & Lyerly, 1963). They obtained descriptions of the behavior of mental patients in the community based on reports by the patient himself and by a relative. Questions about behavior are prepared in booklet form and are completed by the patient and the relative themselves, not by an interviewer.

Adjustment, to Katz, was more than the absence of pathology; he wanted to have a quantified way of describing positive attributes. In order to elaborate the concept of adjustment (with both personal and social referents), the following measures were developed:

Form R1. Relative's Ratings of Patient Symptoms and Social Behavior. This form is an inventory of 127 items designed to record the patient's symptomatology and social behavior which have been observed over several weeks by the relative prior to the rating.

Form R2. Level of Performance of Socially Expected Activities. This was based on work by Freeman and Simmons (1958) and has 16 activities that describe family and social responsibilities, social activities, self care, home adjustment, and community activities.

Form R3. Level of Expectations. This form has the same items as R2 with the relative asked to rate whether he had expected the patient to be doing the behavior within a reasonable time following return home. Discrepancy between R2 and R3 make it possible to infer degree of dissatisfaction of relative without directly asking.

Form R4. Level of Free-Time Activities. This is designed similarly to the Activities and Attitudes Scale (Cavan, Burgess, Havighurst, & Goldhamer, 1949) and has 23 items covering hobbies, social and community activities, and self-improvement activities.

Form R5. Level of Satisfaction with Free-Time Activities. This scale has the same items as R4 to get at the relative's satisfaction with the patient's performance on free-time activities.

Analysis of the tests has been done (1) on one set of data with correlation, cluster-analysis, and factor analysis, and (2) on two different samples of mental hospital patients as a validation procedure. The cluster analysis of Form R1 showed 12 clusters, interpreted as describing types of behavior. The names as proposed by Katz and Lyerly (1963) were 1) Belligerence, 2) Verbal Expansiveness, 3) Negativism, 4) Helplessness, 5) Suspiciousness, 6) Anxiety, 7) Withdrawal and Retardation, 8) General Psychopathology, 9) Nervousness, 10) Confusion, 11) Bizarreness, and 12) Hyperactivity.

From this a factor analysis (principal components) was done yielding three factors, which they hypothesized to underlie the behavior described by the inventory. These factors were named I. Social Obstreperousness, II. Acute Psychotism, and III. Withdrawn Depression. These clusters and factors represent the relationships between the ways in which raters rated patients' behavior. In this sense one can describe, at two levels of abstraction, the ways in which perceived characteristics from Form R1 cluster.

The Katz Adjustment Scales (KAS) approach, as categorized into the descriptive classification of Table 11−2, was assigned the following characteristics.

Purpose. The KAS appears to be oriented towards the reliable categorization of abnormal behavior for the primary purpose of treating and *controlling* it. Secondarily, there is the scientific need to share results with others so that *communication* about disordered behavior and its correlates can advance. *Comprehension* is of interest but given less prominence than the other two (Katz, Lowery, & Cole, 1966) and was therefore listed third.

Unit of Analysis. The focus for collection of data is on descriptive aspects of behavior which are thought to reflect underlying factors or types. The person remains the major unit but he is not regarded as a singular entity to be described with one measure.

Norms. The KAS focused on the social and personal adaptation made by the person to his community. Therefore, social behavior and personality theory provide two frames of reference for judging deviant behavior.

Type. The classification approach is one which is descriptive of behavior characteristics with a functional orientation toward aspects or measurements of personality. The cluster and factor analyses are ways of searching for an explanatory system, but at the present time the approach is still at a descriptive level (Katz, Lowery, & Cole, 1966).

Causality. The methodology used was dimensional in measuring aspects of behavior patterns. This is Newtonian in approach so the author concluded that the causal model (implied here) was interactional.

Behavioral Data. Data were collected about the behavior of the patient in community (nonhospital) settings.

This scale is one of the more sophisticated attempts to take perceptions of behavior, as structured by ratings of characteristics of a persons's behavior, from observers other than a trained interviewer. The statistical procedure is one which does not impose a restricted set of categories on the data until after they are collected. The approach is more accurately a way of showing where, in *n*-dimensional space, the behavioral measures vary in the same ways (i.e., cluster) and it utilizes a completely empirical and relativistic approach to the grouping and reduction of the data. The clusters and the factors are ways of describing stable categories or *classes of variability*. These categories then become the categories for classification.

SUMMARY

Approaches to the classification of disorders of adult behavior have been considered in two ways, *typological* and *dimensional*. Typological approaches are the oldest and most typical in clinical use, as illustrated by *DSM–II* and *ICD–8*. The typology seems to contain an assumption that the basic character (or reality) of the disorder is captured by the category assignment. It should follow then that the category has some predictive power. But the power is apparently not satisfactory (Zubin, 1967). Dimensional approaches are those illustrated by the rating scales. Categorization is accomplished by a complicated set of procedures, usually requiring data processing machinery. Although this is generally a more descriptive approach, there is the continuing interest in types, categories, or classes (Lorr, 1966; Katz, Lowery, & Cole, 1966). It would appear that type means something rather different within different models of causality. If the dimensional approaches yield classes of variability (and locations in multidimensional space) then one is predicting from, and to, locations of measures; and is *not* predicting from assumptions about the character of the entity under various conditions. The two approaches are then, causally, *self-action* (typological) and *interactional* (dimensional) models of action.

As a final note, situational aspects have become a focus of interest recently as a way of improving predictability of the measures, when applied outside the framework of the hospital, as in the case of posthospital adaptation in the community. Following the Katz work (Katz & Lyerly, 1963; Katz, Lowery, & Cole, 1966), some very similar work was conducted by Ellsworth, *et al.* (1968) on Veterans Hospital patients. Both studies support the thesis that if one wants to predict behavior in nonhospital settings, one must go beyond hospital behavior no matter whether it is approached typologically or dimensionally.

CLASSIFICATION OF CHILD BEHAVIOR

Behavior problems of children are a large part of the work of school personnel workers, mental health centers, and family service agencies. While the numbers are sizeable (Glidewell & Swallow, 1968),[16] it is interesting that the resources for children's mental health problems have developed much less rapidly than those for adults or for families. Classification of disorders of children have been attempted via the systems of the American Psychiatric Association, and typically are placed in a few categories such as "Adjustment Reaction of Childhood" or "Transient Situational Personality Disorders" (Dreger & Dreger, 1962). Since many workers have been dissatisfied with this approach, two lines of development have appeared. One is the study of symptoms much like the work with behavior rating scales with adult disorders; the other is the development of family classification and therapy.

Miller (1968), in considering the current state of child psychiatry, addressed himself directly to the matter of classification and described it as a basic issue that divides child psychiatry. The question was whether one can "assign to the childhood years the names for conditions that rule in the years beyond the biological watershed." This is made particularly difficult, he asserted, because organisms are changing and one is confronted both with existent traits and emergent traits (appearing later). He goes on to state that "classification of child disorders may be profoundly influenced by the selecting machine. This is because none of the key persons classifying the child (parents, teachers, mental health professionals) is so objective as to be able to see the child beyond the good and evil which their social, scientific, and religious standpoints force upon them." Thus, for proper classification one must take into account both organismic change and changes in society that affect the prevailing standards for behavior. Viewed in this way, one might state that the task of child psychiatry is the differentiation of the important from the unimportant behavior, and the planning of treatment in such a way as to avoid creating a disorder where one would not have been.

Several research approaches have been taken to the study of childhood behavior problems and their classification. Two will be considered below in detail since they represent substantial attempts to find consistency among the disordered behaviors.[17] Behavior modification and family approaches will also be discussed since these represent two additional means of dealing with children's behavior problems.

Behavioral Classification Project

R. M. Dreger and associates, in 1961, began to describe the problem behavior of children (Dreger & Dreger, 1962; Dreger, et al., 1964). The project was begun after it was found that over 40 percent of children diagnosed by 17 clinics in Florida were placed in the category "Adjustment Reaction of Childhood." The approach was to take 229 descriptions of behavior and to have the respondent sort them into *yes* and *no* categories. A factor analysis was carried out to explore the underlying structure of the answers: This was done for 372 subjects admitted to child guidance clinics and 90 children drawn from a Florida county to serve as a control group. For this trial project, ten *factors* were obtained using 104 of the 229 items:

A. A paranoic, aggressive, and isolative egocentricity,
B. Antisocial aggressiveness,
C. Intellectual and scholastic retardation,
D. Psychoid desurgency,
E. Appreciative, confident, and concerned sociableness,
F. Impulsive and excitable hyperactivity,
G. A sadistic type of aggressiveness,
H. Disturbed sleep and dreams,
I. Social immaturity,
J. Ages of parents.

An alternate approach was attempted. Thirty-two children, six to thirteen years of age, were randomly selected from the 372 subjects, and were clustered by a combination of Holzinger-Harman and Cattell procedures. The *clusters* are summarized below:

A. Relatively mature, semisociable egocentricity,
B. Relatively immature, nonsociable, semisurgent egocentricity,
C. Sociable anxiety,
D. Semisociable, nonanxious, desurgent retardation,
E. Egocentric, antisocial aggressiveness.

Comparing the two suggests that similarities may be found between Cluster A and Factor E; Cluster B and Factor A, Cluster C and Factor I or Factor E, Cluster D and Factor C, and Cluster E and Factor B. The similarities of all five clusters to particular factors is particularly interesting since the clusters were derived by manipulating people, while the factors were obtained from items. One wonders whether this suggests that individuals (along with their characteristics) can be adequately fit into a single category. If so, then there is support for the typological model here. Dreger, *et al.,* (1964) report apparent correspondence of seven factors with those in *DSM—I* (American Psychiatric Association, 1952) and with Patterson's (1964) five factors. This is of interest if comparative research shows the comparison to be reliable since these approaches were developed quite differently. The project has much more work to report before it is clear how it relates to typological and dimensional approaches.[18]

Classification of the Behavior Classification Project into Table 11—2 yielded the following picture.

Purpose. The system was designed to provide more descriptive categories for clinic use than found in standard nomenclature; this was *control. Communication* was assigned to second place due to the emphasis on the statewide need to have consistent reporting. *Comprehension* or understanding would seem to have been the least prominent purpose.

Unit of Analysis. This multivariate, inductive approach describes the behavior of the person in a number of ways. Thus, the person is viewed from a number of different perspectives, yet with the personality as a unifying concept.

Norms. Standards for judging the problem behavior come from those typically found in outpatient mental health work. Parents often respond initially to the problem as social misbehavior and then cast it into mental health terms so that it is eligible for treatment. Mental health professionals using the system would tend to use a mental health frame of reference.

Type. The approach is descriptive of behavior of children coming for outpatient psychiatric treatment. It was categorized as functional in orientation since the item content asked for judgments about behavior (as adaptive or maladaptive) in nonclinical settings. This should reflect the functioning of a person in his relevant environment.

Causality. Interaction was the causal logic seen to be implied and was assigned due to the dimensional approach taken toward the data.

Behavior Data. The behavior judged was reported by an intimate of the subject as typical in settings outside the clinics.

Cromwell's Behavior Dimensions for Emotionally Disturbed Children

Rue Cromwell was interested in identifying and making relevant dimensions of emotional disturbance, useful for application to natural settings (Cromwell, 1967). The project attempted to relate four classes of variables rather than to find descriptive measures to distinguish one group from another (Cromwell & Davis, 1965). The four variable types were: (1) historical etiological, (2) presently assessable (diagnostic), (3) type of treatment, and (4) prognostic. These were designed into a longitudinal study which regarded the diagnostic variables as only one type of several to be studied in the search for specific prediction of outcomes. Objective inventories were designed and developed for all four types of variables. Detailed results are yet to be reported. Data anlysis procedures were multivariate techniques designed to find clusterings in the data and to describe their similarities and differences. In this sense the approach is an empirical one to test whether the four types of variables would reliably cluster. The approach is summarized in Table 11—2 and described below:

Purpose. The system was designed to identify the dimensions of behavior disturbance relevant to such settings as the school classroom and to provide the teacher a way of understanding it so as to plan improved teaching and interpersonal approaches. With this applied focus the system seemed primarily concerned with the *control* of behavior. *Communication* seemed to be the next most important. *Comprehension* or understanding ranked as third and is to be defined, at least in part, by successful application of the system to the matter of prediction.

Unit of Analysis. The behavior and experience of particular children were the focus for study. Behavior was thought to be multiply determined, but the individual personality as the behaving entity seemed to function as the unifying concept.

Norms. The standards for considering the child as having disordered behavior were those of parents and helping agents. The behavior was often described as socially deviant, typically from implicit standards of observers; but the subjects were often from mental health facilities so this perspective could also be at work.

Type. The type of classification system would seem to be a descriptive approach to functional aspects of personality. This classification was on the basis of the multivariate approach to judgments about the person in question, and prediction to future behavior.

Causality. The system was clearly interactional in causal conception. Transaction seemed implied in the author's discussion about the observer problem where some raters apparently could not report reliable (i.e., comparable) data due to different behavior judged by each one.[19]

Behavior Data. The behavioral data included reports on the subject's current behavior, historical factors, parental behavior, descriptions of treatment, and behavior of the subject a year later. The reports are all judgments about the subject by parents or other caretakers.

Cromwell's approach is very similar to Dreger's except that the purpose is much more applied. Both have taken the approach that behaviors to be classified are variable and complex requiring multiple measurements. The several measures are then managed statistically to find how characteristics cluster in time and space. The interrelationships may then describe a series of events or experiences that lead from one particular pattern to another. In this way these approaches to children's behavior are very similar to the adult behavior rating scales described above.

Behavior Modification and Classification

Behavior Modification has developed as a term designating an approach based on Skinnerian learning theory, where the principles of operant conditioning are applied to the change of problematic behavior. It is an approach to symptomatic behavior, often that of children (Cahoon, 1968; Gelfand & Hartmann, 1968). The approach to classification is rather different from what has been discussed heretofore in this paper. Ferster (1965) began his consideration of disordered behavior by asserting that what is labeled as abnormal is a product of the person's interaction with current environmental stimuli, and is an understandable outcome of the individual's history of reinforcement. The operational definition of abnormal is that behavior which important people in the individual's environment wish to increase, decrease, or otherwise change.

Classification to Ferster (1965) is an individual-oriented procedure which requires:

1. analysis of the nature of the actual environments,
2. analysis of the individual's response repertory, and
3. comparison of the individual responses with the behavioral potential of the milieu.

This yields an analysis of the *discrepancies* between the individual's response repertory and the characteristics of the milieu.

Diagnosis for the operant conditioner would be a descriptive matter to determine what environmental characteristics had behavior potential for the subject and what his response repertory was like. This could then be translated directly into a reinforcement schedule to alter the situation. The approach is completely ideographically oriented and allows for the individual to serve as his own criterion. Intervention would be judged effective if there were changes from the typical level of performance for one or more behaviors.

The approach was classified in Table 11–2 in comparison with the other systems considered. The following was considered:

Purpose. The primary purpose is with the *control* of behavior and the *communication* about it with the subject and one's scientific colleagues. *Comprehension* is merely a by-product of the approach and serves to explain the behavior in terms of causal contingencies. In this it seemed somewhat similar to Cromwell's frame of reference.

Unit of Analysis. Analysis was directed toward relationships between stimuli and responses. The person is the beginning point but is not understandable except in relationship to the stimulating milieu.

Norms. Discrepancy is relative to the norms of significant others. Referral or action is taken by someone who wants change.

Type. This approach is a *descriptive* one which focuses on relationships, or the functional aspects of the person's behavior.

Causality. Causality is clearly interactional with characteristics which seem to indicate *transaction.* Transaction was assigned because of the emphasis on relationships rather than entities, the functional systematic orientation, and the presumption of ideography for each person. This suggests belief in time and space specific characteristics, with generalization across time on the basis of probabilities of similarity (and the need for successive approximations in each specific case).

Behavior Judged. Behavior to be observed is studied both in settings where the deviance is reported and in other usual settings both similar and different. This is done to try to determine the stimuli and the reinforcement contingencies which are producing the undesirable responses.

Behavior Modification represents a relativistic and systems oriented approach which considers the person and the situation at a molar level. Relativism refers to the focus on the "fit" among the behavior of the person, the characteristics of relevant stimuli, and the judgment of deviance by someone else. Behavior is altered by "calibrating" the person to several settings, and then attempting to change the stimulus-response relationships.

Family Classification

Family therapy and classification is a current and popular type of approach to disordered behavior, particularly that of children. Here the meaningful unit of study is social, with individuals as components of the larger entity.[20] This view does not regard the disorder as being only psychological, and often leads to treatment directed to other persons than the "patient" or to the social unit as a whole. The approach was included here with the focus on child behavior, although the "social group as the patient" has also been applied to marital counseling and group psychotherapy.

Family as the focus of study has been considered in detail by Handel (1968) who reviewed the research knowledge from studies of the family. The approaches to classification have followed two routes. On the one hand is the approach of Hill and Hansen (1960) which has been directed to the family as a social unit. The

second approach, to be considered here, was directed toward disordered behavior and its treatment within the family. Family therapy was reputedly begun by Nathan Ackerman as early as 1938 (Jackson & Satir, 1961). The field was given a significant boost by Ackerman's (1958) book, *The Psychodynamics of Family Life.* His approach will be described as illustrative of the family treatment field.

Diagnosis is the primary way of considering classification and, for Ackerman, is needed to go beyond the descriptive to something "dynamic, developmental and etiological" (Ackerman, 1958, p. 9). He proposed a three step approach to diagnosis:

1. A theoretical framework for evaluation of psychosocial functioning of family groups;
2. A means for systematic correlation of the emotional functioning and mental health of the individual with that of family; and
3. A method of observation and differential description of families according to their mental health, and a method for contrasting types of families.

The theoretical framework included (1) psychological identity (subsuming strivings, expectations, and values), (2) stability of behavior expressed as (a) continuity of identity in time, (b) the control of conflict, and (c) the capacity to change, learn, and achieve further development. The primary purpose for diagnosis was to plan for treatment.

Data collection for diagnosis follows the following organization (derived from Ackerman, 1958, p. 138–140).

   I. Presenting problem (at level of entry).
      A. Disturbance of family member,
      B. Disturbance of family relationships,
      C. Impaired family functions,
      D. Special stress situation precipitating referral.
  II. Identifying data (family, physical setting, social characteristics, special features).
 III. Family as a group.
      A. Internal organization,
      B. External adaptation of family to community.
 IV. Current family functioning.
      A. Marital relationship,
      B. Parental relationship,

C. Parent-child relationship,

D. Sibling-pair relationship.

V. Personality makeup of each individual member.

VI. Relations with primary parental families.

VII. Developmental history of the primary patient.

VIII. Summary of mental health of family and interrelations between individual and family mental health.

This, along with detailed criteria for the evaluation of marital and parental interaction and for the description of the current state of the child, stands as the diagnosis and classification procedure. The approach is one of completing, in an informal fashion, the above outline and of using that as the primary data source.

Ackerman reports research from 50 families yielding seven forms of family adaptation presented as theoretically "pure" forms:

1. The externally isolated family group,

2. The externally integrated family group,

3. The internally unintegrated family group,

4. The unintended family (goals are parents' individual needs),

5. The immature family group,

6. The (socially) deviant family group (includes internally integrated and unintegrated families),

7. The disinterested or regressed family.

These are types derived from the clinical experience of Ackerman and his associates. The approach is classified in Table 11−2.

Purpose. The diagnostic procedure was designed primarily for treatment (*control*). It has yielded a typology which the author seems to use as means for *communication* about the persons treated. Understanding is implied but was not explicitly a purpose.

Unit of Analysis. Both individuals and the entire family are regarded as units. The primary orientation was toward the family and the interrelationships between individual members.

Norms. Standards for behavior seem to be drawn from two frames of reference. When the family is viewed as the unit, then systems theory and social norms are applied. When the individual is the focus, then personality functioning and mental health norms seem to predominate.

Type. The approach is a descriptive one with a functional orientation. Individual functioning is viewed as importantly a part of the family social matrix.

Causality. Causal explanations of behavior are best described as interactional. An attribute approach is taken to the study of the unit, a unit which has assumptions both of an entity and a set of interrelations.

Behavior Data. The behavior which is judged is that obtained by the clinician in interviews (both individual and joint) and by observation of the family members. It is a collection which is not objectively systematic and relies on the clinician as the data processor leading to the diagnosis.

The consideration of Ackerman's approach shows it to be similar to the other clinically based system. It relies on the clinician for the organization and interpretation of the data in line with the general theoretical framework and the theme areas summarized above. The author regarded this as illustrative of the family therapy orientation, but the serious student of the family therapy area should consult the references cited by Harrigan (1964), The National Clearinghouse on Mental Health Information (1965), and Cardillo (1969). Handel's (1968) book is a very good review of the literature. Hill and Hansen (1960) have provided a descriptive analysis of the several approaches to family research which deserves careful consultation. The field is extraordinarily interesting to mental health workers and, as a result, a sizeable literature is being developed.

SUMMARY

The approaches to children's disorders as discussed above, require the judgments of others about the child's behavior; either the mother or the mental health professional. These judgments are often based on observations of the child in a setting (playroom, classroom, etc.). The systems discussed here seem all based in a psychometric tradition; the Ackerman family diagnosis is the most clinically oriented, producing the most global statements. Based firmly in a clinical tradition, The Committee on Child Psychiatry (Group for the Advancement of Psychiatry, 1966) developed a comprehensive inquiry into the problems of childhood disorders. It developed a statement asserting that a classification of childhood disorders should draw upon 20th century scientific thinking which strives to be multidimensional, relativistic, and dynamic in character—relying on probabilities rather than certainties. *Normal* and *abnormal* were regarded as theoretical or operational constructs in a particular sociocultural and historical context—rather than absolute and incontestable truths. The system would have to include descriptive-cultural, genetic, and dynamic dimensions.

From this beautifully stated preamble, the committee proposed a set of 12 categories based only on a descriptive-clinical set of ideas. The developmental and psychosocial categories were described as "insufficiently crystallized to permit systematic classification." This failure to deliver even a workable system seemed to the author to epitomize the contemporary problem. If a complex and multivariate approach is to be taken, it must use the methodology of multivariate statistics and, perhaps, patterns of scores—it cannot obtain a single diagnosis reflecting the "type" of problem.

One can conclude by observing that the disorders of childhood being clearly an individual-environment complex, empirical study will probably best proceed from a systematic theory and a systematic methodology.

ADOLESCENT BEHAVIOR

Classification of behavior of adolescents varies depending upon the type of behavior to be considered. As indicated by the previous discussion, disordered behavior for adults and for children often is construed in mental health terms—probably most often as emotional or thought disorders. For adolescents, however, one finds that disordered behavior is very often thought of as delinquency. Legal transgressions may be the most likely since this time of experimentation and rule breaking is spent, by and large, out of the home, and therefore the individual is more at risk of contact with formal social control agents.

Over the past 20 years, juvenile delinquency has become a focus of national interest and concern.[21] The years have shown an increasing number of minors associated with violent and serious crimes, and with deviant behavior forms which have caught widespread public attention (e.g., hippies, campus activists, drug users, and demonstrators). The federal government has, for many years, had specific legislation directed toward juvenile delinquency and has lodged the national research and program development responsibility with the National Institute of Mental Health (NIMH). In 1966, as a part of its general program, the NIMH convened a conference to consider the ways of classifying delinquent behavior. Rubenfeld (1967), in the proceedings, reviewed the status of typological approaches and delinquency control. He noted that all current typologies were based on the implicit assumption that the categories (of trait syndromes) are the result of environmental factors—rather than the "older, more widely known typologies presumed to have a hereditary biological basis, such as Sheldon's somatotypes and Jung's introversion-extraversion distinction."[22] Typologies, when they are based on diverse sources of information, are described by Rubenfeld as attempts to get away from situationally specific behavior descriptions. Useful typologies serve three important functions: (1) to discern personality configurations (sets of cognitive, affective, and motivational differences); (2) to indicate the treatment needs deriving from the configurations; and (3) to suggest treatment methods. One of the primary problems in the use of the typology is the *purpose* and *frame of reference* of the user. If one is a clinician and concerned with the change of individual behavior, then the prime focus is on the person. If the concern is with the social structure and its possible change, then the focus must be both on the person and his links with the larger social system.

Rubenfeld developed a cross-classification approach to describe the similarities of the systems under review. From the nine systems considered, five types of delinquents were identified:

1) mentally ill,
2) impulse oriented (aggressive/passive),
3) power oriented (conforming/controlling),
4) neurotic, and
5) normative outsider.

Each system was arranged in parallel fashion with the others. Also included as classification variables were the subject populations, the settings in which the systems have been applied, and the type of applications in the settings.

One of the nine approaches, that developed by Marguerite Warren (1966a, b), will be considered here to illustrate a major system.[23] The typology was an elaboration of that of Sullivan, Grant, and Grant (1957) called *Levels of Interpersonal Maturity.* It is an "ego psychology" formulation of a sequence of personality integrations in normal childhood development. The system describes the ways in which the delinquent is able to understand what is happening interpersonally between himself and others, for the primary purpose of aiding the administrator and practitioner in treatment programming and case management.

Seven stages were described as applicable to the adult population ranging from the least to the most mature, with each stage having a crucial interpersonal problem. Warren noted that the range is more restricted in the delinquent population with three levels being sufficient. Within the three levels, however, nine subtypes were identified. The classification approach was organized to yield treatment goals and prescribed a treatment plan in detail with application to community settings.

Warren's system, along with all of those reviewed by Rubenfeld, was entirely person oriented. The categories described the person as a type, in a reductionistic sense, which has specific characteristics at the several levels of conceptualization (thinking, feeling, overtly acting, and background characteristics of family and culture). The intervention description was to show that persons in one category require different treatment (handling) from those in others.

Classification of the approaches into the authors' classification system was attempted in Table 11–2 with one entry for the entire review. Although the subject populations and procedures varied, this approach suggested that they were all alike. The categorical descriptions and reasons for classification are as follows.

Purpose. All nine systems were described as developed for research purposes. Most were concerned primarily with the problem of control or treatment as well. *Comprehension* was entered first to denote the research purpose. *Control* was listed as second (although for the Warren typology it would be first). *Communication* was apparently the least important, but there was clearly the scientific desire to compare results.

Unit of Analysis. All the systems were person (offender) oriented. Rubenfeld believed, however, that approaches ought to take into account different family and community configurations creating law-violating behavior.

Type. With classification approaches such as these, one tries to achieve order within the area of delinquent behavior. Rubenfeld described some as being trait systems and some as developmental-dynamic systems. The approaches of Horwitz, Jesness, and Quay exemplify the trait systems which tend to be descriptive and data based. On the other hand, Hunt, McGregor, and Warren are based in the theory of ego psychology. They are best described as explanatory. So both types are to be found in this group.

Causality. In the case of the descriptive systems, causality would be implied, but with the explanatory approach causality is properly part of the system. In both cases causality seems to be serial and interactional in character with the interrelationships organized around the centralizing concept of person.

Behavioral Data. The data for use in classification is typically that obtained in interviews, by testing, from the case record and from the particular offense.

Delinquency systems as described by Rubenfeld and viewed in abstracted form within the classification of classifications were all quite similar. They were person-focused, interactional-oriented approaches attempting to describe the commission of delinquent acts as complex resultants of persons and circumstances. They were not oriented toward the behavior as an aspect of the social system, nor interested in transactional behavior events, but Rubenfeld described considerable interest in these orientations by at least some participants at the NIMH conference. One suspects that here, as in all the other fields, the classification systems will continue the search for a way of describing things, and that the various approaches will explain an interesting part of the variance. Whether they will be able to account for a sufficient amount of variance to move the field beyond where it is now is an interesting and open question.

DISCUSSION

The classification systems presented in this first section and summarized in Table 11−2 illustrate a variability of approach dependent largely upon the purpose behind its development and the use to which the classification was to be put. The variability, in an oversimplified way, can be arranged along a continuum with the poles labeled "simplicity" and "complexity." The simplicity approach is that of determining the category of best fit and attaching a label which most describes the condition. The American Psychiatric Association *DSM* and Uniform Crime Reports systems exemplify that. The complexity pole is one which measures the behavior (and the behaver) in question on a number of scales and finds a pattern that best describes the behavior. The multiple variable approach is a way of obtaining a more complete view of behavior and of measuring those variables which contribute most to the particular form of behavior in a particular setting. Should the situation change, or different behavior be selected for prediction, then a new set of variables would be selected. The simplicity view is a very general description, presumably useful for many purposes. The complexity orientation is quite specific and requires a new approach each time the purpose changes.

There is a very interesting parallel development to this in the area of systematics in biology. The "New Systematics" is an approach called Numerical Taxonomy which began in 1957−58 with four independent studies (Sokal, 1966). Since that time Sokal reports over 200 publications dealing with the method. Sokal distinguished between classical taxonomy and numerical taxonomy with the words *monothetic* and *polythetic*. *Monothetic* is the selection of one variable to classify similarity with all members of the class sharing the characteristic; *polythetic* is the use of many characteristics for description where not all measures have to be present.[24] Similarity has been represented as the distance between objects to be classified in multidimensional space as calculated by complex correlational procedures. The similarity is defined by determining the cluster in hyperspace. The approach has been used widely in biology and is reportedly finding application in other disciplines (Sokal, 1966). One is impressed

by the similarity to factor analysis and similar multivariate correlational procedures in behavioral science.

Within the "New Systematics" a struggle between the "old" and the "new" is being waged (Sokal & Camin, 1965; Mayr, 1965; Sokal, Camin, Rohlf, & Sneath, 1965). The basic disagreement can be described as which perspective is more important; longitudinal/historical or current/relational.[25] The development of numerical taxonomy, according to Sokal and Camin (1965) led to a reexamination of the assumptions behind phylogentic reasoning and of the approaches to constructing phylogentic sequences (evolutionary development charts). The computer, used in numerical taxonomy, has required that all procedures and differential weighting of variables be specified and made operational. Mayr (1965), a member of the "old school," emphasized the difficulty, if not impossibility, of programming the cognitive weight of variables assigned by the taxonomist when classifying.

Sokal, *et al.* (1965) countered with the notion that the programming for unequal weighting was trivial compared with the difficulties in finding a logically defensible, operational method of weighting variables *a priori* (as required by subjective classification). This argument has a ring reminiscent of the controversy in psychology over clinical intuition versus statistical prediction (Meehl, 1954). One wonders whether this was, in Psychology as in Systematics, a conflict engendered by the old and established resisting the encroachment of new modes of thought and procedure which are difficult to understand and which do not build directly on the old ways.

PART II: BEHAVIOR DISORDER AS DEVIANT BEHAVIOR

The second section is designed to bring the area of sociology of deviant behavior to the attention of the student of behavior disorders and at the same time introduce him to a mode of thought called Symbolic Interactionism which, like psychology, finds its roots in the Chicago School of Functionalism (and in the thought of John Dewey). This orientation was deemed of particular importance to those interested in community mental health since the disordered behavior needs to be understood in its social context, the community and the family.

Disordered behavior has been considered as "deviant behavior" by sociologists. Deviant behavior, since Durkheim's studies on suicide, has been regarded as an index of social disorganization resulting from the stress between two or more conflicting elements yielding impairment in ability to reach goals. The behavior typically considered has been socially undesirable, such as legal or moral transgressions. The theorizing about deviance has often been with an ultimate hope of eliminating it, and has apparently regarded such behavior as socially undesirable.[26] This derived from the Functionalist view in sociology which regarded the norm-violating (deviant) behavior as producing problems in the equilibrium of society and thus was a potential threat to stability and continuity (Spitzer & Denzin, 1968). From this it can be seen that the perspective of the sociologist is based on a different model of behavior from that of the psychologist or psychiatrist. Spitzer and Denzin (1968) described it as the *normative model* (disordered behavior is judged as not conforming to a modal pattern) in contrast with the *personal adustment model* (disordered behavior is where the person has difficulty in confronting everyday affairs).

Recently there has been the development of a more neutral orientation towards deviance (Becker, 1963, 1964; Dentler & Erikson, 1959; Lemert, 1951, 1967; Rubington & Weinberg, 1968; Spitzer & Denzin, 1968; Wilkins, 1964). Erikson (1962) turned the older Functionalist argument around and asked about the functional properties of deviant behavior, i.e., how it contributes to the stability of society. He described it as being necessary to mark the boundaries of the group and to portray the form and properties of what is undesirable. He suggested, as did Goffman (1957), that the institutions dedicated to changing behavior (prisons, mental hospitals) were more likely to be maintaining and fostering deviant behavior (Erikson, 1957). Perhaps this was a stabilizing process by society to ensure adequate numbers and types of persons to serve as negative referents.

Theoretical Background in Sociology

The view of deviant behavior as an aspect of social disorganization, derived from Durkheim's

(1951) work on suicide and anomie, was most clearly stated by Robert Merton in *Social Theory and Social Structure* (1957). Merton, one of the leading sociological theorists in America, developed a theory in which he treated deviant behavior as arising out of a societal state of anomie which is produced by the social structure. Anomic behavior was seen as a consequence of a strain between means and ends—where the ends are made very attractive but the means are difficult or impossible for a certain segment of society. The society thus produces both conformity and deviation by a disjointed opportunity structure.

Merton (1961) presented deviant behavior as part of the adaptation process of human behavior, and distinguished between social disorganization and social deviance (though they both make up the category of social problems). Social disorganization results from the disjunction between the opportunity structure and goal structure of the social system. Social deviance is the failure of people to live up to normative requirements. These are then at different levels of abstraction, and while deviance may, in some cases, reflect a state of social disorganization, it is not tantamount to it. Merton described deviance as being of two types: a) nonconforming behavior and b) aberrant behavior. *Nonconformity* is characterized by the behaver announcing his dissent publicly, by rejecting the cultural norm, and by using the behavior to try to change the norm. An example of this would be civil disobedience such as a "sit-in." *Aberrent behavior* is where the behaver does not challenge the social norm directly, but uses the the behavior in his own self-interest, tries to hide the fact of his deviation, and thus tries to escape the sanctioning force of the existing norm.[27] Merton presented a set of alternative adaptations based on different patterns of acceptance (by the individual) of institutionalized means and cultural goals (see Table 11−4). This provided a way, according to Merton (1961), to show how cultural/social pressures can cause deviation and that it can be as natural as conformity. Social control in this theory was postulated to be a response to the deviant behavior.

Lemert (1951, 1967) has taken the position that Merton's views need turning around. Deviance, for him, is behavior of individuals which expresses idiosyncratic tendencies overtly or which is a

TABLE 11–4

Merton's Typology of Individual Adaptations

Modes of Adaptation	Institutionalized Means	Cultural Goals
Conformity	Accept	Accept
Innovation	Reject	Accept
Ritualism	Accept	Reject
Retreatism	Reject	Reject
Rebellion	Rejection of old values and substitution of new values	

response to social control institutions, created to maintain deviance. One of the clearest elaborations of this line of thought was the argument by Dentler and Erikson (1959) that deviance was necessary to proper functioning of the group. Erikson (1962) went on to suggest that deviance was the placing of a label, the valuation of behavior, *after* it occurred. This orientation was also elaborated by Howard S. Becker (1963, 1964), Kitsuse (1962), and Scheff (1963). From this orientation, described as a combination of Functionalism and Symbolic Interactionism by Spitzer and Denzin (1968), came the notions of behavior as initially neutral, the importance of the observer in evaluating the behavior and labeling it, and the importance of the label as a way of affecting subsequent behavior towards the deviating person.

To illustrate this line of thought, the sequential model of becoming a deviant as developed by Howard S. Becker (1963) is presented below. It considers deviance as a career from within the interactionist framework.[28]

1. *Commission of a nonconforming act.* These may be either intended or unintended acts of deviance Psychologists would be concerned with finding the motivation; sociologists, in determining the social strain.

2. *Development of interests in the behavior and/or the self-commitment to it.* This can come from pleasure obtained from the deviant behavior; and from the social supports if one joins a group of deviants.

3. *The experience of being identified and publicly labeled as a deviant.* This may serve to hasten the psychological commitment and to structure the ways in which one is viewed socially.

4. *Appelation of a deviant label may carry with it a master status.* If serious, the deviant label is that one which the person is judged on first; all other considerations are secondary. Being psychotic overrides being rich, powerful, a father, etc.

5. *Treating a person as if he is generally deviant produces a self-fulfilling prophecy.* The treatment accorded to the deviant usually denies him the ordinary means for carrying on the routines of everyday life open to most people.

6. *There are means for "immunization."* These stem from a means of action which allows the person to be the victim of another and provides for the necessary changes in label and social supports befitting the status of victim.

7. *Final step is to move into an organized deviant group.* This solidifies the deviant identity and provides means for rationalizing and carrying out the behavior. This is accompanied by a general repudiation of the conventional.

Deviance then can be regarded as the product of a series of experiences which may lead to the status of "outsider" (Becker, 1963), from which, as Erikson (1962) noted, there may be no formalized way back.

Interactionism and Deviant Behavior

Within the contemporary interest in deviant behavior, the approach is often longitudinal with an emphasis on the process of becoming. The career development model has been used to illustrate the process (Lemert, 1951; Goffman, 1959; Becker, 1963). This has served as one of the ways to present the nature of the sequential and interactional development of events from the initial deviant act to the ascription of a status, the acceptance of it by the actor and the subsequent repetitive nature of the deviant behavior (Becker, 1963, 1964; Rubington & Weinberg 1968; Spitzer & Denzin, 1968).

Two books of readings have recently appeared on the sociology of deviance which provide the student of this orientation with both a framework and a variety of examples in which to consider the matter of disordered behavior—from a perspective of the social setting and individual behavior within it (Rubington & Weinberg, 1968; Spitzer & Denzin, 1968). Spitzer and Denzin (1968) have assembled a set of papers dealing specifically with the sociology of mental disorders; this perhaps makes it most relevant to the readers of this chapter.

The orientations of Functionalism and Symbolic Interactionism come together in this approach to understanding disordered behavior. Functionalism has long been an important part of psychology and has a strong base in the fabric of American society. Considered here, disordered behavior is some *function* of the situation and its particular developmental history. Further, the disordered behavior may serve some useful, even important, *function* for the groups contacting it. For the family, it may be a rallying point that brings everyone else together. For the mental health professional it provides work. For the society it may well personify the boundaries of the group and operationally define unacceptable behavior.

Symbolic Interactionism had its most comprehensive early statement by George Herbert Mead (1956, 1934). Symbolic refers to the use of words (and language) as the stimuli to which people typically react. Interactionism refers to the chaining of stimuli and responses between people so that behavior is a complex sequence of each person reacting to and stimulating responses in others.[29] Thus the orientation deals both in observable stimuli (and behavior) such as language and social situation variables, and in postulated psychological processes such as identification with the label and the incorporation of it into the self. As such then, the orientation may properly be termed a social psychological approach.

The Spitzer and Denzin book starts with the general knowledge that social factors (such as social class, residential mobility, family, hospital social structure, area of residence) are related to the nature and amount of mental disorder. They go on to bring attention to the contribution of environmental variables in the behavior sequences—particularly the behavior of others towards the deviant. Of primary interest is the process of *labeling*, i.e., the definition of certain behaviors by certain persons as violations of rules of conduct. The process considered then includes the audience reactions to the behavior, the labeling process itself (including the criteria for the label), the extent of consensus on criteria for the label, consequences for the individual so labeled, and possible career assumption of the deviant status.

This orientation toward behavioral disorder as deviance may be summarized by the following quotation from Erikson (1962): "Deviance is not a property inherent in certain forms of behavior; it is a property conferred upon these forms by the audience which directly or indirectly witness them. Sociologically, then, the critical variable in the study of deviance is the social audience rather than the individual person, since it is the audience which eventually decides whether or not any given action or actions will become a visible case of deviation." This definition may not sit well with the more individually oriented reader since it would seem to require an observer in order for disorder to "exist." Yet the appearance and the maintenance of stable forms of deviant behavior require environmental stimuli. Perhaps translations of the social orientation into stimulus determinants of behavior (as done by Berg & Bass, 1961) will make the matter more acceptable and understandable.

PART III: A RELATIVE PERSPECTIVE

The treatment of behavior disorders in this chapter was designed to provide a variety of perspectives to indicate that the "caseness" of a disorder depends upon how one looks at the behavior and for what purpose. Consideration of the classification problem illustrated, in Part I, some of the thinking in the mental health field, and the diversity of the approaches being taken there. The sociological orientation in Part II was introduced since it is often unknown to workers in the mental health field and since it provides for a way of thinking about behavioral disorders in a social/community context. These two discussions were intended to stimulate the reader to ask what his particular perspective leads him to assume and believe about disordered behavior.

The question "What is a case?" represents one of the critical problems in the field of behavior disorders, since one must begin with something to study, count, and measure. Classification approaches are designed to provide a solution to this question. The analytic model used in this paper suggested that the overwhelming orientation by scientists was an interactional one.[30] This is often based on trait theories of personality which are more descriptive than explanatory. While much of the scientific literature seems to be of this orientation, it does not accurately reflect the orientation of the practitioner nor of the general public. The paradigm used by practitioners is more often based on the notion of disease (APA or ICD systems)—which assumes an *existence* of an entity (or a process). While the disease process is regarded as an interaction, there is a strong underlying logic, which leads to attempts to *reduce* the disorder to what it *is* and what causes it.[31] These two orientations to existence and causality of a "case" of disorder indicate that there is conflict inherent between the paradigms.

Zubin (1968) observed that the pressure on the disease paradigm has occurred as a direct result of the variety of treatments which have been developed and the increasing specification of the outcome desired. When the treatment was to hospitalize or not, then the classification could be simple and gross. But when the decision began to involve consideration of the type of drug to prescribe, the type of psychotherapy, and the nature of the environmental manipulation, many specifics of the situation and the disorder were required. This would seem related to the observation by Katz, Cole, and Barton (1968) that there will be a number of typologies—perhaps as many as there are different purposes to be served by classification.

Is disordered behavior dysfunctional?[32] The answer at this level of generality is usually affirmative. In sociology, deviance has typically been part of courses on social problems and has been regarded as part of the process of social disorganization. In this context, disordered behav-ior has been dealt with at a relatively abstract level, often with emphasis on the institutional means by which the society mobilizes forces against it. Yet there is the paradox that the forces against deviance seem also to perpetuate the behavior by processing the deviant through institutions which lead him to associate with other deviants and to be more likely to repeat the behavior (Goffman, 1957, 1959, 1961). This seems to yield a subculture which maintains the deviant status as a normative one for its members.

It is this aspect of the process which theorists in Symbolic Interactionism have taken up in a framework which is closer to the level of individual behavior, and which is social-psychological in orientation. Symbolic refers to the language and its influence upon behavior—both as stimuli (often called labels) and as responses, most specifically in the form of perceptions influenced as much by the language and situational variables as by intraindividual processes. Interactionism denotes an orientation towards the stream of behavior as subdivided into exchanges of language (or communications). The answer to the dysfunctional question would seem to require a context in which to judge the behavior. It also would seem to require a study of the judgment process to understand what specific behaviors are classified, what standards are applied, and what descriptions of the disorder are formulated.

Lest the reader be tempted to withdraw from consideration of behavioral disorders due to the complexity and lack of consistency of results, it should be noted that a major problem would seem to be the need for a paradigm which can account for multiple perspectives with a standard frame of reference and provide a methodological approach. The paradigm offered by psychophysics will be considered to explore whether it can be helpful in fashioning an approach to the problem.

Behavior Disorder as a Psychophysical Problem

Psychophysics as an area of scientific inquiry was an attempt to specify the nature of the relationships between physical stimuli measured in standard increments and psychological judgments (responses) which did not seem to be based on the same increments. After careful study it was found that responses to physical stimuli were not random nor haphazard but were reliable, if considered through another frame of reference. For example the unit was determined not to be a fixed number of physical increments, but a proportion of the stimulus presented. Approached this way, a judgmental constant was found. The unit became known as a Just Noticeable Difference (JND) and was different in size (in physical units) for different persons or at different stimulus values. Nonetheless, it followed a stable pattern described by the Psychophysical Law.

This model provided for the study of psychological responses to observable physical stimuli and suggested that psychological processes followed unique functions. The model was elaborated into Adaptation Level Theory by Helson (1964) which has been a basis for consideration of the contribution of the stimulus to the study of behavior. Adaptation Level (AL) theory has produced a number of applications including a consideration of mental disorder. Goldstone and Goldfarb (1965) developed a perspective to psychopathology suggesting study both of the judgmental process of the disordered person, and of the judgments by others about the disordered person (where the person and/or his behavior is considered as the focal stimulus). AL approaches require delineation of 1) a focus for judgment, 2) the background or contextual framework, and 3) the standards to be used. While all these may be individual and unique, the means for comparing for similarity across persons or situations is with the *difference score* between any of the components. Applied at a molar level, French (1969) has called this an approach to specifying the characteristics of the *person-environment* fit. The author has been developing a conceptual approach to disordered behavior which incorporates aspects of symbolic interactionism, AL, and transactionalism. It will be presented here to illustrate how such an integration might help to consider behavior disorders from a relativistic perspective.

The Perception of Behavioral Discrepancy[33]

Development of the model began from the notion that "disordered" behavior suggests behavior different from that which is "ordered" (i.e. expected). Judgments of difference are made by some observer of the behavior on the basis of a set of standards which he applies. These standards may be those suggested by a codified system (like the diagnostic and statistical manual of the American Psychiatric Association) or by standards for proper conduct which are the observer's own. Whatever the case, when the threshold between similarity and difference is crossed, the observer judges the behavior and attaches some sort of label (designating the difference). What is subsequently done about the behavior is often influenced by the label attached by the observer and may also be evaluated in terms of who the observer was (e.g., parent, spouse, clergyman, psychiatrist). This process is regarded as generically descriptive of the classification process for behavioral disorders and is derived from the process of making judgments of comparison in a psychophysical experiment.

In specifying the model for Perceived Behavioral Discrepancy three central notions were chosen: labeling, distance, and tolerance.

Labeling. Labeling denotes the process of attaching verbal descriptions (labels) to acts of behavior or to individuals. This process has two stages: first, the psychological process of labeling (i.e., categorizing and naming) the behavior, and second, the use of the label, by the observer or others, as a way of attaching meaning to subsequent behavior of the actor. The label may also serve as a way of deciding whether behavior is tolerable. The chain of relationships encompassed by the approach are:

1) The perception of behavior and its classification by the observer,

2) The label selected by the observer as it relates both to his subjective standards and situational aspects of the behavior,

3) The relationship of the label to the intolerance of the behavior by the observer,

4) The relationship of the label to the intolerance of the behavior by the reference group.[34]

Psychologically, the prime interest for study of labeling is directed to the observers of the actor (and his behavior). Each observer is thought to initially attach a label for his own use. If there is a grouping of observers (either informally as with a family or formally as in a case conference) then a "group label" is likely to emerge from the social interaction and is hypothesized to be a function of the dominance (or power) of one or more observers.[35]

The label is considered to be related to the psychological relationship between the observer and the actor. The function of the label as part of the dynamic interaction would be to suggest the appropriate relationship of the person with the observer. The label would call forth a particular relationship which may be quite different from what had been previously established.

As a beginning to the study of labels as judgmental categories, one might try to obtain the following information for the observers:

1) Specification of the range of labels and the probabilities of their use,
2) relating the use of labels to particular situations,
3) relating the effects of particular labels (in both denotative and connotative aspects) upon subsequent perceptions of all observers.

In addition to these one would want to study the effect of labels upon the actor in communicating what behavior is now expected of him.

From a social function perspective, labeling can be described as stabilizing and controlling situations by telling everyone how to view, feel about, and respond to particular acts or actors. The acceptance of a label can then by hypothesized to reflect some consensus on the perception and definition offered by it.

Distance. Distance has typically served the function of describing (perhaps explaining) the quality of relationships between people. As an example, intimacy has typically been described as close. For our purposes, distance has been taken to denote the working relationships established between particular persons in any situation. A change in the relationships should also lead to change in distance. Change would then be effected by the particular situation and the particular sequence of interpersonal transactions and should be reflected in the label usage.

Research will need to be directed to the establishment of comfortable and uncomfortable distances and the labels used to describe the Perceived Behavioral Discrepancy, and the effect of situations upon the band of distance which is comfortable for the observer in his relationship with the actor.

Tolerance. Tolerance is the concept denoting the "acceptability" of a person and/or his behavior by the observer. It has been used by a number of writers to explain why some persons are kept in their family and others are institutionalized while exhibiting similar behaviors (e.g., Freeman & Simmons, 1958). In our thinking tolerance refers to the lack of overt behavior on the part of the observer to change the behavior of the actor. When the observer does move to action, we have chosen to regard this as the limit of tolerance (and the threshold of intolerance).

In order to approach the labeling problem from the psychophysical perspective, a dimension was postulated with tolerance at one end and intolerance at the other. The threshold of intolerance is defined as that point along a dimension where the observer describes the observed behavior as different from his own standards and, as noted above, where he takes action for the purpose of changing the situation. The label is hypothesized to designate the distance (the new distance) at which the actor or his behavior will be tolerated.[36]

The threshold of intolerance is regarded as relatively moveable and affected by situational factors. This should be particularly the case during the stages of imbalance and coping prior to a formal (or consensual) labeling of the disordered behavior. Tolerance may be achieved through Extenuation in the form of the presence of characteristics which *explain* the behavior (e.g., presence of illness or drugs), which *compensate* for the behavior (e.g., one is peculiar at home but holds down a high paying job), or which *promise* the possibility for *change* (e.g., going to the doctor). These are contextual aspects of the particular situation which are thought to affect the location of the intolerance threshold along the tolerance dimension, and which will, through the process of balance, stabilize relationships. Thus, in studying the threshold it will be necessary to explore the aspects of Extenuation.[37]

Functioning of the Model

Behaviors of actors are perceived, evaluated, and categorized by observers. Some behavior is judged as going beyond the threshold of intolerance. The verbal label assigned by the observer designates the particular status and accompanying role behavior expected of the actor, and reflects the distance relationship between the actor and observer.

TABLE 11-5

Hypothesized Relationships between Labels, Distance, and
Tolerance in the Perceived Behavioral Discrepancy Model

Variables	Categories			
Distance	Normal distance	Approaching limits for normal expectation	Too close or too far	Completely separate
Labels	Designative Mode	Appraisive Mode	Prescriptive Mode	Formal Mode
Tolerance	Tolerance or conformity with standards	At the Tolerance limits	Intolerance	Irrelevant

Note: The labels are considered in the modes of classification suggested by Morris (1946).

The approach taken to the labeling as verbal behavior is a semantic one as developed by Charles Morris (1946).[38] His four modes of discourse (Designative, Appraisive, Prescriptive, and Formal) were related to the other concepts in this model as portrayed in Table 11-5. The *Designative* mode is typically descriptive and should indicate that the observer is describing the normal working distance. The *Appraisive* mode is evaluative. When applied to behavior it serves to communicate how the observer feels about the behavior. The author suggests that it should indicate, when negatively used, that the observer is not comfortable with the behavior and is suggesting readjustment of it (perhaps along a distance dimension). *Prescriptive* mode usage designates command characteristics which, when applied to behavior, suggest that a change in the behavior has been perceived and a readjustment is being called for. The distance is beyond the threshold of intolerance; the label may or may not designate a new status and specifies what the observer regards as the appropriate distance. *Formal* mode is one which describes relationships which are logically related and are not necessarily empirically based. This mode was thought to denote detachment of the observer from the observed behavior and a complete separation, emotionally, so that tolerance/intolerance of the behavior is not relevant.

DISCUSSION

This is an approach which brings together thinking from the sociology of deviance, systems theory, and semantics with an attempt to fit the concepts together around the model presented by psychophysics. It is an approach which provides for the relativity of standards and processes of judgment encountered by most researchers of disordered behavior. Similarity across observers should indicate culturally and socially shared values, with the variability showing the effects of the individual observer's standards and unique contributions from the specific setting. This approach then suggests that discrepancies can be ordered along some dimension (perhaps distance) using a "just perceived difference" for the unit.[39] This removes the categorical yes/no characteristic from the concept of disorder and, as Lewin (1931) suggested, changes the perceived nature of disorder from an Aristotelian "thing" to an interactionist view of process via multiple descriptions of characteristics taken in the setting so as to specify functional relationships. It also provides a way of approaching the dynamic interaction within a situation (such as psychotherapy) which fits best into the transactional framework. Using the distance dimension as a way of ordering types of relationships, one can regard each type of relationship as having different components with different relationships. For example, the measurement of personal values is more likely to predict whether a person will seek psychotherapy, than what will transpire with the therapy process. Prediction to the process might be better from observations made of the person in similar settings under similar emotional stress. This approach then requires 1) identification of the behavior to be predicted or studied or controlled, 2) the specification of the interrelationships of variables which lead to or maintain or describe the process, and 3) the selection of the best related variables when approaching a phenomenon for the purposes of central communication or control.

One of the major aspects of the approach is to provide a way to study the observers' norms without relegating them to error (or individual differences). As noted earlier, lack of reliability in categorization with the standard nosological systems was described by Zubin (1966) as their major fault. If one regards the unreliability as due to the variable standards, then the consistency may best be found through accepting an arbitrary origin for each observer and comparing discrepancies as difference scores.[40] An approach to the study of counseling or psychotherapy would involve the calibration of the therapist and the client to the situation and the specification of desired behavioral outcomes. Then the control process of treatment would become a complex of the labeling, distance, and tolerance variables designed to yield the outcome. Comprehension of the process would take place by exploring the interrelationships of the variables to the behavioral transaction during the process and to the behavioral outcome.

While the model was developed within a community mental health context, one can, as with the Symbolic Interactionist approach, apply it to the study of all forms of discrepant behavior (mental disorder, delinquency, classroom management, senile behavior) with the assumption that the social process of labeling and tolerance of the behavior is mediated through observers who act variously as agents for the person, the family and the community. Perhaps, as Kai T. Erikson has speculated (personal communication, 1965), there is a total deviance rate (which is additive of rates for particular forms of deviance) reflecting the organization and function of the particular social system, and that so long as the system remains stable, so will the overall rate for disordered behavior. Viewed in this framework the work of social agents striving for conformity (e.g., mental health workers) may have the overall effect of changing the standards and the tolerance limits, and thus the particular forms, but never affecting the total prevalence of disorder.

Notes

The writer acknowledges the substantial contributions of John A. Baldwin who was to have been second author until illness intervened. The orientation of the chapter was a joint product; the approach to classification was Baldwin's. Others contributed to this product: Francis Burke, Rue Cromwell, William Dalton, Bruce Dohrenwend, R. L. Dreger, Walter Gove, Wilbert Lewis, Maurice Lorr, and R. J. McCorkel read drafts and offered helpful comments.

1. Related to this is the question of disorders as discrete processes which are confined to the person and operate like a disease which when begun, follow a relatively rigid sequence of processes, *or* whether the disorder is a matter of the person behaving improperly within a setting where the behavior is very strongly affected by the stimuli there and which can change with the shift of environmental circumstances. Miller (1968) noted that Adolph Meyer gave up the disease entity notion many years ago and accepted a set of facts he called *Ergasias* which were behavior patterns only. The work on operant conditioning by Krasner & Ullman (1965) gives considerable credence to this orientation so dramatically presented by Szasz (1961).

2. Miller (1968) suggests that classification involves an hypothesis as to the nature of things to be classified. It would seem that the assumption about generic classification systems is based on notions of stable entities or processes, while the utility view of classification is functionally oriented and assumes no qualitative difference between order and disorder. This illustrates the difference between the discontinuity and continuity hypotheses about disorder (Zubin & Fleiss, 1964; Zubin, 1967), where the discontinuity view is based on the assumption of qualitative difference between normal and abnormal.

3. It is useful to distinguish among classification, diagnosis, nomenclature, and nosology since all appear in discussions of classification. *Classification* in a strict sense means the building of a systematic organization for arranging things. *Diagnosis* is the identification of a person or event within the system and the assignment to one or more categories yielding a classificatory label. *Nomenclature* is a systematic set of names to refer to the categories within the system. *Nosology* is the classification of disease and has relevence where behavior disorder is approached from a disease perspective. Classification is often used to refer to all of these. See Baldwin (1969).

4. The matter of case definition is discussed in the volume by Sells (1969) which is a compendium of invited papers to the National Center for Health Statistics, 1966–67.

5. Similarities of entities or relationships represent quite different underlying philosophical orientations. The *entity approach* assumes that the important focus is the "thing" described in one or more ways. This has its basis in Aristotelian thought (Lewin, 1931) and may be what Katz and Cole called a Typological Model. The

relationships *approach* focuses the concern on the arrangements between entities, and is what Lewin (1931) describes as a Galilean mode of thought (Dewey & Bentley, 1949, call it Newtonian). This seems similar to what Katz and Cole (1968) call the Dimensional Model. Viewed through Dewey and Bentley's (1949) theories of causality, these are self-actional and interactional frames of reference, respectively. No wonder there is argument; the reality is construed differently.

6. This can describe phenomena considered within a field theory or General Systems Theory. It is a person-in-its-environment approach which regards the stability as a function of that particular organization and not necessarily like any other. Taken to its extreme, it is idiography in the purest sense. Prediction is then a matter of probability, as Brunswick argued, and not of certainty.

7. Zubin and Fleiss (1964) noted that one of the reasons for the current difficulties with psychiatric diagnosis is the increased range of treatments now available. In the past when only one treatment was available (sending to the asylum), the classification was relatively simple. But now with an emphasis on remaining in the community and treatments to yield specific results it is a much more complicated matter.

8. This is a debatable point. Kuhn (1962) suggests a course of history which reviews the change from one model (paradigm) to another as based on conflict. The new paradigm wins by capturing adherents, not by its sheer rational appeal. If this be so, then there ought to be conflict when classification paradigms collide. Katz and Cole (1968) described just such an occurrence at their conference.

9. Not included were chronic brain syndromes with neurotic or behavioral reactions, or without qualifying phrases, and transient situational personality disorders (American Psychiatric Association, 1968).

10. From Spitzer and Wilson, 1968, reprinted by permission of The American Psychiatric Association.

11. For a comparison of the *ICD–8* with *ICD–7*, see Baldwin, J. A., *Psychiatric Diagnosis: The Eighth Revision of the International Classification*, 1968. Department of Mental Health. The University of Aberdeen Medical School, Aberdeen, Scotland. Mimeo. Available from author, Oxford Record Linkage Study, Old Road, Headington, Oxford, England.

12. For a detailed study of the *ICD* system, the reader is referred to Stengel (1959), Spitzer and Wilson (1968), Baldwin (note 10), as well as the original publication (World Health Organization, 1968).

13. Lyerly and Abbott (1966) indicate that rating scales for psychiatric purposes were devised and used over 50 years ago. An early example was the Phipps Psychiatric Clinic Behavior Chart used at Johns Hopkins Hospital, Baltimore.

14. The other major work reviewed was that by Wittenborn (1955). It will not be discussed in detail although it has been the focus of substantial work and should not be overlooked by the student of behavior rating scales. Meehl (1962) has developed an extensive behavioral rating approach to the study of schizophrenia.

He seems to be searching for a neurological deficit which is genetically based. The items and procedures are unpublished and available from Meehl.

15. Lorr's work is directed towards finding types (groups) of persons. He is careful to assert that type means commonality only on the variable(s) selected—and does not mean a qualitative category (Lorr, 1966).

16. The prevalence of maladjustment was estimated to be 30 percent of all children showing mild, subclinical adjustment problems, and 10 percent who need professional attention. This could represent a substantial number of children even in a small community.

17. The reader is referred to Patterson's (1964) inquiry since it represented one very similar to these two. He made use of direct observation of children in the clinic setting and evaluated the behavior within the framework of social adjustment.

18. Dreger reported that replication of the factor analysis on new data has shown the factors to be fairly reliable (Personal communication, January, 1969).

19. This was discussed as a relativistic orientation by Mead (1932, 1934) when he considered the matter of various perspectives each occupied by a different person.

20. An alternate approach to the study of children's behavior in units larger than the individual is that of psychological ecology as developed by Barker (1968). It is in many ways similar to behavior modification with its emphasis on behavior in situations, but ecology differs in that the primary focus is on the environmental situation, called a setting, rather than the behavior of individuals. The orientation is one of identifying and describing settings so that behavior can be understood as a function of the situation. This has led to a search for *types* of settings with the notion that a range of behaviors characteristic of the setting type can then be described. Classification has proceeded with two different variables as the organizing ones: (1) authority systems and (2) attributes. This has been developed for use in a behavior setting survey of a town or an institution. Since this orientation is not directly on disordered behavior *per se*, the approach was not treated specifically here.

21. Adult crime, as a form of disordered behavior, was not considered in this paper. For the legally based approach to classification see United States Department of Justice (1965). Clinard and Quinney (1967) have a sociologically derived typology and analysis of the behavior. The former approach is self-actional; the latter is interactional in the analytic framework of this paper.

22. The discussion of typologies, their nature and function is particularly good. Rubenfeld noted that sociologically they may describe normative behavior for groups of people.

23. Rubenfeld described Warren's work as "the most systematic, large-scale application of a typology to effecting change in delinquents so far." See Warren (1966b) for a survey of the field and a cross-classification of offender typologies somewhat different from Rubenfeld's.

24. Sokal (1966) distinguished between classification and identification where the former is the ordering of an

unordered set of objects. Identification is the placement of a single object into the order after it had been established. Identification is what one typically does with disordered behavior although it has been discussed throughout the paper as classification.

25. This has a parallel in the approaches of psychoanalysis and operant conditioning to the changing of behavior. The former looks at historical experience to explain the present problem and to suggest avenues for proceeding. Operant conditioning, conversely, wants to know the behavior in a variety of settings to establish the stimulus contingencies. From a separate grounding each makes predictions into the future.

26. This was embodied in most Utopian societies which placed strong emphasis on conformity. Even in situations where there was considerable behavioral conformity, research (on the Hutterites, at least) suggests that the occurrence of mental disorder, as adjudged by expert outsiders, seems to be similar in frequency to the general society (Eaton & Weil, 1955). The form of the less severe disorders, however, would seem to be more affected by the culture, particularly since there is more variability in form and in label.

27. The mentally disordered might best fit into the aberrent category, yet one wonders about the motivation to hide their behavior. Perhaps this is at work except for the most psychotic. A major difficulty with Merton's system is that it mixes psychological concepts like motivation with social concepts like strain.

28. The seven points are paraphrased from Becker's account with comments added to amplify each one.

29. The closest to this in psychology would seem to be the Interbehavior Theory developed by J. R. Kantor (1958). While the theory never had a major impact, the general approach may be found in psycholinguistics and language development. Symbolic Interaction also includes nonverbal communication such as described by Hall (1964).

30. The approach in this paper was suggested to the author by Arthur F. Bentley's consideration of schools of psychology within an analytic framework derived from the philosophy of science and reported in *Behavior, Knowledge, Fact* (1936).

31. The action model is often a mixed one. Persons holding a disease model seem to see the *process* of the disease as interactional and influenceable at different stages in various ways. Drugs given at different times may have different outcomes (e.g., stopping the process entirely, alleviating symptoms, preventing side effects of the disease). When the disease is thought about as an *entity*, however, it takes on a thingness which assumes sameness across people or illness episodes, and sameness of process.

32. Stated this way, readers may find it difficult to answer beyond a value statement. The nonfunctionality in workable terms must be more specific and include the situation and the purpose for the behavior. This can then provide a set of referents against which to judge the functionality of the behavior, and perhaps as basic a question as whether the behavior is disordered.

33. The presentation is couched in declarative assertions. This is for simplicity in presentation and should be regarded as the description of a hypothetical model. This work has been developed by the author, and John A. Baldwin, Oxford Record Linkage Study, Oxford, England, in collaboration with Geoffrey A. Sharp, Department of Sociology, King's College, Aberdeen, Scotland. It has benefited from periodic conversations with Kai T. Erikson, John Hartley, Richard Royce, and James G. Kelly. A detailed statement of the approach has been prepared as a working paper entitled, *Labelling, distance and tolerance: towards a conceptual model of "perceived behavioral discrepancy" as applied to mental disorder.* This and supporting papers exploring aspects of labelling, distance, conformity, deviance and AL theory are available on loan from the author.

34. This process also can be seen to include two additional aspects: 5) the effect of the label upon the behavior of the actor: 6) the effect of the label upon the behavior of the actor's reference group. These two refer more to the label and to the entire process potentially leading towards career acceptance of a new status.

35. Power or dominance refers to the social process of accepting a group label, with that label then influencing subsequent behavior. The consensus of a group on a label, as noted above, may be a function of agreement with other observers, of explaining the behavior "better" than other labels or of the personal standing of the particular observer. The particularities of the influence remain to be specified by research inquiry.

36. Note two uses of distance in this discussion: 1) the closeness of psychological relationships between people, and 2) the distance along a continuum of tolerance. The latter is assumed to reflect the former.

37. Wilkins (1965) discusses this process in some detail and it was from his discussion that we took the concept.

38. This approach was suggested by Richard Royce and was used in a preliminary form by Geoffrey Sharp in a report entitled *The Language of the House; a study of a halfway house for mental patients* (1964).

39. We have adopted, for working purposes, The Title Perceived Behavior Discrepancy (PBD).

40. The Self-Anchoring Scale is one measurement of personal frames of reference using the difference score approach (Kilpatrick & Cantril, 1960). The cumulative recording approach to the use of the individual as his own control is another approach to the matter of comparing data obtained from persons with different origin points and psychological anchors.

References

Ackerman, N. *The psychodynamics of family life: Diagnosis and treatment of family relationships.* New York: Basic Books, 1958.

American Psychiatric Association, Committee on Nomenclature and Statistics. *Diagnostic and statistical manual: Mental disorders.* Washington, D. C.: American Psychiatric Association, 1952.

American Psychiatric Association, Committee on Nomenclature and Statistics. *Diagnostic and statistical manual of the mental disorders. DSM-II.* (2nd ed.) Washington, D. C.: American Psychiatric Association, 1968.

Baldwin, J. A. Statistical classification in psychiatry: The new international diagnostic code. *International Journal of Social Psychiatry*, in press.

Barker, R. *Ecological psychology.* Palo Alto, Calif.: Stanford University Press, 1968.

Barabee, P., Barabee, E. L., & Finesinger, J. A normative social adjustment scale. *American Journal of Psychiatry*, 1955, 112, 252–259.

Becker, H. S. *Outsiders: Studies in the sociology of deviance.* New York: Free Press, 1963.

Becker, H. S. (ed.) *The other side: Perspectives on deviance.* New York: Free Press, 1964.

Bentley, A. F. *Behavior, knowledge, fact.* Bloomington, Ind.: Principia Press, 1935.

Berg, I. A., & Bass, B. M. (eds.) *Conformity and deviation.* New York: Harper, 1961.

Cahoon, D. D. Symptom substitution and the behavior therapies: A reappraisal. *Psychological Bulletin*, 1968, 69, 149–156.

Cardillo, J. P. Patterns of interaction in dysfunctional families. Nashville, Tenn.: Department of Psychology, George Peabody College for Teachers, 1969. (Mimeo)

Cattell, R. B. (ed.) *Handbook of multivariate experimental psychology.* Chicago, Ill.: Rand McNally, 1966.

Cattell, R. B., Coulter, M. A., & Tsujioka, B. The taxonometric recognition of types and functional emergents. In R. B. Cattell (ed.), *Handbook of multivariate experimental psychology.* Chicago, Ill.: Rand McNally, 1966.

Cavan, R. S., Burgess, E. W., Havighurst, R. J., & Goldhamer, H. *Personal adjustment in old age.* Chicago, Ill.: Science Research Associates, 1949.

Clinard, M. B., & Quinney, R. *Criminal behavior systems: A typology.* New York: Holt, Rinehart & Winston, 1967.

Cromwell, R. L. *The development of behavior dimensions for emotionally disturbed children: A study of relevant indicators for classroom techniques, therapeutic methods and prognosis.* (Interim project report under Grant No. 32–52–0450–5001) Washington, D. C.: Office of Education, United States Department of Health, Education, and Welfare, 1967.

Cromwell, R. L., & Davis, D. Behavior classification of emotionally disturbed children. Paper presented at the meeting of the Council for Exceptional Children, Portland, Oregon, April 1965.

Dentler, R. A., & Erickson, K. T. The Functions of deviance in groups. *Social Problems*, 1959, 7, 98–107.

Dewey, J., & Bentley, A. F. *Knowing and the known.* Boston: Beacon Press, 1949.

Dreger, R. M., & Dreger, G. E. (eds.) *Behavioral classification project.* (Report No. 1) Jacksonville, Florida, 1962.

Dreger, R. M., Lewis, R. M., Rich, T. A., Miller, K. S., Reid, M. P., Overlade, D. C., Taffel, C., & Fleming, E. L. Behavioral classification project. *Journal of Consulting Psychology*, 1964, 28, 1–13.

Durkheim, E. *Suicide: A study in sociology.* New York: Free Press, 1951.

Eaton, J. W., & Weil, R. J. *Culture and mental disorders: A comparative sutdy of the Hutterites and other populations.* Glencoe, Ill.: Free Press, 1955.

Erickson, K. T. Patient role and social uncertainty. *Psychiatry*, 1957, 20, 263–268.

Erickson, K. T. Notes on the sociology of deviance. *Social Problems*, 1962, 9, 307–314.

Eron, L. D. (ed.) *The classification of behavior disorders.* Chicago: Aldine, 1966.

Ferster, C. B. Classification of behavioral pathology. In L. Krasner & L. P. Ullman (eds.), *Research in behavior modification.* New York: Holt, Rinehart & Winston, 1965.

Freeman, H. E., & Simmons. O. G. Mental patients in the community: Family settings and performance levels. *American Sociological Review*, 1958, 23, 147–154.

French, J. R. P., Jr. The conceptualization and measurement of mental health in terms of self-identity theory. In S. B. Sells (ed.), *The definition and measurement of mental health.* Washington, D. C.: United States Government Printing Office, 1969.

Goffman, E. Characteristics of total institutions. In Walter Reed Army Institute of Research, *Proceedings of the symposium of preventive and social psychiatry.* Washington, D. C.: United States Government Printing Office, 1957.

Gelfand, D. M., & Hartmann, D. P. Behavior therapy with children: A review and evaluation of research methodology. *Psychological Bulletin*, 1968, 69, 204–215.

Glidewell, J. C., & Swallow, C. S. *The prevalence of maladjustment in elementary schools.* (A report prepared for the Joint Commission on Mental Health of Children) Washington, D. C.: Joint Commission on Mental Health of Children, 1968.

Goffman, E. The moral career of the mental patient. *Psychiatry*, 1959, 22, 125–131.

Goffman, E. *Asylums: Essays on the social situation of mental patients and other inmates.* New York: Doubleday, 1961.

Gross, M., Hitchman, I. L., Reenes, W. P., Lawrence, J., Newell, P. C., & Clyde, D. J. Objective evaluation of psychotic patients under drug therapy: A symptom and adjustment index. *Journal of Nervous and Mental Disease*, 1961, 133, 399–409.

Group for the Advancement of Psychiatry, Committee on Child Psychiatry. Psychopathological disorders in childhood: Theoretical considerations and a proposed classification. *Group for the Advancement of Psychiatry*, 1966, 6, 173–343.

Hall, E. T. *The hidden dimension.* Garden City, N. Y.: Doubleday, 1966.

Handel, G. *The psycho-social interior of the family: A source book for the study of whole families.* Chicago, Ill.: Aldine, 1967.

Hill, R., & Hansen, D. A. The identification of conceptual frameworks utilized in family study. *Marriage and Family Living*, 1960, 22, 299–311.

Jackson, D. D., & Satir, V. Family diagnosis and family therapy. In N. Ackerman, F. Beatman, & S. Sherman (eds.), *Exploring the base for family therapy.* New York: Family Service Association, 1961.

Katz, M. M., Lowery, H. A., & Cole, J. O. Behavior patterns of schizophrenics in the community. In M. Lorr (ed.), *Explorations in typing psychotics.* New York: Pergamon 1966.

Katz, M. M., & Cole, J. O. Reflections on the major conference issues. In M. M. Katz, J. O. Cole, & W. E. Barton (eds.), *The role and methodology of classification in psychiatry and psychopathology.* Washington, D. C.: United States Government Printing Office, 1968.

Katz, M. M., Cole, J. O., & Barton, W. E. (eds.) *The role and methodology of classification in psychiatry and psychopathology.* Washington, D. C.: United States Government Printing Office, 1968.

Katz, M. M., & Lyerly, S. B. Methods for measuring adjustment and social behavior in the community: I. Rationale, description, discriminative validity, and scale development. *Psychological Reports Monograph*, 1963, 13, 503–535.

Kantor, J. R. *Interbehavioral psychology: A sample of scientific system construction.* Bloomington, Ind.: Principia Press, 1958.

Kilpatrick, F. P., & Cantril, H. P. *Self-anchoring scaling: A measure of individuals unique reality worlds.* Washington, D. C.: Brookings Institute, 1960.

Kitsuse, J. I. Societal reaction to deviant behavior: Problems of theory and method. *Social Problems*, 1962, 9, 247–256.

Krasner, L., & Ullman, L. P. (eds.) *Research in behavior modification.* New York: Holt, Rinehart & Winston, 1965.

Kuhn, T. S. *The structure of scientific revolutions.* Chicago, Ill.: University of Chicago Press, 1962.

Lemert, E. M. *Social pathology.* New York: McGraw-Hill, 1951.

Lemert, E. M. *Human deviance, social problems and social control.* Englewood Cliffs, N. J.: Prentice-Hall, 1967.

Lorr, M. Multidimensional scale for rating psychiatric patients. Hospital form. *Veterans Administration Technical Bulletin*, 1953, 43, 10–507.

Lorr, M. Classification of the behavior disorders. *Annual Review of Psychology*, 1961, 12, 195–216.

Lorr, M. (ed.) *Explorations in typing psychotics.* New York: Pergamon, 1966.

Lorr, M., Klett, C. J., McNair, D. M., & Lusky, J. J. *Inpatient Multidimensional Psychiatric Scale.* Palo Alto, Calif.: Consulting Psychologists Press, 1963.

Lorr, M., & O'Connor, J. P. Psychotic symptom patterns in a behavior inventory. *Educational and Psychological Measurement*, 1962, 22, 139–146.

Lorr, J., & Vestre, N. D. *The Psychotic Inpatient Profile: An inventory of patient behavior for use by hospital personnel.* Washington, D. C.: Department of Psychology, Catholic University of America, 1968.

Lyerly, S. B., & Abbott, P. S. *Handbook of psychiatric rating scales (1950–1964).* (Public Health Service Publication No. 1495) Washington, D. C.: United States Government Printing Office, 1966.

Mayr, E. Numerical phenetics and taxonomic theory. *Systematic Zoology*, 1965, 14, 73–97.

Mead, G. H. *The philosophy of the present.* Chicago, Ill.: Open Court, 1932.

Mead, G. H. *Mind, self & society.* Chicago, Ill.: University of Chicago Press, 1934.

Meehl, P. E. *Clinical versus statistical prediction: A theoretical analysis and a review of the evidence.* Minneapolis, Minn.: University of Minnesota Press, 1954.

Meehl, P. E. Shizotaxia, schizotypy, schizophrenia. *American Psychologist*, 1962, 17, 827–838.

Merton, R. K. *Social theory and social structure.* Glencoe, Ill.: Free Press, 1957.

Merton, R. K., & Nisbet, R. A. (eds.) *Contemporary social problems.* New York: Harcourt, Brace & World, 1961.

Miller, E. The problem of classification in child psychiatry: Some epidemiological considerations. In E. Miller (ed.), *Foundations of child psychiatry.* New York: Pergamon, 1968.

Morris, C. *Signs, language and behavior.* New York: Prentice-Hall, 1946.

National Clearinghouse for Mental Health Information. *Family therapy: A selected annotated bibliography.* Chevy Chase, Md.: National Institute of Mental Health 1965.

Opler, M. K. The need for new diagnostic categories in psychiatry. In *The new physician*, 1963.

Parloff, M. B., Kelman, H. C., & Frank, J. D. Comfort, effectiveness, and self-awareness as criteria of improvement in psychotherapy. *American Journal of Psychiatry*, 1954, 111, 343–351.

Patterson, G. R. an empirical approach to the classification of disturbed children. *Journal of Clinical Psychology*, 1964, 20, 326–337.

Robbins, L. L. A historical review of classification of behavior disorders and one current perspective. In L. D. Eron (ed.), *The classification of behavior disorders.* Chicago: Aldine, 1966.

Rubenfeld, S. *Typological approaches and delinquency control: A status report.* (Public Health Service Publication No. 1627) Washington, D. C.: United States Government Printing Office, 1967.

Rubington, E., & Weinberg, M. S. (eds.) *Deviance: The interactionist perspective.* New York: Macmillan, 1968.

Scheff, T. J. The role of the mentally ill and the dynamics of mental disorder: A research framework. *Sociometry*, 1963, 26, 436–453.

Siegler, M., & Osmond, H. Models of madness. *British Journal of Psychiatry*, 1966, 112, 1203.

Sokal, R. R. Numerical taxonomy. *Scientific American*, 1966, 214(6), 106–116.

Sokal, R. R., & Camin, J. R. The two taxonomies: Areas of agreement and conflict. *Systematic Zoology*, 1965, 14, 176–195.

Sokal, R. R., Camin, J. H., Rohlf, F. J., & Sneath, P. H. A. Numerical taxonomy: Some points of view. *Systematic Zoology*, 1965, 14, 237–243.

Spitzer, S. P., & Denzin, N. K. (eds.) *The mental patient: Studies in the sociology of deviance.* New York: McGraw-Hill, 1968.

Spitzer, R. L., & Wilson, P. T. A guide to the American Psychiatric Association's new diagnostic nomenclature. *American Journal of Psychiatry*, 1968, 124, 1619–1629.

Stengel, E. Classification of mental disorders. *Bulletin of the World Health Organization*, 1959, 21, 601–663.

Sullivan, C. E., Grant, M. Q., & Grant, J. D. The development of interpersonal maturity: Applications to delinquency. *Psychiatry*, 1957, 20, 373–385.

Szasz, T. S. *The myth of mental illness: Foundations of a theory of personal conduct.* New York: Hoeber-Harper, 1961.

United States Department of Justice, Federal Bureau of Investigation. *Uniform crime reporting handbook.* Washington, D. C.: United States Government Printing Office, 1965.

Warren, M. Q. Classification of offenders as an aid to efficient management and effective treatment. Sacramento: Community Treatment Project, California Youth Authority, 1966. (Mimeo) (a)

Warren, M. Q. Interpersonal maturity classification: Juvenile diagnosis and treatment of low, middle and high maturity delinquents. (1966 ed.) Sacramento: Community Treatment Project, California Youth Authority, 1966. (Mimeo) (b)

Wilkins, L. T. *Social deviance: Social policy, action and research.* Englewood Cliffs, N. J.: Prentice-Hall, 1965.

Wittenborn, J. R. *Wittenborn Psychiatric Rating Scales (manual).* New York: Psychological Corporation, 1955.

World Health Organization. *International classification of disease.* (8th rev.) Geneva: Author, 1968.

Zubin, J. Classification of the behavior disorders. *Annual Review of Psychology*, 1967, 18, 110–406.

Zubin, J. Biometric assessment of mental patients. In M. M. Katz, J. O. Cole, & W. E. Barton (eds.), *The role and methodology of classification in psychiatry and psychopathology.* Washington, D. C.: United States Government Printing Office, 1968.

Zubin, J. Clinical, phenomenological and biometric assessment of psychopathology with special reference to diagnosis. In S. B. Sells (ed.), *The definition and measurement of mental health.* Washington, D. C.: United States Government Printing Office, 1969.

Zubin, J., & Fleiss, J. L. Taxonomy in the mental disorders—A historical perspective. Paper presented at the annual meeting of the American Psychological Association, Los Angeles, September 1964. (Published by Human Ecology Fund, New York, 1964)

12

Psychiatric Epidemiology:
An Analysis of "True Prevalence" Studies

Bruce P. Dohrenwend and Barbara Snell Dohrenwend

Investigators of the prevalence and distribution of psychiatric disorder have long been aware that admission to treatment, operationally the clearest definition of a "case," is also one of the most limited (e.g., Dunham, 1961; Felix & Bowers, 1958; Gruenberg, 1955; Mishler & Waxler, 1963). Its limitations are especially evident when research focuses on the possible significance of social factors in etiology. Treatment rates vary, for example, with the availability of facilities and with public attitudes toward their use. Either could be responsible for spurious relations between social factors and rates of disorder measured by number of cases in treatment.

Recognition of such problems has stimulated at least 35 different investigators or teams of investigators to attempt to count untreated as well as treated cases of psychiatric disorder in about 44 different community studies. In this figure, we are counting Strömgren's (1950) summary of 18 small community studies in the same general area as only one study. Excluded from this tally are studies that have reported scores measuring symptomatology but that have not indicated what is to be considered a case (e.g., Gurin, Veroff, & Feld, 1960; Langner, 1965).

Typically, the whole population in a specified geographical area has been included. In the few investigations that have relied on sample estimates, the n's have usually been large; for example, probability samples of 1,660 in the Midtown Study conducted in New York City (Srole, Langner, Michael, Opler, & Rennie, 1962), and 1,010 in a study of a rural county in Canada that

was called "Stirling" (D. C. Leighton, Harding, Macklin, Macmillan, & Leighton, 1963).

VARIABILITY IN RATES OF PSYCHIATRIC DISORDER

The overall rates found in the 44 community studies ranged from less than one percent to more than 60 percent (Dohrenwend & Dohrenwend, 1969). What factors could conceivably account for variation of such magnitude?

For most of the communities studied, the rates we have extracted represent prevalence during a period of a few months to a few years. Of the six exceptions, five present lifetime prevalence rates. In addition, one study (Hagnell, 1966) gives ten year incidence rates—the only published investigation of incidence we could find. By and large, however, these different types of prevalence and incidence made less difference in the rates of disorder reported than a number of other factors. Thus, we are not keeping these studies separate in the analyses that follow. For the reader who would like to investigate these matters further, full references and rates for the summary tables presented below are contained in our recent book (Dohrenwend & Dohrenwend, 1969, chapters 2 & 7) which updates the material in our articles on the epidemiological studies (Dohrenwend & Dohrenwend, 1965 & 1967).

Table 12–1 shows the rates or, where more than two studies were done in a given category, the median and range of rates for communities

TABLE 12–1

Medians and Ranges of Percentages of Psychiatric Disorder According to
Geopolitical Area and Rural versus Urban Study Site

Site		North America	Northern Europe	Asia	Africa
Rural	Median	18.0	10.4	1.1	—
	Range	1.7–64.0	1.1–28.6	0.8–54.0	40.0
	Number of studies	(7)	(14)	(9)	(1)
Urban	Median	7.2	15.6	2.4	—
	Range	1.8–32.0	1.0–33.0	1.1–3.0	11.8–45.0
	Number of studies	(6)	(5)	(3)	(2)

Note: These medians and ranges are based on data presented in Dohrenwend and Dohrenwend (1969). The number of rates on which these figures are based is 47, three more than the actual number of studies because separate rates for rural and urban sites were extracted from the African study by Leighton and his colleagues, and from the study of three sites on Taiwan by Lin.

studied, grouped according to geopolitical area and according to whether the study site was rural or urban. The rates appear to be relatively low in Asia and higher for the rural studies in three of the four geopolitical areas. However, the range in rates within areas is in most cases so much greater than the ranges in medians between areas that these contrasts in setting cannot be said to account for the large variability in rates.

Another possible explanation for the variation in rates is the difference in age ranges, since 14 of the studies excluded certain age groups. In all of these age restricted studies, the youngest ages, usually children under ten, were excluded. Since analysis of the studies that included all ages showed that the minimum rate of disorder is usually found in the youngest age group studied (Dohrenwend & Dohrenwend, 1969, pp. 13–14) the age differences could be expected to have influenced the findings.

Table 12–2 shows that the range of ages included in a study is clearly associated with the rates of psychiatric disorder found. The median rate in age restricted studies is strikingly higher than the median in studies including all ages. However, it is also clear that this is not a sufficient explanation of the variation in rates since the upper end of the range for the all inclusive studies is close to the upper end of the range of rates obtained in age restricted studies.

A number of critics have argued that the factors primarily responsible for variation in rates are methodological (e.g., Blum, 1962; Pasamanick, 1962; Plunkett & Gordon, 1960). One such factor that might affect rates is the conception of what constitutes a case. This conception may, as Szasz (1961) implied, have changed with time, expanding and becoming more inclusive over the years.

As can be seen in Table 12–3, it is clear that more recent investigators have reported higher

TABLE 12–2

Medians and Ranges of Percentages of Psychiatric Disorder for Studies
Including All Ages as against Studies Excluding Certain Age Groups

	All inclusive studies	Age restricted Studies
Median	2.5	21.9
Range	0.8–54.0	2.4–64.0
Number of studies	(30)	(14)

Note: These medians and ranges are based on data presented in Dohrenwend and Dohrenwend (1969).

TABLE 12–3

Medians and Ranges of Percentages of Psychiatric Disorder for Studies
Published Before 1950 and for Studies Published in 1950 or After

| | Date of Publication | |
	Before 1950	1950 or After
Median	2.1	15.6
Range	0.8–9.0	08.–64.0
Number of Studies	(16)	(28)

Note: These medians and ranges are based on data presented in Dohrenwend and Dohrenwend (1969).

rates of psychiatric disorder, since the median rate of studies published in 1950 or later is higher than the highest rate reported earlier.

Another factor which might affect the rates is the thoroughness of the data collection procedures. Investigators who collected data directly from the subjects rather than relying entirely or partially on indirect sources of information might be expected to detect more cases, as has happened with physical illness (e.g., Cartwright, 1957). On the other hand, still more thorough investigation through physical examinations might reveal organic bases of symptoms, thereby reducing rates below those reported when subjects' self-descrip-

tions are the investigator's only source of information.

Four instances in which comparisons were made within studies of the effects of directness of contact are shown in Table 12–4. The results of these studies indicate that rates do tend to be higher when more direct contact is made with subjects. It is important to note, therefore, that the distribution of studies in Table 12–5 shows that investigators who have published their work in 1950 or later are far more likely to have used more thorough data collection procedures than investigators who published earlier. The striking finding in Table 12–5, however, is that directness

TABLE 12–4

Percentages of Psychiatric Disorder for Studies Reporting
Results of Varation in Directness of Contact with Subjects

Author(s)	Indirect contact: records and/or informants	Partial direct contact: records and/or informants, and interviews with same subjects	Direct contact: interviews with all subjects
Rosanoff, 1917		1.3	3.6
Roth & Luton, 1943		6.4	12.4
Eaton & Weil, 1955	1.2	2.3	2.9
Cole et al., 1957		28.0[a]	35.4[a]

[a]Calculated by B. S. Dohrenwend; rates for wives were calculated for direct contact and other family members for partial contact on the basis of the statement that wives were usually interviewed; the base for each rate is the number of families interviewed.

TABLE 12-5

Medians and Ranges of Percentages of Psychiatric Disorder Reported
According to Thoroughness of Data Collection
Procedures and Date of Publication

Directness of contact with subjects		Date of Publication	
		Before 1950	1950 or After
Indirect contact: records and/or informants	Median	2.3	
	Range	1.1–9.0	1.2–14.8
	Number of rates	(5)	(2)
Partial direct contact: records and/or informants, and interviews with same subjects	Median	1.3	19.9
	Range	0.8–6.4	2.3–28.6
	Number of rates	(5)	(4)
Direct contact: Interviews with all subjects	Median	3.6	13.6
	Range	2.7–12.4	0.8–50.0
	Number of rates	(6)	(19)
Interviews and physical examination of all or most subjects	Median	–	18.0
	Range	–	10.9–64.0
	Number of rates	(0)	(7)

Note: These medians and ranges are based on data presented in Dohrenwend and Dohrenwend (1969). The number of rates on which this study is based is 48 due to inclusion of separate rates for studies using varied methods as shown in Table 12-4.

of data collection does not account for the tendency for rates of disorder to be higher in the more recent studies. This table also provides no evidence that physical examination lowered the reported rates of disorder.

It could be argued, of course, that rather than reflecting changes in the researchers' concepts, the results shown in Table 12–5 are a consequence of the times we live in. However, in view of statements suggesting a shift from exclusive concern with avoiding overestimation (e.g., Cohen, Fairbank, & Greene 1939, p. 113; Lemkau, Tietze, & Cooper, 1941, p. 635; Rosanoff, 1917, p. 137) to concern with complete enumeration (e.g., Bremer, 1951, p. 12; D. C. Leighton, et al.,

1963, p. 195), it seems premature to infer a true change in prevalence between the 1940s and 1950s. Moreover, there is ample evidence from studies in which both inclusive and relatively exclusive standards were applied to the same populations that rates can be markedly affected by these standards. Essen-Möller (1956, p. 95), for example, reported a rate of 13.6 percent for "diagnoses constituting the main subject of most psychiatric population studies," but an average of 54.7 percent (calculation by B. S. Dohrenwend) for whom pathology was not definitely absent. A similar contrast is offered by the figures 23.4 percent in the impaired group, and 81.5 percent judged less than "well" in the Midtown Study

(Srole et al., 1962, p. 138). Another comparison with the Midtown Study is provided by an investigation (Manis et al., 1964) which used the 22 Midtown items. While obtaining a distribution of repsonses similar to that reported by the Midtown researchers, Manis and his colleagues found that their decision to include only severe psychological disorder resulted in a rate of 3.4 percent.

The continuing importance of methodological problems is emphasized by the difficulty of comparing results even from studies carried out by the same investigators. For example, the Leightons and their colleagues (A. H. Leighton, Lambo, Hughes, Leighton, Murphy, & Macklin, 1963) concluded, concerning their own studies: "the differences and similarities between the Yoruba and Stirling figures are to an unknown degree under the influence of differences in the procedures employed in the two studies (p. 124)." To complicate the problem of comparison further, various procedures used within one of these, the Stirling County study, yielded different rates of psychopathology (D. C. Leighton et al., 1963, pp. 123, 127).

PROBLEM OF VALIDITY

Given the variability of both procedures and results in attempts to assess "true" prevalence, the salient question is which, if any, among these field studies has produced valid measures of psychological disorder. Despite their deficiencies, studies restricted to treated disorder had a clear advantage. The fact that a person is in treatment usually indicates that he cannot function unaided in his customary social environments. The clinician diagnosing a patient has a "presenting problem" with which to start, so that the question he must answer is not *whether* something is wrong, but rather *what* is wrong. The diagnostic result of this analysis, moreover, can be changed on the basis of repeated observations and interviews over a course of treatment.

The investigator of untreated disorder must work without the aids to diagnosis inherent in the clinical setting. Evidence of the difficulties he faces are found in the results of the psychiatric screening attempts associated with Selective Service in the United States during World War II.

The psychiatric judgments were extremely unreliable, rejection rates within the same region varying in a number of areas by a factor of three to one (Star, 1950b, pp. 552, 554). Moreover, there is no evidence that among the unreliable judgments one or another was more effective, since strictness of screening procedures bore little relation to subsequent rates of separation on psychiatric grounds (Ginzberg, Anderson, Ginsburg, & Herma, 1959b, Chapter 11).

Nevertheless, clinical judgment was the tool relied upon for case identification in almost all studies that included untreated as well as treated psychological disorder. In most, psychiatric diagnoses were made, and findings were presented in terms of categories such as those described in the *Diagnostic and Statistical Manual* of the American Psychiatric Association (1952). Neither the information available to the judge, nor the criteria on which the diagnoses were based were usually reported in detail in these investigations. The validity of the results was assumed to be implicit in the diagnostic process, a shaky assumption in light of the World War II experience with psychiatric screening.

A few investigators, recognizing the difficulty of placing untreated cases in diagnostic categories, also made judgments in more general terms, such as probability of pathology (Essen-Möller, 1956; Rosanoff, 1917), likelihood of being psychiatric cases (A. H. Leighton et al., 1963; D. C. Leighton et al., 1963), or degree of severity ranging from "well" to "incapacitated" (Langner & Michael, 1963; Srole et al., 1962). Among these relatively sophisticated investigations, the Leightons' Stirling County and Nigeria studies, and the Midtown Study by Srole and his colleagues stand out. Although they differ in several aspects of their assessment procedures, they share an important innovation. Both used structured questionnaires, thereby providing a standard, explicit set of data for psychiatric assessment. In this respect, these studies represent the methodologically most advanced epidemiological investigations of untreated and treated psychological disorder, possibly excepting a Polish study which has not yet been completely reported (Piotrowski, Henisz, Gnat, 1966). The question is whether procedures of the Midtown, Stirling County, and Nigeria studies have dealt adequately with the central methodological problem of validity.

Content Validity

Content validity involves a demonstration that the items used are a representative sample from a universe generally accepted as defining the variable to be measured (Cronbach & Meehl, 1955). In the Midtown Study, the universe from which items were drawn was defined by Srole et al. (1962) as "the most salient and generalized indicators of mental pathology (p. 41)." Behavioral scientists selected a group of items from the Army Neuropsychiatric Screening Adjunct (Star, 1950a) and the MMPI (Dahlstrom & Welsh, 1960) "consisting principally of the psychophysiologic manifestations and those tapping the anxiety, depression, and inadequacy dimensions (Srole et al., 1962, p. 42)." In addition, the psychiatrists independently contributed 40 items "bearing particularly on psychosomatic symptoms, phobic reactions, and mood (p. 60)." The final decision determining the 120 items actually included was made by the senior psychiatrist on the basis of "clinical experience (p. 60)." Thus, in the absence of systematic sampling of items, no argument can be made for the content validity of the Midtown measure of psychological disorder. The same is true of the Stirling and Yoruba studies, where items were taken from the NSA and other test sources without explicit specification of the selection procedures (e.g., A. H. Leighton et al., 1963, p. 85; D. C. Leighton et al., 1963, pp. 202, 205).

It is doubtful whether content validity, in the strictest sense, can be achieved in the measurement of untreated psychological disorder, since there appears to be no universe of items which experts agree on as defining the variable. Four different sources have been cited by the relatively few researchers who related their procedures to an established diagnostic system: the Sjöbring system used at Lund University, Sweden (Essen-Möller, 1956); the system used in the Department of Psychiatry of the National Taiwan University Hospital, Taipeh, based on Henderson and Gillespie's *Textbook of Psychiatry* and on Bleuler's *Lehrbuch der Psychiatrie* (Lin, 1953; Rin & Lin, 1962); the World Health Organization *International Classification of Diseases* (Primrose, 1962); and the American Psychiatric Association *Diagnostic and Statistical Manual* (D. C. Leighton et al., 1963; Rin, Chu & Lin, in press). As Clausen

pointed out (1961, pp. 131–132), the last two differ markedly as a function of the greater emphasis placed by European psychiatrists on hypothetical constitutional determinants.

Criterion-Oriented Validity: Concurrent and Predictive

Of the two types of criterion-oriented validity, concurrent and predictive (Cronbach & Meehl, 1955), there is no evidence in the field studies for the latter. Typically conducted at one point in time, these studies have thus far not tested their assessments of disorder against criteria of future psychiatric condition, admission to treatment, or social functioning. What evidence, then, is provided for concurrent validity?

In Midtown (Srole et al., 1962), the NSA and MMPI items proposed by the behavioral scientists were tested in a study involving 139 diagnosed neurotic and remitted psychotic patients, and 72 persons judged well by a psychiatrist on the basis of a half-hour interview. The result was that "almost all the NSA and MMPI symptom questions emerged with validity confirmed (p. 42)." Twenty-two of the items included in the final questionnaire discriminated between the patient and well groups at the .01 level of significance (Langner, 1962). The remainder of the items contributed by the behavioral scientists discriminated at the .05 level (Thomas S. Langner. Personal communication. February 1964). While the Midtown psychiatrists reported that, in rating cases well or not well, they gave special weight to eight of the 22 items which discriminated at the .01 level, they also paid special attention to six items which failed to discriminate at this level (Srole et al., 1962 p. 396). Thus, in the Midtown Study, while the data from which the psychiatrists worked had been tested for concurrent validity in the manner described above, this test did not guide the use of these data by the psychiatrists.

In the Stirling County study, an attempt to identify valid items was made by administering NSA questions and items from other tests to untreated community samples and to patients diagnosed as neurotic. The selection of items included in the survey interviews, however, was not wholly determined by the results of this study (D. C. Leighton et al., 1963, p. 205). As in the Midtown Study, the Stirling County psychiatrists did not make use of objective scores based on these items in the judgmental assessment of psychiatric disorder.

Before considering how the psychiatrists actually used the symptom items in the Midtown and Stirling County studies, questions must be raised about concurrent validity of the items themselves. In attempts to validate these items, the patient criterion groups were homogeneous with regard to type of disorder (e.g., all neurotics in a study by Macmillan in D. C. Leighton et al., 1963, chapter 7). or unspecified as to diagnostic composition (e.g., Manis, Brawer, Hunt, & Kercher, 1963). Moreover, the stubborn problem of well controls has not been met head-on, much less solved. For example, in Langner's (1962) study identifying 22 items which discriminated at the .01 level between patient and well groups, the fact that the well group was identified by means of clinical judgment brings the problem back to its origin, since the items can be no more valid than the psychiatrist's judgments against which they were tested.

Nor does the solution appear to lie in avoiding clinical judgments by using an unselected sample of the nonpatient population as the healthy criterion group. Reports of community rates up to 64 percent from the field studies themselves argue against such a procedure. An attempt by Manis et al. (1963) to cross-validate the 22 Midtown study items, using samples from patient and nonpatient populations as criterion groups, both illustrates the problem and raises another. They found that a group of predischarge ward patients had an average symptom score lower than those of a community cross section, and a group of college students, and argued that the result indicated a failure of the test since "there is little reason to believe that the mental health of these pre-discharge patients is equal to or better than the non-hospitalized populations (p. 111)." In the absence of independent evidence concerning the mental health of their nonpatient populations, however, it seems difficult to interpret this result. It is conceivable, though unlikely, that the predischarge ward patients are cured, while the nonpatients need treatment.

It is also possible, and perhaps more plausible, that the predischarge ward patients, in the interest of "getting out," are simply less willing than nonpatients to admit socially undesirable behavior. That is, it appears that there is evidence of the impact of response style on these items. What are the implications of such influence for the psychiatric evaluations which have relied heavily on the "face validity" of the items?

The measure of disorder in the Midtown Study consisted of psychiatrists' ratings of the symptom data which ranged respondents on a scale from well through five degrees of severity of symptomatology: "mild," "moderate," "marked," "severe," and "incapacitated." Almost a quarter, 23.4 percent, of the respondents were classified in the last three categories: marked, severe, and incapacitated. These are referred to collectively as "impaired," and are the "cases" in the Midtown Study. Michael, one of the evaluating psychiatrists on the Midtown Study, put it this way:

The individuals in the Impaired category of mental health . . . are represented as being analogous to patients in psychiatric therapy. . . . When it is urged that the mental ratings "Marked" and "Severe" are comparable to the clinical conditions of patients in ambulatory treatment, and the rating "Incapacitated" to the clinically hospitalized, the distinction is presented . . . as an attempt to anchor our conceptualizations in relation to known degrees of psychopathology (Srole et al., 1962, p. 333).

There is evidence that this claim requires scrutiny. In the Midtown sample, 40 respondents reported being current outpatients in psychotherapy at the time of the interview; 182 reported that they were expatients. The evaluating psychiatrists had full knowledge of these facts when they made their judgments. Since expatients might be expected to have benefited from treatment, it is not remarkable to find that 54 percent of the 182 expatients in the Midtown sample were judged unimpaired. However, if respondents placed in the impaired categories indeed resemble psychiatric patients, as the Midtown researchers claim, it is hard to understand why the study psychiatrists placed 48 percent of the 40 *current* patients in the unimpaired categories (Srole et al., 1962, p. 147).

In the Stirling County study, disorder was defined in terms of judged similarity to descriptions in the 1952 *Diagnostic and Statistical Manual* of the American Psychiatric Association, rather than judged similarity to actual patients with whom the psychiatrists had had experience. The main rating was a psychiatric evaluation of "caseness" based on written summaries of symptom data collected for the most part by lay interviewers. It is described by D. C. Leighton et al. (1963) as "a rating of the probability that at some time in his adult life, up to the time of the interview, the individual would qualify as a psychiatric case (p. 53)." The evidence for the validity of their conclusion "that at least half of the adults in Stirling County are *currently* suffering from some psychiatric disorder defined in the APA *Diagnostic and Statistical Manual* (p. 356)" rests largely on the study psychiatrists' blind evaluation of the likelihood that 47 former clinic patients, mostly neurotic, were cases. Of these 47, 81 percent were rated "almost certainly psychiatric," and 11 percent more were rated "probably psychiatric (p. 175)." Their problems, moreover, were viewed mainly as present rather than past (pp. 178–179). Thus the Stirling evaluators saw more disorder in their expatients than the Midtown evaluators saw in their current patients.

These results of the application of Midtown and Stirling County study evaluation procedures to patients and expatients suggest a number of possible interpretations: that patients get and remain sicker in Stirling County than in Midtown Manhattan; or that treatment in Stirling is less effective than in Midtown; or that Stirling methods are less able to distinguish between past and current problems; or that the definitions of cases are vastly different in the two studies; or that some combination of these circumstances has operated simultaneously. In brief, there is considerable ambiguity about the relations between the Midtown and Stirling judgmental ratings of untreated disorder.

In a subsequent study, the Leightons had several psychiatrists conduct clinical interviews and made "caseness" ratings based on these interviews for respondents, the great majority of whom had previously been evaluated as either most or least likely to be psychiatric cases. These ratings showed a high level of agreement with the psychiatric ratings previously made from the survey data collected by lay interviewers (Leighton, Leighton, & Danley, 1966). However, the decision to use predominantly respondents who were originally evaluated either most likely to be ill or most likely to be well, grossly underrepresenting the majority who had been given intermediate ratings, seriously limited the test. Moreover, the procedure whereby each psychiatrist reconciled his rating with the

original rating before proceding to his next case reduced the independence of the second set of ratings, and may have artificially increased the agreement between the two sets of ratings.

There is, then, much to criticize and improve upon in these past attempts to investigate the criterion-oriented validity of both objective and judgmental measures of untreated disorder. There is, first of all, the absence of evidence of predictive validity, evidence that can only be supplied by prospective studies. Criterion-oriented attempts to establish both concurrent and predictive validity, however, face a common problem. Even with more attention, for example, to larger and diagnostically more heterogeneous patient criterion groups, independent criteria of "wellness," and problems of response style, there are strong reasons not to rely primarily on attempts to establish criterion-oriented validity. Foremost is the present fact that there are no generally agreed upon criteria of psychological health or disorder (cf. A. H. Leighton et al., 1963, p. 264).

Construct Validity

Cronbach and Meehl (1955) have argued that when no generally accepted criteria for the variable of interest are available and when no universe of content is fully agreed upon as defining the variable, we must become interested in construct validity. These are the circumstances of untreated psychological disorder. In Cronbach and Meehl's formulation, "A necessary condition for a construct to be scientifically admissible is that it occur in a nomological net, at least *some* of whose laws involve observables (p. 290)." Furthermore: "*unless the network makes contact with observations and exhibits explicit, public steps of inference, construct validation cannot be claimed* (p. 291)."

As noted above, the Midtown Study measure of mental health consisted of psychiatrists' ratings which ranged subjects on a scale from "well" through five degrees of severity of symptomatology: "mild," "moderate," "marked," "severe," and "incapacitated." The two rating psychiatrists (Srole et al., 1962) explained: "Throughout the volumes of this Study, the data must be evaluated *as a rating of mental health based on the rating psychiatrists' perceptions operating through a questionnaire instrument* (p. 66)." Although they reported that positive responses to any of 14 specific items ordinarily precluded the classification of a subject as well, and positive responses to other items suggested various degrees of severity of symptomatology (pp. 396–397), the psychiatrists summarized their impression of the rating process: "We used our clinical judgment to the best of our ability. It would be a mistake, however, to overlook the fact that there remain some aspects of the process which are not altogether in our awareness (pp. 62–63)." To the extent that this measurement of psychological disorder is private and hence not replicable, a claim for construct validity is precluded.

The same problem exists in the Leightons' Stirling County and Yoruba studies (1963). Although the problem of achieving public steps of inference in psychiatric evaluation concerned them, they did not attain this goal in either of these studies. Optimistically, they suggested that the development of the procedures to date: "brings within sight the possibility that the evaluations could be done by a computer. To achieve this the steps would have to be broken down into even more specific items, and the intuitive leaps that are still allowed would have to be dissected so that their components could be identified (p. 267)."

A computer program would certainly be a step toward construct validation of measures of psychological disorder. However, the construct validity of such a program could be evaluated only in relation to a nomological net. It is not clear in the work of the Leightons how such a net would be formulated. Although the Stirling County study was introduced with a theoretical volume (A. H. Leighton, 1959), the propositions in this theory are developed at a level of abstraction such that it does not make direct contact with observations. Instead, the guide for psychiatric evaluation was the American Psychiatric Association *Diagnostic and Statistical Manual* (1952). While this Manual often includes etiological propositions in its descriptions of nosological types, etiological inferences were avoided in the Stirling and Yoruba studies in the interest of interrater reliability. Thus, the psychiatric evaluations were removed entirely from a nomological framework within which construct validity could be evaluated.

Where, then, can we look for propositions placing psychological disorder in a nomological net? Not, it appears, to clinical experience. Unlike tuberculosis and pellagra, which are commonly cited as subjects of successful epidemiological research, psychological disorder does not constitute an etiologically defined disease entity (Clausen, 1961; Gruenberg, 1955). Instead: "With symptoms still our primary basis for classification, we are at the same stage of knowledge about mental disease that medicine occupied a century ago with reference to the 'fevers.' Typhoid, malaria, and a number of other diseases, all readily distinguishable now, were lumped together (Clausen, 1961, pp. 131–132)." Recognition of this situation has led a number of investigators to avoid psychodynamic inferences and assumptions in attempting to identify untreated disorder (e.g., A. H. Leighton et al., 1963, p. 89; D. C. Leighton et al., 1963, p. 48; New York State Department of Mental Hygiene, 1959, p. 83; Srole et al., 1962, pp. 63, 134). This avoidance of assumptions about connections between symptoms and individual psychodynamics, however, removes the symptoms from the theoretical frameworks of nomenclatures that rest on such assumptions, without providing a substitute nomological network for validating them as measures of psychological disorder.

Thus we are faced not only with the fact that the researchers who have done these field studies do not agree on how to conceptualize and measure psychiatric disorder, but we are confronted also by the problem that there is no basis in evidence for choosing the more valid among them. Are there, nevertheless, general trends that can be discerned in the relationships these studies report between social factors and symptomatology? If so, do such trends contain clues to etiology?

RELATIONS BETWEEN SOCIAL FACTORS AND SYMPTOMATOLOGY

Four social factors have been studied sufficiently frequently to show a pattern of relationship to rates of judged psychopathology. These are age, sex, race, and socioeconomic status. Of the four, however, we found that only the last yielded a consistent relationship with total prevalence rates. As Table 12–6 shows, 20 of the 25 studies that provided data on social class reported the highest rate of disorder in the lowest stratum. Moreover,

TABLE 12–6

Number of Community Studies Reporting Minimum and Maximum
Rates in Different Socioeconomic Strata

| | Minimum in: | | | |
Maximum in:	Lowest stratum	Middle stratum	Highest stratum	Total
Lowest stratum	0 ·	5	15	20
Middle stratum	4	0	0	4
Highest stratum	0	1	0	1

Note: This tabulation is based on data presented in Dohrenwend and Dohrenwend (1969, p. 17).

15 of these showed an inverse relationship, having also found the lowest rate in the highest stratum.

Further analyses of relations reported between social class and major subtypes of disorder (Dohrenwend & Dohrenwend, 1969) showed no consistent relationship between class and neurosis. The relationships were quite consistent for schizophrenia and the personality disorders, however. Of the seven studies that reported rates of schizophrenia by class, five yielded the highest rate in the lowest stratum. And of the 13 studies that provided rates of personality disorder by class, ten showed the highest rate in the lowest class.

It seems, therefore, in the face of other inconsistencies in the studies here reviewed, that a relationship of such apparent strength must command attention. The cumulative evidence that it represents appears to establish the association of low socioeconomic status with a high rate of judged psychopathology as an important source of working hypotheses.

AN ISSUE OF SUBSTANCE

Taken at face value, the central issue raised by this finding is the one so vividly underlined by the work of Faris and Dunham over 30 years ago (1960). For these results can be explained with equal plausibility on the one hand as evidence of social causation with the pressures of low status producing psychopathology; and on the other hand

as evidence of social selection, with the disability of preexisting disorder leading to low social status (e.g., Dunham, 1961). The latter interpretation is compatible with the position that genetic factors are important in the etiology of disorders widely held to be of psychogenic origin.

Consider as an illustration of the dilemma some recent results from the Midtown Study of untreated and treated disorder in a section of New York City (Srole et al., 1962). In an advance over previous work on this problem, the Midtown researchers attempted to choose between social causation and social selection interpretations by investigating the impact of parental class position, a factor clearly antecedent to the current psychiatric condition of their adult respondents. Finding a significant inverse relation between their respondents' symptomatology and the socioeconomic status of their respondents' parents, the investigators suggested that environmental deprivation in childhood is a causal factor in psychiatric disorder. However, they also found that the relation between parental socioeconomic status and impairing symptoms was weaker than the relation of respondents' own socioeconomic status to impairing symptoms. Moreover, respondents rated impaired were most likely to be found among those who were downwardly mobile relative to their parents, and least likely to be found among those who were upwardly mobile. Accordingly, the Midtown researchers concluded that perhaps both social causation, in the form of childhood deprivation, and social selection, in the form of intergeneration mobility, contribute to the strong inverse relation between rates of impairing symptoms and the respondent's own socioeconomic status (Srole et al., 1962, pp. 212–213, 228–229). However, as Michael, one of the Midtown researchers, implies, genetic predisposition could with equal plausibility be substituted for childhood deprivation in this interpretation (pp. 329–330).

The problem of finding a basis for assessing the relative importance of social causation versus social selection factors in class differences in rates of disorder, then, has proved persistent. Obstacles reside in the nature of the epidemiological surveys, each conducted at one point in time and necessarily without experimental controls. Causality is inherently difficult to demonstrate in such studies. Short of experiments involving the manipulation of social class, and, possibly, prospective surveys over long periods of time, is there any key to a solution? We will argue that potentially at least one such key does exist.

Theoretical Formulation of the Problem

In formulating our argument, let us start with some social history. The growth of New York City has been marked by great successive waves of new immigrant groups: the Irish and Germans in the 1840s; the Jews and Italians starting in the 1880s; the blacks after World War I; and the Puerto Ricans after World War II. Possibly excepting Germans, the initial conditions of these new groups in the city have been those of poverty, slums, and working-class jobs. The Jews, Irish, and to a lesser extent the Italians, have moved up over succeeding generations into relatively affluent and largely middle class circumstances. In this process of assimilation, these three ethnic groups have achieved a substantial share in the wealth and power of the city.

In sharp contrast to these now relatively advantaged ethnic groups are the blacks and Puerto Ricans—concentrated geographically in the city's slums, and occupationally in its low-paying unskilled and semiskilled jobs.

Glazer and Moynihan (1963) see the situation faced today by black and Puerto Rican New Yorkers as different from Jews, Irish, and Italians at the start of their climb. At the same time that the supply of black and Puerto Rican labor has increased, relative industrial wages have been decreasing. Of the consequences of these trends, coupled with ethnic and racial prejudice for black and Puerto Rican New Yorkers, Glazer and Moynihan write: "To a degree that cannot fail to startle anyone who encounters the reality for the first time, the overwhelming portion of both groups constitutes a submerged, exploited, and very possibly permanent proletariat (1963, p. 299)."

It would be consistent with the reports of an inverse relationship between social class and psychological disorder to expect relatively high rates of such disorder among New York's blacks and Puerto Ricans. Indeed, Srole makes just this prediction on the basis of the Midtown Study results with white, non-Puerto Rican groups (1962, p. 365). If such an expectation were confirmed by the facts, what would it suggest? In social selection terms, it would indicate that high rates of prior psychological disorder, probably genetically produced, are causing the low status of blacks and Puerto Ricans in New York City. Against the background of the history and contemporary circumstances of ethnic groups in the city, however, such an explanation would strain credulity. It makes sense only as an explanation of high rates of disorder among the low status members of ethnic groups which, as wholes, are relatively advantaged.

Let us, then, make the more plausible assumption that the pressure maintaining the low group status of black and Puerto Rican New Yorkers stems more from such social factors as society's reactions to difference in skin color and to difference in the culture of new immigrant groups than from hereditary defects of personality. Let us also assume that such social pressure on white Anglo-Saxon Protestant, Jewish, Irish, and Italian New Yorkers is much less strong, since many of the social obstacles to achievement now facing blacks and Puerto Ricans have either been removed or never were encountered by these more advantaged ethnic groups. If, therefore, we hold such indicators of class as income and education constant and find that blacks and Puerto Ricans show higher rates of psychological disorder than their class counterparts in the more advantaged ethnic groups, this would be strong support for the social causation interpretation of class differences in rates of disorder. The reason is that increased social pressure would clearly be shown to produce an increment in psychopathology over and above that produced by the lesser pressure on members of more advantaged ethnic groups.

If, on the other hand, we were to find that rates of psychological disorder among blacks and Puerto Ricans are lower than rates among their class counterparts in more advantaged ethnic groups, the implication would be that class differences in rates of disorder are due less to social causation than to social selection. The reason is that less psychological disorder among blacks and Puerto Ricans would demonstrate that increased social pressure does not lead to increased psychopathology. Rather, these pressures would be seen to block upward mobility to a greater extent for psychologically healthy blacks and Puerto Ricans than for psychologically healthy members of more advantaged ethnic groups. As a result of these social selection processes, there would be what Gruenberg has termed a "residue" (1961, p. 269) of ill among the low status members of the more advantaged ethnic groups.

On the basis of this argument, we can set forth two diametrically opposing hypotheses, each plausible depending upon the point of view:

1. The social causation hypothesis predicts that blacks and Puerto Ricans will have higher rates of psychiatric disorder than their class counterparts in more advantaged ethnic groups.

2. The social selection hypothesis predicts that blacks and Puerto Ricans will have lower rates of psychiatric disorder than their class counterparts in more advantaged ethnic groups.

State of the Facts

We appear, then, to have something quite rare: a major substantive issue that could turn on a simple question of fact. This question is: what are the rates of psychiatric disorder among blacks and Puerto Ricans relative to the rates for their class counterparts in more advantaged ethnic groups? Consider first what can be learned from existing research about the state of the facts bearing on this question.

Of the field studies of "true" prevalence reviewed earlier, eight provide data from which

rates comparing blacks and whites can be obtained. As it turns out, the eight divided evenly, with four showing higher rates for blacks and four showing higher rates for whites—an altogether inconclusive state of affairs (Dohrenwend & Dohrenwend, 1969, p. 16).

Only one previous investigation of untreated disorder provides data on Puerto Ricans, and this is the Midtown Manhattan study. Although there were very few Puerto Ricans in the area of New York City studied by the Midtown researchers, a small group of 27 were included in the sample of about 1,600 respondents. These Puerto Ricans were evaluated as having the largest proportion with impairing symptoms of all the subgroups in the study (Srole, 1962, pp. 290–292). But the finding, based on so few Puerto Rican respondents, would be weak on grounds of sample size alone even if we were willing to accept the measure of psychiatric disorder used.

In our preliminary studies in the Washington Heights area of New York City (upper Manhattan), we used interview procedures similar to those of the Midtown Study and the Stirling County study. As in Midtown and Stirling, our interviewers were neither psychiatrists nor clinical psychologists. Our subjects consisted of probability samples of adults, aged 21 to 59 from Washington Heights—about 1,000 for a first interview and about 150 for a follow-up—and also a group of about 100 psychiatric outpatients attending various clinics in the area. Further description of procedures, including ethnic matching of interviewers and respondents in the smaller sample, is given elsewhere (Dohrenwend, 1966).

Unlike the section of the city studied by the Midtown researchers, Washington Heights has sizable numbers of blacks and Puerto Ricans, along with members of other major ethnic groups in New York City, such as Jews and Irish. Of these four main ethnic groups in Washington Heights, blacks and Puerto Ricans are far more disadvantaged social and economically than the Jews or the Irish. The proportion of blacks and Puerto Ricans in the Washington Heights sample with family incomes below $5,000 (roughly one-half) was double that among the Irish and Jewish families. The clearest evidence of downward pressure by the larger society on blacks and Puerto Ricans is in the relation of education to income. Table 12–7 shows that, at any given educational level other

TABLE 12–7

Percents with Family Incomes Under $5,000 Per Year According to
Advantaged (Jewish and Irish) Versus Disadvantaged (Black and Puerto
Rican) Ethnic Status, Controlling on Educational Level

| | Ethnic Status | | | |
| | Advantaged (Jewish and Irish) | | Disadvantaged (Black and Puerto Rican) | |
Years of Formal Education	%	(N = 100%)	%	(N = 100%)
7 or less	47.6	(21)	57.6	(85)
8–11	31.3	(131)	59.3*	(189)
12–15	22.4	(264)	47.4*	(175)
16 and over	22.4**	(49)	12.5	(24)
Total Respondents	26.0	(465)	52.2	(473)

Note: Figures in parentheses indicate base for percent and exclude "no answers" on Family Income or Educational Level

*Differs significantly at 0.05 level or better from advantaged (Jewish and Irish) counterparts according to one-tailed t-test of difference between proportions.

**Includes a number of graduate students with temporarily low incomes.

than college graduate, income in the black and Puerto Rican groups is well below that of their counterparts among the Jews and Irish. Thus, although a person's education determines to a large degree what income he can hope to earn, a black or Puerto Rican high school graduate is likely at present to have to settle for less than a Jewish or Irish high school graduate.

Potentially, then, this research setting is almost ideal for the investigation of our problem. Results from our preliminary studies, however, have proved tantalizingly inconclusive as they have run into two important and complex problems in the conceptualization and measurement of untreated psychiatric disorder. The first involves cultural contrasts in symptomatic modes of expressing psychological distress. The second centers on the question of persistence of symptomatology over time. Consider the following illustrations.

As mentioned earlier, the Midtown researchers found that 22 symptom-items, many of them psychophysiological in nature, from their questionnaire showed strong ability to discriminate between patients and nonpatients. Moreover, they also found that these 22 items could be scored to provide a close approximation of the Midtown

psychiatric ratings (Langner, 1962). Langner described a score of four or more on these 22 items (i.e., indicating the presence of at least four symptoms according to respondent's own report) as useful "since it identifies only one percent of the psychiatrically evaluated Wells, but ... almost three-quarters of the entire Impaired group (Langner, 1962, p. 275)." On this evidence, it seemed useful to include these 22 items from the Midtown Study in the Washington Heights interviews. If this 22 item index of psychiatric disorder showed the same relationship with class in the Washington Heights sample populations as was found in the Midtown Study with the full psychiatric evaluation, we reasoned, this would give us increased confidence that it provides a close approximation to Midtown ratings.

As Table 12–8 shows, there is an inverse relationship between impairing symptoms and family income in the Washington Heights sample. Table 12–9 shows that the relationship is even stronger between high symptom scores and level of education. Thus, in general, the inverse relationship between social class and psychiatric disorder reported in the Midtown Study holds for Washington Heights. What, then, of the crucial

TABLE 12–8
Symptom Score According to Family Income (Percent)
(Excluding "No Answers" on Income)

Symptom Score	Income Group			
	< $3,000	$3,000-$4,999	$5,000-$7,499	$7,500 and over
4 or more	24.3	27.0	18.1	17.4
Base for %	(140)	(226)	(337)	(236)

Note: –Chi-square=9.39; p < 0.05.

question about rates of psychopathology among blacks and Puerto Ricans in comparison with rates in other ethnic groups?

Table 12–10 shows that at every level of family income the Puerto Ricans have larger proportions with four or more symptoms than their counterparts in the other ethnic groups. The results are much the same if educational level is used as the index of class. If our comparisons involved only Puerto Ricans and members of more advantaged white groups, the results would support a social causation explanation of class differences in rates of disorder. But, as Table 12–10 indicates, blacks do *not* show higher rates of symptoms than Jews or Irish, thus contradicting expectations from the social causation hypothesis. If accepted at face value, these results would leave us in an extremely unparsimonious state of theoretical affairs.

Further investigation, however, provided considerable evidence that there are strong ethnic and class differences in modes of expressing distress that are affecting these results (Dohrenwend,

1966). We found that the responses of our group of psychiatric outpatients to the 22 symptom-items from the Midtown Study directly parelleled our finding in the nonpatient sample. As Table 12–11 shows, the Puerto Ricans had higher scores than the patients in the other three ethnic groups. The fact that the patients were matched across ethnic group on type of disorder strongly suggests that this ethnic difference indicates more about subcultural contrast in modes of expressing distress than about difference in underlying psychiatric condition.

We also found that both Puerto Ricans and blacks tended to score higher than subjects from the other two ethnic groups on additional sets of items chosen to indicate possible sociopathic tendencies (e.g., "most people are honest for fear of being caught") and possible paranoid tendencies (e.g., "it is safer to trust nobody") (Dohrenwend, 1966). Accepted at face value, this result suggests that there may be subcultural differences in types as opposed to amount of disorder (cf. Eaton &

TABLE 12–9
Symptom Score According to Education Level (percent)
(Excluding "No Answers" on Education)

Symptom Score	Years of Education			
	0–7	8–11	12–15	16 or more
4 or more	30.2	24.3	17.8	8.4
Base for %	(116)	(342)	(471)	(83)

Note:–Chi-square=18.99; p < 0.01.

TABLE 12–10
Percents with Four or More Symptoms According to
Family Income and Ethnicity

| | Ethnicity | | | |
Yearly Family Income	Jewish	Irish	Black	Puerto Rican
Less than $3,000	10.5 (19)	26.7 (15)	24.4 (82)	33.3 (24)
$3,000–4,999	30.8 (52)	20.0 (35)	16.2 (80)	42.4* (59)
$5,000–7,499	20.5 (117)	11.1 (81)	14.0 (93)	32.6* (46)
$7,500 or more	15.3 (98)	13.7 (51)	18.8 (64)	30.4 (23)

Note: Figures in parentheses indicate base for percent
*Differs significantly at 0.05 level or better from combined Jewish and Irish counterparts according to one-tailed t-test of difference between proportions.

Weil, 1955; Field, 1960; Henry & Short, 1954; Hollingshead & Redlich, 1958; Langner & Michael, 1963; Opler & Singer, 1956).

However, there are indications that the ethnic groups differ in tendency to "yeasay" and "naysay" (Couch & Keniston, 1960). The lower educated blacks tended to yeasay on some items, and the Irish, by contrast, to naysay on some items. And there appear to be sharp differences in the ways members of the different ethnic groups rate the social desirability of many of the symptom items (Edwards, 1957). Small samples of blacks and Puerto Ricans, for example, see the items concerned with sociopathic and paranoid tendencies as less undesirable than small samples of Jews and Irish (Dohrenwend, 1966). This suggests that some of the symptom items themselves may have different meanings and hence different implications in the different subcultures.

There is, as was mentioned earlier, another problem in assessing the psychiatric implication of those symptoms. A usual characteristic of the symtomatology observed in psychiatric patients has been described as its stereotypy, repetitiveness, and intractability (e.g., Wilson, 1963). Do the symptoms reported by respondents in such studies as Midtown, Stirling, and our own research in Washington Heights show these qualities of persistence? The fact of the matter is that there are very few data over time from these cross-sectional studies. To explore this issue we made use of our follow-up interviews, conducted an average of two years after the first interview, with the subsample of about 150 nonpatient respondents. The results were startling. There was a strong tendency for symptom scores on the 22 item measure from the Midtown Study to increase with negative intervening events such as serious physical illness of spouse, and decrease with positive intervening events such as job promotion (Dohrenwend & Dohrenwend, 1966; cf. Haberman, 1965). Thus these symptoms appear in part at least to be reactions to stressors (Dohrenwend, 1961), that is, to events which, at one time or another, disrupt the usual activities of most individuals. Though of common occurrence, we have little systematic knowledge of reactions to such events.

We have more data on reactions to massive stressors such as physical disaster, civilian bombing, and combat (e.g., Dohrenwend & Dohrenwend, 1969). And only a few years ago, we had a

TABLE 12–11

Mean Number of Symptoms on the 22-Item Screening Instrument among
Jewish, Irish, Black and Puerto Rican Psychiatric Out-Patients
According to Behavior Type

Behavior Types	Ethnicity			
	Jewish	Irish	Black	Puerto Rican
Suspicious, etc.	11.0 (3)	8.0 (3)	9.8 (8)	14.0 (3)
Quiet, afraid, etc.	6.7 (3)	5.7 (3)	10.1 (8)	14.3 (3)
Worry, moody, unhappy, etc.	7.9 (10)	5.4 (7)	8.4 (12)	11.9 (10)
Drinks too much, etc.	3.0 (1)	6.3 (3)	5.2 (8)	5.0 (1)
Checks stove, afraid of elevator, etc.	5.7 (6)	8.2 (4)	6.0 (9)	13.0 (7)
Lies, steals, etc.	– (0)	– (0)	7.0 (2)	– (0)
All Behavior Types	7.4 (23)	6.6 (20)	7.9 (47)	12.5* (24)

*Differs significantly at the 0.05 level or better (two-tailed t-tests) from Jewish mean, Irish mean, and Black mean.

report on reactions to a tragedy affecting the entire nation—the assassination of President Kennedy. In this National Opinion Research Center study, Sheatsley and Feldman (1964) found that 89 percent of a national sample said that during the four days following the assassination, they experienced one or more of 15 physical and emotional symptoms such as "Didn't feel like eating," "Had headaches," "Had an upset stomach," "Had trouble getting to sleep," and "Felt nervous and tense." However, five to nine days after the assassination when these interviews were conducted, only 50 percent replied that they still had one or more of the symptoms.

Note that it is symptoms such as these, supplied in response to questions whose temporal reference was often ambiguous, that have been taken in studies such as Midtown and Stirling to indicate extremely high rates of psychiatric disorder in nonpatient groups. Yet we know from our own research that stressful events of everyday life are not infrequent in community populations. Moreover, we know from studies of reactions to massive stressors, such as the one just described, that normal individuals react with symptoms resembling those observed in psychiatric patients. However, for most people in such situations, the symptoms do not have the "peculiar recalcitrant obstinacy" (Field, 1960, p. 296) of the symptoms observed in patients. Tyhurst (1957), indeed, has suggested that in some circumstances, the symptomatology may indicate something quite different from the presence of psychopathology or disorder. From the vantage of his clinical observation and analysis of "transition states" (e.g., marriage, childbearing, promotion, retirement, migration, and physical disaster), Tyhurst writes:

> Our tendency to regard the appearance of symptoms as invariable signs of illness, and therefore a need for psychiatric treatment, requires some revision. It would be probably more appropriate if we regarded the transition state and its accompanying disturbance as an opportunity for growth. When an impasse develops in the resolution of the "hitch," we may speak of illness. Signs of psychological distress—somatic, emotional or intellectual—are thus not necessarily equivalent with that person's being a case of mental illness. . . . Thus, for example, prevalence surveys of such symptoms . . . can have little meaning for the incidence of mental illness unless the *contextual relevance and timing* of the symptoms is determined at the same time. If symptom incidence [sic] is not close to 100 percent in such surveys, this is probably because the survey has been incomplete in some way or the memories of informants were faulty (1957, p. 161).

The harsh reality is that the determination of whether something is wrong in a psychiatric sense has proved extremely difficult to make about persons not in treatment. We have mentioned that this was evident in the results of psychiatric screening during World War II (Star, 1950; Ginzberg et al., 1959); it is apparent from our previous analysis of rates ranging from over 60 percent to under one percent in the field studies of "true prevalence"; and it can be seen in the results of our own preliminary studies. It would seem that the firm fact that we can take from the results of field studies of the "true prevalence" of psychiatric disorder in community populations is that there is an inverse relationship between social class and psychological symptomatology. However, the psychiatric meaning of such symptomatology is very much at issue.

REFORMULATION OF THE PROBLEM

Only very small minorities of those judged to be psychiatric cases in high rate studies such as Midtown and Stirling have ever been in treatment for psychiatric disorder. If the above analysis of the state of the facts bearing on our problem is correct, it seems possible, even likely, that much of the untreated symptomatology reported in community studies consists actually of normal and reversible responses to stressors in the contemporary situations of the respondents. Further, the environments of lower status groups may well be fraught with harsher stress situations than those of higher status groups. If so, such situations would themselves contribute to the higher rates of symptoms in the low status groups. In the light of these compelling possibilities, the question of social causation versus social selection explanations of an inverse relationship between class and psychiatric disorder is premature. There is a prior issue, the issue of the extent to which the higher rates of symptomatology in the lower class groups represent higher rates of persistent disorder of the kinds observed in psychiatric patients.

Let us try to spell this out. The question being raised is: to what extent is the excess of symptomatology in lower status groups generated by personality defects, of whatever origin (e.g., genetic, childhood deprivation), and to what extent does such symptomatology consist of normal reactions to unusually harsh and numerous stressors in the contemporary situation? To answer this question, we will have to learn a good deal more than we now know, first, about the cultural and situational factors that lead to different modes of expressing distress and second, about the conditions under which the symptomatic expression of distress becomes evidence of underlying personality defect.

These are not easy problems to solve. The symptoms most characteristic of low status groups appear to be not only those of the psychophysiological variety (Crandell & Dohrenwend, 1967), but also behavior similar to that described in the American Psychiatric Association's *Diagnostic and Statistical Manual* under the heading of "Personality Disorders" (Dohrenwend & Dohrenwend, 1969). Such symptoms often involve antisocial acting out which is difficult to measure with personal interview techniques. Moreover, the main test of whether a symptom is stressor-induced or a result of personality defect is its disappearance after the stress situation is altered. Many of the stress situations of everyday life, perhaps especially those associated with low status positions of groups such as blacks and Puerto Ricans, are themselves enduring, e.g., racial discrimination. The test is thus often difficult to apply.

Reacting to some of these problems in his discussion of one of our earlier papers, Bradburn wrote:

One might well ask whether the distinction between stress-or-situation-induced symptoms and psychological disorder is worth making for extremely disadvantaged groups. If people live in conditions of extreme deprivation all of their lives and manifest symptoms as a result, isn't this the same thing as saying they are suffering from psychological disorders? . . .

I think the distinction is important, even crucial to make. . . . Why are we concerned with the rates of untreated disorders? One answer might appear obvious—although it is not the only possible one—because we want to provide treatment for those who need it but are not now getting it. What is not so obvious, however, is how the treatment is going to be provided, given the already overtaxed facilities available and shortage of trained personnel, not to mention some serious questions concerning the efficacy of treatment procedures currently in use. The most important question . . . here is—what is the nature of the treatment we have in mind? The answer to this question is bound up with the distinction between the stressor-induced symptoms and true psychological disorders. If observed differential rates are due to true psychological disorders, then the type of treatment we would engage in should be appropriate to that disorder, making the assumption that we now have some effective treatments. If, on the other hand, the observed rates are stress induced, then we would want to concentrate our energies on removing the stressors. One way leads to allocating more funds to community mental health programs, the other to the War on Poverty. . . . (Bradburn, 1966).

It would seem, then, that we have a tall order before us. On practical as well as theoretical grounds, however, to undertake it may well be worth the effort.

Note

This chapter has been adapted from three previously published articles: (a) Dohrenwend, B. P., & Dohrenwend, B. S. The problem of validity in field studies of psychological disorder. *Journal of Abnormal Psychology*, 1965, 70, 52–69 (copyrighted 1965 by the American Psychological Association). (b) Dohrenwend, B. P. Social status and psychological disorder: An issue of substance and an issue of method. *American Sociological Review*, 1966, 31, 14–34 (copyrighted 1966 by the American Sociological Association). (c) Dohrenwend, B. P. Social status, stress, and psychological symptoms. *American Journal of Public Health*, 1967, 57, 625–632 (copyrighted 1967 by the American Public Health Association). Grateful acknowledgment is made to the American Psychological Association, the American Sociological Association, and the American Public Health Association for permission to use this material here.

The work was supported in part by Grants OM–82, Mh 07327, MH 07328, MH 10328, and MH 13356 from the National Institute of Mental Health, United States Public Health Service. It has also been supported in part by Grant U1053 from the New York City Health Research Council to the Community Population Laboratory of the Columbia University School of Public Health and Administrative Medicine.

References

American Psychiatric Association, Committee on Nomenclature and Statistics. *Mental disorders: Diagnostic and statistical manual.* Washington, D. C.: American Psychiatric Association Hospital Service, 1952.

Blum, R. H. Case identification in psychiatric epidemiology: Methods and problems. *Milbank Memorial Fund Quarterly*, 1962, 40, 253–288.

Bradburn, N. Discussion of Dohrenwend, B. P. A study of untreated psychiatric disorder in samples of urban adults. Paper presented at Symposium on Social Psychological Approaches to the Conceptualization and Measurement of Psychological Disorder at the annual meeting of the American Psychological Association, New York City, September 1966.

Bremer, J. A. Social psychiatric investigation of a small community in northern Norway. *Acta Psychiatrica et Neurologica Scandinavica*, 1951, Supplement 62, 1–166.

Cartwright, A. The effect of obtaining information from different informants on a family morbidity inquiry. *Applied Statistics*, 1957, 6, 18–25.

Clausen, J. A. Mental disorders. In R. K. Merton & R. A. Nisbet (eds.), *Contemporary social problems.* New York: Harcourt, Brace & World, 1961.

Cohen, B. M., Fairbank, R., & Greene, E. Statistical contributions from the Eastern Health District of Baltimore. III. Personality disorder in the Eastern Health District in 1933. *Human Biology*, 1939, 11, 112–129.

Cole, N. J., Branch, C. H. H., & Orla, M. Mental illness. *American Medical Association Archives of Neurology and Psychiatry*, 1957, 77, 393–398.

Couch, A., & Kenniston, K. Yeasayers and naysayers: Agreeing response set as a personality variable. *Journal of Abnormal and Social Psychology*, 1960, 60, 151–174.

Crandell, D. L., & Dohrenwend, B. P. Some relations among psychiatric symptoms, organic illness, and social class. *American Journal of Psychiatry*, 1967, 123, 1527–1538.

Cronbach, L. J., & Meehl, P. E. Construct validity in psychological tests. *Psychological Bulletin*, 1955, 52, 281–302.

Dahlstrom, W. G., & Welsh, G. S. *An MMPI handbook*. Minneapolis: University of Minnesota Press, 1960.

Dohrenwend, B. P. The social psychological nature of stress: A framework for causal inquiry. *Journal of Abnormal and Social Psychology*, 1961, 62, 294–302.

Dohrenwend, B. P. Social status and psychological disorder: An issue of substance and an issue of method. *American Sociological Review*, 1966, 31, 14–34.

Dohrenwend, B. P., & Dohrenwend Barbara S. The problem of validity in field studies of psychological disorder. *Journal of Abnormal Psychology*, 1965, 70, 52–69.

Dohrenwend, B. P., & Dohrenwend, B. S. *Social status and psychological disorder: A causal inquiry*. New York: Wiley, 1969.

Dohrenwend, B. S., & Dohrenwend, B. P. Field studies of social factors in relation to three types of psychological disorder. *Journal of Abnormal Psychology*, 1967, 72, 369–378.

Dunham, H. W. Social structures and mental disorders: Competing hypotheses of explanation. In *Causes of mental disorders: A review of epidemiological knowledge, 1959*. New York: Milbank Memorial Fund, 1961.

Eaton, J. W., & Weil, R. J. *Culture and mental disorders*. Glencoe, Ill.: Free Press, 1955.

Edwards, A. L. *The social desirability variable in personality assessment and research*. New York: Dryden, 1957.

Essen-Möller, E. Individual traits and morbidity in a Swedish rural population. *Acta Psychiatrica et Neurologica Scandinavica*, 1956, Supplement 100, 1–160.

Faris, R. E. L., & Dunham, H. W. *Mental disorders in urban areas: An ecological study of schizophrenia and other psychoses*. Chicago: University of Chicago Press, 1939.

Felix, R. H., & Bowers, R. V. Mental hygiene and socio-environmental factors. *Milbank Memorial Fund Quarterly*, 1948, 26, 125–147.

Field, M. J. *Search for security*. Evanston, Ill.: Northwestern University Press, 1960.

Ginzberg, E., Anderson, J. K., Ginsburg, S. W., & Herma, J. L. *The lost divisions*. New York: Columbia University Press, 1959.

Glazer, N., & Moynihan, D. P. *Beyond the melting pot*. Cambridge, Mass.: Massachusetts Institute of Technology Press, 1963.

Gruenberg, E. M. Problems of data collection and nomenclature. In C. H. H. Branch, E. G. Beier, R. H. Anderson, & Carroll A. Whitmer (eds.), *The epidemiology of mental health*. Brighton, Utah: Departments of Psychiatry and Pathology, University of Utah and Veterans Administration Hospital, Fort Douglas Division of Salt Lake City, Utah, 1955.

Gruenberg, E. M. Discussion of Dunham, H. W. Social structures and mental disorders: Competing hypotheses of explanation. In *Causes of mental disorders: A review of epidemiological knowledge, 1959*. New York: Milbank Memorial Fund, 1961.

Gurin, G., Veroff, J., & Feld, S. *Americans view their mental health*. New York: Basic Books, 1960.

Haberman, P. W. An analysis of retest scores for an index of psychophysiological disturbance. *Journal of Health and Human Behavior*, 1965, 6, 257–260.

Hagnell, O. *A prospective study of the incidence of mental disorder*. Stockholm: Scandinavian University Books, Svenska Bokförlaget Norstedts-Bonniers, 1966.

Henry, A. F., & Short, J. F. *Suicide and homicide*. Glencoe, Ill.: Free Press, 1954.

Hollingshead, A. B., & Redlich, F. C. *Social class and mental illness*. New York: Wiley, 1958.

Langner, T. S. A twenty-two item screening score of psychiatric symptoms indicating impairment. *Journal of Health and Human Behavior*, 1962, 3, 269–276.

Langner, T. S. Psychophysiological symptoms and women's status in Mexico. In J. M. Murphy & A. H. Leighton (eds.), *Approaches to cross-cultural psychiatry*. Ithaca, N. Y.: Cornell University Press, 1965.

Langner, T. S., & Michael, S. T., *Life stress and mental health*. New York: Free Press of Glencoe, 1963.

Leighton, A. H. *My name is legion*. New York: Basic Books, 1959.

Leighton, A. H., Lambo, T. A., Hughes, C. C., Leighton, D. C., Murphy, J. M., & Macklin, D. B. *Psychiatric disorder among the Yoruba*. Ithaca, N. Y.: Cornell University Press, 1963.

Leighton, A. H., Leighton, D. C., & Danley, R. A. Validity in mental health surveys. *Canadian Psychiatric Association Journal*, 1966, 11, 167–178.

Leighton, D. C., Harding, J. S., Macklin, D. B., Macmillan A. M., & Leighton, A. H. *The character of danger*. New York: Basic Books, 1963.

Lemkau, P., Tietze, C., & Cooper, M. Mental hygiene problems in an urban district. *Mental Hygiene*, 1941, 25, 624–646.

Lin, T. A study of the incidence of mental disorder in Chinese and other cultures. *Psychiatry*, 1953, 16, 313–336.

Manis, J. G., Brawer, M. J., Hunt, C. L., & Kercher, L. C. Validating a mental health scale. *American Sociological Review*, 1963, 28, 108–116.

Manis, J. G., Brawer, M. J., Hunt, C. L., & Kercher, L. C. Estimating the prevalence of mental illness. *American Sociological Review*, 1964, 29, 84–89.

Mishler, E. G., & Waxler, Nancy E. Decision processes in psychiatric hospitalization: Patients referred, accepted, and admitted to a psychiatric hospital. *American Sociological Review*, 1963, 28, 576–587.

New York State Department of Mental Hygiene, Mental Health Research Unit. A mental health survey of older people. *Psychiatric Quarterly Supplement*, 1959, Part I, 45–99.

Opler, M. K., & Singer, J. L. Ethnic differences in behavior and psychopathology: Italian and Irish. *International Journal of Social Psychiatry*, 1956, 2, 11–22.

Pasamanic, B. Thoughts on some epidemiologic studies of tomorrow. In P. H. Hoch & J. Zubin (eds.), *The future of psychiatry*. New York: Grune & Stratton, 1962.

Piotrowski, A., Henisz, J., & Gnat, T. Individual interview and clinical examination to determine prevalence of mental disorders. *Proceedings of the Fourth World Congress of Psychiatry*, Madrid, September 5–11, 1966, (Excerpta Medica International Congress Series No. 150, pp. 2477–2478).

Plunkett, R. J., & Gordon, J. E. *Epidemiology and mental illness.* New York: Basic Books, 1960.

Primrose, E. J. R. *Psychological illness: A community study.* London: Tavistock, 1962.

Rin, H., Chu, H., & Lin, T. Psychophysiological reactions of a rural and urban population in Taiwan. *Acta Psychiatrica Scandinavica*, in press.

Rin, H., & Lin T. Mental illness among Formosan aborigines as compared with the Chinese in Taiwan. *Journal of Mental Sciences*, 1962, 108, 134–146.

Rosanoff, A. J. Survey of mental disorders in Nassau County, New York, July–October 1916. *Psychiatric Bulletin*, 1917, 2, 109–231.

Roth, W. F., & Luton, F. B. The mental hygiene program in Tennessee. *American Journal of Psychiatry*, 1943, 99, 662–675.

Sheatsley, P. B., & Feldman, J. The assassination of President Kennedy: Public reactions. *Public Opinion Quarterly*, 1964, 28, 189–215.

Srole, L., Langner, T. S., Michael, S. T., Opler, M. K., & Rennie, T. A. C. *Mental health in the metropolis: The Midtown Manhattan Study.* Vol. I. New York: McGraw-Hill, 1962.

Star, S. A. The screening of psychoneurotics in the army: Technical development of tests. In S. A. Stouffer, L. Guttman, E. A. Suchman, P. F. Lazarsfeld, S. A. Star, & J. A. Clausen (eds.), *Measurement and prediction.* Princeton, N. J.: Princeton University Press, 1950. (a)

Star, S. A. The screening of psychoneurotics: Comparison of psychiatric diagnoses and test scores at all induction stations. In S. A. Stouffer, L. Guttman, E. A. Suchman, P. F. Lazarsfeld, S. A. Star, & J. A. Clausen (eds.), *Measurement and prediction.* Princeton, N. J.: Princeton University Press, 1950. (b)

Strömgren, E. Statistical and genetic population studies within psychiatry; methods and principal results. *Actualités scientifiques et industrielles, Congrès International de Psychiatrie, VI, Psychiatrie Sociale.* Paris: Herman & Cie., 1950.

Szasz, T. S. *The myth of mental illness.* New York: Paul B. Hoeber, 1961.

Tyhurst, J. S. The role of transition states–including disasters–in mental illness. In *Symposium on preventive and social psychiatry.* Washington, D. C.: United States Government Printing Office, 1957.

Wilson, R. S. On behavior pathology. *Psychological Bulletin*, 1963, 60, 130–146.

13

Building Foundations for Strength in the Preschool Years: Preventing Developmental Disturbances

Lois B. Murphy and Caroline A. Chandler

INTRODUCTION: SOME BASIC CONSIDERATIONS

Theoretical

The field of anthropology has emphasized mutual adaptation of the individual and the culture. As Ruth Benedict (1934) has pointed out, individuals who survive well or "fit" in one culture may be deviant or unadjusted in another. Thus, prevention of disturbance, or development of adequate adaptation in any culture, is relative to the demands of the culture and the capacities of individuals to meet those demands. Human beings seem capable, within limits, of developing a wide range of adaptational styles. Handicapped persons may have special limitations in this regard; some who might fit into rural or urban unskilled jobs would not be able to meet the more complex demands of work which requires higher levels of intellectual functioning. Mental limitations are obviously not alone in influencing the adaptational capacity of an individual. Sensitivities to stimulation and limits in the capacity to integrate the rapid input of stimulation from modern life also interact with other adaptational limits. These seem evident in persons who report such things as "I can't stand the noise of the city" or in children who can learn well only in controlled classrooms or in small groups. Different geographic and subcultural areas, as well as vocational groups, seem to attract and to develop different personality styles and values: a Texas cattleman does not usually resemble a Boston bank accountant.

The problem of prevention of adaptational failure, and the related problem of development of strength, are partly a matter of the mutual selection of organism and environment. However, this is made more complex by the failures of certain areas of our culture to meet basic human needs consistently. Years ago, Shaw (1929) demonstrated that most delinquency comes from "delinquency areas." Ernest Schachtel and Anna Hartoch (in Glueck & Glueck, 1950, pp. 217–19) were given the task of differentiating 1,000 boys from a slum area into delinquent and nondelinquent categories on the basis of Rorschach records alone. Excluding 135 out of 496 records of delinquent boys as inconclusive, the Schachtels correctly classified 91 percent of the remaining 361 as delinquent; a similar proportion of the actual nondelinquents were correctly classified. Fear of and dependence on authority was regarded as the critical aspect of character which they expected would operate to inhibit the tendency to become delinquent in a depriving slum environment. Beyond this, 15.8 percent of the delinquents were seen as markedly defiant in contrast with only 1.5 percent of the nondelinquents, and an additional 34.6 percent of the delinquents were considered slightly defiant, in contrast to only 10 percent of the nondelinquents.

Contemporary research is exploding with studies—of varying degrees of breadth, depth, and technical excellence—of the effects of ghetto deprivation on the very intelligence of our children (Deutsch, 1967), as well as the relation of frustrating conditions to the violence in our cities, and the relation between lower socioeconomic conditions and mental illness (Srole, Langner, Michael, Opler, & Rennie, 1962). The foundations of both inadequate mental and emotional development and of delinquency are seen to lie in inadequate prenatal care of mothers (Pasamanick & Lilienfeld, 1955; Rogers, Lilienfeld, & Pasamanick, 1955), inadequate maternal care of infants (Ourth & Brown, 1961; Prugh & Harlow, 1967; Coleman & Provence, 1957; note 1), and other distorting conditions in infancy and the preschool years.

In other words, building physically and mentally healthy participants in our democratic culture requires that the culture meet certain requirements. This is also implied by the protests in recent times from varying groups of young people from even middle class, relatively privileged backgrounds—protests against what they feel to be the excessively militaristic, materialistic, competitive values in our culture. Such protests, as well as the protests of the deprived, raise the question whether the adaptational problem of this generation is merely a problem of individuals, or rather of the interaction between the culture and the needs and values of many groups of youths.

In this regard we have to consider the contributions to developmental stress of the intensely competitive, self-aggrandizing culture as seen by hippies (Time, 1967; Newsweek, 1967), the "uncommitted" (Keniston, 1966), some artists, and other creative seceders from the culture, as well as by observers of the "corporation family" (Whyte, 1957). Oddly enough, psychologists absorbed in studies of "need achievement" (need-Ach) (McClelland, Atkinson, Clark, & Lowell, 1953) seldom discuss in depth the possible destructive consequences of an excessively high degree of need-Ach. While thousands of young people express disgust with what they observe of the back scratching, status seeking, cut throat competitive life of much of the business, advertising, and academic world, or plead for "brotherly love," neurotic brothers and sisters may not be so articulate (Menninger Quarterly, 1967). They get depressed, seek out the school counselor, or exhibit other forms of internal stress, often resulting in self-destructive behavior. Suicide is a major cause of death in the late "teens" (USPHS, 1968a).

But it may not be just the intensity of competition and materialistic values which pro-

duce stress. Our hedonistic culture may have laid the foundation for rejection or depression partly as a product of lack of the tolerance typical of certain aspects of pioneer life when the focus was on a struggle for the essentials of living (Stegner, 1962). In a happiness-centered culture, a serious personal loss or even frustration may seem to involve a collapse of the world in which happiness is possible. Within this context, some depressed mothers may bring up depressed children;[1] the latter may be deprived as a result of the withdrawal, preoccupation, and paralysis of the mother, as well as emotionally depressed in empathy with the depressed mother.

In contrast to our pleasure oriented culture which has tended to equate adaptation with happiness rather than with strength in coping with life problems, other civilizations or subcultures have fostered one or another of a different range of values. Sparta reared her boys for endurance, as school books have long taught us. Contemporary religious groups such as the Amish and the Mennonites have reared children to be devout and to be good workers.

The contemporary middle class American focus on "fun" (Wolfenstein, 1955) and pleasure for the "haves" seems to have generated a blindness to the needs and the positive potentialities of the more deprived members of the community, while simultaneously intensifying the sense of deprivation of the "have nots." The identification of the deprived with the pleasure culture may in turn contribute to their own emphasis on immediate gratification at the expense of long-term, problem-solving efforts, the development of strength, control, and sublimation of impulses; that is, there is a lack of early channeling of aggressive impulses into constructive activities. In this connection we can note Eleanor Glueck's (1966) finding that infantile aggression in children from deprived homes correlates with later delinquency.

The dichotomous quality of our culture which both saves and destroys can be frustrating and confusing to those who want to make sense out of their world. On the one hand, antibiotics, blood transfusions, open heart surgery, and prosthetics for almost every kind of defect, all contribute to save life and conserve basic physical and mental functioning, though we still have a high rate of neonatal mortality (USPHS, 1968b), infant morbidity (Schiffer & Hunt, 1963), adolescent suicide

(USPHS, 1967), and accidents (USPHS, 1968c), some of which are preventable.

At the same time, the culture does not consistently allow a niche for the fragile, or respect for the "different" child. With rare exceptions, it does not encourage *individual* solutions. There seems to be strong pressure to adjust to a conforming pattern of life which may not allow room for the enormous range of individual differences of all kinds (Williams, 1956). Such pressures toward conformity, achievement, competition, and self-control, and failure to guide expressiveness or to channel aggression into creativity in the preschool and school years contribute to disturbed behavior in adulthood. These and similar considerations are relevant to the question of prevention and of the development of strength in the earliest years of life.

Technocratic Education

Our technological culture with its strong drives toward automated or mechanized education *even of the preschool child* (Moore & Anderson, 1967) threatens an even more dangerous denial of human values than the callous and competitive commercialism which our society has already fostered. Children isolated with machines may learn to solve arithmetic problems, but they are not learning to solve problems with peers or authorities, much less how to cooperate with others, or how to use their own imaginations for creativity in any area.

If our culture is going to place decreasing value on stable, warm, cooperative human relationships, and if technological values are to have top priority, the early years of childhood will be even more shortchanged and will fail to prepare for humane living under changed value systems. If future values are to emphasize adaptability to change rather than fostering the stability of a subcultural group, early experience will have to be guided accordingly. In the following discussion we are going on the assumption, rightly or wrongly, that the coming generation of children will grow into a culture with both increasing demands for a capacity to adapt to change, and the need to respect basic human and democratic values. These must include values of respect for individuals regardless of differences in color or race; independence and responsibility for one's own behavior; cooperation; creativity and capacity to contribute to or to enhance the culture itself. These values stand alongside the value of maintaining sufficient integration or stability to think coherently and to develop competence in one's adaptational situation. Thus, our conception of strength will emphasize constructive coping (Murphy, 1962) with the opportunities, demands, and obstacles of the changing culture and the ability to maintain internal integration. This must be not only sufficient to withstand the pressures and stress involved in sequences of change but sufficient to develop productivity and to help solve the human problems which threaten the security of this culture and the mental, physical, and emotional health of large segments of its population.

Historical Evolution of the Child Development Field: Research and Clinical Studies

While the evolution of science *can* proceed by a process of thesis-antithesis-synthesis, as Hegel outlined, it seems unnecessary for rational people in one discipline to ignore important work in other fields, as happens when thinking swings from one extreme to the other. It would seem to be desirable to build on all of the important relevant work of the last 100 years. While major observations and research studies of young children and even infants were carried out between 1870 and 1920 (Shinn, 1900; Sully, 1910; Canestrini, 1913; and others), the big push toward study of early childhood began in the 1920s. The following are a few major examples from a huge list of centers and investigators.

The work of the major Child Development Institutes, notably longitudinal and other observational studies, at the Universities of California, Minnesota, and Michigan, as well as Iowa, Fels Institute, etc., document the approaches of Harold E. Jones, John E. Anderson, Willard Olson, L. Sontag, Arthur Jersild, and other leaders in Child Development for 30 years. Reports of their contributions are readily available in the Manuals of Child Development (e.g., Carmichael, 1954). Outstanding social psychological experiments under the leadership of Kurt Lewin (1939) of Moreno (1934), and of Sherif (1967) have implications for the preschool stage as well as older ages of childhood. The University of Denver and its medical school have supported basic experimental and psychoanalytic studies of infants and young children (e.g., Benjamin, 1961). In addition, the studies at the Yale Child Study Center under Gesell (Gesell & Ilg, 1943), and later under Ernst Kris and Milton Senn (Solnit & Provence, 1963; Senn & Solnit, 1968) are significant. Gesell's material, although it seems to require certain revisions of the more global concepts, provides important observations to supplement both the statistical material from the Child Development Institutes and the theoretical contributions of Freud, Piaget, Heinz Werner, and others. Abroad, the continuing studies of Anna Freud, Dorothy Burlingame, and their colleagues at Hampstead Clinic, London (*The Psychoanalytic Study of the Child*, 1945–1972), as well as R. Spitz (1945, 1946, 1965), Piaget (1952), Heinz Werner (1964), and others have contributed insights, hypotheses, and syntheses important for the assessment of children. Charlotte Buhler's (1931; Buhler & Hetzer, 1930) developmental studies in Vienna contributed methods of studying children as well as data on sequences in maturation; and other German studies, especially of the Hamburg school, enriched our approaches to social interaction. Intermittent Soviet studies (Brackbill, 1962) on environmental control of social behavior add to the substantial body of work, which includes also pediatric, neurological, and comparative studies of human and infrahuman infants and children (Richmond, 1964).

A major lack in most of the work mentioned above results from the predominant use of middle class children in research. Thus, we have inadequate knowledge about interrelations between social and cognitive development and mental health of migrant children, those in minority groups such as the Mexican-American, Puerto Rican, American Indian, and also very poor children, and children of socially marginal or alienated parents such as criminals, prostitutes, and the isolated handicapped.

Other major limitations in research result from the relative lack of interdisciplinary collaboration; and many important hypotheses formulated on the basis of intensive case studies have not been tested by research on larger samples. For instance, there has been little or no large-scale study of early childhood foundations for control of aggression, conscience, capacity to cope with frustration, stability, or flexibility. And finally, detailed studies of the strengths and coping methods of children in different subcultural, socioeconomic, and national groups have begun only in recent years (Murphy, 1962; Havighurst, 1964).

Similarly, much of the research on children in ghettos, in "poverty areas," in "deprived groups," fails to distinguish important qualitative differences among subgroups. Overgeneralization from so-called hard data leads to errors just as premature generalization from limited samples may do. Especially important for our dicussion is the difference between young children among whom prevention of emotional disturbance, delinquency, or learning failure is chiefly a matter of social environment, and those who need special medical or psychiatric care. While a substantial proportion of children in Head Start groups make significant gains in response to the help of warm teachers, together with varied new experiences, an important fraction of them—from 10 to 20 percent—make little or no progress because of constitutional or other organic deficits which require special diagnosis and help.

The significant correlations in early years between physical, motor, and mental development (as measured by intelligence tests in children) (Terman, 1925; Thompson, 1954) suggest that some effects are due to biochemical and metabolic factors (nutritive, oxygen, hormone, etc.) operating from the neonatal period through childhood; there also seem to be multiple factors involved in neuropsychological activation in some children. This activation accompanies increased (stimulated or released) motor and especially exploratory activity in adequately rich and varied environments. Data from many animal studies are extensive on this point and even show that such rich environments permit better biochemical and physiological development of the brain (Rosenzweig, 1966). It is reasonable to assume that the same process goes on in infants and young children. Moreover, important experimental and exploratory studies of infants are showing differences in sensory-motor and social responses such as smiling directly due to specific types of stimulation at different stages of infancy (Rheingold, 1956).

Stimulation effects are more than a matter of neural stimulation and of content input; confinement or limitation of activity, or the lack of objects and spaces to explore, may preclude opportunity to observe. Stimulus lack is also involved in failures to develop eager responsiveness and curiosity, since there is nothing interesting to discover. The passive or tired mother in a meager home not only fails to provide information and personal stimulus; she may prevent activity, including cognitive activity such as asking questions, which feeds the spontaneous interest of the child.

Individual Differences

At all socioeconomic levels, individual differences are found. M. Shirley (1933) and others have documented the *range* in the ages at which new perceptual-motor and other cognitive and social functions emerge in babies within a middle class socioeconomic sample. This is important for recognizing the child's own contribution at any one stage to the "antecedent" factors followed by certain behavior. Individual differences may also be seen in the need for stimulation; infants have different preferences, different degrees of tolerance for and different response to varying types and intensities of stimulation in different modalities (Heider, 1966; Escalona, 1968).

Knowledge accruing in the fields of physiology, biochemistry, neurology, and neuropsychology all contribute to understanding of the child by the pediatrician and the psychiatrist. In one brief chapter it is not possible to review even the most important facts in detail; but we can present a point of view which grows out of all of these, demands the further use of knowledge from these fields, and also calls for further research.

While many studies illustrate the effects of certain internal or external factors on given aspects of development, the *interaction of mutually potentiating factors* needs more study. At Ibadan, in Nigeria, biochemists and pediatricians agree that the high death rate of children between two and five is frequently an outcome of malaria *plus* protein deficiency *plus* culturally sanctioned but traumatic separation of mother and child (Lambo, 1961; see also Jelliffe, 1955). That is, biochemical, nutritional, parasitic, and cultural factors are seen to interact cumulatively in producing developmental failure. The model of interaction will help us to understand many types of maladaptation: what are the limitations or exaggerations within the organism, and in the environment, and how do they worsen each other? The study of interaction

requires detailed "process" studies of individuals by interdisciplinary teams. In the United States we need to study the interaction of poor nutrition, inadequate cognitive stimulation and emotional support with congenital vulnerabilities related to poor prenatal and birth conditions—all of which are often involved simultaneously and cumulatively in the poor development of deprived children.

A major tragedy in psychology (and other social sciences) and medicine is the gulf between "academic"—be it statistical or experimental—and "clinical" work, with the respective snob and status patterns that support this gulf. Each side has much to learn from and with the other and the major problems will not be solved without the necessary integration to permit thinking about the interaction of broadly documented statistical trends and idiosyncratic patterns and processes observable only in a few cases.

A related problem arises from the fragmentation of disciplines and the tendency to work at one aspect of a problem at a time. Head Start has been trying to prepare children for school by providing adequate cognitive stimulation. Eyes and ears get checked along with any obvious illnesses (Cooke, 1969). But what about the total physiological functioning of apathetic children, hyperactive children, oversensitive children, those with unusual autonomic reactivity, restless, irritable, or chronically anxious children? What about the physiological condition of limp, exhausted mothers who have no energy to encourage the interests begun in Head Start? What about the interaction with his children of an alcoholic, arthritic father who gets disability payments but no help with his emotional problems? What about the emotional development of the child in Head Start whose unwed mother entertains her boyfriends in the two-room apartment where the child is constantly being overstimulated sexually and brings this excitement to school (Murphy, 1969b)? It seems obvious that we need a comprehensive, multidisciplinary approach in which the entire situation of the child as an organism in his physical, cultural, and personal or family environment will be understood and all of this seen in relation to his cognitive development, his emotional and social orientation, and his coping resources.

The close relation to each other of major forms of disturbance in development is reflected in the correlations between behavior problems, learning difficulties, emotional illness on the one hand, and pregnancy and birth difficulties on the other hand (Pasamanick & Lilienfeld, 1955; Rogers, Lilienfeld, & Pasamanick, 1955; Knobloch & Pasamanick, 1960; Wiener, 1965; Drillien, 1967). All of these are higher in poverty areas and are also associated with inadequate mothering (Drillien, 1964, 1967). This relationship between many expressions of disintegrative response to stress supports Dr. Karl Menninger's (1963) hypothesis of the unitary nature of disturbance. This concept implies that body and mind are never completely autonomous or separate from each other and that different patterns of expression of disturbance may have related basic sources. If we focus on the development of strength we must deal simultaneously with the development of intelligence, emotional integration, and social constructive behavior.

In agriculture, "prevention" of disease or of growth failure is seen largely in terms of providing for health and sturdy growth. Scientific data relevant to total development are made accessible from federal, state, and county agencies and are readily applied to growth of cattle, hogs, wheat, and corn. Soil analysis, study of biochemical needs, irrigation needs, favorable climatic conditions, and the like are under constant study. Data are made available to growers and the result is the astonishing and outstanding agricultural productivity of the United States, which is able to contribute substantially to the feeding of the rest of the world.

Contrast this situation with the failure to produce comparably healthy children. In the area of child development, utilization of all of the scientific knowledge relevant to optimal development is spotty and inadequate. Important here are Roger Williams' (1956) data on the extraordinary range of biochemical needs as well as individual differences in body structure of different individuals—at least as wide as the variations in biochemical needs of different breeds of stock and grain. Yet appraisal of such needs in relation to muscle tonus, resistance to infection, etc., of individual children as we see them in Head Start and in public schools is limited. In extreme cases—as of Mongolism (Jacobs, Baikie, Court Brown, & Strong, 1959; Bazelon, Paine, Cowie, Hunt, Houck, & Mahanand, 1967) or blindness in infants (Sandler, 1963; Omwake & Solnit, 1961;

Fraiberg & Freedman, 1964; Burlingham, 1965; Klein, 1967; Lowenfeld, 1964), or prematurity (Gold & Stone, 1968)—we take hold of the problem. But possible biochemical factors in apathy, slow learning, poor impulse control, and hyperactivity do not get much attention.

Or let us consider the situation in the automobile field. In order to prevent accidents with loss of life and limb, we demand repair of recognized defects in cars and we develop a system of safety checks; we also find ways of improving the roads and developing better control of traffic. With combinations of increased strength and protective measures we hope to save a percentage of deaths and injuries that occur each year.

But what about the 161,000 infant deaths every year (Lesser, Gershenson, Hunt, Bonato, & Pratt, 1968)? And the related birth hazards which predispose the infant to disturbances of functioning in all areas? Can we think in terms of a *comprehensive* program to produce stronger babies, better equipped for survival in a changing, stressful culture, comparable to the programs for agricultural productivity? Can this be achieved when human values are those most directly involved and economic factors are only secondary? (The cost of even minimal custodial care of the mentally ill [Rice, 1966] and delinquent [USPHS, 1965] alone amounts to more than two and a half billion dollars per year.)

Handicapping Conditions

There are many children who are institutionalized because of handicapping conditions; and there are also many handicapped children who never reach an institution. In 1965, eleven and a half million children, or over 23 percent of the 5- to 17-year-old group, had a handicapping eye condition that needed care. The most handicapping conditions in our child population (as estimated by the Children's Bureau) are revealed in the following table. These estimates are important, since most of these handicaps affect early experience and development in cognitive, social, and emotional areas.

Disturbances and Failures in Development in Infancy

The most glaring failures result in early death: the infant mortality rate is higher in the United

TABLE 13–1

Estimates of Number of Children with Handicapping Conditions

Handicapping Condition	Age Basis for Estimates	Year 1965	Expected in 1970[a]
Eye conditions needing specialist care	5–17	11,404,000	12,637,000
Emotionally disturbed	5–19	4,600,000	4,920,000
Speech	5–20	2,829,000	3,026,000
Mentally retarded	0–20	2,440,000	2,528,000
Orthopedic	0–20	2,153,000	2,231,000
Rheumatic fever	?	977,000	1,063,000
Hearing loss	0–20	597,000	619,000
Cerebral palsy	0–20	406,000	421,000
Epilepsy	0–20	400,000	414,000
Cleft palate–cleft lip	0–21	103,000	107,000

Note:–Source of data: Children's Bureau, United States Department of Health, Education, and Welfare, 1966.

[a] Assumes little improvement will be made in prevention and care.

States than it is in 14 of the other advanced countries of the world (World Health Organization, 1968). And if we compare infant mortality rates by counties in the United States, those in the worst quintile are experiencing rates which are 50 percent higher than the national average and twice as high as the counties having the lowest infant mortality rate (Lesser et al., 1968). Child mortality rates are of course higher in the poorer and most deprived regions of the country: the South Atlantic, East South Central, West South Central, and Mountain areas exhibit the highest mortality rates for each age grouping up to age 24. Such high childhood mortality rates reflect the fact that infants and children are not receiving medical care or are receiving poor care; also nutritional inadequacy is often involved. It is significant that the areas with high child mortality largely overlap the areas in which states or counties have not received federal grants for children's lunches and/or food stamps for the poor because of failure to provide the required matching funds. As a result, children are malnourished and have lowered resistance, if they do not literally starve.

Deaths in the younger age groups tend to occur from causes that have been shown to be treatable medically. The deaths due to respiratory diseases, infective and parasitic diseases, and diseases of the nervous system are largely unnecessary with present medical knowledge and adequate nutrition.

The deaths of babies from sudden and unexplained causes are a reflection at the least of the special vulnerability of the young infant (Geertinger, 1968). Adequate assessment of possible hazards–such as unstable respiration, unusual sensitivity, and possible vulnerability to shock–could lead to better protection and care of at least some of the young babies who are lost or who have a bad start at present. The same factors contributing to mortality presumably undermine the strength and resources of many survivors as well.

Possible factors in early developmental failure or disturbance as expressed in obvious vulnerabilities, poor cognitive development, marasmus, autism, schizophrenia (Bender, 1953), and related conditions include basic functional difficulties in areas such as breathing, sleep, feeding, elimination, as well as hypotonia. Precursors to adaptive difficulties include marked sensitivities handled chiefly by withdrawal (Bergman & Escalona, 1949); lack of response to environment due to lack of stimulation (Spitz, 1945) or to undiagnosed sensory or sensory-motor defect, etc.; and imbalances in development of psychological functions. Perceptual difficulties as well as inadequate stimulation may contribute to failure of differentiation of self or mother-figure (Jacobson, 1954); failure of perceptual-motor development and active exploration of the environment; failure of ego-directing and ego-control functions; failure to develop basic identification as a socially responsive person, internalizing the positive and negative values and directives from the environment (Goldfarb et al., 1969).

Extreme autonomic reactivity (Richmond & Lipton, 1959), affective lability, etc., may contribute to disturbed relations with the environment and may also be related to or involved in a predisposition to anxiety (Greenacre, 1952), hostility, or ambivalence. Contributing factors may be birth damage (Schwartz, 1965) or trauma (Greenacre, 1952), chronic distress,[2] or disturbed reactions to neglect (Prugh & Harlow, 1967; Coleman & Provence, 1957).[3] Understimulation, isolation, lack of maternal response to crying or other evidences of discomfort may also lead to incomplete differentiation of self and others, due to lack of sustained, devoted care from a mother figure (Ainsworth et al., 1967).

When the above interferences with adequate development have not been present, disturbed weaning (Caldwell, 1964) or toilet-training (Hushka, 1942)—at whatever age and by whatever method these are carried out—may have diffuse effects on the child's general mental and social development. Ego organization previously well-developed may crumble or split, and the child's self-image and identification with parents may be threatened. Marked withdrawal in reaction to separation trauma may lead to inhibition or regressive loss of speech, or lack of motor progress, depending in part on the condition of the child or the phase at which separation occurs.

Developmental retardation and/or sensory-motor delay or inhibition may result from confinement or restriction due to illness,[4] institutionalization (Spitz, 1945), or atypical care patterns.[5] For instance, extreme confinement in the crib of infants 9 to 24 months old because of infantile eczema, chronic upper respiratory illnesses, or other difficulties may not only interfere with motor development but with the broadened and deepened autonomy which normally accompanies the triumphs attending mastery of motor skills.

Withdrawal, apathy, suspicion, distrust, and anxiety may become chronic in reaction to severe handling, chronic strain, etc., as with battered children or those subject to adult hostility. Inadequate communication[6] and often affective exchange and "sending power" (Erikson, 1963) in the second year of life, and subsequently, may result from lack of encouragement during the early efforts toward communication. Inadequate play materials, space, and zones for exploration may interfere with the development of curiosity, the capacity to experiment and to solve problems of space relationships, and the flowering of imagination seen in play of normal preschool children (e.g., see *Colin: A Normal Child*, Murphy, 1956, vol. 2).

Assessment

Neurological and pediatric assessments will pick up defects in the baby's equipment and basic functioning. However, beyond these it is important to assess the skeletal structure, musculature, autonomic reactivity, and somatic stability in the newborn. Biochemical factors and needs (Williams, 1956) affecting blood and brain development or functioning are being increasingly appreciated. The implications of high autonomic reactivity and variability need to be considered in relation to the infant's vegetative functioning in general and the development of emotional tone.

The biological substrate will have much to do with the early outlines of personality and beginning dynamics of interaction with the environment which may contribute irreversible patterns in the early stages of personality formation. Unstable vegetative functioning, with the colic, vomiting, and diarrhea which reflect this, also contributes to diffuse distress which prevents the basic sense of well-being, comfort, and bliss needed to give the baby a foundation of good self-feeling.

In the first neonatal period, it is hardly possible to assess the future growth pattern and pace except as these may be inferred or guessed at from the range of patterns in the family. Later, but still in the early weeks of life, however, alertness, intensity, drive, adaptability, and capacity to accept change may be assessed along with smoothness of motor coordination, steadiness of attention, and selective positive and negative responses to various kinds of stimulation (Escalona & Heider, 1959; Escalona, 1968; Heider, 1966; Murphy, 1968a; Thomas, Birch, Chess, Hertzig, & Korn, 1964).

Both the baby's tolerance for and need for stimulation in the earliest weeks, along with changes in these as the baby grows, need to be watched. What is adequate stimulation to one baby may be deprivation to another or overstimulation to a third. Similarly, what is stressful to one baby may be merely challenging or interesting to another.

To sum up, although *all* infants share certain common, basic needs—physical, developmental, and emotional—individual infants vary greatly in the specific terms of their needs as individuals.

Pregnancy and Delivery

Among the common pregnancy problems (Montagu, 1962; Sever, 1965) which may interfere with the health and adequate development of the growing fetus (and therefore the early integrity of the child) are the Rh incompatibilities, and infections (especially rubella, kidney infection, etc.). Drugs which may affect the fetus adversely include various antibiotics, antidepressants, and LSD, as well as large amounts of alcohol or nicotine. Dietary inadequacies (Scrimshaw & Gordon, 1968), if extreme, or extreme vomiting contributing to malnutrition in the mother, may also hamper the development of the fetus. Anxiety (Sontag, 1958), trauma, or shock involving disturbances in the mother's own autonomic, biochemical, and metabolic functioning may disturb the fetus.

Education of parents as to these and other important factors that might injure a baby before it is born is important, in addition to actual availability of the obstetrician and prenatal care—since not only the mother's understanding but also supportive help from fathers and other family members can influence both physical and emotional aspects of the mother's condition during pregnancy.

Problems in delivery, in addition to actual injury during difficult births or precipitate births, may include effects of excessive medication (Stechler, 1964), anoxia (Jakab, 1965) due to delay in delivery, etc. Prematurity (low birth weight) is strongly correlated both with neonatal and infant mortality (Shapiro & Unger, 1965) and with handicapping conditions in surviving children and with learning and behavior difficulties (Pasamanick & Lilienfeld, 1955; Drillien, 1967).

If we are going to produce greater health and strength in all babies, further research is needed in order to identify (a) the communities in which prenatal and delivery care are inadequate, and (b) ways of providing adequate care for mothers who otherwise would not receive it (Deschin, 1968).

Infancy

L. K. Frank's (1966) review of some 400 studies of infants presents an organized picture of general and individual aspects of organic development, learning, and coping and the effects of care as contrasted with different kinds of deprivation. Longitudinal studies such as those by Escalona and Heider (1959), Murphy and Moriarty (to be published), Macfarlane and Honzik (1954) show that some children can outgrow or compensate for infantile deficiencies or problems. At the same time, Escalona and Heider, and Murphy and Moriarty, in detailed studies of individual infants at older stages, also show that some infancy patterns continue, or strongly influence later functioning in a substantial proportion of children. This is congruent with clinical data from many sources which indicate the importance of adequate infantile functioning and freedom from serious traumata for later adaptation.

Factors in Development in the Preschool Years

Reports of medical follow-ups on Head Start children (North, 1968) include basic information on teeth, vision, hearing, nose-throat and ear infections, heart, kidneys, anemia, etc., of large samples of children. As we noted above, these are important beginnings, but many other conditions underlying general and individual problems are not analyzed. Adequate programs should provide for thorough medical and developmental assessment of all the vulnerabilities in preschool children as early as possible, with recommendations for support of all of the child's developmental needs; these are basic to both mental and emotional integration and the development of socially adaptive behavior.

Physical and/or emotional illness may contribute to a pathological disruption of the normal growth pattern and this in turn makes for discontinuity and interference with the continuous process of *integration* and capacity for control accompanying healthy development. The zones of development most seriously distorted or disrupted by illness or by severe disintegrative responses to stress are naturally those in which maturation is incomplete.

In fact, the entire area of mental health in a young child has to be considered from a developmental point of view. We have to ask, how does this child's reaction to this specific stressful experience affect the whole spectrum of motor, cognitive, affective integrations that are important at this phase of his development? The answer will require knowledge of not only developmental sequences and processes, but also the wide range of individual differences in all aspects of equipment, drives, and personality—differences which influence the child's vulnerability to particular types of stress at a given phase and to related patterns of disturbance.

Mastery of Stress

All children go through some stressful periods and potential crises; many children can not only handle these with support, but can gain a sense of added mastery, progress, and self-assurance from these experiences (Murphy & Moriarty, to be published). We can think of "normal, expectable stresses" of childhood in our culture and also of individual variations in the severity of these, and in the child's capacity to cope with them, depending on the particular pattern of vulnerabilities and strengths the child brings to the stressful experience, and the support provided by his family and community.

Characteristic threats experienced and mastered by young children in our culture are implied in the extensive records of problem behavior studied by Jean Macfarlane, Marjory Honzik, et al. (1954) in a large, random sample of children studied from infancy (see also Jones, M. C., et al., 1971). The frequency of fears of the dark and of animals,

sibling rivalry, toileting problems, etc., at the preschool stage is clearly documented in many other studies (Jersild & Holmes, 1935) of children from different groups in the United States. These all imply that learning to control elimination, to share parental attention with a sibling, to live with the fantasies evoked by darkness and animals, is not easy for many children; any specially intense area is potentially a zone of stress.

Hazards during the preschool years include loss or prolonged absence of the mother due to illness, operation, death; or even the partial loss due to the birth of a new sibling before the child has achieved adequate self-sufficiency. A new sibling evokes far less rivalry after the prior child is four years of age, for instance, than when the intruder interrupts the mother's support of a two-year-old (Sewall, 1930). At this early stage, losing accessibility to her lap, care, and playtime can be far more critical than it is after the child has achieved full autonomy. Depression or other mental illness of a parent may be especially disturbing when a child is in the active process of identifying with the parent, including day-by-day learning from, imitating, etc. Parental harshness, punitiveness, explosiveness, especially with chaotic, disorganized, alcoholic, or impulsive parents disrupts the child's effort to organize his own behavior at a stage when impulse-control is still difficult.

Persistent fears may follow tonsillectomies performed before the age of three years (Levy, 1945; Jessner, Blom, & Waldfogel, 1952), or experiences of disaster such as a tornado or fire (Murphy & Moriarty, to be published). With help, all of these can be mastered and even contribute to strength.

We have been using the term stress to refer to the experienced interactions of inner and outer factors that strain the child's coping capacity or that arouse anxiety that he will not be able to manage the experience. Deprivation is sometimes considered stress, and it may be when it involves frustration of a deeply cathected expectation.

Privation which has been continuous since birth, so that the child knows nothing different, may produce less anxiety, but it may prevent adequate development in another way—through lack of "nutriment" required for growth and integration, as we indicated above (p. 306). In these instances, failure of basic aspects of cognitive development, such as curiosity, problem-solving, capacity to organize, adequate space and time concepts; or failure to develop capacity for self-control or for planning, may result from the lack of family, or, more broadly, cultural stimulus and support for such functions.

While from the point of view of pathology, stress is a threat, our longitudinal studies indicate that not only does every child experience some developmental stress, but that stress well-managed in a context of family support contributes to strength, just as exercise itself contributes to muscular development and motor coordination. A child who has had little need to struggle with difficulties may have little capacity to meet stress or challenge in adolescence or early adult years (Murphy & Moriarty, to be published).

However, chronic privation limits coping resources, although it may lead to passive endurance or resignation which contribute to at least a capacity to survive in a meager environment.

Let us now consider a broad range of factors involved in the development of strength.

Ecology

If we undertake a total approach to adaptation we will have to begin with ecology. Ecology includes everything from climate, air pollution, and other factors affecting health itself, to space, safety, noise, and factors affecting the child's opportunities for exercise, development of motor skills and coping resources, exploration and education through satisfying curiosity, and other freedoms to develop independence and a sense of relatedness to the environment.

Physical Environment. This includes architecture. Expensive big new schools being planned to promote good learning have *no windows*. The rationale for this is greater economy on the one hand, controlled temperature and humidity and protection from external noise sources on the other. Everything that might distract the child from learning his math is shut out. So is much that might help him to learn about the world he is living in. We can speak here of *built-in* sensory deprivation, which occurs also in many an institution for the care of infants, as well as in urban day care centers in factorylike buildings with no access to the outdoor environment. It is not only sensory deprivation as such, but

deprivation of the flexibility to shift attention from burdensome work to varied stimuli outside of the child's confining school world—the clouds with their evocative shapes floating by, the gradual stretching of leaves in spring, or their drifting down in a fall breeze; or in the city, varied passing vehicles. Such architectural thoughtlessness is due to the failure of educators and social scientists to communicate human, and especially children's, needs in relation to architecture.

If psychologists or child psychiatrists had been consulted, some other considerations beyond climate control could have been brought to the attention of the architects. This type of isolated, unidisciplinary thinking spawns a new set of problems. Architecture in urban renewal high rise apartments in the large city has typically paid attention to needs for adequate sunlight and air, without providing for indoor activity needs of children, or even for adequate outdoor needs. Meager, hard surface playgrounds with swings and slides allow for only limited, repetitious activity with no room for development of imagination or resourcefulness. This is not true in all countries. Small children in parks in many American cities have to keep off the grass, are punished for digging, and are not allowed to play in fountains; Soviet parks provide large sandboxes for digging and allow children far more freedom in public places.

Ecology, or the study of the influence of the environment on child development, also includes study of the psychological as well as physical aspects of architecture of the home. The location of the parents' and children's rooms affects privacy—freedom of the children to enjoy themselves without disturbing parents' need for quiet; freedom for parents to enjoy their private marital relationship without stimulating excessive curiosity of the children. The child's freedom includes his need for experimenting, for healthy, active use of energy even in confining weather when he has to remain indoors, and healthy discharge of tension.

The nearly total absence of protection for childhood privacy and play opportunity in poor homes may underlie the chronic suppression by parents of activity and childhood conversation. "Shut up, be quiet!" may be necessary to protect the "nerves" of the harassed mother but the resulting inhibition of the infant and young child can interfere seriously with adequate development of speech, communication, active initiative, curiosity, and problem-solving.

Psychological Environment. The "environment" also includes the psychological atmosphere of the home and the community. Unity and harmony between the parents (Baruch, 1937) is the most important aspect of home atmosphere. The atmosphere created by adults' attitudes toward infants and small children has either supportive or disturbing effects. One travels in countries where everyone seems to have a warm interest in children, and in other areas where adults are intolerant of and irritable toward them.

Thus, attitudes toward infants and young children underlie the quality and quantity of stimulation provided by the adults in their interaction with children. Appropriate stimulation for the child is as necessary as fertilization and cultivation of the growing things in a garden. Despite the fact that studies at the University of Iowa (Skeels, 1940; see also Skeels, 1966) many years ago demonstrated the importance of adequate materials, affectionate, individual care, and other aspects of stimulation for cognitive development, the general public has been slow to use this knowledge. We have referred above (p. 306) to the mass of studies of animals, including monkeys (Sackett, 1967) and rats (Rosenzweig, 1966), which have shown that an adequately rich, varied environment with opportunities to explore is necessary for optimal growth of the brain itself, along with the development of problem-solving and other learning capacities. Many studies of children have demonstrated that similar principles are basic for their development as well. While this work has aroused great hopes for and efforts toward prevention of the kinds of retardation which result from ecological and material deprivation, there is a danger that the comparable need for planned cultivation of social and emotional capacities, along with broad coping resources, will be neglected.

The psychological environment also includes the quality, content, and quantity of stimulation of values, concepts of reality, assumptions regarding the nature and workings of human relationships, and the place he may hold in the community. Demands from mother to fight back (Davis & Havighurst, 1947), daily bombardment by t.v., observation of violence in the ghetto, but also other areas, observation of and induction into delinquent activities—these and other cumulative influences from the psychological environment help to channel the early aggression reported by Eleanor Glueck (1966), and tendencies to deviant behavior found by Schachtel to identify delinquents.

In order to build self-control, constructive purposiveness, and social as well as emotional health, the environment must supply accessible ways of channeling vigor into achievement instead of destruction (Clausen, 1968). In order to build emotional well-being and integration, the environment needs to provide for a balance of gratification and rewarded frustration tolerance.

Summary of Environmental Needs. In our planning for an adequate environment, then, we need to include the requirements of 1) bodily nutrition and exercise; 2) mental stimulation and challenge; 3) emotional support and stimulation; and 4) social experience, and the opportunity to develop strong personal ties as a basis for identification with positive values of one's culture and participation in it.

As a setting within which these provisions are available, the growing infant and young child needs sufficient harmony, structure, or organization. A climate of too great conflict, extreme contrasts, fluid, inconsistent values, and chaotic living is evidently hazardous for both cognitive and personality development. Enough order as a background for experiencing change and variety, and for development of a cognitive map; enough peace and unity as a background against which to discriminate differences—these help the child to develop strength, just as enough sun, rain, and wind, without blistering heat or devastating storms, are necessary for most things that grow.

Thus a broad approach is needed, not only for the comfort of the children and for survival, but also in order to develop the strength, flexibility, and creativity required for active participation in and coping with a rapidly changing culture.

We do not assume that every child must be prepared to take a place in the middle class culture of the large cities. Only half of our population[7] live in the big metropolises now, and there are trends toward dispersion. This dispersion is already allowing for the development of new varieties of community as well as support for subcultures which now struggle for the right to survive. Disappearance of the small, multicrop farm which supported many families at the turn of the century does not need to mean disappearance of the opportunity for quiet living close to nature preferred by many people.

Maternal Environment. The "ordinary good mother" (Winnicott, 1957) loves the baby, stimulates him by her interest and active attention—her tender cuddling and play, her encouragement of his efforts to achieve new steps in progress, her friendly way of setting limits and providing substitutes for aggressive or dangerous activity, her support for his development of frustration tolerance. She observes and respects his autonomy (Murphy & Moriarty, to be published), preferences, rhythms, his energy limits, the sources of his discomfort, the most successful ways of soothing him, and the new steps in development which need to be encouraged.

The mother contributes to the baby's strength through a balance of respecting and tuning-in to the baby's needs, timing, and sources of pleasure on the one hand, while still helping him to gradually "become one of the family," adapting to a reasonable schedule not only of sleeping, feeding, etc., but also of play and attention. An example of this is:

Suppose that a baby is in the first stages of being weaned from breast to bottle. The mother has been told that, on the whole, reasonably spaced self-demand is a pretty good idea so that the baby sets up a sort of rhythm and knows when he is hungry. Then, if you are counselling a mother, something else has to come into play. You ask her to begin to see if he can't learn to postpone his feeding time a little bit. When he first cries for the bottle and she knows he is hungry, she doesn't give him the bottle right away. She postpones it just a little bit because this is a very important learning experience. If the baby can learn, with his mother's help, to postpone this immediate gratification for later gratification, then he's learned something very important. He has learned to give up satisfaction now in order to get more satisfaction later on. In its simplest terms, this is the business of learning to tolerate anxiety. It is learning how to live with certain kinds of frustrations, frustrations that come about because you don't always have a choice. Some things you just have to endure. If frustration goes on and on, it is none of your choosing, but you still have to endure it. You don't endure it blindly, however, because you know from past experience—and this is learning, too—that this frustration won't last forever (Chandler, 1965).

Another way in which the mother can help build tolerance is by encouraging the baby to "play by himself" for short periods of time at first; she provides objects, toys, materials that he can manipulate and explore—things which give him sufficient feedback to make his independent efforts satisfying and which help him to tolerate his mother's absences. Without some patterned surroundings (Fantz, 1965) and objects such as toys to manipulate, the baby may find the inevitable disappearances of his mother intolerable.

While Ainsworth (1967), Brody (1956), and others have made some significant studies of mother-infant feeding transactions, a complete understanding of mother-baby interaction is still in the future. A major difficulty in much thinking about mother-child relations has been the tendency to think in terms of absolutes: if attention, talking to the baby, affection, are good—then more attention, more talking, more affection, are better. Actually, in the Topeka study (Murphy & Moriarty, to be published) the only aspects of the mother that had such an absolute value were her adjustment, her harmony with the father, and her respect for the baby's autonomy. In such matters as attention to the baby, correlations were curvilinear—that is, too much and too little both interfered with the development of the baby. What is too much or too little varies, of course, with the needs, tolerance, and adaptability of the individual baby.

This is in line with our previous discussion of the importance of a *balance* of gratification and frustration—not an arbitrary or arithmetical balance but enough gratification to contribute to adequate trust (Erikson, 1963) that needs will be met, and support for the effort to obtain more; and enough frustration to develop both tolerance and resourceful coping.

The ideology of parents, and their beliefs about the kinds of behavior to encourage and to suppress, are also important. For instance, some parents will overemphasize independence, where during infancy and the early years a *balance of independence and ability to accept help* contributes to optimal coping with the developmental challenges of early childhood. The child needs both support for his drive to grow up and also tolerance for his inevitable periods of regression (A. Freud, 1965), or the plateaus that permit consolidation and preparation for the next stage.

Pediatric handling, in and out of the hospital (Bowlby, Robertson, & Rosenbluth, 1952), is also important for the development of strength. Doctors and nurses can help infants and young children to *get used to temporary pain*, to master their anxiety, by the way "shots" and vaccinations are handled. Uncomfortable intensive examinations, treatment of injuries, and extended periods in the hospital can be made more bearable if the mother is nearby to reassure the child (Robertson, undated). Help in mastering anxiety in one area can build the child's pride, courage, and self-respect in a way that extends to his total feeling about himself and his ability to cope with other stress.

Pediatricians and public health nurses can also help prepare mothers to support the baby's and young child's active response to the environment. They can help mothers to provide optimal protection during the crucial early months when somatic integration, emergence of basic ego functions (such as perception and manipulation), and organization of the central controlling ego are under way.

The history of both medicine and social science has included broad swings, from one extreme to the other, of freedom and controlled direction. Yet there are creative periods when a fine balance has been struck. We are at a point in the progress of knowledge about human development when such a balance can be achieved—a balance which includes full attention to both medical and psychological contributions, and which allows room for each value, whether of independence or need for warm support.

Hopefully the pediatrician will make increasing and maximum use of biochemical assessment with its constantly improved knowledge of nutritional needs and the contributions of drugs to the stabilization of damaged or sick nervous systems. The pediatrician can also provide guidance and assistance to nursery school and day care center teachers. The latter need more understanding of children, especially those who come with hyperactive or severely inhibited behavior or other expressions of emotional disturbance. The pediatrician will be able to watch for transition points in development which constitute especially vulnerable or critical periods for the individual growing infant or young child.

CRITICAL PERIODS: WORKING HYPOTHESES DERIVED FROM RESEARCH AND CLINICAL STUDIES

The term critical period has been used in many ways (Scott, 1962), but we shall use it in reference to the period of greatest importance for the emergence of a new sort of function. During the critical period for the development of any function, *relevant stimulation* needs to be supplemented with *protection* from disturbing experiences which could interfere with the adequate organization and integration of the new function.

This is important because the rapidly developing infant or young child not only maintains a precarious equilibrium generally but he is especially prone to instability at times when emerging functions disrupt the old balance. J. Kagan considers the first three years as a critical phase (Kagan & Moss, 1962). Yet within this rather broad span of growth sequences, each new specific stage which involves a basic reorientation to the environment and to self is a critical phase in a more precise sense. When a child gives up the breast or bottle or achieves control of elimination or can pull himself to an upright position or learns to walk, or when he learns to talk and communicate through verbal symbols, he takes a major step toward autonomy (Erikson, 1963; Murphy et al., 1962) and toward the status of a child who can manage for himself. Simultaneously he relinquishes a part of his infantile dependency on the mother, with its reassuring feelings of lap, encircled arms, and other kinds of warm, physical contact. Just as birth threw him out of his warm uterine nest into a relatively cold world, so his own maturational efforts take him still further from maternal comfort. Each step may be felt ambivalently and alternations of progressive and regressive behavior are normal. The baby switches from insecure toddling back to his speedy creeping; although proud of using the toilet, he gives up once in a while and "has an accident." The new achievements are not yet tightly tied into his self-image or the structure of his active ego; and this immature looseness also exposes the new developments to the danger of easy disorganization when too much stress burdens the child at this particular critical phase.

Parallel to these developments are critical phases in the development of *relationships*: when he clearly recognizes mother as different from all other persons he becomes newly sensitive to "separation anxiety" (Murphy, 1964) and to "stranger anxiety."

We can also think of each *major new experience* in the first years as potentially contributing to a critical phase. If mother goes to work and he is left with a strange baby-sitter or in a day nursery, his familiar world is gone and he is confronted with the perhaps desperate necessity (accompanied by trembling chin and pale cheeks) of coming to terms with a new world, without his trusted supports.

The way in which the child masters such challenges determines the degree to which he gains an added increment of strength, or is weakened by sometimes thinly-covered-over conflict or acute anxiety. Since he is still so young and his personality so incompletely jelled, his ego so vaguely organized, any additional threats may dissolve his mask of brave conformity, so that he is reduced to terror or rage (temper tantrums) "over nothing," as the grownup sees it. But the "nothing"—some small frustration—was the straw that broke the camel's back. This process is all too frequent in the second and third years of life. It may still yield to new strength, if the tempest or the collapse is handled supportively and understandingly by the adults.

In this connection we may ask in summary, when does a "crisis" exist? In essence, a crisis is a threat of disorganization or the occurrence of disintegrative reactions which carry the possibility of long-term loss of some aspect of previously achieved progress, or long-term strain on the child's capacity for integration. Prolonged illness, or severe anxiety unrelieved for a long period, or a severe regression, may be followed by recovery or repair. But the developing ego structure may still be weakened so that the child is never again as solid or stable as he was at the precrisis period. On the other hand, the crisis may be thoroughly mastered, as when the child accepts the fact that although mother goes away, she does come back; and that while she is away he can still be well taken care of and can manage for himself. In such instances the growing ego is strengthened by the experience.

Vulnerability Resulting from Interactions of Different Factors

There are critical *combinations* of internal factors, each one of which in itself need not be disrupting or disturbing. For instance, myopia or other disturbances of vision combined with very high drive and high activity level, especially if very high autonomic reactivity is also present, may lead to frequent, intense upsets. These are apt to be triggered by the frustration, pain, or punishment resulting when a fast-moving child with poor vision bumps into, knocks over, or inadvertently damages precious objects or gets hurt by others. High sensitivity combined with a high activity level makes a child vulnerable to overstimulation resulting from his own reactions to the many encounters produced by his high activity level.

Strong drives combined with poor adaptive resources may predispose an infant to endless frustration. High social responsiveness will tend to evoke much stimulation from adults; this may be overwhelming to a child who is very sensitive to stimulation or who has high autonomic reactivity. A child with a strong sense of rhythm and delight in kinaesthetic movement, who is confined or not allowed to be very active because of a poor heart or other dangerous condition, will suffer more than a child to whom movement is less important.

It is impossible in this short space to outline all the possible combinations of equipment and temperament which contribute to individual vulnerability (Murphy & Moriarty, to be published; Murphy, 1968b) and difficulties in coping with stress or mastering adaptational tasks. In each instance, then, it is obligatory to think in terms of the interaction within a given combination of factors in the child and between this combination of factors and the environment, and what this interaction means to the child. Along with a clarification of factors which create developmental and adaptational difficulties, the potential coping resources of the child need to be assessed. Only when this is done can we obtain an adequate basis for guidance of mothers of infants and young children.

New Understanding of Children's Management of Stress

When we look at infants and children in terms of "problems" and "symptoms," we note the role of withdrawal, resistance, dependency, rigidity, compulsiveness and impulsiveness, aggression, etc., in disturbing behavior. This often leads to overgeneralizations and a tendency to assume pathology in even normal forms of such behavior. A more balanced view of the child's management of stress can be found by careful observation of normal children who are on the whole getting along well in their environments. In Topeka, an infancy-to-young-adulthood investigation of normal children included an intensive multidisciplinary study at the preschool stage (Murphy et al., 1962). The children were examined by a pediatrician, a psychiatrist, and by several psychologists; they were also observed in play and party situations as well as in the test situations by independent recorders of behavior. All of these situations presented new and challenging experiences to these preschool children, few of whom had been to nursery school or a play group. Each child had to remain alone with an adult stranger, in a strange place, and respond to the challenging new demands and opportunities presented there. Tests, new toys, games, demands for climbing, jumping, finding a way to eat marble-hard ice cream, and cooperating with a pediatric examination by a new doctor were some of the situations in which the children were observed.

When these children were confronted with potentially overwhelming stimulation such as entrance into a very complex new situation, few reacted by overcomplying, inhibiting activity, crying, or other extreme emotional or physiological reactions, or exaggerated intellectual reactions or denial of reality. From one- to two-thirds did deal with the stress by efforts to alter the situation, or increased efforts toward organization and integration; handling the stress in fantasy or humor; by taking action to avoid the stimulation or to engage in other constructive activity, and with "proud self-control" suppressing disturbing reactions.

The importance of such early efforts to cope with overwhelming stimulation in active ways or with humor or fantasy is clear from the later capacity of most of these children to manage the stressful years of adolescence.[8] The background of these preschool capacities can also be seen in the infancy records. Grace Heider's analysis (Heider, 1966) showed the beginnings even during the first six months of life of some of these capacities to do something about unwanted or excessive stimulation—capacities which correlated significantly with later coping strengths (Murphy & Moriarty, to be published). She found that normal infants in the first six months of life may withdraw from, turn away, pull away, or in other ways avoid stressful stimulation. Or they may protest, push away, throw away, or in some other fashion try to get rid of the unwanted object. They may use some self-comfort device such as sucking thumbs or fingers. Observations of children from the second to the fifth years include similar forms of strategic withdrawal, protest, attack, or efforts to change or restructure the situation (Murphy et al., 1962). Healthy children may protect themselves by stubborn refusals, by setting up protective barriers and organizing a play situation in a seemingly rigid way. Or they may run to mother, teacher, or babysitter for help. A *balance of ability to use help and to make autonomous efforts*, or a balance of dependence and independence, is thus a healthy pattern. So is a flexible capacity to retreat or avoid when necessary; or to protest, attack, or actively change the situation. Both withdrawal and aggression have a normal place in effective coping.

When we look at the earliest precursors of coping efforts we note the contribution of early *infant decisiveness* to later coping capacity of the Topeka children as seen in correlations of .5 or above between "infantile protest, capacity to resist disliked foods, and to terminate feeding when satiated" on the one hand and active preschool coping capacities on the other (Murphy & Moriarty, to be published). The latter include: ability to control the impact of the environment, impulse control, struggle capacity, and also clarity regarding one's own identity, and accuracy of perception and reality testing. Obviously it is important for mothers and other people who are handling the infant and young child to respect these early efforts to deal with the environment actively.

The Topeka data also imply that the infant's ability to express oral (and probably other) demands freely may be part of (and when it leads to adequate fulfillment reinforces, many other aspects of) open, outreaching expressiveness and efforts of the baby. The correlation of this infancy *capacity to express demands openly* with later competence and with flexibility in adapting means to ends, implies that the former may be one of the earliest indications of active capacity for and efforts toward adaptation. Open expressiveness of oral demands in early infancy is one of the first steps in interacting with the environment and coming to terms with its opportunities.

Children who as infants showed a high degree of oral demand, gratification, and ability to cope actively with unwanted or excessive oral stimulation—that is, to protest, withdraw from, or to terminate what was being offered or pressed upon the infant—tended to show at the preschool level positive capacities of similar kinds.

Positive ratings of the infantile oral experience of the Topeka children also correlated negatively with preschool aggressiveness and destructive activity and with such difficulties in relating to others as being critical, tending to deprecate others, or to be tense.

By contrast, the good infantile oral functioning correlates *positively* in this group with warmth, range of social skills, ability to ask for help, being stimulating to others, and the capacity to use substitute gratification. In addition to these evidences of a positive infancy foundation for good social relationships at the preschool level, the good infantile oral experience also correlated significantly with separate and with global aspects of positive feelings about self at the preschool level: pride, autonomy, freedom from doubt and ambivalence, clarity regarding own identity, and feeling good ("healthy narcissism").

The simultaneous existence of these social and self patterns was also expressed in the capacities to balance dependence and independence, and the ability to synthesize drives such as love and aggression. These relationships are congruent with results of studies of preschool children over many years.

Interestingly enough, the good oral experience in infancy also correlated positively with the capacity to mobilize resources under stress and to be stimulated to greater effort following failure. Obviously the latter capacities would be supported by the deep self-assurance and accompanying freedom to act positively on one's own behalf

involved in the group of favorable feelings about self discussed above.

We can get some help in understanding the interdependence of all of these variables when we consider the factor analysis performed by Dr. Riley Gardner (Gardner & Moriarty, 1968) on the data obtained when these children were at the prepuberty stage. The same types of interrelations appeared and the factor analysis revealed a broad global factor which might be called "an active orientation to the environment;" this includes positive affective and cognitive orientations as well as capacities for action like those discussed above. Dr. Gardner's analysis and its finding of a broad positive response tendency is congruent with Dr. H. Witkin's (Witkin, Dyk, Faterson, Goodenough, & Karp, 1962) discussions of the outcome of maternal "growth-supporting child-rearing methods." On the basis of independent studies of other groups of school-age children, he finds that autonomy allowed by the mother from the beginning, along with adequate support, is followed by adequate differentiation in the child.

We have discussed the importance of basic organization of physiological functions; of being able to obtain enough gratification to sustain a sufficient equilibrium and to reinforce efforts to deal with the environment; and the ability to cope in a constructive way with unwanted, excessive, or overintense stimulation by protest, useful avoidance or withdrawal, or ways of changing one's relation to the situation.

Tolerance of obstacles, disappointment, frustration, and anxiety is another major capacity shown by many of the children in the Topeka sample. The child who has had sufficient satisfaction to maintain his trust that his needs will be taken care of and who has developed sufficient competence to be able to cope with a considerable proportion of ordinary frustrations by getting substitutes, for instance, is able to tolerate frustration and delay of immediate gratification.

Learning to Participate in a Changing World— To Enjoy Newness, and New People

The infant's response to strangers has not been studied extensively, yet important records are available in the data from a few longitudinal studies. In the Topeka studies, as in the Yale study (Wolf, 1952), instances are recorded in which babies of two, three, or four months were frightened by encounters with new persons—in each case a woman who apparently resembled mother enough to evoke the expectation of seeing her but who was strikingly different in some ways. In one case the visitor was an energetic, loud voiced, older woman who contrasted with the soft voiced young mother. In another case the woman had very black hair in contrast to the blonde mother. These sensitive babies generalized from such experiences to other strangers, retaining a fear of new persons for many months, and shyness, at least, for some years (Murphy & Moriarty, in press).

We are emphasizing this because of the importance of the earliest experiences with people for later capacities to accept differences, to accept people as they are, to be unthreatened by different colors, appearance, or behavior patterns—capacities important for full democratic participation. The "capacity to accept people as they are" was another important variable in the behavior of the Topeka children at the preschool stage.

In a rapidly changing world like that of today, an important group of capacities includes those to enjoy newness and discovery, to develop a wide range of areas of enjoyment and gratification, as well as to gain pleasure from the concrete results of one's own activity, and to develop a variety of coping patterns—along with the flexibility to use them appropriately. These capacities can help the growing child to respond to changes positively, without too much nostalgia for lost gratification, or helplessness if one coping resource is withdrawn or blocked.

The capacity for fear is inborn in humans (and many animals), and absence of fear and anxiety handicap the individual's capacity to deal with danger. We do not want to eliminate fear, or anxiety either; we do want to help the infant and young child to use them effectively. The capacity to use anxiety constructively was a variable correlating significantly with overall capacity to maintain inner equilibrium in the Topeka children.

By "constructive use of anxiety" we mean the capacity to be alert to anxious reactions as signals: signals which indicate the need for caution, selective control in managing a situation, perhaps even new or problem-solving solutions to a dangerous problem. Examples would be seen when one young child carefully and slowly negotiates a narrow, raised plank (Murphy et al., 1962), while another heedlessly dashes along, risking a potentially injurious fall. In our contemporary life, young children need to develop useful caution in regard to crossing streets, handling electronic instruments or heating apparatus, drinking unknown substances from bottles, and climbing on high places from which they could fall on hard surfaces.

A major cause of death in children is accidents, many of which the child himself could have avoided by more discriminating use of normal activity. Here our cultural value on courage may sometimes be distorted into acceptance of bravado or recklessness; lack of impulse control may be wrongly interpreted at first as simple masculine vigor. Again, a balance of energy expression with constructive use of anxiety will contribute to survival and healthy development.

HELPING THE CHILD COPE WITH STRESS AT LATER STAGES

We have dealt so far with some of the basic foundations of strength in the organic intactness of the child, good vegetative functioning, primitive capacities for active interaction with the environment through making demands and expressing needs, finding gratification in what the environment offers, and being able to fend off or terminate what is not wanted; finally, we noted the basic importance in early development of some capacity for delay, and tolerance of frustration.

But more and more as the child matures and new skills can be developed, the mother can support his efforts to solve problems by himself—to "come and get it," to find out what he can do with things, to utilize his own resources for comfort, as well as to let her know when he needs some help.

The Contribution of Restitution

While the earliest months and years are crucial for the development of fundamental strengths and capacities to cope with the environment, many early failures or inadequacies can be compensated, developmental gaps filled in, and weak areas strengthened through restitutive experience (Alpert, 1959). It may not be possible to restore all of the original potentialities possessed by the child's original genetic resources, yet great progress can be made, even within a day care or nursery school setting, provided the comprehensive guidance for supportive one-to-one relationships is made available.

With patient, warm care, the immobilized, battered child begins to trust adults; the overanxious, apparently mute child begins to talk; the stiff, resistant, suspicious child begins to explore interesting materials; the frighteningly aggressive child begins to control his angry impulses; the glazed-eyed, anxious child of a psychotic mother grows more relaxed and becomes attached to a healthy teacher; the war-shocked child begins to trust (Collis, 1953). Moreover, as we read in *Child of Our Time* (Del Castillo, 1958), the child himself, separated in disaster from his mother, may search for a new love-object and through a new relationship find support for growth. Anna Freud illustrated the way that children from a concentration camp provided support for each other (Freud & Dann, 1951).

The Role of the Child Psychiatrist

In Robert Coles' beautiful description of his experiences and observations of children, both black and white, undergoing integration (1967), we have an example of a psychiatrist functioning as leaven, sowing seeds of human values. He is one who can take it, who can listen, who can provide support through understanding, through appreciating the need for time, and through his ability to accept touchiness and hostility as understandable reactions of people who have grown up being rejected and experiencing stress. We see the psychiatrist as a person whose warmth can generate warmth.

Related to this is the response of many of our 60 longitudinal research subjects in Topeka. Many of them want more contact with the investigators, they want the research to go on. What is it they really want? Is it perhaps simply the alert, objective, but warm listening and attention, the sense of being valued, respected, and cared for, as well as being understood?

We can also think of the psychiatrist as a possible contributor to more cultural flexibility—even to a multidimensional culture where there would be room for the strong and the "tough-minded," in the best sense of the term, and also the "tender-minded," in the best sense of the term as well.

The psychiatrist can, moreover, help to stimulate adult imagination in regard to ways to *include* the fragile in our culture, as we have poured energies into ways to keep them alive.

The Potential Contribution of Head Start

In the late '60s, Head Start was initiated as a federally financed program to provide some of the resources for prevention we have just discussed. In many day care centers—established under the Office of Economic Opportunity, in urban renewal housing, in established settlement houses such as Hudson Guild in New York and St. Vincent de Paul in Chicago, under church and other local auspices—experienced directors integrated contributions from the neighborhood, and from community professional agencies, to enrich the care and experience of the children.

Examinations of children in a North Carolina study had found 17 percent with vision and hearing defects, and 42 percent with inadequate medical care for handicapping conditions (North, 1968, Table IV). A summary of diagnoses of 15 categories of disorder in Summer Head Start children in 1966 showed 63 to 87 percent of the diagnoses to have been first identified in the Head Start medical examination (Ibid, 1968, Table VI).

In addition, workers in Head Start, and other observers of the children, reported that many arrived in the morning without breakfast; this led to emphasis on nutrition as well as medical care. As of this writing, research reports were largely limited to evaluations of changes in intelligence (as measured by standard middle class tests) at the end of year-long Head Start experience; and improvements in ability to meet demands of school, despite the stated aims of Head Start to improve the physical and social functioning as well as cognitive development of the children. As might be expected, the widely different samples of children (from metropolitan ghettos, migrant workers' families, deprived rural areas, and of different ethnic backgrounds, as well as from Head Start centers differing widely in program and staff skill) showed widely different levels of cognitive progress. As indicated, improvement in physical development and socialization were not measured.

From some 800 hours of direct personal observation of Head Start groups, and from records by professional observers and aides, one of the authors (LBM) has concluded that the changes seen in individual children and mothers are of the greatest significance and demand much more comprehensive and intensive analysis. It is especially urgent to identify factors in and processes of change when it occurs, and the factors deterring progress when improvement is too limited (Murphy, 1969).

New efforts are needed to study qualitative deficiencies in cognitive development of deprived preschool children: the much discussed limitation of curiosity (Mattick, 1965), of organized play, of foundations for sublimation, for example, and the relation of these to the autonomous drive to learn, to impulse-control and constructive use of aggressive drives, as well as to mental health.

Interdisciplinary programs such as of parent-child centers (Murphy, 1970) promise to begin prevention from pregnancy and birth, and to provide necessary restitution and correctives for the infant and his family. As programs like these eventually succeed in reducing pockets of destitution and earliest deprivation, and in making whole neighborhoods better environments for child development, a new generation of children will have a better chance for health and competence.

A number of experiments are now in process which undertake to demonstrate the effectiveness of adequately designed infant care programs; these emphasize one or another pattern for providing personal attention in a one-to-one relationship, sufficient cognitive and emotional stimulation, and exploratory opportunities to insure normal development. Some of these are described in detail in *Early Child Care: The New Perspectives*, by Chandler, Lourie, and Peters, edited by Dittmann (1968). A brief review of some of the research problems is contained in Murphy's "Issues in Research" (1969a), followed by descriptions of several projects.

We do not yet know the extent of potential elimination of poverty and reduction of ill health, mental illness, school failure, and delinquency, but whether these can be reduced 75 percent or only 25 percent, the social and economic saving to the nation would be enormous. Just as many years were required for development of the airplane, and for many other major innovations, time is needed to revise and perfect the rehabilitation of neglected children and families in America.

OPERATIONAL GUIDELINES FOR PREVENTION OF DISORDER AND DEVELOPMENT OF STRENGTH

The following is a *suggested outline* of factors to be considered in development of the infant and preschool child (development of strength and prevention of disturbance or of developmental failures):

Ecology and the Culture

1. The broad culture: values, expectations, demands placed on children, and broad support for development.
2. The physical environment: protection from excessive heat, cold, wind, air pollution; and from other physical-environmental disturbances to health and equilibrium.
3. Architecture and equipment for the infant: stable "home base," space for motor activity and exploration; varied visual surroundings; protection from excessive noise and other overstimulation, from exposure to parents' marital activities. Play equipment.

Neighborhood. Adequate congruence between home and community values, standards of living.

The Family. Health and harmony of parents; mother's "optimal" warmth, attention to and contact with baby (not too little or too much). Father's support to mother and child. Support from siblings and the extended family.

The Organism. Genetic counseling to assist parents to avoid hereditary defects.

Prenatal-Birth Care. To prevent prenatal damage and assist optimum prenatal development and safety in delivery.

Infancy Assessment

Birth to Six Months

1. Defects, vulnerabilities, and special help required. If a baby is limp, unresponsive to visual or auditory stimuli, does not vocalize, is extremely disturbed by inoculations, loud sounds, or change and new stimuli, is oversensitive to touch, does not smile when smiled at, for example, he will need special help to approach normal

development. The same is true in the case of other sensitivities or defects. If he is in a cast for a club foot or confined because of infantile eczema, special resourcefulness will be needed to prevent the development of extreme passivity and failure to exert effort.

2. Biochemical needs, individual nutrition, vitamin, mineral, medication needs must be assessed, especially when a baby is apathetic despite loving care, susceptible to infection, etc.

3. Experiences related to early physiological integration: assessment of sources of pain and stress, effective soothing methods, appropriate timing and selection of need-gratification, feeding, cleaning, rest—important for smooth functioning as an organism and also foundations of ego strength.

4. Stimulation: qualities, quantities, duration and change appropriate to sensitivities and needs of the baby must be evaluated individually.

Infant's Psychological Development
First Year of Life

1. Support for infant's communications and expressions is needed to sustain his interest in and trust in the environment and interaction with it.

2. Support needed for cognitive development: a) adequate sensory (visual, auditory, tactile) stimuli, patterns, variety, b) communication; response to early vocalization and other signals, c) adequate support for autonomy, selectivity and choice, coping, effort, functional use of motor resources in adjusting posture and development of motor skills, participating in feeding, reaching and manipulating objects, exploring the environment, d) assistance to development of capacity for delay, attention, scanning, development of a cognitive map.

3. Support for social-emotional development: a) enjoyment of infant, interest in his individual expressions, his achievements, and patterns of development; support for his pleasure in self and in people, b) assistance to infant's coping with separation or change in image of mother-person, substitute mother, strangers, pain, and other sources of anxiety, c) help in management of early anger and aggression as aroused by teething, frustration, restriction of movement in changing clothes, etc., d) support for development of affection, love through play, cuddling, fondling to mild degrees (not too little or too much), e) help in laying foundations for maturation and sublimation of primitive drives—oral demand, motor, and aggressive drives, f) support for development of flexibility through accepting substitutes, getting used to new situations and frustrations, g) support for communication of needs for help.

Simultaneously, through all of the above, support for identification with mother, a relationship to a stable mother-figure, and a foundation for an awareness of self as differentiated from others.

These can contribute to a subjective sense of well-being—narcissism, or comfort and positive self-feeling—in the infant; and also to the development of *basic cognitive functions* dependent upon a positive response to the environment. These functions include curiosity and observation (looking); recognition, memory; the organization of sensory-motor functioning, capacity to experiment and to carry on *reality testing*, to cause things to happen by manipulating the environment, and the *development of concepts of stability in objects* in the external world and their potentialities, along with their qualities; the development of a cognitive map.

The above also contribute to the following: The development of positive basic social *relationships*, the ability to *communicate*, "sending power," capacity for perception of self as one who is human, one who can relate to and communicate with others, one who can belong to his own sex, one who is growing up and is part of one's own culture; the capacity for flexible relations with peers and adults, with a workable balance of trust and caution.

Second Year of Life

1. Enrichment of relationships and of cognitive development and coping capacity through shared experience and interaction in play, body games, looking at pictures, sharing simple stories and songs with adults; also companionship and play with other children.

2. Development of communication: a) response to child's efforts to express wants, observations, thoughts, fantasies in gesture, action, and language, b) providing vocabulary for objects, body parts, events, actions, routines, colors, etc., c) verbal play.
3. Assistance to perceptual and conceptual differentiation through verbalizing experiences: big-little, up-down, mine-yours, go-come, one-two, one-many, night-day, hot-cold, etc.
4. Developing respect for limits and rules: a) not touching dangerous objects, b) not throwing, breaking, c) not biting or hitting poeple, etc.
5. Assistance in sphincter control: opportunities for comfortable toileting, and encouragement within the child's realistic control capacities.
6. Respect for development of autonomy: a) support for child's self-help efforts in feeding, bathing, toileting, undressing, b) support for choices of play materials, excursions, foods (more of favorites; not forced acceptance of disliked foods, but gradual help in accepting), c) support of constructive coping devices: strategic withdrawal and fending off unwanted stimulation; protest, evoking help when needed, etc.
7. Support for maintenance of integration: a) protection from: i) unmanageable stress and anxiety; from excessive stimulation, ii) overwhelmingly frightening experiences with pets, trains, hospitalization, etc., iii) harsh discipline, excessively guilt-provoking pressures. iv) extreme frustration of autonomy needs in relation to hunger, sleep, etc., b) assistance in coping with manageable stress.
8. As an outgrowth of these, the development of trust in oneself and in others, the capacity to evoke and give love, and a balance of autonomy and cooperation. These include: a) self-attitudes that are positive and include a capacity for feeling good about oneself, or pride and triumph, as well as comfort in autonomous and self-initiated activities; freedom to express preferences, needs, demands; freedom to reject distasteful stimuli, to terminate after satiation, to fend off excessive stimulation, and also to evoke help and support, b) the beginnings of tolerance, the capacity to wait, to control impulses and to sublimate drives into socially constructive activities.

From Three to Five Years of Age

At this stage the child needs:
1. Materials, equipment, and space to use his new motor skills: Things to climb on, push, pull, swing in, ride on. He learns concepts of high-low, up-down, far-near, fast-slow, together-away, through verbalizing his activities and experiences.
2. Materials and spaces to express his ideas in: a) boxes and corners, boards and large blocks with which he can recreate the fire engine station or garage or farm he visits. These help him to begin to understand balance, heavy, light, short, long, b) paints, fingerpaints, clay, play-dough, crayons, scissors, paste; through these he discovers colors, the results of mixing, the effects produced by different ways of handling materials. Gradually, around the age of five—not at three—he begins to draw people, houses, or things he cares about.

Control, channeling of energy and directing of it, satisfaction in achievement, in what he can produce, are all stimulated by these experiences and the learning and growth they bring. A child *who learns to care about what he creates* loses interest in destroying things.

3. New experiences to stimulate curiosity and give him new ideas.
4. Help and support from his teachers and other grownups to respect his productions, and to develop pride and self-respect, and to develop his initiative toward leadership, not intrusiveness.
5. His competitive, exhibitionistic, domineering drives need the teacher's help in becoming socialized and balanced with cooperation, helping others, participating in joint undertakings.
6. As his skills and energies expand he needs help to respect limits and reasonable rules and to learn that these ground rules for living together do help him to control

unruly impulses. In severely deprived children we sometimes see extreme forms of aggression and sexuality (such as tearing down curtains, biting, spitting, violent kicking, screaming, ripping up doll clothes, erotic behavior toward teachers) which are rarely seen in middle class groups.[9] Such lack of beginning impulse-control may provide the roots for later reckless outbursts of violence and sexual aggression if his early school years do not evoke sufficient identification with socially acceptable standards.

7. Now that he has the capacity for expanded vocabulary he needs help in learning how to communicate his feelings in words—to tell the teacher when he is scared or mad or sad instead of running away or exploding or weeping in silent misery.

8. He needs opportunities to relate to and identify with others besides teachers, so that he can select roles to which he can tie his hopes for the future—whether he dreams of becoming a policeman or a mailman or a grocery-store man.

9. The children need help in developing frustration tolerance, a capacity to wait, and to stand the inevitable disappointments that come at times. This help will include help in accepting substitutes, in solving a problem that requires several steps to reach a goal.

10. They need help in management of fears, shock, or anxiety resulting from operations or other stressful experiences.

11. Those who have had inadequate mothering, who have been mistreated, need restitution; that is, patient, loving care, close contact, affection—large doses of what they did not have before.

12. All children need encouragement to express their wants, needs, feelings, and observations. Progress in use of concepts accompanies increase in communication, listening to, participating in, telling over, and finally telling their own stories.

From all of the above we see that building of strength in learning, control of behavior, social participation, and emotional integration come through the same rich experiences. A trip to the zoo can provide helpful intellectual, emotional, and social learning at the same time, and all of the child's positive development intrinsically fortifies the child against the breakdown of integration which becomes emotional disturbance or blocks to learning.

If these goals in the earliest development of the child are realized, delinquency, behavior problems, mental illness are less likely to occur in the child who is actively related to a positively satisfying and consistently socialized community, since the problems are chiefly outcomes of combinations of failure to meet the requirements proposed above. The child who is identified with the values of his social group and who has adequate control of impulses along with constructive channels for energy, initiative, and aggression is not likely to become delinquent. The child who is supported in coping with typical emotional problems and who is able to maintain positive attitudes toward himself and the relationships with the family and community is less likely to become mentally ill. This is not to say that children will cease to show transitory behavior problems and even symptoms growing out of the variable interacting stresses of development; but these not lead to pathology (barring disturbing brain damage, constitutional imbalances, and other defects, and overwhelming trauma).

Common errors in care of infants and young children include:

1. Forcing the baby to fit arbitrary norms of: a) sleep schedules; quantity, pace, etc., of food intake; toilet-training progress, b) disregarding individual differences in daily rhythms, nutritional needs, sphincter control capability, competing interests related to the infant's individual developmental timetable.

2. Underestimating or overestimating the baby's need for contact, sensory stimulation in different modalities, affection, protection, freedom, etc.

3. Underestimating the importance of early ego development growing out of: selective choices, receiving respect for expressions of needs, desires, protests, wish to terminate (feeding, play); manipulation of objects, exploration of environment, mastery of body and of environment.

4. Underestimating long-term effects or sequelae of early anxiety, trauma, deprivation, prolonged disintegrative reactions, and predispositions to anxiety, ambivalence, hostility arising from early disturbances.

5. Underestimating the importance of infantile foundations of cognitive development, curiosity, desire to learn, capacity to exert efforts toward mastery.

6. Underestimating positive aspects of earliest socialization.

Summary

Doctors, nurses, social workers, teachers, and many other persons can be helped to understand the process of development of personal strength and can help it go in the right direction. In medicine, the pediatrician thinks first of the physical needs of the individual child. The formula for the infant is adjusted in terms of how strong or how weak, how much sugar, which kind of prepared milk, what extra nutrients, and so forth, should be added in order to meet the needs of this individual child. Similarly, allergies are now recognized and, when solid food is added, those foods are utilized which the child can assimilate without allergic reactions, and any that create gastric disturbances are omitted; substitutes are found for them.

We need this kind of individualized thinking in dealing with children's feelings and mental development. We need to recognize the emotional equivalents of allergies, low sugar tolerance, high protein requirements, and the like in terms of both the direct effect on the child and the long-time influence on the mother-child relation. We are at a point where it is not only possible but desirable to think of babies in such terms as *the amount of stimulation they can stand, the quality, timing, and extent they need.* Experienced nurses and mothers can share their realization that one baby sleeps best when tightly wrapped up, where another one will respond to being stroked and patted, and still another responds to being cuddled or held, kitten-like, on a shoulder. One baby wants very early to be sufficiently vertical to be able to see as much as possible, where another baby is content to lie down and bang at toys on a cradle-gym.

Mothers may need more than good diets from pediatricians; they often need guidance in providing feeding experiences that allow the babies to follow their own rhythms and pace, and to do as much for themselves as they can with satisfaction. They need suggestions for individually measured stimulation, play, communication, opportunities for many different kinds of mastery, gratifying experiences with the new and strange, and other contributions to ego development that are of equal importance to the meeting of basic physiologic and libidinal needs.

A comprehensive program for building strength in young children would involve a full assessment of the strengths and vulnerabilities of the infant, the strengths and limitations of the mother in relation to her baby, other strengths and hazards presented by the environment to the individual child. Young parents today take the youngest babies on trips by car, train, or plane, often exposing the young sense organs and nervous system to amounts of stimulation that even adults find uncomfortable. Thus, the pediatrician can help the mother to think about "How much can this baby take at this stage?", "How can this experience be made bearable?"

Understanding of babies and little children can also be brought into the churches. Helpful attitudes can be stimulated in mothers by contagion, imitation, or identification with the supportive, kindly, observant, understanding approach of a wise leader in any field of service. As fast as persons most closely in touch with children in their homes, in clinics, hospitals, churches, and schools can recognize the danger signals in individual children, their individual needs for support, and ways of helping themselves, the more able we shall be in helping children to turn potentially overwhelming and damaging crises into managable stress, mastery of which can contribute to greater strength and capacity to handle new stress.

Building strength in children requires child-oriented and family-oriented thinking and planning throughout the culture: community planning and architecture, theology and the church, education, mass media of communication, all contribute their share to defeat or support the child's effort to maintain stability in an increasingly complex and changing world.

Notes

Much of this discussion is based on work done by L. B. Murphy over a period of 15 years at the Menninger Foundation under USPHS grants M680 and 5 R12 MH 9236–02, and also with support from the Menninger Foundation and the Gustavus and Louisa Pfeiffer Foundations, as well as grant MH 10421 at Children's Hospital of D. C.; and work by C. A. Chandler over a period of five years as Chief, Child Mental Health Section, NIMH.

1. Unpublished data from the Topeka longitudinal studies under L. B. Murphy, Menninger Foundation.

2. L. B. Murphy's review of infancy experience of severely disturbed children at Children's Hospital, Menninger Foundation. Unpublished.

3. L. B. Murphy's observations of individual cases at the Sarah Lawrence Nursery School.

4. One example is the case of Rachel reported in Murphy and Moriarty (to be published).

5. L. B. Murphy's personal records from Sarah Lawrence Nursery School; for example, autisticlike behavior in a child cared for by a deaf nurse, and another child kept on a leash tied to a tree.

6. Unpublished observation of L. B. Murphy.

7. Census data, World Almanac; 1965 compared with 1955.

8. Volume on the Topeka children in adolescence; by Alice Moriarty and Povl Toussieng, in press.

9. Observations by L. B. Murphy in day care centers for very deprived children.

References

Ainsworth, M. D. *Infancy in Uganda.* Baltimore: Johns Hopkins University Press, 1967.

Alpert, A. Reversibility of pathological fixations associated with maternal deprivation in infancy. *Psychoanalytic Study of the Child*, 1959, 14, 169–185.

Baruch, D. W. A study of reported tension in interparental relationships as co-existent with behavior adjustment in young children. *Journal of Experimental Education*, 1937, 6, 187–204.

Bazelon, M., Paine, R. S., Cowie, V. A., Hunt, P., Houck, J. C., & Mahanand, D. Reversal of hypotonia in infants with Down's syndrome by administration of 5-hydroxytryptophan. *Lancet*, May 27, 1967, 1130–1133.

Bender, L. Childhood schizophrenia. *Psychiatric Quarterly*, 1953, 27, 663–681.

Benedict, R. Anthropology and the abnormal. *Journal of General Psychology*, 1934, 10, 59–79. Reprinted in M. H. Fried (ed.), *Readings in anthropology.* Vol 2. New York: Crowell, 1959.

Benjamin, J. D. The innate and the experiential in development. In H. W. Brosin (ed.), *Lectures in experimental psychiatry.* Pittsburgh: University of Pittsburgh Press, 1961.

Bergman, P., & Escalona, S. K. Unusual sensitivities in very young children. *Psychoanalytic Study of the Child*, 1949, 4, 333–352.

Bowlby, J., Robertson, J., & Rosenbluth, D. A two-year-old goes to the hospital. *Psychoanalytic Study of the Child*, 1952, 7, 82–94.

Brackbill, Y. Research and clinical work with children. In R. A. Bauer (ed.), *Some views on Soviet psychology.* Washington, D. C.: American Psychological Association, 1962.

Brody, S. *Patterns of mothering.* New York: Hallmark Press, 1956.

Buhler, C. *Kindheit und Jugend (Childhood and adolescence).* (3rd ed.) Leipzig: S. Hirzel, 1931.

Buhler, C., & Hetzer, H. *The first year of life.* New York: Day, 1930.

Burlingham, D. T. Some problems of ego development in blind children. *Psychoanalytic Study of the Child*, 1965, 20, 194–208.

Caldwell, B. E., Hoffman, M. L., & Hoffman, L. W. (eds.) *Review of child development research.* New York: Russell Sage Foundation, 1964.

Canestrini, S. Über das Sinnesleben des Neugeborenen. In *Monograph. Gesamtgeb. Neurol. Psychiat.* No. 5. Berlin: Springer, 1913.

Carmichael, L. (ed.) *Manual of child psychology.* (Rev. ed.) New York: Wiley, 1954.

Chandler, C. A. The role of the community treatment facility in prevention. In R. H. Ojemann (ed.), *Proceedings of the Fifth Institute on Preventive Psychiatry.* Iowa City: University of Iowa Press, 1965.

Chandler, C. A., Lourie, R. S., & Peters, A. DeH. (L. Dittman, ed.) *Early child care: The new perspectives.* New York: Atherton, 1968.

Clausen, J. A. *Socialization and society.* Boston: Little, Brown, 1968.

Coleman, R., & Provence, S. Environmental retardation (hospitalism) in infants living in families. *Pediatrics*, 1957, 19, 285–292.

Coles, R. *Children of crisis.* Boston: Little, Brown, 1967.

Collis, R. *The lost and the found; The story of Eva and Laszlo, two children of war-torn Europe.* New York: Womans Press, 1953.

Cooke, R. E. Statement before the Committee on Education and Labor of the House of Representatives; hearings on Head Start, April 28, 1969. (Mimeo)

Davis, W. A., & Havighurst, R. J. *Father of the man.* Boston: Houghton Mifflin, 1947.

Del Castillo, M. *Child of our time.* New York: Knopf, 1958.

Deschin, C. S. The need to extend medical services beyond the hospital if maternal and infant care is to become comprehensive. *American Journal of Public Health*, 1968, 58, 1230–1236.

Deutsch, M., & Associates. *The disadvantaged child.* New York: Basic Books, 1967.

Drillien, C. M. *The growth and development of the prematurely born infant.* Edinburgh & London: Livingston, 1964.

Drillien, C. M. The incidence of mental and physical handicaps in school age children of very low birth weight. *Pediatrics*, 1967, 39, 238–247.

Erikson, E. *Childhood and society.* (2nd ed.) New York: Norton, 1963.

Escalona, S. K. *Roots of individuality.* Chicago: Aldine, 1968.

Escalona, S., & Heider, G. *Prediction and outcome.* New York: Basic Books, 1959.

Fantz, R. L. Visual perception from birth as shown by pattern selectivity. In *New issues in child development. Annals of the New York Academy of Sciences,* 1965, 118, 793–814.

Fraiberg, S., & Freedman, A. Studies in the ego development of the congenitally blind child. *Psychoanalytic Study of the Child,* 1964, 19, 113–169.

Frank, L. K. *On the importance of infancy.* New York: Random House, 1966.

Freud, A. *Normality and pathology in childhood.* New York: International Universities Press, 1965.

Freud, A., & Dann, S. An experiment in group upbringing. *Psychoanalytic Study of the Child,* 1951, 6, 127–168.

Gardner, R. W., & Moriarty, A. E. *Personality development at preadolescence: Explorations of structure formation.* Seattle: University of Washington Press, 1968.

Geertinger, P. *Sudden death in infancy.* Springfield, Ill.: Charles C Thomas, 1968.

Gesell, A., & Ilg, F. L. *Infant and child in the culture of today.* New York: Harper, 1943.

Glueck, E. T. Identification of potential delinquents at 2–3 years of age. *International Journal of Social Psychiatry,* 1966, 12, 5–16.

Glueck, E., & Gleuck, S. *Unraveling juvenile delinquency.* Cambridge: Harvard University Press, 1950.

Gold, E. M., & Stone, M. L. Total maternal and infant care: A realistic appraisal. *American Journal of Public Health,* 1968, 58, 1219–1229.

Goldfarb, W., Mintz, I., & Stroock, K. *A time to heal.* New York: International Universities Press, 1969.

Greenacre, P. *Trauma, growth and personality.* New York: Norton, 1952.

Havighurst, R. J., Dubois, M. E., Csikszentmihalyi, M., & Doll, R. A cross-national study of Buenos Aires and Chicago adolescents. *Bibliotheca, Vita Humana, Fasc. 3.* S. Karger Ag (Albert J. Phiebig), 1964.

Heider, G. M. Vulnerability in infants and young children. *Genetic Psychology Monographs,* 1966, 73–74.

Hushka, M. The child's response to coercive toilet training. *Psychosomatic Medicine,* 1942, 4, 301–308.

Jacobs, P. A., Baikie, A. G., Court Brown, W. M., & Strong, J. A. The somatic chromosome in mongolism. *Lancet,* 1959, 1, 710.

Jacobson, E. The self and the object world. *Psychoanalytic Study of the Child,* 1954, 9, 75–127.

Jakab, I. The role of neonatal anoxia and its prevention. *Acta Paedopsychiatrica* (Basel), 1965, 32, 329–338.

Jelliffe, D. B. *Infant nutrition in the tropics and sub-tropics.* Geneva: World Health Organization, 1955.

Jersild, A. T., & Holmes, F. B. Children's fears. *Child Development Monographs,* 1935, No. 20.

Jessner, L., Blom, G., & Waldfogel, S. Emotional implications of tonsillectomy and adenoidectomy on children. *Psychoanalytic Study of the Child,* 1952, 7, 126–169.

Jones, M. C., Bayley, N., Macfarlane, J., Honzik, M. P. *The course of human development.* Waltham, Mass. Xerox College Publishing, 1971.

Kagan, J., & Moss, H. A. *Birth to maturity: A study in psychological development.* New York: Wiley, 1962.

Keniston, K. *The uncommitted: Alienated youth in American society.* New York: Harcourt, Brace & World, 1966.

Klein, G. S. Blindness and isolation. *Psychoanalytic Study of the Child,* 1962, 17, 82–93.

Knobloch, H., & Pasamanick, B. Environmental factors affecting human development, before and after birth. *Pediatrics,* 1960, 26, 210–218.

Lambo, T. A. Growth of African children (psychological aspects). In T. A. Lambo (ed.), *Pan African Psychiatric Conference.* (Abeokuta, Nigeria, Nov. 12–18, 1961) Ibadan, Western Nigeria: Government Printer, 1961.

Lesser, A. J., Gershenson, C. P., Hunt, E. P., Bonato, R. R., & Pratt, M. N. *Infant and perinatal mortality rates by age and color. United States, each state and county, 1956–1960, 1961–1965.* (Children's Bureau, United States Department of Health, Education, and Welfare) Washington, D. C.: United States Government Printing Office, 1968.

Levy, D. M. Psychic trauma of operations in children. *American Journal of Disease of Children,* 1945, 69, 7–15.

Lewin, K., Lippitt, R., & White, R. K. Patterns of aggressive behavior in an experimentally created social situation. *Journal of Social Psychology,* 1939, 10, 271–299.

Lowenfeld, B. *Our blind children.* (2nd ed.) Springfield, Ill.: Charles C Thomas, 1964.

Macfarlane, J. W., Allen, L., & Honzik, M. P. *A developmental study of the behavior problems of normal children between twenty-one months and fourteen years.* Berkeley: University of California Press, 1954.

Mattick, I. Adaptation of nursery school techniques to deprived children. *Journal of the American Academy of Child Psychiatry,* 1965, 4, 670–700.

McClelland, D., Atkinson, J., Clark, R., & Lowell, E. *The achievement motive.* New York: Appleton-Century-Crofts, 1953.

Menninger, K. A. *The vital balance; The life process in mental health and illness.* New York: Viking, 1963.

Menninger Quarterly, 1967, 21(3 & 4). (Whole issue: Adolescence: The troubled and troubling years.)

Montagu, M. F. A. *Prenatal influences.* Springfield, Ill.: Charles C Thomas, 1962.

Moore, O. K., & Anderson, A. R. The responsive environments project. In R. D. Hess & R. M. Bear (eds.), *Early education: Current theory, research and practice.* Chicago: Aldine, 1967.

Moreno, J. L. *Who shall survive?* Washington; Nervous and Mental Disease Publishing Co., 1934.

Murphy, L. B. Some aspects of the first relationship. *International Journal of Psycho-Analysis,* 1964, 45, 31–43.

Murphy, L. B. Assessment of infants and young children. In L. Dittman, C. Chandler, R. Lourie, & A. Peters (eds.), *Early child care: The new perspectives*. New York: Atherton Press, 1968. (a)

Murphy, L. B. The vulnerability inventory (Appendix A). In L. Dittman, C. Chandler, R. Lourie, & A. Peters (eds.), *Early child care: The new perspectives*. New York: Atherton Press, 1968. (b)

Murphy, L. B. Children under three—Finding ways to stimulate development. I. Issues in research. *Children*, 1969, 16, 46—52. (a)

Murphy, L. B. Statement before the Committee on Education and Labor of the House of Representatives; hearings on Head Start, April 28, 1969. (Mimeo) (b)

Murphy, L. B. Curing a social cancer. Unpublished paper evaluating the Parent Child Centers, 1970.

Murphy, L. B. Later outcomes of early infant and mother relationships. Paper presented at the 1971 Annual Meeting of the American Orthopsychiatric Association.

Murphy, L. B., & Associates. *Personality in young children.* Vol. 1. *Methods for the study of personality in young children.* Vol. 2. *Colin—A normal child.* New York: Basic Books, 1956.

Murphy, L. B., & Associates. *Widening world of childhood.* New York: Basic Books, 1962.

Murphy, L. B., & Moriarty, A. E. *Development, vulnerability and resilience.* In press.

Newsweek, 1967, 69, 92—95.

North, A. F. Pediatric care in Project Head Start. In J. Hellmuth (ed.), *Disadvantaged child.* Vol. 2. Seattle: Special Child Publications, 1968.

Omwake, E. B., & Solnit, A. J. "It isn't fair": The treatment of a blind child. *Psychoanalytic Study of the Child*, 1961, 16, 352—404.

Ourth, L., & Brown, K. B. Inadequate mothering and disturbance in the neonatal period. *Child Development*, 1961, 32, 287—295.

Pasamanick, B., & Lilienfeld, A. M. Association of maternal and fetal factors with development of mental deficiency. I. Abnormalities in the prenatal and paranatal periods. *Journal of the American Medical Association*, 1955, 159, 155—160.

Piaget, J. *Origins of intelligence in children.* New York: International Universities Press, 1952.

Prugh, D. G., & Harlow, R. G. "Masked deprivation" in infants and young children. In M. D. Ainsworth (ed.), *deprivation of maternal care*. New York: Schocken, 1967. (Paperback)

Psychoanalytic study of the child. New York: International Universities Press, 1945.

Rheingold, H. L. The modification of social responsiveness in institutional babies. *Monographs of the Society for Research in Child Development*, 1956, 21(Special No. 63).

Rice, D. *Estimating the cost of illness.* (United States Department of Health, Education, and Welfare Health Economics Series No. 5; Public Health Service Publication No. 947—6) Washington, D. C.: United States Government Printing Office, 1966.

Richmond, J. B. Observations of infant development: Clinical and psychological aspects. *Merrill-Palmer Quarterly*, 1964, 10, 95—101.

Richmond, J. B., & Lipton, E. L. Some aspects of the neurophysiology of the newborn and their implications for child development. In L. Jessner (ed.), *Dynamic psychopathology in childhood.* New York: Grune & Stratton, 1959.

Robertson, J. *Going to hospital with mother.* (Movie, 16mm, sound, 45 min., in English and French) London: Tavistock Clinic, undated.

Rogers, M. E., Lilienfeld, A. M., & Pasamanick, B. *Prenatal and paranatal factors in the development of childhood behavior disorders.* Baltimore: School of Public Health, Johns Hopkins University, 1955.

Rosenzweig, M. R. Environmental complexity, cerebral change, and behavior. *American Psychologist*, 1966, 21, 321—332.

Sackett, G. P. Some effects of social and sensory deprivation during rearing on behavioral development of monkeys. *Inter-American Journal of Psychology*, 1967, 1, 55—77.

Sandler, A. M. Aspects of passivity and ego development in the blind infant. *Psychoanalytic Study of the Child*, 1963, 18, 343—360.

Schiffer, C. G., & Hunt, E. P. *Illness among children.* (Children's Bureau, United States Department of Health, Education, and Welfare) Washington, D. C.: United States Government Printing Office, 1963.

Schwartz, P. Parturitional injury of the newborn as a cause of mental deficiency and allied conditions. In C. H. Carter (ed.), *Medical aspects of mental retardation.* Springfield, Ill.: Charles C Thomas, 1965.

Scott, J. P. Critical periods in behavioral development. Science, 1962, 138, 949—958.

Scrimshaw, N. S., & Gordon, J. E. (eds.) *Malnutrition, learning and behavior.* Cambridge: MIT Press, 1968.

Senn, M. J. E., & Solnit, A. J. *Problems in child behavior and development.* Philadelphia: Lea & Febiger, 1968.

Sever, J. L., Nelson, K. B., & Gilkeson, M. R. Rubella epidemic, 1964. Effect on 6,000 pregnancies. *American Journal of Diseases of Children*, 1964, 111, 395—407.

Sewall, M. Some causes of jealousy in young children. *Smith College Studies in Social Work*, 1930, 1, 6—22.

Shapiro, S., & Unger, J. *Weight at birth and its effects on survival of the newborn in the United States.* (Public Health Service Publication No. 1000, Series 21, No. 3) Washington, D. C.: United States Government Printing Office, 1965.

Shaw, C. R. *Delinquency areas.* Chicago: University of Chicago Press, 1929.

Sherif, M. *Social interaction: Processes and products.* Chicago: Aldine, 1967.

Shinn, M. W. *The biography of a baby.* Boston: Houghton Mifflin, 1900.

Shirley, M. M. *The first two years.* Vol. 3. *Personality manifestations.* Minneapolis: University of Minnesota Press, 1933.

Skeels, H. M. Some Iowa studies of the mental growth of children in relation to differentials of the environment: A summary. In *Intelligence: Its nature and nurture.*

39th Year Book of the National Society for the Study of Education, 1940, Part II, 281–308.

Skeels, H. M. Adult status of children with contrasting early life experiences. *Monographs of the Society for Research in Child Development*, 1966, 31(3, Serial No. 105).

Solnit, A. J., & Provence, S. A. (eds.) *Modern perspectives in child development*. (In honor of Milton J. E. Senn) New York: International Universities Press, 1963.

Sontag, L. W. Maternal anxiety during pregnancy and fetal behavior. In *Physical and behavioral growth*. (Report of the 26th Ross Pediatric Research Conference) Columbus, Ohio: Ross Medical Company, 1958.

Spitz, R. A. Hospitalism: An inquiry into the genesis of psychiatric conditions in early childhood. *Psychoanalytic Study of the Child*, 1945, 1, 53–74.

Spitz, R. A. Anaclitic depression: An inquiry into the genesis of psychiatric conditions in early childhood, II. *Psychoanalytic Study of the Child*, 1946, 2, 313–342.

Spitz, R. A. *The first year of life*. New York: International Universities Press, 1965.

Srole, L., Langner, T. S., Michael, S. T., Opler, M. K., & Rennie, T. A. C. *Mental health in the metropolis: The Midtown Manhattan Study*. Vol. 1. New York: McGraw-Hill, 1962.

Stechler, G. Newborn attention as affected by medication during labor. *Science*, 1964, 144, 315–317.

Stegner, W. E. *Wolf Willow*. New York: Viking Press, 1962.

Sully, J. *Studies of childhood*. New York: Appleton, 1910.

Terman, L. M. *Genetic studies of genius*. Stanford: Stanford University Press, 1925.

Thomas, A., Birch, H. G., Chess, S., Hertzig, M. E., & Korn, S. *Behavioral individuality in early childhood*. New York: New York University Press, 1964.

Thompson, H. Physical growth. In L. Carmichael (ed.), *Manual of child psychology*. (Rev. ed.) New York: Wiley, 1954.

Time, 1967, 90, 18–22.

United States Public Health Service. *Statistics on public institutions for delinquent children: 1964*. (United States Department of Health, Education, and Welfare, Children's Bureau Statistical Series No. 81) Washington, D. C.: United States Government Printing Office, 1965.

United States Public Health Service. *Suicide in the U. S., 1950 through 1964*. (Vital and health statistics series; Public Health Service Publication No. 10000, Series 20, No. 5) Washington, D. C.: United States Government Printing Office, 1967.

United States Public Health Service. *Monthly vital statistics report*. (Vol. 16, No. 12, Suppl.) Washington, D. C.: United States Government Printing Office, 1968. (a)

United States Public Health Service. *Vital statistics of the United States*. (Vol. 2, Part A, Section 2: Infant mortality; Section 3: Fetal mortality) Washington, D. C.: United States Government Printing Office, 1968. (b)

United States Public Health Service. *Monthly vital statistics report*. (Vol. 16, No. 12: Annual summary for the United States: 1967) Washington, D. C.: United States Government Printing Office, 1968. (c)

Werner, H. *Comparative psychology of mental development*. (Rev. ed.) New York: International Universities Press, 1952.

Whyte, W. H. *The organization man*. New York: Doubleday, 1967.

Wiener, G. Correlates of low birth weight; Psychological status at six to seven years of age. *Pediatrics*, 1965, 35, 434–444.

Williams, R. J. *Biochemical individuality*. New York: Wiley, 1956.

Winnicott, D. W. *Mother and child*. New York: Basic Books, 1957.

Witkin, H. A., Dyk, R. B., Faterson, H. F., Goodenough, D. R., & Karp, S. A. *Psychological differentiation*. New York: Wiley, 1962.

Wolf, K. M. Observation of individual tendencies in the first year of life. In M. J. E. Senn (ed.), *Problems of infancy and childhood*. New York: Josiah Macy Jr. Foundation, 1952.

Wolfenstein, M. Fun morality: An analysis of recent American child-training literature. In M. Mead & M. Wolfenstein (eds.), *Childhood in contemporary cultures*. Chicago: University of Chicago Press, 1955.

World almanac and book of facts. New York: Newspaper Enterprise Association, 1955, 1965.

World Health Organization. *World health statistics report*, 1968, 21(2–3), 145–146.

14

The Social Environment of the High School: Guidelines for Individual Change and Organizational Redevelopment

Edison J. Trickett, James G. Kelly, David M. Todd

The impact of an ever increasing rate of social change and the growing complexity of our urban communities is hitting the adolescent "where he's at," in the high school. The social system of this organization reflects not only the social characteristics and the goals of the community it serves but also the community's tensions and conflicts. Under the mandate to prepare adolescents for adult life, the high school becomes a very visible battleground for social issues, with the result that the schools face recurrent crises. Students, demanding a voice in the governing and disciplining process, threaten to strike; police are increasingly stationed in school buildings in more than one part of the country; and in increasingly more communities black parents are insisting not only on more equal staff representation at their local high school but also on the right to interview job applicants in order to screen out "Uncle Toms."

Mental health professionals share the interest of various community groups in the high school. This interest stems from a consideration of the school as a place for preventive interventions to curb the growing mental health problems of the country. Several years ago the Joint Commission on Mental Health and Illness and, more recently, the Joint Commission on the Mental Health of Children, brought "into the national consciousness in a clear and compelling way the staggering extent of the mental health problem, the inadequacy of numbers of professionally trained personnel, the limitations of exclusive dependence on the hospital, clinic and private-practice setting, the need to explore the use of and training for subprofessional groups, and the consequences of the neglect of a truly preventive approach" (Sarason et al., 1966, p. 16).

What are the costs of these inadequacies? While it is difficult to find statistics on the incidence of mental illness in adolescents as a group, Osterweil (1966) estimates that about ten percent of children attending school have emotional difficulties in varying degrees of seriousness. Kvaraceus (1968)(a) paints a somewhat more serious picture:

"If we add to all those disturbed children who remain passive and manifest silent symptoms of their maladjustment to the overt, aggressive norm-violating group, we will be dealing with a minimum of 10 percent of the school's population and, depending on the socioeconomic-cultural forces as well as on the tolerance of local authority to deviancy, the school and community may need to give special attention to a third of its clientele" (p. 1).

The statistics compiled by Dukelow (1961), based upon reports from 143 large city school systems, suggest that about 7.5 percent of the pupils in these schools could benefit from mental health services. Although this estimate is conservative by Kvaraceus' standards, its comparison with the reported number of children receiving such help dramatizes the inadequacy of current services (see Figure 14–1).

The discrepancy between reported needs and available mental health services is wide for all geographic regions, ranging from a 400 percent increase in services needed in New England to a reported need for an increase of around 700 percent in other areas. Nationally, school systems

REGION

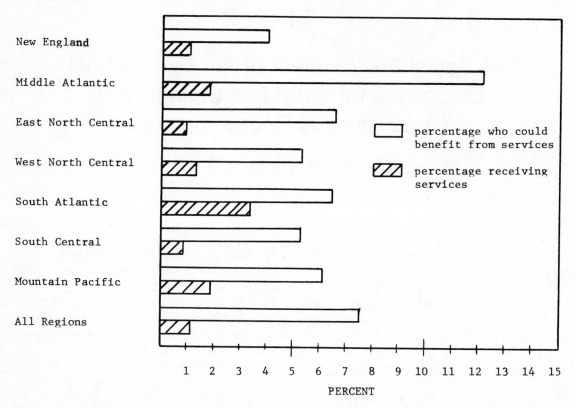

Fig. 14—1. Percentage of pupils in large city schools who could benefit from mental health services and percentage receiving such services. (Data reprinted with permission from Dukelow, 1961. Copyrighted 1961 by the American School Health Association.) Based on reports from 143 large city school systems with over 5½ million pupils.

of this size report a need for more than six times the current mental health services to provide help to all the pupils who could benefit from it.

In seeking ways to ameliorate mental illness in children and to develop means of preventing its occurrence, many mental health professionals turn to the school. Why? Hunt (1968) presents one explanation:

"In suggesting the American School System, my basic premise is that the school is the one common institution that touches every American for a long and extremely important period of his life. He is gathered up and made accessible to his culture in a common location. Not only is he made accessible, but he is made invisible, as an individual and as a member of a group. He is in a controlled environment which can be manipulated for the social good. His continuance in the system is rigidly enforced, legally by the truant officer, economically by the state and federal financing

based upon attendance figures, and familially by the educational and supportive (such as school lunches, etc.) benefits made available to him. The school, then, is the one institution that involves every American and from which he cannot escape" (p. 37).

While Hunt's statement concerns the entire range of public schooling, it serves to clarify the importance of the high school as the one *controllable* force in the socialization of adolescents (Bardon, 1968). Recent statistics based upon estimates from the United States Office of Education and the National Education Association (*Saturday Review*, 1968) suggest that roughly 14,200,000 adolescents are attending 31,306 secondary schools (including 1,400,000 who are attending nonpublic schools). Over $30 billion is invested in elementary and secondary education. These statistics emphasize the importance of understanding and enhancing this socialization process, and the high school's place in preventive and rehabilitative mental health services for adolescents.

This chapter will focus on the conceptual and empirical bases for creating interventions for the adolescent in the high school. It is the premise of this chapter that the source for preventive interventions for the student and faculty of the high school will derive from a point of view that focuses directly upon the relationship between the individual student and the high school environment. It is the thesis of this chapter that the task of designing preventive programs is a *new* problem for the behavioral sciences, not simply a matter of translating or applying current or past knowledge. For some time, the topic of community mental health services has been related to concepts of primary, secondary, and tertiary prevention, the touchstones of public health programs (Caplan, 1964). Too often, however, such applications have been literal and discrete, as if the prevention of mental illness is identical with the prevention of an infectious disease.

The heritage of public health has relied upon a conception of disease etiology that is dynamic, multivariate, and primarily concerned with the relationship between various environmental sources and combinations of carriers or agents of the infection. Much has been lost in the translation, for there is a tendency in community mental health practice to search for *the* cause, and then to offer *a* treatment to a specific population, denying the heritage of public health practice. There is little in the psychological literature that presents a view of man as a dynamic part of his social environment and that presents the task of psychological theorizing as a problem of how persons are bounded or related to a social setting and how their behavior varies from place to place. It is this preference for viewing individual behavior in a natural setting that is the recommended context for the topics of both personal and organizational change. The view asserts that any real change in the performance of individuals will affect other members of the immediate setting and the functions of the social structure. Similarly any substantial changes in the structuring of the environment will have effects upon at least some individuals. The grist for the mill of the change agent is advocated as the coupling between the

person and the social setting just as much as the individual *or* the social setting. This point of view, while laudable and even venerable in the biological sciences, is idiosyncratic for the behavioral sciences. The closest analogy is the ecological analogy in biology. This chapter will present principles derived from biological ecology that are relevant for designing preventive interventions and that can help to anticipate the effects of such interventions upon the members of the immediate setting.

Because of the unfamiliarity of ecological writings in mental health literature, the authors have organized the chapter so as to present the ecological principles after a review of current research of the high school. The reader is alerted that ecological principles will come at the end of the chapter and that they dominate the authors' point of view. In part this organization reflects a viewpoint about the development of knowledge as an inductive, cyclical process. The development of theory in this view represents an attempt to provide an integrative perspective on existing knowledge and to provide direction to the verification, elaboration, and extension of that knowledge through continued research.

To begin, there is a review of current mental health practices including a discussion of mental health consultation methods. Mental health services provided within the high school as well as mental health services provided for adolescents in the community will be summarized. This section will present a view of the types of services that currently are provided as well as pointing out the gaps in such services. The next part of the chapter will review current knowledge regarding the performance of critical adult roles serving the high school, including the superintendent, principal, classroom teacher, and provider of special service resources along with some brief comments about the adolescent in the high school. The focus for this section is an analysis of the influence of these critical roles upon the social structure of the high school, particularly how these roles affect the expression of innovation. This section then presents a working knowledge of the high school as the student meets it. The next section will look at the high school as a socialization agent, as a social institution for influencing the competence of the adolescent. Here the emphasis will be to look at the formal and informal social structure of the high school, including the peer structure of the adolescent. This section in combination with the preceding section is designed to present a realistic view of how the high school works as a natural social organization. Given the lack of research on social change and disruption in the high school, the last part of this section considers directions for naturalistic observation and case reporting on high schools in crisis.

The last part of the chapter presents ideas for taking the ecological analogy and making it work to affect individual change and organizational redevelopment. It is hoped that the thesis will be more relevant and its validity upheld by coming late in the chapter and referring back to the previous material.

CURRENT MENTAL HEALTH PRACTICES IN THE HIGH SCHOOL

A primary consideration for viewing the high school as a setting for preventive interventions is to assess the total range and scope of existing mental health services for the adolescent, both within the school and in the community. This assertion derives its significance from two assumptions which are rooted in the basic ecological premise of interdependence between the various structures and functions of a dynamic system, and between the system and its environment. The first of these assumptions is that treatment and prevention are highly interdependent functions. An adequate response to adolescent mental health problems demands a network of differentiated preventive and treatment-rehabilitative services, a social network in which existing mental health resources play a critical role. The second assumption is that the nature and adequacy of mental health services in the school is highly dependent upon their relationship to mental health resources in the surrounding community.

The following section provides an overview of current mental health services for adolescents in the school and the broader community as a basis for considering the development of preventive interventions in the high school.

Mental Health Services in the School

Facing the pressures of inadequate "traditional" services, not to mention the growing interest in

preventive measures, mental health and guidance professionals are increasingly stressing the need and responsibility to utilize existing resources more fully in the school (Hunt, 1968; Bardon, 1968; Thoreson, 1968). Here, as in many related areas of mental health services, the question is a dual one of manpower and role definition. Both guidance counselors and school psychologists, traditionally identified as the "core" of student services, find themselves in far greater demand than there is supply (Wrenn, 1965; Reed & Steffler, 1963). Indeed, Trachman, speaking of school psychologists, pointed out that "if every qualified psychologist in the country went to work for the schools, the proposed ratio (of one psychologist for every 900 pupils) would still not be met" (Reed & Steffler, 1963, p. 157). Coleman and his associates (1966) found that the average secondary pupil attends a school in which a guidance counselor has 391 students assigned, counsels 39 students per week, and deals with "personal or emotional adjustment" problems only about 22 percent of his counseling time. Estimates such as these provide the basis for skepticism that the demand, defined in existing terms, can be met.

In response to this situation, traditional school mental health professions are experiencing increasing pressure to redefine their functions toward roles of enhancing the ability of teachers and the school as a whole to cope with student mental health problems. Such developments have several important implications for mental health services in the schools. One of particular interest is the emergence of more differentiated, specialized roles such as psychometrician, and in elementary schools, the crisis teacher. No systematic investigation of the extent and impact of such roles on the high school is known to the authors.

Another implication of current trends is a concern for the informal help-giving processes in the school. Unfortunately, extremely little has been written about these resources and their importance to adolescent socialization. Coleman and his associates (1966) found that the average secondary school teacher reports spending almost two hours a week in counseling activities. It is likely that there are important individual and situational differences in such activity and that particular school personnel, such as athletic coaches and extracurricular advisors, can have a significant impact on some adolescents. It is difficult to assess the contribution of these resources without any systematic knowledge about who they are and how they function, and the process of strengthening informal help giving in the school must remain a very ad hoc operation until such knowledge is created.

In addition to the various mental health personnel in the school, it would be helpful to know of the existence and effect of relevant programs. One estimate of the extent of such programs is that just ten percent of secondary school pupils in the United States attend schools with programs for children with "behavior and emotional problems" and 51 percent have access to a program for the mentally retarded, with 44 percent having a speech therapist available (Coleman et al., 1966). Unfortunately this kind of statistic provides only the most cursory picture of the scope, fears, and quality of existing programs.

Other more differentiated and comprehensive information about mental health services in the school is clearly needed. The inadequacy of existing knowledge is striking and it represents a major constraint on effective planning. Our best estimates do suggest that the mobilization of mental health services in schools is already quite deficient and that preventive programs will have to offer much harder evidence than ideological hope and public health analogy to gain support and implementation. However, even more basic implications derive from the interrelationship among various mental health interventions in terms of their effectiveness. To cite a rather obvious example, a program to help teachers learn to make earlier assessments and referrals for disturbed adolescents can expect little support if the students who are referred are simply put on a waiting list. The problem is a reciprocal one. It may be true that existing mental health services can never meet current needs if effective preventive measures are not developed. However, it is equally likely that the effectiveness of preventive measures will depend in the long run upon an adequate range of treatment and rehabilitative resources.

This problem is infrequently noted within the confines of the high school. The ecological view asserts that major constraints upon an organization exist in its relationship to the environment. A key to the mobilization and utilization of existing resources within the school is the relationship of those resources to other mental health services in the community.

Extra-School Mental Health Services and Links to the Community

The notion that education, and not mental health, is the responsibility of the schools is an overly simple one, but its truth is important. The school is one unit of an extensive array of institutions and "agents" which comprise the "socialization community" for children and youth (Lippitt, 1968). In terms of mental health services, the school may be viewed as part of a system of community resources for enhancing the psychological well-being and social effectiveness of young people (see Figure 14–2). Some of these agencies collaborate with the school in working directly with troubled children or in more intensive programs away from the schools and homes of more severely disturbed or less manageable children.

The various institutions listed in Figure 14–2, Column D, represent key community resources which can serve mental health functions for adolescents. The critical interdependence of the institutions in this network, which includes the school, is represented in its most simple form by their dependence on one another for consultation, referrals, and the collaboration in joint efforts to help particular adolescents. However, their interdependence is represented at a more abstract level by the fact that the various mental health functions of the total community must be distributed in some way through this network of institutions (Column C). These functions represent the demands placed upon the community by the total range of maladaptive conditions characteristic of adolescents, ranging from emergent difficulties in coping with various life crises to the critical disequalibrium associated with severe psychopathology and chaotic, nonnutrient, or abusive environments (Column B). Adequate help for all adolescents who need it depends upon the community's ability to allocate its mental health functions to available institutions and provide the necessary resources. The network in Figure 14–2 represents, in simplified form, a comprehensive example of such allocations. However, a major implication for the school as a socialization agent

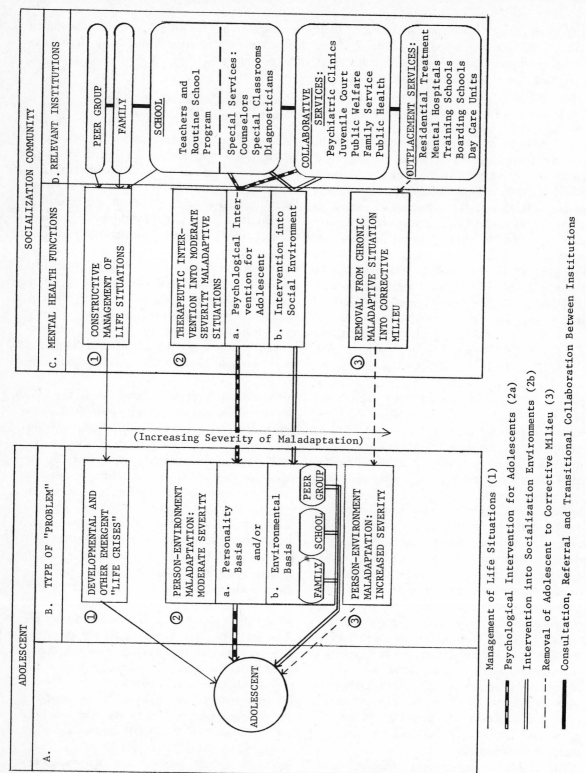

Fig. 14–2. Mental health services for adolescents in varied adaptive conditions.

is that these functions for which no other resources are available will be laid at the door of the school. When treatment is not available in the community, for example, the school has little choice but to work with children who cannot function effectively in its regular programs. We expect that the availability of special resources within the school system is all too highly correlated with the availability of collaborative community services, and the school is very often left with a range of problems with which it is ill-prepared to cope.

Of course, the existence of resources need not imply their ready availability or efficient mobilization. The difficulties in coordination between school and community agencies is especially clear, for example, in disadvantaged areas where multiproblem families are served by a variety of agencies (Sarason et al., 1966). The school may make unique contributions to the community's efforts to help such families by providing diagnostic information about the family and offering various services to the children. An example would be the creation of group recreational programs for boys without adult males in the family or providing the adolescent opportunities to increase his ability to cope with such family life-crises as births, divorces, deaths, and parental unemployment. In turn, the school may be very limited in what it can do with any child as long as the family remains disorganized or excessively conflicted. The availability of relevant community resources is crucial in such cases and may assume a greater priority than any particular work with the child in the school setting. In many cases, the information gained from community agencies—especially through welfare or social workers—can become crucial sources of data for the school personnel to consider in evaluating adolescents. Such agencies can, in addition, serve an important role in the coordinated planning of what to do and can serve to alert school personnel of impending crises in an adolescent's life such as the family's moving to another neighborhood or city.

Unfortunately, many mental health professionals who remark on the importance of close and constant communication between school and community agencies "learned the hard way" and have realized its importance after a lack of such communication. Discouragement among profes-

sionals in this respect comes close to unanimity when speaking of schools in disadvantaged areas (Newman, 1967). Indeed, Sarason et al. find the problem sufficiently pressing to devote an entire chapter to the frustrations of working within the web of the many agencies who often have dealings with disadvantaged children. Their discouragement is very evident: "Most disheartening, in everyday work, is that it's easy to develop the paranoid attitude that the major concern of the community agencies is to keep teachers and other school personnel as uninformed as possible about problems and actions that affect the child in school" (Sarason et al., 1966, p. 270). Of additional importance is that the quality of the relationship between school and community agencies can have a profound effect not only on the adolescent who may get lost—or at least misplaced—in the shuffle, but on the morale of the teachers. If we are to accept Sarason's analysis, there is an equivalent impact on the already abundant cynicism of many mental health professionals.

In fairness to the community agencies it must be noted they are generally in no better position than the school with respect to the manpower and facilities necessary for effective school-agency cooperation. To compound the tragedy, those schools whose students' families have most contact with community agencies are the least likely to be adequately staffed themselves. These families are the most critical clients for establishing community services in disadvantaged areas.[1] This is by no means to imply that planning and coordination have not occurred simply because of negligence or lack of interest on the part of school personnel and mental health professionals. Our cultural context provides little perspective or precedent for such planning, and social science is only beginning the search for a viable antidote to this historical void.

Community Referral Resources. Sometimes community agencies play a more direct role in the school's work with children than the collaborative one of providing services to their families; they also participate in the task of enabling the child to grow and learn through treatment or counseling. Again, the school's relationship to these referral agencies is multifaceted, with the school and the agencies serving interdependent and complemen-

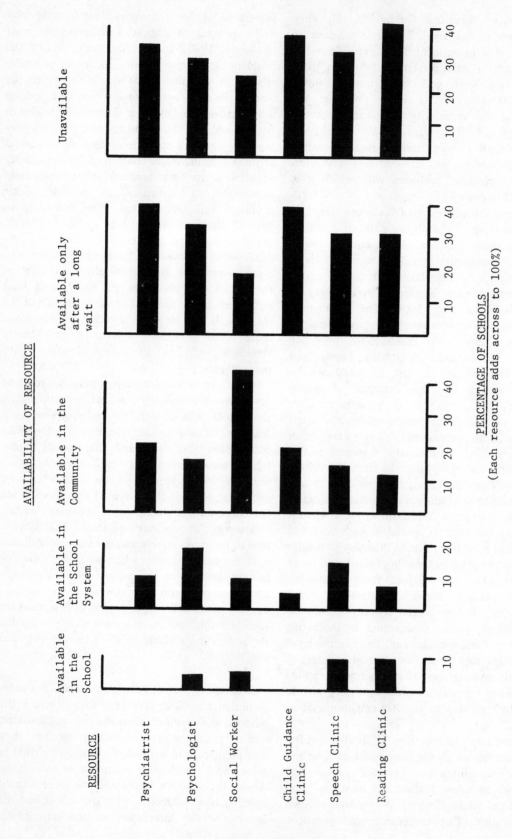

Fig. 14—3. Availability of resources reported by schools with guidance programs in 1960. (Reproduced from Project TALENT (USOE funded) with permission of the American Institute for Research and the University of Pittsburgh; Flanagan, 1962.)

tary functions. It is estimated that approximately one-fifth of the 16-year-olds who terminated in outpatient clinics in 1966 had been referred by the school (with a greater frequency for boys than for girls), with the percentage of males in such clinics dropping off rather sharply for 18-year-olds (Rosen et al., 1968). These are indications of the very significant "case-finding" function the school serves for the community and its various treatment agencies.

At the same time, the availability of community referral services is a major environmental constraint on the school's ability to meet the educational and socialization needs of the children. Given insufficient referral options, the school may have to maintain extremely disruptive and disturbed children within its classrooms, with waiting lists as very small consolation. At the other extreme, of course, a relative abundance of treatment services could result in "problem" children being referred out when they ought to serve as a stimulus for altering attitudes, management competencies, or practices within the school. The point is that the nature of the relationship, no matter what form it takes, may have major implications for the impact of the school on adolescents.

We found no recent or comprehensive estimates of the availability of various referral resources to schools. Because such data is not readily available the limited information which does have relevance will be reported here in some detail. Flanagan et al. (1962) do provide data on some resources available to 13,000 public high schools which had guidance programs in 1960. This survey data, as presented in Figure 14–3, does not indicate the combination of services available to a given school and community. But assuming that the presence of various services is somewhat highly correlated and that drastic positive changes have not occurred in the past ten years, the picture is not encouraging. Even social workers, who were a prevalent professional resource, were available in only 58 percent of the communities surveyed. Child guidance clinics, which generally serve a basic and comprehensive referral function for the schools, were presented in only 24 percent of the communities.

Another view of referral resources for the high school is provided by data brought together for the Joint Commission on Mental Health and Mental Illness on the utilization of psychiatric services by adolescents (Rosen et al., 1968). For the year 1966, information was available on the utilization of four types of service by high school aged adolescents (15–17): outpatient psychiatric clinics (terminations), general hospital inpatient psychiatric facilities (discharges), state and county mental hospitals (first admissions), and private mental hospitals (first admissions). This data is presented in Figure 14–4 in terms of the four diagnostic classifications which were most often assigned to these patients (accounting for 76 percent of the adolescents utilizing these services), with the "other" category including acute and chronic brain syndromes, psychophysiologic disorders, mental deficiency, no mental disorder, and undiagnosed cases.

Adequacy of Services Provided for Adolescents. The total number of 15- to 17-year-olds served by these agencies (which include roughly 3/4 of the known agencies of these types) in 1966 was about 46,000. Given an estimate of ten and one-half million adolescents in this age group in the same year, the conservative estimate is that two percent of school children need psychiatric services. Approximately 212,000 high school aged adolescents were in need of psychiatric services in 1966 (Rosen et al., 1968). The surveys cited by Rosen et al. which suggest that an estimated two to three percent of children are in need of psychiatric care indicate that "an additional seven percent [are] in need of some help for emotional problems" (p. 22). This brings the overall estimate of children needing some kind of mental health attention in line with Osterweil's (1966) ten percent estimate cited earlier. These estimates indicate that only one-fourth of the adolescents who needed such help obtained it in the agencies surveyed. Considering the existence of other services such as residential treatment centers and private practioners, this seems in agreement with the estimate of Rosen et al. (1968) that only a third of the 1,400,000 children who needed psychiatric care in 1966 received such help.

Patterns of Psychiatric Facility Utilization. Several patterns of facility utilization as displayed in Figure 14–4 are of interest. Outpatient clinics are clearly the major source of treatment for adolescents (69 percent of those agencies surveyed

TYPE OF
DISORDER

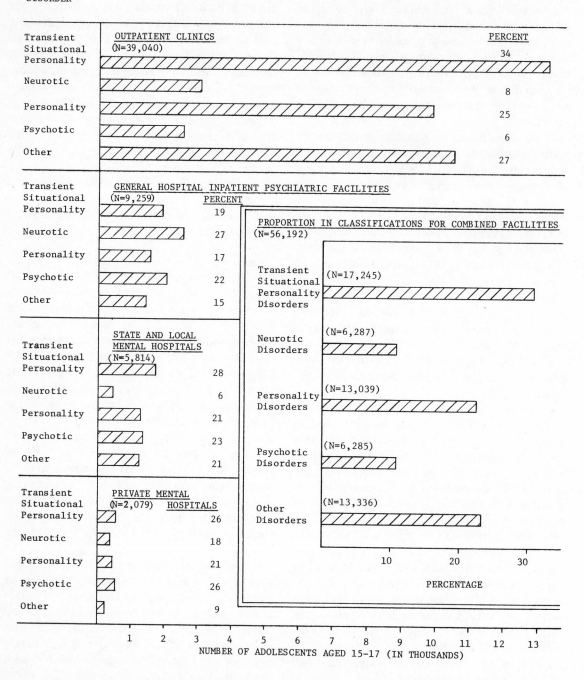

Fig. 14—4. Utilization of psychiatric facilities by adolescents aged 15—17 in 1966 by type of disorder. (Statistics from Rosen et al., 1968.)

here). In suggesting that "outpatient clinics have failed to meet the needs for which they were intended," Sowder (1968) points out that "of 53,000 adolescents seen in such clinics in 1962, two-thirds received no treatment, i.e., most simply had admission and diagnostic interviews" (p. 5). Other data (Rosen et al., 1968) suggest that approximately one-half of the adolescent referrals to these clinics with diagnoses of psychoneurotic, psychotic, personality, and transient situational personality disorders received treatment.

Transient situational personality disorders account for one-third of the adolescents in outpatient treatment, a figure which is roughly indicative of the prevalence of these disorders in the total group of adolescents utilizing the psychiatric facilities included in the table. It is especially interesting that a nearly proportionate number of adolescents in this classification were treated in state and county mental hospitals (28 percent) and in private mental hospitals (26 percent). These facilities, especially the public insitutions, are not often thought of as treatment centers for "crisis" reactions. These data may reflect, among other factors, the notorious difficulty of diagnostic assessments with adolescents, such as the opinions of many that a considerable amount of personality disorganization and identity confusion is "stage-appropriate." With this in mind, it is interesting to speculate on the preventive potential of strengthening the ability of adolescents to cope with stress, of reducing "psychologically hazardous" conditions in the school and other settings, and of providing adequate opportunities for adolescents to resolve crisis situations in growth-promoting ways.

Psychoneurotic disorders (predominantly depressive reactions in the 15–17 age group) were proportionately more often treated in general hospital psychiatric units (27 percent) and private mental hospitals (18 percent), and less often seen in outpatient clinics (eight percent) or public mental hospitals (six percent). Psychotic disorders represented about one-fourth of the adolescent population in all inpatient settings (as opposed to six percent in outpatient clinics). Socioeconomic data were not included in these statistics, but it would be interesting to know whether such factors are related to the tendency for hospitalized neurotic adolescents not to be placed in public mental hospitals.

In all of these data, of course, the quality or kind of treatment obtained cannot be sufficiently assessed from "body counts" alone. Mayer (1968) makes this point clearly in describing hospital facilities for adolescents:

"A number of hospitals have established exquisite treatment facilities for a limited number of adolescents. These hospitals serve as pioneers in research and in the practice of residential treatment. Other hospitals have reluctantly developed adolescent grouping, etc. Sometimes the adolescent who is relatively intact is thrown together with a psychotic youngster who cannot benefit from group living at all. A part of the problems seem to lie in the unavailability of post-hospitalization facilities. Youngsters are discharged too late or too early or indeed both" (Mayer, 1968, p. 23).

Mayer's statement again stresses the importance of a range of interrelated agencies and resources to provide adequate mental health care for adolescents.

Transitional Facilities. Noting again the difficulty in securing statistical information about community services for adolescents, Mayer provides a view of "in-between" treatment alternatives, such as foster family homes and group homes, which involve neither living at home nor being hospitalized. Though it is predicted that 247,000 children were in foster homes (family and group) as of 1970, the problems surrounding coordination of services to the children and adequate financial remuneration to the foster parents are often prohibitive. However, the possibility of increasing group homes—where a number of youngsters live together under adult supervision—is encouraging. "The dearth of foster homes makes group homes the most desirable and available choice of all foster care and perhaps in the long run the least costly one" (Mayer, 1968, p. 14). These homes offer important alternatives for working with adolescents in the community, and the fact that young people in these settings will probably attend public schools will make coordination and planning essential. Beyond the general estimate of needed services discussed earlier, it is difficult to assess the impact of these current mental health resources on the high school and the services it provides for adolescents. That they do not offer anything near a panacea is further evident in data on referral source and the disposition of adolescent patients terminated from 780 outpatient clinics in the United States in 1962 (Rosen et al., 1968). Almost one-third of the adolescents aged 16–17 who were referred by the school withdrew either before or during treatment and before final disposition (less than one-fourth of these were treated). Another 14.5 percent were referred back to the school for services (with only ten percent of these having received treatment in the clinics before referral back to the school). Rosen et al. conclude that "the clinic is frequently used as an evaluating service only" (p. 6). Nearly half of the 16- and 17-year-olds referred to outpatient clinics by the school return there without having having completed evaluation and/or treatment, or specifically in need of additional services from the school. No matter what services are available in the community, the school may still have to cope with many children for whom some kind of help is needed. One increasingly important resource for the development of the schools' capacity to cope with these mental health issues and with the prospects of prevention is the psychological consultant.

Psychological Consultation

The basic concern for many years has been with the child as an individual and not with the school as an important environmental context for adolescent development. There is nothing inherent in the school's contact with traditional clinical services in the community to press toward changing this emphasis. However, school consultation in many of its forms represents forces toward both a pragmatic reevaluation of modes of intervention and a theoretical reassessment of the concept of the child as patient to include a specific focus on the environmental context of behavior.

There are many accounts of approaches to school mental health consultation in the literature which represent divergent points of view and techniques (e.g., Caplan, 1959; Gildea, Glidewell, & Kantor, 1967; Isoce, Pierce-Jones, Friedman, & McGehearty, 1967; Klein, 1967; Newman, 1967; and Sarason, Levine Goldenberg, Cherlin, & Bennet, 1966). To distill the various themes pursued by all of these consultation modes into a few words would be to ignore the all-important variety of a newly emerging field, and to pursue

the complexity would not be appropriate to this chapter. Perhaps it is fair to say that one principle which underlies most or all of these approaches is that the role of the consultant is less to provide direct services to children than to develop the ability to the school to utilize its resources effectively in finding solutions for its own problems.

It may be noted that as in most areas of emergent mental health services in educational settings, most accounts of psychological consultation relate experiences in elementary school settings. Few deal with high schools. This is understandable given the smaller size of elementary schools, the younger age of their pupils, and the relative simplicity of their organizational structure, but these are the very factors which cloud the applicability of these approaches to the high school and adolescents. One study of school mental health programs at various levels (Bloomberg & Salzman, 1961) anticipated differences due to these factors but found them to be even more significant than had been expected. They presented data, for example, which suggests that high schools make proportionately less use of pupil personnel services than other level schools, and they reported that the principal of at least one school felt that there was little value in referring individual adolescents. As a result, the referral clinic was viewed as much more relevant to the elementary schools and of little relevance to the high schools. On the other hand, results in a high school which received multiple services seemed to indicate that case conferences, and the resulting involvement of the teachers, "resulted in heightened interest in individual children, greater tolerance and understanding of adolescent behavior, and more concern with helping children complete their school experience" (Bloomberg & Salzman, 1961, p. 210). This approach seemed very relevant for increasing teacher communication in the more differentiated setting of the high school and suggested to the investigators that "it is not impossible to go further in affecting total school mental health in a high school" (Bloomberg & Salzman, 1961, p. 210). One of the central recommendations derived from this project, a suggestion of particular relevance to the development of mental health programs in the high school, is that "consultants should be chosen who have a total mental health approach rather than a clinical one" (Bloomberg & Salzman, 1961, p. 222).

Some of the approaches to consultation described by Newman (1967) and by Sarason et al. (1966) are limited because of the historical emphasis on the elementary school. The latter, especially, is very much focused on the elementary school as a consultation setting and neither of these authors goes very far in conceptualizing the relevant features of the school as an organizational environment. At the same time, Newman and Sarason and his associates are not unaware of the importance of these features, and they do provide some of the most sensitive "clinical" description of what consultation is all about. It is clearly worth discussing their approaches briefly if only to raise some issues and give some "feel" for the consultation process as a resource for the organizational development of the high school.

Newman (1967) begins by focusing on the conditions in the school which make student learning possible, i.e., the climate for learning. Her particular approach to promoting this climate is through continuous, on-the-spot consultation with staff around particular problems. She sums it up as follows:

How our method differs from or is similar to others seeking to grapple with school problems is less imortant than the fact that multiple services are needed to help high school staffs . . . One has to be realistically aware of what must be done to fulfill more deep-seated needs in a school than the individual disturbances of any one child—considering the growth of population, the limited number of trained personnel, and urgent pleas from teachers who must deal with all these things at all times. We firmly believe that what ever method of consultation is tried, for it to be successful over the long run, it must include a concept of continual, on-the-spot service by trained people, sufficiently flexible to change procedures, though not principles, as the personnel or conditions of a school demand (p. 10).

And indeed Newman's tactics do prove flexible, including not only consultation with teachers around behavior problems, but also including such innovations as the organization of a teacher institute to facilitate idea-sharing and communication in a school badly in need of both. Though her formal conceptualization leaves much to be desired, it is clear that her focus is on the school as a social system. She elucidates on how innovations are contingent on pressures within the school, cites the devastating effect of staff anomie in a ghetto school on the "climate," and allows the reader to "tap in" on a sensitive "third ear" about clinical problems manifested in the context of the school environment.

Somewhat more systematic is the conceptual framework of Sarason et al. (1966), who draw on Lewin's famous $B = f(P,E)$ in identifying school behavior (B) as a function of the interaction between person (P) and environment (E). They point out that both by tradition and training clinical psychologists have had little contact with middle class schools and virtually no contact with inner-city schools, and urge that this narrowness of training cease. Sarason et al. define their consultation aims as threefold: (1) Not duplicating any existing service; (2) serving one or both of two functions: (a) anticipating and mitigating potentially serious problems, and (b) making the effects of the consultative effort such that they will be transferred by those involved to other individuals and problems; and (3) making a primary consideration and goal the intimate knowledge of the setting in which the services are to be rendered. "Rather than be consultants, we would be participant observers" (p. 43).

Space does not allow us to do justice even to the rich buffet of clinical sensitivity and innovative approaches to classroom problems of elementary school children with which the Sarason book is filled. The discussions of the "loneliness" of the teaching profession and the immense problems of coordinating services to children in inner-city schools demonstrates an intimate knowledge of many organizational problems faced by faculty as well as by mental health professionals "just trying to do their job." And the emphasis that since $B = f(P,E)$ a change in behavior (B) should result from an alteration of the environment (E) as well as the person (P) independently provides supports for the ecological approach which runs throughout this chapter.

Psychological consultation as thus defined can be construed as a *potential* stepping stone to a more sophisticated ecological approach to the redevelopment of the high school. Both Sarason and Newman implicitly see the school as an interdependent system and both imply that because schools are facing multiple and varied problems, interventions in these schools must themselves be multiple and varied. The concern with interdependence and the necessity of fitting the treatment to the setting are important steps. In addition, the importance of gaining a thorough knowledge of the setting in which one consults means that consultation—originally sought after around specific problems—may lead from the individual pupil or the teacher-pupil dyad as the focus of intervention to seeing the school itself as an entity in need of diagnostic and planning services. In short, such involvement allows the mental health professional to view the school as an ecological niche where *all* students and staff live and try to survive.

Despite their many strengths, the approaches of Newman and of Sarason reflect a general prejudice in the development of school mental health services toward discrete, pragmatic, and reactive modes of responding. Such an approach does provide valuable data about the school and it guards against premature prejudices and abortive large-scale programs generalized to different schools. At the same time, however, it fails to produce a much needed conceptualization of the social environment of the high school itself, and to draw upon such a view in designing appropriate interventions. Though justifiably lamenting the impact of organizational or environmental constraints on their functioning in the school, these consultants have not yet—to the authors' knowledge—made a primary commitment to intervening on the level of organizational redevelopment or to considering such intervention as an attractive and appropriate consultation goal.

The ecological view which is developed here is an orientation which directs the consultant's attention to both individual personality characteristics and to the structure and functions of organizational environments, and assigns primary importance to the interaction of these factors as the focus for the development of preventive interventions. The following two sections review knowledge about the high school, from which an ecological view appropriate to that setting can be further developed.

THE SOCIAL SYSTEM OF THE HIGH SCHOOL: ORGANIZATIONAL ANALYSIS OF CRITICAL ROLES AND POTENTIALS FOR INNOVATION

The social system of the school is no longer simply a "context" for individual functioning; it is part of a complex, reciprocal, dynamic relationship, and the context or superordinate system becomes the total community as it affects the high school as an organization.

However, especially lacking at present is knowledge about the ways in which school organizational structure and behavior are constrained or facilitated by forces in the environment of the school. Very few research examples exist. Bidwell (1965) has cited several studies which suggest in a general way that "school systems differ markedly in external vulnerability according to the characteristics of the communities they serve" (p. 1009). An example of a more differentiated study of the environmental relationships of the school is provided by McDowell (1954) as quoted in Carlson (1964): "As aspects of the school environment change, the job of principal also changes. When the environment contains largely lower socio-economic children, principals encourage parent participation in school affairs; when the environment contains mostly upper class children, the principals attempt to suppress parent participation in school affairs" (Carlson, 1964, p. 263). Heriott and St. John (1966) note the existence of research which suggests that the socioeconomic status of the student body affects not only the relationship of the principal with parents, but also the closeness of his relationship with teachers.

The ecological perspective places a high value on understanding the relationship between external forces and the structure and functions of the organization, as represented in this research. The absence of studies and comments like the above are serious limitations for the development of knowledge for preventive interventions. Consequently, we have few concepts or data to help us understand organizational functioning, let alone planned change or natural disruptions, in the high school.

Given the basic assumption that any intervention in the social system of the high school alters or affects any number of the interrelated aspects of that system, lack of knowledge about the so-called side-effects of a planned change is particularly disturbing. It is a safe bet that many a well-intentioned planned change effort has been undone by unanticipated or poorly understood organizational resistances to it. To learn how to anticipate and account for the impact of a proposed intervention in an organization, we need to gain more sophistication about how to assess

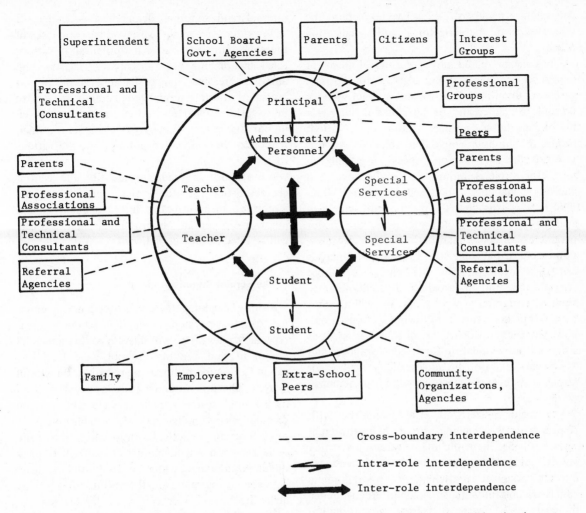

Fig. 14—5. Role interdependent and external constraints on role performance in the high school.

the organization, its current functioning, and its relationships to its environment.

One source for making such an assessment of school social structure and functioning is an understanding of the role requirements and interdependence of the various personnel comprising the social system of the high school. The classical example of naïvete in this important area is given by Berkowitz (1966), citing a consultant who "when told by a public school teacher of his patient's tendency to have tantrums in the classroom, suggested 'when he's like that when I see him, I take him out for a walk around the block for an ice cream cone—couldn't you try that?' " (p. 225). Although it is unlikely that such blatant failures to understand the role constraints of school personnel are common, it is far from unusual to hear complaints that recommendations made by mental health professionals would be

very helpful—if only there were any chance they could feasibly be implemented.

A more subtle but equally important concern is that when the realities of role constraints and organizational structure have been taken into account, many external change agents view these factors as constraints on the change process which must be counteracted or circumvented in order to bring about effective change in the clients, as if the clients are not an organic part of the environment. We are suggesting that an understanding of the role system (as well as other views of the social structure) is crucial as a basis for planning intervention programs which are the most relevant for the system and its members. Not only is such knowledge important in determining what form an intervention should take to be acceptable to and compatible with the system but it can serve as a basis for developing changes in the system which will enhance its adaptive capacity and increase the effectiveness of the educational and socialization process.

The concept of role provides a useful means of expressing major social and organizational forces which act upon the individual and interact with his personal characteristics to determine his behavior in organizational settings (Kahn et al., 1964; Biddle & Thomas, 1966). The relevance of this view to the socialization process, especially in terms of "role learning" in adolescence and adulthood has been discussed by Brim (1966, 1968). It is true that the clarity with which an analysis of critical role represents the major parameters of social relationships in an organization is achieved at some cost. In itself, role analysis not only over-simplifies the nature of those relationships, but it provides a predominantly static or structural view of them. We will attempt to develop this point in following sections. First, however, a discussion of school roles can serve as an important foundation for trying to understand the social system of the adolescent, as well as for posing new research questions related to organizational change.

The major pattern of interdependence with respect to roles in the high school are illustrated in Figure 14—5. These include relationships which are hierarchical (e.g., the teacher's dependence upon the principal for disciplinary support), others which are horizontal (such as the interdependence of peers, e.g., teachers' sharing of curriculum ideas), and still others which involve relationships to sets of roles outside the formal structure of the school (e.g., a student's response to his parents' academic expectations).

Of central importance to the effective functioning and adaptation of the school to its environment is the capacity of its "role occupants" to identify and anticipate internal and external sources of stress or demand, to define constructive responses to emergent problems, and to take effective action. An important consideration in this regard is the innovative potential of the individual, given the role pressures which constrain his behavior and his patterns of influence and interaction with other role incumbents. The capacity of the school for innovation is especially important when focusing on organizational redevelopment. A superordinate goal is often to enhance the organization's ability to cope with its internal and external demands for change. It follows that one of the earliest diagnostic tasks of the consultant is to assess the potential of various role incumbents to anticipate, accept, and advocate creative change. Because of the importance of these factors in planning preventive interventions, particular attention has been given in our discussion of the role system of the high school to the innovative potential of the various roles.

An attempt is made to identify the central characteristics of the roles and to suggest important facets of the interdependencies and innovative potential. Major references on each role will be cited as they are relevant.[2]

The School Superintendent

Strictly speaking, the superintendency is external to the role system of the high school, yet it is especially relevant to a discussion of the individual school in that the high school is at least one subunit of a superordinate organization, the school system. The superintendency is the focal position of a school system which is responsible for the formulation of policy and the establishment of procedures and practices within whose limits the social system of the high school functions. To view the superintendency, then, is to consider at least important constraints on the various roles of the high school.

Given the complex set of expectations which impinge upon the superintendent, it is no surprise that one of the major recent studies of role behavior and role conflict has been concerned with this position (Gross, Mason, & McEachern, 1958). Few other systematic studies of this position have been done, but it is possible to gain some sense of the demands made upon the superintendent and the impact of those demands on his role performance as they interact with the characteristics of the superintendent himself.

Just as the school functions in a community context, so does the school administrator function in a social system bound to that context (Brookover & Gottlieb, 1961). Because the school is a service organization, the superintendent is responsible to those persons who are the recipients of the service—or in this case, more often to the parents of the recipients. Parents can either exert pressure directly through personal contact or indirectly through the elected board of education. The superintendency evolved as a result of "slow, reluctant, and recent relinquishment by boards of education of direct managerial functions" (Bidwell, 1965, p. 995). The board's legitimate authority and its power to hire and fire render it a formidable constraint on the superintendent's activities and make his relationship with the board a critical factor affecting his willingness to innovate and his freedom to exercise professional judgment. From below him in the organizational hierarchy, teachers and principals can support or resist his decisions on such matters as school policies, the allocation of resources, etc. Thus, the superintendent must mediate between subordinate personnel and the board, as well as parents (and students) who intervene directly.

Because the superintendent operates in a system, his role as mediator often causes him to face conflicting demands from above (the board), below (teachers or principals), and "outside" (parents). Pressure from one source is likely to beget counterpressure from another. As an example, let us take the case of a superintendent who is being pressured by the board to force a principal, at whose school student uprisings have occurred, to "run a tight ship," to clamp down and strongly suppress such activity. Let us assume further that the principal already has faculty support for his handling of the uprising. Upon hearing of what the superintendent is trying to do, the dissident students now rally strongly behind the principal. How can the superintendent mediate? If he follows the "suggestion" of the board, he maintains status with them but is suspect not only with the particular principal involved but with all the principals of the school system who see him as an agent of the board. If he resists the pressure from the board and supports the principal's action, he may be respected by the principal and faculty as a man who "understands," but he may be fired. Increasingly, school superintendents have been forced to make the choices and without a conscious exposition on their part.

The example of role conflict offered here may be somewhat of a caricature, but it does serve to illustrate the very real potential for conflict inherent in the superintendent's responsibility to a variety of groups whose points of view are often divergent. Gross, Mason and McEachern (1958)

have documented superintendents' perceptions of such conflicting expectations for various personnel decisions; also they have explored the implications of such conflict for the gratification afforded occupants of the superintendency and isolated some of the factors which determine the individual's approach to resolving the inconsistent demands. Their study provides a framework for more extensive empirical investigations of the role of the superintendency as perceived by people in various influential, interdependent positions as well as for investigating the determinants and effects of various resolutions to conflict which ensue from incongruities in those varied role expectations.

At least one implication of this study stimulates a more detailed commentary from the point of view of an ecological approach to the functioning of individuals on organizations. Although this work by Gross and his associates has established an important basis for considering the interaction of individual and organizational variables in its attempt to determine the antecedents of varied responses of individual superintendents to the kind of role conflict examined in the study, a broader perspective is needed. The only factor which might be termed a dimension of personality functioning was the superintendents' "predisposition" to weigh the importance of legitimacy or sanctions. Current personality theorists do not include this type of variable, a variable which is tied to coping performance in naturally occurring job situations. Hopefully, future research will broaden our knowledge about the attributes of the person—as well as the conditions of influential expectations— which determine the superintendent's response to role conflict and, indeed, to role demands of any kind. The addition of a third type of role conflict, that of "person-role" conflict, to the interrole and intrarole forms of conflict would contribute to such a broader analysis (Kahn et al., 1964).

The Superintendent and Innovation

An important concern for mental health professionals involves the degree to which a school system will tolerate, or perhaps foster, innovative activity, whether instigated within the system or outside. While the influence of the superintendent may be slight, if the innovation is a minor one in a single school it is likely to be a sine qua non in matters affecting a group of schools or the entire system. Further, it is expected that the superintendent's influence in setting a general tone which encourages or inhibits various kinds of innovation will be of particular importance in at least some types of systems. Although there appears to be little research on this point, Dreeban and Gross (1965) did find that the expectations of higher administrators were of significant influence in determining the willingness of principals to support innovation in the urban high schools included in their study.

Although the study by Dreeban and Gross suggests that the superintendent's support of innovation may have important implications for innovation behavior in the system, it does not indicate any determinants of the superintendent's tendency to provide such support.[3] A study of Carlson (1962) provides clues to an aspect of the personal history of the superintendent which contributes to his role behavior in this area. Carlson suggests that whether the superintendent defines himself as an innovator or not may be inferred from his career pattern. He defines two such patterns as prevalent: place-bound and career-bound. The place-bound superintendent is one who ascends to the superintendency from within the same school system with which he is affiliated. He is a low risk taker and prefers to "wait for the call" from his own school system rather than seeking out career advancement in another geographical area. The career-bound superintendent, on the other hand, is a reformer who prefers to "go where the action is." Not only is his administrative style geared toward innovation, he is likely to be selected by a board of education which is unsatisfied with the previous incumbent of the superintendency and is looking for change. While Carlson fails to clarify whether superintendents themselves are the basic change agents or whether school systems which had "institutionalized innovation tended to hire superintendents with the appropriate outlook" (Erikson, 1967, p. 418), he does imply that entering a school system from outside does increase the probability of policy innovation being successfully carried out (Lipham, 1964), and that characteristics of the individuals who are likely to seek such positions contribute to the fostering of innovation in such systems. Still this does not address itself directly to the question of how or in what circumstances career-bound administrators

would be receptive to innovations not initiated by them. This empirical question remains unanswered.

Surely far more than the career pattern of the superintendent is involved, however. There are, in addition, certain role-related dispositional characteristics which are of potential importance in assessing how a superintendent may respond to a request for change. Among these are his orientation toward the board (Bidwell, 1965), toward power versus ideology, toward creativity versus conventionality, and towards action versus contemplation (Katz & Kahn, 1966). Yet all these dispositional characteristics are modified by the social context of his job: how he was recruited and why, the previous stresses the school system has undergone, and how it has responded to them, etc. Because an understanding of the complexities of this role may be an important factor in understanding the functioning of the high school as a part of the school system, and because the response of the superintendent may be an important factor in the success of initiating mental health programs, the superintendent's role and the nature of the men who fill it deserve much more systematic study (Allinsmith & Goethals, 1962).

The Principal

While the superintendency developed to assume functions previously carried out by the board of education, the principalship evolved in response to the need for someone to coordinate growing schools and take over some of the administrative tasks which were formerly a part of every teacher's duties (Pierce, 1935, cited in Bidwell, 1965). Today, the principal is responsible for the direct management of the school, which involves a variety of responsibilities as outlined by Dreeban and Gross (1965):

"Principals are supposed to: (1) orient new teachers by making them aware of their formally defined rights and obligations; (2) see that all staff members carry their teaching and extracurricular responsibilities at least at a minimum level of satisfactory performance; (3) cope with problems arising out of personal misunderstandings and conflicts; (4) deal with problems of deviant behavior that so often arise out of rationally designed efforts to run a stable organization; (5) implement policy decisions made at higher levels in the school system; (6) resolve the conflicts presented by teachers and parents who are disgruntled or apathetic; (7) interpret the school program to the community served; (8) assess the capabilities of teachers. In short, principals occupy a strategic managerial position at the lower levels of the school system bureaucracy; they are the administrative officials with the closest contact to the core functions of schools—teaching and learning" (Section 1–3 to Section 1–4).

It is clear even from such a brief listing of the duties of the principal that, like the superintendent, his task is in large part the management and mediation of pressures and forces from a variety of sources: higher administration, faculty, parents, and students, not to mention the growing number of staff specialists with their demands for more specialized programs, and an increasingly prevalent figure from outside the school, the mental health consultant. In a typical industrial organization, the chief administrative officer would probably create a number of specialized administrative positions or departments to respond to the demands and needs of these various people. Although this happens as well in some larger schools, it is probably true that a majority of school principals continue to take primary responsibility for responding to the incumbents of this array of positions inside and outside the organization.

Again, we find that the complexity of this role has been attractive to social scientists concerned with the development of theory and knowledge to account for role behavior and the resolution of role conflict (Gross & Herriott, 1965; Dodd, 1965). Gross, Mason, and McEachern (1958) express a central premise of the ecological view—that of the interdependence of the units of an organization when they suggest that "whatever the implications of the label, a position cannot be completely described until all the other positions to which it is related have been specified" (p. 51). Dreeban and Gross (1965) provide a more extended description of some of the role interdependencies from the point of view of the principal than we are able to offer here, and Dodd (1965) describes the nature, determinants, and effects of principal role conflict in much greater detail. But we can attempt to give some picture of the tasks and trials of the school principal.

Like the superintendent, the principal must also deal with pressures from outside and inside the formal structure of the school. In his role as principal he serves as a very visible mediator between his school and the local community; indeed, some evidence suggests that because of his role the principal is more closely identified with the community values than the rest of the school staff (Nicholas, Virjo, & Wattenberg, 1965). Conversely, this may imply that those principals whose values are in conflict with community values provide an easy target for community resentment (viz., a white principal who cannot relate well to Negro students in a predominantly Negro school).

In addition to this link with the community, the principal also serves as "middleman" with the school staff, mediating between the demands of teachers in his school and the demands of his supervisors in the organizational hierarchy (Bidwell, 1965). The manner in which he balances the dual allegiances of colleague ties to the teaching group and felt responsibilities to his superiors is probably a critical dimension for predicting the sources of tension between himself and the teachers, on the one hand, and him and the supervisors on the other. As an administrator, he must work out within the school a suitable compromise between administrative efficiency and granting teachers the autonomy necessary for successful teaching. Moeller (1964) points out that both excessive efficiency and excessive "laissez-faire" have predictable effects for school functioning, thus providing another salient dimension of the principal's behavior in understanding his role constraints.

Several other dimensions of principal behavior have been noted as especially relevant to his relationship vis-à-vis teachers and students. Newman (1967) reports a teacher diary which reflects the devastating effect that a condescending and infantilizing principal can have on teacher morale and the openness of teacher-principal communication. Kelly (1968) has remarked on the potential impact that principal availability to students may have on student behavior.

While such case reports serve to emphasize the crucial importance of the principal in the functioning of the school, there is more generalizable empirical data regarding contextual aspects of principal role behavior in schools of varying socioeconomic class. Herriott and St. John (1966) found that the performance of the principal is more crucial to the performance of teachers in schools with a lower socioeconomic status (SES) student body than in the schools with a higher student SES. Nicholas, Virjo, and Wattenberg (1965) forcefully point out differences in the principal role in "high" and "low" socioeconomic settings: "Urgency, crisis, and harrassment characterized the challenge confronting principals in 'low' school settings, whereas businesslike routine operations were the nature of the challenges presented to principals in 'high' area schools" (pp. 121–122). From this it seems reasonable to conclude that different types of principals would be appropriate for these different settings, underscoring the ecological assumption that one "style" may be adaptive in one particular environment but not in another.

The Principal and Innovation

One point of view about the differential adaptiveness of principals in varied high school settings has been voiced by the National Educational Association Policies Commission which includes a plea that creative and innovative principals be assigned to schools "not only in deprived areas but also in changing neighborhoods" (Nicholas et al., 1965, p. 17). While the present authors would also stress the importance of organizational redevelopment in dealing with the unusual problem plaguing schools in deprived areas and changing neighborhoods, it is agreed that the capacity of principals for innovative approaches to change is crucial.

If the superintendent's receptiveness to innovation contributes to the school system's responsiveness to change and openness to innovative efforts, it is likely as well that the principal's support for innovation contributes to the extensiveness and quality of new ideas and new practices within the individual high school. Dreeban and Gross (1965) found that principals' support for innovation (more specifically, the conformity of the principals' behavior to their self-expectations to support innovation) was related positively in their sample to teacher morale and teacher effort, although not to pupil academic achievement at the high school level. They did not directly study the implications of such support for innovative behavior on the part of the faculty; no such study is known to the present authors. The study by Dreeban and Gross did establish that the support of innovation is

quite commonly a self-ascribed function of the principal role, and Dodd's (1965) data suggests that "introducing change into instructional program" is a major area of role conflict which derives from discrepant expectations of administrators and teachers. But Gallaher (1965), citing the "man in the middle" or balancing role of the school administrator, doubts that he can serve as an effective advocate for broader change in the school system, or in this case, the high school itself. He suggests that it is necessary "to create positions that have as their special role function the management of educational change" (Gallaher, 1965, p. 51). Hayes (1966) has outlined a model for a "council for instruction" which would serve much the same purpose.

Until such programs or some workable variants of them are established it remains the task of the principal and his fellow school administrators to respond in some way to the demands of a changing community and a changing school. Ochberg and Trickett (1970) and Trickett and Ochberg (in preparation) study the manner in which the principal responds to the threatened disruptions caused by such social strains as racial tensions and student power movements. Any threatened school disruption strikes at the core of one of the principal's primary role obligations, and his response to impending crises is assumed to be critical in its resolution. In attempting to understand the principal in response to crises, efforts are being made to see him "in context," to view not only his personality make-up but also his relations to and communication patterns with both teachers and students. Finally the nature and extent of the community pressures brought to bear on him are being explored. Thus, the principal is seen as operating in and constrained by a particular social context. It is hoped that his perspective will generate useful information not only about a particular crisis but also about the social environments of high schools in general. Such knowledge should provide a basis for creating administrative structures which are increasingly able to undertake a planning role with respect to change and potential disruption, and decreasingly forced to respond only under "crisis" conditions.

Our discussion of administrative roles has dealt with those aspects of the high school social system which influence the socialization of the adolescent in relative indirect ways, e.g., through setting school policy and supervising the personnel who work with him more directly. In turning to a discussion of teachers and staff specialists, we consider what might be called the *direct* socialization agents of the high school.

Teachers

In his discussion of the school as a formal organization, Bidwell (1965) notes the absence of studies of the "teacher society" (in contrast to greater interest in the "adolescent society") and suggests that there is no empirical literature on the "teacher office" outside of "studies on the student society, as they bear also on teacher performance" (p. 993). If we include as relevant to the "teacher office" studies directed at the definition of the role of the teacher and the assessment of the adequacy of teacher role performance, additional areas of research must be included. It has been suggested that "of studies of role conceptions held for the teacher there is no end" (Biddle, Fraser & Jellison, 1965, p. 326). Though most of these studies are concerned with role definitions obtained from teachers, they include, as well, the conceptions held by other educators, school administrators, pupils, parents, and others.[4] It would seem that research on teacher effectiveness has been at least equally popular: "Literally thousands of studies have been reported dealing with characteristics of teachers (rated or measured), effects of teaching, goals of education, and other related issues. Yet, few if any 'facts' seem to have been established concerning teacher effectiveness, no approved method of measuring competence has been accepted, and no methods of promoting teacher adequacy have been widely adopted" (Biddle, 1964, p. 2).[5] In considering the socialization process in the high school, the particularly relevant research in this area will be discussed, with suggestions for directions future investigations of teacher-student relationships and the classroom might take. But in general we must agree with the thrust of Bidwell's evaluation that relatively little is known about the organizational context and implications of the teacher role. Enough is known, however, to characterize essential features of this role and its relationship to other positions in the high school systems, as well as the interaction of teacher personality with organizational demands to influence teacher role performance.

An integral part of the teacher's functioning, central to many of the conflicts he must face, is concerned with his role vis-à-vis students. Such conflicts, according to Waller (1932), may be inherent and are consequences of the disjunction between the task of learning or gaining knowledge and the demands of the world of adolescents (Bidwell, 1965). In the classroom the teacher faces two immediate and continuing tasks. One is to focus on classroom activities and student motives in order to form the personal and warm relationship which is so important as a motivation for learning. The other is to control the classroom and maintain discipline so that learning can occur. This second task calls on the teacher to be the authority, to be the adult. As such it is in conflict with the personalized role necessary for effective teaching. Thus, the teacher's task is one of continuous *integration* and *adjustment* of these conflicting expectations (Gordon, 1957; Bidwell, 1965). It is likely that some teachers, young teachers especially, also wish to serve as models for their students in various respects. Although little is known about the bases for this kind of modeling, to the extent that it depends on the teacher's contact with the student culture and ability to communicate in its terms this may well be another major source of conflict with the authority function.

One aspect of the teacher's authority is the power to assign grades, and the manner in which he uses this power affects the way he is perceived by students. Gordon's (1957) example is perhaps classic in this regard: Miss Jones was thought to ascribe status in the classroom on the basis of social class. Lower class members thought her fair because she practiced a "not too subtle" form of "underdog" ascription. Mr. Highly, who affected a manner of rigid universalism (in grading practices), was thought by the lower class members to be unfair and by all to particularize in favor of more attractive, physically mature girls (Gordon, 1957).

But being a teacher involves far more than relating to pupils. The teacher is part of the social system and is constrained by that system. Often, for instance, the maintenance of order in the classroom is seen as symbolic of teacher competence not only by the principal but by colleagues, parents, and, indeed, by students. Gordon (1957) speculates that when the principal rates competence via the degree of classroom order (i.e., when he supports the "discipline aspect of the teacher role"), it is more likely that the teacher will use disciplinary measures to control the classroom. When the principal is less likely to support this kind of authority, the teacher is more likely to resort to a more personalized leadership or "charisma" to avoid endemic conflict.

Gordon's focusing on the interdependence of the teacher and principal roles represents an important conceptual advance over the "good guy-bad guy" era. It suggests, for instance, that a teacher whose classroom coping style relies heavily on "classroom order" would be seen in a more favorable light by the principal who equated competence with classroom order than by a principal such as A. S. Neill of Summerhill (Neill, 1960). More of this synthetic emphasis is needed.[6]

Complicating the issue further for the teacher are the problems which may arise from the conflicting expectations of administrators, teachers, and parents for the characteristics of the teaching role (Allinsmith & Goethals, 1962). For instance, Fishburn (1962) found that the teacher role perceived as most important by administrators (liaison between school and community) was perceived as least important by teachers. This differential perception of teacher role by different groups need not, of course, lead to conflict. The most critical instances in this regard would probably occur when the group holding divergent expectations is in a position of power over the teachers (Twyman & Biddle, 1963).

Teachers may be shielded from the pressures of differing expectations by specific structural characteristics of schools. Miles (1965, 1967) has discussed the lack of goal clarity and the "invisibility of teacher role performance." This raises a very critical question about interdependence between the teacher role and other related roles in the high school environment.

Bidwell (1965) has suggested that one of the salient characteristics of schools as formal organizations is their relative "structural looseness," i.e., the low interdependence of their various roles. This observation is a theoretical statement which has not been subject to the kind of relevant research which might include comparative studies of organizations. However, low interdependence of school personnel is a frequently attributed condition of organizational structure which has important implications for organizational functioning and change. Miles has suggested that under conditions which support the "autonomy" of the teacher role a number of important problems exist: "teachers who wish support find it difficult to get; administrators who are concerned about inadequate teaching behavior find it difficult to get enough data to be helpful; and parents exert erratic pressure based on children's reports of what the teacher did" (Miles, 1967, p. 9).

What is needed of course is a much more sensitive and differentiated exploration of various aspects of the teacher role with respect to the degree of interdependence between that role and organizational or community forces which might either facilitate or disrupt the teacher's work. We have mentioned some thinking and research which take this direction, and it should at least be clear that there are certain aspects of the teacher role which, aside from the personality of the teacher, can be expected to be issues with which teachers must deal in the performance of their duties. Understanding how they deal with these issues necessitates not only a knowledge of personality characteristics of the teacher but also an awareness of the particular social structure of the school in which the teacher works.

In outlining some of the probable organizational constraints on teacher role performance, we have briefly mentioned the relevance of personality factors. However, the viewpoint of this chapter is that the consideration of personality effects on role behavior without an understanding of their interaction with organizational forces can shed little light on the problems of effective individual and organizational functioning. Research on teacher effectiveness provides an illustration of this point. For a long time research on the teacher-pupil classroom relationship revolved around the educational objective of discovering the teacher personality characteristics which discriminated "good" or "effective" teachers from "bad" or "ineffective" ones. In essence, teacher "personality" was assumed to operate similarly in all situations. The low efficacy of this research strategy is summed up by Storlurow (1965): "The most significant conclusion that can be drawn from efforts to use teachers as a basis for information about teaching is that effective instruction can be produced by a variety of combinations of characteristics and conditions rather than by one unique combination. If this were not the case, efforts to enumerate the characteristics of good teachers would have resulted in the identification of at least one or two critical characteristics" (p. 226).

While there are probably a small number of "master teachers" who would be effective with most children in most schools (a few teachers being expected to thrive in multiple and varied environments), the general dearth of nuggets in this research vein can in part be attributed to the lack of appreciation for the interactional determinants of pupil performance and teacher behavior. As in any ecological approach, the question of effectiveness (adaptive "teacher-pupil behavior") is shifted from a classical "personality" approach to one of teacher-pupil interaction in a particular setting (Gump, 1964). Some research which illustrates this approach to the classroom will be included in a later section. The point to be made here is that relevant personality variables of the teacher should be considered in terms of their interaction with social system variables in what has been called a "transactional" approach (Pervin, 1968). An interesting and unstudied variable of potential relevance to teacher performance, for example, is the teacher's latent identity (Bidwell, 1965). Here, one would anticipate that as the teacher becomes a long-standing member of the community served by the school, he becomes increasingly susceptible to community pressure and experiences increased constraints against being innovative if being innovative violates community norms.

A broader question involving the interaction of personality and organizational factors in affecting role performance centers around the recruitment or selection of individuals into the teaching profession. Miles (1967) ventures that the self-selection process for teachers in the American public school tends to attract "persons who are less able verbally, more passive, more deferent and less competitive than other professionals . . ." (p. 18). Although some of these characteristics may be linked to role-compatible qualities, he suggests they also limit the readiness of teachers to "learn, grow and develop" (Miles, 1967, p. 19).

The Teacher and Innovation

Some of the most important "barriers to change" in the school system have to do with the performance of teacher roles. Miles (1967) extends his analysis of the "properties of schools as social systems" to consider some of these implications. In spite of evidence that some aspects of teacher functioning (e.g., the assignment of grades) are subject to conflicting expectations held by others, it appears that "what the teacher does in the classroom" is quite rigidly and consistently defined by the role system and the teacher's self-expectation. Miles suggests that this condition is "relatively independent of the personality of the incumbent of the teacher role. Biddle, after extensive research on teacher role behavior (see Biddle and Rosencranz, 1964) suggested that 'the teacher is on rails,' and almost nothing can be done to alter the role performance short of radical structural change, such as that involved in team teaching" (Miles, 1967, pp. 9–10).

In addition to the problems of internal integration which arise out of the school's "structural looseness," significant barriers to organizational change are inherent in such a condition. Again, Miles states the case succinctly: "It is important to note that a low degree of interdependence ordinarily makes a system much more difficult to alter, since if changes occur in one part (e.g., in one teacher's practices), there are no meaningful channels or linkages by which they can travel to other parts of the system" (Miles, 1967, p. 12). This analysis suggests that a major aim for enhancing the innovative process among teachers is the alteration of structural conditions to break strong expectations and the increase of interdependence between members of the high school social system.

Social Change and the Development of Teacher Roles

Some of the social changes which are making innovation increasingly important to the school's functioning may also be contributing to a struggle in the teaching profession which is having and will have a profound effect on the evolving teacher role and the functioning of high schools. According to Stinnett (1968), an emergent "new breed" of teachers dedicated to teaching as a career is actively striving for increased autonomy and participation not only in bargaining for salary but with respect to working conditions as well. These teachers are intent on altering their role, their professional image, and, in many cases, the basic nature of the educational process. While the impact of the move toward more control over their teaching destiny has already been felt in the form of strikes or professional sanctions (the terms are not synonymous, says Stinnett) the effect of this force on organizational functioning or student behavior is, to the authors' knowledge, unreported. One tentative result found by Trickett and Ochberg (in preparation) is that the rise of a student power movement in two high schools resulted in a faculty split, with the younger "new breed" of teachers more supportive of the student demands and the "old guard" tending to make a more "hawkish" line. In sum, the many traditional stresses and strains which inhere in being a teacher are being increased as more and more teachers attempt to increase their control over their professional dealings. If there ever was a time when "those who can, do; those who can't, teach," it shows signs of changing.

Mental Health Specialists and Supportive Services

Paralleling the development of the teacher role, with the increasing complexity of expectations held for it, various "pupil personnel" services have emerged to serve more specialized functions in the education and socialization of children. A particularly prominent example of this process in recent years has been the addition to the staff of elementary schools of the "crisis teacher" (Morse, 1962). Long-standing specialized roles at the high school level are those of guidance counselor and school psychologist, and our discussion of the role of staff specialists will center around their place in the functioning of the school.

Normative Roles of Guidance Counselors and School Psychologists. Traditionally, the roles carried out by guidance counselors include administration of vocational tests, helping students plan their high school programs, counseling with "underachievers," and generally aiding individuals in mobilizing their current resources while they plan for their future. While these may constitute the broad role requirements, the content of these areas is largely dependent on many factors, including a knowledge of what the student expectations are and what they bring to the counseling or guidance situation, as well as a clearer understanding of the participation of the

students in the settings of the high schools. This would indicate that the particular knowledge necessary for guidance purposes is closely tied to the school context in which the counselor functions. In a wealthy community of college-bound aspirants, it is incumbent on the guidance counselor to have information about colleges and universities; in a deprived neighborhood, a greater demand would be placed on the counselor to know of local job opportunities and training possibilities.

The current functions of a school psychologist may vary greatly in emphasis depending on the type of program, the individual psychologist's theoretical bias, the pupil-psychologist ratio, and so on. White and Harris (1961) identify four major services which encompass most of their activities. These include (a) educational diagnosis (as assessed by testing, observation, etc.); (b) educational remediation (a program based on "a"); (c) personality diagnosis (more comprehensive than "a" and including personality tests and diagnostic interviewing); and (d) personality remediation (a program for change based on "c"). As with guidance counseling, the specific tools necessary for effective functioning in this role would be specific to the situation and would depend on such knowledge as developmental differences in disadvantaged and advantaged children, knowledge of social agencies or private therapists, etc. An important implication of this is that a monolithic training program for guidance counselors and school psychologists will equip these professionals for school situations where the student population is congruent with the values and styles of the training program.

Presently, both guidance counselors and school psychologists are showing signs of discontent at maintaining a constant role in a changing world (Bardon, 1968; Thoreson, 1968). Members of both professions are moving away from an exclusively intrapsychic view of behavior towards a more ecological one which places heavier emphasis on the adolescent "in context" (Stern, 1968). In an article entitled "Guidance: The Ecology of Students," Danskin, Kennedy, and Friesan (1965) present their idea of the emergent guidance counselor as a "human development engineer" oriented toward understanding pupil learning in interactional terms and investing a "much larger part of his total resources into observation of and systematic research into the learning climate of the school" (p. 135). Thoreson (1968), also speaking of guidance counselors, proposes that a new breed of specialists be trained combining scientific rigor with humanistic commitment and a constant concern with the total school environment as seen through a "systems" approach.

Similar emphases are becoming visible in school psychology. Bardon (1968) envisages a model for school psychologists "based upon the idea that the school is unique enough to call for special training and that the application of psychology to the school requires something more than the study and education separately" (p. 193). Gray (1963), in describing the George Peabody College for Teachers program for "psychologists in the schools," emphasizes not only an indirect consultation model but one which is aimed towards prevention and research rather than cure.

Normatively speaking, however, the hopeful directions outlined above are predominantly in the "pipe dream" phase. The current services provided by guidance counselors and school psychologists, while valuable, are limited not only by manpower problems but by an inadequate appreciation and conceptualization of the adolescent's current school environment as a critical factor in his personal development and career aspirations.

As traditionally construed, these specialists have been seen as providing services to individuals, either counseling or testing with a student or limited case consultation with particular teachers. It is not surprising, then, that there has been little or no research on the organizational constraints upon these roles. If these roles are redefined in the directions outlined here, it becomes even more imperative that such research be undertaken. We will consider further some of the functions these specialists might serve in this school in a later discussion of the development of preventive mental health services for adolescents.

Students: Adolescence and the High School

Although we have been concerned with the role system of the high school as a *system*, our review has not been without an "ulterior motive," that of defining important aspects of the socialization of the adolescent in the high school. Since it is the "focal role" of our analysis, "studentship" will be discussed in the broader context of adolescent development and the school's influence on the socialization process. In doing so, we do not intend to review the vast literature on adolescence, but rather to focus on critical aspects of the relationship between adolescents and the high school. The understanding of this relationship demands a complex frame of reference since the definition of student membership in the school is likely to differ widely when viewed from the perspective of administrators, teachers, parents, and students themselves. After outlining the reciprocal relationships between adolescents and school life we will review available empirical knowledge for a view of adolescent socialization in the schools that is relevant for ecological theory and for developing programs for individual change and organization redevelopment in that setting.

Perhaps the most comprehensive approaches to adolescence have evolved from a psychoanalytic viewpoint, focusing primarily on the biological changes and intrapsychic conflicts of that developmental period (Blos, 1962; Group for the Advancement of Psychiatry, 1968). From an ego-analytic frame of reference, Erikson (1959, 1968) has more systematically attacked the problems of ego development in varying cultural contexts and has emphasized the critical adolescent problems of sense of identity and identity formation. From a broader perspective, Douvan and Adelson (1966) have coupled psychodynamic hypotheses with data from a national sample of adolescents regarding such topics as values, family and peer relationships to yield valuable *normative* data on "the adolescent experience." While these and related investigations provide a basic understanding of psychic development in adolescence, with some attention to role of family and peer relationships, they provide no link to the organizational context of the school in which a large part of the adolescent experience occurs. Within the frame of reference of this chapter, adolescence is less a biological or physiological given than a psychological and social opportunity (Kenniston, 1968). One of the primary creators of opportunities for psychological and social development of the adolescent is the high school environment with its near total involvement of the adolescent population (Coleman, 1961; 1966).

The high school serves many functions in adolescent development and behavior. As an agency whose primary task is that of training and socializing the adolescent for adult roles, it provides alternative avenues to crystalizing a sense of identity and can help to consolidate the present and chart a course for the future. It is a place where one can "try on different bags" to see what works and what does not; it allows for heterosexual experimentation and provides a laboratory for training in social conventions; it provides a peer cohort with which the adolescent can compare himself and where he can find "soul mates" for his attempts to reconcile the idealism of boyhood with the realism of manhood. Status and the peer group assume unparalleled importance. The sense of social worth developed in the high school becomes a core component of the growing sense of identity. The peer group helps support the "struggle for independence" and helps guide the adolescent in the art of self-governing.

It has been suggested that the mandatory attendance requirement for students contributes to organizational arrangements which yield the peer group an even more cohesive and influential influence than might be otherwise (Bidwell, 1965). It is aruged that because of this requirement, school personnel confront a client society characterized by values and activities which are at best irrelevant and at worst opposed to the service of the school. The students have no choice about attending nor does the public school regulate who comes through its doors. Thus the stage is set by organizational constraints for staff-student conflict of goals which serve to unite the students and enhance the importance of peer socialization.

In sum, the high school serves as a significant locus for adolescent socialization. But most germane to this chapter is that the course which this socialization takes is highly contingent on the quality and form of the high school experience. For the developing adolescent, school is perhaps second in importance only to the family as an area in the search for identity, and is at least as important as family in areas such as college aspirations (Boyle, 1966). The near total involvement in school as a way of life gives the school and the varied activities which take place within its boundaries great formative power. At the same time, much of the formative power rests with the peer group, and is presently tangential to the "formal" educational process (Coleman, 1961).

It is precisely because the high school, in all its facets, makes such an impact on adolescent socialization that it should be studied as an ecological niche—as an environment with multiple and varied opportunities for development in some directions and constraints on development in others. The influence of such cultural factors as socioeconomical class and demographic variables like rural or urban place of residence are known to be important in presenting different opportunities for childhood development, consequently resulting in differing coping styles (Miller & Swanson, 1960; Reissman, 1962; Reissman, Cohen, & Pearl, 1964; Kobrin, 1962; Douvan & Adelson, 1966). In like manner, high school environments differ in the opportunity structures (overt and covert) that they present to students, differences which have important implications for the development of adult competence (Havighurst, Bowman, Liddle, Matthews, & Pierce, 1962). For instance, decisions about occupational choice are surely affected by such environmental constraints as the range of available courses, by the peer group in which the adolescent moves, and by the high school's implicit value system of what "its" students should do, to mention only a few of the possibilities.

The peer group with its status system, values, and opportunities for interaction, and the adult social system of the school with its powers to give information, distribute grades and honors, provide leadership for extracurricular activities, influence curricular and life decisions, and decide on suspension, dismissal, and recommendations, are important aspects of what we have been calling the socialization structure of the high school. This structure is responsive to a variety of forces in its environment and is a major segment of what Lippitt has called the "socialization community," that aspect of the community which is responsible for instilling socially desirable values, goals, and skills in its youth (Lippit, 1967).

Our discussion of the role system of the high school has explored important elements of the school's socialization structure, the interdependence of its varied parts, and the organizational constraints upon its response to changing internal and external conditions. This same socialization structure, in turn, defines a variety of roles for the adolescent in response to which his behavior may be adaptive or nonadaptive, with significant implications for his self-esteem, coping styles, values, self-expectations, and readiness for adult life. In the next section the socialization function of the school environment becomes the explicit focus of investigation as we examine research which might serve as knowledge base for an ecological view of adolescent socialization in the high school.

CURRENT KNOWLEDGE OF THE HIGH SCHOOL AS AN ENVIRONMENT FOR ADOLESCENT SOCIALIZATION

An understanding of the critical roles in the school—in terms of their behavioral prescriptions, sources of conflict, and constraints on innovative behavior—is important knowledge for the development of preventive interventions, but it is not enough. It is true that with such an understanding the mental health professional should be better prepared to assess the internal strengths of the system, to anticipate the "rites of passage" likely to surround his entry, and to identify sources of support for, or resistance to, change efforts. But a descriptive map of critical roles does not provide much help in determining what kinds of interventions are likely to have what effects on the mental health of adolescents, because it does not include a consideration of the dynamic process of socialization in the school. It does not identify those aspects of the interaction between the adolescent on the one hand, and the social system and surrounding organization of the school on the other, which have significant influence on various socialization outcomes—adaptive and nonadaptive.

An approach to preventive intervention which is directed at the socialization of the adolescent in the high school must be derived both from an understanding of the social system of the school and from knowledge about the dynamic interaction between individual and environmental variables in that setting. Although enough research has been done to suggest the general value of an "interactional" approach (Pervin, 1968), it has rarely been applied to schools. Typically, studies in this area have been directed at *either* the organization *or* the individual. Such unilateral research, as Forehand and Gilmer (1964) suggest, can prove frustrating: "formal models of the organization and its parts provide neat symbolic devices, but members of the organization often do not behave as the model says they should. On the other hand, attempts to predict what an individual will do on the basis of his own personal characteristics often lead to the reluctant conclusion that behavior depends in part on the situation" (p. 362).

The change agent who focuses his efforts at either the organizational or the individual level is likely to develop considerable empathy for the researcher's frustration. The therapist may find that the behavior of his child patient reverts to its pathological form as soon as he returns to the classroom. Or the organizational consultant may induce increased communication between teachers only to find that it has consolidated their hostility toward an unsupportive administration and legitimized a norm of minimal classroom involvement. These are unintended, and presumably unwanted, consequences of the interdependence between individuals and their organizational environments. But a change agent, if he can identify such relationships, may also use them to advantage. Focusing on the treatment of severely disturbed children in the classroom may be an important step toward reducing classroom tensions and increasing teacher commitment to positive socialization efforts in the school. Increasing teacher communication in a school may promote the sharing of constructive classroom management techniques and improve the mental health impact of that setting on the child.

We have suggested that research which is to be relevant to preventive intervention into the socialization process must be interactional, i.e., it must explore the relationship between individual and environment. Kahn et al. (1964) have suggested more specifically that research relevant to individual and organizational change must be based upon attempts to integrate knowledge at three levels of abstraction—organizational, group (or interpersonal), and individual. This conceptualization takes into account the special role of the social system in mediating the reciprocal relationship between broad characteristics of the organization and the efforts of the individual to establish an adaptive relationship to his environment. High schools are tremendously diverse organizations, and the relatively little research on organizational characteristics and the modes of coping employed by adolescents in the varied settings of the high school does not provide an adequate analysis of the socialization process for planning preventive interventions and "organizational redevelopment." Some relevant research is available, and we will attempt to suggest guidelines for an integrated

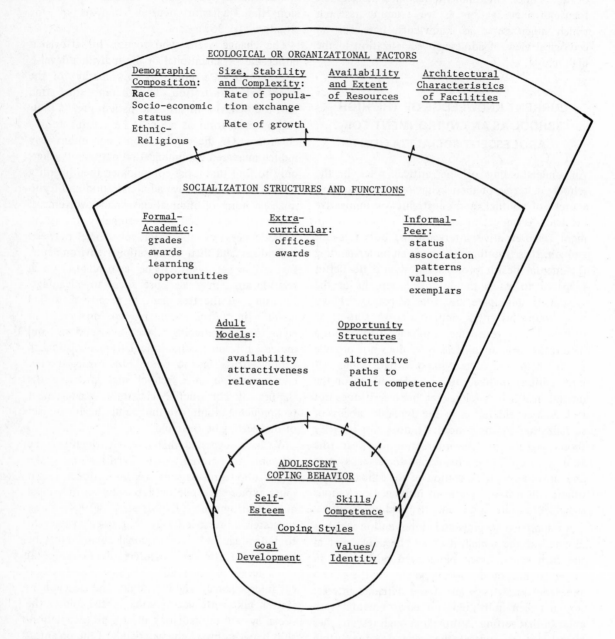

ECOLOGICAL OR ORGANIZATIONAL FACTORS

Demographic Composition:	Size, Stability and Complexity:	Availability and Extent of Resources	Architectural Characteristics of Facilities
Race Socio-economic status Ethnic- Religious	Rate of popula- tion exchange Rate of growth		

SOCIALIZATION STRUCTURES AND FUNCTIONS

Formal- Academic:
grades
awards
learning
 opportunities

Extra- curricular:
offices
awards

Informal- Peer:
status
association
 patterns
values
exemplars

Adult Models:

availability
attractiveness
relevance

Opportunity Structures

alternative
paths to
adult competence

ADOLESCENT COPING BEHAVIOR

Self- Esteem   Skills/ Competence

Coping Styles

Goal Development   Values/ Identity

Fig. 14—6. An ecological view of adolescent socialization in the high school: Levels of analysis and some relevant variables. (Adapted with permission from a conception of person-environment relationships used by Douvan and Gold in a seminar on "The Individual and the Social Environment" at the University of Michigan. This model allows for some direct influence of broader social structural variables, e.g., ecological or organization factors on individual behavior but illustrates the predominant mediation of such effects through intermediate levels, e.g., socialization structures and functions such as peer groups.) (Another way of conceptualizing and illustrating the relationships between these kinds of variables can be found in Bachman et al., 1967.)

understanding of the socialization function of high school environments by exploring relationships between three types of variables—organizational or ecological characteristics, socialization structures and functions, and the coping behavior of the adolescent. The main variables at each of these levels which are included in the research to be reviewed here are presented in Figure 14—6.

Organizational and ecological characteristics, such as school size and socioeconomic composition of the student body, reflect the social, economic, and geographical nature of the surrounding community. These features of the external environment, as they are manifested in the organizational environment of the school, are important determinants of the basic socialization functions allocated to the school and generate the quantity and quality of the resources available for pursuing its mandate. Between these cultural, economic, and social forces on the one hand, and the adolescent on the other, are other aspects of the school—largely linked to its social system— which most directly determine the nature of the socialization process. These socialization structures and functions include, among others, the adolescent social system (informal and extracurricular activities, as well as classroom functions), and the unique educational and social opportunities provided by the school. The opportunities and need satisfactions provided by these aspects of the school will have implications for the individual functioning of the adolescent. The nature of that impact is dependent upon, and in turn is a determinant of, the adolescent's coping behavior. The sense of competence, time perspective, relevance of personal goals, and characteristic modes of relating to the social environment not only affect the adaptiveness of the adolescent's response but also are aspects of individual functioning which may be altered as a result of the coping process. A discussion of these topics will focus on research literature which explores the many links which are assumed to exist between the kinds of variables listed in Figure 14—6. In doing so, we hope to suggest a view of this research which will be relevant for the planning of preventive interventions in the high school and for the research process which must increasingly provide a basis for the development of such interventions.

Organizational and Ecological Factors

Several broad organizational characteristics of the school and its relationship to the community have been identified as probable determinants of the nature of the socialization process in the school. These variables reflect or determine important characteristics of the population of adolescents served by the school, as well as the nature of the physical, social, and educational environment. In turn, these organizational and ecological factors place important constraints on such aspects of the socialization system as status requirements and the relevance of adult models, and therein lies their relevance to preventive interventions. Not only are such features of the school as its demographic composition very visible and available sources of data for the change agent, but changes at this level may be desirable and effective means of altering the course of adolescent socialization. It is possible to look at the bussing of Negro children into white schools, for example, as an attempt to change the socialization process for children of both groups by altering the ecological variable of racial composition. Such changes at the organizational level may have profound implications for the values, competences, and coping styles children develop—a prospect to which both "revolutionaries" and "reactionaries" are acutely sensitive!

The development of increased knowledge about the potential impact of such organizational-level changes—whether they are "natural" or "planned" —will depend upon careful investigations of relationships between broad organizational characteristics of the school and the structures and roles which bear most directly upon adolescent functioning and growth in that setting. The current research on relevant variables at the organizational and ecological level can be summarized in terms of the socioeconomic and racial composition of the student body, school size, and school architecture.

While earlier sociological studies were more concerned with the effects of the socioeconomic status of the community on the educational process (Hollingshead, 1949; Coleman, 1961; Havighurst et al., 1962), some recent work has indicated that the socioeconomic status of the student body has implications not only for student socialization but for the principal role and principal-teacher interaction as well (Herriott & St. John, 1966). Among those variables mediated by the average socioeconomic composition of the school are aspirations for entering college. To quote Boyle (1966), "when high schools are classified according to *average* socio-economic status of the student body, the aspirations of the *individual* students are influenced in the direction of the majority. Working class students attending predominantly middle class schools plan to attend college much more frequently than those attending more working class high schools" (Boyle, 1966, p. 628). The reverse holds true among middle class students attending predominantly working class high schools. Such evidence seems congruent with the "Coleman Report" (Coleman et al., 1966), where, in an effort to identify chacteristics of schools that appear to affect pupil performance, the authors singled out the proportion of highly motivated, high ability pupils enrolled as the most critical variable. Goslin (1967) believes that this phenomenon is implicitly, if not explicitly, understood by those minority groups who are struggling to realign school districts along more racially and socioeconomically balanced lines. A further conclusion from Boyle is that even though the effect of socioeconomic composition on aspirations for college is considerable, it varies as a function of the size of the community in which the school is located. In large cities, the effect of the socioeconomic composition of the high school is roughly equivalent to that of the family, while in smaller communities the effect of the school is much weaker.

Thus, from these studies we see that the high school can have an impact which, for instance, can counter the less developed aspirations of a working class student by providing an academic environment geared toward a college education. An important question concerns whether or not college aspirations are incorporated into the normative structure of the adolescents (Coleman, 1966) or whether they result from the high quality academic system found in schools with higher socioeconomic student bodies (Boyle, 1966; Ryans, 1960; Herriott & St. John, 1966). At this point it is unclear. To the extent that such aspirations result from the higher quality academic system, then faculty enrichment is suggested. If

higher aspirations are generated by the normative student structure as is suggested by the Coleman Report (Coleman et al., 1966), then socioeconomic mixture in a ratio favoring the middle class students would seem to be an appropriate approach for increasing the proportion of working class college aspirants.

A second ecological variable related to the structure of the adolescent social system and one of extreme concern today is the racial composition of the student body. Gottlieb and Tenhouten (1965), for example, studied the social systems of three schools—one primarily white, one primarily black, and the third about equally divided by race. They found that black students entering a previously all-white school enter first into activities involving a minimum of informal cross-racial interaction and seek rewards in the formal system of the school. As the proportion of black students increases, they suggest, two separate social systems emerge and students of each race receive prestige from their activities in their social systems. When racial changeover reaches a critical level, black students "spread out" into all activities and behave much like the white students in the white school. This study suggests that the opportunities for socialization through participation are constrained by the racial composition of the school.

The most thorough initial attempt at assessing the impact of a third variable, school size (number of students), on the behavior and experience of high school students is that of Barker and Gump (1964). These investigators determined the number of behavior settings at schools of varying sizes and related this measure to student participation at the same schools. While larger schools were found to provide a greater number of settings for their students, smaller schools provided a greater number of settings per student. Thus students in smaller schools were given more of an opportunity to participate relative to large school students and they held more positions of responsibility per student than did students in large schools. In short, Barker and Gump's results imply that because of the increased participation and responsibility evident in small schools, the socialization opportunites and experiences of students attending schools of divergent sizes are signficantly different. The structural characteristic of school size is therefore added to the list of ecological variables relevant to adolescent socialization.

While size as studied by Barker and Gump certainly implies architectural design differences in the schools of varying sizes, the physical plant per se was not the subject of inquiry nor has it been a focus in much research. That the physical plant involves important constraints on student behavior has long been known by the school principal whose old building makes flexible scheduling difficult and by the school psychologist who searches in vain for a spot where Johnny can "be alone and think." Indeed such concerns as these are being reflected in the growing interdisciplinary efforts among city planners, mental health and educational professionals, and architects (Good, Siegal, & Bay, 1964; Sapir, 1968).

Meanwhile, there is a growing body of empirical data on the relationship between architectural design and student social structures. Myrick (1965a; 1965b) and Myrick and Marx (1968) have found that the layout of a building can, by affecting interaction rates among students and between students and faculty, indirectly affect the process of meeting education requirements. A more direct illustration of the impact of architectural design and the utilization of facilities on the social system of students is found in the following quote:

"Architects and administrators, without being particularly aware of it, often create homogeneous mixes (of students). This occurs when, in the interests of efficiency or cutting down on noise or disruption, similar activities are located adjacent to each other—as for example, when all related offices or departments, or classes of one grade level are located in the same wing of a building. A common illustration is that in many high schools the vocational education facilities are located in a separate wing from the academic facilities. The result is to decrease interactions between the academically and vocationally oriented students to an even greater extent than would otherwise occur" (Myrick and Marx, 1969, p. 70).

A different aspect of the (unanticipated) consequences of architectural design on student social structure is related by Snyder (1967). The subjects in his study were students in a high school which was moving from an old high school

building to a plant designed on a campus plan which essentially subdivided the new school into three "little schools" in an attempt to achieve some of the advantages of the small school (such as intimacy and greater cohesiveness) while maintaining the advantages of the large (such as a broader range of opportunities and facilities). Two aspects of the student social structure were assessed: the *formal* structure (participation in voluntary, formally organized school clubs, organizations, and activities) and the *informal* social structure (as assessed by sociometric best-friend choices). Results indicated that the change from a single building where there was a high degree of interaction to a campus high school with students dispersed into separate buildings seemingly contributed to a lack of integration in the formal aspects of the school system. Consequently, while the informal social system was not altered by the switch to a new building, there was significantly less social participation in the *formally* organized activities in the new school.

Snyder also remarks on the relation between physical space and teacher social relationships. Informal comments by teachers who had worked in both schools suggested that there was less cohesion and lower morale at the new school due to greater physical distance between teachers and the resulting lack of opportunities to talk with each other. These changes in the social system of a high school suggest that (1) planning for alteration in physical structures should include consideration of possible effects on social interaction patterns, and (2) changes in architectural design may be effective means of producing particular effects on the social systems of the school.

Aside from these relatively scattered and exploratory efforts, there is little data to link organizational-level variables to the socialization process in the schools. For example, Miller, Saleem, and Bryce (1964), in reviewing literature relevant to the study of "drop-outs," suggest that "the crucial importance of organizational form and style has been largely ignored. Restraining cannot be sprinkled through an organization with the expectation of big change unless the organization as an entity changes." But only three studies are listed under the heading "The School as a Factor" and the only one of these which seems at all relevant is a study by Liddle (1962). He shows that a lower class student is more likely to remain in a middle class school than he is in a lower class school; and he suggests that the greater "holding power" of the former is due to a greater expectation that students will remain.

Against the background of this research, which at least demonstrates the relevance of ecological and organizational variables to the socialization process of adolescents in the high school, we now consider research which bears more directly on the nature of the socialization structure.

Socialization Structures and Functions of the High School

It is a somewhat arbitrary task to define discrete socialization structures and functions of the school as they relate to particular outcomes at the individual level. In outlining some important features of "the structure of formally organized socialization settings," Wheeler (1966) summarizes the current "state of the art": "There is really no appropriate and logical end to a list of the properties of socializing organizations that may influence socialization outcomes. At least at this point in organization theory, questions of the distinctive relevance or the explanatory power of various dimensions are just beginning to be answered with empirical data" (p. 107).

The selection of aspects of the school to be included in this discussion is guided more by the available literature than by any coherent conceptualization of the socialization process in the school. Indeed, none of this research appears to have been derived from or explicitly related to such a conceptualization. Still, research has been done which provides some knowledge about organizational aspects of the school, formal and informal, which are presumed to have a direct bearing on such outcomes of the socialization process as the adolescent's formation of an identity or self-concept, his self-evaluation, and the development of a mode or style of coping with various features of his social environment. We shall focus more directly on these outcomes in the next section; what is important to note at this point is that the concern of the present discussion is to explore research which relates structures and functions of the school to such aspects of adolescent functioning.

In line with our assertion that the socialization process in the high school is mediated for the most part by its social system this discussion will be organized in terms of various segments or spheres of this social system. Almost all of the relevant research available concerns two of these spheres, the adolescent social system, and the interaction of students and teacher in the classroom. Within each of these "subsystems," various structures can be identified—such as status systems and patterns of association—which define the particular focus of various studies. Two additional areas of concern will be cited which have as yet received little, if any, systematic attention from social scientists, and which potentially hold great import for the socialization of adolescents in the high school. The first of these is the out-of-class interaction of the student with adults in the school, including extracurricular advisors, administrators, and staff specialists, as well as teachers, and the relevance of these figures to "modeling" and other socialization processes. The second concerns the "structure of opportunity" in the school as it is manifested, among other places, in the relevance and availability of role models and the legitimation of various "paths to adult competence." Taken together, these spheres and features of the socialization structure of the school reflect the fact that either peers or adults in the school may be "agents" of socialization, and that the outcomes of interaction with these agents depend upon the setting and organizational context of that interaction as well as the particular salient dimensions of the relationship to the agent (e.g., status, expertise, affectivity, modeling).

The importance of these aspects of the school to the mental health professional should by now be clear: they are the features of the school environment which impinge most immediately on the psychological "lifespace" of the adolescent and which most directly determine and define the adaptiveness and mental health value of his behavior. The mental health professional may attempt to bring about change in the socialization process directly, as in counseling with a particular teacher about the management of aggressive behavior in classroom management. Or he may attempt to include change in the interaction between adolescents and "direct socialization agents" by altering broader characteristics of the school, e.g., by facilitating the redefinition of relevant policy at the administrative level. In either case, the ultimate aim of the change agent will be the development of a system of socialization agents and structures which maximizes the school's utilization of its resources and provides relevant, growth-encouraging experiences for adolescents, while ensuring the on-going and effective functioning of the school itself.

One problem which illustrates the importance of careful assessment and planning for change in the socialization process is the oft expressed need for relevant and available role models for black adolescents in "ghetto" schools. The notion that white, middle class, suburban teachers may not be well-suited to serving this function is not a new one, and the intervention usually proposed is a broad restructuring of the school to include black teachers with whom the students can identify. The change agent who takes a systematic view of the socialization process in the school will weigh the simplicity of this solution against its unrealistic nature as a large-scale move. He may explore the possibility that some kind of experience can be created to increase white teachers' sensitivity, relevance, and availability to their students. Or he may resign himself to the limited relevance of white teachers to the modeling function, while accepting the possibility that they may still provide some available teaching, and consider ways that appropriate black role models can be introduced into the school experience, including as teachers. The ability of the change agent to help the school create a solution to such a problem will depend to a great extent on his assessment of the existing social system and the socialization functions served by its various segments, as well as resources available to that system which can be applied to the unmet socialization needs of its students. The following discussion is a summary of research knowledge which may provide some guidelines and orientations for such assessments and serve as the basis for further study.

Adolescent Social System

Increasing attention has been given in recent years to the impact of the adolescent social system on socialization and education in the school. There is growing recognition that the system of peer relationships may be cohesive enough to develop a "culture" or "society" with norms, values, and status systems which significantly constrain the behavior of adolescents within the school. As is the case in work groups in a variety of organizational settings, the impact of a cohesive peer group on the achievement of organizational goals may be either inhibiting or facilitating, depending upon the commitment of members to those goals. It has been suggested by some (Coleman 1961; 1966) that it is at least true that the socialization power of the adolescent society is not being applied to educational goals as it could be. Others maintain that the perceived irrelevance of many current educational practices to the needs of adolescents insures that peer influence will act against the accomplishment of educational aims. Either of these positions asserts that peer influences on the socialization process in the school can be considerable.

The system of adolescent peer relationships may be described along any number of dimensions, including status systems, value climates, and structures of association (Coleman, 1961). To this point, however, systematic investigations of peer-cultural influences have been very narrowly defined. Just as a predominant and early focus of sociological interest in the schools was the impact on education of socioeconomic status in the community, a major view of the adolescent society in the school has centered on a descriptive analysis of status allocation among the student body. The critical importance of status in the development of the adolescent's identity and self-esteem has been cited by many authors, with Gordon (1957) going as far as to hypothesize that "the dominant motivation of the high school student is to achieve and maintain a general social status within the organization of the school" (p. 1). Most research on the adolescent society, with its solitary interest in the status dimension, suggests that Gordon is not alone in his assumption.

In an early study which remains one of the most systematic approaches to the status system of the high school, Gordon (1957) distinguished between three society systems which involved the students at "Wabash High:" formal involuntary (academic), formal voluntary (extracurricular), and informal voluntary (peer group). Gordon devised measures of status in each of these three social systems and suggested that the individual's total status in the school could be defined as a composite of these three ratings. Gordon concluded generally that the "social behavior of the students was functionally related to the general social positions they occupied in the social structure of the school" (p. 2). More specifically, intensive interviewing of students suggested that a student's general status among his peers in this school was most strongly related to his position in the formal voluntary (extracurricular) system. Normatively speaking, the most highly valued male social type in this school was the "big wheel" whereas the highest status for girls was defined by competition for the position of "Yearbook Queen." Gordon's observations suggest that informal peer association tended to follow the status lines established in the extracurricular system. Peer-group status rewards for adolescents at Wabash High were less related to academic goals and accomplishments than toward peer-directed activities and relationships.

In addition to providing some normative breadth to Gordon's findings by studying ten Illinois high schools, Coleman's (1961) research focuses more specifically on the relationship between status and the value climates, patterns of association, and characteristics of elites and popular heroes in the "adolescent society." Though he found significant variation among the ten schools in the extent to which the student normative structures valued such areas as academics, athletics, and dating, Coleman substantially agrees with Gordon in concluding that "athletic ability" for boys and "charm and beauty" for girls were dominant in determining status among peers. However, Coleman's analysis goes beyond the identification of the dominant source of status in each of the schools. It suggests that the status system of a given school may be quite complex, conferring highest prestige, for example, on individuals who excel *either* in athletics *or* academics or perhaps on those who excel in *both* simultaneously.

An adequate view of the status system of an adolescent society must not stop with an analysis of its dominant features, however complex. Questionnaire studies of high school students suggest that values promoting status differ considerably *within* schools as well as between them (Gottlieb, 1964). Coleman begins to deal with this issue in identifying various association patterns or cliques in the schools which represent divergent parts of the peer value system. For example, even though academics were rarely dominant in determining social status in a school, Coleman suggests that the "formal involuntary" system may have significant effects on the school through particular groups of students. "The school-oriented cliques, who conform to the standards and desires of teachers, are those whom the teachers and the administrators reward . . . Thus, so long as the administration and teachers are not faced by widespread rebellion, the cliques which they 'sponsor' by the use of their rewards will gain some attention from the adolescents, and they will always be at least in contention for dominance of the system" (Coleman, 1961, p. 217).

This example not only indicates the internal complexity and dynamic quality of the student status system, but also points out that there may be adaptive roles for particular adolescents in a variety of nondominant parts of the social system. Some students may be able to deemphasize predominant peer norms, associate with subgroups which share their interests, and seek status primarily from adults in the formal academic system. Schools will vary in the extent to which such subgroups can flourish; there is some evidence, for example, that the extent of racial integration is one relevant variable. Gottlieb and Tenhouten (1965) imply that the distinction between a staff-supported formal status system and the informal, interpersonal ways of gaining status may have special relevance for schools with a small racial minority. Specifically, their findings suggest that the minority students will tend to seek status in the formal (academic) system and in those areas of the extracurricular system which minimize interpersonal and cross-racial interaction. As the racial balance becomes more equal, this difference does not appear.

We have already pointed to the predominant focus on status in research on the adolescent peer culture. In its overall design, Coleman's research represents no exception to this focus, although he investigates a number of dimensions of that culture as they are related to social status. However, those other dimensions of student culture may have important functions for socialization which are not totally dependent upon their relation to status. The investigation of such functions is an important research task for the future and examples of directions for that research can easily be drawn from Coleman. In viewing association patterns among student peers, Coleman demonstrated that the structure and the content of these patterns could be characterized as either complex or simple and as stable or variable. Though Coleman did not explore such a relationship, one might expect that variations along these dimensions could have different and significant import for the socialization of adolescents with varied coping styles. For instance, an adolescent who is very intolerant of ambiguity and change might face a number of difficulties in a school with a system of associations which could be described as complex and variable in both content and structure (Kelly, 1966). Another aspect of the adolescent social system which Coleman identifies is the exemplary student or "exemplar." Coleman's attention, however, was directed to the effects on a student of being in that position. As we shall point out later in more detail, the function of models in adolescent socialization is relatively unexplored and Coleman's type of analysis might provide a basis for investigating such modeling at the peer level.

Some important gaps in research on the adolescent social system reflect the need for more comprehensive designs. First, very little of the research cited here or in the following sections makes explicit links between variables of the "socialization structure" and the broader organizational variables which we assume to be major determinants. One model for the kind of research needed is provided by McDill (1966), who describes his study as "a further development of *The Adolescent Society*" (Coleman, 1961). McDill systematically investigated potential sources in the community and in the organization of the school affecting variations in "educational climate" within the school. This study includes many relevant findings with respect to various indices of academic achievement in the high school, including the especially interesting indication that differential rewards for academics in the adolescent status system seem to have no systematic bearing on student achievement. But the only dependent variables included in the study were academically focused and the relevance of this

approach to other socialization processes has yet to be demonstrated.

Student-Teacher-Classroom Interaction

Since the classroom is the major educational unit of the school, it is naturally a prominent unit for research on the socialization process as well. Understandably, but unfortunately, nearly all research on the classroom as a setting for socialization is focused on the elementary classroom.[7] This is understandable because constant and exclusive contact of the elementary school pupil with his classroom is much greater than that of his secondary school counterpart. It is unfortunate because the high school classroom is still a major setting for the interaction of a variety of socialization forces: the adolescent social system as it is constituted in the classroom, the teacher as a focal representation of the organizational forces of the school as they are filtered through this particular personality, and the physical and informational segments of the teaching-learning process. Our ability to ascertain the relevance of the research mentioned here to the high school is severely limited by the absence of research at the high school level; but we intend to at least call attention to a number of variables of potential relevance to investigations of this focal setting for the interaction of socialization forces on the adolescent in the high school.

We have already noted the lack of research which considers the *interaction* of several classroom variables, but a few examples of such research may be cited. Grimes and Allinsmith (1961), studying the relationship among compulsivity, anxiety, and performance in structured and unstructured settings, found that anxiety and compulsivity interacted with one another and with teaching methods. In a structured setting, compulsive children performed better than noncompulsive children with anxiety making no difference. In the unstructured setting, however, compulsivity made no difference and anxiety impeded performance. Amidou and Flanders (1961), studying the relationship between degree of structure in the environment and learning, found that while independent children were unaffected by the nature of the teaching method, dependent children performed better under "indirect" than under "direct" teaching. Using college students, McKeachie (1961) found a significant interaction between student motives and classroom environments in determining grades. This kind of emphasis has not, to the authors' knowledge, been extended to noneducational criteria such as student self-esteem or student isolation. In short, the in-class influence of the teacher-pupil relationship of adolescent socialization is unknown, although the studies cited here provide a basis for relevant research.

Some mention needs to be made about out-of-class parameters which may affect the in-class teacher-pupil relationship. For instance, it is reasonable to assume that the compatibility of a teacher's preferred teaching style with the organizational structure of the school would have implications for his classroom performance. An innovative teacher demanding considerable autonomy to function in his preferred mode may thrive in an "open" organizational climate and may feel stifled in a "closed" one where teachers are expected to "go by the book." On the "pupil" side, it is also not simply the adolescent's personality which affects his relationship to the teacher. As an example, the informal student norms may help govern what the "acceptable" responses to teachers are. We would anticipate that a strong adolescent norm to "play it cool" would have visible constraining effects on the nature and intensity of the pupil-teacher relationship. Thus, both the organization context of the teacher role and the informal student norms are at least partial determinants of the teacher-pupil relationship, effects which, to our knowledge, have yet to be investigated. The ecological perspective helps broaden the conception of the determinants of this relationship and places it in a context for important research on its relevance to adolescent socialization.

Although the concept of "climate" or "atmosphere" has been successfully studied with respect to colleges (Stern, 1968), and correctional institutions (Moos, 1968a, 1968b), and psychiatric wards (Moos and Houts, 1968a, 1968b), until recently no economical and sufficiently reliable instruments assessing "classroom climate" were located by the present authors. Early work in this direction (Anderson & Brewer, 1946; Withall, 1951; Mitzel & Rabinowitz, 1953) has proved both cumbersome and time consuming. Thus,

much of the folk lore about specific effects of classroom climate draws heavily on research not germane to the classroom environment. The early work of Lewin, Lippitt, and White (1939) on democratic versus authoritarian leadership style has thus been transposed wholesale by those whose ideological predilection is congruent with those findings to the teaching situation. Hence, we see the oft uttered textbook comment on the superiority of being a "democratic teacher" and providing a "democratic climate" while the relevance of various classroom situations has yet to be explored.

Recently Walberg, in connection with the Harvard Physics Project, has developed a measure of perceived classroom environment which promises to fill a significant research void in the study of classroom atmospheres (Walberg, 1966; Walberg & Anderson, 1967). Because heavy stress is laid on classroom dimensions particularly relevant to the academic or learning environment and because thus far the scale is standardized on a national sample of experimental physics classes, its utility and relevance to the psychosocial classroom experience awaits further empirical work and extended standardization. Yet, by dimensionalizing the classroom environment in a systematic manner, it may allow the testing of interactional hypotheses within an ecological conceptualization.

Though at present the classroom seems to remain an area of recognized importance and little systemic knowledge, significant empirical efforts such as that of Walberg are being made. How a particular classroom environment affects a particular adolescent is, of course, an important problem not only from an educational but also from a mental health perspective.

A more specific area of research, classroom social structure, has been viewed as related to the identification and perhaps the amelioration of mental health problems in the classroom. While the research cited here is again based on the elementary school classrooms, the variables considered may be especially important to the high school as well. While these variables are much the same as those which have been considered as aspects of the broader peer social structure, it is true that one of the main opportunities for school personnel to understand individual students in these terms is as the peer structure is translated into the classroom. While we have not found a great deal of research relating to the classroom social structure with regard to mental health, the implications of the available research are provocative. Lippitt and Gold (1959) demonstrated that a child's position in the social structure of the elementary school classroom is related to certain mental health criteria. "To summarize, we can say that children in low positions in the socio-emotional structure of the classroom (as assessed by peer ratings on the dimensions of social power, affectivity, expertness, and coerceability) tend to have mental health difficulties which are reflected in the inner psychological processes, in interpersonal relationship difficulties, and in behavior patterns which disrupt the life of the classroom group" (pp. 44–45).

Not only do students low in the social structure have a continuous experience of failure and social rejection from peers, teachers also behave differently toward them. Teachers pay more attention to the social behavior than to the performance behavior of low status pupils, more so than for high status pupils.

A closely related line of research is that dealing with the "classroom isolate." Epperson (1963) reports that in a combined elementary and secondary school population "exclusion by peers is not significantly related to feelings of isolation from them ... [but] there is a strong relationship between peer exclusion and the other forms of alienation and task and social powerlessness" (p. 375). Further, high isolation and high powerlessness are both related to low actualization of a pupil's academic potential. In the only study we found relating teacher characteristics to the amount of classroom isolation, Gold (1962) found more isolates in classrooms of higher-authoritarian teachers (as defined by the F scale) than in classrooms of low-authoritarian ones.

Taken as a group, these studies suggest that the elementary classroom social structure does have mental health implications for student experience and that knowledge of this social structure can serve as a basis for creating preventive attempts to aid those who are "at risk"—such as the isolate. Once isolates are identified, the course of intervention depends on the resources of the school. If there are teachers' aides, they can be used to free the teacher for more personalized attention. If aides are not available and teachers have no time, a high-status student may serve in

the change-agent role. Of particular importance are those isolates who are characteristically quiet and passive, for they often can be overlooked—especially in a class with many "troublemakers"—precisely because they cause no trouble. This scene reminds one of Paul Goodman's remark: "As is common in our society, in order to get a fair deal and ordinary human attention to one's needs, it is necessary to be an exceptional pain in the neck" (Goodman, 1968, p. 10). It does, however, have important implications in terms of the effects such variables as composition of the class might have on how the quiet and passive isolate is labeled by the teacher.

These studies do not, of course, deal at all with the critical implications of the differences between the classroom's function in elementary and secondary schools. Very important questions as a result are left unanswered and, in fact, have been heretofore relatively unasked. To what extent is isolation a function of a student in a particular class with a particular teacher and to what extent is it true of the student across classes? How do different teachers affect the manifestation of extra-classroom social structure within the classroom? Can teachers be identified in terms of the relevance of their teaching styles and personal characteristics to classes of particular student composition? Only new types of research directed to questions such as these will clarify the importance of the classroom social structure for socialization and mental health in high school.

Finally, the classroom includes many other variables which affect its social structure. Such variables as socioeconomic composition of the students, racial composition, organizational climate of the school, etc., all affect what goes on in the classroom. At this point it seems safe to say that we really know very little about what goes into making up the classroom climate nor do we understand the process by which pupil-teacher relationships and classroom social structure contribute to the social environment of the high school and the socialization of the adolescents therein.

Extra-Classroom Contacts with the Adult Social System

It is unfortunate that much of the research done on teacher-pupil relationships seem to assume implicitly that this relationship is entirely a classroom phenomenon. While common sense and personal experience testify that pupil-teacher contact out of class (or lack of it) may be of immense importance in determining the quality of the high school experience, we know of no research on this phenomenon, its effects, or which teachers tend to "fraternize" and under what conditions. Perhaps even more serious is the lack of research on more formalized extra-class contacts between the student and school personnel: extracurricular advisors, athletic coaches, counselors, and administrators.

Closely related to this void is an equally vacuous one around the function of role models for adolescents. Although the importance of such models is stressed in discussions of adolescent socialization (e.g., Douvan & Adelson, 1966), no relevant research is known to deal with the school in this respect. Bachman et al. (1967) have included the influence of adult role models in the conceptual design of their study, but no analysis is available as yet.

Opportunity Structure

We have mentioned the obvious significance of the opportunity structure of the high school for the alternative routes to adult competence available to the adolescent. Quite apart from such issues as status, schools vary in the extent to which they provide programs relevant to the wide range of skills and interests of their clientele. Havighurst et al. (1961) have suggested, for example, that the nonacademically-oriented students in the "River City" school were given little opportunity to develop appropriate areas of "adult competence," defined as an essential goal of socialization. They suggest that such structures as work-study programs for boys, and domestic and family management training for girls should be instituted for these students. Carlson (1964) has suggested that these students—for whom the schools have no appropriate courses of study—are generally victims of "internal selection" procedures and they get channeled into programs where they can be "kept out of the way." Unfortunately, no direct, formal analysis of the opportunity structure of high schools and their impact on the development of social and vocational competence is known to the authors. The potential contribution of this type of

analysis is demonstrated in Cloward and Ohlin's (1960) treatment of the relation of opportunity structures of the community to various delinquent adaptations on the part of adolescents. Research is needed to explore such questions as the relevance of the opportunity structure of the school for the general client population, as well as subgroups and individuals, the flexibility of the school in responding to unique individual characteristics and needs, and the response of various adolescents to fixed and limited alternatives. The absence of such studies would seem to be one of the most significant research voids in the area of adolescent socialization.

Adolescent Behavior: Socialization and Coping

How are we to view the individual adolescent's behavior in terms of his response to environmental conditions and the socialization process? Individual outcomes which have most concerned students of socialization include values, self-concept or identity, self-esteem, and at times the more diffuse criteria of mental health. But if individual behavior is to be considered in relation to particular socialization environments, its relevance to interaction with such environments must be made quite explicit. It is clearly possible to set such individual variables as values, and even much less well-defined processes as "needs," in a framework which considers their relevance to features of the environment; at a later point we shall present one such framework as it has been applied to an especially relevant research task (Bachman et al., 1967). At this point, we suggest that one possible way of organizing a view of the individual and making the interactive or relational features of his behavior especially explicit is to consider the relevance of various behavior and attributes to his modes of coping with the environment. It is important to know from a mental health standpoint, for instance, if a set of conditions in the school is producing low self-esteem and reducing a student's chances of coping with such a condition. On the individual side we can assume that this adolescent is likely to experience some degree of lowered self-esteem and confidence as a result of leaving fewer options to deal with the problem. Important in the long run, both for the individual *and* the organization, is his behavioral response to such a situation. Does he withdraw, and if so, how? Does he attempt to change the basis for status allocation in the school or perhaps to locate a subsystem within that environment in which his behavior is more adaptive? Or does he seek changes in his own behavior which will be more congruent with the prevailing system and merit a more positive evaluation? Our particular interest in coping behavior as a view of the individual as he relates to the social environment stems from its potential relevance to such questions. As ways are developed to understand and conceptualize individual behavior in these terms the socialization process in the high school can be increasingly viewed as ways that are highly relevant to improving the functioning of both the school and the people within it. Research on the high school has been especially weak in applying such a view of individuals and conceptualizing a range of relevant variables to deal with coping behavior. The development of this area depends upon efforts to build upon exploratory research cited here.

To repeat a central point, the development of sufficiently complex and representative ways of describing and measuring adolescent behavior which is socialized in school has not proceeded very far. Those studies which have contributed most to an understanding of the social system of the school have generally been either suggestive or simplistic with respect to assessing the impact of the social system on the adolescent. Gordon (1957), for instance, indicates that his index of general status might be viewed as a "measure of personal adaptiveness" in that "it reflects the individual's capacity for performing a wide range of roles in the various structures which confront him in the school situation" (p. 24). While Gordon's idea of using cumulative status as a measure of adaptation is an ingenious inroad to studying the impact of the school social system on the adolescent, his particular study did not attack this problem directly.

Coleman (1961) begins a relevant analysis by linking low social system status with low self-esteem and high status with high self-esteem. Though he does not study the individual's reaction to this low status and how he copes with it, he does speculate on some of the possible reactions to negative self-feelings: "In short, a person with any ego strength will not sit by while his self-evalua-

tion is being lowered by the social system of the school. He may attempt to gain status through those activities that give status. If this is not possible, either because status is ascribed to a predetermined group, or because he has no talents in status-bringing activities, he will take his psychological self elsewhere, leaving only a physical self in the school" (p. 228). Coleman does note that the proportion of students who express dissatisfaction with their position in the social system decreases over time, suggesting that some processes of withdrawal from, resignation towards, or mastery of the system do occur.

Several authors have discussed or implicated the relationship of organizational or ecological variables to the possible range of adaptations in the high school, though the specific channels of such influence remain unspecified. Carlson (1964) has delineated some possible dimensions of adolescent coping style resulting from the extent to which students accept the school's definition of their role. The student who totally accepts the mandatory school-pupil relationship is making a *receptive adaptation*. The total rejection of the school is *drop-out adaptation*. Other more in-between ways in which the student can "redefine the school" include situational retirement (a body present, mind absent adaptation), rebellious adjustment (a limit-testing adaptation), and a side payment adaptation (attending school for the fringe benefits such as athletic competition). Carlson lays no guidelines as to how these differential adaptations may be identified nor does he attack the problems of how they may be differentially distributed in a school and who may choose one versus another. They do refine Coleman's dimension of withdrawal from the school, however, and present useful hypotheses for further inquiry.

Another underdeveloped but potentially useful method for studying dimensions of coping behavior is through the use of high school behavior settings (Barker and Gump, 1964). Barker and Gump found that students in smaller schools are more likely to occupy a wide range of positions in the extracurricular system because of the "undermanned" nature of the settings and they suggest that a small school with undermanned settings represents a pull toward a *"generalist"* type of competence with more people doing more different things. In larger schools with "overmanned" settings there are more people for fewer positions, thus pulling for a *specialist* type of competence to develop. Conversely, it would seem that the relative scarcity of opportunities per student in the larger schools would result in more of a "vicarious participation" adaptation among those lacking the relevant skills necessary to specialize. It might be noted that the relation of school size to the types of competencies likely to develop is less clear-cut than Barker and Gump's data suggest. Coleman (1961) did not find that degree of specialization increased with size of school, and Bachman et al. (1967) suggest that a curvilinear relationship exists between school size and opportunities for self-actualization.

Kelly (1966a, 1966b, 1967, 1968, 1969) is conducting a study to describe how the high school student adapts to the environment of the high school. The work is a longitudinal study of male students attending three Detroit metropolitan area schools. Two of the schools are located in suburban, white communities. One of the schools is in a black, inner-city location. Each pair of suburban schools also varies according to the rate of the total number of students who enter and leave during the school year. One school is a "high" exchange school; the other school of each pair is a "low" exchange school. The study is attempting to specify the conditions under which students who vary in their coping styles have different adaptive histories in schools of contrasting cultural and demographic properties. The specific coping style of primary interest is exploratory behavior, and it is assumed that students who vary in their preferences for exploratory behavior have differing adaptive histories. Exploratory behavior is being measured by multiple methods—a 30-item questionnaire, a thematic assessment of response to social structures, and a developmental inquiry of past exploratory behaviors (Kelly et al., 1971). On the basis of preliminary studies conducted in Columbus, Ohio, it was found that schools which had varied social structures had contrasting modes of operation and utilized different styles for absorbing new students. Further preliminary studies in high schools in the Detroit metropolitan area have provided correlational status for the questionnaire assessment of exploratory behavior (Edwards, 1971). It has been found that exploratory behavior is *not* related to other established measures of personality traits or socioeconomic status (Rice & Roistacher, 1968) but has been found to correlate significantly with peer nominations of this behavior (Kelly, 1968; Edwards, 1969). As the major work developed, it includes organizational assessments of faculty-student interactions as well as naturalistic observations of relevant social settings. The longitudinal framework allows for a detailed and comprehensive analysis of socialization processes at each of the four schools as these processes relate to the performance of coping styles and the generation of adaptive roles. The purpose of this work is to generate a conceptual base for planning preventive interventions that will be valid for each of these varied environments. The goal is to build a workable theory for interventions created from an intensive analysis of these natural settings over time.

Research is urgently needed to develop a more sophisticated view of adolescent coping behavior as it is relevant to the school. Especially important in this respect is the concept of competence, as reviewed by Smith (1968), not only in its relevance to the development of socially valued skills but also in the broader sense of the "competent self" as a prerequisite to effective coping with social environments. Again the significance of behavioral response to the environment should be stressed. Smith (1968) suggests, for example, that a view of the self as competent will allow the person to "risk disapproval in order to master a task on [his] own terms," while the absence of such a view will lead to conforming behavior. Relationships of this sort demand much more conceptualization and careful study.

The Integrative Task for Research on Adolescent Socialization in the High School

In this section and the one previous to it, we have explored some of the knowledge currently available which is relevant to understanding the school broadly as an organization and social system, and more specifically as an environment for the socialization of adolescents. A variety of "needed research" areas have been mentioned throughout, including a better understanding of the school's relationship to the larger community, constraints on innovative behavior in various roles in the school, and the conceptualization and operational definition of important socialization variables (e.g., opportunity structure, coping style, etc.). However, the broader task for the research involves the direct development of integrative links in and between these areas of knowledge about the high school environment and its impact on the adolescent. This integrative task demands the use of multiple and complementary research methods to expand the research which has been reviewed here. One of these methods involves focused, systematic studies of the links between selected variables at different levels of analysis such as those listed in Figure 14–6 at the beginning of this section. What is the impact, for example, of low status in the high school on adolescents who view themselves as generally competent as compared with those who do not? How do varying degreees of racial integration in the school affect the relevance of adult role models to adolescents with divergent racial characteristics? How do students with varied coping sstyles and preferences react to inadequate opportunities for personal expression and growth in different school environments? The exploration of such questions demands intensive research which systematically poses alternative hypotheses and investigates them through field and laboratorylike methods.

A second, complementary need is for multivariate, longitudinal studies of socialization in the high school to generate and test hypotheses and to provide a normative and integrative framework for the development of knowledge. One study which attempts to satisfy many of these conditions is now under way (Bachman et al., 1967). Although the entire scope of this project cannot be reviewed here, a brief consideration of salient features can illustrate both a point of view and a research strategy for viewing the ecology of the high school.

The Bachman study concerns a representative national sample of 2,213 high school age boys, during the time from their beginning of tenth grade to their first year after graduation, and the 87 schools these boys attend (Johnston, 1968). The study views the impact of the social environment (in work settings as well as in school) on these adolescent boys under the single overarching hypothesis that "the contemporary objective environment of a person has profound effects on his physical and mental health, that these effects are always part of a causal sequence which includes as intervening terms his psychological environment and his immediate responses to it, and that the causal sequence from objective environment to health will be modified by the genetic endowment and personality of the individual" (Bachman et al., 1967, p. v in preface).

This general hypothesis derives from the conceptual framework that is a variant of role theory applied to research in prior organizational settings (French, Kahn, & Mann, 1962; Wolfe, Quinn, Snoek, & Rosenthal, 1964). In this approach, social roles are seen as points of contact between the organization and the individual, and the focus is the degree of "person-environment fit" along various dimensions important to the effective functioning of both the organizations and the individual. This requires measurement of individual and environmental characteristics along commensurate dimensions. The importance of this problem has been stated succinctly by Brim (1966):

"Personality processes have been analyzed with concepts which do not articulate with analyses of the outside social structure and what is needed are personality concepts which permit easy and direct movement from characteristics of the social organization to its consequences for personality. For example, if a man lives in a highly differentiated, complex social structure, one can describe his significant reference figures. Similarly, where he is involved with persons who make conflicting and unresolvable role demands the concept of identity confusion permits one to move directly from the existence of conflict in the objective social order to its consequences for personality" (pp. 7–8).

Within this framework, data is being collected at each of the three levels relevant to organizational analysis: (1) broad characteristics of the organization (size, administrative policies, and practices, etc.); (2) socialization structures and functions (role models, demand, and opportunity structures); and (3) coping behavior of the adolescent (self-concept, value and attitudinal aspects of mental health, social behavior, job successes, etc.). Bachman and his associates have included measurements of such commensurate variables as opportunities and demands for achievement, self-development, and affiliation in the environment, and needs for achievement, self-actualization, and affiliation in the individual.

In addition to this approach to measurement, the promise of the Bachman study lies in its longitudinal panel design. This will allow the study of changes in adolescent socialization over time and within different social environments (e.g., work and school). The design does have the limitation of considering the organizational environment to be a constant factor though the value of studying organizational change as well has been argued convincingly by Miles (1965).

This brief discussion can do justice neither to the complexity of the particular study summarized here nor to the integrative task to which it is directed. But it does provide an example of an approach to research which is highly relevant to the development of ecological knowledge as a perspective on mental health and preventive intervention in the schools.

Other research methods involve the naturalistic observation and "case reporting" of life in natural environments (Raush, 1969). Such studies can add a measure of richness and integration to the understanding of environments that more discrete and manipulative methods cannot provide. As a general method, naturalistic observation includes a broad range of research approaches from the attempts of a participant or consultant to understand his experience in a particular environment, to the systematic use of observations to complement differences in environments found by other experimental methods (Kelly, 1967). The authors know of few detailed, systematic reports based upon extended observations of life in high schools. We suspect that this vacuum is attributable to at least two major conditions. One is a low value in current psychological research circles of "purely descriptive" accounts of ongoing social systems. This seems to hold in spite of the pioneering research of Barker and others (Barker 1965; Barker & Gump, 1964). Another constraint is the limited development of conceptions of social environments which are complex and authentic enough to provide a point of view as well as integrate hypotheses about life in a natural social system. The development of one such conceptual framework is an ultimate goal toward which the work of this chapter is directed. What can we suggest at this point about research needs which could be served by systematic naturalistic

observation in high schools? What guides can be offered to the observer in collecting and reporting data which will be of greatest relevance to extending our understanding of adolescent socialization in the school setting? For a number of reasons, these questions are especially relevant to a pressing need for knowledge about the impact of social change on the high schools, the responses of schools to various forms of crisis or disruption, and the opportunities and dangers for adolescent socialization which can be found in this facet of school experience. The behavioral scientist sometimes rushes, or is yanked, into the position of "expert" and consultant in periods of disruption. He is asked to help clarify the situation and pose alternative outcomes and means of resolution, and often to aid in the implementation of the plans which result. Whatever form this school involvement may take, it is our belief that an ecological assessment of the school environment is an indispensible requisite for effective "consultation" in that setting, no less in time of crisis than at any other point. Consultation by professionals at times of threats or incidents of school disruption, then, represents a growing opportunity to assess and report the response of school social systems to social change and internal stress. Methods of naturalistic observation assume a special importance in this assessment because of the often unpredictable (or perhaps more correctly, the often unpredicted) character of organizational disruption, the rapid shifting of involvements and courses of response which they may involve, and the frequent mobilization of many diverse elements of the social system. Because of this special relevance, the opportunities and needs for naturalistic observation in high schools will be discussed in more detail in the context of their response to social change and organizational disruption.

Social Change, Organizational Disruption, and Naturalistic Research in the High School

Social change is both an outgrowth and expression of the individual human condition, and a set of societal forces which act to shape that condition (Reiff, 1968). Individuals—or indeed organizations and professions—may respond to such change by helping to shape its course or by yielding to frustration and anger or disparagement and confusion. In any case, the kind of response which is made will significantly affect the impact of change on the people or social systems concerned.

At the high school level, the most visible occurrence of changing times is seen in the variety of disruptions in the traditional educational process. Student strikes and racial tensions are in many high schools part and parcel of the living curriculum. In addition to reflecting broad social forces and issues, such incidents invariably involve major personal investments and needs on the part of many participants. In that sense, they must be taken as expressions of the hopes, problems, prejudices, and anxieties of the involved adolescent. There are innumerable indications that many adolescents feel hampered, if not oppressed, in their search for a meaningful, satisfying, and productive role, in part because in their eyes the school system fails to provide opportunities for adequate experiences in many important areas (Joint Commission on Mental Health of Children, 1968). Moreover, this is a time in which traditionally powerless subcultures have developed more of a voice and have become more of a power to reckon with as their dissatisfactions have become more openly expressed. Student power groups such as the United Student Movement are agitating for rapid change in the direction of greater student control in decision making and rule enforcing. The rise of Black Identity and the struggle for Black Dignity has already had visible effects upon the curriculum and hiring practices of many schools and school districts.

The disruptions resulting from these social forces are potentially important socialization experiences for all involved. While a variety of hypotheses have been put forward as explanations for the discontent, to view the disruptions either as mere expressions of individual restlessness or purely as national social malaise would be a gross oversimplification. Student discontent and activism do not form in a vacuum nor is the high school merely a passive victim of broader social strains and stresses. The knowing or unknowing role played by the high school itself in sustaining, increasing, or alleviating tensions is one worthy of critical investigation.

Selected research relevant to conflict in the high school has been reviewed by Chesler, Franklin, and Guskin (1969) who derive four major principles about such conflict:

"(1) certain aspects of the structure and operation of schools make student-student, student-adult, and professional-community conflict inevitable; (2) societal racial patterns reflected in the schools encourage much school conflict to be expressed in racial terms; (3) school personnel resist changes in the management of staff and student human resources; and (4) certain aspects of educators' roles and assumptions and student status prevent the use of mediating processes that could intervene between the existence of grievance and conflict and the development of student and community protest and rebellion" (p. 34).

There are few published accounts of attempts to gather data which would substantiate, correct, or elaborate these principles. The discussion to follow relies heavily upon two reports, as yet unpublished, which were available to the authors. The first is an account of a "racial incident" in a high school and observations of adminstrative responses to the incident (Ochberg & Trickett, in preparation). The second is a preliminary report on a study of organizational crisis in seven high schools throughout the United States, with a focus on the development of alternative means of resolving or utilizing such disruptive conditions constructively (Chesler et al., 1969). These case study materials are used to help generate a set of questions about the response of high schools to social change, questions which reflect the conceptual basis of this chapter and which can direct the collection and reporting of further naturalistic data. These questions are not meant to be exhaustive, but to stimulate further development and inquiry.

One set of questions revolves around the impact of the broader community on the school, i.e., the relation of the organization to its environment. We noted previously the absence of knowledge about environmental constraints on the organizational functioning of the school, even though "vulnerability" to external influence has been identified as one of its primary characteristics. The extent and focus of this vulnerability, as well as organizational means of trying to cope with it, should be especially apparent in the response of various schools to social change in the community. How do community factions attempt to bring pressure to bear on the school social systems and at what point? How does the school attempt to maintain its autonomy and what roles does professionalization play in staff positions? How effective are these coping strategies under varied conditions? The account of racial disruption in a high school by Ochberg and Trickett (in preparation) provides an illustration of one interesting response of the school to community pressures. In this case the school "internalized" the conflicting community positions. The principal essentially withdrew and allied himself with the school board and the white citizens, while a vice-principal served as the school's link to the black community and the students. The organizational response to community conflict was patterned primarily by the rather subtle and informal ways the vice-principal could find of working around and with his "superior," toward whom he was quite sympathetic. This example illustrates both some of the community forces to be contended with by the school as well as one noninstitutionalized form of response to them. How representative this kind of informal, makeshift "division of labor" is for school administrators we do not know. Most formal accounts of school role structure fail to differentiate the allocation of administrative functions, but such a monolithic view seems called to question if this example is at all representative.

Similar questions ought to be raised about the response of the student and faculty social systems of the school to community issues. The impact of socioeconomic status in the community on these social systems has long been a subject of speculation and research. It is expected that the goals, expectations, and dissatisfactions of teachers and adolescents in the school will reflect in an even more dynamic and differentiated way their life styles and places in the flow of community life. This is seen dramatically, of course, in the increased expression of the frustrations and hopes of the black communities within the school, even at the elementary school level. Also in some areas, adolescents in white suburban schools have been the target of propaganda from white radical groups with sexual liberty, drugs, and freedom of verbal expression as the central topics. The impression of the authors is that there is wide variation in the extent to which community groups and adolescents define the school as a microcosm and battleground for community issues. Available data, however, does not allow more than the most impressionistic analysis of some of the sources of

this variation in community structure and school organization, and of its differentiated effects on adolescent socialization. The systematic study of school "crisis" should provide valuable data about these aspects of interdependence between the school and its environment. Especially important is knowledge about alternative ways schools can develop to assess community change and to respond to impending needs and demands with foresight and constructive action, guiding the course of this response in directions which create positive socialization and educational experience for adolescents.

Obviously, the attainment of these ends depends not only on the school's relation to its environment, but also on the nature of the internal organization of the school and the patterns of interaction between the various subgroups within the school society. Chesler et al. (1969) comment upon a central aspect of the response of school administrators and staffs to disruption in their midst:

"One of the most distressing products of these situations is the perspective that nothing of any educative value can be accomplished. The resulting administrative postures of instituting repressive school or policy controls, of expelling students, of surrendering a school to chaos, or of wholesale teacher resignations are essentially disastrous examples of our inability to resolve conflict productively. Often schools are patched up enough to delay or drive underground the expression of real concerns and the exploration of important issues; a strategy guaranteed to create other explosions later. A useful perspective for educators could be an indication that these situations are not entirely hopeless, and that some educationally fruitful means of preventing, managing, rebuilding from, or responding to such crises may indeed exist" (p. 1).

Moreover, Chesler and his associates reject the notion that the school must be at the mercy of forces in the broader society, and that improvement in the school can come only from change in its environment: "Although it is a truism that school life and community life are interdependent, we think there are some immediate policy alternatives for local schools that do not depend for success upon wholesale change in the political, social and economic character of the American society" (Chesler et al., 1969, p. 2). The research which is resulting from these views explicitly recognizes the position that constructive alternatives for action must be based in both intensive and comparative naturalistic observations of high school social systems as they attempt to deal with crisis.

This is a second guidepost for the naturalistic researcher. Along with current, situational responses to the problem at hand, a crisis may bring forth conflicts, alienation, and strengths in the social system which may have been subtle, covert, or denied previously. Careful observation during these times can provide a somewhat biased, but nonetheless informative, picture of these characteristics which are critical to the functioning of the system at all times. It is difficult for informal aspects of the social system to remain implicit during crisis. The faculty may be unable to ignore very strong and basic differences in their conceptions of their own role and the educative process which is the responsibility of the school. In one of the reports available to the authors, it appeared that a majority of teachers in a disrupted high school were unwilling to see their active involvement in problem solving as a legitimate or desirable part of their role requirements. The fact that they resolved to ignore the crisis in classroom discussion seems bound to have had an effect on the resolution of the conflict and the students' view of the relevance of the school to their own concerns. Other critical questions center around the available channels of communication and influence for the students and the extent to which they feel they can affect their own experience. What role does the student council or newspaper play in a tense situation? Do committed and involved students have access to decision makers or adults who have informal power within the system? Are there communication and decision-making mechanisms within the student body and whom do they include? Extensive observations of these and related matters in high schools in conflict can serve as a basis for a more complete and accurate understanding of the social functions served by the high school social system, not only for adolescents but for the adults. As such a comparative knowledge is created it will also be possible to specify the ways in which those functions can be variously distributed in individual schools and how those distributions are related to community structure and to adolescent experience in the school. One place where the allocation of functions seems highly variable in the school is the role of the counselor. The central characteristic of this role seems to range freely between "administrative assistant," "mental health professional," friend and advocate for students, educator, and disciplinarian, to name a few. Moreover, a particular definition seems predominant in a given school. The obvious question is: What happens to the other functions in those schools? When the counselor is disciplinarian, is the principal or teacher the friend and advocate, or is no one? Are their rivalries to define the most valued functions for various roles in the school? These seem to be critical questions about the nature of the school as an agent of socialization, which can be clarified through the case reporting of how these roles are expressed in different settings.

Following our earlier conceptual framework for viewing research in an ecological context, the third area of focus for the "crisis observer" is coping behavior, not only of adolescents, but of the adults who constitute much of their social environment in the school. Again, we repeat our bias, that the critical question is what patterns and styles of coping lead to adaptive and maladaptive outcomes under varied environmental conditions. Just as a crisis situation often makes covert properties of the social system of the school more visible, so does a crisis put to the critical test the commitment, resiliency, and responsiveness of individuals in the system to resolve it in the direction of increased personal effectiveness and more relevant and productive role performances. An administrator or teacher who generally provides support and guidance to peers or students in a subtle way, may have to put his concern on the line and become more visible. Doing so may strengthen or weaken his overall contribution depending upon his sensitivity to the situation and his own resources. We mentioned previously a vice-principal in a racially disrupted school who played a significant informal and subtle role in buttressing and supplementing the inadequate response of a withdrawn principal. Subsequent evidence suggests that he was unable to maintain this thankless position under fire and that he resolved some of the conflict in the same maladaptive direction taken by the principal. We need rather desperately to understand the personal qualities and situational conditions which allow and support sustained constructive coping with such stress. When and how is support for problem-solving provided in the formal and informal social structure? What processes of selection and socialization generate persons who can tolerate ambiguity, create support for their efforts, and maintain their commitments under fire? These are important questions for individuals in all the segments of the high school social system. It may be the student whose typical life experience is alien or irrelevant to the ongoing life of his school who emerges as one who can roll with the punches, confront the issues, and encourage problem-solving efforts under conditions of stress. Which students emerge as leaders in efforts to assert student demands? Where does their power originate and how do they sustain it? Assessing the place of these "effective copers" in the day-to-day social system of the school may be one way of viewing the total high school environment in some depth. Are these resources actualized by the school or does their strength and relevance develop only through marginal membership? Data which bears upon these issues should have significance for understanding the life of the high school which goes far beyond the immediate issues and problems which draw the behavioral scientist into that setting.

Let us be clear about the perspective we take on this discussion. We do not mean to imply that crisis is the whole, or even the essence, of social change. Careful long-term accounts of change and the socialization process, as well as more structured and controlled probes, are prerequisite to an adequate knowledge of the social system of the school and its potential for constructive response to social change. We do suggest that a poverty of descriptive and analytic accounts of school life and crisis is a serious impediment to a valid ecology of the high school. This discussion has suggested a general perspective and some representative questions to guide the observation and reporting of such accounts. A more sophisticated approach to the high school and adolescent socialization depends upon the inseparable tasks of generating knowledge and formulating more sophisticated theoretical conceptions. It is to the latter task that we now turn our attention.

ECOLOGICAL CONCEPTS FOR THE REDEVELOPMENT OF THE HIGH SCHOOL

The previous sections have documented the state of current knowledge regarding relationships between the functions of the high school and how the styles of adaptation for both students and faculty are changing. What has been absent in this literature is a point of view that provides a basis for developing ideas for change that are immediately practical. This section will provide a discussion of ecological principles relevant for designing preventive interventions.

Proposals for the validity of ecological analogies have previously appeared (Barker, 1965; Kelly, 1966; Kelly, 1967; Kelly, 1969) and the term is mentioned with increasing frequency in the literature of the mental health professions. Ecology, however, like many orienting concepts, has multiple and even contradictory meanings. The specific source for the derivation of the ideas in this chapter comes closest to the biological heritage for this term, rather than the meaning in the psychological, sociological, or public health literature.

The discipline of ecology has arisen in the biological sciences from a need to understand the interaction of the many varied components of natural environments. The conceptual basis for biological ecology is the "ecosystem." The biological world is seen as a series of reciprocal processes whereby organisms are dependent upon their nonliving environment for fulfilling basic needs for food, shelter, and reproduction, with the interaction of organisms producing environmental changes. An organism or group of organisms, therefore, is seen as existing in a dynamic equilibrium with its environment—hence the term eco*system* (Odum, 1959; Tansley, 1935). While biological ecology has this single unitary concept for identifying this relationship, the ecological perspective in psychology as yet has not developed such a concept. At the present time the term ecosystem has the status of an axiom in psychology without empirical verification.

Kelly (1968) previously has proposed four principles, derived from biological ecology, as a guide for assessing social environments for the purpose of change and redevelopment. These four principles represent ideas that are applicable for designing change programs for the redevelopment of individuals and organizations. The purpose of this section is to present these principles and to illustrate how they are applicable for conceptualizing and changing the high school environment.

These principles refer to the following ecological formulations: interdependence, entropy, adaptation, dynamic equilibrium, and succession. The interdependence principle, a corollary from the axiom of the ecosystem, states that a biological environment consists of reciprocal units; the principle of entropy refers to patterns by which energy is transferred through environments; the adaptation principle asserts that the present level of functioning of the environment directly affects the form of survival for the individual of the species; the dynamic equilibrium principle explicitly states that biological communities are continually changing in response to environmental influences; the succession principle refers to the predictable development of biological communities. The focus for the discussion in this chapter is to illustrate how these four principles (interdependence, cycling of resources, adaptation, and succession) can provide a basis for describing the functions of high school environments.

The Principle of Interdependence

The principle of interdependence is a direct derivative of the ecosystem principle of biological ecology. Research has shown that whenever any component of a natural ecosystem is changed there are alterations in the relationships between all other components in the ecosystem. When the Welland Canal was built to allow passage of commercial vessels around Niagara Falls, for example, the canal enabled the sea lamprey and the alewife (a small minnow-like fish) to enter the Great Lakes ecosystem. Before a selective poison could be found to control the lamprey, it had virtually eliminated the lake trout and whitefish from the Great Lakes. The removal of the lake trout as a predator permitted the alewife population to expand relatively unchecked and shortly resulted in an alewife population explosion. Following spawning, many alewives die.

Consequently, bathing beaches along Lake Michigan and Lake Huron became swamped with piles of dead alewives several feet high, which needless to say quickly drove away bathers. The interrelationships do not stop here, however, as alewives have collected sizeable quantities of DDT in their bodies and have passed it along to coho salmon, which has in turn made the salmon unfit for human consumption and damaged the reproductive capability of the salmon (McKee, 1968). It is suggested that similar intricated interdependencies exist in high school ecosystems.

An additional ecological principle which supports the importance of the principle of interdependence is the concept of *limiting factors*. Originally conceived by the German botanist Justus Liebig as the "Law of the Minimum" (Liebig, 1840), the concept of limiting factors implies that no organization or organism is stronger than the weakest link in the ecological chain of requirements which comprise its ecosystem. The chief value of the concept of limiting factors is that it gives ecologists an entering wedge for the study of complex situations. Ecosystems are complicated, and it is important to recognize that not all functions are of equal importance. High schools and other organizations are assumed to provide a number of functions, and the function which is in shortest supply relative to its demand will usually have the greatest potential for affecting the effectiveness of the organization.

In thinking about the specific functions of a high school that have direct relevance for the performance of individual students, as well as the behavior of the total high school environment, at least four types of variables can be enumerated as examples: (1) the expressive behavior of individual faculty and students; (2) the roles that these faculty and students perform; (3) the characteristics of the social policies that are generated for the particular school; and (4) the purposes and styles of managing the classroom. For each of these variables there are specific examples of observable behavior that can be cited to show how persons and roles are linked together, and how school policies can be coupled with the functions of any particular classroom (see Table 14–1).

This point of view defines the school as a series of couplings by which students, faculty, and the

TABLE 14–1

Ecological Principles for the Redevelopment of the High School

		I. The Principle of Interdependence	
		Predictions	
Variables	Selected Topics	Changing Environment	Unchanging Environment
Persons:	Channels for Help-Giving:	Maintains Survival	Maintains Status Positions
Roles:	Sources For Role Definitions:	Competences are Relevant for Momentary Events	Competences are Relevant for Seniority and Status
Policies:	Criteria for Revision of Social Conditions:	Pragmatic Validity	Normative Validity
Classrooms:	Definitions of Teaching Unit:	Supplemental	Central

governing ideas for the life of the classroom are interrelated rather than separate elements of the environment. This linkage is defined by processes that allow students and faculty to work or not work together in developing the social norms and the goals for the high school. Students and faculty who are active in defining the direction of the school society will affect not only the social life of the school but can become the grist for the change agent's mill, in that such spontaneous groupings define the social structure of the school. It is commonplace for change agents to remark that the social atmosphere is the most critical data for assessing the organization. Current work, however, has been unable to articulate the dimensions of psychological climates. This section of the chapter is one attempt to develop suggestions for this dimension of the social environment.

An ecological principle states that *how* interdependence is mediated will directly affect the types of behavior and the types of individuals who will emerge as adaptive members of the society. For example, high schools are likely to vary in how students and faculty help each other. Do they each go their own way, and rarely attend to the needs of each other, or are there occasions, either planned or spontaneous, that encourage teachers and students to collaborate and actualize needs of students? How teachers and students express help

will relate to how they codify the rules for the school. Will the students be asked to appear at the principal's office to listen and acquiesce to the adult world, or do faculty and students meet at a mutually convenient time with a shared concern for solving a problem that is seen by both parties as making a real difference to them? An enterprising student finding himself in a restricted dialogue with the faculty is likely to express his convictions in ways that will not be adaptive for that school. The student who values structure and is more receptive to the advice and direction from the faculty will feel uncomfortable in a quixotic conversation with a mixed group of faculty and students who are attempting to clarify conflicting issues during a confrontation. How faculty and students deal with their school life has practical value for the development of students *and* for changing the high school; it defines the boundaries for the management of student behavior.

One of the critical sources of data for defining the forms of interdependence is an understanding of how help is given—when it is given, to whom it is given, under what circumstances, and to what extent individuals will express helpful behavior to others over periods of time. Is help-giving spontaneous, improvised behavior, or is it segmental and expressed under restricting conditions? Looking at ways in which help is expressed is one source for seeing how help-giving roles are identified with specific individuals. Concurrently, which of many types of help-giving roles are defined in a school, how they are developed, and under what conditions they are expressed provides a diagnostic view of the school that is relevant for understanding the adaptive behavior of the organization.

To illustrate the application of ecological principles for the high school environment, the variable of population exchange will be used. This variable refers to the rate at which students enter and leave the high school during the school year, including the addition of new students and the loss of students who drop out. This variable was selected for several reasons. First, the rate of population exchange is expected to have an effect on how the individual student functions. Secondly, it is expected to affect how the total high school responds to a range of changing conditions. Much of psychological research that has been ecological in scope has focused upon variables like size, variables that are not directly applicable to assessing the functioning of an organization over time (Barker & Gump, 1964).

To provide an example of how population exchange can mediate different styles of interdependence, the case of the changing and unchanging high school is presented. A changing environment is defined as a high school where at least 40 percent of the faculty are new every year and where 40 percent of the student body come and go during the school year. The multiple factors that contribute to such an event are assumed to be equivalent and additive (e.g., urban renewal, residential mobility, emigration from Appalachian areas) and to collectively contribute to this population exchange. An unchanging high school environment is hypothesized as a school of equal size where less than five percent of faculty and students leave during a calendar year. The social functions that are generated in a changing society are expected to be different from the selection process generated in a high school with a constant population rate.

Population exchange is a demographic variable that is expected to have direct and visible effects upon the social life of the school. Living in a fast moving revolving door is predicted to have effects perceptibly different from living in a more slowly generating environment; surviving in a rapidly

changing environment is distant from living in a predictable and constant setting. The impact of population exchange is mediated through the rapidity with which people come and go, the number of new roles that are generated from moment to moment, and the effects of the repopulated roles upon the functions of the classroom. Observations of these activities can clarify how the students and faculty go about helping each other to fulfill the work of these contrasting worlds.

The ways in which help is expressed in social environments that vary in population exchange can document the nature of interdependence within these two places. The ways in which faculty and students help one another in a rapidly changing world is predicted to be expressed in how they assist each other to survive; the basis for generating help in an unchanging society is expected to be in terms of how the members of the society help each other to enhance their status positions. In a changing world, criteria for help-giving are more rudimentary; while the form of giving help in a constant environment is to protect what one already has and to embellish the performance of individuals.

If this rationale is correct, it is likely that there are different social definitions for the helper in these two schools. In the changing school, the student who knows where the action is, who is informed about resources, and who is accessible, can develop into an immediate help-giving agent and accrue social position, completely independent of traditional or formal definitions of achievement. If this hypothesis can be verified, it may help to explain why in many inner-city schools the faculty will tolerate a student who is academically marginal because of his ability to "swing" the organization. In a less changing school, help-giving becomes more specialized and less improvised. Here the help-giving takes a circumscribed and a more structured function than in the changing environment.

These differences in expressive modes have their corollary in the ways in which the critical roles for these schools are defined and allocated. The way in which help-giving is allocated and the characteristics of the individuals who will perform these roles in a constant environment will be in direct contrast. In the unchanging school, the primary basis for the definition of helping roles to be performed by both faculty and students is the seniority of membership or their status in the high school. In some instances, this may not be functional. The status position or length of service may bear little relationship to competence to perform tasks for that school.

Help-giving in the changing environment is expected to be expressed in diverse ways and can be assessed by a broad range of behaviors; students in a changing environment may go to great lengths and great risks to do a good deed. Fixing cars, tipping a buddy off about the expected inquiry of police, loaning money, and doing favors is a daily routine for those students in a changing world. Students attending a more constant environment are limited in their natural expression of spontaneous acts of kindness. A helpful act is more studied and is facilitated by the position and status of the members of the organization and the form in which the help is given. An act of generosity in a constant world is expressed when there is explicit social accounting and is the basis for labeling the good guy. The question then becomes "How much has he done for me?" and "How has it helped me achieve status?" The validity for membership in a changing society is defined by what he can do *now*; his other talents or blemishes are irrelevant to the performance of tasks demanded at the moment. In a more constant setting, social position can compensate for what one doesn't do at a particular place or specific time. If it's clear who one is, it matters less what good things a person fails to do or what unacceptable behaviors he expresses.

Help-giving, a valued aspect of our American heritage, is less understood than various forms of individual and social pathology. The psychodynamics of the doing of good deeds is not only a critical topic in this period of our country's history but is a salient issue for rediscovering the joy of adolescence. Of primary interest in this chapter is to illustrate how the social structure of contrasting environments can channel styles of help-giving behavior and affect the modes of adapting to new social situations. How often have we observed in our personal experience that an act of kindness can have unexpected side effects for a new member of an organization!

In addition to an examination of help-giving behavior, the principle of interdependence can also be useful in predicting how the school environment develops policies for managing the organiza-

tion. An additional part of the interdependence of these contrasting organizations can be assessed in terms of what counts whenever there is a crisis. Our guess is that the most critical and basic definition of what people do in a changing society is whether it meets pragmatic needs, whether it works and does a job (pragmatic validity). In an unchanging society, the basis for validating policies for school rules will be whether these rules are consistent with the values of the past and the conventions of the present (normative validity).

Life in a changing high school is expected to produce a shifting social fabric where the social norms vary from time to time and place to place. The pragmatic feature of the social structure relates directly to contributions that assist the school to survive as a social institution. The fact that new guidelines emerge very rapidly adds an additional constraint on the students and the faculty. Consensus revolves around whether a program succeeds in meeting immediate goals or not. The instability and flux of the high school produces more emphasis upon expectations for behavior that are useful, relevant, and workable. The only workable tradition may be an awareness of making the rules fit the requirements of the task. The faculty and students can be mobilized to root for the football team, to support a fellow student who is undergoing duress, to freeze out a faculty member who is unsympathetic to student needs. All these activities involve the organization of loose or temporary social structures for specific social functions. The criterion for performance in all these social affairs is whether the job gets done, the school spirit gets aroused, the student is exonerated, or the faculty member is expelled.

The unchanging school has a contrasting social order. There is a close correspondence between the past and the present, and a more literal reverence of the roles of the school. The range of valued behavior is restricted and there is less allowance for alterations to meet new and different events that appear in the surrounding community. There is reluctance to alter the self-imposed course of history. New and unpredictable experiences are seen as intrusions into an orderly life. Which social norms will be selected will depend upon the demographic and social characteristics of the school and the traditions. In each case, however, the history of the intact social institution is the superordinate criterion for the regulation of the society. If the school has emphasized athletics, then the basis for assigning status positions and the basis for planning for change will be a preference for maintaining these traditions. Life in this type of school does not encourage revision, it reveres established ways. Evaluation of interpersonal behavior depends largely upon whether that behavior supports these traditions. The social pressures upon the students are to contribute to their environment in terms of these given traditions. The nonathlete in an athletic world, the nonintellectual in a college prep environment, or the less sociable student in a well-organized social world will be a visible misfit and is likely to have few avenues for redefining himself. Social membership is not only stratified, but it is binary and there is little opportunity to redefine one's social position without a conversion from one world to another. The traditions in this society are so embracing that the individual faculty member or student can find himself locked into an environment without any recognition of his unique competencies.

The definition of the classroom follows from these examples of the criteria for policy development. In a changing society, the classroom is supplemental to the major activities of the school—it is not the only justification, or the only setting, where the educational and social life of the school are expressed; the athletic field, the band, the shop, and many extracurricular activities, become equally essential for this environment. In an unchanging school, the classroom is the primary and most valued unit for representing the society; the other places and settings are supplementary to it.

The development of social norms in these contrasting schools has different effects upon the functions of their classrooms. In an unchanging high school environment the classroom lecture becomes the primary method for implementing the social policies of the school. Other formal and informal social settings are viewed as extensions of the teacher-pupil relationship or supplemental to the classroom. In the changing high school, the classroom is only one of many settings for developing and communicating the rules for the society. In many instances what happens between the students and between teachers and pupils in the classroom is irrelevant to the social condition. Both faculty and students realize that "real" learning takes place in the hallways, cafeterias, and multiple settings off campus. For many students,

going to class is a ticket of admission or entrée to social relationships. At the unchanging school, on the other hand, taking part in extracurricular activities is a means for enhancing social status and social position and for embellishing or refining one's primary role functions. In this case the student relies on the availability of supplementary social settings which are equivalent to the classroom to define his social status. For students attending changing school environments the classroom and the extracurricular activities are at best supplementary, most often irrelevant.

The settings for the expression of help-giving behavior will also vary as the functions of the classroom. Help-giving may take multiple and far-ranging forms in the changing school. Such acts will seem randomly expressed with the result that students may express this behavior in any of the social settings. What this behavior accomplishes is the development of a definition of the environment that focuses upon multiple expression of varied behaviors in diverse settings. The informal social norms say, "If you succeed, then it's help; if it's help, it's good." In the unchanging school, the adverse is so—most of the altruistic behaviors center around classroom-related activities, and their expression is to enhance the traditions of the school and support the power and influence of persons that are expressed via the classroom and to maintain and support such settings. To the casual observer of the constant school, the classroom is the stage and the students are rehearsing in other settings for their performance in this one type of setting. For many of the students attending a constant school, learning could not take place except in a classroom. Consistent with these same directions, we could also guess that in an unchanging environment, there would be more ceremonies, more celebrations of good deeds, while in the changing society the appearance of such celebrations would be less frequent. There would be less need for symbolic performances or rewards for helpful behavior; in an unchanging school helpful deeds are germane and present essential elements of life.

The Cycling of Resources

The second ecological principle offered as a tool for assessing organizations is the principle of cycling of resources. The natural ecosystem is driven by radiant energy from the sun which is

TABLE 14–2

Ecological Principles for the Redevelopment of the High School

		II. *The Principle of Cycling of Resources*	
		Predictions	
Variables	*Selected Topics*	*Changing Environment*	*Unchanging Environment*
Persons:	The Salience of Diverse Experience:	Instrumental	Incidental
Roles:	Technical Competences Required:	Undeveloped	Specialized
Policies:	Goals for Change:	Maintenance of Total Organization	Maintenance of Current Roles
Classrooms:	Criteria for Evaluation:	External to the Class-room	Internal to the Classroom

converted first to carbohydrates by plants and then second to protein by plant-eating animals. As energy is passed from one link to another through the ecosystem some energy is lost in each transfer, until it has been completely dissipated. In animal ecology, a traditional and primary research activity is the measurement of the production of energy in different plant or animal communities so as to specify variations in net and gross productions of the species of these communities.

Except for discussion by Katz and Kahn (1966) and by Pugh (1966) there are few approaches to the study of personal resources in social environments. Yet, a focus upon the utilization of resources is considered relevant for discussing any changes in the function of the high school. Before beginning a change program a sense of how the organization is currently defining and distributing its resources is advocated as an essential step. This principle emphasizes the utility of a historical approach to social organizations, a perspective which the behavioral sciences in general, and the mental health professions in particular, do not include as a part of assessments for organizational change. The traditions that bind an organization for managing its talents are expected to be major constraints against change, as well as suggesting an opportunity to redefine and reallocate resources.

The details of the principle of cycling of resources for relating school policies, critical role functions, and personal styles is presented in Table 14–2. How persons are developed and how talent is shared is predicted to have much to do with the life of social settings and how these settings are utilized by students and faculty. A person with a more diverse background is expected to be able to generate a more resourceful repertoire of problem-solving skills than a person who utilizes more restricted or more redundant social settings.

In addition to differentiating individuals in how they express resourceful behavior, it is also possible to differentiate the types of school policies, and activities of the classroom that are developed for utilizing resources of the school Continuing our discussion of the unchanging (constant) and the changing (fluid) high school environments, it is expected that these two schools do differ in their definition of resources and the social norms for utilizing both faculty and students. It is expected that in the constant high school there is not only less turnover of resources but there are also restrictions against defining new resources. Guidelines and policies for the operation of the school will not only reflect well-defined ground rules for such different elements as job descriptions, curriculum, and relationships with nonschool personnel, but there will be a large number of persons who occupy the various roles in the school according to these traditions. Of particular relevance to the change agent is the well articulated nature of the social structure and the development of informal social customs about definitions of the tasks of the school. Both of these characteristics are expected to present major obstacles against the development of new resources, along with a stereotyped definition of existing resources.

The implications of this principle for the constant school are the unexpected, hidden costs of a well-defined social structure, e.g., its resource cycle is involutional and defines the same tasks in the same ways over time, and it views specified people with identical past experiences as the primary candidates for these roles. The redistribution of rare resources and the creation of new types of resources is not only a salient issue for the change agent, but it is likely to be an excellent set of criteria for predicting how the school will cope with new crises. The management of resources also applies equally well to the organization's response to faculty members. For example, new or young faculty members will not be expected to have the "right" ideas about the routine of the schools. A faculty member who once was troublesome or ineffective is likely to continue to be seen as troublesome or ineffective, even when there have been observable changes in his behavior. Likewise, there are likely to be limitations upon the role of faculty and students to function in roles which are beyond their status positions. When natural events occur, such as an accident of a student at school, a sick leave of a faculty member, or spontaneous attempts to organize the faculty around a new activity, relevant resources, however available, will be underutilized.

On many occasions, nonprofessionals such as secretaries, janitors, bus drivers, and community aids can emerge as important resources for the school. The mobilization of these resources in times of community conflict often is the critical link in the management of school affairs. How the school utilizes such persons will be a barometer of the extent and direction of change in the school system. It is expected that such resources will be drawn upon in a fluid school as part of the everyday life of the high school environment.

Personal and organizational survival in a fluid school depends directly upon the easy absorption of ready and scarce talent.

In this case a prediction is suggested which goes hand in glove with the ideas about the relevance of varied experience for the cycling of resources. The guess is that in a high school with a changing population, variety of experience becomes more essential for organizational development than in a less changing school. By definition, a changing environment generates instrumental value for varied experience, it accentuates the expression of those experiences, and serves as an incentive for the seeking out of more varied contacts. In a changing school, it is more difficult to sit on the sidelines—the environment is continually asserting itself upon each of the members to engage in new and different experiences. Not all of these experiences may be considered socially acceptable, but that is also one of the characteristics of the changing society—social norms are more fluid and behavior is more transitory. In the unchanging school, varied experience becomes accidental, if not irrelevant, in the lives of the people. There is no way in which diverse experience can easily become a social norm. In a changing society, the competencies required for the performance of critical roles are latent; in the unchanging society roles are not only developed but they are also specialized. The assertion here is that the changing society with underdeveloped competencies has a more efficient cycling of its rare resources than does a constant environment. Using a criterion of efficiency we could affirm that in the changing school, while the level of technical competence is low, the efficiency of the organization is high in terms of its use of resources. Persons living in a changing society get more for their money. In an unchanging school the level of available competencies is high but its efficiency is low.

This principle also applies to the way in which policies are defined and how roles are performed. Because the fluidity of a changing society presents problems for continued organizational functioning, more effort will be given to define educational policies that can facilitate the continued maintenance of the organization. The criterion of pragmatic validity that was utilized for the principle of interdependence once again can provide survival value for maintaining the organization. The principal's behavior, the faculty's values, the student's concerns, while varied and elusive, have a common characteristic of being directed towards maintaining the organization in the face of its changing membership.

In the unchanging high school, where there is very little population exchange, the policies will have a contrasting effect. In this case, attention is not towards maintaining the organization as a whole but rather to increasing the *quantity* of individuals performing relatively the same roles within the organization, even when a Parkinsonian expansion of the organization may reduce the effectiveness of the organization. It is characteristic of the unchanging organization to replicate itself independent of the surrounding environment. Here interdependence is expressed through the maintenance of the status quo such as rewards for seniority, and preferences for normative validity. The dominant style of this unchanging organization is to define its way of life in terms of the relevance of past traditions, previous role assignments, and the location of influence roles occupied by more senior status persons. The conventional process for change is to promote upward through accustomed channels. Under these conditions, the utilization of resources is accomplished by promotions via very clear and explicit criteria, while for the changing environment the utilization of resources is haphazard and depends on the availability of talent to meet momentary conditions. In contrast, the effect of the exchange of membership in the low exchange school is reduced on the premise that new members will be socialized only via a restricted number of roles before they assume new positions. The socialization process for new members, like other features of the unchanging environment, emphasizes a way of life which affirms that *past* traditions are the standards for doing business.

The unchanging nature of the population affects the life of the school by limiting opportunities for the faculty to agree on how to cope with troublesome behavior. Such consensus is rare. When it does come it is presented in formal terms. The few faculty who are developing wisdom in dealing with a wide variety of "nonconformity" are unable to create settings to discuss workable solutions. In this case, the most relevant knowledge of the school's operations is not fed back into the school's decision making body, thereby reducing the efficiency of the organization's use of resources.

One of the unanticipated effects of population exchange is the continuous input of diverse knowledge from incoming students and faculty, e.g., new persons from outside the school offering sources of unplanned growth. Life is informal, even chaotic, reinforcing the axiom to make most of what is available. With all of the apparent disarray and confusion, the changing school paradoxically can be a stimulus for the development of coping styles. What is needed in future work is to spell out in detail how these processes work.

The Adaptation Principle

The principles of interdependence and cycling of resources provide a basis for conceptualizing the organization of the high school, and a point of view for defining how the life of the high school develops and how it can redevelop. Two additional principles, the adaptation principle and the succession principle, provide additional ideas for understanding both the functioning of individuals and the style of the organization.

The adaptation principle is derived from experimentation in biological ecology concerning environmental factors affecting the survival of an organism. The premise of the ecosystem asserts that for an organism to survive over time it must be able to cope with environmental changes. Animal species vary greatly in their ability to cope with changes in the environment. The dinosaurs, once rulers of the earth, were not able to cope with environmental changes produced by volcanic activity and the coming of the Ice Age; consequently they became extinct. Other animals can seemingly thrive under a wide variety of conditions. The Norway rat, for example, seems to have little trouble becoming established anywhere in the world (Leopold, 1966).

In response to studies of animal adaptation, Levins (1966) has developed the theorem that environmental randomness leads to increased niche breadth (the variety of conditions under which a single species can successfully function) while unchanging environments lead to specialization of species.

Discussions of adaptation and maladaptation have primarily been of two forms. One has emphasized the deficiencies or inadequacies in undifferentiated environments. Such theories of pathological behavior in psychology must often

TABLE 14-3
Ecological Principles for the Redevelopment of the High School

| | | III. Environment Affects Adaptation | |
| | | Predictions | |
Variables	Selected Topics	Changing Environment	Unchanging Environment
Persons:	Coping Styles:	Exploratory Behavior	Citizenship
Roles:	Adaptive Roles:	Personal Effectiveness	Achievement of Status
Policies:	Goals of the Organization:	Survival of Students	Control of Social Influence
Classrooms:	Purposes of the Curriculum:	Reduce Individual Casualties (Leader is Focus)	Promote Excellence of Classroom (Problem Student is Focus)

refer to forms of conflict resolution, defensiveness, past reinforcement histories, etc., with little direct attention to a view of man in a social setting and how such couplings create a man-environment fit which is not only unique but which is also explanatory. The sociological approaches emphasize effects of specific social structures upon an undifferentiated class of individuals. The significance of the adaptation principle is that maladaption is not only a consequent of malfunctioning social units but is a reciprocal process. As the functions of the social environment change, so do responses of individuals. As individuals express different coping styles the form of the social setting shifts. This notion of mutuality and binding of causes and effects is an idea which has been very difficult for psychologists to affirm. We seem to view life as a series of contingent polarities, rather than as an evolving, interdependent open process. To the extent that this analogy from biological ecology can generate operational methods for assessing person-environment relations, it may contribute to a view of coping behavior as a sequence of multivariate behaviors tied to specific social settings.

The premise of this chapter is that the high school is a group of social settings that are critical for the development and refinement of coping styles. It is the setting where an individual can easily be defined as a casualty, and where academic, social, and personal constraints provide

a continuous press for the individual to lead his immediate world. The ways that students perform these tasks in turn contribute to the school's development (see Table 14-3). Determinations of role functions are of interest as they were for the previous principles, for they help to concretely define adaptive and maladaptive behavior of the school and individual students. Appraisal of the curriculum, likewise, is expected to relate directly to the adaptation of the school and to the performance of students.

Continuing our use of the changing and unchanging high school as examples, the coping style that is generated in a changing, transient environment is predicted to be a coping style which facilitates exploratory behavior. The student who lives and attends a world in which only 50 percent of the membership is constant *must* be open to change, select varied experience, and be able to initiate and involve himself in an effective performance in his environment. In this kind of setting, the adaptive functions of his roles are also geared more towards facilitating personal effectiveness for the members of the society.

In a changing high school the functions of the classroom take on the additional role of being sensitive to maladaptive behavior. The classroom is not only a setting for academic work but one of the key places to reduce the prevalence of individual maladaptive behavior in the population. There can develop a climate to do whatever is possible for students with low reading ability, substandard spelling, and nonachievement. Not by planning, but as a result of emergencies the classroom takes on a pragmatic tone to reduce maladaptive behavior. While this set of purposes is expressed in informal ways, climates emerge where both faculty and students gear up to reduce the number of personal casualties. This contagion can work so well that the student who bubbles to the top is revered and honored. Awards for achievement take on the proportions that are equivalent to honoring a local hero.

In the constant or unchanging school, the modes for adaptation offer contrast. Here the requirements for the coping styles of students and faculty emphasize the citizenship of the student, his participation in the society along prescribed channels, his fulfillment of societal expectations, his absorption, and his reverence for the society. Definitions of adaptive roles are primarily in terms of the achievement of the society, the status of the society, rather than the achievement of the individual student. The society is salient rather than the individual. Rules and social conventions are oriented towards control of the school, in contrast to the life style of the unchanging school where the rules of the game are to personally "make it." In the unchanging school the classroom becomes a symmetrical replica of the norms of the society and it is expected that each classroom is competing not only against itself, but against all the other classrooms as well. The consequence of this style of life presents what is often found in schools serving permanent populations: the student with the problem receives attention.

In pronounced yet unplanned ways, these two environments tend to select students who present striking differences in their coping styles and their potential for taking adaptive roles in other societies. For example, the unchanging school selects on citizenship, with exploratory behavior likely to be maladaptive. For the changing society exploratory behavior is essential and citizenship is maladaptive. Our guess is that most forms of citizenship involve coping styles that are for specific times and places and foster skills which are not easily transferable to other societies. Exploratory behavior, facilitating a set towards mastery of the environment, is assumed to have a greater survival value and will allow the individual, through his subsequent personal development, to adopt varied roles and to be in a better position not only to adapt to social change but also to effect change himself.

It is these consequences of the ecological analogy that provide a point of view not only for viewing the limitations of our current knowledge but also for generating new methods for thinking about preventive interventions which take into account the ecology of the specific high school. The set of recommendations for interventions in the fluid and the constant school would also involve contrasting styles of implementation (Kelly, 1968). It is with this in mind that the recommendations for preventive interventions in the latter part of the chapter will be presented.

The Principle of Dynamic Equilibrium and Succession

The fourth ecological principle is derived from accumulated research and naturalistic observations of biological communities over extended periods of time. Biological ecologists have found that natural communities are not stable. Although they may appear to be in the short run, instead they are in a constant process of change in response to changing environmental conditions. As a grassland community persists in an area, for example, the annual die-off of grasses produces more mulch than can be completely decomposed during the next year. Thus, eventually the site becomes more moist due to the increased water-holding capacity of the humus, and produces a site less favorable to the continued growth of grasses and more favorable to the growth of annual flowers like asters and golden rod. Because such environmental changes produce resultant changes in community structure, natural communities are said to exist in dynamic equilibrium with their environment (Clements & Shelford, 1939). The most immediate implication of this principle is to emphasize the value of having a time perspective, a long range view, for our efforts in the prevention of maladaptations. But the principle also is relevant for viewing the current high school environment and can help to predict the rate at which schools will achieve a new level of succession as well as the form that these changes will take (see Table 14–4).

The previous focus with reference to the individual has been the channels available to him

TABLE 14-4

Ecological Principles for the Redevelopment of the High School

IV. Dynamic Equilibrium and the Succession Principle

Variables	Selected Topics	Predictions	
		Changing Environment	Unchanging Environment
Persons:	Options for new Roles:	Infinite and Lateral	Restricted
Roles:	Sources for Role Definition:	External	Radiates from the Top of the Organization
Policies:	Means for Change:	Availability of New Resources	Changes in Current Roles
Classrooms:	Requirements for Change:	New resources	New definition of organization

for help-giving, the significance of varied experience for his present behavior, and the relevance of his coping styles for adaptation. This view of the individual emphasizes a concern for the options a person has for taking new roles. For the principle of dynamic equilibrium and succession, the interest is to examine the sources for redefining new roles. In the rapidly changing high school, options for new roles are expected to be infinite. New role options will become available as new functions are required or as new persons are added. In the unchanging high school the options for new roles are restricted and are generated from the top of the organization irrespective of organizational or personal needs. If we examine the sources for role redefinition in the changing high school, they are external to the school, eminating from events occuring outside the immediate environment of the high school—urban renewal, the availability of new health care services, or the demands and influences of parents. In the unchanging environment, as has been mentioned, there will be a finite number of new roles and these will be primarily defined by authorities. In some cases they will be expressed by the school board, the superintendent, or the principal; in other cases a faculty-student code will define the process for change. These

decisions even after some discussion are passed along as a statement of tradition rather than working principles.

In sum, revision of policies comes about in an unplanned way in the changing environment, while in the unchanging environment revision is stimulated to the extent that it is valued and initiated by the key decision-makers. It is further predicted that as a result of the accessibility to outside events in the changing environment there is a greater probability of natural succession occurring than in the constant environment. Top decision-makers in constant schools are expected to initiate a change orientation less often and to know less how to do it. The principle of dynamic equilibrium and succession points to the issue of shifts in environmental functions as criteria for differentiating whether change efforts have long term effects or whether they are more simply just tinkering with a short life history.

This principle also has implications for how we view the emergence of policies and the viability of the classroom unit. It was mentioned previously that such criteria as revision of school policies, purposes for changing policies, and other principles have been discussed. In terms of redevelopment of the school, the critical topic is what means these environments generate for producing change—what procedures, what resources are accessible for changing these policies? In the previous discussions we were interested in what criteria were employed to evaluate the social environment. Here, we are more concerned with the mechanisms that are necessary for changing the functions of the classroom. As an example, if we look at a high exchange high school, the means for revising the classroom are going to depend largely on the availability of new resources, the creation of supplementary teaching aids, the blending into the school environment of non-school resources that are available but not directly involved in the teaching enterprise. In the unchanging high school, a primary means for changing the classroom will be incidental changes that can be brought about by the participants. This is an important distinction since in an unchanging high school only a limited amount of roles have a change quotient. The impact of this principle for the function of the classroom is the creation of school-wide policies that are directed toward long-term evolutionary change. Achieving this goal requires change in the very environmental functions of the high exchange school.

Following extensive research and observation, biological ecologists have found that not only do natural communities change over time but that the direction of change is roughly predictable if the environmental conditions are known. For example, providing there are are no unusual climatic changes such as the sudden appearance of an ice age, an ecologist can predict with a good degree of assurance that what we might see today as a shallow lake in the Midwest will someday be replaced by a forest community of beech and maple trees, barring disruptive influences of man. Further, the ecologists have found that the existence of a natural community at any time is attributable to its ability to make the most effective use of the sources of energy and nutrients under the existing conditions. Those communities which are capable of reproducing themselves in the same area over relatively long periods of time, such as a beech-maple forest, are termed "climax communities" (Clements & Shelford, 1939).

There are at least two implications of the succession principle for the study of social organizations. One is that if we can gather the proper environmental data and master the processes of organizational structure and function, perhaps it will be possible to not only predict organizational changes over time but to be able to design organizations which will be better able to adjust to change. The payoff of such knowledge for high schools is that it might be possible to design high schools which would be flexible enough to meet the changing demands of contemporary society by translating these demands into appropriate curriculum and counseling functions.

The goal for such social organizations as the high school is suggested by the concept of a "climax community." The existence of a climax community under natural conditions is attributable to its ability to make the most efficient usage of energy and nutrient sources under the existing environmental conditions. The "climax community" for a high school would be an organizational structure which would be able to maximize its function for converting students into functioning members of society. In many cases today the structure of schools has not been responsive to changing social conditions and consequently the loss of students through "entropy" is great. Moving to the next level of organizational development, the principle of dynamic equilibrium requires that the high exchange school make sufficiently efficient use of its resources so that new needs can be recognized and new resources recruited to fulfill these needs. It is predicted that one of the effects of the high exchange environment upon student members is that they are encouraged to take on an emergency role as required by the events of the day. In the unchanging environment differences are qualitative. The critical dimension for the changeability of the school is the extent to which the combination of faculty and students in the school can alter their conceptions and redefine the purposes of the school. Succession becomes a conceptual or a cognitive task.

These two contrasting processes also present new demands for the adaptation of the change agent. Most of the change programs that have been developed for high schools have been congruent with the past history of the professional change agent, namely his ability to conceptualize and alter the views of the members of the society. To the extent that the changing environment can be helped to attain the next higher level of evolutionary development, the intervention is not necessarily concerned with psychological intervention, but instead may involve interventions which contribute to redevelopment of resources that are economic or social in character, such as part-time employment linked with local resources, or providing a new type of research technician. Simply altering the point of view of the students of a high exchange environment may aid a revolution or increase the expression of unresolved conflicts, leading to the expression of new forms of maladaptation rather than a new level of organizational development.

The previous discussion has attempted to present concrete instances of how ecological concepts can be relevant and useful for grasping the meaning of the relationships of the students in their high school setting. It is this thesis that provides the envelope for the new types of interventions for American high schools.

ECOLOGICAL PLANNING AND PREVENTIVE INTERVENTIONS

The ecological principles presented in the previous section represent extrapolations from biology in order to derive ideas that are salient for assessing and changing natural social environments. The choice of the ecological analogy is deliberate. It is the premise of the present writers that the formulation of change programs for natural environments requires that such ideas go beyond current knowledge in the behavioral sciences. The present writers are advocating that the task of developing new knowledge can be solved by adopting a view of man which focuses directly upon the assessment of the interaction of persons in natural settings. Viewing man as an integral part of his social environment is expected to be an effective aid in deriving preventive interventions since it focuses continuously and directly upon the specific aspects of the unique social setting.

In the previous section, ecological principles were offered as concepts for looking at how individuals and social groups of various sizes adapt to the environment. Such a delineation has implications for the design of preventive interventions in the following ways: (1) interventions will deal directly with local conditions; (2) they will derive from a longitudinal assessment of the

social organization; (3) they will focus upon expected effects of a change program upon the members of the setting; and (4) they will include a wide variety of potential interventions. The ecological principles presented in the previous section are assumed to be relevant for affecting change of individuals in a locale because of these properties. The noise of the environment is trapped within the ecological perspective and then utilized. Effects of interventions are anticipated and mechanisms are created to reduce negative effects and actualize positive effects.

Some mention should be made of the choice of the term intervention to describe ecological planning. While this term has certain negative connotative meanings, reflecting perhaps an impulsive, unilateral invasion of another person's personal space, it also denotes that every man-made change in an immediate environment produces effects that must be anticipated. Concern with the long-term effects of change programs is conspicuously lacking in many change efforts, whether we are talking about changing the individual, the small group, the organization, the community, or segments of the larger society. The choice of the term intervention, then, represents a deliberate step to conceive of change processes interdependent with the environment. The term denotes an assertion that quality control and accountability are aspects of the process of affecting change and that accountability derives directly from the requirements of the local situation.

Another important corollary to accountability is the concern about future side effects. Anticipation of immediate and long-term effects of interventions in natural environments may sound like an appeal for clairvoyance. The ecological analogy does represent a series of built-in mechanisms to deal with negative and positive responses to indigenous and external changes. The ecosystem formulation provides an opportunity to establish empirical relationships between direct and indirect effects of alterations in the life cycle of the organization.

The implications of this approach for changing high school environments are several. First, most of the high schools in our country lack any specific commitment to see their problems or successes as at least partially due to local conditions. Second, few faculty or administrators view their organization over time as a system of interrelated units. Third, many community mental health professionals view change as a permanent result of their efforts. If there is lack of conspicious responses to their efforts, ineffectiveness is attributed to properties of the client system rather than the intervention per se or any interaction between the intervention and the client system. Fourth, the range of our methods for affecting change tends to be restricted to the past heritage of the professional rather than the unique requirements of the situation facing the social environment. Accountability has been limited to the survival of the professional and anticipation has been restricted to very brief periods of time.

Traditionally, high schools have had little opportunity or necessity to develop anticipatory functions. While industrial organizations often allocate a substantial portion of the budget to scan other resources in an effort to anticipate the effect of social change on their operation, schools by and large have planned no such activity (Katz & Kahn, 1966). On the other hand, schools lack the necessary number and type of staff for this work. More significant are organizational constraints against developing this function. Carlson (1964) attributes at least part of this "institutionalized resistance" to their "domesticated" nature. Because schools are assured by law of a student clientele they do not have to fight for survival as do businesses. Not having to compete, they—like domesticated animals—become "fat" and "lazy" and tend to see change more as an imposition than a necessity for successful survival.

Today, however, when evidence indicates that the rate of change itself is accelerating, it is clear that schools are suffering from a lack of ability to adapt to the changing society (Goslin, 1967). Such events as student turmoils, the perceived irrelevance of the curriculum, and high teacher turnover are all straining the school as a system.

It is the contention of the present writers that an ecological plan is a necessary first step for the redevelopment of the high school. Planning for change does not mean "scheming for change or proclaiming utopias . . . but (refers) to mobilizing anticipatory problem solving not only for clients but for professionals as well" (Kelly, 1966, p. 538). This chapter will be concluded by presenting examples of how an ecological framework can be used in planning for change and for assessing the result of the executed plan. Included

will be suggestions for (1) designing interventions; (2) creating a framework for encouraging anticipatory problem-solving for school faculties; and (3) designing research on the planning process.

The Design of Interventions

Programs are currently being developed and are underway in an effort to deal with the present turmoil and social upheaval reflected in high schools. Unfortunately, many are hastily thrown together and often are ill-designed, and the low ratio of innovative programs suggested to innovative programs implemented is discouraging (Kvaraceus, 1968; Sarason, 1966). As Bennis states, "we often seem to have analyses and prognoses, but no programs for change" (1963, p. 135).

Some guidelines for change can be drawn from an ecological perspective. First, the variety of student needs and the diversity of high school environments implies the need for *a plurality of programs for dealing with environmental and organizational variables and selected individuals*. Secondly, *efforts are made to anticipate the organizational side-effects of proposed programs* so that their relative costs and benefits can be assessed *prior* to action. A brief elaboration may be helpful.

Any proposed intervention by definition disrupts the current functioning of a school by intruding on and altering the ongoing social structure. Goslin (1967) gives an example of the relative lack of increase in academic achievement made by black children who were "integrated" into previously all-white Southern schools. He hypothesizes that the ongoing informal social structure of the white students made the school such an antagonistic learning environment for the black children that their ability to progress academically was hindered if not destroyed.

In like manner, Waite (1968, personal communication) tells of an exciting weekend encounter group of 150 students from various high schools to plan to make their high schools a "less bigoted environment." Because there were so few students from any particular school, it is expected that only in those high schools where the climate is ripe for action will the students attending the group have success as change agents. The good intentions of such efforts—if they are directed toward social change—can be hampered by a lack of attention to the potentially noxious environment into which individuals return. Many strategies for change disrupt the organizational functioning, at the native environment. Lack of knowledge as to how a particular school—both students and faculty—will deal with a particular disruption, narrows the chances of a change surviving. With respect to such problems as those of bigotry, the particular approach would depend on the nature of the school. But a focus on organizational properties of the high school environment as well as personality variables is essential. An additional approach might be to have guest speakers on "Interracial Topics" offer a course on "Mutual Racial Stereotypes," and couple these two inputs with student and/or faculty encounter groups. The next level of approach would pay more attention than is often the case to the constraints of the total school environment and deal with both organizations as well as individuals.

A Planning Perspective for Organizations

The aim of this type of intervention is to mobilize the problem-solving ability of the faculty and administration. It may involve long-term planning to alleviate a current problem facing the faculty to alert them about a social change which may have an impact on their role.

The nature of the particular topic will vary from school system to school system. For instance, one problem anticipated in lower socioeconomic districts may revolve around teacher turnover. "Estimates are that 8 percent of the full-time teachers in the fall of 1965 will interrupt or terminate their careers before the opening of schools in the fall of 1966" (National Education Association, 1966, p. 30). Since turnover is known to be greater in schools of lower socioeconomic composition this constitutes a significant organizational problem which can have great impact on the intellectual and emotional development of the students (Herriott & St. John, 1965). In this connection, efforts can be made to create administrative and faculty committees to develop orientation plans for new teachers in school systems with large departure rates in order to redefine the natural selection of talent for such schools. Not only is such a program geared toward a "looking inward" on such recurrent organizational problems as teacher turnover, but it also involves a "looking outward" by faculty to assess

what may be in store for them in their school. Mention has already been made of the national Education Association's recommendation that both innovative principles and organizational flexibility are helpful in deprived areas and changing neighborhoods (Nicholas, Virjo, & Wattenberg, 1965). While this combination of resources may allow quick and, hopefully, adaptive *responses* to change, a planning orientation also can include flexibility for accommodating to change and enhance the ability to anticipate changes and be in a position to act rather than to react.

An example of such a perspective is the behavior of a principal whose school was beseiged with a wave of demands for student power. Being "tuned in" to student sentiment as well as social ramblings, he anticipated in early summer that "the students were restless." During the summer he read up on student power in an effort to understand it and when fall came he appointed some students to previously all-faculty committees of significant importance. Later on during the year when a student-proposed "Vietnam Day of Conscience" boycott of the schools threatened to mushroom into a student strike, he set up an "open mike" at lunch hour for student speakers to talk at will on any topic. His perception was that the open mike served not only the purpose of meaningful student debate but drained off some of the fervor for the proposed strike (Trickett & Ochberg, in preparation). In this case the mobilization of the anticipatory problem solving skill of an individual principal contributed an opportunity for the high school organization to continue its development. This same treatment is relevant for the mental health professional in his efforts to view the high school as a changing ecological niche. Not only must the mental health professional be "tuned in" on the current formal and informal social structure of the school, he must see the school as a changing organization in varying phases of life cycle, and as such must attend to new data sources for his own "planning for change" (Kelly, 1968).

The Design and Planning of Interventions

Kelly (1970) has outlined three complementary approaches for the design and evaluation of preventive interventions. In this section of the chapter a few comments will be made concerning

TABLE 14–5

Ecological Principles and Sources of
Data for Planning Clinical Interventions

Ecological Principles	Mode of Intervention
Interdependence	Assessment of Individual Resources Assessment of Supplemental Helping-Roles Assessment of New Roles
Cycling of Resources	Linking of Internal Resources Mechanisms for Redefining Roles Mechanisms for Assessing Goals of Organization
Adaptation	Assessment of Functions of Environment Development of Criteria for Adaptive Behavior Assessment of Adaptive Behavior Over Time
Succession	Defining Boundaries for Membership in a Social Setting Mechanisms for Crossing Status Lines in Social Interactions Changes in Coping Styles While a Member of a Setting

the process of interventions. This particular discussion will be limited to an intervention that follows closely the clinical tradition. Premises about the amount of resources expended in developing the intervention, the time period required to realize the intervention, and the assumption about the clients will be presented. Statements will be offered about the types of data required to evaluate the change process in terms of these premises.

The four ecological principles discussed in the previous section have utility for discussing the "how" of preventive programming as well as the "whys" and the "whats." Table 15–5 illustrates examples of variables that can be derived from each of the four principles for an intervention utilizing the clinical method. As the table indicates, each of the four principles is relevant for a different state in the chronology of the change process. The principle of interdependence is salient for conceptualizing the entry process and the initial assessment of the client systems; the principle of cycling of resources is useful in generating predictions about the potential of the organization's development; the adaptation principle is relevant for developing hypotheses about the social norms for effective and ineffective

behavior emerging in the organization; while the principle of dynamic equilibrium and succession is valid for developing hypotheses regarding the long term development of the social setting. These four principles can then define dimensions for studying the intervention process, and can highlight varied levels of change induction.

For each principle and method there is a unique content that is distinct from the other principles and has validity for the particular combination of theory and real world elements. As an example of how these principles and methods relate, comments will be made first about the application of the principle of interdependence.

The Principle of Interdependence

Two aspects of the clinical heritage can be separated. One is a commitment to helping others, a desire to reduce suffering. The second historical root is a commitment to intrapsychic explanations about the troubled person. The significance of the principle of interdependence for the clinical method is that while preserving the compassionate perspective, it revises the unit of analysis; the individual becomes part of a social setting, and the coupling between the individual and his social environment defines the treatment process. Many types of consultation techniques discussed earlier in the chapter can have an ecological feature. Many of the writings and observations about consultation techniques, however, present appraisals of natural settings not as theoretically expected findings but as aphorisms about the real world accumulated through direct experience. The nonecological clinician working in a natural environment is faced with an integration of his professional role with the politics of social change, a mix often giving rise to cognitive dyspepsia. The translation of ecological ideas for the design of interventions can improve the conceptual range of the change agent and reduce the disparity between academic theorizing and confrontations with community events.

When the principle of interdependence is applied to clinical methods, the emphasis is upon the interdependence of roles that key persons assume in the client's organizational setting, and the task for the design of the intervention is to assess how roles are performed and how they are related. The early diagnostic function of the change agent is to deal with those phases of the client's setting which relate to the management of a particular clinical issue whether it be a truculant youth in the high school or an uninvolved faculty member. Each of the presenting problems can be dealt with by a variety of existing clinical methods. The relevance of the approach described here is to define the problem as involving resources within the school. The design of the intervention will require a diagnostic assessment of the informal social structure of the relevant social settings out of which help can be offered. This diagnostic activity is expected to involve at least three processes: (A) An assessment of individual resources in the client setting; (B) assessment for redefining supplemental roles of key helping agents; (C) assessment for creation of new helping roles. Each of these steps is interlaced and considered as a sequence from A through C, with the result that if step A is effective, there will be a diminishing amount of energy required to implement the next steps over time. A few comments will be made about each of the three phases using the truculent youth in a classroom as the example.

A. Assessment of Individual Resources. The educational heritage for dealing with classroom behavior is to define many problems out of bounds of the competence and the resources of the classroom teacher and to adopt one of the following solutions: (a) transfer of the youth to another regular classroom; (b) initiation of evaluation procedures for placement in a special classroom; (c) referral to school administration; (d) parent-teacher conferences; and (e) referral to community agencies. All of these decisions are preemptive for they not only include removal of the youth and the classroom teacher from the immediate situation but they reduce the possibility of other educational resources in the school being engaged.

The ecological assessment generates questions like the following: (a) What helping roles do the youth and the teacher perform in the classroom? (b) What are both the youth's and teacher's relationships with their peers? (c) In which social setting in the school do the youth and the teacher participate together? (d) In those settings with whom do they relate and how? (e) In what settings do the teacher and the youth perform very well and in which ones do they perform ineffectively? and (f) In what settings do they express the most sustained interactions? A comparable set of questions could be generated for the teacher and the youth separately for nonschool settings, as well as those places where the potential client spends his leisure time. The responses to these questions should indicate the type and range of ties that the client has to his immediate environment and should provide an empirical basis for planning an intervention that will not only continue to assist the definition of the problem but will identify those resources which have the potential of becoming part of the therapeutic environment.

B. Assessment of Options for Redefining Supplemental Roles of Key Helping Agents. Following the above assessment and the location of salient and valued persons in the client's world, the next phase of the planning process is to identify to what extent key resources can be drawn into the treatment process and to what extent roles can be created and tied to the client. Such resources may consist of the following: (a) the principal's availability for weekly conference; (b) a second teacher to work with the classroom teacher to create a new relationship with the client; (c) an older, esteemed peer assigned to the client as a tutor; (d) developing a member of the teaching faculty to serve as a liaison between school and the family; (e) assisting the client in learning a new skill that will be salient for himself, his peers, and his parents; and (f) providing didactic and therapeutic consultation to the parents, etc. All of these plans derive from building a minor but relevant role for key persons already available and accessible in the high school community. Planning is an inductive process derived from the unique interdependent roles that are already ongoing and proximal to the individual client.

C. *Assessments for the Creation of New Helping Roles.* The preceding analysis documents the nature of the interdependent relationship of the client and potential persons in the immediate environment who may be developed to help with the therapeutic plan. This third portion of the assessments assumes that the preceding analysis will identify helping roles that are not now being provided in the school system in coping with indigenous problems. The third phase consists of designing new roles that complement existing environmental resources, that can help the client, and which create an opportunity in the school to deal with future similar issues. The power of this last phase of the assessment process is to identify unique additional elements that can improve the school's capacity to deal with future events. This assessment is based on the premise that every environment will have some part that is not functioning effectively and that the addition of a new ingredient based upon a knowledge of the linkages of previous roles can assist the evolution of the organization. Continuing the example of the truculent youth in the classroom, the assessment for planning new resources in the school could include the following: (a) a recreation leader, to improve the use of the school facilities for year round and after school programs; (b) a member of the community who can develop as a liaison between the school and the community for creating salient out of school activities; (c) a coordinator for work-study programs for those students attending school and working part time; (d) a coordinator of tutorial services, utilizing college and community residents to supplement classroom instruction; (e) adult education services to assist parents with continuing education; and

(f) a coordinator of youth services to assist faculty in dealing with changing customs and habits of adolescents. These examples are designed to focus on the creation of new forms that not only sanction but also encourage innovation in the local environment. One of the important contexts for the assessment and planning of new resources will be to provide mechanisms so that new roles can be evaluated and adaptations to the new environment studied. These types of assessments, derived from the principle of interdependence, are most congruent with the clinical method. They can also be applied to methods of organizational change and community development.

The Cycling of Resources Principle

Clinical work is often restricted to a very particular contract between the professional and the client. Few additional persons are defined as part of the therapeutic staff and there are few occasions or settings outside of the treatment relationship where the professional and the client interact. The ecological principle cycling of resources has a definite implication for this state of affairs, e.g., that effective treatment involves more than professional resources in order to meet the requirements of the local situation. How these resources are utilized depends upon the norms of the organization for talent development and the internal mechanisms available within the organization to redefine its aims. This principle affirms that effective personal change comes about as the result of the help of many people of varied skills in contrast to a few persons with specific competences. The power of this principle is that it derives from observations and studies of the life processes in lower organisms and suggests that the success of any intervention will depend upon the range of available resources and the potential of the organization to develop new resources.

At least three functions can be derived from this principle which have definite implications for the assessment of the social setting. These activities are similar to those generated by the principle of interdependence; together they suggest a viable means for defining the ecology of the individual's adaptation to a social setting. These functions are: *Linkage of internal resources, mechanisms for redefining roles,* and *mechanisms for assessing goals of the organization.* Each of these functions focuses upon different levels of the organization and reflects the complexity of a social setting; first, focusing on the relationship between individuals, secondly, focusing on the processes available within the setting to alter existing roles, and, thirdly, considering the process available to alter the mission of the organization.

A. Linkage of Internal Resources. The principle of interdependence suggested the assessment of individual resources. The present principle, in suggesting the linkage of resources, refers to the larger school environment beyond the classroom. In the same way that the principle of interdependence suggests a point of view which goes beyond the student and teacher, and focuses upon those aspects of the high school that could emerge as relevant resources, the present principle suggests a mechanism for defining how available resources are tied together. Here the emphasis is focusing upon how new resources can be brought together to expand the effectiveness of the school environment. Examples of questions are: (1) What are the impediments restricting the interaction between the relevant teaching faculty? (2) What settings are populated by students and faculty and how can these be strengthened? (3) What occasions exist for the key segments of the faculty and students working on key issues? Each of these questions is focusing on the ease with which persons can relate and work together independent of their heritage, their status, and their expressive behavior. Related questions refer to how these resources are linked together, e.g., is it by common background, common interests, or political ideology? How the talent is related is a defining attribute of the social environment and specifies the conditions and the tasks for the intervention. If the intervention is to be effective it should specify how these resources will be drawn together during the intervention and following it.

B. Mechanisms for Redefining Roles. In many school environments, the day-to-day operation of the school is defined by a series of formal communication procedures. Memos are sent from teacher to department head, from teacher to counselor, and from administrator to administrator. Except for faculty meetings, which tend to be restricted to very specific and current topics, there is not likely to be either very many media or social

settings for faculty and students to focus upon generating revisions for their work roles.

The particular function that is suggested is concerned with (a) What are the available media for faculty and students to define their response to the demands of the school? (b) In which setting can representatives of all the roles define their way of relating to one another? (c) Which persons in the school are trying new ways of expressing their views on how tasks can be performed? (d) What are the options for creating new functions for the organization of the school? In order for an intervention to be begun, the design should involve a detailed statement of current communication styles and the resources for developing new styles of communication. What is often left unstated is the finding from ecological studies that the sources for indigenous change often come from informal, undeveloped settings. They are the "watershed" for innovation in the social system. The assessment requires that these informal settings must be noted and characterized in order to heighten their contribution to the organization. One task for the intervention will be to create new ways for encouraging the organization to communicate within its local environment.

C. Mechanisms for Assessing Goals of the Organization. This particular function is difficult to achieve. It is guessed that it can be successful only after actualizing of the first two principles. Adequate performance of the first two issues increases the probability that the high school environment can create its own principles of accountability. At the present time there are few opportunities for the total high school to set major goals for itself; instead it tends to exist on the basis of ad hoc procedures which primarily are concerned with the survival of the organization and with graduating students. It is the opinion of the present writers that many of the difficulties facing the contemporary high school are conditions which reflect the inability of educational administrators to redefine the goals of secondary education based upon changing local conditions. Few high school faculties initiate in an explicit fashion short-term and long-range goals that attempt to match the needs of the students and the immediate community. Drawing from the ecological principles presented in the previous section there are a number of questions that can stimulate an approach to this topic: (1) How are the various constituencies within the school organization linked together? (2) How are students and community leaders involved in the operation of the school? (3) How are such evaluations distributed throughout the organization? (4) How has the organization defined roles to insure the practice of accountability? and (5) What persons in the organization are involved and committed to the organization? The answers to these questions can suggest limits that the high school is currently facing in adapting to change. The answers to these questions will define the type of intervention that will be required; whether the high school can benefit from recruitment of new resources or the creation of new settings. All of these options may be desirable and feasible and some are apt to be more relevant to the life of the high school than others. The task for the design of the intervention is to identify those specific mechanisms which will meet the needs of the organization, and will be useful in the efforts of the school to define its own goals for change. This ecological principle implies a commitment to the locale and a tolerance for revision that is infrequently observed. It is precisely this role combination that is required for both personal change and organizational development.

The Adaptation Principle

This principle advocates a focus upon criteria that describe the performance of the organization as a social system. How the high school relates to the surrounding community, how it absorbs external resources and identifies current local resources and makes them available for the students, how it recruits new members, how it performs under emergency conditions, who is selected to emerge as an effective citizen; these criteria are offered as examples of the types of variables that determine the types of demands made upon members of the organization and the types of coping styles that will survive best under specific conditions of the particular environment. The gist of the idea is that the ecological point of view is generating questions about the relationship of the high school to its surrounding environment as opposed to approaches which focus primarily upon the internal structure of the organization. Adaptation is not so much an issue of meeting internal norms and standards as much as a question of the performance of the members in dealing with external events. This point of view is at variance with current thinking which defines successful socialization in terms of functions internal to the organization. One premise of the ecological point of view is that maladaptive behavior in one setting may affect successful adaptation in a new setting. Upon the basis of this idea, the design for interventions must include ways to identify the diverse requirements of the social structure and the varieties of responses to such structures to which the student will be asked to adapt.

As has been mentioned in commenting on the previous examples, the high school does not often operate with a diverse number of functions; its mission, on the contrary, is singular and geared for a particular time and place, lacking resources for generating activities that go beyond the academic roles. Three functions which are considered very relevant for assessing how the high school environment will adapt to change and how it will deal with resources will be presented in order to give examples of criteria for the redefinition of the high school.

A. Assessment of Functions of the Environment. As mentioned above, this is a different way of viewing the activities of the high school environment and suggests new types of data sources. The types of questions that are suggested are as follows: (1) What types of resources are available to identify needs of students before they enter high school? (2) What resources of the high school are allocated to identify post-high school opportunities such as changing vocational requirements and then training for these needs? (3) What means are created for the members of the high school to affect policy changes? (4) What opportunities are provided for the results of new knowledge about the educational process to be diffused through the school system? and (5) How can students with minority opinions change the policies of the school?

Each of these questions is suggested in order to identify how the high school, as a total social system, works to define the major purposes for its future. An additional criterion relating to the behavior of the high school is how the high school adapts to crises, emergencies, and conflict. The importance of the criteria is to focus on the relationship of the school to its neighboring locale.

B. Development of Criteria for Adaptive Behavior. The previous criteria referred to measures of the high school in terms of its performance with the external world. This concept focuses on the process by which the high school develops criteria to clarify norms for adaptive behavior. It is complementary to the previous criteria in that it specifies the steps that the organization will go through to create its working definitions for effective performance. Questions can be asked such as: (1) What are the sources for current guidelines used to assess individual organizational performance? (2) Who shares the responsibility for the definition of adaptive behavior? (3) How many different norms for adaptive behavior are there in the organization? and (4) How closely tied are these criteria to the values of the community?

It is important to identify how aware faculty and student body are of how the rules of their organization affect their daily behavior. To the extent that members of the organization are not aware of the immediate social condition, it might be expected that life is similar to their traditional society. It also is expected that the process for reawakening attention to specific goals may take a long period of time and many resources. In nontraditional high school settings the process of developing criteria for adaptation is expected to be related to variables such as (a) trust among members and (b) the prevalence of crises. In a noncrisis condition, the process of developing guidelines for effective performance is expected to be related to the mutual trust that is present in the school. On the other hand, a crisis situation which speeds up interaction may affect a more rapid development of criteria for the high school environment. These two factors may be the catalysts for resources to move toward specifying ends and means for their organization. A factor which is more closely tied to the indigenous social structure of the high school environment is the range of settings that are present and those that can be created for representations of all the various groups in the high school to meet and work out their common goals. The processes are expected to vary depending upon the type of setting that it utilized. Memos from the principal are not going to elicit the responsiveness of the

same audience as informal meetings with key members of the student-faculty coalitions. Each of these forums is expected to generate different norms for adaptive behavior illustrating the scope of the interdependence principle, e.g., that there is interdependence between the method of work and the product. The adaptation principle provides a basis for documenting the functions of the total environment needed for redevelopment.

C. Assessment of Adaptive Behavior Over Time. This function is seldom employed, but its significance for the design for organizational redevelopment is primary. This function calls for data on changes in the types of adaptive behavior that is expressed over time. It implies a longitudinal analysis of the high school environment; it also implies a sufficient grasp of the workings of the school so that the various relationships between individual behavior and organizational behavior can be defined. It also provides an empirical basis for the accountability of the organization. As adaptive behavior varies over time it provides independent checks for the natural development of the organization and can assess the effects of any interventions.

The Dynamic Equilibrium and Succession Principle

This last principle has the least obvious historical tie to the study of social environments and yet has the most direct relevance for the social organization's ability to carry out a long-range plan of organizational development. As was discussed in the previous section this principle relates to the biological process of species emerging and declining as the immediate environment alters its functions. The implication is that alteration of the pattern of the dominant species and communities is inevitable. Over specific periods of time the total ecosystem shifts so that new functions emerge and a pattern of adaptation is expressed.

The ecological premise adopted by the present writers is that social environments *do* function in this manner as well. It is an implicit assumption that change programs generated by most professionals have universal applicability over a long period of time. To the extent that the contemporary social scientist denies the social evolution of the organization he is denying a reality that makes his efforts ineffective at best and delusional at worst. The effective change program derived from ecological analogies takes the succession principle as a given and attempts to work with the succession process rather than against it. The ecologist Odum has commented that organisms which man cultivates are members of communities in periods of early versus late succession. He states:

Thus, most game birds, many fresh-water game fish, and many of the most valuable timber trees thrive best in what are actually temporary communities. Since a particular organism cannot be maintained in nature without maintaining at least the essential parts of its community the problem is to learn how to halt succession and keep the desired community permanently in existence. This has often times proved easier said than done. An alternative would be to allow succession to proceed normally but to arrange to have a sufficient number of areas continually coming into the desired stage (Odum, 1959, pp. 259–260).

As the biological ecologist takes into account the natural evolution of the environment, the design of preventive interventions can also be developed to take account of this process. In this case there are several questions that can be asked to clarify the assessment process prior to the design of the intervention. Some comments will be made about each one.

A. Criteria for Membership in Social Settings. If the social organization is going to continue its development, then its criterion for membership will be both diverse and changing. If the level of organizational development is stabilized then membership in the organization will be more restricted and will be relatively unchanging. The implication from the ecological analogy is that diverse criteria for membership will facilitate the succession process while more restricted criteria for membership will stabilize the succession process. Criteria for membership can include the usual items such as ethnic status, social status, and occupational aspirations. Criteria can also include participation in informal and formal activities in the high school, academic performance, and activities which involve innovative changes within the high school. Are such criteria implicit or explicit? Are the criteria defined by tradition or

by the exigences of the moment? Do they emerge as a result of social interactions between multiple groups of students or are they defined by a small group of faculty?

The process by which persons are defined and how they are involved in the membership of the high school environment can define how this particular social structure utilizes its talent. How students, faculty, community leaders, and administrative staff are involved in the operation of the school are suggested as guideposts for detailing the operation of the development of the school's future. Of equal importance to the description of the criteria for membership is the assessment of types of events that are shared by the members, the amount of mutual trust that can emerge, and the type of social relationships and social effectiveness that can emerge outside the more formal criteria that define the structure of the membership groupings. The succession principle allows an easy transition to the social processes by which students and faculty can form new alliances, can develop new consitituencies, and can contribute to the redevelopment of the high school.

B. Mechanisms for Crossing Status Lines in Social Interactions. This criterion is a direct outgrowth of the first criterion and addresses more specifically those features of the social environment that can enable criteria cited under the previous heading to become workable. One means for defining how well the social setting can move toward the next level of its development is to determine the opportunities persons have to cross internal structures that divide the organization into its various parts. It is assumed that every high school has a social order and that this order dictates the flow of communication, influences, and the norms for social control. One way of defining the relevance of these parts of the organization for the adaptation of its members is to specify how these portions of the organization can be revised, and under what circumstances. Are the circumstances rare and created by external events? Are the circumstances initiated by the requirements of the social structure? Or are they generated as the result of the effectiveness of the individual members of the organization? Does the organization have planned occasions whereby its members review the criteria for social status or are such activities related to the accidental performances of individuals? The answers to such questions are not easy to obtain and must often rely on naturalistic observations of informed social settings in order to provide an index of the activities that may reflect the functioning of these environments. The development of a realistic view of the workings of social settings will depend upon the talents of the observer to be accessible and be a participant in the activities of the critical settings. The implication of this point is that a science of interventions is developed only if the knowledge is derived from settings that reflect the life of the environment and not the life of the scientist.

C. Changes in Coping Styles While a Member of a Social Setting. This criterion is presented in order to focus upon the interaction between expressiveness of the individual and the functions of the social setting. This is one of the defining properties of ecological analogy and one of the essential defining properties of the succession principle. This interaction between individual coping styles and the functions of the social setting allows for an empirical assessment of the adaptation of persons to a variety of settings. It is assumed that cross-sectional views of such relationships will specify the particular adaptations while longitudinal analyses of such relationships can be another index of the development of the social environment. The design of interventions can be improved by answers to questions that derive from this type of criterion. Do the preferences for coping styles shift in their intensity or frequency over time in the same setting? How do changes in the functioning of the environment affect the expression of coping preferences? How do the coping styles expressed in one setting compare to the coping styles expressed in another setting? How much variability is there in the coping preferences of members of a social setting? The answers to such questions can provide data that will force the design of the intervention to account for how the change program will alter the ecological balance of the social setting. It is the spirit of the ecological analogy that the introduction of a change program can anticipate the ways in which the intervention will serve to redefine the coping styles of persons and the norms for adaptation. It is assumed that there will be differential effects for interventions. Change

programs that focus on affecting the organizational climate are expected to have fewer effects upon individual coping styles than will interventions which focus upon the expressive modes of individuals dealing with the environment. With adequate knowledge of these relationships, the intervention can meet and more clearly specify external changes that can complement the dynamic properties of the natural environment. As this coupling is defined predictions about the succession process can be made.

The above criteria are examples of the types of data that are suggested for an analysis of the social organization of a setting and the development of interventions. The emphasis has been on the types of persons who are members of settings, how members can move across status levels, and how coping preferences change over particular periods of time. All of these criteria are presented as examples of how the varieties of adaptation of individuals serve as examples of the range of developmental patterns of social organizations.

Summary

As Table 14–5 portrays, each of the four ecological principles is complementary for generating sources of data for planning interventions. The interdependence principle which has been presented is useful in developing methods to assess the type of current resources as well as the potential for developing new resources in that setting. The cycling of resources principle is relevant in developing criteria for the process by which resources are utilized and the manner and style in which resources are combined. Both the interdependence principle and the cycling principle focus on data about individuals in social settings. The adaptation principle suggests data for defining how the social setting deals with the individuals residing in the setting and to what extent its norms change over time. The succession principle, like the adaptation principle, focuses on the behavior of the social setting and its response to individuals in that setting. The particular relevance of the succession principle is in suggesting data for evaluating how the social setting adapts to externally induced change. These principles generate different types of criteria depending upon whether the change method is primarily focusing on the behavior of individuals, the functions of an organization, or the institutions of a community.

Looking at how all four principles apply to the clinical method, collectively they provide a context for a combination of information from the environment and its members in order to plan an intervention which focuses on the expressive behavior of one or two members of the social setting. These same four principles are also relevant as guides in suggesting concepts and criteria that are relevant for defining change at the level of the total organization. Here the focus is on how the organization develops and how it fosters the development of its members. When these four principles are applied to the topic of community change, the focus shifts again to the relationship between community groups and their effectiveness in producing means for change in their geographical area.

The present discussion has focused on the relevance of these four principles for only the clinical method. Such principles are useful in drawing out the implications of other change programs such as organizational change and community development.

The implication of this discussion is that new types of data are needed to design preventive interventions if not to validate ecological theories of human environments. These tentative and initial formulations are presented as a start in this direction.

Bringing It All Back Home

These principles have been presented as examples of how the ecological point of view can be useful in deriving new criteria for the assessment of persons and environments. At the moment each of these principles has received meager verification. It is the authors' belief, however, that the process of validating these principles can develop new data that is relevant for the practical tasks of assessing the differential benefits of adaptation for individuals and organizations.

It is the opinion of the authors that the tasks of community mental health which include the design of preventive interventions depend upon defining how a change program varies for the specific requirements of the local setting. The above principles suggest, for example, that

help-giving behavior not only has a different function in contrasting environments, but that such acts will be likely to be performed by persons with varying coping styles. If succeeding efforts can establish the empirical properties of contrasting settings, then a knowledge base can be evolved for change programs that do, in fact, meet the requirements of the local setting. The community mental health field has two simultaneous efforts to build upon; first, the reassessment of social settings and, second, the creation of workable methods for personal change. The achievement of these two tasks can provide an ecological theory of social change that is relevant and valid. This quest has been the purpose of this chapter.

The preceding discussion brings—or rather returns us—to a final critical point regarding ecological planning for mental health services; namely, that we have little available data to draw on as an aid in planning for change. We are not used to viewing the high school as an ecological niche nor are we geared toward a planning orientation. To develop this new analogy, we need to understand more about specific environments. We must learn about organizational functioning if we are to anticipate organizational side effects of our interventions. We must learn more about the links of the high school to surrounding environments if we are to assess the alternative costs and benefits of contrasting programs for change. Because of these gaps in knowledge and relevant training, we must learn how to learn about how environments vary. We need to know more about: (1) *the structural aspects of the school environment itself*—how ecological variables, such as size and racial composition, affect styles of adaptations and the opportunity structures of high schools; (2) *populations at risk*—how individuals and groups of students emerge as candidates for service in different social environments; (3) *the adaptation process*—how personal values and coping styles are affected over time by the high school environment, and how opportunity structures of the high school absorb students and differentially socialize them as a function of their varying coping styles; and (4) *changes in the functions of environments over time*— how the organizational history of the environment provides constraints for generating the change process. This is a plea for knowledge which has pragmatic utility to help the development of a design to capitalize on the benefits of the past and not on the mistakes. These needs for new facts about the nature of the high school environment and its effect on adolescents—needs which we have explored in the early parts of this chapter—are the context for planning for change.

In addition to new knowledge, a conceptual approach to planning for change—such as the one we have suggested—also necessitates an expansion and a redefinition of the available roles of the mental health professional. One of these changes involves a movement from an intrapsychic orientation to one which focuses on the reciprocity of man and environment. At this point in time, the training of most mental health professionals ill prepares them for the assessments, planning, and change induction in natural settings.

But the need is great and the time is short to strengthen high schools in their own development as social institutions. Those of us who believe that "the game is worth the candle" must indicate a willingness to develop new competencies and try new professional experiences lest we mould our training into a kind of trade school philosophy where we do what we were taught because it's all we know. Finally, we must cultivate the ability to tolerate the fact that effective change in a school environment is a long-term proposition. It is our belief that successful intervention in and redevelopment of the high school lies in an adequate conceptualization and understanding of the forces impinging on it.

EPILOGUE

The mounting social and mental health problems faced by our high schools far surpass our manpower available. Recognition of this problem has necessitated a search for ways of intervening in high schools in such a manner as to reduce ultimately their need for service and insure that such interventions that are made do not wither as the mental health professional walks out the door. The traditional services offered by schools are of obvious necessity, though chronically inadequate. They tend to focus on individuals and generally do not direct themselves to organizational problems or environmental properties. In this chapter, an ecological approach has been proposed as one which attempts to take sufficient account not only

of personality characteristics but of organizational constraints. By focusing on the interdependence of these two types of knowledge, this approach bridges the gap between personalogists and organization theorists (Forehand & Gilmer, 1964; Pugh, 1966).

We have elucidated this ecological orientation with regard to many aspects of the social environment of the high school, and in each we have tried to summarize some of the current knowledge as well as highlight the research gaps which appear when the high school is seen as ecological data. Underlying this emphasis is the assumption that such knowledge is critical to a truly preventive approach to intervention in the high schools. In addition, we have contended that such interventions revolve around a commitment to a planning orientation. This orientation was elaborated on two levels: (1) providing guidelines for action programs and (2) focusing on ecological research data for planning future interventions.

Hunt has written: "The most fascinating and as yet relatively undeveloped field for mental hygiene is the restructuring of the educational system itself in such a fashion that it produces the least possible number of tensions and conflicts that may generate new emotional disorders or exacerbate existing ones. This will involve administrative as well as educational readjustments, not the least important of which will be the promotion of emotional health and stability among the teachers and administrators themselves" (Hunt, 1968, p. 38). It is the task of the professional in the high school to work toward organizational redevelopment and in the process create a scientific basis for both planning and evaluation of preventive intervention. If this process is successful, we will evolve from a psychology *in* the schools to an ecology *of* the schools. This chapter represents one attempt to contribute practical and theoretical guidelines for this expedition.

Notes

This work was carried out while the first author was completing a Postdoctoral Research Fellowship under the direction of Rudolph Moos, Department of Psychiatry, Stanford University (NIMH Grant #MH 8304). Appreciation is expressed to him for his support of this work. A substantial amount of the work contributed by the second author was made possible by the support of a NIMH research grant, Adaptive Behavior in Varied High

School Environments, R01 MH 1–5606–01. The contributions of the third author were made possible by an NIMH Predoctoral Research Fellowship 1–F1–MH34, 359–01A. The authors wish to thank Robert Bush of Stanford University for his extensive help in suggesting relevant literature within the field of education and for his constructive suggestions regarding the scope of the entire chapter. The authors also acknowledge the incisive and helpful suggestions regarding the Principles of Ecology made by James A. Swan, School of Natural Resources, University of Michigan. Judy Black, Kathleen Powers, and Penelope Trickett were extremely helpful in reviewing relevant literature and typing earlier drafts of the manuscript. Appreciation is expressed to Janice LaRue, Merikay Bryan, and Colby Schneider for their excellent editorial work and for typing the final drafts.

1. The issue of communication between school and community services is, of course, critical not only in mental health areas. The emerging role of "community liaison worker" is specifically tied to the linkage of school with community opinion. Whereas mental health services are at this point in time generally involved with individual children, the "community liaison" role reflects a concern with the school's "mental health" and as such represents an awareness that the school's success with adolescents is a multidimensional problem.

2. A more extensive review of "research on the school as bureaucracy," along with integrative and theoretical commentary, can be found in Bidwell (1965).

3. Although Dreeban and Gross made directional interpretations (e.g., superintendent support for innovation leading to increased innovative behavior of teachers), their correlational analysis does not preclude reversed influences (e.g., the innovative behavior of teachers resulting in the superintendent's greater willingness to support innovation). The application of research techniques which allow causal inference, such as the cross-lag correlational analysis described by Pelz and Andrews (1964), should help to clarify these relationships.

4. See Biddle et al., 1965, for a selected bibliography of these and related references.

5. These issues and recent approaches to their solutions are the topic of *Contemporary Research on Teacher Effectiveness*, edited by Bruce J. Biddle and William J. Ellena (1964).

6. See Halpin and Croft, 1964, for a scale discussing the principal-teacher relationship in greater detail.

7. See Glidewell, Kantor, Smith, and Stringer, 1966, for a review of this research.

References

Allinsmith, W., & Goethals, G. W. *The role of the schools in mental health.* New York: Basic Books, 1962.

Amidou, E., & Flanders, N. A. The effects of direct and indirect teacher influence on dependent-prone students learning geometry. *Journal of Educational Psychology*, 1961, 52, 286–291.

Anderson, H. H., & Brewer, J. M. Studies of teachers' classroom personalities II. *Journal of Applied Psychology*, 1946, No. 8.

Bachman, J. G., et al. *Youth in transition: Blueprint for a longitudinal study of adolescent boys.* Ann Arbor, Mich.: University of Michigan Press, 1967.

Bardon, J. I. School psychology and school psychologists. *American Psychologist*, 1968, 23, 87–194.

Barker, R. G. Explorations in ecological psychology. *American Psychologist*, 1965, 20, 1–14.

Barker, R. G., & Cump, P. *Big school, small school.* Stanford, Calif.: Stanford University Press, 1964.

Bennis, W. A. New role for the behavioral sciences: Effecting organizational change. *Administrative Sciences Quarterly*, 1963, 8, 125–165.

Berkowitz, H. Clinical child psychology in the school. *Psychology in Schools*, 1966, 3, 223–228.

Biddle, B. J., & Ellena, W. J. (eds.) *Contemporary research on teacher effectiveness.* New York: Holt, Rinehart & Winston, 1964.

Biddle, B. J., Fraser, G. S., & Jellison, J. M. Teacher role: Conceptions and behavior. In B. J. Biddle et al. (eds.), *Essays on the social system of education.* Columbia, Mo., 1965.

Biddle, B. J., & Rosencranz, H. A. The role approach to teacher effectiveness. In B. J. Biddle & W. J. Ellena (eds.), *Contemporary research on teacher effectiveness.* New York: Holt, Rinehart & Winston, 1964.

Biddle, B. M., & Thomas, E. J. (eds.) *Role theory: Concepts and research.* New York: Wiley, 1966.

Bidwell, C. The school as a formal organization. In J. G. March (ed.), *Handbook of organizations.* Chicago: Rand McNally, 1965.

Bloomberg, C. M., & Salzman, A. *School mental health programs: Description and evaluation.* Washington, D. C.: Washington School of Psychiatry, 1961.

Blos, P. *On adolescence: A psychoanalytic interpretation.* New York: Free Press, 1962.

Boyle, H. P. The effects of high school on students' aspirations. *American Journal of Sociology*, 1966, 71, 628–639.

Brim, Q. G., Jr. Socialization through the life cycle. In O. G. Brim, Jr., & S. Wheeler (eds.), *Socialization after childhood: Two essays.* New York: Wiley, 1966.

Brim, O. G., Jr. Adult socialization. In J. A. Clausen (ed.), *Socialization and society.* Boston: Little, Brown, 1968.

Brookover, W. R., & Gottlieb, D. Sociology of education. *Review of Educational Research*, 1961, 31, 38–56.

Caplan, G. *Concepts of mental health and consultation.* Washington, D. C.: Children's Bureau, United States Department of Health, Education, and Welfare, 1959.

Caplan, G. *Principles of preventive psychiatry.* New York: Basic Books, 1964.

Carlson, R. *Executive succession and organizational change: Place-bound and career-bound superintendents of schools.* Chicago: Midwest Administration Center, University of Chicago, 1962.

Carlson, R. Environmental constraints and organizational consequences: The public school and its clients. *National Society for the Study of Education Yearbook*, 1964, 63 (Pt. 2), 262–276.

Chesler, M., Franklin, J., & Guskin, A. Development of alternative responses to interracial and intergenerational conflict in secondary schools. Unpublished manuscript,

Institute for Social Research, Ann Arbor, Michigan, April, 1969.

Clements, F. E., & Shelford, V. E. *Bio-ecology*. New York: Wiley, 1939.

Cloward, R. A., & Ohlin, L. E. *Delinquency and opportunity: A theory of delinquent gangs*. New York: Free Press, 1960.

Coleman, J. *The adolescent society*. New York: Free Press of Glencoe, 1961.

Coleman, J., et al. *Equality of educational opportunity*. Washington, D. C.: National Center for Educational Statistics, United States Department of Health, Education, and Welfare, 1966.

Danskin, D. G., Kennedy, C. E., Jr., & Friesen, W. S. Guidance: The ecology of students. *Personnel and Guidance Journal*, 1965, 44, 130–135.

Dodd, P. C. *Role conflicts of school principals*. (Final Report No. 4, Cooperative Research Project No. 853) Cambridge, Mass.: Graduate School of Education, Harvard University, 1965.

Douvan, E., & Adelson, J. *The adolescent experience*. New York: Wiley, 1966.

Dreeban, R., & Gross, N. *The role behavior of school principals*. (Final Report No. 3, Cooperative Research Project No. 853) Cambridge, Mass.: Graduate School of Education, Harvard University, 1965.

Dukelow, D. A. Mental health services in large city schools. *Journal of School Health*, 1961, 31(3), 75–82.

Edwards, D. W. The development of a questionnaire method of measuring exploration preferences. In M. J. Feldman (ed.), *Buffalo: Studies in psychotherapy and behavioral change*. No. 2. *Theory and research in community mental health*. Buffalo, N. Y.: State University of New York at Buffalo, 1971, 99–107.

Epperson, D. C. Some interpersonal and performance correlates of classroom alienation. *School Review*, 1963, 71, 360–376.

Erikson, D. A. The school administrator. *Review of Educational Research*, 1967, 37, 417–432.

Erikson, E. The problem of ego identity. *Psychological Issues*, 1959, 1(1), 101–164.

Erikson, E. *Identity: Youth and crisis*. New York: Norton, 1968.

Fishburn, C. E. Teacher role perception in the secondary school. *Journal of Teacher Education*, 1962, 13, 55–59.

Flanagan, J. C., et al. *Studies of the American high school*. (Final Report to the United States Office of Education, Cooperative Research Project No. 226) Washington, D. C.: Project TALENT, University of Pittsburgh, 1962.

Forehand, G. A., & Gilmer, B. Environmental variation in studies of organizational behavior. *Psychological Bulletin*, 1964, 62, 361–383.

French, J. R. P., Kahn, R. L., & Mann, F. C. (eds.) Work, health and satisfaction. *Journal of Social Issues*, 1962, 18(3), 1–129.

Gallaher, A., Jr. Directed change in formal organizations: The school system. In R. O. Carlson et al. (eds.), *Change processes in the public schools*. Eugene, Ore.: University of Oregon Center for the Advanced Study of Educational Administration, 1965.

Gildea, M. C. L., Glidewell, J. C., & Kantor, M. B. The St. Louis school mental health project: History and evaluation. In E. L. Cowen, E. A. Gardner, & M. Zax. (eds.), *Emergent approaches to mental health problems*. New York: Appleton-Century-Crofts, 1967.

Glidewell, J. C., Kantor, M. B., Smith, L. M., & Stringer, L. A. Socialization and social structure in the classroom. In L. W. Hoffman & M. L. Hoffman (eds.), *Review of child development research*. New York: Russell Sage Foundation, 1966.

Gold, H. A. The classroom isolate: An additional dimension for consideration in the evaluation of a quality education program. *Journal of Experimental Education*, 1962, 31, 77–80.

Good, L. R., Siegal, S. M., & Bay, A. P. *Therapy by design: Implications of architecture for human behavior*. Springfield, Ill.: Charles C Thomas, 1964.

Goodman, P. Catalyst for failure. *Psychiatry and Social Science Review*, 1968, 2, 8–11.

Gordon, C. W. *The social system of the high school*. New York: Free Press of Glencoe, 1957.

Goslin, D. The school in a changing society: Notes on the development of strategies for solving educational problems. *American Journal of Orthopsychiatry*, 1967, 37, 843–858.

Gottlieb, D. Sociology of education. *Review of Educational Research*, 1964, 34, 62–70.

Gottlieb, D., & Tenhouten, W. Racial composition and the social system of three high schools. *Journal of Marriage and the Family*, 1965, 27, 204–212.

Gray, S. W. *The psychologist in the schools*. New York: Holt, Rinehart & Winston, 1963.

Grimes, J. W., & Allinsmith, W. Compulsivity, anxiety and school achievement. *Merrill-Palmer Quarterly*, 1961, 7, 247–271.

Gross, N., & Herriott, R. E. *Staff leadership in public schools*. New York: Wiley, 1965.

Gross, N., Mason, W. S., & McEachern, A. W. *Exploration in role analysis: Studies of the school superintendent role*. New York: Wiley, 1958.

Gross, N., & Trask, A. E. *Men and women as elementary school principals*. Cambridge, Mass.: Graduate School of Education, Harvard University, 1964.

Group for the Advancement of Psychiatry. *Normal adolescence: Its dynamics and impact*. New York: Scribner, 1968.

Gump, P. V. Environmental guidance of the classroom behavior system. In B. J. Biddle & J. Ellena (eds.), *Contemporary research on teaching effectiveness*. New York: Holt, Rinehart & Winston, 1964.

Halpin, A. W., & Croft, D. B. *The organizational climate of schools*. Chicago: Midwest Administration Center, University of Chicago, 1963.

Havighurst, R. J., et al. *Growing up in River City*. New York: Wiley, 1962.

Hayes, P. C. The effect of planned change on the local school. *Theory into Practice*, 1966, 1, 46–50.

Herriott, R. E., & St. John, N. H. *Social class and the urban school: The impact of pupil background on teachers and principals*. New York: Wiley, 1949.

Hollingshead, A. B. *Elmtown's youth: The impact of social classes on adolescents.* New York: Wiley, 1949.

Hunt, W. A. The American school system, a possible locus for a national mental health program. *Psychology in the Schools*, 1968, 5, 35–40.

Iscoe, I., Pierce-Jones, J., Friedman, S. T., & McGehearty, L. Some strategies in mental health consultation. In E. L. Cowen, E. A. Gardner, & M. Zax (eds.) *Emergent approaches to mental health problems.* New York: Appleton-Century-Crofts, 1967.

Johnston, L. T. Design and sample for a nationwide longitudinal study of adolescent boys. In J. G. Bachman, R. Bloom, T. N. Davidson, L. Johnston, M. T. Mednick, & J. O. Raynor, *Working Paper 3: Some studies of background factors, achievement and mental health in a nationwide sample of adolescent boys.* Ann Arbor: Institute for Social Research, University of Michigan, October 1968.

Joint Commission on Mental Health of Children. Statements and tentative recommendations. Prepared for discussion to annual meeting of affiliate organizations, board of directors, and task force chairman of Joint Commission on Mental Health of Children, January 22, 1968.

Kahn, R. L., et al. *Organizational stress.* New York: Wiley, 1964.

Katz, D., & Kahn, R. L. *The social psychology of organizations.* New York: Wiley, 1966.

Kelly, J. G. Ecological constraints on mental health services. *American Psychologist*, 1966, 21, 535–539. (a)

Kelly, J. G. Social adaptation to varied environments. Paper presented at the annual meeting of the American Psychological Association, New York, September 1966. (b)

Kelly, J. G. Naturalistic observations and theory confirmation: An example. *Human Development*, 1967, 10, 212–222.

Kelly, J. G. The quest for valid preventive interventions. In C. D. Spielberger (ed.), *Current topics in clinical and community psychology*, Vol. II. New York: Academic Press, 1970.

Kelly, J. G. Towards an ecological conception of preventive interventions. In J. W. Carter, Jr., (ed.), *Research contributions from psychology to community mental health.* New York: Behavioral Publications, 1968.

Kenniston, K. *The tasks of adolescence.* (Preliminary report for the Joint Commission on Mental Health of Children) Washington, D. C.: Joint Commission on Mental Health of Children, 1968.

Klein, D. C. Consultation processes as a method for improving teaching. In E. M. Bower & W. G. Hollister (eds.), *Behavioral science frontiers in education.* New York: Wiley, 1967.

Kobrin, S. The impact of cultural factors on selected problems of adolescent development in the middle and lower class. *American Journal of Orthopsychiatry*, 1962, 32, 387–390.

Kvaraceus, W. C. *Report to Task Force III: The adolescent in school.* Washington, D. C.: Joint Commission on Mental Health of Children, 1968. (a)

Kvaraceus, W. C. The disadvantaged learner: Some implications for teachers and teaching. Paper presented at the Sixth Work Conference on Curriculum and Teaching in Depressed Urban Areas, Teachers College, Columbia University, New York, June 1968. (b)

Leopold, S. Adapatability of animals to habitat change. In F. F. Darling & J. Milton (eds.), *Future environments of North America.* Garden City, N. Y.: Natural History Press, 1966.

Levins, R. The strategy of model building in population biology. *American Scientist*, 1966, 54, 421–431.

Lewin, K., Lippitt, R., & White, R. K. Patterns of aggressive behavior in experimentally created "social climates." *Journal of Social Psychology*, 1939, 10, 271–299.

Liddel, G. P. Psychological factors involved in dropping out of school. *High School Journal*, 1962, 45, 276–280.

Liebig, J. *Chemistry and its application to agriculture and physiology.* (4th ed.) London: Taylor & Walter, 1847.

Lipham, J. M. Organizational character of education: Administrative behavior. *Review of Educational Research*, 1964, 34, 435–454.

Lippitt, R. Improving the socialization process. In J. A. Clausen (ed.), *Socialization and society.* Boston: Little, Brown, 1968.

Lippitt, R., & Gold, M. Classroom social structure as a mental health problem. *Journal of Social Issues*, 1959, 15, 40–49.

Mayer, M. The adolescent in placement. Unpublished manuscript, Joint Commission on Mental Health of Children, Washington, D. C., 1968.

McDill, E. L., Meyers, E. D., Jr., & Rigsby, L. C. *Sources of educational climate in high schools.* (Final project) Washington, D. C.: United States Department of Health, Education, and Welfare, December 1966.

McDowell, H. D. The principal's role in a metropolitan school system. Unpublished doctoral dissertation, University of Chicago, 1954.

McKeachie, W. J. Motivation, teaching methods and college learning. In M. R. Jones (ed.), *Nebraska symposium on motivation: 1961.* Lincoln, Neb.: University of Nebraska Press, 1961.

McKee, R. Defeat of the killer eel. *Audubon*, 1968, 70(4), 40–47.

Miles, M. B. Planned change and organizational health: Figure and ground. In R. O. Carlson et al. (eds.), *Change processes in the public schools.* Eugene, Ore. Center for the Advanced Study of Educational Administration, University of Oregon, 1965.

Miles, M. B. Some properties of schools as social systems. In G. Watson (ed.), *Change in school systems.* Washington, D. C.: National Training Laboratories, National Education Association, 1967.

Miller, D. R., & Swanson, G. E. *Inner conflict and defense.* New York: Holt, 1960.

Miller, S. M. Saleem, B. L., & Bryce, H. *School dropouts: A commentary and annotated bibliography.* Syracuse, N. Y.: Youth Development Center, Syracuse University, 1964.

Mitzel, H. E., & Rabinowitz, W. Assessing social-emotional climate in the classroom by Withall's technique.

Psychological Monographs, 1953, 67(18, Whole No. 368)

Moeller, G. Bureaucracy and teacher's sense of power. *School Review*, 1964, 72, 137–157.

Moos, R. H. The assessment of the social climate of correctional institutions. *Journal of Research in Crime and Delinquency*, 1968, 5, 174–178.

Moos, R. H. Differential effects of social climates of correctional institutions. *Journal of Research in Crime and Delinquency*, 1970, 7, 71–82.

Moos, R. H., & Houts, P. S. The assessment of the social atmosphere of psychiatric wards. *Journal of Abnormal Psychology*, 1968, 73, 595–604. (a)

Moos, R. H., & Houts, P. S. Differential effects on the social atmosphere of psychiatric wards. Unpublished manuscript, 1968. (b)

Morse, W. C. The crisis teacher public school provision for the disturbed child. *School of Education Bulletin*, 1962, 37, 101–104.

Myrick, R. A new concept in the the architectural planning of dental schools. *Journal of Dental Education*, 1965, 29, 382–386. (a)

Myrick, R. Summary progress report on the planning study: Behavioral factors in dental school design. Washington, D. C.: George Washington University, 1965. (Mimeo) (b)

Myrick, R., & Marx, B. S. An exploratory study of the relationship between high school building design and student learning. (Final Report, Project No. 5-8006) Washington, D. C.: United States Department of Health, Education, and Welfare, 1968.

National Education Association. *Teacher supply and demand in public schools.* (Research Report 1966–R–16) Washington, D. C.: Research Division, NEA, October, 1966.

Neill, A. S. *Summerhill: A radical approach to child rearing.* New York: Hart, 1960.

Newman, R. *Psychological consultation in the schools.* New York: Basic Books, 1967.

Nicholas, L. N., Virjo, H. E., & Wattenberg, W. W. *Effect of socio-economic setting and organizational climate on problems brought to the elementary school offices.* (Final report of Cooperative Research Project No. 2394) Detroit: College of Education, Wayne State University, 1965.

Ochberg, F. M., & Trickett, E. Administrative responses to racial conflict in a high school, *Community Mental Health Journal*, 1970, 6, 470–482.

Odum, E. P. *Fundamentals of ecology.* Philadelphia: Saunders, 1959.

Osterweil, J. School psychology and comprehensive community mental health planning. *Community Mental Health Journal*, 1966, 2, 142–145.

Pelz, D. C., & Andrews, F. M. Detecting causal priorities in panel study data. *American sociological Review*, 1964, 29, 836–848.

Pervin, L. Performance and satisfaction as a function of individual-environment fit. *Psychological Bulletin*, 1968, 69, 56–68.

Pierce, P. R. *The origin and development of the public school principalship.* Chicago: University of Chicago Press, 1935.

Pugh, D. S. Modern organization theory: A psychological and sociological study. *Psychological Bulletin*, 1966, 66, 23–252.

Raush, H. L. Interaction sequences. *Journal of Personality and Social Psychology*, 1965, 2(4), 487–499.

Raush, H. L. Naturalistic method and the clinical approach. In E. P. Willems & H. L. Raush (eds.), *Naturalistic viewpoints in psychological research.* New York: Holt, Rinehart & Winston, 1969.

Raush, H. L. Dittman, A. T., & Taylor, T. J. Person setting and change in social interaction. *Human Relations*, 1959, 12, 361–379.

Raush, H. L., Farbman, I., & Llewellyn, L. G. Person, setting and change in social interaction II. A normal-control study. *Human Relations*, 1960, 13, 305–333.

Reiff, R. Social intervention and the problem of psychological analysis. *American Psychologist*, 1968, 23, 524–531.

Reissman, F. *The culturally deprived child.* New York: Harper, 1962.

Reissman, F., Cohen, J., & Pearl, A. *The mental health of the poor.* New York: Free Press of Glencoe, 1964.

Rice, R., & Roistacher, R. Questionnaire and monimation methods of identifying exploratory behavior. In *Adaptive behavior in varied high school environments progress report I.* Ann Arbor: Institute for Social Research, University of Michigan, 1968.

Rosen, B. M., Kramer, M., & Rednick, R. W. Utilization of psychiatric facilities by children: Current status, trends, implications. In *Mental health statistics—Analytical and special studies reports.* Series B, No. 1. Bethesda, Md.: National Institute of Mental Health, 1968.

Ryans, D. *Characteristics of teachers.* Washington, D. C.: American Council of Education, 1960.

Sapir, B. What to tell the architect. *Community Mental Health Journal*, 1968, 4, 17–26.

Sarason, S. B., Levine, M., Goldenberg, I. M., Cherlin, D. L., & Bennett, E. M. *Psychology in community settings: Clinical, educational, vocational, social aspects.* New York: Wiley, 1966.

The Saturday Review. The magnitude of the American educational establishment (1968–1969). November 16, 1968, 51, 105.

Sherif, M., & Sherif, C. W. *Reference groups: Exploration into conformity and deviation in adolescents.* New York: Harper & Row, 1964.

Short, J. F., & Strodbeck, F. L. *Group process and gang delinquency.* Chicago: University of Chicago Press, 1965.

Smith, L. M., & Klein, P. F., The adolescent and his society. *Review of Educational Research*, 1966, 36, 424–436.

Smith, M. B. Competence and socialization. In J. A. Clausen (ed.), *Socialization and society.* Boston: Little, Brown, 1968.

Snyder, E. E. The differential effects of innovation on the student social structure of a high school. *Sociology Quarterly*, 1967, 8(1), 103–110.

Sowder, B. The question of effective treatment for adolescents. Unpublished manuscript, Washington, D. C., Joint Commission on Mental Health of Children, 1968.

Stern, G. G. *People in context*. New York: Wiley, 1968.

Stinnett, T. N. *Turmoil in teaching*. New York: Macmillan, 1968.

Storlurow, L. M. Model the master teacher or master the teaching model. In J. D. Krumboltz (ed.), *Learning and the educational process*. Chicago: Rand McNally, 1965.

Tansley, A. G. The use and abuse of vegetational concepts and terms. *Ecology*, 1935, 16, 284–307.

Thoreson, C. A. A need for a new education specialist. Unpublished manuscript, Stanford University, 1968.

Twyman, J. P., & Biddle, B. J. Role conflict of public school teachers. *Journal of Psychology*, 1963, 55, 183–198.

Walberg, H. J. Classroom Climate Questionnaire. Cambridge: Harvard University, 1966. (Mimeo)

Walberg, H. J., & Anderson, G. J. Learning environment inventory. Cambridge: Harvard University, 1967. (Multilith)

Walberg, H. J. Structural and affective aspects of classroom climate. *Psychology in the Schools*, 1968, 5, 247–252.

Waller, W. *The sociology of teaching*. New York: Wiley, 1932.

Watt, K. E. F. *Systems analysis of ecology*. New York: Academic Press, 1966.

Wheeler, S. The structure of formally organized socialization settings. In O. Brim & S. Wheeler (eds.), *Socialization after childhood*. New York: Wiley, 1966.

White, M. A., & Harris, M. W. *The school psychologist*. New York: Harper & Row, 1961.

Withall, J. The development of a climate index. *Journal of Educational Research*, 1951, 45, 93–99.

Wrenn, C. G. A second look. In J. W. Loughary (ed.), *Counseling, a growing profession*. (Report of the American Personnel and Guidance Association concerned with the professionalization of counseling) Washington, D. C.: American Personnel and Guidance Association, 1965.

15

Mental Health in Later Life

Carl Eisdorfer

The focus of crisis intervention and disease prevention in this decade is on youth. Yet maturity and aging are the targets for which childhood disease-prevention techniques are developed. Interest in early childhood development, supported by the theoretical formulations of psychoanalytic and neoanalytic personality theory, yields to a structural disease-oriented approach from adolescence onward. Such an orientation implies that successful personality growth in the early years is all that is necessary for lifelong mental health, that nothing of significance happens to personality structure beyond adolescence, and that preparation for personal and interpersonal trauma early in life leads to effective coping with all subsequent crises. These ideas seem tenuous at best.

While changes in the professional mental health community have yielded vastly different patterns of institutional care and outpatient approaches, the aged have not, by and large, profited from such change. Butler (1970) has reported that there was no one on the Joint Commission on Mental Illness and Health charged with the responsibility of investigating factors involved in the prevention or treatment of mental health problems of the aged nor were any of the members of that distinguished group familiar, by virtue of training or professional commitment, with problems of later maturity. In a 62-minute-long film describing the needs and functions of community mental health centers, the National Institute of Mental Health (Bold New Approach, NIMH, 1960) devoted scarcely 30 seconds to the need for services to the aged. In fact the aged are wanting in

receipt of social services throughout the nation and their unmet need is reflected in an underrepresentation in outpatient contacts in psychiatric settings (Redick, 1970).

At least three possible explanations would appear to account for this tendency to ignore the aging process and the aged as a focus for significant activity in the field of mental health. The first is that the aged do not represent a particular mental health problem, neither are they any special risk, nor do they require any special help. A second explanation is that aging, while a serious problem for mental health workers, is hopeless and defies solution. The first hypothesis runs counter to the facts; the second is not only tautologic and a poor rationalization by those who have neglected this area but also is denied by the available data on those few programs which have attempted to deal with this problem. A third possible explanation requires a more complicated analysis and involves attitudes toward aging and the problems of dealing with the aged, nearness to death, and the decrement and decline anticipated in all persons postmaturity.

The most frequently used justification for the mental health professionals' attitude toward the aged is "they don't have much time left and we are better off investing in youth." Such justification has limited validity only when one is prepared to make specific life expectancy statements about a given individual and is invalidated by the evidence of sympathetic generosity given to such patients as leukemic children who themselves have a greatly restricted life span. This orientation also ignores the potential effect upon all generations of what has been referred to as "ageism" (Butler, personal communication) and the treatment of the aged as a minority group with negative stereotyping (Palmore, 1969) when in fact aging is a universal phenomenon.

THE AGED IN THE UNITED STATES

Before discussing the mental health of the aged it is probably valuable to describe the target populations and the special problems they present. The aged, as popularly defined in our culture, are those persons who have reached their 65th birthday (Axelrod & Eisdorfer, 1961; Tuckman & Lorge, 1953) and comprise some ten percent of the total population of the United States (approximately 20,000,000 persons). Not only has there been a recent increase in the absolute number of persons in this category but the proportion of aged in our society has also increased during the past several decades. In the year 1900, with the total population in the United States amounting to 76,000,000 persons, the aged comprised 3,000,000 individuals. Thus, while the total population in the United States has approximately tripled during the past seven decades, the aged segment of the population has increased sevenfold. Perhaps of more relevance is the postulate that the aged are a group with definable characteristics and properties. While such a notion has a certain amount of face validity, this static concept ignores the fact that the group membership is rapidly changing and many characteristics are being modified. By the year 2000 between forty-five and fifty million Americans (now in their middle age) will reach their 65th birthday. It is also true that the number of persons 75 and over will increase at about twice the rate of the 65+ group as a whole and at better than twice the rate of the population at large.

Income

Apart from these simple population statistics, it is important to consider that aged persons are poorer than the young. In 1966, 50 percent of the families headed by persons 65 and over had annual incomes of less than $3,650 or less than half of the median income obtained by younger families. For older persons living alone, the median income (for this group of 5,000,000) was $1,480 during the year 1967 (Havighurst, 1969). Of the 7,000,000 elderly families, two out of five had incomes of less than $3,000 a year, and half of that group earned less than $2,000 a year.

Health

Older persons are in poorer physical condition than the general population. Approximately three-fourths of the aged population have some chronic illness, they receive medical care more frequently, and they spend more time in the hospital. The probability of long-term hospitalization is correlated with age. Thus, while only two percent of the population between 65 and 72 require long-term care, approximately seven percent of the group 73+ require such help. On the other hand, five-sixths of the elderly get about on their own. The problems of physical illness are most important in the life of the older person and represent a threat to his mental health. It is not accidental that high bodily concern and hypochondriasis are heightened among the aged and that much of the interpersonal interaction of aged persons is mediated by health concerns. As Ostfeld (1966) has demonstrated, the behavior pattern of aged persons is often mediated by illness even when the victim is unaware of the illness and accepts the limitations on his activity as secondary to old age.

Change

The aging population is changing and the change in the characteristics of those persons entering the group over 65 is particularly dramatic. Today about 20 percent of the United States population aged 65 or over is foreign-born and 50 percent of them never went beyond elementary school. (As a matter of fact, a million elderly never went to school at all and only five percent are college graduates.) Clearly, this pattern is shifting and consequently it is predictable that the educational and social level of the elderly population will be improving markedly. In the immediate future a more articulate, better educated aged group will emerge as a potent social and political force. It could be predicted that the attempts to communicate with such a group would become effective as soon as the "new aged" are recognized and appreciated by the populace at large. This ongoing change in the socioeconomic and educational level of the aged, with its implication for a different life style and cultural patterning, could change the nature of mental illness among the aged. The shift from a poor, uneducated, and relatively physically ill group to a more affluent, cognitively active, and healthy older population might well be reflected in different types of mental disease with different presenting symptomatology. Its significance should be reflected in community programs.

Social Relations

Social isolation constitutes a particular problem among the aged, largely as a result of the deaths of relatives and friends. This is compounded by the age limitations in our social and work settings which frequently result in diminished job contacts. Lessened opportunity for social interaction further aggravates the isolation of older individuals. A majority of the aged live alone and older persons seem more likely to be cut off from close and deep interpersonal relationships. More than half (54.4 percent) of older women are widows and there are approximately 131 older women to 100 older men. Life expectancy for women is longer and increasing more rapidly than for men and consequently this gap should even widen.

The relationship between mental health and socialization in adult life needs to be more definitively explored. At present there is much evidence to suggest that older persons show less participation in community activity than do younger adults (Cumming & Henry, 1961). According to Cumming and Henry, this pattern is an aspect of the normal psychosocial aging process which involves a progressive "disengagement" during the later years of life. The disengagement hypothesis has been a central theme of much research and criticism in social gerontology. It would appear to be derived implicitly from an energy conservation approach to postmature development and is based on the interpretation of data describing social activity patterns of aged persons in Kansas City. Cumming and Henry contend that the reduction in social participation on the part of many older persons in the absence of any noticeable decline in happiness indicates that disengagement is a normal and healthy adaptational process and is a reflection of reduced motivation for social and interpersonal participation.

A number of investigators, however, have reported that the cessation or reduction of activities is not clearly associated with heightened morale. Maddox and Eisdorfer (1962) demonstrated that subgroups of a population of normal aged varied in their affective response to loss of roles. Palmore (1969) has supported this finding. Eisdorfer (1970) has suggested that disengagement is a more complex variable involving personal style and life history. In their study of response to crises, Lowenthal and Haven (1968) report that the significance for adaptation of widowhood or retirement is not a simple function of the apparent loss of existing interpersonal relations. While being socially privileged (i.e., having more social contact) appears to enhance one's morale and self-evaluation, being socially deprived (having fewer contacts) does not necessarily deflate it, and poor morale is not necessarily associated with psychiatrists' ratings of poor mental health. The crucial variables identified by Lowenthal and Haven are the maintenance of a stable intimate relationship with another individual, a "confidant." The existence of such a relationship is more highly associated with good mental health and good morale than is a high level of social interaction or role status or social stability. Recent interpersonal loss to an individual, e.g., widowhood, is considerably softened by the presence of the confidant. Lowenthal and Haven report that while psychiatrists' ratings of individuals who have just experienced loss take into account the potential for intimacy and response to loss, these clinicians often ignore the fact that this potential does not serve the needs of the individual if there is not one to fill the loss. Indeed, it might be anticipated that persons capable of forming and sustaining close personal ties may, in fact, be more immediately vulnerable to loss.

In exploring the question of who is more likely to develop a confidant relationship, the investigators found important sex differences: women develop such close relationships more often than men; there are socioeconomic differences: white collar persons have more such involvements than blue collar; and role differences: married persons more than single persons develop such relationships; and perhaps not unexpectedly, persons with a history of a heightened number of social roles sustain these relationships better than those with a history of fewer such relationships. In summary, the married, the upper socioeconomic classes, women and upper status men, for whom a rigid concept of masculinity and virility that discourages intimacy is less likely to hold, are more likely to have formed an intimate relationship inside or outside of marriage. This relationship may have definite survival value and may explain, for example, why the rate of suicide and mental illness for men including bachelors and widowers, despite their greater potential for remarriage, is much higher than for women. Potential for being fulfilled versus actual filling of a need is very much an issue with the aged and supplying the needs of an older individual following a loss is an unexplored area of crisis intervention.

WORK AND RETIREMENT

Work and retirement are two important factors affecting the isolation of older persons and are also decisive variables in attempts to understand the behavioral ecology of aging persons. Because age 65 is highly correlated with mandatory retirement and the beginning of social security compensation, as well as a variety of private pension programs, there is established a circularity of definition with loss of work characterizing persons of this age, and this in turn defining "the aged." Being thought of as "old" seems intimately tied to the variety of legislated and private plans which establish the 65th birthday as a time when most Americans enrolled in the Old Age Survivors Insurance (OASI) program receive their pension. In this regard, it is noteworthy that the retirement age has been lowered to age 62 through OASI and for at least one union pension fund (UAW), to age 55. In a recent report to the United States Senate, Kreps et al. (1969) have indicated that with increased productivity and size of labor force, it may be that this age will drop even more dramatically. Their projections indicated that if we choose to take our economic growth in the form of leisure (and the leisure came in reduced work life rather than shorter hours or longer vacations) we could within two decades lower retirement age to 39. It should also be noted that "labor force participation rates beginning with the middle-aged fall consistently with increasing rapidity with increasing age. Once unemployed, older workers remain unemployed significantly longer than the younger workers" (Brotman, Useful Fact #5, AoA, 1966).

A POPULATION AT RISK: VULNERABILITY TO MENTAL ILLNESS

Given the facts as elaborated above, it is hardly surprising that aging in the United States is associated with a heightened risk for mental illness. This does appear to be the case. Among the impressive statistics in this regard are the data on suicides which indicate that though the base rate for white males aged 15 to 24 is 7.4/100,000, it climbs steadily so that for the group 65 to 74, the rate is 45.5, and for the 75+ group, 54.5. Suicide rate for females is lower, plateaus at 55, and drops after 74. While the aged comprise about nine percent of the population for the years studied, they contribute 25 percent of the suicides (Resnik & Kantor, 1970).

Major mental illness is not easily studied and the aged are often underreported for reasons discussed below. When data are collected the heightened risk of severe emotional and mental illness is dramatically apparent. Pasamanik's study of the prevalence of psychosis by age, in Baltimore, for persons outside institutions indicates a weighted rate for those aged 35 to 64, of 5.8 per thousand in comparison with the rate of 27.8 for persons in the 65+ category. In state and private hospitals, the 65+ group has considerably higher rates for psychotic illness. However, Pasamanik found little difference in the rate of psychoneurosis by age past the age of 15. This finding of an increasing rate of psychotic symptomatology but no difference in "neurosis" seems to be stable throughout many studies here and abroad. The Midtown Manhattan Study (Srole et al., 1962) shows a clear monotonic increase in the proportion of persons "severely" disturbed with increasing age. That study excluded persons aged 60 and over, however. Of considerable importance, too, are Srole et al.'s data on economic status which demonstrates a monotonic increment in more severe psychopathology with decreasing socioeconomic level. Since the aged group is vastly overrepresented in the poverty categories, it is quite probable that this correlation between poverty and mental illness will be further supported by an increased incidence of difficulty among the aged.

It seems quite clear that the proportion of the aged who are reported to show mild deviance appears to be relatively small. However, those showing significant mental or emotional illness as expressed in suicide and psychotic symptomatology and perhaps in psychophysiologic illness would indicate a much increased risk factor for older individuals. The Dohrenwends (1969, see chapter 12) found that of those studies on rate of psychosis which included populations over 60 years of age, six out of nine showed maximum disease rate in the 70+ years. Kramer, Taube, and Starr (1968) report that "in mid-1963, about 292,000 persons 65 years of age and over were residents in either long-stay psychiatric inpatient facilities or in nursing homes, geriatric hospitals, homes for the aged, and related facilities in the United States" (page 92). They further report that this "is a minimum estimate" based upon an interview survey rather than psychiatric review. About half (51 percent) of these patients were being cared for in state and county mental hospitals, and another five percent at Veterans Administration Hospitals; the remainder were in nursing homes and related facilities. Approximately 125,000 elderly patients in nursing homes could be regarded as manifesting obvious mental disorder. Given these data it is startling to find the aged so vastly underrepresented in the mental health clinic and psychiatric outpatient population. In New Haven, Connecticut, (1950) only about one percent of the treated senile cases were under the care of a private psychiatrist. In the New York City study (Srole, 1962), the rate for persons who have sought psychiatric care is approximately 8.9 percent of the population at age 20–39; five percent at 40–49; and only 1.5 percent in the age group 50–59. Among the group rated by psychiatrists as incapacitated or showing marked symptom formation, it is impressive that 79.2 percent of the 50–59 year old group have never sought or received help. The Midtown Manhattan Study did not include persons over age 60 and again we can only project that, extrapolating from figures obtained from the data collected, the ratio would be even greater for older persons.

The National Clearing House for Mental Health Information of the National Institute of Mental Health reporting on psychiatric outpatient terminations (Clearing House for Mental Health Information, 1969) indicates that of the 703,054 outpatients terminated in 1967, 14,977 were 65+. The rate per 100,000 was 82.1 for patients aged 65+, and 167.1 for those aged 55–64, in contrast to a high of 567 for the 25–34 age group. This analysis of the case load of psychiatric and mental health center outpatient facilities throughout the country also indicated that while patients under 18 accounted for 36.3 percent of all cases and the group aged 24–34 comprised 17.8 percent of those being seen, only 4.4 percent of the patients were 55–64 and the oldest group (65+) comprised 2.1 percent of the clinic load. The implications of these statistics are quite clear: with increasing age postmaturity, the risk for severe psychiatric disease increases but the aged are largely underrepresented in outpatient care facilities and preventive services in their communities. The possibility exists that the aged turn instead to other social institutions and are overrepresented, receiving help from churches, medical centers, etc. This does not appear to be the case, however, and indeed if one extrapolates from the report of Ossofsky (Hearings, U. S. Senate Special Subcommittee on Aging, 1969) on Project FIND, quite the opposite may be true for the very poor aged, who, so far as social agencies are concerned, and Ostfeld's work (1966), would give little credence to the notion that health sciences are overused by older persons.

PROBLEMS IN PLANNING
FOR THE AGED

The factors responsible for this paradoxical situation are difficult to assign and research evidence is sparse. One interpretation of the disparity between psychiatric outpatient and inpatient rates may lie in self-referral as distinct from referral by others. The elements of the decision-making process in going for help have not been adequately explored. The lower level of education, the rigidities of personality, and the apparent constriction of affect (Banham, 1951) as well as a sense of loneliness, isolation (anomie), and despair would appear to lead to negative attitudes toward mental health professionals and a lower self-referral rate for mild and moderate mental illness among the aged. The historic posture toward psychiatric illness and mental health practitioner would further support a condition of fewer self-referrals by older persons.

It is, of course, possible that for aged persons the rate of mild mental illness is quite low but that there is a heightened risk of disease associated with central nervous system or organic disorders with syndromes involving dramatic and acute onsets of symptomatology identifiable as psychopathology of severe proportions and requiring institutionalization upon identification. This would explain why older persons are not likely to require or profit from outpatient care and first appear as inpatients. Unfortunately, such a simple explanation runs counter to the facts.

Referral by others involves a somewhat different set of issues. In her analysis of the factors which brought 530 elderly patients to the psychiatric screening wards of the San Francisco General Hospital, Lowenthal (1964) reported that "the most striking characteristics of these predisposing factors was their duration: two-thirds of them had prevailed for a year or more, one-third for five years or more, and only nine percent were of less than a month's duration" (page 32). It would seem that the aged do show clear signs of mental or emotional illness for some time but the capacity of the patient's social network to cope with or tolerate the symptoms of deviance or disability in older persons is fairly high. Of the precipitating causes for admission to the psychiatric ward the most frequent is "harmful behavior" and "potentially harmful behavior." Disturbances of thought or feelings or environmental factors have a relatively lower status. Excessive drinking, when listed as a predisposing factor, was the most important in 70 percent of the cases and typically considered the basis for all other symptoms. While depressive symptomatology was apparently not a particularly significant factor in the frequency count of precipitating factors, "irrational fears and thought deterioration" were given some emphasis. There were socioeconomic differences among patient categories—harmful behavior "for some time" was a background factor among the younger men of very low socioeconomic status within this geriatric group and disturbances of thought and affect was a central variable among lower and middle socioeconomic status women.

The impressive characteristic mediating admission of these older patients is the longevity of symptomatic deviance prior to hospitalization. Though a variety of social and familial supports were brought into play as the patient's problems became manifest, psychiatric help was almost judiciously avoided, even at the level of consulta-

tion to the family physician. This tendency to avoid psychiatric help persisted until some acute socially visible precipitant emerged, typically in "acting out" behavioral terms. Lowenthal further reports that by far the most prominent specific act which brought persons into contact with the psychiatric inpatient facility was harmful or potentially harmful behavior best characterized by "unmanageability." This pattern accounted for a combined total of 54 percent of all referrals. Environmental crises were responsible for 23 percent of the difficulties, and disturbances of thought and affect or physical problems the remaining 13 and ten percent of the referrals respectively. It seems fair to conclude that there was manifest denial of the symptoms of mental or emotional disorders by relatives and friends or a decided reluctance to openly label aged persons as showing signs of mental illness.

Such observations lead us to a serious dilemma. Lowenthal's findings may reflect a desirable tendency toward greater tolerance of deviant behavior among the aged on the part of relatives, neighbors, and the broader community and a reluctance to institutionalize older persons. An alternate analysis could lead to the hypothesis that denial plays a major role in our societal attitude toward mental impairment and deviance in the aged. In such a pattern, three factors could be operating: the aged person himself denying his difficulty, or denial of symptoms by the family or persons caring for the aged individual, and the larger community whose attitudes are best reflected by the attitudes and mores of the culture on the one hand and the availability of facilities on the other. Take, for example, the stance used by majority groups toward minorities. The expectation of poorer performance or disability plays an important role in protecting the majority groups from responsibility for substandard treatment or impoverishment of minority groups. This social pattern becomes most insidious when it causes the minority group to accept its inferior status and to show the "expected" deviance from the cultural norms, thereby lowering its own expectations. Thus, if the aged are supposed to be sick, to be a little senile, or to experience a "second childhood," nothing needs to be done for symptoms of depression, severe regression, or minor acting out behavior; indeed, planning for mental health care for the aged becomes an unnecessary and wasted activity, or at best, a charitable act. This expectancy pattern would also lead us to defer on the labeling of questionable behavior as deviant or as a condition which requires help or intervention.

The dilemma is this: is it more desirable to seek for a broader acceptance of individuals with some minor or moderate degree of emotional and mental disturbance, or is it more desirable to work for the early diagnosis and treatment of disorders? On a broad conceptual scale it seems simple to question the need for choosing between such alternatives; on the level of the individual, however, the situation becomes much more complex. Indeed, it should be recognized that identifying deviant individuals as disturbed or needing help could prevent progressive deterioration and permanent change, rejection from the community, serious embarrassment and self-rejection, and the amelioration of undesirable feelings and impulses on the part of many persons. The problems associated with too rapid labeling stigmatization and the fulfilling effects of social expectations of deviant behavior are also apparent. The conflict in the two approaches—acceptance of deviance and minimization of its socially undesirable consequences to the individual versus intolerance and concomitant treatment of disorders—requires continuous resolution. The distinction between stable behavior which reflects individual needs and eccentricities and that which can be identified as showing early signs of more serious disturbance can be delineated with careful scrutiny of the situation and it is necessary that we do so where such delineation has social and clinical significance. The problem of social control of deviant behavior and suppression of the individual is an important and relevant concern. Safeguards upon professional care must be imposed but the problems generated by early response to deviance cannot be used as a basis for therapeutic nihilism. It is probably the case that frequently the denial of early signs of mental illness reflects a common professional and social misconception that such illness or behavioral deviance is progressive and irreversible, and, in short, "hopeless."

A specific problem which emerges in dealing with the aged mentally ill is the relationship consistently discovered between physical and emotional pathology in the aged (Kahn, Goldfarb, Pollack, & Gerber, 1960; Rosenblum & Bachrach, 1963). This interaction warrants special considera-

tion since treatment programs established by most mental health professionals tend to focus on intrapsychic or behavioral therapies while they ignore physiological and medical difficulties in the patient. Typically, medical distress is seen as belonging to another province of patient care and often only after the patient is "medically cleared" does he get appropriate psychological help in many institutions. In recent years, the antagonism toward a "medical model" of mental illness has led to an overreaction and rejection of physical disease and medically-oriented practitioners in the field of community mental health. To this extent then the aged represent a particular enigma for many community mental health programs. Since most of the professionals in the mental health field often feel distinctly uncomfortable with medical problems, regardless of their background and training, patients who have a major component of medical disability to their problem are often rejected in favor of patients whose difficulties appear to be purely "psychosocial" or "educational" where the principles of behavior modification and psychotherapy can be said to be maximally effective.

In developing services for the aged, we must take cognizance of the attitudes of professional personnel in dealing with aged persons with mental symptoms. Sapolsky (1965) shows that patient-therapist compatibility appears to be an important predictor of hospital or therapeutic outcome. The aged patient and his doctor or therapist are considerably less compatible than doctor and younger adult patients and indeed, in one study a majority (60 percent) of older persons felt that they knew more about their own health than did most doctors (in contrast to persons 21–34, only 28 percent of whom agreed with this statement; Riley, 1968, page 319). Older persons themselves report that doctors prefer to take care of younger patients (Shanas, 1962). These data are, unfortunately, confirmed by findings which examine the attitude of health care personnel toward the aged (Spence, Feigenbaum, Fitzgerald, & Roth, 1962). Another issue resulting in poorer care for older persons resides in professional rivalries.

Such professional rivalries within a mental health center may well be exacerbated if a member of the team with a medical background, usually the psychiatrist, is placed in an apparently essential role while the nonmedical workers are given adjunct duties and find themselves uncomfortable in the diagnostic or treatment situation. Obviously, this need not be the case but such is the situation quite often and it is not particularly eased by the patient's focus on the health aspect of his problem or the family press for institutionalization in order to obtain needed care and relieve the situation in the home. It is quite clear that in many cases aged mentally ill patients are not evaluated carefully enough or with enough precision to warrant complete trust in the initial diagnosis, be it medical or psychiatric.

Based upon the existing literature and their own extensive studies, Simon, Lowenthal, and Epstein (1970) have stated that "It is obvious that the majority of elderly patients who require emergency psychiatric care in a given year are seriously in need of general medical treatment as well" (page 161). This does not obviate the need for psychiatric care or the help of the other mental health disciplines, and Simon, Lowenthal, and Epstein (1970) also point out that the mental and emotional impairment of the patient is more severe than the physical in three-fourths of the cases. The relatives and informants as well as the patients, however, present their initial complaints as physical health and self-care problems of the patient. Since problems of management and care seem more dominant than affective or emotional difficulties in predicting older patients' institutionalization, the need to recognize the patient's concerns about his health, and particularly about his ability to do things for himself as these involve the daily routine of living, must be understood. This places the mental health worker in a peculiar position since often the aged person's difficulty may reside in the persistence of life-long patterns of adaptation no longer effective in the face of changing physical or socioeconomic status. Identification of individual abilities and limitations, physical and psychological, as potential for change and the opportunities which are available (or can be made available) in the environment all become central to the understanding (diagnosis) and help (prevention-treatment) of deviant older persons. Frequently it is the failure to appreciate the abilities of the older person to care for himself and his need to do so which result in over support by the environment and regression by the older individual.

THE IMPLICATIONS OF MODELS OF MENTAL HEALTH CARE

There are two major models which may be applied to the understanding of mental illness in the aged—the medical-pathologic or the social-adaptational. It should become clear that these approaches are not mutually exclusive and that "the medical model" is no more restricted to physicians than the social-adaptational model is to social workers or sociologists.

A concern with the failures in providing a satisfactory combination of medical with psychological treatment in the care of the aged mentally ill and the prevention of mental illness in the aged should not be taken as a defense of a particular medical model. Szasz (1961) has refocused our attention on the legal versus the psychiatric and social definitions of mental illness. His arguments have particular applicability to the aged. It would appear that treatable aged mental patients may suffer from an application of an exclusively medical-pathology[1] versus social-adaptation model to their condition. The term "medical-pathology" is used here to refer to a dichotomy in the sickness-health continuum. This conceptualization presupposes that there are specific symptom clusters which may be classified into groups which have a common etiology in some discernible physical or biochemical abnormality. The concept emerged historically as a result of anatomic pathologists who defined, for the medical practitioner, a given disease based upon the status of an organ or tissue taken from a patient or former patient. Thus, a complex of symptoms in regular association with an abnormal anatomic state and related clinical (i.e., physical and laboratory) findings could be used to define a specific illness. The constancy of this complex is often such that a "diagnosis" can be made on the basis of the data from only a few of the components, e.g., symptoms reported by the patient or the physical signs derived from his examination. Indeed, the stability of the pattern of findings associated with a particular abnormal biochemical or anatomic situation frequently is such that a physical sign (or laboratory finding) could be used in the absence of symptoms to define or predict pathology, often to the surprise and consternation of the individual being evaluated. While there is no desire to challenge this approach for a large array of disease states, it has its difficulty in predicting to adaptational distress or to malaise in an individual when the lesion, or abnormal anatomic or biochemical situation, is borderline or where the physiologic toll of a particular activity is unclear. Thus, in borderline metabolic or genetic abnormalities, where an individual is environmentally well protected, no discernible effect on life-span or functional adaptational capacity may be noted. In many instances human adaptation may appear unimpaired in the face of apparent illness—given an appropriately supportive ecosystem.

An attempt to use such a pathology model for mental health or illness, however, creates very serious problems. In describing deviant behavior an observable response pattern is necessarily referred to but the definition of pathology in behavior is not nearly so obvious. Take the case of the man who fires a pistol at another. Before we can decide whether our man is "pathologically" abnormal, it is essential that we know whether he was suffering from the misconception that he was an important government official and the victim a member of a large international conspiracy out to assassinate him, after following him, observing him day and night, attempting to poison his food, etc., (and whether indeed this is not the case); or whether he had a badge in his wallet, shouted "Stop thief" several times, and fired a shot into the air before he attempted to hit his victim in the legs; or whether he was wearing a uniform including a steel helmet and appropriate insignia so that as a result of his act he would be commended by his unit commander or chief of state. In these instances, the individual act cannot be thought of as pathological or nonpathological except by reference to the total situation and frequently only by understanding its antecedents. This rather obvious example is presented only to highlight the difficulties in dealing with mental health and mental illness. Behavior then needs to be characterized not in absolute terms but in relative social and adaptational terms.

Our understanding of the dynamics of acute brain syndrome and pathologic cerebral vascular changes in reducing functional capacity needs to be more firmly established. Given the two models for understanding the behavior and adaptation in the aged, a pathology model as a basis for a strategy of detecting the extent of organic dysfunction in the aged seems legitimate. Indeed, programs involving the prevention of organic deficit and its behavioral sequelae need to be incorporated into any program for the prevention of mental illness.

It is the case, however, that the behavioral sequelae of organic or functional deficit have traditionally been subsumed under the same pathologic model. Thus, the traditional psychiatrist practitioner's role emerged from that of a state hospital superintendent who was charged with protecting society from the aberrant or "pathologic" behavior of some of its more deviant members. In the case of much mental and emotional disorder in the aged, this concept must be replaced by a social adaptational approach. There has been relatively little exploration of the extent to which patients with mild or even moderate brain damage could be helped to function better in their community using such techniques as behavior shaping, sheltered workshops, or group therapeutic experiences. Diagnoses need to be recast to assess the strengths of elderly persons, particularly in the face of inappropriate and misleading psychodiagnostic devices (Eisdorfer, 1969). It is now apparent that environmental factors are important in determining the extent of self-care and adaptation on the part of many such organically impaired individuals. Epstein and Simon (1968) have demonstrated that the placement of geriatric mentally ill patients in a state hospital or nursing home setting results in quite different consequences. It is evident that the environment established within the nursing homes leads to a greater loss of self-maintenance skills by patients and that in their follow-up study the patients in the state hospital setting appear to remain more intact. The state hospital geriatric patients were the match of the nursing home groups at the outset but a year later many more had recovered or maintained skills involved in caring for their own needs, e.g., utilization of money, grooming, and the like. The crucial role of environmental, including social, determinants upon the behavior of presumably hopeless patients has been similarly documented by Fairweather (1964) who reported upon the dramatic impact of democratization and socially relevant therapy in a hospital setting. Presumably chronically mentally ill patients who were given responsibility and authority showed marked improvement. The work of Robert Kastenbaum (1964) in introducing into a hospital setting conflicting behavior, e.g., "the cocktail hour" to alter the relationship of nurse and patient, also demonstrated conclusively that approaches involving elemental social modification may have profound effect on patient behavior and staff response even in the absence of extensive alteration of the physical environment or patient-staff ratio.

PREVENTION OF MENTAL ILLNESS AND MENTAL HEALTH MAINTENANCE

The context of the foregoing discussion should lead us to a recognition that there are superb opportunities for utilizing preventive services and intervention techniques in the clearly predictable crises in health status, retirement, the loss of loved objects, role relationships, and financial distress. Despite the predictability of age-related crises, however, research, planning, and program implementation for these events are still not frequent in mental health settings.

For the aged person in the community the disengagement concept held that the failure of older persons to remain involved in many activities is normal given the process of aging and decline and the need to conserve energy. Alternatively, one could, of course, question the subjective effect of a decline in activities and social roles on mental health and question the locus of the pressure to withdraw from involvements. Edward Albee in his play *The Sandbox* (1964) has described the situation with which many aged are presented. "Mommy and Daddy" bring "Grandma" to a sandpile on the beach to wait for her demise. As the end comes Mommy states, "It means the time has come for poor Grandma . . . and I can't bear it." Daddy's response is "I . . . suppose you've got to be brave. You'll bear up. You'll get over it." Grandma is now shoveling sand over herself and finally she exclaims, "I don't know how I'm supposed to do anything with this goddammed toy

shovel. . . ." Thus, the loss of social roles by the older person and his loss of control over significant environmental variables puts him in the position of being useless. Because he is mourned far before he is dead, his mourners can justify depriving him of those social and psychological tools necessary to keep him viably alive. Albee seems to be suggesting that we do not even provide the aged with the most basic means to cope with the world nor indeed even to exit from it.

The "activity" concept holds that the aged would be active if they were given the opportunity but, in our culture, they are deprived of the tools and roles which allow for the expression of their needs. An activity theory orientation would indeed have striking implications for an approach to the mental health of older persons in programming for their later years. One implication of such a concept would suggest reallocation of our resources. Thus, we should allot far more funds for leisure activities in later life, and part-time employment rather than full retirement should be the norm. Programs should turn to aged volunteers for their assistance and involvement and an attitude toward the aged as participator rather than observer needs to be pursued. Perhaps the major difficulty is that of accepting the aged and their heightened degree of participation in community and social activity. The tendency of older persons to interact more with age-related peers (Rosow, 1967) may reflect this complex "ageism" as well as personal preference. Certainly at this time many older Americans prefer to live among their age peers.

In a valuable reformulation of one aspect of social theory, Weiss (1969) suggested that perhaps in concerning ourselves with role theory we have forgotten the interactional components and their effect on the individual. As he points out, roles may have greater specificity than we have appreciated. The notion that the role of spouse is equivalent to the role of friend or acquaintance is erroneous and, in fact, replacement of one with the other is not a satisfactory trade-off. The social roles reflect a variety of individual needs. Thus, the need for someone or something to nurture may not be replaced by the healthy interaction with a peer. Intimacy needs which may be filled by a spouse, a very close friend, or indeed a "confidant" may not at all be satisfied by a heightened number of superficial social contacts and roles. This pattern of fulfillment of personal needs in the context of the individual's ecosystem has been relatively little explored so far as the aged are concerned. While we consider losses as potential crises, there has been surprisingly little evaluation of the specific context of losses to the individual and its meaning to him in coping with the world and with his own internal state. As a parallel, defined patterns of behavior of an individual may be appropriate to specific interpersonal needs and have significant symbolic status. This author would suggest that self-help activities are fundamental to the ego-integrity of an adult and that the loss of basic self-help skills, or the loss of opportunity to exercise these skills, will be marked by ego regression. A most significant feature should be pointed out in describing the aged. It is the case that following maturity the variance in a given population increases with the age of that population. These psychologic differences tend to increase with advancing age and older individuals are a more varied group. It is then even more difficult to make generalizations about this population and to provide one formulation and one set of alternatives for their needs. The difficulties would appear to be better resolved with more, rather then fewer, options.

In an attempt to study the effects of preretirement counseling, Greene et al. (1969) found that for retirees finances, health, activities, attitudes about retirement planning, morale, and job skill level all appeared to be definitely related to postretirement adjustment. Setting up a prediction model based on a factor analytic scheme, they discovered that attitude toward health stereotypes and the number of activities engaged in and attitude toward the company were the most closely related to adjustment and explained 53 percent of the variance. A complicating issue was that the number of activities was highly correlated with planning and that health stereotypes and activities were all related to finance and morale. Thus, all of these issues could be said to account for predicting adjustment.

In predicting "resistance" to retirement on the part of workers, the crucial variables appear to be plans for retirement, attitudes toward health, stereotypes of retirement, and enjoyment of present activities. Low morale appears to be a product of high resistance and the imminence of retirement rather than the basis for the resistance.

The most important finding of this study, however, may lie in the difference found between subjective and objective state in predicting to retirement. While the several hundred retirees studied accurately assessed their expected income, they were unrealistic about the "adequacy" of that income. "Adequacy" calls for a subjective judgment. Employees awaiting retirement typically were hoping for the best, irrespective of their degree of resistance to retirement. Surprisingly, a larger percentage of retirement resistors reported high expectation (based on blind optimism) while it was the nonresistors (who also turned out to be the planners) who based their report of expectations on a more realistic planning. Thus, on many subjective variables there was a higher expectation on the part of the potential resistors than on the part of the nonresistors. Overall, however, the impressive extent of the overoptimism (denial?) of employees is indicated by the finding that only ten percent of the total group expected their income in retirement to be less than adequate, but to questions concerning the adequacy of their current income, about 90 percent felt it either to be just adequate or inadequate. This is an impressive distortion on the part of the preretirees who expect their future income levels (certain to be reduced) to be "adequate" when current level of income is "just adequate" or "less than adequate." These authors suggest that resistance to retirement is characterized by a high degree of "wishful thinking" which allows the potential retiree to rationalize away the need for planning, and even the need to admit that someday soon he must retire. They further question the validity of current patterns of preretirement counseling because they fail to confront the resistors with a more realistic view of his present and future needs. Indeed, while those who partook of it praised preretirement counseling, they appeared to have done very little by way of planning based on the counseling sessions.

While the investigators do not discuss their finding in psychodynamic terms, the parallels between resistance to retirement and what could be called denial is obvious. It is reasonable to suppose that such a pattern of denial leads to difficulty in the retirement years. While the data on adaptation to retirement are equivocal and leave unanswered the question of whether indeed there is significant psychological crisis postretirement (Eisdorfer, in press), one such retirement syndrome has been reported. Berkey and Stroebner (1968) found that for career army officers forced to retire because of failure to reach the rank of full colonel by a specified period, a crisis with associated anxiety, depression, and somatic complaints was apparent. This is similar to the findings reported for the middle-level white collar worker who appears to show the greatest difficulty during the early retirement years.

A point of some concern in dealing with approaches toward maintenance of mental health and the prevention of mental illness is the previously cited relationship between mental health and the practical issues of living as these are perceived by older persons. The data on retirement would indicate that financial status pre- and postretirement may be the best single predictor of adaptation postretirement (Eisdorfer, in press). Such a finding is reminiscent of the report by Leighton (1965) on the high degree of relationship between poverty and mental health in the community of his group so carefully studied.

Chronic illness affects more than three-fourths of the population over 65 (Terry, 1961) and large segments of the middle aged community have similar health problems. It is clear that chronic physical illnesses have a decided emotional concomitant. Bogdonoff and Nichols (1960) describe the process as a six-stage progression. First there is a functional abnormality of an organ or system identified by person, physician, or both. The second stage involves a shift in the patient's previous activity pattern with discomfort associated with attempts to return to previous behavior. The next stage involves the patient's social network which necessarily changes as a result. Phase four is the patient's recognition that there is no solution to his situation in the foreseeable future. In the fifth phase, the patient tries new adaptive measures in response to his altered psychological state and a need to reduce the stress of his illness. The sixth and final stage is reached as a consequence of the patient's upset and his attempts to reestablish his equilibrium physically and psychologically. As a result of his turmoil affective changes including anxiety and depression as well as a feeling of helplessness ensue.

Perhaps the most impressive feature of this reaction pattern is the failure of physicians caring for the chronically ill or of the mental health professionals to be more actively involved with the psychological difficulties of this group which constitutes a heightened risk for mental illness.

Busse (1962) suggests that physician self-esteem is lowered by the failure of chronically ill patients to improve and that chronically ill patients rarely show appreciation to the physician. Eisdorfer (1969) points out that often aged chronically ill patients have outlived their physician and have considerable difficulty in finding a doctor to take care of them in anything more than a perfunctory and technical manner.

In this context, it should be noted that the sick role is preferred by many as an alternative to the "aged role." Such a shift leads to many complications. For one, it may unnecessarily restrict activity and involvement to a degree greater than necessary in terms of physical incapacity; for another, it may result in a tendency toward high bodily concern or hypochondriasis as a mode of coping with the world (Busse, 1962).

The high bodily concern often leading to hypochondriasis and the depression most often accompanying physical loss, real or apparent, are amenable to intervention techniques. Indeed, with appropriate care at the time of the physical work-up and diagnosis such behavior-shaping consequences can be modified. This constitutes a challenge for the mental health professional in the community. Relationships between the community mental health program and the total health care system of the area must be close with good communication between them. The health care agents for older persons and the chronically ill should be a special target for education and consultation by mental health professionals in dealing with the crises of adult life and the aged. Combining the talents of health and mental health systems in affecting the social welfare and other community facilities may also prove essential in an effort to improve the environment of those in need. Crisis intervention for the emotional concomitants of chronic physical illness, particularly for the aged, is a very significant practical alternative to the extensive use of medical and long-term mental institutional services by the aged. There is a dramatic need, in addition, for a community mental health strategy to operate effectively in the social system in which so much of the care of older persons is, or should be, taking place.

CONCLUSION

We are failing to meet the needs of a large portion of our population. The data on utilizaton of outpatient psychiatric and community mental health services for older persons in the light of institutional admissions, and the extent of the needs of this group, may reflect less a failure of the mental health profession alone than of the larger segment of the community's social, welfare, and health services. It is more probable that it signals the lack of enthusiasm on the part of any of these groups for coping with the problems of the aged. Until there is an open reappraisal of the role of the aged in our culture, it may be expected that the tendency to ignore the mildly deviant and to incarcerate, "nurse," and infantalize the more deviant or dependent aged person will continue to occur. Perhaps it is symptomatic of a more serious deficit in the state of the community at large that the potential contributions of any portion of the population is negated in favor of benign rejection.

Note

At the time of writing, Carl Eisdorfer was Director, Center for the Study of Aging and Human Development, and Professor of Psychiatry and Professor and Head, Division of Medical Psychology, Duke University.

1. This author holds little brief for the unspecified term "medical model" since there are a multiplicity of models used in medicine, conceptual as well as applied.

References

Albee, E. *Sandbox and the death of Bessie Smith.* New York: New American Library, 1964.

Axelrod, S., & Eisdorfer, C. Attitudes toward old people: An empirical analysis of the stimulus-group validity of the Tuckman-Lorge Questionnaire. *Journal of Gerontology*, 1961, 16, 75–80.

Banham, K. M. Senescence and the emotions: A genetic theory. *Journal of Genetic Psychology*, 1951, 78, 175–183.

Berkey, B. R., & Stroebner, J. B. The retirement syndrome: A previously unreported variant. *Military Medicine*, 1968, 133(1), 5–8.

Bogdonoff, M. D., & Nichols, C. R. Perspectives of chronic illness. *Journal of the American Medical Association*, 1960, 174, 1936–1938.

Bold new approach. (Movie) Mental Health Film Board, 1966. (Made by Affiliated Film Board, 62 min. Sd. B. & W. 16mm., with the cooperation of the National Institute of Mental Health, Bethesda, Maryland.)

Brotman, H. B. The older worker in 1965. In *Useful Fact No. 5.* Washington, D. C.: Administration on Aging, United States Department of Health, Education, and Welfare, 1966.

Busse, E. W. Some emotional complications of chronic disease. *The Gerontologist*, 1962, 2(3), 153–156.

Busse, E. W. Therapeutic implications of basic research with the aged. (Strecker Monograph Series. No. IV): Institute of Pennsylvania Hospital, 1967.

Butler, R. N. Need for commission on mental health and illness of the aging and retired. (Letter to the Editor) *Journal of the American Geriatrics Society*, 1970, 18(7), 555–556.

Committee on Research and Development Goals in Social Gerontology. The status of research in applied social gerontology. *The Gerontologist*, 1969, 9(4), Part II.

Cumming, E., & Henry, W. E. *Growing old: The process of disengagement.* New York: Basic Books, 1961.

Dohrenwend, B. P., & Dohrenwend, B. S. *Social status and psychological disorder.* New York: Wiley-Interscience, 1969.

Eisdorfer, C. Intellectual and cognitive changes in the aged. In E. W. Busse & E. Pfeiffer (eds.), *Behavior and adaptation in late life.* Boston: Little, Brown, 1969. (a)

Eisdorfer, C. Observations on medical care of the aged. In R. R. Boyd & C. H. Oakes (eds.), *Foundations of practical gerontology.* Columbia, S. C.: University of South Carolina Press, 1969. (b)

Eisdorfer, C. On the issue of relevance in research. (The 1969 Robert W. Kleemeier Award Lecture) *The Gerontologist*, 1970, 10(1), 5–10.

Eisdorfer, C. Retirement: Psychological perspectives. In F. Carp (Ed.), *Framework for retirement.* New York: Behavior Science Publications, 1970, in press.

Epstein, L. J., & Simon, A. Alternatives to state hospitalization for the geriatric mentally ill. *American Journal of Psychiatry*, 1968, 124(7), 955–961.

Fairweather, G. W. *Social psychology in treating mental illness: An experimental approach.* New York: Wiley, 1964.

Greene, M. R., Pyron, H. C., Manion, U. V., & Winklevoss, H. *Preretirement counseling, retirement adjustment and the older employee: An experimental study measuring the interrelationship of factors affecting retirement adjustment, resistance to retirement, and the effectiveness of the older employee.* Washington, D. C.: Administration on Aging, Social and Rehabilitative Service, United States Department of Health, Education, and Welfare, 1969.

Havighurst, R. J. Research and Development Goals in Social Gerontology, *Gerontologist*, 1969, 9, chapter 4.

Kahn, R. L., Goldfarb, A. I., Pollack, M., & Gerber, I. E. The relationship of mental and physical status in institutionalized aged persons. *American Journal of Psychiatry*, 1960, 117, 120–124.

Kastenbaum, R., & Slater, P. E. Effects of wine on the interpersonal behavior of geriatric patients: An exploratory study. In R. Kastenbaum (ed.), *New thoughts on old age.* New York: Springer, 1964.

Kramer, M., Taube, C., & Starr, S. Patterns of use of psychiatric facilities by the aged: Current status trends and implications. In, *Psychiatric Research Report 23.* Washington, D. C.: American Psychiatric Association, 1968.

Kreps, J. M., et al. Economics of aging: Toward a full share in abundance. Part I of Survey Hearing before the Special Committee on Aging, United States Senate, Washington, D. C., April 1969.

Leighton, A. H. Poverty and social change. *Scientific American*, 1965, 212(5), 21–27.

Lowenthal, M. F. *Lives in distress: The paths of the elderly to the psychiatric ward.* New York: Basic Books, 1964.

Lowenthal, M. F., & Haven, C. Interaction and adaptation: Intimacy as a critical variable. *American Sociological Review*, 1968, 33(1), 22–30.

Maddox, G., & Eisdorfer, C. Some correlates of activity and morale among the elderly. *Social Forces*, 1962, 40, 254–260.

Ossofsky, J. Hearing before the Special Committee on Aging, United States Senate. Ninety-First Congress, 1st session, Part 8, Nat. Organization, Washington, D. C., October 29, 1969.

Ostfeld, A. Frequency and nature of health problems of retired persons. In F. M. Carp (ed.), *The retirement process.* Bethesda, Md.: National Institute of Child Health and Human Development, United States Public Health Service, 1966.

Outpatient psychiatric services, 1967. (Mental health statistics, Series A, No. 5; Public Health Service Publication No. 19. National Clearinghouse for Mental Health Information, National Institute of Mental Health) Washington, D. C.: United States Government Printing Office, August 1969.

Palmore, E. Sociological aspects of aging. In E. W. Busse & E. Pfeiffer (eds.), *Behavior and adaptation in late life.* Boston: Little, Brown, 1969.

Pasamanik, B., Roberts, D. W., LemKau, P. W., & Krueger, D. B. A survey of mental disease in an urban population: Prevalence by race and income. In B. Pasamanick (ed.), *Epidemiology of mental disorder.*

Washington, D. C.: American Association for Advancement of Science, 1959.

Redick, R. Age, Sex, Diagnostic Distributions of Additions to Community Mental Health Centers, 1968. Statistical Note 13, National Clearing House for Mental Health Information: Biometry Branch, N.I.M.H., January 1970.

Resnik, H. L. P., & Kantor, J. M. Suicide and aging. *Journal of the American Geriatric Society*, 1970, 7, 152–158.

Rosenblum, M. P., & Bachrach, D. L. Study of behavioral aspects of the aging psychiatric patient. *Geriatrics*, 1963, 18, 247–250.

Sapolsky, A. Relationship between patient-doctor compatibility, mutual perception, and outcome of treatment. *Journal of Abnormal Psychology*, 1965, 70, 70–76.

Shanas, E. *The health of older people: A social survey.* Cambridge: Harvard University Press, 1962.

Simon, A., Lowenthal, M. F., & Epstein, L. *Crisis and intervention: The fate of the elderly mental patient.* San Francisco: Jossey-Bass, 1970.

Spence, D L., Feigenbaum, E. M., Fitzgerald, F., & Roth, J. Medical student attitudes toward the geriatric patient. *Journal of the American Geriatric Society*, 1968, 16, No. 9.

Srole, L., Langner, T. S., Michael, S. T., Opler, M. K., & Rennie, T. A. C. *Mental health in the metropolis: The Midtown Manhattan Study.* Vol. 1. New York: McGraw-Hill, 1962.

Szasz, T. S. *The myth of mental illness: Foundations of a theory of personal conduct.* New York: Hoeber-Harper, 1961.

Terry, L. L. Health needs of the nation. *Public Health Report*, 1961, 76, No. 10.

Tuckman, J., & Lorge, I. When aging begins. & Stereotypes about aging. *Journal of Gerontology*, 1953, 8(4), 489–492.

Weiss, R. S. The fund of sociability. *Trans-action*, 1969, 6(9), 36–40.

16

Prevention of Alcoholism

Thomas F. A. Plaut

CLARIFICATION OF TERMS: ALCOHOL PROBLEMS, DRINKING PROBLEMS, AND ALCOHOLISM

In any field where "common sense" and personal experience overlap with scientific and professional concerns, there are bound to be serious problems of terminology. When, in addition, attitudes about the topic are emotionally charged and deeply rooted in the culture, matters of definition loom even more important. These problems are graphically highlighted by the subject of alcohol use and abuse. The only constitutional amendment that ever was repealed was the Prohibition Amendment. Clearly then, behavior and attitudes regarding alcohol occupy a unique but rarely understood position in contemporary American society.

The term "alcoholism" generally refers to the most pathological and destructive types of drinking. Emphasis is placed on deviant types of drinking behavior and particularly on "loss of control."

Historically, viewing alcoholism as a "disease" or "illness" has been of great significance in developing more professionalized and scientific approaches to this problem area. It has functioned as a "legitimizing" slogan and also has helped speed the removal of discriminatory practices in hospital policy and insurance coverage. In the continuing efforts to remove alcoholism from the domain of "preaching" and "punishing," emphasis has been placed on assimilating alocholism to the classical medical model of disease. The belief that physiological factors underlie the drinking behav-

ior of alcoholics has supported the use of this label. However, despite considerable research, no metabolic or physiological factors have yet been discovered which differentiate alcoholics from social drinkers. Furthermore, reports of "alcoholics" who are able to engage in "normal drinking" following treatment also cast some doubts upon narrowly conceived notions of alcoholism as a "disease" (Pattison et al., 1968, p. 610).

Numerous recent attempts at defining alcoholism have focused on impaired social functioning. Reference here particularly is to the ability of the person to be effective in his community, in his job, or home situation. One recent report (*Alcohol Problems, 1967*) goes further and proposes a virtual abandoning of the term "alcoholism" and a substituting of the term "problem drinker." In this view a "problem drinker" is any individual whose drinking causes substantial harm to himself or others. Such socially oriented definitions clearly represent a substantial departure from classical medical models. Others still stress a predominantly disease-oriented conception (Keller & McCormick, 1968, p. 14). Persons advocating the newer terminology are confronted with a difficult dilemma by recent legal efforts to find alternatives to the "revolving door" method of handling chronic alcoholics. The strategy being used in these legal approaches[1] emphasizes that chronic alcoholics are "sick people" totally unable to control their drinking. It clearly would be far more difficult to obtain the desired court action if socially-oriented rather than medically-oriented definitions were emphasized.

"Alcoholism" or "problem drinking" represents only a fraction of the totality of "alcohol problems" which abound in American society. The heritage of the Temperance Movement and of Prohibition is evident everywhere (see p. 426). The term "alcohol problems" is increasingly being used to include such diverse phenomena as disagreement about appropriate penalties for drunk drivers, legislative and public controversy regarding minimum age for drinking, conflict within school systems and communities about "alcohol education," confusion regarding the role of drinking in crime and civil disorders, student conflict with college administration regarding drinking rules, and informal agreements between the alcoholic beverage industry and the television industry regarding the nature of advertisement of distilled spirits on TV. Many of these "alcohol problems" involve basic disagreement regarding the nature of drinking, appropriate and inappropriate uses of alcoholic beverages, and the relationship between drinking and other forms of socially approved or disapproved behavior. An important element underlying the relatively limited attention that alcoholism and other drinking problems have received and the continuing ambivalence and even rejection practiced by many "helping agencies" towards these persons is the fact that virtually all Americans, whether they are "problem drinkers," social drinkers, or abstainers, relate in curiously ambivalent ways to the whole subject of drinking. Furthermore, the evident fact for most Americans who drink (these, of course, constitute a vast majority of all adult Americans) that they have no difficulty in controlling their drinking behavior often makes it hard for them to understand the drinking behavior of other individuals, i.e., "alcoholics" or "problem drinkers" who seem to have such difficulty avoiding destructive and socially damaging uses of alcohol. The residual moralistic views of drinking and drunkenness, together with the uncertainty whether problem drinkers could really "control their drinking" if they wanted to, contribute greatly to the ambivalence regarding these persons.

MAGNITUDE OF DRINKING PROBLEMS

Large numbers of problem drinkers are "known to" various community helping agencies. For example, over one-quarter (27 percent) of the men admitted to the nearly 300 state mental hospitals in the United States each year are diagnosed as "alcoholics" (Patients in State and County Mental Hospitals–1967, p. 21). In recent years more psychiatric patients of all kinds have been admitted to the psychiatric wards of general hospitals than to state mental hospitals. However, here too, the proportion of male patients admitted to these community-based psychiatric facilities who are diagnosed as alcoholics is about 25 percent. These figures are not meant to suggest that the bulk of state hospitals or psychiatric wards in general hospitals are providing adequate care and treatment for alcoholics. Unfortunately, with a small but increasing number of exceptions, this certainly is not the case. Less than 10 percent of the male patients seen in general psychiatric clinics are diagnosed as alcoholics. Nevertheless, the total number of alcoholic patients receiving treatment in adult psychiatric clinics exceeds 20,000 per year.

Not only do very large numbers of "problem drinkers" appear in the emergency wards of general hospitals but a surprisingly large proportion of patients admitted to the medical and surgical wards of hospitals turn out also to have serious drinking problems. In one study of 100 consecutive male admissions to a general hospital (Pearson, 1962), over one-quarter of the patients could readily be classified as "alcoholics" and another nine percent had serious drinking problems but the information was incomplete. In this hospital there was no psychiatric service and no preselection had been made in terms of the admitting causes or diagnosis of the patient. Several studies undertaken of public welfare caseloads indicate that serious drinking problems are found in between ten to 25 percent of all households involved. (See Plaut, 1967, pp. 43–44.) As in the previously reported study of general hospitals, this is not to suggest necessarily that the drinking problem was the cause of the economic dependency. However, such reports do confirm that a very sizeable proportion of problem drinkers are "known" to various health and welfare agencies.

A significant and highly visible kind of drinking problem is public drunkenness. Close to 40 percent of the more than five million arrests made in the country each year are for the offense of public drunkenness. (See *Task Force report: Drunkenness*, 1967.) While Skid Row "alcoholics" constitute only a small proportion (probably less than ten percent) of all alcoholics, they do constitute a highly visible and distressing problem for most communities. Finally, there is the very significant relationship between drinking and motor vehicle accidents. (See Bacon, 1968, and *Alcohol and Highway Safety Report*, 1968.) A sizeable proportion of persons involved in fatal motor vehicle accidents (ranging from 25 to 40 percent) are found to have extremely high blood alcohol levels. Whereas formerly it was believed that the bulk of persons involved in alcohol-related motor vehicle accidents were "social drinkers," it now appears that this is not the case. Both in terms of the high blood alcohol levels and in terms of other social and demographic characteristics, it is clear that persons with serious drinking problems are tremendously over-represented among any population of drinking drivers involved in accidents.

Although the precise number of problem drinkers is not known—both because of difficulties of case finding and lack of agreement on definition—clearly such individuals exist in large numbers in the contemporary United States. Problem drinking is a major social problem that until recently had received extremely little attention.

AN OVERVIEW OF PREVENTION

The concept of prevention, as it is used in the field of public health, refers to reductions in rates of some illness or other undesirable condition. Traditionally, of course, public health has been concerned with environmental sanitation and infectious illnesses. It is only recently that any stress has been placed on the prevention of chronic illnesses or other conditions. Modifying dangerous or potentially harmful characteristics of the environment or protecting large groups of persons through immunization have been the traditional approaches in public health. Some such activities have been based on rather complete knowledge of the total disease process. Examples include the control of poliomyelitis and the virtual elimination of amebic dysentery in the United States. Other significant public health programs, however, have

been developed in the absence of any complete understanding of the "disease process." Sometimes it is possible to significantly influence the rate of a phenomena by appropriate interventions even if the total causal chain of events is not entirely understood. For example, the reduction of oxygen concentration in incubators used for premature infants turned out to be a significant means of reducing cases of retrolental fibroplasia. This interventive method was based on epidemiological findings rather than on any clinical investigation of the precise factors which accounted for the retinal damage in tiny newborns. Similarly, the utilization of artificial fluoridation of water supplies has turned out to be an extremely effective method of preventing dental caries. Observations on differential rates of caries in communities with naturally high and low rates of fluoride in the water supply immediately suggested this public health program.

The general theory underlying such approaches is that modification of certain environmental factors or "experiences" impinging on large numbers of persons may significantly reduce *rates* of a particular illness or condition. This can occur although the particular factor affected is not the single or even principal cause of the illness or other condition. Clearly this type of prevention is rather unlikely to completely eliminate a disease but nevertheless it can substantially reduce the rates.

When public health concepts, originally developed around infectious and communicable disorders, are applied to chronic illnesses and behavioral problems, the resultant programs often will take radically different forms than traditional public health programs. Thus, when one talks about the "prevention" of poverty or of juvenile delinquency or even of a war, this introduces a host of factors which traditionally have not been seen as lying within the purview of public health. The area of drinking problems, involving as it does at least some medical aspects, is in a sense a bridge between more orthodox public health approaches and far broader ones which at times appear indistinguishable from social change. Modification of social attitudes and alteration in social behavior are essential components in reducing the occurrence of many contemporary problems. Still unresolved, however, is the extent to which planned efforts at such changes can really be effective. Clearly, prevention within the social change model represents a substantial departure from earlier public health models which placed primary stress on modifications of host, agent, and environment.

THE SOCIAL CONTEXT OF ALCOHOL USE

Historical Elements of Alcohol Use in the United States

The 18th Amendment prohibited the manufacture, sale, or transportation of alcoholic beverages in the United States. It was repealed by the 21st Amendment in 1933. The Temperance Movement began nearly 100 years before the passage of the 18th Amendment. Thus, this Amendment did not represent primarily an impetuous response to World War I but rather the culmination of scores of years of energetic work by a very broad segment of the American population.

About 1825, relatively small temperance groups began to develop in the United States. Their initial emphasis was only on abstinence from distilled spirits. However, within 20 years the Bible had been "reinterpreted" so that the "wines" referred to in it were considered unfermented. With this reinterpretation of biblical teachings, it became possible for some early temperance workers to advocate total abstinence on moral grounds.

In the 15-year period between 1845 and 1860, 13 states passed statewide prohibition laws. However, after the Civil War all of the states except Maine either repealed these laws or had them declared unconstitutional. The period immediately following the Civil War also marked a great growth of the liquor business. Within ten years after the end of the Civil War, the Prohibition Party and the Women's Christian Temperance Union were organized. However, it was not until 1893 that the Anti-Saloon League was formed. Before the Prohibition Party was founded, efforts were made to get the Democrats and Republicans to consider inclusion of prohibition planks in their national platforms.

The early years of the Temperance Movement, i.e., between about 1850 and 1900, were marked by a far broader concern than merely abuse surrounding beverage alcohol. Many of the persons identified with the Women's Christian Temperance Union, and the organization itself, sought to achieve a range of social and economic reforms. These included such matters as improved penal institutions, shorter working hours, abolition of child labor, defending the right of unions to strike, Women's Suffrage, the graduated income tax, government ownership of railroads, and the direct election of members of the U.S. Senate. Frequently, temperance groups were concerned also about other issues and certainly throughout the latter years of the 19th century most of the leaders of the Temperance Movement were also in leadership positions regarding other "social reforms."

A recent student of this period has described the Temperance Movement as follows:

It is the breadth of the temperance movements in the late 19th century which is so impressive. Almost every progressive, radical, or conservative movement had some alliance with it. Populists and Progressives, labor and farmer, urban and rural, male and female, Christian and secularist had for some reason or opportunity to be an adherent or a sympathizer in the temperance movement. To belong to one was not to be disloyal to the other. The overlapping of conservative, progressive, and radical is the outstanding quality of the Movement in this period of history (Gusfield, 1962 p. 111).

Around the turn of the century, the Movement had become considerably more focused in its efforts. For example, the Women's Christian Temperance Union now was concerned only about alcoholic beverages. The Anti-Saloon League placed primary emphasis on the holding of local elections in which communities would vote on whether or not to "go dry." Long before the entry of the United States into World War I, there already was widespread antialcohol sentiment in the United States. For example, in 1913, the Webb-Kenyon law was passed by Congress. This law provided that no alcoholic beverages could be shipped from "wet" to "dry" states.

In 1913, a "Prohibition Amendment" did pass the House of Representatives but it fell far short of the required two-thirds vote. In 1917, the year the United States entered World War I, statewide prohibition was voted in Indiana, New Hampshire, Utah, and New Mexico. In the same year it was soundly defeated in Missouri and California and, by a close vote, in Minnesota. By the end of that year, Prohibition was the law in 25 out of 48 States. And, by 1918, still prior to the national Prohibition Amendment, Florida, Nevada, Ohio, Texas, and Wyoming had also voted for prohibition. At the federal level, Congressional action prohibited the manufacture of whiskey after September 8, 1917. The Prohibition Amendment became effective on January 16, 1920, and at this time 85 percent of all the counties in the United States were already "dry" and these counties included 63 percent of the total population of the country. Eventually, all of the 48 States except for Connecticut and Rhode Island voted for enactment of this Amendment. Thus, almost exactly 100 years after the initiation of the first temperance activities, America was embarked on what many have called the greatest "social experiment" of modern times.

In the fall of 1919, the Volstead Enforcement Act was passed by Congress over President Wilson's veto. This set up details for enforcement and defined the terms included in the constitutional amendment. For example an "intoxicating beverage" was specified as any beverage which was one-half of one percent of alcohol by volume. Because of the very magnitude of the problems involved, the Act ran into administrative difficulties almost from its inception. For example, federal-state-local cooperation in enforcement was always on a shaky and uncertain basis. There had been just too long a history of limited cooperation between these agencies. Local, state, and even the federal courts were soon flooded with cases involving enforcement of the Act. Although both the United States Supreme Court and lower jurisdictions repeatedly sustained local governments and Congress in their exercise of fullest enforcement powers, it rapidly became clear that the enforcement of the Act would be extremely difficult. Little or no stress was placed on educational approaches and all emphasis was focused on enforcement. A rather extensive illicit bootlegging business soon developed. Clearly, such an enterprise could not have survived in the absence of illegal purchases by otherwise law-abiding citizens of large amounts of alcoholic beverages. Increasing concern about these matters led President Hoover in May 1929 to appoint the Wickersham Commission on Law Observance and Enforcement. This Commission held widely publicized hearings which highlighted both the widespread violations of the Volstead Act and the inadequacies of enforcement measures. Although the final report of the Commission in early 1931 did not urge repeal of the Amendment, it was

highly critical of enforcement measures and implied that their future success was quite uncertain.

In the nearly two years between the creation of this Commission and its report, there was a substantial increase in opposition to the Prohibition Amendment. While, in part, this represented the successful activities of advocates of Repeal, it also reflected a change in the opinion of many highly significant American leaders who previously had favored Prohibition. An increasing number of adherents were being won to the view that the sale of beer and light wines should be sanctioned while distilled spirits and the saloon should continue to be prohibited.

In 1928, both party platforms spoke only of enforcement of the Volstead Act (although Alfred Smith—Democratic candidate for President—personally was in favor of Repeal). However, two years later one-quarter of the State party platforms opposed the Prohibition Amendment. By 1932, the Democratic Convention was unequivocally for Repeal and the Republicans urged revision of the Amendment but actually were very split on this issue. In February 1933, the United States Senate and House of Representatives urged adoption of the Repeal Amendment. In less than ten months this Amendment had been ratified by the necessary 36 states. It failed of ratification in only two states where it was considered (North Carolina and South Carolina).

One of the most controversial aspects of the whole Prohibition period has to do with the effects of the Amendment and the Volstead Act. It does appear, from relatively "soft" and incomplete data, that certain types of drinking problems were reduced—at least during the early years. For example, arrests for public drunkenness and alcoholic admissions to mental hospitals were substantially lower during the early Prohibition years. However, these changes may have been mainly a continuation of previous long-term trends and probably also reflected differences in law enforcement and hospital admission practices. However, it was also clear that large numbers of Americans now drank "illegally" where previously most of them had drunk in conformity with the law. In addition, it is the general impression that drinking by youth increased substantially. Whether the growth of organized crime would have occurred even in the absence of Prohibition is, of course, impossible to determine. During the Prohibition years and thereafter, both opponents and proponents marshalled much evidence pointing to the economic effects of Prohibition. However, there is an amazing lack of any convincing data on this question.

Prohibition was in effect from January 1920 until December 1933–just six weeks short of 14 years. There is no question that this issue was more bitterly debated in the United States than any since the time of slavery. Although the "anti-alcohol" position has few adherents at present, it should not be forgotten that a very large number of highly idealistic persons worked for Prohibition in the half century or so following the Civil War.

While originally the advocates of Repeal wanted only the return of beer and low alcohol content wines, in 1931 there came for the first time the realization that total Repeal would be possible. The 21st Amendment in actuality was an extremely broad grant of authority to the states. For all practical purposes it removed the federal government from regulating the conditions of the manufacture and sale of alcoholic beverages. Less than 30 years after Repeal, the sale of alcoholic beverages was again legal in all states of the Union.

By the mid 1960s, over two-thirds of all adult Americans reported that they drank alcoholic beverages. Of the remaining 25 to 30 percent, probably less than half could be considered "anti-alcohol" in the sense that they had strong sentiments for a return to total prohibition. The period since World War II has seen an increasing proportion of local option elections resulting in defeat for the "drys." For example, liquor-by-the-drink was recently approved in Iowa and Virginia.

In the years following Repeal, particularly since World War II, the Temperance Movement has been primarily linked to small town, rural values and defense of an extremely conservative economic order. Whereas previously the Temperance Movement had had substantial upper middle class support, it now represents mainly a lower middle class fundamentalist right wing group.

Heritage of the Prohibition Controversy

Although more than 35 years have now passed since repeal of the Prohibition Amendment in December 1933, the residual effects of this long-standing controversy are still evident in many aspects of contemporary American culture. Every year "local option" elections are held in numerous communities to determine whether or not "liquor-by-the-drink" shall be permitted in that jurisdiction. Although these "minicontroversies" rarely excite the emotion that characterize earlier Prohibition elections, they do serve to keep alive the strange ambivalence about drinking that exists in the United States. Local, state, and national laws, regulations, and policies regarding the sale and advertising of alcoholic beverages are an amazing mixture of contradictory and haphazard approaches to the subject of alcoholic beverage control. They both reflect and reinforce the confusion in the United States regarding whether or not it is acceptable to drink, under what circumstances drinking is acceptable, who should be permitted to drink, what kinds of drinking behavior ought to be sanctioned, and which should be prohibited.

All 50 of the states have laws regarding the purchase of alcoholic beverages by youngsters. Some states also prohibit the serving of alcoholic beverages to youngsters by adults–including their own parents! This latter type of law, however, obviously is rarely enforced. One of the most effective ways of removing such legislation probably would be to demand its enforcement. Some states distinguish between distilled spirits and beers and wines; others apply the minimum age uniformly to all three types of alcoholic beverages. Until recently, only in New York and Louisiana were youngsters permitted to purchase all alcoholic beverages at the age of 18. In other states (South Carolina, Kansas, Ohio and West Virginia, for example) beer can be purchased at 18. In the District of Columbia and Wisconsin both beer and light wines are available at 18. Until recently, in the state of North Carolina the minimum age for the purchase of all alcoholic beverages was 21, except that unmarried women could purchase liquor at the age of 17! Quite likely this law reflected some linkage in the public's mind between drinking behavior and sexual behavior.

In a number of states "liquor-by-the-drink" can be sold only in places that also provide food. Recently, for example, in "local option" elections held in Virginia, voters determined whether or not their community was going to permit liquor to be sold only by restaurants. It was further specified that each such establishment must gross at least 50 percent of its business from food rather than from alcoholic beverages. In North Dakota, on the other hand, places with a liquor license are only permitted to sell food of "inconsiderable size or amount."[2] States—and communities—vary greatly also in the hours which liquor stores and bars are permitted to remain open. Although strong feelings generally arise when efforts are made to modify any of these laws or regulations, conclusive or even persuasive evidence regarding the impact of such regulations on actual drinking behavior is virtually nonexistent.

The ambivalence and confusion regarding drinking is perhaps nowhere seen more dramatically than in advertising policies and practices. For example, although beer and wine are frequently advertised on television—everyone of the major league baseball teams has a brewery as one of the sponsors for its games—even a cursory examination of these television commercials demonstrates their artificiality. Only rarely are family situations depicted as part of these commercials—even though a very large proportion of beer and wine is now consumed as part of family situations—and even more strikingly the actual drinking of beer or wine is never depicted in the commercial. Somehow the actual act of drinking is seen as too "tabooed" for the American public! Is it any wonder that American youngsters are somewhat confused in their attitudes towards alcoholic beverages when the images presented on television are so unrealistic and out of touch with actual practices! Distilled spirits are not advertised at all on television. This does not represent any legislative or judicial action, but rather is "self-policing" on the part of the distilled spirits industry and the television industry. Similarly, at least until recently, most newspaper and magazine advertising of alcoholic beverages excluded women.

These restrictions on advertising represent, at least partially, a fear on the part of the media and the alcoholic beverage industry of evoking prohibitionists and "anti-alcohol" sentiments. There is concern lest latent "dry" sentiment be aroused if alcohol is "pushed too hard" or made to seem too attractive. This wish to avoid reawakening old controversies and to stay completely "neutral" in relation to "wet-dry" issues is also reflected in the public statement and policies of most governmental alcoholism treatment and educational agencies. There is the fear that health-oriented programs directed at alcoholism might be jeopardized if issues regarding the propriety of drinking were to arise. Thus, most state alcoholism agencies, for example, have carefully avoided any explicit statements that some uses of alcohol might be acceptable.

Although the question of whether the country should be "wet" or "dry" is not an important issue for the vast majority of Americans—rather it is settled for them that Prohibition is entirely a thing of the past—many persons still become very concerned about some kinds of drinking behavior. Alcohol is seen, for example, as the cause of much teenage misbehavior and as an important factor in the economic dependency of welfare recipients. Efforts at alcohol education—particularly in the public schools—are confronted with an almost insurmountable task. In virtually all states education about alcohol is required by law. Generally these requirements reflect legislation enacted—under pressure from temperance organizations—more than 50 years ago. Many educators now realize that education "on the evils of alcohol" is likely to be ineffective with a large proportion of high school youngsters. In most parts of the United States the majority of high school juniors and seniors already have more than experimented with alcohol. On the other hand if it is even suggested in the classroom that teenage drinking might be acceptable, repercussions are likely to develop from at least two groups. The first of these, of course, are persons in the community who are opposed to all drinking—or to all teenage drinking. The second group are law enforcement authorities who frequently have great difficulty enforcing state laws regarding minimum age. Consequently, most alcohol education efforts are only token gestures to meet the state law. Where broader programs are conducted, the emphasis frequently is on being "objective" and implying—or stating explicitly—that it would be preferable if youngsters delayed their drinking until they were 21 years of age.

Drinking—and getting drunk—have a variety of meanings for many Americans. This, of course, is particularly true for men. Drinking—and holding one's liquor—is identified with masculinity. Some of the terms used to describe drinking behavior demonstrate the linkage of drinking with aggressive impulses. For example, the expressions "have a blast," "really hanging one on," or "sneaking a quick one" all reflect certain ambivalences. Drinking is seen as a symbol of adulthood. Many youngsters report that they feel really accepted by adults when they are permitted by adults to smoke, to drink, and when adults tell "off color" stories in their presence! Although there are clear taboos against drunkenness in many situations, attitudes about this also are uncertain. The masculine pride in "getting drunk" was graphically illustrated recently when the actor, Dean Martin, telegraphed three American astronauts to congratulate them on their space accomplishments. He concluded his message with the following comment: "I bet I was higher last night than you were!" This telegram—especially the last sentence—received wide publicity throughout the country and was reported on the major television networks. Dean Martin has made a name for himself as somebody who is frequently more than slightly intoxicated. This image certainly does not appear to have hurt his career!

One of the peculiar—and perhaps extremely unfortunate—consequences of the residual conflict and uneasiness remaining from the prohibition days is the unwillingness of the vast majority of American drinkers to take any steps at all to modify the drinking of other persons. There are strong attitudes which prevent Americans from commenting at all on another person's drinking unless the drinking is of a highly extreme and practically "alcoholic" nature. There is, for example, a far greater reluctance to criticize another person's drinking behavior than his excessive eating behavior! Since the days of the Prohibition controversy, the area of drinking behavior has become one of great privacy. Even persons who are inclined to comment unfavorably about a colleague's, relative's, or friend's drinking behavior, are reluctant to do so for fear they will be labeled as puritans or as "drys." Thus, drinking behavior is considered almost entirely a matter of the individual's private freedom. Over the past 100 years, virtually the only persons, outside the alcoholic beverage industry, who have made any efforts to modify American drinking patterns have been the "drys." And clearly the bulk of American drinkers are not likely to be influenced at all by the attitudes of this small minority.

The many years of controversy surrounding drinking and prohibition left a substantial mark on American laws, regulations, and practices. In addition, their impact is still seen in the feelings and attitudes of the vast majority of persons. The topic still is so highly emotionally charged that only very recently has it become possible to focus on distinctions between different kinds of drinking and to move away from the past heated exchanges between "wets" and "drys."

Current American Drinking Patterns

Drinking—and abstaining—are not randomly distributed throughout American society. Numerous studies have demonstrated that drinking behavior is highly correlated with social factors such as age, sex, social class, religious affiliation, etc. Far less is known about the psychological correlates of different types of drinking behavior. Sanford has noted that there has been little interest by psychologists in studying the meaning and functions of drinking for different individuals (Sanford, 1968). Virtually all psychological studies of drinking behavior focus on severe problem drinkers or alcoholics.

Several major studies of American drinking practices have been conducted in recent years. One of these, (Cahalan and Cisin, 1968) using a national sample, has reported the following major findings:

1. Thirty-two percent of American adults can be classed as "abstainers" (either never drinking or drinking less than once a year).

2. Fifteen percent of American adults drink less than once a month. Thus, slightly over half of the adult population (53 percent) can be classed as regular drinkers.

3. There is a wide variation of the proportion of drinkers among different age, sex, and social class groups.

4. The largest proportion of drinkers (88 percent) were found among men in the age group 21–39 who were in the highest of the four social class categories.

5. The lowest proportion of drinkers (34 percent) were found among women age 60

or more in the lowest socioeconomic group.

6. Sex differences are considerably greater than differences between social class. For all social class levels, more men are drinkers than women. However, in the highest social class group—particularly in the age groups under 60—the proportion of drinkers among men and women are virtually the same.

7. In the lowest socioeconomic groups there are almost 30 percent more drinkers among men in the age groups over 40.

8. Not surprisingly, the highest proportion of drinkers are found in the suburbs of larger cities and the lowest proportion in rural settings.

9. Among Jews, over 90 percent are classed as drinkers, and among Baptists the figure is less than 50 percent.[3]

Although the proportion of drinkers is greatest among the higher socioeconomic groups, both national samples and community surveys indicate that heavy drinking and very heavy drinking are substantially more frequent in lower socioeconomic strata. Since the proportion of abstainers, even among men, is higher in the lower socioeconomic groups, this means that a far greater proportion of drinkers in the lower strata are likely to drink in large quantities.

Historically, drinking has been associated with significant social ceremonies and rituals. These include birth, marriage, death, celebration of victories, the signing of contracts, and various holidays (religious as well as secular). Contemporary use, of course, extends far beyond these types of occasions. Several years ago Fallding presented a typology of four different social functions of drinking. This category system focuses on the extent to which individuals feel themselves part of a genuine "community." Thus, the first type of drinking is called "ornamental, community-symbolic drinking." The bonds between individuals preexist and the drinking is not needed in order to develop any relationship of trust. The author points out that this type of drinking now appears

relatively rare in Western society. He cites the orthodox Jews' religious use of wine as a prototype of such drinking behavior. The second category in this typology is referred to as "facilitation drinking." Under these circumstances individuals still retain basic feelings of trust and community. However, some individuals—and perhaps all individuals at some time—are unable to participate fully without some use of alcohol. In this sense then the drinking "eases adjustments" and helps to bind people together. It is this type of drinking, which involves some release of impulses, which probably is predominant in contemporary American society. The drinking helps individuals to relax and breaks down reserve.

In the third category—referred to as "assuagement drinking"—the drinking behavior and drinking situations become substitutes for genuine relationships of mutual trust and social support. The emphasis is placed on abandonment and excitement and immediate gratification. Here the drinking is not genuinely binding people together. Fallding (1964, p. 721) suggests that many of the social relationships in contemporary American cocktail parties fall in this category rather than in the category of "facilitation drinking." Finally, and this would appear to be the least satisfactory of Fallding's categories, is a type of drinking called "retaliation drinking." Such drinking is seen as an explicit (conscious?) attack by the person on the society through his drinking behavior. The drinking is an expression of his distrust against the community. In extreme form it may represent an effort to make himself dependent on the society through his drinking. Drinking at college reunions or "stag" parties would appear to be a blend of facilitation and assuagement drinking. Missing from typologies of this type are adequate consideration of more strictly psychological considerations. The businessman who always has one or two drinks on the airlines or the young executive who has a drink when he returns home from work is using the alcohol more as a drug and yet less as a "social lubricant." In these circumstances it would appear that the pharmacological effects of the particular substance are more important than any expression of feelings towards social groups.

The last 50 years have seen some remarkable changes in American drinking practices. Perhaps most striking among these is the increased acceptability of drinking by women. Also, a far greater proportion of drinking now occurs in mixed groups (both men and women present). In contrast to earlier years, a much larger proportion of alcohol is consumed in the form of beer and wine than in the form of distilled spirits. Finally, the locus of drinking has altered. Whereas in the past the bulk of drinking occurred in public, relatively anonymous, settings–such as bars and saloons–currently the largest proportion of drinking occurs in private homes and clubs. There has then been, especially since the end of World War II, a far greater social acceptance of drinking. Finally, it should be noted that although the proportion of drinkers among adults has continued to increase, there is no evidence for any increase in the rate of alcoholism. This suggests that the proportion of drinkers becoming alcoholics probably is lower at present than it formerly was.

TOWARDS AN ETIOLOGICAL
THEORY OF ALCOHOLISM
Introduction

Information regarding the causes of alcoholism still is limited. However, much of the same can be said for other psychosocial problems such as schizophrenia or "character disorders." Many therapeutic as well as preventive measures are taken in relation to other psychiatric disorders, even though knowledge regarding the causes of these conditions is no better than knowledge in the area of alcoholism. In part, this difference reflects the complicated attitudes towards alcoholism and the residual "therapeutic nihilism," i.e., the belief that alcoholics cannot be helped. In actuality, of course, very significant numbers of alcoholics have been assisted to return to lives of effective functioning both through the efforts of various professional workers and through Alcoholics Anonymous.

It is generally accepted that three classes of factors should be considered in any discussion of the causes of problem drinking. These are: (1) physiological factors, (2) psychological factors, and (3) sociological factors. The exact role of each of these factors is not currently known.

The Role of Physiological Factors

Because the drinking behavior of many alcoholics seems qualitatively different from the drinking behavior of social drinkers, it is natural to search for physiological differences to account for this variation. The notion of an "alcohol allergy," while lacking any sound experimental basis, has been widely propounded through Alcoholics Anonymous. Nutritional theories received a great deal of prominence because of the work of Williams (1952). Nutritional theories attempt to explain the "craving" for alcohol in terms of certain deficits. Experimental efforts to verify Williams' theory generally have not been successful. Furthermore, it is not at all clear whether the supposed vitamin deficiency is a consequence of the alcoholism or can be considered a cause or antecedent of the drinking problem.

Another frequently mentioned physiological theory emphasizes the role of possible endocrine disturbances in alcoholics. In recent years efforts to find metabolic differences between alcoholics and social drinkers have increased. To the present time, however, no significant differences in rates of metabolism have yet been demonstrated. For example, Mendelson, reporting some recent data, stated, "The data indicate that there are no significant differences in the rates of ethanol metabolism in alcoholic and nonalcoholic individuals after administration of a large dose of alcohol (1968)." He concludes that the increased tolerance to alcohol (requiring larger amounts to obtain the same effects) noted in many alcoholics, perhaps needs to be understood in terms of adaptational processes in the central nervous system rather than in changed rates of metabolism.

In discussing alcoholism, reference is often made to the phenomena of "loss of control." Jellinek (1960) made a major contribution in clarifying the difference between two types of "loss of control." The first refers to the inability to abstain, i.e., the apparent necessity for many alcoholics to drink in certain situations. The second type of "loss of control" refers to the inability to stop drinking once a particular episode has been initiated. It is widely believed that certain physiological changes make it difficult for alcoholics to stop drinking once they have begun. The reduction in levels of alcohol in the blood and central nervous system are often followed by striking psychophysiological changes, generally called "withdrawal symptoms." Clinical evidence suggests that only chronic alcoholics are likely to experience withdrawal symptoms on the cessation of a drinking episode.

Psychological Theories

The most widely held etiological view of alcoholism emphasizes psychological factors. That is, Americans tend to view alcoholism primarily as a psychological, rather than physiological, disorder. For a considerable number of years psychologists, as well as psychiatrists, believed that there was an "alcoholic personality." That is, individuals with certain types of character structure were far more likely to become alcoholics than others. The search for the "alcoholic personality" has more or less been abandoned in recent years. This is primarily due to the failure to discover any single set of factors uniformly associated with alcoholism. A wide range of different types of individuals are found in any group of alcoholics.

Clinicians often agree on reporting that certain characteristics frequently occur among alcoholics. These include dependency, hypersensitivity, depression, inability to develop meaningful interpersonal relationships, etc. Systematic studies, however, have failed to demonstrate a higher frequency of these characteristics among alcoholics than among other psychiatric populations. Even if it did turn out that certain personality traits predominate among alcoholics, this would not, of course, demonstrate that these characteristics were "causes" of the problem drinking. It is highly likely that persons who have been serious problem drinkers for a substantial number of years and who have repeatedly evoked certain responses in others, will develop personality changes that are consequential on their problem drinking rather than causal. The generally negative and highly ambivalent reaction of Americans to alcoholics certainly could bring about important personality changes.

Thus, frequently, there are many years of normal drinking before the person can clearly be classed as an alcoholic or as a problem drinker. A relatively small proportion of alcoholics evidence unusual or "deviant" drinking behavior from their first or even from early drinking episodes. Far more characteristic is the history of a substantial number of years—often as high as ten—of relatively normal or undistinguished drinking.

Sociocultural Theory

The major sociocultural theory postulates a relation between the "normal" drinking patterns in a particular cultural group and the "deviant" drinking patterns in that population. The records of various treatment facilities show great differences in the percentage of alcoholic patients drawn from various ethnic-religious groups. Most striking in this regard is the overrepresentation of Irish-Americans and the underrepresentation of Jewish-Americans. Even granting the importance of social class and educational factors as determinants of the utilization of public facilities, these differences appear to be maintained. For example, a report on World War I army "selectees" (*Medical Department of the United States Army*, 1929) substantially confirmed this difference. Ten percent of all Irish-Americans were classed as alcoholics and only 0.5 percent of Jews. In a study of World War II selectees, controls were made for social class and other demographic factors and, here too, Irish had far higher rates than Jews (Hyde & Chisholm, 1944). Several other studies, some including appropriate controls for social class, confirmed these differences in Jewish and Irish alcoholism rates.

Italian-Americans and Chinese-Americans are other groups with relatively low rates of alcoholism. Northern European and other Anglo-Saxon groups, as well as French-Americans, tend to have higher rates (see, for example, Barnett & Skolnick, 1955). The classical work of Bales (1946) represented an early effort to identify cultural patterns which might either increase or decrease the likelihood of the development of serious drinking problems. The attitudes towards drinking (and towards drunkenness) appear to be substantially different in the "low alcohol cultures" than in those with higher rates.

A recent work analyzes a large number of studies relevant to the social cultural approach (Wilkinson, 1970). Some of the significant differences are highlighted by comparing Italian and French drinking patterns. In traditional Italy, alcoholism has been quite low while in France it has been relatively high. The sanctions against drunkenness are far stronger in Italy than France. In Italy, most drinking of alcoholic beverages traditionally has occurred with meals. In France, drinking is far more pervasive. Finally, there appears to be substantially more emotionalism about drinking in France. For example, it is harder to turn down a drink in France than Italy—in this regard the French pattern is more similar to the contemporary American one.

However, this has not yet been demonstrated under experimental conditions, because most nonalcoholics are unable to consume sufficiently large amounts of alcohol so that withdrawal symptoms would occur upon cessation of the drinking. Several investigators have noted that nonalcoholics experience severe gastrointestinal distress upon the consumption of large amounts of alcohol and usually such experiments have to be terminated.

Most physiological theories have focused on explaining only one type of "loss of control." That is, the inability to stop drinking once the drinking has been initiated. Physiological explanations of the other type, i.e., "inability to abstain," are rarely attempted.

One of the strong arguments cited by advocates of physiological theories has been the "fact" that alcoholics can never return to "social drinking." This was seen as an indication that physiological differences between alcoholics and social drinkers were of an irreversible nature. Consequently alcoholics, even if they had learned to abstain from alcohol, could never drink again socially. However, the original work of Davies (1962) and subsequent work by others, including most recently Pattison and his colleagues (1968), demonstrate that at least certain alcoholics can return to some forms of social drinking without exhibiting the "loss of control" pattern that previously characterized their drinking. Pattison feels that this ability to return to social drinking argues against physiological conceptions of alcoholism. He prefers to describe alcoholism as a "psychosocial behavior syndrome . . . dependent on a variety of social and cultural variables (p. 630).

No consistent differences in other psychiatric disorders have been found, for example, between groups such as Jewish-Americans, Chinese-Americans, and Irish-Americans and persons of Northern European backgrounds. When corrections are made for social class and educational levels, Jewish-Americans do not have unusually low rates of mental illness, suicide, or drug addiction. However, they do have distinctly low rates of alcoholism. This suggests that the elements of traditional Jewish life which "protect" against alcoholism are rather specific and do not reflect factors such as family solidarity, emphasis on control, etc. It is possible, but unlikely, that these factors affect rates of alcoholism but not rates of mental illness. Irish drinking patterns apparently are an extreme example of conflict and ambivalence. Most men drink—and many drink heavily— but there is much friction between sexes in

relation to drinking. Youngsters are not supposed to drink and there is considerable ambivalence about drunkenness. In summary then, there is strongly suggestive, although not conclusive, evidence that different attitudes towards drinking and different types of drinking patterns in the "normal population" are associated with different rates of alcoholism and other types of problem drinking. It appears then, that certain cultures have built-in safeguards against the development of alcoholism among their members.

An Integrated Etiological Theory

An etiological model, involving physiological, psychological, and sociological factors is suggested. Since even among those groups with the highest rates of alcoholism only a minority of drinkers develop alcoholism, it is clear that sociological factors themselves cannot be viewed as the total explanation. A corollary to this is the fact that alcoholics are found also in those groups which afford the highest degree of protection against this disorder—Jewish-Americans and Chinese-Americans. It may well be that certain combinations of the three types of factors must be present in order for the alcoholism to develop. And the relative contribution of the three factors may vary from one person to another. Of 100 men living in a "high risk" culture, only 15 may have the psychological characteristics necessary for the development of alcoholism. And, of these 15, only five may have the physiological characteristics which, in combination with the other factors, lead to the development of serious drinking problems. It is thus possible to conceive of various "loadings" of the factors in different individuals coming together to "cause" the alcoholism.

At one extreme there may be some persons whose psychological characteristics are of such a nature that they are extremely likely to develop into alcoholics even if reared in the "most protective" cultures and even though they are lacking the physiological factors generally associated with alcoholism. Comparable would be those hypothetical persons who were born with (or developed) physiological or metabolic dysfunctions which made them extremely vulnerable to alcoholism. Possibly a small proportion of such individuals could develop alcoholism even in the absence of any major psychological disorders.

Clearly, the status of current knowledge does not permit any definitive assessment of such an etiological theory. If, however, such a model has any validity, it would have important implications for prevention. Since in any population all three types of factors are involved, any significant reduction of one or more of these factors would probably be accompanied by a reduction in the rate of alcoholism. However, it is unlikely that alcoholism could be completely eliminated by dealing with only one of the three factors.

NONSPECIFIC APPROACHES TO PREVENTION

Introduction

Specific approaches to prevention are those activities which are initiated primarily, or even exclusively, because of their anticipated effects on rates of a specific condition or disorder. In relation to problem drinking "specific prevention" refers to steps that are taken primarily to reduce rates of problem drinking. Nonspecific activities are those which, while they are directed at other problems, may also help to reduce rates of problem drinking.

Four quite specific approaches to the reduction of rates of problem drinking will be discussed in the next section. Improving general mental health and creating a "better society" will be the focus of this section.

Improving Mental Health

As has been indicated earlier, if psychological factors are an important component in the development of problem drinking and if it is further postulated that such psychological factors are nonspecific, then improvements in the mental health of a population would probably be accompanied by a reduction in rates of alcoholism. If preventable efforts in the general field of mental health were somehow to reduce rates of, say, schizophrenia and other major psychiatric disorders, this probably would also be accompanied by a reduction in rates of alcoholism.

The goal then, in this approach, is one of achieving lower rates of mental illness and generally improved mental health. This would include increasing a person's competence to deal with his own feelings, interpersonal relationships, and life in general.

During the last 15 years there has been a rapid growth of interest in the whole field of preventive psychiatry. Persons particularly concerned about alcoholism and other types of problem drinking should view activities in the area of preventive psychiatry as one key element in efforts to reduce rates of alcoholism. Examples of approaches that have been suggested in this field are: (1) improving the quality of family life (see Caplan, 1961), (2) assisting persons to cope more effectively with various types of crisis situations, and (3) increasing the general understanding in the society of the nature of human emotions and interpersonal relations (see Ojemann, 1957).

Creating a "Better Society"

Since problem drinking is not an inevitable characteristic of the human organism or, apparently, even of social existence, it seems reasonable to assume that a "better society" might well have a lesser rate of alcoholism. The substantial reduction of poverty, other forms of deprivation, certain obvious types of inhumanity of man to man, and a reduction of injustice presumably would be accompanied by lower rates of various social-behavioral problems including psychiatric illnesses and alcoholism. Increasing people's sense of community or belongingness and reducing feelings of alienation are other goals of a "better society." Insuring for all persons equal access to the "opportunity structure" and eliminating discrimination would also be steps in this direction.[4]

SPECIFIC APPROACHES TO PREVENTION

Early Case-Finding

This approach emphasizes activities directed at individuals or groups who could be considered "high risk" for the possible development of drinking problems. Reference here is to individuals who for either physiological, psychological, or social-cultural reasons appear to be particularly vulnerable or susceptible to the development of drinking problems. If such persons could be identified through mass screening or other procedures, primary preventive programs could be developed for them. Focusing on "high risk" individuals or groups clearly would be a more efficient procedure than attempting to reach total populations. At the present time, however, no physiological or psychological factors have been discovered which could be considered precursors of later drinking problems.

An even more focused preventive approach consists of activities directed at individuals who already appear to be exhibiting some signs of pathological or destructive drinking behavior. Such persons could be considered to be in the "early stages" of the disorder. It is generally believed that efforts at intervention, therapy, and reeducation (or resocialization) are more likely to be successful if they are initiated before the condition reaches this more serious or chronic stages. Current efforts to identify persons with incipient drinking problems are made far more difficult because of the cultural attitudes referred to earlier. That is, Americans generally are extremely unwilling to intervene in any fashion in the drinking behavior of their family, friends, or working colleagues unless this behavior already is very deviant and rather extreme. However, if certain major modification of drinking patterns were to occur, it would be easier to assist such persons to obtain help before their problems became far more serious.

Modifications of Alcoholic Beverages

Theoretically, it is possible that means could be discovered of altering alcohol so that its habit-forming properties are greatly reduced. For example, some substances could be added to alcoholic beverages which would alter the manner in which the alcohol is absorbed or metabolized. Possibly such changes would not reduce the utility of alcohol as a "social lubricant" but still would reduce its potentially addictive qualities. The blood-alcohol levels associated with the usual "social" uses of alcohol are far lower than the alcohol levels frequently found among problem drinkers. Hypothetically then, it would be possible to create a modified type of alcoholic beverage that would still allow the pharmacological effects that have made this substance so universally used, but would not entail the dangers currently associated with alcoholic beverages.

Functional Equivalents of Alcohol Use

The major "function" of current alcohol use patterns in the United States is to enable individuals to relax, to release some of their inhibitions and thus achieve certain psychological states which otherwise are relatively difficult for many people to attain. However, it is not only the pharmacological aspects of alcohol that help to bring about these states. Both the situations in which the drinking occurs and the symbolic meaning of drinking are important factors in creating the sense of well-being. Many persons report the experience of arriving at a party somewhat late and after only the first few sips of a drink feeling as "high" or "happy" as other persons who have had several drinks already. There also is no question that most persons are able to achieve the state of relaxation of the usual control mechanisms without any alcohol being involved. Thus, one could conceive of other beverages (or other agents)—without any pharmacologically intoxicating constituents—which could become socially defined as signals for relaxation and the release of social inhibitions. A still further step, of course, would be the creation and establishment of such "functional equivalents" which did not involve use of any substances.

Prevention of Drinking Problems through Modifications of Drinking Patterns

At this time the most feasible approach to the prevention of drinking problems appears to be through modification of existing American drinking practices. There is substantial evidence that rates of alcoholism are significantly higher in some sociocultural groups than in others (see pp. 431–432). It is now increasingly being suggested that the occurrence of certain changes in American drinking practices would be followed by a reduction in rates of problem drinking.[5] The concern in such an approach is neither with promoting nor preventing the use of alcoholic beverages, but rather with bringing about changes in American drinking practices that are likely to lead to a reduction in drinking problems. The proposed changes may lead to either an increase or a decrease in the number of drinkers. They may lead to either an increase or a decrease in the total amount of alcohol consumed. The policy, however, is not concerned with either of these two possible areas of change.

Below are listed four major changes in American drinking patterns that have been proposed (*Alcohol Problems*, 1967, pp. 138–152):

1. A reduction of the emotionalism associated with the whole topic of drinking and abstinence.

2. A clarification of the distinctions between socially acceptable and socially unacceptable types of drinking behavior.

3. Discouraging drinking that occurs for its own sake and encouraging drinking that is integrated with other activities.

4. Assisting young people to prepare themselves for participation in a predominantly "drinking" society.

The subject of the use of alcoholic beverages has long been surrounded with highly emotionally-charged feelings and attitudes. This was most strikingly evident, of course, during the days of the Temperance Movement and the period of Prohibition. An essential precondition for the development of a reasonable approach to alcohol problems is the creation of a climate in which rational discussions can occur on this topic. Recent years have seen increased activity in relation to alcoholism but these have not been accompanied by equal activity in relation to the broad area of drinking behavior. As a matter of fact, most official and voluntary alcoholism agencies have gone to great lengths to indicate that they are completely "neutral" in relation to the "wet-dry controversy." By saying this they have in effect abdicated any concern about drinking behavior that is short of alcoholism or serious problem drinking. The first priority then is a legitimatization of the whole area of drinking behavior for examination and study by specialists and—more importantly—for thoughtful discussion by the American public generally. Symptomatic of the current feelings in this area is the total lack of mutual respect between social drinkers and abstainers. A large portion of the members of both groups feel somewhat superior to members of the other group and also are perhaps slightly discomforted by their behavior in relation to alcohol.

Ever since the Prohibition years—and even prior to that time—the principal discussions and arguments have been about the "rights and wrongs" of drinking. This has led to an almost complete neglect of another set of distinctions which may be far more important. These are the distinctions between different kinds of drinking behavior. For too long it has been assumed—especially by the "drys," of course—that all kinds of drinking behavior were one and the same. As a corollary of this, virtually the only persons in the United States who have been trying to bring about any changes in American drinking practices (aside from the alcoholic beverage industry) have been persons in the Temperance Movement. Clearly, they have been quite unsuccessful in this effort since the bulk of American social drinkers consider the attitudes of abstainers quite irrelevant to their own drinking behavior.

No hard and fast across-the-board rules can be established for drinking behavior. The appropriateness (or inappropriateness) of a particular kind of drinking behavior will depend on the situation in which the drinking occurs and the activities that the persons involved will undertake in the period of time immediately following. For example, if the members of a football team drink heavily as part of their celebration of a victory in the season's final championship game, this is very different than the same kind of drinking behavior the night before this championship game. What is "safe" or acceptable drinking in one situation may not be in another. The objective then is to encourage various groups to be responsible for the drinking behaviors of their members and to envoke appropriate sanctions when the drinking deviates significantly from such agreed-upon standards. At present, persons in any social group are extremely reluctant to intervene against the drinking behavior of other members of their group unless the drinking is very extreme. Persons inclined to intervene in this fashion are often constrained from doing so because of a fear that they will be considered "prudes" or "stuffed shirts."

If appropriate social controls against unacceptable drinking behavior could be developed, they would probably significantly reduce many of the problems associated with the drinking of alcoholic beverages. For example, it is the failure to make distinctions between different kinds of drinking behavior—and the persistent emotionalism surrounding this topic—which have made it so difficult to develop any successful educational programs in relation to drinking and driving problems. It is both pathetic and ludicrous that hosts at most American parties feel a strong obligation to keep their guests' glasses full but only rarely do they think of any obligations in terms of their guests driving home after the party with considerable alcohol in their bloodstreams and central nervous systems. The confusion and ambivalence in this area is highlighted by the varied and complicated attitudes towards drunkenness in our society. Drunkenness is often considered a source of amusement and even envy. Here again the frequent unwillingness to intervene can be traced to the failure to recognize that disapproval of inappropriate drinking is not a condemnation and disapproval of all drinking.

Evidence from cross-cultural comparisons suggests that drinking integrated with other activities is less likely to cause difficulties than drinking occurring in situations where the primary purpose is drinking itself. When the drinking of alcoholic beverages is incidental to other activities, the "rules of the game" in relation to those other activities generally operate as a constraining force on the drinking behavior. If the drinking is merely incidental to other activities, it already becomes less of a primary focus and less of an issue for the group generally. For example, the members of a company or union bowling team who are part of a league are not likely to look kindly upon one of their members drinking so much that his average is seriously affected. Similarly, if a person's drinking substantially interferes with his ability to play bridge, his partner is likely to object. Finally, the integration of drinking with meals is another example of "safer" drinking behavior. This is not only because the primary focus is on the eating rather than drinking but also because of the known "buffering" effects of food.

One of the logical and necessary concomitants of a reduction in the emotionalism associated with drinking and a clarification of distinctions between acceptable and unacceptable drinking practices would be the creation of conditions for effective and realistic alcohol education for youngsters. Current approaches to alcoholic beverages seem to maximize the "forbidden fruit" aspects of drinking behavior. It is only recently that a minority of parents have begun to feel that they have some responsibility for preparing their youngsters for subsequent participation in a predominantly drinking society. The adults themselves, of course, have generally not been good role models for the younger generation. Many opportunities have been missed for the creation of situations in which youngsters can do some

appropriate learning in relation to drinking. The last few years have seen a number of colleges modifying their rules about campus drinking and delegating to the student body the responsibility for the "policing" of drinking on campus. Previous college rules—almost completely unenforceable—had, of course, precluded any opportunities for formal learning about drinking since all drinking on campus was prohibited.

Proposals such as the four listed above do not, of course, constitute any clear-cut prescription for changes in American drinking practices. Rather, they are an initial framework for bringing about badly needed changes. Clearly, the drinking customs of other sociocultural groups, such as the Chinese, the Jews, or the Italians cannot be grafted onto the complex heterogeneous American culture. These proposals merely are a first step towards a new approach to drinking behavior. Hopefully they can be a rallying point for diverse groups in the society that previously have either operated in total isolation—and with little effectiveness—or have not been concerned at all about problems attendant upon certain uses of alcoholic beverages.

While it is not certain that social changes of the kinds outlined above would result in significant reductions in alcoholism and other types of problem drinking, there is little reason to believe that these changes could have undesirable consequences. Certainly, a lessening of emotionalism around this topic and the creation of a new approach would be a significant social gain. However, it should not, of course, be assumed that this approach, even if highly successful, would lead to the elimination of alcoholism and other types of drinking problems. What is being suggested is a virtual revolution in American attitudes and practices in this important area of social behavior. Long-standing and deep-seated attitudes and practices would have to be overcome. Lest one believe that such major changes are impossible, it is worth recalling the radical modification of attitudes and practices in relation to family planning and sexuality that have occurred over the last 30 years.

Prevention of drinking problems presents a unique opportunity to combine individually and socially focused strategies of change. Cultural conflicts—as represented by nonintegrated drinking patterns—provide a readily available vehicle for the expression of intrapersonal conflicts. In addition, such cultural ambiguities can themselves help to create psychological problems for the individual. Thus, it is postulated that a society with a more balanced, less guilt-ridden and ambivalent, attitude towards drinking (and abstaining) would have fewer drinking problems. Furthermore, the creation of a "mentally healthier" society presumably would lead to a reduction in drinking problems. The ultimate outcome of American efforts to "do something" about drinking problems may well also be dependent upon the resolution of current conflicts regarding the social acceptability and desirability of the use of various mood-modifying and tension-reducing agents. It should never be forgotten that the reason ethyl alcohol is such a universally used substance is because of its particular pharmacological properties. How alcohol is viewed in the future may well depend on generally social attitudes regarding "altered states of consciousness." The clarification of differences between the acceptable and the unacceptable uses of certain mind- and feeling-modifying substances may be a necessary precondition to the eventual reduction of alcoholism and other types of problem drinking.

Notes

1. For example, *Powell v. Texas*, 393 U. S. 514; *Driver v. Hinnant*, 356 F.2d 761; and *Easter v. District of Columbia*, 361 F.2d 50.

2. See letter dated January 26, 1965, from the State Attorney General to the North Dakota Beverage Dealers Association.

3. For a discussion of the role of social factors in rates of alcoholism, see p. 431 of this chapter.

4. For an interesting discussion of the relation between values, expectations, and access to the opportunity structure and the extent of drinking problems in several cultural groups, see Jessor, Graves, Hanson, and Jessor, 1968.

5. This position is spelled out in some detail in *Alcohol and Alcoholism* (1967), *Alcohol Problems: A Report to the Nation* (1967), and *Thinking about Drinking* (1968).

References

Alcohol and alcoholism. (Public Health Service Publication No. 1640) Washington, D. C.: United States Government Printing Office, 1967.

Alcohol and highway safety report. (A study transmitted by the Secretary of the Department of Transportation to the Congress, in accordance with the requirements of Section 204 of the Highway Safety Act of 1966, Public Law 89–564, 90th Congress, 2nd Session) Washington, D. C.: United States Government Printing Office, August 1968.

Alcohol problems: A report to the nation. (Prepared by T. F. A. Plaut for the Cooperative Commission on the Study of Alcoholism) New York: Oxford University Press, 1967.

Bacon, S. D. (Spec. ed.) Studies of driving and drinking. *Quarterly Journal of Studies on Alcohol*, May 1968, Supple. No. 4.

Bales, R. F. Cultural differences in rates of alcoholism. *Quarterly Journal of Studies on Alcohol*, 1946, 6, 480–499.

Barnett, M. Alcoholism in the Cantonese of New York City. In O. Diethelm (ed.), *Etiology of chronic alcoholism.* Springfield, Ill.: Charles C Thomas, 1955.

Cahalan, D., & Cisin, I. H. American drinking practices: Summary of findings from a national probability sample. I. Extent of drinking by population sub-groups. *Quarterly Journal of Studies on Alcohol*, 1968, 29, 130–151.

Caplan, G. (ed.) *Prevention of mental disorders in children.* New York: Basic Books, 1961.

Davies, D. L. Normal drinking in recovered alcohol addicts. *Quarterly Journal of Studies on Alcohol*, 1962, 23, 94–104.

Fallding, A. G. The source and burden of civilization illustrated in the use of alcohol. *Quarterly Journal of Studies on Alcohol*, 1964, 25, 714–724.

Gusfield, J. R. Status conflicts and the changing ideologies of the American temperance movement. In D. J. Pittman & C. R. Snyder (eds.), *Society, culture and drinking patterns.* New York: Wiley, 1962.

Hyde, R. W., & Chisholm, R. M. The relation of mental disorders to rates in nationality. *New England Journal of Medicine*, 1944, 231, 612–618.

Jellinek, E. M. *The disease concept of alcoholism.* New Haven, Conn.: College and University Press, 1960.

Jessor, R., Graves, T. D., Hanson, R. C., & Jessor, S. L. *Society, personality, and deviant behavior: A study of a tri-ethnic community.* New York: Holt, Rinehart & Winston, 1968.

Keller, M., & McCormick, M. *A dictionary of words about alcohol.* New Brunswick, N. J.: Rutgers Center of Alcohol Studies, 1968.

Medical Department of the United States Army in the World War. Vol. 9. *Neuropsychiatry.* Washington, D. C.: War Department, 1929.

Mendelson, J. H. Ethanol–1–C14 metabolism in alcoholics and nonalcoholics. *Science*, 1968, 159, 319–320.

Ojemann, R. H. *Four basic aspects of preventive psychiatry.* Iowa City, Iowa: State University of Iowa, 1957.

Patients in state and county mental hospitals. (Public Health Service Publication No. 1921) Washington, D. C.: National Institute of Mental Health, United States Public Health Service, United States Department of Health, Education, and Welfare, 1967.

Pattison, E. M., Headley, E. B., Gleser, G. C., & Gottschalk, L. A. Abstinence and normal drinking: An assessment of changes in drinking patterns in alcoholics after treatment. *Quarterly Journal of Studies on Alcohol*, 1968, 29, 610–633.

Pearson, W. S. The hidden alcoholic in the general hospital: A study of "hidden" alcoholism in white male patients admitted for unrelated complaints. *North Carolina Medical Journal*, 1962, 23, 6–10.

Plaut, T. F. A. Alcoholism and community caretakers: Programs and policies. *Social Work*, 1967, 12, 42–50.

Sanford, R. N. Personality and patterns of consumption. *Journal of Consulting Psychology*, 1968, 32, 13–17.

Skolnick, J. A study of the relation of ethnic background to arrests for inebriety. *Quarterly Journal of Studies on Alcohol*, 1954, 15, 622–630.

Task force report: Drunkenness. (The President's Commission on Law Enforcement and Administration of Justice) Washington, D. C.: United States Government Printing Office, 1967.

Thinking about drinking. (Public Health Service Publication No. 1683) Washington, D. C.: United States Government Printing Office, 1968.

Wilkinson, R. *The prevention of alcoholism: Liquor control and public education.* New York: Oxford University Press, 1970, in press.

Williams, R. J. Alcoholism as a nutritional problem. *Journal of Clinical Nutrition*, 1952, 1, 32–36.

17

The Prevention of Drug Abuse

Arnold Bernstein, Leon J. Epstein, Henry R. Lennard,
and Donald C. Ransom

An important contribution that community mental health has made to the study of problem behavior is to change the focus from the individual and his personality dynamics to a contextual and systems framework. Models in community psychology have also emancipated a range of important questions from consideration within only the conventional medical model. At the same time most of the research on psychoactive agents, their usefulness, and effect has heretofore been based on a symptom, disease, and treatment model. Information collected within this framework has by design been limited to an assessment of the effects of drugs on symptoms associated with emotional disturbance, and attention to other drug effects generally focuses upon troublesome physiological side effects. But emphasis clearly needs to be paid to the other pervasive problems surrounding drug use by studying the relation between drug usage and psychological, social, and interactional functions and patterns. This includes the study of drug effects upon social groups and settings, considering effects on both the drugged and the nondrugged participants.

Before one can formulate a program for the prevention of drug abuse, one needs to know more about the functions drug giving and drug taking serve for physicians as well as patients. We need to learn more about the nature of the social settings and systems which encourage their members to seek drug solutions for personal and human problems. We need to know whether the use of drugs furthers the achievement of intimacy and relatedness between persons and satisfies their need for novel experiences and/or whether certain modes and functions of interaction are being sacrificed by their use. More significantly still, we need to explore a new, uncharted territory regarding how the introduction of drugs into social systems affects the participants in these systems; what the critical thresholds are for changing the nature or character of social systems (families, wards, neighborhoods, societies, etc.). For example, how many persons on what sorts of drugs will bring about what sorts of changes in a social system as a whole? Certainly alterations of the psychological and social modes of behavior of a significant segment of a population can be expected to alter the population as a whole in significant respects. The approach taken in this chapter will be to examine questions relating to drug abuse and its prevention within this broad context (Lennard et al. 1971).

Drug abuse has traditionally referred to the medical and social problems associated with the illegal, excessive use of drugs for "nonmedical" purposes. The term "drug abuse" conjures up associations of heroin addicts, traumatic withdrawal, "pushers," and the underworld traffic in drugs with which these are connected. More recently, to these stereotypes have been added the colloquial descriptive terms "acid head" and "speed freak." Problems associated with drug abuse have tended to be formulated in such terms as the recruitment of "susceptible" young persons into illegal drug use and hypotheses concerning eventual physical and psychological deterioration if they persist in their use.

During a time when the attention of the public and that of most officials has been concentrated upon use of "illegal" drugs, however, the steady, marked increase in the giving and taking of legally prescribed or purchased psychoactive drugs has gone relatively unnoticed. From time to time there have been warnings to the effect that the increased use of such drugs represents a much greater public health problem, and that, in terms of cumulative consequences, their abuse has much wider and more serious consequences.

A former president of the American Academy of General Practice has stated, "I have become deeply concerned about the use, overuse and abuse of the psychic drugs—particularly the ones most commonly called tranquilizers. I believe these drugs are not only used wrongly, to excess and without adequate indication but that in many instances their indiscriminate use has led to dependency, habituation and addiction with all of the consequent results thereof . . ." (Witten, 1966, p. 21).

Such warnings have gone largely unheeded and the steady increase in the prescribing and taking of psychoactive drugs has not abated.

A large part of this paper will be devoted to a discussion of forces in our society which are generating increased drug use. These, in our view, include, in addition to the criminal elements to whom this role is conventionally assigned, the pharmaceutical industry, the medical profession, the psychiatric practitioner, and prevailing social ethos. Hence, a discussion of drug abuse and its prevention must proceed from a framework that includes both legal and illegal drugs, medical and nonmedical aspects of drug use, and effects of drug use upon persons other than the individual who uses the drugs.

THE ROLE OF THE DRUG INDUSTRY

Pharmaceutical companies comprise an active industry, constantly seeking a wider market for their products; both physicians and the general public are targets for their retail men and intensive advertising campaigns.

For drugs which require prescription, the industry believes it must educate physicians on their usefulness. Drug advertisements abound in medical journals and in many hospital lobbies. Scarcely a day passes in which a physician's mail does not include drug literature.

Pierre Garai, a medical writer, states: "Tranquilizers have become a big business in the past 8 years, a new national habit. . . . The physicians have been sold. So has the country. . . . Three quarters of a billion dollars are spent yearly by some 60 drug companies to reach, persuade, cajole, pamper, outwit and sell one of America's smallest markets, the 180,000 physicians . . . no other group in the country is so insistently sought after, chased, wooed, pressed and downright importuned . . ." (Garai, 1964, p. 10).

Most pharmaceutical firms have experienced substantial growth since the early 1950s. For example, in 1951 one company reported a net income of 9.5 million dollars; by 1968 this income had reached 80.2 million dollars. Among the principal products of this company are central nervous stimulants (amphetamines and amphetamine-barbituate combinations) and antipsychotic agents (phenothiazine compounds). While the sale of all drugs has increased greatly for the industry as a whole, the sale of psychoactive drugs has increased to a greater extent.

For nonprescription drugs, the industry advertises and sells to the public directly rather than to the physician, and this they also accomplish with increasing success. From antacids to Compōz, there is a drug on the over-the-counter market for a remarkable variety of occasions. The Federal Trade Commission has recently instituted an investigation of advertising practices and claims concerning such over-the-counter drugs.

The pharmaceutical industry alone can hardly be indicted for this. It is an American tradition that growth is good, and increased earnings per share demand a larger market. If an automobile manufacturer is to grow it must convince American families they need two cars, not one, and the same logic holds for the pharmaceutical industry. We call attention to this factor mainly to suggest that there are steady pressures from the pharmaceutical industry that encourage the use of drugs.

In addition to the obvious types of drug abuse, the mere volume of increased drug use may also have dysfunctional side effects, leading to a more subtle or secondary kind of drug abuse. In the same way that too many cars on the road results in an outcome opposite to that for which cars were designed—to get us from place to place more comfortably, safely, quickly—an extensive pattern of drug ingestion may undercut the very goals for which drugs were initially intended. The problem then may not be so different from the one we now experience with the pollution of our earthly environment. The introduction and spread of psychoactive drugs in the human population may represent another kind of pollution, one which may have the potential for an ecological catastrophe. An ecological model may indeed be relevant to an understanding of drug use and its consequences upon patterns of human interaction and the quality of human experience.

Mystification of Drug Use

While the pharmaceutical industry has been expanding its market of both prescription and nonprescription drugs, it has created an increased need, and in the construction of that need it has promoted its products in part by engaging in what we feel can appropriately be called "mystification." The concept of mystification involves the communication of false constructions of events and experiences in place of more accurate ones, constructions which serve one party at another party's expense.

We shall focus here on only two kinds of mystification which contribute to the total pattern leading to drug abuse. These mystifications involve redefining or relabeling of an increasing number of minor disturbances and problems of the human condition as medical problems, and the presentation of a misleading model of drug action and drug effects.

As more of the range of ordinary human experience is defined as a medical problem relievable through drugs, both physicians and the public are persuaded that intervention by means of drugs is a desirable or required practice.

On the inside front cover of the *Journal of the American College Health Association* (1969) an advertisement reads: "A Whole New World . . . of Anxiety . . . to help free her of excessive anxiety . . . adjunctive Librium." Accompanying the bold print is a full page picture of an attractive, worried looking young woman, standing with an armful of books. In the caption surrounding her, the potential problems of a new college student are foretold: "Exposure to new friends and other influences may force her to reevaluate herself and her goals. . . . Her newly stimulated intellectual

curiosity may make her more sensitive to and apprehensive about unstable national and world conditions." The text suggests that Librium, together with counseling and reassurance, "can help the anxious student to handle the primary problem and to 'get her back on her feet'." Thus, normal problems and conflicts associated with the status change and personal growth that accompany the college experience are relabeled as medical-psychiatric problems, and as such are subject to amelioration through Librium. There is, however, no substantial evidence for the proposition that drugs facilitate a student's progress or participation in the college experience.

This contemporary tendency to increase the prescription of psychoactive drugs no doubt contributes to the recruitment of more and more persons into a way of life in which the regulation of personal and interpersonal processes is accomplished through the ingestion of drugs. Paradoxically, such drug use, at a future time, without a physician's prescription, will be deplored by both the medical profession and the community at large.

Our second observation pertains to descriptions of drug effects in advertisements and circulars to physicians and in the media aimed at the general public. Librium is claimed to "reduce anxiety," Compoz to "calm the nerves," and Elavil "lifts depression." Such representations suggest that specific psychotropic drugs directly alter specific emotional states and psychological processes. This paradigm of drug action is patterned after Paul Erhlich's conception of drug specificity embodied in his notion of a "magic bullet," a given chemical agent seeking out a specific target in the organism, creating a specific desired but highly circumscribed effect, leaving the surrounding processes un-effected. Although this model has proven to be useful in the management of many somatic states, particularly in the control of infectious diseases with antibiotics, even within the framework of the theory that drugs have specific effects it is now well established that with any agent there is a diffusion of both physiological action and bodily effects.

The question that must bear exhaustive scrutiny is the appropriateness of using the medical model of the "magic bullet" as a rationale for the employment of chemical agents to accomplish psychological as distinguished from physiological alterations in human beings; whether specific chemical agents can be found to alter and control specific cognitive and emotional states. This notion is at best misleading and at worst is simply erroneous. So many significant determinants of a psychological and contextual sort seem to be at work in the determination of emotional and cognitive states that the supposition that these can be turned on and off by specific chemicals simply cannot be taken for granted.

The increased use of drugs in our society, especially the spread of psychoactive agents, represents a phenomenon too important to be left entirely to the drug industry and the medical profession. These two institutions are themselves implicated in the abuse problem. We have already described how essential it is for manufacturers to recruit new groups to drug use, and to find new uses for their products. We shall now extend our argument to suggest that it is in the interest of physicians to do so as well.

THE ROLE OF THE MEDICAL PROFESSIONAL

The question as to where ethical drug use ends and drug abuse begins is of course a question not easily answered. We would suggest that drug abuse occurs when the costs of the "latent fallout" or side effects of the use of a drug outweigh its benefits (irrespective of whether these costs are to be reckoned in social, psychological, economic, or medical terms) or when the benefits of drug use accrue more to the giver than to the taker. While some of the costs are apparent, many of them are hidden, and it is essential that the hidden costs and benefits be identified.

The giving of drugs has always been and still remains the hallmark of a physician.[1] The role of the drug giver has not only been assigned to him as part of his social role but the role of drug giver has, for many drugs, been written into law as his exclusive prerogative. The giving of drugs by a physician is a performance that is essential, if not intrinsic, to the practice of medicine. But at the same time it must be realized that the act of drug giving is a form of social behavior, and as such entails social and psychological consequences that may transcend the purely medical purposes for which it is undertaken. Attention must therefore be paid to the latent (hidden) functions of the act of drug giving (and drug taking) as well as to the manifest (explicit) ones.

The manifest functions of a social process are "those objective consequences which are intended and recognized by participants in the system. Latent functions are those consequences neither intended nor recognized." Merton (1957) writes that "It is precisely the latent functions of a practice or belief which are *not* common knowledge." The administration of a drug serves latent functions for physicians as well as for patients, and for pushers as well as addicts. Because these latent functions of drug giving go unrecognized, and because they tend to promote drug giving for other than bona fide medical reasons, their operation tends to encourage drug abuse. Some of the medical practices of drug prescription leading to drug abuse will be described below. These practices tend to accomplish two major latent functions of drug use, i.e., benefits to the physician and mystification.

The availability of an effective drug legitimizes the physician-patient contract. Patients seen in everyday practice present physicians with complaints that are obviously troublesome for the patient and a source of personal concern. But often a physician cannot discover a specific cause for a complaint nor clearly define it for himself or for the patient. The physician may nonetheless prescribe medication. In such cases the drug prescribed is likely to be a minor tranquilizer to "relieve the patient's discomfort." But such an action also serves latent functions. Prescribing a drug, such as a minor tranquilizer, legitimizes the doctor-patient relationship. Through the giving of a drug the physician accepts a patient's discomfort as legitimate and he agrees with the patient's definition of himself as in a sick role. Through prescribing a drug, a physician also reduces a patient's anxiety by the implication that he has defined the problem and has recourse for alleviating the complaint. This is clearly a form of mystification, albeit "in a good cause."

Prescribing a drug may also help a physician to maintain a sense of accomplishment and to allay his frustration. As studies of medical students suggest, physicians are likely to be most pleased by patients who permit them an opportunity to effectively apply their skills and knowledge. Physicians are likely to prefer to work with patients whose symptoms are definite and with whom, in applying their knowledge, they can facilitate healing (Martin, 1957).

The patients whom most physicians are likely to meet in general medical or psychiatric practice do not always make this possible, however. In the presence of an undefined and fluctuating symptomatology, a physician is less able to render the service he prefers and is less able to use his knowledge to the fullest. We assume this situation to be frustrating for the physician, and the administration of a drug, even when based on the assumption of a partial "placebo" effect, may serve to reduce his feeling of impotence.

Administration of drugs may help some physicians retain a sense of mastery in ambiguous situations. There is nothing quite as frustrating for a psychiatrist or mental health professional as a seriously ill psychotic patient who does not respond to treatment. The readiness of some psychiatrists to use even new drugs, some with incompletely determined hazards, may be testimony to such a perhaps unarticulated sense of exasperation.

There are a number of studies which, to our mind, support some of the observations offered here. These (Hayman & Ditman, 1966; Klerman, Sharaf, Holzman, & Levinson, 1960) suggest that prescribing a psychoactive drug helps a physician to preserve a sense of mastery in the doctor-patient relationship. Psychoactive drugs will tend to be prescribed more frequently by physicians who "value" being in control or who feel more helpless in managing a patient or an interpersonal transaction without drugs.

For example, Mendel (1967) reports that medical students, interns, and residents who participated in an experiment in which the prescription of psychoactive drugs was not permitted for a patient during the first 12 hours of hospitalization tended to markedly decrease the number of prescriptions they wrote for patients in subsequent weeks on the service.

A publicized example of overzealousness and mystification in the application of drugs to the solution of primarily nomedical problems has recently come to national attention in a report that between five and ten percent of the 62,000 school children in the city of Omaha were being given "behavior modification" drugs (such as Ritalin, Tofranil, and Dexedrine). The children, virtually all of them in grade school, were identified by their teachers as "hyperactive" and unmanageable. By November 1969, the school administration found itself swamped with the problems that grew out of the fact that thousands of elementary school children had potentially dangerous drugs in their pockets and in their lunch pails. "They were trading pills on the school grounds," it was reported by the assistant school superintendent. "One kid would say, 'Here, you try my yellow one, and I'll try your pink one'."

An Omaha pediatrician was instrumental in introducing the "behavior modification" program to the public schools after he attended a seminar in Syracuse in 1968 in which he said several prominent physicians described the positive results they had achieved by using drugs on hyperactive students. Physicians have thus introduced thousands of elementary school children to drugs which the United States Food and Drug Administration warns are addicting and about which it has urged physicians to exercise extreme caution in prescribing (*San Francisco Chronicle*, June 29, 1970).

This example seems to us to be a paradigm of medical drug abuse and to exemplify within it the gamut of practices which must be reversed if such abuse is to be prevented:

—The use of drugs for social control.
—The use of drugs with dangerous or unknown side effects in the absence of generally accepted need to do so for serious illness.
—The use of drugs without sufficient knowledge and research about their mode of action or uses.
—The induction of large groups into the drug-taking mode for solving problems.
—The substitution of a medical for a social model of influencing social behavior.
—Mystification of and by the physician as to the nature of the problem, the nature of drug action, and the description of drug effects.

DRUGS AND THE PATTERNING OF SOCIAL INTERACTION

Psychoactive drugs are probably most often employed to resolve problems which arise in the course of social interaction. Their use is intended to modify the behavior of individuals within their immediate social context when their behavior is either disturbing to them or to the others with whom they are interacting.

A variety of drugs, whether available on prescription, available over the counter, or illegally obtained, are taken to achieve desired interactional and relationship states. Furthermore, so-called psychedelic drugs require, so say "connoisseurs," the presence of other people, in very special social configurations.

But theory, research, speculation, or mythology about legal and illegal psychoactive drugs has either proceeded from a symptom-disease treatment framework or has dwelt upon effects of drugs on "inner" experience. Not much effort has been invested in developing a more comprehensive theory that includes the effects of drugs on social interaction, how drugs affect the sensory modalities involved in human interaction process, and how drug ingestion by one or more members of a social group alters the expectations, behavior, and configuration of the group and the system of which they are members.

Comtemporary approaches to the understanding of drug abuse appear to us to suffer from severe limitations because they manage to avoid coming to grips with the more significant problems, very much as if physiologists or physicians were to exhibit great interest in the effect of salt intake or diuretic medication on clinical hypertension, but neglected to pay the least attention to a study of the function of sodium in metabolism and particularly in relation to the role of electrolytes in cardiovascular function.

Our purpose here is to propose a framework within which questions can be raised about drugs and social interaction, and to draw attention to some hypotheses about the prevention of drug abuse which flow from this framework.

Some Propositions about Social Interaction

Human interaction provides the medium through which societies and, indeed, all social systems perform their functions and carry out their purposes. For, unless individuals interact, no social system can exist. Interaction serves purposes such as information exchange, socialization, and the maintenance of physical and emotional well being. Different social contexts demand different forms and patterns of interaction.

Interaction serves a multiplicity of functions. For example, interaction at the work place may be conceived of as primarily instrumental (task oriented); while at a party it may be primarily expressive (socioemotional). Among scientists at a conference interaction may be primarily, though not wholly, concerned with the exchange of ideas and the acquisition of information; while interaction among the customers at the neighborhood bar may serve to assuage loneliness and to affirm group membership.

Human interaction embodies a complex of different levels and channels, as well as different sensory modalities. One interacts through such media as sight, sound, touch, and smell. Although each occasion for human contact may simultaneously involve any number of these, one or the other may constitute the primary modality of interaction from time to time.

Social interaction takes place within social settings that exhibit system properties. Units or elements of interaction are not discrete but interdependent, and are contingent upon each other. Furthermore, interaction process involves tendencies towards homeostasis. It follows, from this position, that whenever the behavioral contribution of a member of a social group is changed (as through drug administration) it will inevitably affect the behavior of the others in that group with whom he is interacting and, therefore, the group's interaction process as a whole.

To the extent that psychoactive agents alter the behavior of individuals they will also alter the interaction processes in the social groups in which the individual under drugs participates. One general effect of psychoactive drugs which has not yet been explored is their tendency to alter the balance of interactional processes and functions in a social group in which one or more members are using such drugs.

Psychoactive agents must then be seen as agents which alter the functions, types, and modalities of social interaction. In fact, self-administered as well as prescribed drugs are usually taken and given for that very purpose.

This hypothesis, of course, still requires much additional empirical documentation, but nevertheless does seem to be supported by clinical observation as well as pilot studies. It is not difficult to see how the introduction of alcohol, marijuana, amphetamines, or heroin tends to change the nature of the interaction taking place in a social context, such as a party. The effect of the introduction of phenothiazines into the state hospital setting upon the character of the interaction there is considered by some in the field of mental health to be a major medical breakthrough. In like manner, it has been noted that the use of LSD among youth groups has become associated with the dramatic changes in the mode of interaction characteristic of the so-called hippie way of life.

To fully understand the attraction that the giving and taking of psychoactive drugs exercises upon physicians, responsible adults, and especially the young, one must appreciate the essential role that interaction plays in normal human development. Human beings are characterized by their strivings for and dependence upon interaction with other human beings. Interaction is an end in itself. Interactional deprivation leads to anguish, loneliness, and depression. Relevant, too, is the function served by interaction in defining and affirming the "humanness" of the self. By being recognized socially and responded to by another person, one acquires identity. Interaction also defines and redefines the self and roles among interactors and enhances and authenticates the identity assumed by an individual vis-à-vis other persons (Lennard & Bernstein, 1969).

Drugs are often given and taken for the purpose of modifying unsatisfactory interaction patterns, especially interactions which in the view of the patient or the physician (or youthful drug user) are painful, disordered, or stressful. Drugs may be given or taken for the purpose of diminishing the pain associated with stressful interaction or the pain caused by lack of interaction (e.g., lonely adolescents or isolated old people). Drugs are also often given or taken in order to facilitate interaction, to make it possible for persons to enter into and maintain human interaction. This provides a motivation for ingesting such substances as alcohol and marijuana on social occasions.

Apparently, drugs can act as a special medium or modality of human interaction. Persons interacting under the influence of the same psychoactive agent (whether this be marijuana, a phenothiazine, or LSD) sometimes exhibit certain similarities in the structure of their mutual expectations and the modalities within which they find interaction intensified or facilitated. In other words, they are more "interactionally attuned to each other."

Persons who wish to join groups or social settings in which many of the participants are on drugs may find it difficult to interact, to maintain contact, unless they too are under the influence of the same drug. When it becomes important to maintain contacts with peer groups one can see where the pressure for drug taking (e.g., in the youth culture) stems from. The oft-noted desire of drug takers to "turn on" their nonuser friends and interactional partners, whether to the use of marijuana, LSD, or alcohol may also be motivated similarly. We also take note of the observation that family members on major tranquilizing medication often find themselves bypassed and isolated in family conversation and family decision making. Human beings in general show preference for interacting with persons who have something in common with them. The energetic wife soon tires of the passive husband and the involved student gets turned off by an apathetic fellow student.

It is also reasonable to assume that people will take similar agents for similar reasons, and to accomplish similar ends. One common end that drugs accomplish lies in the bypassing of means, whether this be an immediate imitation ecstasy or a sense of interactional communion. It is this attitude of drug action which makes drugs especially attractive to young people. To achieve a drug-induced mystical experience does not take the practice which, for example, a true mystical experience may require. To achieve a sense of social belonging or human intimacy through drugs does not require the complex social rituals involved in the transition from casual acquaintanceship to friendship. Drugs bypass the means but the effect may be short lasting and illusory.

Interaction process involving persons under drugs, then, can be seen as qualitatively different from interaction process in general. The dimensions and character of these differences deserve further attention and study.

IMPLICATIONS FOR THE
PREVENTION OF DRUG ABUSE

The conceptual framework proposed here seems to us to be equally applicable to understanding the use (and abuse) of both legal and illicit drugs; drugs prescribed by the physician as well as drugs used outside the medical context.

Our perspective, however, leads to very different conclusions about the prevention of drug abuse from that implied in most discussions of psychoactive drugs presented in medical journals and by the mass media, since most such discussions focus upon the individual as the target for intervention, rather than upon the larger system of which the individual drug user is just a symptom. Our approach calls for imaginative social engineering rather than limiting attention to the victims of the system and to what appear to us to be merely patchwork remedies, for it should now be clear that the drug user himself represents only a small part of the problem of preventing drug abuse.

Two analogies should serve to clarify what steps in principle should be taken to implement any program for the prevention of drug abuse with any reasonable probability of success. The first illustration concerns the problem of preventing accidents from taking place at a dangerous intersection. One approach to this problem, the traditional one, is to formulate an accident prevention program, including safety education, driver training and screening, warning signs, and traffic regulations requiring police enforcement (and, incidentally, adequate medical services to treat the victims). We see this as analogous to current efforts to prevent drug abuse through educational campaigns aimed at potential drug users, police and law enforcement and medical and psychiatric treatment for the victims. A very different approach to prevention of accidents at a dangerous intersection would be to engineer the intersection out of existence, that is, to construct an overpass, etc. We believe that efforts to prevent drug abuse must likewise deemphasize the role of interventions at the level of the individual in favor of efforts to modify the nature of the situation or contexts that encourage drug use.

Consider also the example of the treatment at an army field hospital of soldiers wounded in combat. No amount of medical and surgical know-how, however successful at patching up wounded soldiers, will succeed in solving the larger problem, i.e., how to prevent soldiers from getting wounded; to do this one must bring an end to the war. In many respects, drug use, like war, is not a medical problem but a social, political, and economic one.

These analogies may be readily accepted when we consider, for instance, drug use among disadvantaged social groups such as blacks or Puerto Ricans in Harlem, or if we consider the prescription of sedating or mood-elevating drugs among older people.

In the first instance, it is quite clear how the social and economic contexts contribute to the use of drugs (such as heroin) which alleviate pain and make the user, for a time, oblivious to the reality of his life circumstances.

In the second example, it is also clear how the social organization of modern life, with the physical isolation of the aged, with normative instructions restricting their participation in the social systems, and with the negative values attached to "being old," generates the unhappiness and misery experienced by many old people.

The analogy, in our mind, is equally as relevant to the range of so-called psychoneurotic symptoms and complaints brought to the physician or the professional specializing in psychological problems.

The discomfort, anxiety, or pain—however one wishes to describe it—experienced by the unhappily married woman, the salesman insecure in his work, the adolescent caught between parental values and those of his peer group, can all be conceived as consequences of forces operating in the social context of which the individual or the patient is a member. Such social factors may be incompatible demands made upon the individual, the guilt induced by unfillable expectation, or they may consist of profoundly inadequate social arrangements of systems.

The prescription of psychoactive drugs for persons "victimized" in this way may permit them to survive with less agony, to operate, though with some sort of impairment, despite the disturbing social and normative arrangement. At the same time, an individually oriented "repair emphasis," the very act of defining the problem as medical, may well be dysfunctional for an understanding of the social determinants. It may, furthermore, detract from the attention required to alter social systems and the normative instructions prevailing within them.

The increasingly accepted definitions of human problems as medical problems and their solutions through psychoactive agents will only result in the use of *more* drugs by *more* people. There is ample evidence that this is already the case.

Note

1. Pages 442–443 are adapted from H. L. Lennard and L. J. Epstein, "Sociopharmacology," December 1967. (Mimeo)

References

Garai, P. As quoted by S. Malitz. Psychopharmacology: A cultural approach. Paper presented in symposium on non-narcotic drug dependency and addiction, Proceedings of the New York County District Branch, American Psychological Association, March 10, 1966.

Hayman, M., & Ditman, K. S. Influence of age and orientation of psychiatrists on their use of drugs. *Comprehensive Psychiatry*, 1966, 7, No. 3.

Journal of the American College Health Association, 1969, 17, No. 5.

Klerman, G. L., Sharaf, M. R., Holzman, M., & Levinson, D. J. Sociopsychological characteristics of resident psychiatrists and their use of drug therapy. *American Journal of Psychiatry*, 1960, 117.

Lennard, H. L., & Bernstein, A. *Patterns in human interaction.* San Francisco: Jossey-Bass, 1969.

Lennard, H. L., Epstein, L., Bernstein, A. & Ransom, D. C. *Mystification and Drug Misuse.* San Francisco: Jossey-Bass, 1971.

Martin, W. Preferences for types of patients. In R. K. Merton, G. Reader, & P. L. Kendall (eds.), *The student physician.* Cambridge: Harvard University Press, 1957.

Mendel, W. Tranquilizer prescribing as a function of the experience and availability of the therapist. *American Journal of Psychiatry*, 1967, 124, No. 1.

Merton, R. K. Social theory and social structure. (Rev. ed.) Glencoe, Ill.: Free Press, 1957.

Witten, C. Address given by president-elect to the American Academy of General Practice. In Symposium: Non-narcotic drug dependency and addiction, Proceedings of the New York County District Branch, American Psychiatric Association, March 10, 1966.

18

Prevention of Suicide:
A Challenge for Community Science

Edwin S. Shneidman

Although this chapter on suicide prevention is part of a section of this volume entitled "The Prevention of Disorder and the Promotion of Effectiveness," it should be noted at the outset that prenecessary suicidal deaths will not be viewed as evidences of a "disorder," but rather as manifestations of various sociopsychological blights and existential distortions. Further, the converse of suicide prevention is not related to "effectiveness" but rather to the promotion of a self-exulting existence, specifically to the elevative use of life's time. All this is to say that suicidal phenomena are not simply to be understood as disease or disorder, and, at the other and positive reach, the most overarching goal is not simply to lift depressions or to avoid benighted feelings but rather to permit the developmental fulfillment and complete individuation of each person in every community.

CONCEPTS OF DEATH AND SUICIDE

Neither suicide nor death has been adequately conceptualized, even though current writings on these topics are certainly not lacking. Among the recent works of more than ordinary interest one can cite especially the following: Choron (1963, 1964) has performed a signal service by tracing Western man's ideas of death over the past several centuries and by focusing and synthesizing the notions of death in our own time. Feifel (1959) and Fulton (1965) have provided us with separate symposia of harmonic and disparate voices on the topics of death and dying; and, perhaps most

important for our current needs, Murray (1967) has invited our attention to the concept of partial death, including death of the inner self and death of the outer or social self; Weisman and Kastenbaum (1967) have explicated one of our own favorite notions (see Litman, Curphey, Shneidman, Farberow, & Tabacknick, 1963), namely, the Psychological Autopsy; and Shneidman as editor (1967) and as author (1963) has tried to add an additional symposium on the broader topic of self-destruction in man and to focus on the role of the individual in his own demise, especially in the large majority of subintentioned deaths. All these are to mention but a few of the current writings in this general area. In sum, there is a lively interest in death.

And what of suicide? Suicide is, by definition, a certain kind of death and, as such, obviously relates to other kinds of death. Suicide has been defined as "the human act of self-inflicted, self-intentioned cessation" (Shneidman, 1968b). Suicide relates to motivation and is intentioned (as opposed to death due to trauma from without, apsychological failure from within, or assault from others); it is total cessation (as opposed to partial deaths or temporary interruption of consciousness); it is individual (as opposed to the decimation or disappearance of a group); it is technically "suicide" (as opposed to Natural, Accident, and Homicide in the NASH (Natural-Accident-Suicide-Homicide) classification of modes of death used for reporting purposes in the death certificates (and statistics) in the Western World;[1] and, in practically every ordinary case, it appears, from the point of view of the surviving relatives, to be stigmatizing (as opposed to honorific, uplifting, ennobling, comforting).

The extent of the community and mental health problems created by or associated with suicidal deaths is difficult, perhaps impossible to enumerate. The National Center for Health Statistics (1967) estimates over 20,000 suicidal deaths in the United States each year. Some other experts on this topic, notably Dublin (1963), believe that this is a minimum figure, representing a significant underreporting. My own belief is that the veridical data are half again as high, well over 30 thousand self-inflicted deaths per year—and if subintentioned deaths were added, the number would be ten times as high. Further, there are about eight suicide attempts for each reported suicidal death (Farberow & Shneidman, 1961) so that conservatively we are dealing with over 180,000 suicidal episodes each year. The number of people alive in the United States who have attempted suicide at some time in their lives is estimated to be in the millions (Dublin, 1963). Although it seems obvious to say that the primary goal of any suicide prevention effort is to save lives (i.e., to effect a reduction in the suicide rate), it is no contradiction to state that, given the suicide figure at any given time, by far the more important mental health problem relates to the fate and well-being of the survivor-victims of the suicidal deaths. If we can assert that the typical suicide directly affects four people (a surviving parent, a spouse, and two children)—not to count the larger number he less directly touches—then we are talking about the dire and inimical mental health sequelae imposed (usually for the lifetime of that person) on around 100,000 additional persons each year, burdens of guilt, shame, puzzlement, taint, fear, and mystery which are never satisfactorily resolved and often reach through the generations, benighting many lives.

CENTERS FOR SUICIDE PREVENTION

Currently, there is a great deal of activity related to suicide prevention in this country. One of the most impactful developments on the national scene was the establishment, in 1966, of a Center for Studies of Suicide Prevention within the National Institute of Mental Health. The first announcement of this Center was made by Dr. Stanley F. Yolles, Director of the NIMH, at a Symposium on Suicide at the George Washington University School of Medicine in October 1965. At that time, Dr. Yolles (1967, pp. 15–26) indicated that "the Center will have five basic functions in support of the development of this nation's capability to prevent suicide," which he listed as follows:

1. It will serve as the focal point within the Institute to coordinate and direct Institute activities in support of research, pilot studies, training information, and consultation designed to further basic knowledge of the problem of suicide and techniques for aiding the suicidal individual. Studies to be supported will include continued basic and applied research in cultural, sex and age differences in suicide and the relationship of suicidal acts to behavioral disturbances, social and medical problems. Among the latter are homicide, personality disturbances, fatal accidents, occupational and educational stress, terminal illness, use of drugs and alcohol, cultural deprivation, and other aspects of several social stresses. In addition to studies of environmental stress, the Institute will continue to support research into the possible relationship of biochemical processes to suicide. . . .

2. The Center will also compile and disseminate information and training material designed to assist mental health personnel, clergy, police, educators and others in obtaining a better understanding of suicidal actions and learning to utilize research findings.

3. It will assist in developing and experimenting with a variety of regional and local programs and organizational models to coordinate emergency services and techniques of prevention, case finding, treatment, training, and research.

4. The Center will maintain liaison with studies and programs on suicide prevention undertaken by other Federal agencies . . . and with appropriate national and international groups. . . .

5. The Center will promote and maintain the application of research findings by state and local mental health agencies.

On that historic occasion, Dr. Yolles appropriately implied that the intellectual permissiveness for the creation of a national suicide prevention center had been given, in large part, by the successful demonstration of research, training, and clinical effectiveness of the Los Angeles Suicide Prevention Center, started by two psychologists in 1958, after a decade of research and publication, itself supported by an NIMH demonstration grant.

There had, of course, been organized suicide prevention activities in this country since 1906, the year the Save-A-Life-League was founded in New York City, but the Los Angeles Center was apparently the first multidisciplinary Center within the tradition of a scientifically-oriented training and research clinical unit. Within the past decade, four edited books—*Clues to Suicide* (Shneidman & Farberow, 1957), *The Cry for Help* (Farberow & Shneidman, 1961), *Taboo Topics* (Farberow, 1963), *Essays in Self-Destruction* (Shneidman, 1967), and *Psychology of Suicide* (Shneidman, Farberow, & Litman, 1971)—and over one hundred professional articles have come from the Center, in addition to the numerous training workshops, institutes, seminars, consultations, and conferences (Shneidman & Farberow, 1968)—not to mention the substantial number of lives-in-balance believed (by staff and by citizen-caller) to have been saved.

In a recent "progress report" (Shneidman & Farberow, 1965) the cofounders of the Los Angeles Center discussed their own work in terms of its having been a demonstration of public health feasibilities:

If we have been a demonstration project, what have we demonstrated? Primarily we believe that we have demonstrated certain important *feasibilities*. Webster's dictionary defines "feasible" as "capable of being done or carried out; practicable, possible; reasonable or capable of being used or dealt with successfully." . . . We propose that our experiences at the Suicide Prevention Center in Los Angeles over the last several years have demonstrated the *feasibility of*: (a) Preventing suicide; (b) Discovering prodromal clues to suicide; (c) Doing social research on this topic; (d) Using active therapeutic techniques, often involving the "significant other"; (e) Acting as a consultation service for established health agencies; (f) Working with a chief medical examiner-coroner, especially by use of the "Psychological Autopsy" procedure; (g) Having an around-the-clock service; (h) Employing a truly multi-professional approach; (l) Reconceptualizing some time-worn (and inadequate) concepts of suicide and death; (j) "Un-booing" some unnecessary taboos; (k) Showing the desirability of establishing regional training centers; and (1) Operating a specifically focussed suicide prevention center.

In the past decade, there has been a spirited growth of suicide prevention centers throughout this country. The figures detailing this trend are themselves interesting. As recently as 1958 there were three more-or-less comprehensive suicide prevention centers in this country; in 1959, there were four; in 1960, five; in 1964, there were nine; in 1965, there were 15; in 1966, 30; in 1967, 40; and in 1968 there were 60; in 1972, over 200. Not all of the centers of the future will be autonomous and have separate identification; indeed, most of them will be—as they ought to be—integral aspects of hospitals, universities, and especially of Comprehensive Mental Health Centers, but, nonetheless, they will exist. Of the over 250 Community Mental Health Centers already supported (by staffing or construction grants) by NIMH, there are about 20 in which suicide prevention services and activities were indicated as integral aspects of their initial plans. In terms of geographic distribution, suicide prevention centers now exist in about half the states—21 in 1968—and the District of Columbia—in every major section of the nation. But, obviously, with less than half the total number of states represented, there is much to be done.

A suicide prevention center provides an example par excellence of a kind of service that, literally in order to stay alive (much less to function with any degree of effectiveness), needs to coordinate closely and well with a large number of agencies and key persons within the community. Perhaps more than most, the prevention of suicide is a *community* mental health operation. Experience teaches us that the establishment of suicide prevention facilities within a community is an experience in liaison and coordination. The interest (or, at the least, the passive approval) of several pivotal groups should, in most cases, be secured: the local medical group, the police, local government, hospitals, resource therapists in private practice, some civic groups, a number of social agencies, and the press. A recent Public Affairs Pamphlet (Shneidman & Mandelkorn, 1967) contained the following advice:

A suicide prevention center cannot open shop all at once like a supermarket. Rather, the entire process, if it would be successful, must be gradually and tactfully woven into the community. From the beginning, the organizers must solicit help—at the very least, cooperation—from the city or county medical authorities. The hospitals, the coroner's office, and the police chief should know about the beginning of any suicide prevention service. In fact, suicide prevention needs their help. This is reasonable, since the new service ultimately will ease police and hospital emergency-room workloads. But, on occasion, the suicide prevention service will have to call on them for help. The local press, radio, and television should be informed about what's afoot and asked to cooperate. If a story breaks before the budding suicide prevention service is ready, this premature news could be disastrous. Of course, the city government must know what plans are being made. If city officials are not the initial sponsors of such a community service, certainly their endorsement should be heartily pursued. Without local cooperation, successful suicide prevention is practically impossible.

The recent establishment of a new multiprofessional discipline, *suicidology*, serves as the intellectual catchment area for a wide variety of *scientists* (epidemiologists, demographers, statisticians, sociologists, social psychologists, etc.), *clinicians* (psychiatrists, clinical psychologists, psychiatric social workers, trained volunteers, clergy, police, etc.), and *educators* (school and university personnel, health educators, etc.). Suicidology is the study of, and concern with, suicidal phenomena and their prevention. This term was chosen advertantly in order to give the special visibility and identity which such a new discipline required (Shneidman, 1964). As part of the activities of the new Center for Studies of Suicide Prevention at the National Institute of Mental Health, we had sought to create some sense of special excitement in the burgeoning fields of suicide and suicide prevention and to unite the interests of a number of kinds of people concerned either with suicidal phenomena or with suicide prevention. Suicidology seemed to provide a reasonable solution.

In March 1968, the American Association of Suicidology was organized in Chicago, just prior to the annual meetings of the multiprofessional American Orthopsychiatric Association. On that occasion, a number of eminent suicidologists—Jacques Choron, Louis Dublin, Paul Friedman, Robert Havighurst, Lawrence Kubie, Erich Lindemann, Karl Menninger, and Erwin Stengel—"reconvened" the famous 1910 Viennese symposium "On Suicide." The edited proceedings of this meeting are presented in a recent publication (Shneidman, 1969b). A new quarterly journal *Life Threatening Behavior* has been established.

In this chapter, suicide has been viewed as a sociopsychological blight. I am one who believes that psychologists (and other social and behavioral scientists) would do well to focus, even to specialize, in the *substantive* areas of specific sociopsychological blights—suicide, homosexuality, urban perturbation, to name a few. The psychologists's stake—indeed, his responsibility—in suicide and suicide prevention is a vital one. In this, of course, he joins with his colleagues in sociology, psychiatry, public health, philosophy, health education, to name a few. The role of the psychologist in suicidology permits him to do exciting things: research, training, and clinical functions. At this moment, the opportunities in suicide prevention for psychologists in public service would seem to be limited only by the resources of their own imaginations and energies.

A TEMPORAL CONCEPTUALIZATION FOR SUICIDAL PHENOMENA

It is possible that a useful understanding of the prevention of suicide as related to community and mental health issues might be achieved in terms of any one of a number of models or paradigms. At the outset, however, it can be argued that among the models to be chosen, the medical model (with its notions of disease, cause, cure, and a specially anointed curer) seems especially limited and inappropriate. In this connection, Dr. Bertram Brown, Director (then Deputy Director) of the NIHM (and a contributor to this volume) and Dr. Eugene Long (1967) have appraised the situation realistically in their discussion of "The Medical Muddle," a paper presented at the 1967 annual convention of the American Psychological Association.

How to conceptualize an approach to suicidal phenomena within the context of community practice? A rather simple scheme along a temporal dimension is proposed which divides all activities in terms of whether they occur before, during, or after the suicidal crisis. From this (temporal) point of view—using the Latin word *venire* meaning "to come"—one can come (or do) before (*prevention*); one can come (or do) during or between (*intervention*); and one can come (or do) after (*postvention*). These three temporal points exhaust the possible times at which action—community or otherwise—can be effected. They focus on the *whens*, rather than the *whos* (M.D., Ph.D., D.D.), the *wheres* (*inpatient, outpatient,* at home, on the telephone), or the *whats* (manic depressive-depressed, paranoid schizophrenic, benighted citizen, perturbed housewife, etc.). This way of "seeing the action" has the additional advantage of "opening the field" to anyone who can help at any crucial point in time: a trained volunteer, a significant (or even insignificant) other, a relatively untrained psychiatrist, an epidemiologist, a demographer, a psychoanalyst, a vital statistician, a clergyman, a sociologist, a policeman, a social psychologist, a health educator, a clinical psychologist—a whole panoply of individuals who can practice prevention, intervention, or postvention, as clinicians, research scientists, or as emphathic human beings seeking to help someone in duress (Shneidman, 1971).

A simple pictorial representation in this scheme might be contained in a grid, in which the major threads of this proposal—prevention, intervention, and postvention—would be represented by the rows, and the major functions of any enterprise—clinical services, training and education, research and investigation, and administration and liaison—might be represented by the columns. Within this potentially fruitful nexus, any suicidologist ought to be able to find a useful area for his own special talents—the direction, leadership, or supervision of any professional person who is most suited to these latter tasks.

In general, there are three main avenues to the reduction of suicidal deaths which emerge from their temporal framework: 1) to increase the acumen for recognition of potential suicide among all possible rescuers; 2) to facilitate the ease with which each citizen can utter a cry for help; and 3) to provide resources for managing suicididal crises.

The key to the reduction of suicide lies in recognition and diagnosis—the perception of the premonitory signs and the prodromal clues. Most individuals who are suicidal typically cast some verbal or behavioral shadows before them. Prevention lies in recognition. This task of early case-finding must be shared by both professionals and lay people. The "early signs" of suicide must be made known to each physician, clergyman, policeman, and educator in the land—and to each spouse, parent, neighbor, and friend. There is a giant body of mythology and erroneous folklore concerning suicide. One of the first tasks is to disseminate the solidly known facts to all possible citizens.

The tabooed nature of suicide must be recognized. Part of a successful program of suicide prevention lies in reducing the taboos and giving a greater permissiveness for citizens-in-distress to seek help and to make their plight a legitimate reason for treatment and assistance.

Both facilities and personnel will be needed. The personnel will need to acquire relevant skills and appropriate attitudes. Management and treatment of the suicidal individual, as well as his "significant others"—within their own cultural setting—will be required for reduction of suicide rate.

The remainder of this chapter will attempt an explication of these notions of prevention, intervention, and postvention. Under each of these three basic categories—prevention, intervention, and postvention—an attempt is made to develop a number of key foci for action, which, when taken together, should constitute a somewhat comprehensive community program for suicide prevention.

PREVENTION

In the context of suicide prevention has the general meaning of "to forestall," to make unnecessary, to preclude, avert, or to ward off. In common usage, it means not only to prevent the occurrence of a suicidal condition or state of mind. In a much broader sense—in terms of long-range policy planning, perhaps—prevention planning would have to include two major goals, which might seem, at one level, to be contradictory ones: (a) the goal of reducing the number of suicidal deaths (and the simultaneous unequivocal demonstration that the reduction claimed had, indeed, been effected); and (b) the reduction in the stigma or taboo on suicide, so that even if it did occur the mental health sequelae would be less severe and less crippling These two major goals would, it seems to me, also be applicable in other mental health areas, such as schizophrenia or homosexuality.

With these notions in mind, the following are suggested as parts of a comprehensive program in suicide prevention, especially relating to the preventive aspects of such a program.

A Redefinition and Refinement of Concepts and Statistics on Suicide

It would seem to be part of the elementary logic of a clinical science to believe that remediation optimally follows from one's understanding of etiology and that both of these follow from one's understanding of the nature of the phenomena. Good conceptualizations (including definition and taxonomy) must precede any effective action (prevention, intervention, or postvention).

It is generally agreed that current statistics on suicide are grossly inadequate and that comparisons of suicidal incidents between cities, between states, and between countries, based on available figures, are at best sometimes inaccurate and often obfuscatory and misleading. The current inaccuracies are due to many reasons, including the following:

(a) Confusion as to how to certify equivocal deaths, for example, those which lie between suicide and accident;

(b) Dissembling on the part of police and physicians who wish to protect the family, and public officials who wish to protect the reputation of their community;

(c) Inaccurate record-keeping, where what could be known and ascertained simply is not accurately tabulated;

(d) The irremediable inadequacies of the present concepts.

More will be said of this last point in the paragraphs below.

Two additional points should be made in relation to statistics: An opportunity now exists to introduce improved classifications and to conduct pilot studies to determine (for the first time) the veridical suicide rates in some selected communities; and further, the specter exists that unless there is a refinement of the concepts related to self-destruction, there will never be accuracy of reporting, because the present concepts are simply not conceptually strong enough to reflect accurately the events which they are purported to represent.

At all levels, special thought should be given to the redefinition and refinement of statistics and to the problem of record-keeping to the end of suggesting new concepts and a comprehensive program for uniform national record-keeping in relation to self-destruction. We have already suggested that the greatest difficulty in accurate reporting of self-destructive deaths is that it is currently tied to the archaic NASH classification. The greatest shortcoming of this classification is that it completely omits the role of the individual in his own demise.

The traditional NASH classification of death robs us of the possibility of generating meaningful statistics. The approach suggested above, focusing on the *intention* of the individual, if used in conjunction with the traditional approach, might well provide an important step in the psychological understanding of a broad spectrum of deaths and lead to more effective assessment and prevention.

Special Programs for the "Gatekeepers" of Suicide Prevention

An important key to suicide prevention lies in detection and diagnosis. One of the most important findings from the last decade's experience in suicide prevention is that practically every person who kills himself gives some verbal or behavioral clues of his intention to do so. These prodromal clues are often in "code," are cryptic or disguised, but nonetheless they are clues, and one can learn to recognize them. These are the "handles" to prevention.

In practice, a variety of kinds of people hear the presuicidal clues—spouse, friend, neighbor, clergyman, policeman, bartender, physician, employer, etc.; however, it is a most important fact that over 65 percent of all individuals who commit suicide have seen a *physician* (usually a general practitioner) within three months of the event. It is therefore crucial to have a program of education relating to detection and diagnosis which focuses on physicians, and secondly on clergy, police, and other "gatekeepers."

There are a number of ways in which a program for educating general practitioners about the diagnostic indices of suicide can be done. These include the following:

(a) Preparation of special educational materials for physicians focused on the premonitory signs of suicide. These materials can be in the form of brochures, pamphlets, long-play training records, film strips, films, etc.;

(b) A similar program directed toward physicians in hospitals and clinics;

(c) Including instruction on suicide prevention for medical school students by introducing such materials into the medical school curriculum;

(d) Courses on suicide prevention in postgraduate medical education in medical schools throughout the country;

(e) The use of resources of the American Academy of General Practitioners (AAGP);

(f) Special national and regional conferences on suicide prevention sponsored by the AMA and the AAGP, perhaps with cosponsorship by the American Psychological Association and the National Association of Social Workers;

(g) Suggesting that the drug companies train their drug detail men in suicidal prevention. Although every doctor in the United States does not read every journal or attend conventions, every doctor does see drug detail men. The major drug companies ought to be most willing to train these drug detail men in the principles and content of suicide prevention and to have them distribute appropriate literature to the physicians on whom they call. This could be done not only through the drug companies, but with the additional coordination of the AMA, state medical societies, etc.

Clinical experience, now over the past several years at the Los Angeles Suicide Prevention Center, indicates that it is not only possible but advisable for physicians to ask direct questions about a patient's suicidal intent without any harmful effects. In interviews with 10,000 suicidal patients and reviews of 3,000 suicidal deaths, the staff at the Los Angeles Center found no evidence that such questions had ever harmed patients; indeed, the questions often relieved the patients and permitted them to discuss their own problems with their physicians.

Additional special programs, tailor-made for clergy, police, educators, and others, should, without question, also be considered.

Carefully Prepared Programs in Massive Public Education

This is probably the most important single item for effective suicide prevention and at the same time one of the most difficult to put into practice in ways which would be both acceptable and effective. The basic notion is that one major avenue to reduction of suicidal deaths is through the use of the lay citizen as one for first-line detection and diagnosis. The rough model may be found in cancer detection, wherein more and more citizens know the prodromal clues for cancer (e.g., bleeding from an aperture, a lump in the breast, a wart or sore that does not heal or which grows, etc.). The same model, with appropriate changes, might well be adopted in suicide prevention.

A study of massive public education might be done initially in a few carefully preselected communities. This study would need to involve experts in epidemiology, biostatistics, and the use of communication media, especially. This type of study would need to be preceded by a long-term comprehensive study of the actual state of suicidal (and suicidal equivalent) incidents in those areas. The public education activities might include planned and careful use of all the public media: schools, TV, newspapers, radio, advertisements, placards—and these might be done in both usual and unusual places, where appropriate, such as doctors' offices, pool halls, public lavatories, etc.

One or two cities might be selected as large scale pilot projects (or one or two sections of cities might be selected with equal catchment areas). There is the need for control scientific data in order to ascertain the effects and effectiveness of such a program of public education. In part, this can be done by selecting other cities (or sections of cities) which are comparable to the experimental cities in terms of the major variables thought to be relevant.

The use of certain carefully selected target cities as a pilot attempt in suicide prevention is in line with current scientific practice. There currently exist many concepts in suicide prevention which have been found useful; there is already a base of knowledge from which to predict a hope of success.

Although a program of massive public education would seem to be very important in any full-scale assault on the problem of suicide, it would need to be done with the reservations concerning the unanticipated consequences of public information and of popularizing the topic of suicide prevention. We do not know enough about what the short-term effects of such a program might be. However, it needs to be further stated that this in itself is a legitimate subject for serious study and one in which sociology consultants would play an important role.

The Development of a Cadre of Trained, Dedicated Professionals

The fact is that there do not exist at present trained professionals in sufficient number to man the proposed and projected projects in suicide prevention. There is an acute need for the creation of a core group of individuals who might then direct and staff the suicide prevention programs in the communities throughout the country. It should be pointed out that what is being proposed here is not the training of individuals to be specialists in suicide in the sense of only being therapists for suicidal people, but, rather, that individuals be given sufficient training in the basic ideas and facts about suicide and suicide prevention so that they can then act more meaningfully in their administrative and technical capacities.

This aspect of the total suicide prevention program has already been implemented by the establishment of Fellowships in Suicidology at The Johns Hopkins University. The goal is to have similar programs at main centers of learning at several strategic places throughout the country. Already, it appears that there may be Fellowships in Suicidology programs soon on the West Coast, the Midwest, and the Southwest. The concept seems viable and the future seems to be one of expansion of such training sites.

The main point to be made is that the establishment of these multiprofessional Fellowships in Suicidology will, within a relatively few years, create a corps of trained professionals specifically concerned with suicide prevention and able to staff effectively a variety of suicide prevention activities throughout the country.

INTERVENTION

Most suicide prevention activities are interventative in nature. In part, this is so because this is where the light is, but this fact does not gainsay another fact that great needs, especially for more fundamental research, lie in the areas of prevention and postvention. Intervention has the apparent attractions of immediacy, drama, and relatively quick response. The issue has been identified—he *is* suicidal—and the need is real. Intervention is a kind of secondary prevention, having to do with the effective treatment of an existing, identifiable (suicidal) crisis. The increase in the number of suicide prevention centers from three to over 60 in the past decade is only one of several evidences of the legitimate appeal and humane worthwhileness of intervention. It is largely, but not entirely, the clinician's domain; his and the effective volunteer's.

Making Available Service and Treatment and the Improvement of Treatment Procedures

Although there is great need for systematic research on intervention, the heart of intervention is the service itself. The challenge is a logistic and tactical one: that the services which can be rendered be made *available* to whom they are needed when they are required. This routinely means some kind of 24-hour-a-day operation, usually involving the use of the telephone as the life-saving instrument. The use of the telephone willy-nilly changes the clinical interviewing task, presenting fresh challenges and offering new opportunities. Suicide prevention personnel need to become expert in quickly rating each caller's *lethality* (see Shneidman, 1969a)—his probability of *committing* suicide in the immediate future—as opposed to his perturbation or degree of upset or distress. Admittedly, workers at a suicide prevention center will probably handle more nonsuicidal calls (of individuals lonely, perturbed, intoxicated, psychotic, fundless—but not lethal) than suicidal ones, yet they do well constantly to remember that their clinical goal is to keep people out of the coroner's office, to prevent their killing themselves, and that everything else takes its place subsumed under that primary aim.

The improvement of treatment procedures involves the search for new and improved methods. Within the last decade, a number of changes have already taken place. Among these can be listed a more active approach to treatment in general, the dyadic form of most treatment of suicidal persons actively involving the "significant other," and a great movement "out of the office" into the community, using the resources within the community and putting the organized and unorganized helping hands which exist in the community on the handles which can be identified on the caller. In this special sense, it can be said that the best suicide prevention worker is the one who is able to get others to do most of the life-saving.

Studies of Special Groups

For any one of a number of reasons, the closer scrutiny of certain groups seems to merit special interest and attention. These groups, in the suicide domain, should include such high-risk groups as college students, military personnel, certain professional groups such as physicians, particularly psychiatrists, the aged, and the identification of other high-risk groups, whatever their composition.

On the topic of college students and suicide, there are currently a number of studies throughout the country. The identification of high-risk groups is a way of redefining individuals who manifest the prodromata or premonitory signs associated with suicidal behaviors. The key issue is whether *groups* of such persons can be found or whether this kind of search is not always a quest for individuals.

Selection and Training of Volunteer Groups

The "manpower problem" in suicide efforts cannot be ignored. One way of addressing it is through the Fellowships in Suicidology program, giving focused training to individuals who already possess graduate or professional degrees. Another way is to turn to the much larger resource pool of mature and willing individuals, carefully to select them, and then rigorously to train them. This has been the route of many of the suicide prevention centers through the country, and there are some excellent reports of these experiences (see Heilig, Farberow & Litman, 1968). In general, selection has focused on such traits as flexibility and trainability, absence of "overinvestment," or previous emotional difficulties, considerable maturity and some experience with life's problems—the avoidance of "psychological virgins"—and the ability quickly to master the difference between a conversation (which is social and coequal) and an interview (which is clinical and betokens the helper and the helped). In the training of volunteers, many usual and innovative techniques have been employed, including the use of taped telephone calls, psychodrama, role playing, and the preceptor method—most of which cost very little but yet have the potential of enormous yield in dedicated and high-morale and low-cost personnel—usually the womenpower of the community.

POSTVENTION

We have tried to indicate that the largest mental health problem in relation to suicide relates to the survivor-victims, who outnumber the deceased in the order of five to one. Appropriate care or treatment of a surviving widow, or, especially, surviving young children is obvious good mental health practice (Silverman, 1969). We know a good deal about the nefarious sequelae of a parent's suicidal death and much is known relating to remedial and prophylactic psychological treatment of these unfortunates. And obviously, follow-up programs which study and help individuals who have attempted suicide are needed, in order, at least, to learn more of the "natural history" of suicidal behaviors. Apropos of prophylaxis: postvention of individuals in the present becomes prevention for the next decade, or even for the next generation. Postvention relates to the reduction in the amount of disability in the survivor caused by the irreversible suicidal event, or in the individual subsequent to his own attempted suicide.

A Special Program for Follow-up of Suicide Attempts

We know that about eight out of ten people who commit suicide have previously attempted or threatened it, but the data relating to the percentage of people who have attempted or threatened suicide who subsequently commit suicide are contradictory and equivocal. The primary purpose of follow-up of suicide attempts would be to prevent the commission of suicide. Some people who committ suicide do so the first time they attempt it, but the more common pattern is that of a series of attempts, with increasing lethality, and there are too many reports of individuals who have been sewn up or pumped out and released only to complete the task within hours. Like the suggested programs for the gatekeepers and the program in public education, this also is meant to "nibble" at the suicide problem and to help effect a reduction in the suicide rate.

A program of follow-up of suicide attempters could be done in sites where the conditions are propitious for success, and with especially cooperating hospitals, police departments, and public health officials. The actual follow-up could be done by a variety of types of personnel, including public health nurses, social workers, psychologists. The data already available particularly from the work of Stengel (1964) would serve as a beginning for further and better understanding.

There is great confusion about the relationship between attempted suicide and committed suicide. (Again, this confusion exists largely because clinicians and investigators fail to think in terms of lethality, as opposed to perturbation. A suicidal event—whether a threat or an attempt or a commission—is best understood in terms of its lethal intention, rather than its method, or how much general upset accompanies it.) We need to know the characteristics of those with low lethality. Obviously, prevention of suicidal deaths lies in dealing with the former.

It might be well to pattern the follow-up procedures for suicide attempts roughly after that of health educators working with VD or TB follow-up, and look forward to the time when suicide attempt follow-up can be built into routine health services. The follow-up could be seen as "postcrisis follow-up" and would be a legitimate aspect of a comprehensive approach to suicide prevention. It is known that the most dangerous period with relation to suicide is within three months after a suicidal crisis. A follow-up procedure might be one effective way in saving some lives and would furnish excellent data for significant study and research.

A Special Follow-up Program for the Survivor-Victims of Individuals Who Have Committed Suicide

It is not inaccurate to state that from the point of view of the survivor, there are two kinds of deaths: all the deaths from cancer, heart, accident, etc., on the one hand, and suicidal deaths on the other. If one stops to consider the kind of grief-work and mourning that one has to do on the occasion of a death of a loved one who dies of a natural or accidental cause on the one hand, and then what he has to do for the rest of his life if his parent or spouse has committed suicide, the contrast is then clear. The individual who commits suicide often sentences the survivor to obsess for the rest of his life about the suicidal death. The suicide puts his skeleton in the survivor's psychological closet. No other kind of death in our society creates such lasting emotional scars as does a suicidal death. A comprehensive suicide prevention program should attend to the psychological needs of the stigmatized survivors, especially the children who survive a parent who has committed suicide.

Although this aspect of the program is not directed especially toward reducing suicide—dealing as it does with an individual who has already killed himself—nevertheless, because it relates to the survivors of the suicidal death, it is directly in the center of mental health concern. Today each citizen enjoys many rights in this country; we would hope that he might be granted the right to lead an unstigmatized life, especially a life unstigmatized by the suicidal death of a parent or a spouse.

The Los Angeles Suicide Prevention Center has pioneered in developing a procedure which they have called the Psychological Autopsy. This process is used in cases of equivocal suicidal-accidental deaths, and consists of interviewing a number of individuals who knew the deceased, to obtain pertinent psychological data about the nature of the death. The relevance of this is that it has demonstrated that it is easily possible, always therapeutic, to work with survivors of a suicidal death especially immediately after the death and even for some interval thereafter.

Studies of the effects of suicides on survivors need to be done. Two kinds of studies immediately suggest themselves: retrospective studies of individuals whose parent committed suicide one, five, ten, 20 years ago; and prospective studies, where the suicide has occurred in the very recent past, and the effects on the survivor are followed through time.

We do not at present know of the "cost" of each suicide in terms of the deleterious mental affects on the survivors—how many survivors of a father's or a mother's suicide subsequently need mental hospitalization or other mental health care—and in ascertaining of what these facts are, we need to develop special ways for effectively helping individuals who have suffered this kind of traumatic loss. Just as there are better and worse ways of responding to, for example, the loss of a limb or to blindness, so we must develop better ways to help survivors respond to the grim fact of suicide in their family, and thus to reduce the overall mental health toll.

A Rigorous Program for the Evaluation of the Effectiveness of Suicide Prevention Activities

Evaluation is a necessary part of effective follow-up. The goal of effecting a reduction in suicidal deaths carries with it the simultaneous charge of doing so in such a way as to be able to demonstrate unequivocally that those lives have been saved.

Although, in the individual case, suicide can best be seen as reflecting "a damp, dismal November in the soul," it also seems to be so that, in the large, suicide rates vary with such items as the nation's position in relation to peace and war; changes in the economic state of the nation (prosperity or depression); changes, in any one place, in the percentage and the role of Negroes, etc. All this is to say that it is an extremely thorny methodological problem in epidemiology to make a single test or to prove the effectiveness of a suicide prevention program in terms of a single measure, especially suicidal deaths. Nevertheless, efforts to establish the effectiveness of suicide prevention activities must, from both a scientific and moral point of view, be a part of a comprehensive suicide prevention program from its very beginning. Without this feature of rigorous evaluation there can be no accounting by any clinician or investigator, either to himself or to the scientific community.

This aspect of the total program, perhaps more than some of the others, requires close consultation with people in biometry, in epidemiology, in sociological methodology, in research design, and in statistics. Perhaps special committees might be formed specifically to deal with the issue of evaluation.

The basic issues in a suicide prevention program are: What can a local suicide prevention program do which will affect the suicide rate of the people of that community, and how can we find out whether this is being accomplished.

In general, three levels of prevention have been envisaged: Primary prevention, in which the goal is to make it unnecessary for the suicidal crisis ever to occur; secondary prevention (intervention) which has to do with the effective treatment of an existing suicidal crisis; and tertiary prevention (postvention) which relates to the reduction in the amount of disability in the survivor caused by the irreversible (already occurred) suicidal event.

And if there are three levels of prevention, there are at least three criteria for the effectiveness of any suicide prevention program. The first, and most obvious, and by far the most important, is the reduction of suicidal deaths; the second is the evaluation of the effectiveness of various types of approaches to and treatments of suicidal phenomena; but the third should not be entirely ignored: it is the reduction of the over-all "lethality" in the individuals who make up a community. ("Lethality" is the measure of the probability of an individual's effecting his own death—whether naturally, accidentally, suicidally, or homicidally—within the immediate future.) Just as one might ask what a random study of blood samples of individuals entering a business or government building would reveal in terms of barbiturate and ethanol levels, so in the same spirit one might ask what a random study would reveal in relation to individuals' lethality indices, i.e., their general ties to life. A successful suicide prevention program should, in addition to overtly saving lives, also serve to lower the "lethality level" and "suicidal index" of a community. We need much baseline data in this area.

The very establishment of a suicide prevention program has a salutary effect on the mental health within its own community. It can provide a model for the effective approach to a variety of other sociopsychological blights, as well as provide useful information which can help reduce the inimical effects of these blights. It would be hard to conceive that information generated in the area of suicide prevention would not have implications (both methodological and substantive) for accident fatalities, addiction, alcoholism, delinquency, homicide, schizophrenia, and other maladaptive and self-destructive patterns.

Notes

Written while the author was Chief, Center for Studies of Suicide Prevention, National Institute of Mental Health, Chevy Chase, Maryland, 1966–1969.

1. We would do well to abandon completely the NASH classification of deaths—for it is Cartesian and apsychological in that it entirely omits the role of the individual in his own death and totally disregards the teachings of 20th century psychodynamic psychology. Instead we should attempt to conceptualize all human deaths in terms of a motivational dimension of intention-toward-death. As a beginning, three large subcategories are suggested: intentioned, subintentioned, and unintentioned, which might briefly be defined as follows: An *intentioned* death is any death, from whatever cause(s) or of whatever apparent mode, in which the decedent played a direct, conscious role in effecting his own demise; a *subintentioned* death is one in which the decedent played an indirect, covert, partial, conscious, or unconscious role in *hastening* his own demise by such behaviors as imprudence, excessive risk-taking, abuse of alcohol, misuse of drugs, disregard of life-extending medical regimen, death-risking life style, etc.; and an *unintentioned* death is one in which the decedent played no effective role in effecting his own demise, in that the death is due entirely to assault or trauma from without or nonpsychologically tinged failure from within. The reader is referred elsewhere for a further explication of these notions (Shneidman, 1963, 1968a, 1968c).

References

Brown, B., & Long, S. E. Psychology and community mental health: The medical muddle. *American Psychologist*, 1968, 23, 335–341.

Choron, J. *Death and Western thought.* New York: Collier Books, 1963.

Choron, J. *Modern man and mortality.* New York: Macmillan, 1964.

Dublin, L. *Suicide: A sociological and statistical study.* New York: Ronald Press, 1963.

Farberow, N., & Shneidman, E. (eds.) *The cry for help.* New York: McGraw-Hill, 1961.

Farberow, N. (ed.) *Taboo topics.* New York: Atherton, 1963.

Feifel, H. (ed.) *The meaning of death.* New York: McGraw-Hill, 1959.

Fulton, R. (ed.) *Death and identity.* New York: Wiley, 1965.

Heilig, S. M., Farberow, N. L., & Litman, R. E. The role of non-professional volunteers in a suicide prevention center. *Community Mental Health Journal*, 1968, 4, 287–295.

Litman, R. E., Curphey, T., Shneidman, E., Farberow, N., & Tabachnick, N. Investigations of equivocal suicides. *Journal of the American Medical Association*, 1963, 184, 924–929.

Murray, H. A. Dead to the world: The passions of Herman Melville. In E. Shneidman (ed.), *Essays in self-destruction.* New York: Science House, 1967.

National Center of Health Statistics. *Suicide in the United States.* (Publication No. 1000, Series 20, No. 5) Washington, D. C.: United States Government Printing Office, 1967.

Shneidman, E. Orientations toward death: A vital aspect of the study of lives. In R. W. White (ed.), *The study of lives.* New York: Atherton, 1963. (Reprinted in *International Journal of Psychiatry*, 1966, 2, 167–200.)

Shneidman, E. Pioneer in suicidology: A review of Dublin's "Suicide." *Contemporary Psychology*, 1964, 9, 370–371.

Shneidman, E. (ed.) *Essays in self-destruction.* New York: Science House, 1967.

Shneidman, E. The deaths of Herman Melville. In H. P. Vincent (ed.), *Melville and Hawthorne in the Berkshires.* Kent, Ohio: Kent State University Press, 1968. (a)

Shneidman, E. Suicide: Psychological aspects (1). *International Encyclopedia of the Social Sciences*, 1968, 15, 385–389. (b)

Shneidman, E. Prevention, intervention, and postvention of suicide. *Annals of Internal Medicine*, 1961, 75, 453–457.

Shneidman, E. Suicide, lethality, and the psychological autopsy. In E. Shneidman & M. Ortega (eds.), *Aspects of depression.* Boston: Little, Brown, 1969. (a) (*International Psychiatry Clinics*, 1969, 6, 225–250.)

Shneidman, E. (ed.) *On the nature of suicide.* San Francisco: Jossey-Bass, 1969. (b)

Shneidman, E., & Farberow, N. (eds.) *Clues to suicide.* New York: McGraw-Hill, 1957.

Shneidman, E., & Farberow, N. The Los Angeles Suicide Prevention Center: A demonstration of public health feasibilities. *American Journal of Public Health*, 1965, 55, 21–26.

Shneidman, E., & Farberow, N. The Suicide Prevention Center of Los Angeles. In H. Resnik (ed.), *Suicidal behaviors.* Boston: Little, Brown, 1968.

Shneidman, E., Farberow, N. L., and R. E. Litman. *The Psychology of suicide.* New York: Science House, 1970.

Shneidman, E., & Mandelkorn, P. *How to prevent suicide.* (Public Affairs Pamphlet) New York: Public Affairs Committee, 1967.

Shneidman, E., & Swenson, D. (eds.) *Bulletin of suicidology.* Washington, D. C.: United States Government Printing Office, 1967.

Shneidman, E. Orientations toward cessation: A re-examination of current modes of death. *American Journal of Forensic Sciences*, 1968, 13, 33–45. (c)

Silverman, P. R. The widow-to-widow program: An experiment in preventive intervention. *Mental Hygiene*, 1969, 53, 333–337.

Stengel, E. *Suicide and attempted suicide.* Baltimore, Md.: Penguin Books, 1964.

Weisman, A., & Kastenbaum, R. The psychological autopsy: A study of the terminal phase of life. *Monograph of the Community Mental Health Journal*, 1967, No. 4, 1–59.

Yolles, S. F. The tragedy of suicide in the United States. In *Symposium on suicide.* Washington, D. C.: George Washington University, 1967. (Reprinted in Public Health Service Publication No. 1558. Washington, D. C.: United States Government Printing Office, 1967.)

19

Is the Concept of Prevention Necessary or Useful?

Nevitt Sanford

In order to seriously raise the question "Is the concept of prevention necessary or useful?" it must be made clear that the concern here is with *mental disorder* rather than with physical disease and with a condition or *persisting organization of processes in the person* rather than with overt behavior. As will be stressed later on, we must, of course, be concerned about preventing such overt acts as suicide or murder or other crimes against persons. The question here is whether it is necessary or useful to speak of preventing psychological conditions from developing in individuals.

Ten years ago it would have been inappropriate to raise this question. At that time the whole accent in psychiatry and in clinical psychology was on treatment, and it seemed important to remind professionals in these fields that mental disorders would never be controlled by treatment alone, that ways to prevent these conditions had to be found. Specialists in public health provided this reminder, pointing out that wherever control of diseases such as malaria or diptheria had been attained, it was by means of preventive actions directed to the environment, and to infecting "agents" as well as to the "host." Having moved from treatment to prevention of mental illness it now seems appropriate to shift the focus of our energies to an even more fundamental level—the promotion of health development.

It may still be premature to raise the question posed in the present title in some circles or with respect to some problem areas. In the field of alcohol-related problems, for example, there are influential groups of professionals and amateurs who are not really interested in prevention, but devote themselves instead to the treatment of the "inevitable." They think either that "alcoholism" cannot be prevented—without eliminating alcohol—because some people are just born that way, or else that preventive action must await discovery of the biological causes of the condition.

There is a point, however, in asking whether the idea of prevention as applied to mental illness has not outlived its usefulness. Instead of focusing upon this or that specific disorder and asking how it might be prevented, would it not be better to devote our energies to promoting mental health in general?

That we should do this was, of course, forcibly argued in the 1950s by members of and consultants, including the present writer (Sanford, 1955), to the Joint Commission on Mental Illness and Health. Far from winning the day, however, this program was labeled "visionary," and the "core problem" of mental illness was said by the Commission to be the treatment of the mentally ill in hospitals. But no sooner was the Commissions's final report published (1961) than Dr. Rene Dubois of the Rockefeller Foundation disagreed, stating eloquently that the "core-problem" was not treatment at all but how to prevent mental illness from developing in the first place (1961). The debate has continued, the general position I am taking being ably espoused by Murphy and Chandler (chapter 13), by Keniston (1968), and others in reports for the Joint Commission on Mental Health of Children (1968).

The shift in emphasis I am advocating would be in keeping with some important trends in contemporary thought about mental illness and health. It is not only that the last ten years have seen a marked increase in interest in positive mental health—in defining it and in experimenting with ways to promote it (Jahoda, 1958; Sanford, 1966; Menninger, 1963)—but the concept of mental disease itself has been called into question. One would not need go all the way with Szasz (1961) and Becker (1964) in their attacks on psychiatry in order to agree with these writers that what is called mental disease may sometimes be in fact ethical conflict and sometimes mere deviance from social norms, and that for conceptualizing and attempting to cope with these and other psychological troubles medical models of disease are inappropriate and probably harmful.

Particularly relevant to the argument to be advanced here, as to the very similar argument of Murphy and Chandler (Chapter 13), is Menninger's (1963) notion that mental illness is all of one piece. This writer points out that the history of psychiatry could be written as a story of how a long list of categories of mental illness was built up and then gradually reduced to three or four, and finally, in his own work, to just one, i.e., mental illness. Menninger's conception is of a single process underlying diverse manifestations of mental illness and mental health and, hence, of a single dimension extending from serious disruption of "the vital balance" to a condition of being "weller than well." If specific kinds of illness do not exist there is obviously no point in assuming that a diagnosis must be made before people with psychological difficulties can be treated, no point in supposing that illnesses can be prevented by discovering and removing their specific causes. Actions affecting people in the role of patients as well as actions directed to people who might later have psychological difficulties must be guided by conceptions of what, in general, favors individual well-being.

It is not proposed here that we define mental illness out of existence or that we go along with Menninger in reducing the number of kinds of mental illness to one; it *is* proposed, however, that where our concern is with people who are not yet disordered we dispense with the assumption of various diseases each with its specific causes which can be discovered and removed, and that we accept fully the organismic view of the person that is fundamental to Menninger's conception of "the vital balance." If we do this last, it will become clear that any planned action affecting a person's welfare must take into account his complexity and potentialities for further development, and that the goal of full development should take precedence over goals of preventing particular forms of disorder.

To evaluate these proposals, to see their implications, it will be necessary first to examine the most sophisticated of the medical models of prevention, the one known as the public health approach.

THE PUBLIC HEALTH APPROACH TO PREVENTION

This approach is based on the assumption that diseases are caused by multiple interacting factors—factors in the *agent* (e.g., microorganisms or a toxic substance), in the *host* (the human organism or organ system), and in the *environment* (the physical and social environment in which both agent and host have their being). It is concerned with rates of occurrence of diseases in populations (rather than in the particular affected individual) and with aspects of the environment that are widely influential, that impose strains or provide support for the great mass of people. It also embraces several general strategies of prevention.

Multiple Interacting Causes. The idea of the complex causation of disease is of very great importance, for there is good reason to believe that adherence to a single factor theory has held up progress toward prevention for a long time, and is still doing so.

The very old medical belief that each disease has a single dominating cause received strong support from the success of public health workers in controlling diseases such as malaria (by eliminating the responsible germ) and diphtheria (by immunizing populations against the germ). In the case of communicable diseases such as tuberculosis and syphilis, however, matters were by no means so simple. Although the responsible microorganisms have been identified and counteracting drugs discovered, these diseases are still very much with us. Following the single cause logic one would say that the cause of tuberculosis is the *tubercle bacillus.* But how are we to explain the fact that of

100 people exposed to the *bacillus* in the United States, only three actually contract tuberculosis?

Cassel (1963) has offered a theory of the causation of tuberculosis that illustrates well the interaction of multiple factors. He writes: "Exposure to mounting life stresses in people deprived of emotional support from society will lead to their being overwhelmed with a resulting increase in depression and apathy. Such emotional states may lead to an alteration in hormone balance which increases susceptibility to *tubercle bacillus*. If any of these factors are missing, tuberculosis is unlikely to occur." Cassell assembled much evidence that supports—though it does not prove—his theory. The point here is that an understanding of causation would seem to hold for a variety of conditions—noninfectious chronic diseases, mental disorder, problem drinking, social maladjustment—as well as for infectious diseases. Indeed, if it holds for a disease like tuberculosis about which much is known and in which some of the determining factors are readily identified and measured, there is all the more reason why it should hold for the more complicated and obscure mental disorders or disorders in which psychological factors loom large.

If causation is multiple, success in removing or sharply reducing any one of the determining factors or in building up a factor that favors recovery would reduce the rate of occurrence of the disease in question; and so would some slight success in modifying in a favorable way all of the factors involved. The possibility of reducing the rate of occurrence of a disease before knowing precisely how it is caused is illustrated by Cassel's story of tuberculosis. Knowing of an association between socioeconomic marginality and this disease would be enough to indicate that improving the lot of homeless men would reduce rates of this disease, even without invoking a theory about hormone imbalance as a basis for susceptibility to the *bacillus*. Again, to take an example from the field of mental health, Bowlby and his associates (1951, 1956) did not need to prove conclusively that a two-year-old child's separation from his mother for periods of two weeks or longer is a cause of psychopathology in later years. Their thesis was persuasive enough so that the British Ministry of Health issued a directive permitting and encouraging mothers to visit their children in hospitals for unlimited

amounts of time. This administrative action might lead to a reduction in the rate of mental illness in general; and, in any case, it seemed a humane thing to do.

Obviously, however, *something* must be known or strongly suspected about the causative factors, and the more that is known the better.

Strategies of Prevention. Public health workers seek to reduce rates of occurrence of diseases by actions aimed at causative factors known to be, or suspected of, operating widely in the population in question. The idea is to interrupt the chain of causal events, or to intervene in the system of causation, in such a way as to affect in a favorable way the largest possible proportion of those who are exposed to the disease in question.

In seeking to prevent disease, the focus may be on the *host* or on factors in the *environment*, and within each focus the major effort may be either to remove identifiable strains or to strengthen defenses and supports. In the case of tuberculosis, for example, one might seek to maintain or to achieve normal hormone balance in individuals by removing inner psychological sources of emotional upsets, or to develop psychological and physical stamina in individuals so that critical situations would be less upsetting to them; or, turning to the environment, one could try to arrange things so that people were not subjected to mounting strains, or were always assured of someone to talk to or to lean upon when they were in trouble.

What was actually done would depend further upon the aim of the preventive activity, whether it was to prevent the development of any signs or symptoms of a disease or disorder (*primary prevention*) or to detect early signs or symptoms in order to prevent a more serious condition (*secondary prevention*). Primary prevention may be *specific* (directed to a particular disease or disorder) or *nonspecific* (directed to bringing about changes, either in the host or in the environment, that are presumed to have value over and above their impact on any particular disease or disorder).

Improving the lot of homeless men is an example of nonspecific primary prevention; and it is here, I am suggesting, that emphasis should be placed. It seems beyond doubt that improving the psychological functioning of people, reducing the strains under which they have to live, and providing support for them when they are in trouble would reduce the rates of other ills in addition to tuberculosis. Specific primary prevention would be exemplified by efforts to eradicate the *bacillus* itself or to prevent its spread or to prevent exposure to it. For many years, the main approach to the control of tuberculosis has been secondary prevention by early diagnosis and treatment. Rates of this disease have steadily declined but there is no evidence that the rate of decline bears any relation to programs of case finding, medical care, and hospital treatment (McGavran, 1963). It seems, instead, that the decline of the disease has been associated with improving economic conditions, which have brought better housing and nutritional status—an example of nonspecific primary prevention.

A DEVELOPMENTAL MODEL

Preventive actions may be motivated by the simple faith that mental illness is bad, but they must be guided by a positive model of human development. Actions deemed necessary to prevent a particular unhealthy condition may affect a person in various ways, some good and some bad; and in order to weigh these actions, we need a goal that includes, but goes far beyond, the prevention of a single illness. We know that tuberculosis is embedded in a wide context of other problems in the individual. One might hope that the prospects of reducing rates of this particular disease would not be the only incentive that policy-makers could conceive for improving the lot of homeless men. On the other hand, those who are interested in helping these men in order to prevent some other condition, e.g., alcoholism, would do well to cooperate with agencies concerned with the prevention of tuberculosis. From the present point of view, action to improve the lot of homeless men need not be motivated by a concern to prevent anything in particular; a concern with human welfare in general would be sufficient. The basic question is, what would improving the lot of these men consist of? To reply we need a broad and well-articulated model of human welfare. I have argued, in various places (Sanford, 1955, 1962a, 1962b, 1966, 1967, 1968), that the overriding value is full development, the greatest possible differentiation and integration of the personality. Actions to achieve this broad objective would

include, as Murphy and Chandler point out in chapter 13, overcoming arrests in, removing barriers to, and providing stimuli for development. This holds for the homeless man as well as for the hospitalized child.

The mental health specialist who wants to be sure that his actions do more good than harm cannot limit his consideration of goals to the single dimension of increased or decreased "mental health," for it is unthinkable that all desiderata of human development can be derived from this rubric. To be convinced of this one has only to ask what should a person who has achieved mental health do with himself, or whether one would be willing to give up one's ideals of individualism in order to eliminate psychological strains and thus to reduce rates of mental illness. It would be hard to imagine circumstances in which the goal of reducing or preventing mental illness should take precedence over humanity, or justice, or the fullest possible development of the individual's potential.

The literature on positive mental health provides two conceptions of it. One of them posits a resistance to, or relative immunity from, mental illness. There would seem to be a place for this conception, and for research that could specify what such a condition might be. The criticism that positive mental health is incapable of definition would seem not to apply with any great force here, for to define resistance to illness, and to specify it experimentally, would seem to be no more difficult than to define and to specify susceptibility to illness. The second conception of positive mental health embodies a set of ideals referring to what a person might become, and is analytically distinct from the first since not all qualities that contribute to resistance to illness fit in with such positive ideals. For example, a relatively simple personality, with relatively few needs and a narrow but highly integrated cognitive structure reinforced by a homogeneous culture, might be highly resistant to mental illness but also unlikely to develop such ideal qualities as autonomy and creativity. In this sense, the conception based solely on resistance or immunity is less a positive than a sort of double negative.

Conceptions of positive attributes are, of course, central to the developmental-nonspecific preventive approach being advocated here. Psychologists have not been backward about offering such conceptions. In addition to that of Jahoda (1958), schemes of desirable attributes have been put forward since 1950 by Erikson (1950), White (1952), Allport (1961), Maslow (1954), and Barron (1957). In the work of these and other writers the value orientation is sometimes brought under the heading of, or even labeled, "mental health," sometimes "maturity," and sometimes "goals of development." I have argued elsewhere (Sanford, 1962b) that these three desiderata ought to be separated conceptually, and that relations among them should then be studied. Not only can the person be mentally healthy without being highly developed, as suggested above, but a person can be highly developed—complex, autonomous, creative, and the like—but full of painful conflicts. The word "maturity" is sometimes used to stand for desirable levels of development in various qualities, but there is an older, value-free meaning of the word that seems well worth retaining: the possession of a great deal of that which generally distinguishes adults from younger and older people. Efficiency, discrimination, and realism seem more or less distinctively adult, while spontaneity, wholeheartedness, and, of course, honesty are more characteristic of children than of adults. People no doubt differ in their preferences for these two sets of characteristics, as they do respecting most goals of development. This is not to be lamented or wondered at. The point to be emphasized is that when we speak of developmental goals or conceptions of the highly developed person we are in the realm of values. Instead of trying to find some way to achieve ethical neutrality we should, instead, strive to think well about values. It is well known that particular value orientations are easy to criticize, for they frequently can be shown to be bound by culture, social class, or historical era. For example, until quite recently—until the early 1950s probably—the goal of "social adjustment" was highly regarded by many American psychologists. This was viewed with amused tolerance by European intellectuals, who considered it a typical manifestation of our immaturity as a nation. Today "social adjustment" seems definitely passé, not only among articulate student activists but among psychologists, such as those mentioned above, who write about goals for man.

Competence seems more of an "in" thing today, whether the concern be with mental illness or with education. It is particularly interesting to consider *incompetence* as a major dimension of Menninger's "lowest common denominator." A great advantage of this view is that those who take it can always think of something to do for the mentally ill in hospitals. One may not be able to "cure" a patient's "disease" but one can certainly teach him some skills—which may set in motion a process of general improvement. That competence, broadly defined, is to be promoted in all kinds of educational settings is generally taken for granted in our society.

Competence is not, however, universally acclaimed. Many students of the current college generation are questioning the emphasis on this value in institutions of higher learning, and urging that other values, such as humane feeling, ought to have higher priority. At the same time many educators are pointing out that using competence, as measured by school achievement measures, as a basis for admission to higher educational institutions is a form of discrimination against ethnic minorities—that, at the very least, a wide range of kinds of competence ought to be taken into account.

The point for us here is that it is probably a mistake to consider values such as competence by themselves, as if they were in fact separated in the person. It is fine to decide that something is *a* value and to set about promoting it; but it should never be forgotten that virtues and strengths, like illnesses and weaknesses, tend to be interrelated, and to be related as well to other qualities of the person. This means that whatever we do in the interest of a particular value ought to be done with attention to the consequences for other values. Nobody doubts, for example, that academic competence is often attained at the expense of other desirable personal qualities; but it seems equally clear, as Brigante has point out (chapter 23) that intellectual and emotional development can be regarded as parts of the same process; and that it ought not to be beyond *our* competence as educators to make arrangements whereby various aspects of the person develop in concert.

If we are to do this last, however, we must be guided by a general theory of personality and its development, with open-ended conceptions of what people can become, while continuing our efforts to improve thinking about values.

My own thinking about actions to promote personality development has been mainly in the context of education beyond the high school. I have argued that what is needed is an education that concentrates not so much on what it regards as the straightforward process of imparting facts and technical skills as on developing the student as a fully functioning human being. In attempting to summarize this thinking I recently wrote as follows:

> By education for individual development, I mean a program consciously undertaken to promote an identity based on such qualities as flexibility, creativity, openness to experience, and responsibility. Although these qualities depend in part on early experience, college can develop them further and in new ways, as shown by our research at Vassar College a few years ago (Sanford, 1956; Webster, Freedman, & Heist, 1962) and by subsequent studies at other instituions. A college must use all of its resources for this sort of developmental education. The curriculum, methods of teaching, organization of teacher-student relationships, living arrangements, extracurricular activities, activities of the president and his assistants—all should be studied anew, with attention to how they may contribute to individual development. In this effort, the college's plan for a total educational environment must be guided by a theory of personality.

Personality, an inferred organization of processes within the individual, may be conceived as comprising three major systems: a system of primitive impulses and feelings; a system of inhibiting or punishing forces that have been automatically taken over from the social environment—the primitive conscience; and a system that controls and adapts and integrates in accordance with the demands of reality—the ego. The inner life of a person consists largely in conflicts and alliances among these systems; and it is to patterns of their interaction that we may largely attribute observable traits of personality.

A high level of development in personality is characterized most essentially by complexity and by wholeness. There is a high degree of differentiation, a large number of different parts or features having different and specialized functions; and a high degree of integration, a state of affairs in which communication among parts is great enough so that different parts may, without losing their essential identity, become organized into larger wholes in order to serve the larger purposes of the person. In the highly developed person there is a rich and varied impulse life—feelings and emotions having become differ-

entiated and civilized; conscience has been broadened and refined, and it is enlightened and individualized, operating in accord with the individual's best thought and judgment; the processes by which the person judges events and manages actions are strong and flexible, being adaptively responsive to the multitudinous aspects of the environment, and at the same time in close enough touch with the deeper sources of emotion and will so that there is freedom of imagination and an enduring capacity to be fully alive. This highly developed structure underlies the individual's sense of direction, his freedom of thought and action, and his capacity to carry out commitments to others and to himself. But the structure is not fixed once and for all. The highly developed individual is always open to new experience and capable of further learning; his stability is fundamental in the sense that he can go on developing while remaining essentially himself.

Helping people to attain these ideals is a common aim of both psychiatry and education, though educators need more often to recognize these goals consciously or explicitly. The college years of late adolescence are a time when development toward these characteristics can be helped or hindered by what the college does.

Like everyone else, a student develops when confronted with challenges that require new kinds of adaptive responses and when he is freed from the necessity of maintaining unconscious defensive devices. The fulfillment of these conditions results in the enlargement and further differentiation of the systems of the personality, and sets the stage for integration on higher levels (Sanford, 1968, pp. 858—859).[1]

At the same time I have been concerned in recent years with the prevention of alcoholism and other drinking problems. Here my colleagues and I (Cooperative Commission, 1967; Sanford, 1965, 1967; see also Plaut, chapter 16) were led to the view that highly important determinants of problem drinking had to do with the ways in which young people were first introduced to drinking, and that preventive actions should be directed to helping young people to integrate their drinking—or their abstaining—with their developing personalities. Plaut has suggested in chapter 16 some actions that can help prevent problem drinking by reducing the emotionalism associated with drinking, clarifying the distinctions between acceptable and unacceptable drinking, discouraging drinking for its own sake, and helping young people to prepare themselves for life in a predominantly "drinking society." I have sought to view these and other actions in the perspective of a general theory of personality development (Sanford, 1967, 1970a). Drinking that is maximally enjoyable and neither problem causing nor expressive of problems that already exist in the person must be *integrated* with, that is, all-of-a-piece with, the personality. When such integration has been achieved—in a person in whom various needs have been differentiated—the same drinking behavior may provide gratification for a number of different needs while interfering with the gratification of few or no other needs. How hard it is for a person in our society to attain this integration has been suggested by Plaut. Not only have many drinkers—and young people who are tempted to drink—been taught that drinking is bad in and of itself but drinking is readily connected with and becomes an expression of impulses that are ordinarily proscribed in our culture. The problem for the drinker, then, is how to obtain the pleasures of drinking, or satisfaction of the deeper needs of which drinking is an expression, without having to deal with bad conscience or actual punishment of some kind. But this is a special case of a major problem faced by every teenager: how to achieve genuine freedom of impulse. To solve this problem he must find means by which basic emotional needs may be expressed without too much conflict with his other needs or with society. This is largely a matter of acquiring the cultural symbols that enable him to live vicariously and imaginatively and of attaining to the kind of flexible self-control that goes with a relatively high level of ego development. To help the young person perform these tasks is the central purpose of education for individual development.

It has been highly gratifying to discover that Soskin and Korchin (1968) have been thinking along similar lines. Starting out with the aim of developing a therapeutic program for reducing "the incidence and prevalence of the use of hallucinogens and stimulants among high school and junior high school students" they are now operating a sort of "after-school school" which is the very model of a personality-developing institution. They write: "The therapeutic program is designed to promote three personal outcomes in these youth that will enhance ego development at this stage in the maturational process:

(1) to improve their sense of self-identity,
(2) to promote a strong sense of personal competence, and
(3) to effect a commitment to one's personal goals, to community, to one's fellow men. (p. 8)"

They are undertaking to achieve these outcomes through a program embracing group therapy, seminars, small group activities, retreats, work projects, individual consultations, parent-youth consultations, and sessions with groups of parents—all designed in accord with hypotheses concerning ways in which these procedures work to promote development.

Soskin and Korchin note that the activities of their "place" are not ordinarily carried out in public schools and are not likely to be. They envision, therefore, the eventual institutionalization, with support by parents, of centers such as theirs. In my writings about higher education (Sanford, 1962a, 1966, 1967) I have insisted that all the activities of undergraduate institutions, including curriculum making and teaching, have implications for personality development and ought to be guided by developmental theory; I have suggested also that if we were deliberately to set about building institutions for personality development in late adolescence these institutions would turn out to be much like colleges—this because cognitive development cannot be separated from development in other areas or aspects of the person and because these other areas or processes, e.g., emotional and characterological, can be influenced via cognitive processes.

Here it will be apparent to the reader that Brigante (chapter 23) and I have adopted the same general approach. We agree that personality development in schools and colleges depends upon the whole institutional system and that we must attend to all of its parts and functions with a view to how they help or hamper development. As Brigante says, this involves for the mental health specialist a greatly expanded role. He must get out from behind his desk, work with students in groups wherever they are to be found, and seek to improve the whole educational environment. He must do more. He must become an educator, joining with faculty members and administrators in the formulation of educational purposes as well as in the search for means by which they can be realized. He will find that few faculty members are prepared to discuss education, and that few conceive of goals beyond narrow academic ones. He will find also that a major theoretical task—one almost totally neglected by educational psychologists—is to show how the curriculum may be used for such developmental purposes as the stabilization of ego identity, the extention of the self, and the expansion of the domain of "object relations" to include love of subjects or disciplines.

This approach has not exactly revolutionized higher education, but it has had some impact. For example, it influenced the planning of the Santa Cruz campus of the University of California and of Johnston College of the University of Redlands. It wins its way slowly. Meanwhile, it has often been called to my attention that programs of the sort I am talking about were better offered to younger people. In this connection it is most interesting to note the large number of new schools—"experimental schools," "free schools," "in-community schools"—that are springing up around the country. There are at least a dozen in the San Francisco Bay area, for example, the Martin Luther King In-community School in Berkeley. They are being started either by educators who have been "turned off" by the public school system or by educators with a special concern for the young people who have been "turned off" by that system. These schools vary widely in philosophy and specific aims, but it is fair to say that all of them have conceptions of what young people need for their development and some kind of theory, however implicit, about how these needs are to be met by the new school's program.

This is an area that cries out for research. An investigator with the means to measure personal qualities that are supposed to change under the impact of education broadly conceived can find here excellent opportunities for "natural experimentation." Whatever his preferred theory concerning what it takes to develop some important personality dimension he can probably find a school in which precisely that educational procedure is being tried; and it will be easy for him to compare the accomplishments of that school with those of one or more others that have different ideas and proceed in quite different ways.

One area that is especially ripe for research, in view of strains between conflicting ethnic ideologies in contemporary American society,

pertains to the needs of young people of ethnic minorities and how educational or personality-developing institutions can help to meet their needs. Like all others, these young people need cultural identity, a sense of having roots or a tradition of which they may hope to be worthy; but, if some of the newer theories of black culture are valid, their case is special, for they live in a predominantly white society which tells them in one breath that they must conform with *its* superior culture but that they cannot fully do so because by its standards they are inferior and must remain so. It is reasonable to ask how, in these circumstances, they are to acquire the self-respect necessary to the development of their personalities; how they can avoid the self-contempt that is a fundamental cause of delinquency, alcoholism, and drug addiction. There is good reason to believe that people can attain to a suitable degree of self-love only if they are permitted to live during their most formative years in a culture that affirms them as they are, whatever their color, and that is relatively free of conflicts respecting basic values. It has been this knowledge, one may believe, that has persuaded American Indians that they had to preserve their cultures—which they have done in the face of almost inconceivable odds; they have seen too many of their children corrupted by a dominant society that would neither respect their differences nor permit them full membership in it. This is consistent with the report of Ortega (1969) that Spanish-speaking Americans who emerged as leaders in the Southwest lived during their formative years in Chicano enclaves where they were relatively untroubled by the intrusions of "Anglo" culture—until they had enough security in their identity to enable them to cope with the surrounding dominant culture. In this light, the efforts of black people to preserve, to reconstruct, and to create a cultural heritage of their own may be seen as fitting directly into the emphasis on personality development that I am advocating.

All this must, however, be seen in a developmental perspective. Cultural identity is by no means all that a person needs in order to participate fully in a society such as ours, and what is at one time necessary for self-definition can at another stage become restrictive. People whose personalities develop securely in one culture can learn without great difficulty to live in one or more other cultures; they can become citizens of the world. But first they must have a secure sense of identity in *one* culture. Everybody is familiar with the white, middle class adolescent who goes abroad and compares everything unfavorably with what he has known at home; we sympathize with him in his need to be sure of himself and what he belongs to before he can appreciate differences or adapt himself to foreign ways. We ought to consider in this light the young black militant who is striving for a sense of identity with a newly conscious black community and to recognize that it is imperative for him to accomplish this phase of personality development before he is fully open to the kind of education that can prepare him for a creative role in a wider and more pluralistic community.

Community-run schools and ethnic studies programs within schools and colleges are thus highly significant as personality-developing institutions; they should be supported and then carefully evaluated. Although members of ethnic minorities are, as individuals, no less susceptible to ethnic prejudice than other people, it seems unfair to label as "racism in reverse" or as "separatism" the efforts of these minorities to establish some cultural basis for identity and pride. When these minorities have what they want and need, namely, their own cultural identity *and* the freedom to go where they please, we will find them mingling freely with white people in all places where the good things of our society are to be had. This suggests that educational programs for ethnic identity can very well be carried out in integrated schools, provided these schools are not run by white people for the benefit of white people, and provided white people do not say, in effect, "we'll accept them when they become like us" nor feel guilty or anxious every time minority students are observed to stick together—in the cafeteria, or on the playground, or in classes of their own.

CONCLUSION

A shift of emphasis from preventing particular problems to building up personality in general would have implications for various kinds of professional workers. College and school counselors, for example, instead of waiting in their offices for students who feel they have problems

to come in, would devote themselves to activities designed to promote the well-being and development of all the students in their institutions. Again, mental health specialists who work with adults and older people will do well to consider that, given the right conditions, personality development can occur at any age; and that health, well-being, and development are better promoted by dwelling more on possibilities and potentialities than on difficulties, weaknesses, and failures. My colleagues and I have found, both in our studies of middle aged college alumni (Freedman, 1962) and in our studies of college professors (Sanford, 1970b), that adults who come to us in order to help with "our study" and are then studied in some depth almost universally report considerable benefit from the experience. Some of them, indeed, change the directions and styles of their lives.

A great advantage of this approach, here as with college students, is that people are able to have the benefits of seeing themselves in fresh perspectives, of discussing matters ordinarily not thought of, of experiencing a new kind of interpersonal relationship, of personal stock taking, without having first to be labeled as "problems"—a process which is itself problem causing.

We must note here, however, as we did in the beginning, that all this discussion concerns structures in the personality and that personality and behavior are two different things. Probably we shall always have to be concerned about preventing certain kinds of destructive and self-destructive behavior—regardless of our success in building up healthy dispositions of personality. Behavior, after all, always depends upon the situation of the individual and thus there will probably continue to be a place for cultural and legal controls. For example, fewer people would be shot if we had adequate gun control laws. Many deaths have occurred because a gun happened to be handy. This could occur even though all members of the population were within normal limits as far as personality was concerned: There could be killings in fits of anger or fits of depression or merely by accident. Again, there would probably be a slight reduction in the rate of suicide if people who fell into periods of depression could immediately walk into some kind of mental health center and find someone to talk to. To take yet another example, if our young people who are brought into court for running away from home or being called incorrigible by their parents or guardians were not thrown into jail or otherwise labeled delinquent, but instead were given some help with their problems, we would probably have a reduction in the rates of delinquency.

But, be it noted, actions that would offer depressed people someone to talk to, or reduce the number of loaded guns in homes, or provide decent attention to the problems of runaways need not be justified on the grounds that they help to prevent problematic behavior; in an enlightened and humane society such actions would be taken anyway, on the ground that they favor or express a high quality of life.

The argument of this paper is still that the bulk of our resources should go into general building-up activities rather than to efforts at preventing particular problems. A major objection to this thesis may turn out to be practical. This is, it seems much easier to raise money in order to prevent or to ward off some evil than to raise money for some imagined good. For example, it is certainly easier to get money in order to prevent tuberculosis than to get money for the purpose of making poor people happy. This may be an aspect of human nature or it may be simply an expression of the way things work in a society such as ours. It does seem that the organization of research and services within the helping professions assumes the persistence of this way of looking at things. And there is no doubt that this organization is going to be hard to change. Nevertheless, as we are fond of saying to college students, it is possible to achieve something by working within the system; those professional people who are really convinced of the priority of personality development can find ways to promote their ends through the flexible use of the present agencies for funding, while bending their efforts toward converting more and more people to their way of looking at mental health and illness.

Notes

Work on this chapter was supported in part by a Research Scientist Award (K5–MH–12, 829) from the National Institute of Mental Health.

1. Reprinted with permission from Sanford (1968). Copyright 1968 by the American Orthopsychiatric Association, Inc.

References

Allport, G. W. *Pattern and growth in personality*. New York: Holt, Rinehart & Winston, 1961.

Barron, F. What is psychological health. *California Monthly*, 1957, 68, 22–25.

Becker, E. *The revolution in psychiatry*. Glencoe, Ill.: Free Press, 1964.

Bowlby, J. *Maternal care and mental health*. Geneva: World Health Organization, 1951.

Bowlby, J., Ainsworth, M., Boston, M., & Rosenbluth, D. The effects of mother-child separation: A follow-up study. *British Journal of Medical Psychology*, 1956, 29, 211.

Cassell, J. C. Potentialities and limitations of epidemiology. In *Key issues in the prevention of alcoholism*. (Report of the Northeast Conference) Harrisburg, Pa.: Pennsylvania Department of Health, 1963.

Cooperative Commission on the Study of Alcoholism. *Alcohol problems: A report to the nation*. (Prepared by T. F. A. Plaut) New York: Oxford, 1967.

DuBois, R. J. An outsider's view of *Action for mental health*. Unpublished paper presented at the annual meeting of the National Association for Mental Health, Miami, November 16, 1961.

Erikson, E. H. *Childhood and society*. New York: Norton, 1950.

Freedman, M. Studies of college alumni. In N. Sanford (ed.), *The American college*. New York: Wiley, 1962.

Jahoda, M. *Current concepts of positive mental health*. New York: Basic Books, 1958.

Joint Commission on Mental Illness and Health. *Action for mental health*. New York: Basic Books, 1961.

Joint Commission on Mental Health of Children. Statements and tentative recommendations. Prepared for discussion at the annual meeting of affiliate organizations, board of directors, and task force chairmen of Joint Commission on Mental Health of Children, January 22, 1968.

Keniston, K. The tasks of adolescence. Preliminary report for the Joint Commission on Mental Health of Children, 1968.

McGavran, E. G. Facing reality in public health. In *Key issues in prevention of alcoholism*. Harrisburg, Pa.: Division of Behavioral Problems and Drug Control, Pennsylvania Department of Public Health, 1963.

Maslow, A. H. *Motivation and personality*. New York: Harper & Row, 1954.

Menninger, K. *The vital balance: The life process in mental health and illness*. New York: Viking, 1963. (With M. Mayman & P. Pruyser)

Ortega, G. Discussion of Sanford's paper. Presented at the annual meeting of the Association of Governing Boards of Colleges and Universities, Washington, D. C., November 6, 1969.

Sanford, N. The findings of the commission on Psychology. *Annals of the New York Academy of Science*, 1955, 63, 341–364.

Sanford, N. (ed.) Personality development during the college years. *Journal of Social Issues*, 1956, 12(4), 1–70.

Sanford, N. Developmental status of the entering freshman. In N. Sanford (ed.), *The American college.* New York: Wiley, 1962. (a)

Sanford, N. What is a normal personality? In J. Katz, P. Nochlin, & R. Stover (eds.), *Writers on ethics.* Princeton, N. J.: Van Nostrand, 1962. (b)

Sanford, N. The prevention of mental illness. In B. Wolman (ed.), *Handbook of clinical psychology.* New York: McGraw-Hill, 1965.

Sanford, N. *Self and society.* New York: Atherton, 1966.

Sanford, N. *Where colleges fail.* San Francisco: Jossey-Bass, 1967.

Sanford, N. Education for individual development. *American Journal of Orthopsychiatry*, 1968, 38, 858–868. Copyright, The American Orthopsychiatric Association, Inc. Reproduced by permission.

Sanford, N. The prevention of alcoholism. In D. Adelson & B. Kalis (eds.), *Community psychology.* San Francisco: Chandler, 1970. (a)

Sanford, N. A model program for improving college teaching. Berkeley, Calif.: The Wright Institute, 1970. (Mimeo) (b)

Soskin, W., & Korchin, S. Therapeutic explorations with adolescent drug users. Unpublished manuscript, Psychology Clinic, University of California, Berkeley, 1967.

Szasz, T. *The myth of mental illness: Foundations for a theory of personal conduct.* New York: Hoeber-Harper, 1961.

Webster, H., Freedman, M., & Heist, P. Personality changes in college students. In N. Sanford (ed.), *The American college.* New York: Wiley, 1962.

White, R. W. *Lives in progress.* New York: Dryden, 1952.

IV

Community Mental Health:
The Conception, Practice, and
Effect of Intervention

Previous chapters of the Handbook have been concerned with intervention, but with differing purposes from the chapters in part IV. The chapters in part IV, in developing the conception, practice, and effects of intervention more fully, stress indirect strategies such as consultation, education, and community development. Included are case histories telling of the struggle for program survival and effectiveness at institutional, community, and national levels.

Part IV begins with a primer for the consultant and a guide for the mental health educator. In his chapter "Mental Health Consultation," John Altrocchi provides practical guidance on theory, techniques, roles, phases, and pitfalls in consultation. Daniel Adelson and Lawrence Lurie, in "Mental Health Education: Research and Practice," provide a conceptual frame of reference drawn from empirical findings, and offer practical tools for the planning and practice of mental health education.

In part III, Trickett, Kelly, and Todd (chapter 14) described the high school environment and anticipated issues of mental health intervention in differing educational settings. Now, in chapters 22 and 23 of part IV, Murray Levine and Anthony M. Graziano evaluate the literature regarding the application of mental health concepts in educa-

tion, and Thomas R. Brigante examines the issues of establishing college and university mental health programs. Both chapters advocate particular intervention strategies: Levine and Graziano see intervention at the elementary classroom level as holding maximum potential for behavioral science efforts toward social change; Brigante offers plans for increasing the emotional availability of campus personnel to students.

In chapter 24–32, the dimensions of program development strategy described in part I are further illustrated in case studies and program descriptions. Innovation in helpers and direct service recipients may be seen in programs which use parents as therapists for their own children and in other uses of paraprofessionals. Experimentation with services provided is illustrated in the use of consultation and psychotherapeutic intervention with delinquent youth. Experimentation with location and occasion of service delivery are apparent in separate chapters on rural and urban mental health programs. The nine case examples, by chapter, are as follows:

In chapter 24, "Parents as Agents of Behavioral Change," Leopold O. Walder, Shlomo I. Cohen, Dennis E. Breiter, Frank C. Warman, David Orme-Johnson, and Stanley Pavey describe a sample program which attempted to give parents the technical information and skills needed to better handle their problems in raising children and to guide their children's behavioral development. The authors stress the learning theory basis of their approach and its nonreliance on diagnostic labeling.

In Frances Kaplan and Donald Quinlan's "Mental Health Consultation to Community Settings: A Case Study of a Failure to Achieve Goals," the reader has opportunity to encounter in practice the theory of consultation developed in chapters 20 and 21 of this part. The authors have recorded their consultation experience within a small hospital in the form of an informal and often intimate diary of the consultative relationship, to provide a concrete example of the complexity of dealing with a social system that at best can be only partially understood when the consultant enters. Interspersed with the authors' process notes is discussion enriched by their knowledge gained from the experience.

In "Psychological Consultation in a Maximum Security Prison: A Case History and Some Comments," Edward S. Katkin relates his experience that the traditional framework of clinical psychology fits poorly within the walls of a highly restricted prison institution. He describes the failed attempts to provide traditional psychological services within a large maximum security prison in upstate New York, presents reasons why this traditional orientation failed, and describes the emergence of a changed role for the consultants involved. He extrapolates from this particular experience to the experience of clinical consultants to alien institutions in general, and emphasizes the necessity he and his colleagues found for deep involvement in institutional administration and politics.

Milton F. Shore and Joseph L. Massimo, in "An Innovative Approach to the Treatment of Adolescent Delinquent Boys Within a Suburban Community," descibe their efforts to reach "unreachable" delinquent youth. Using a community model, the program was designed to provide vocational assistance, remedial education, and psychotherapy to youths at the crisis point of suspension or dropout from school; mental health professionals met the youths in the youths' milieu.

In "The Politics of Mental Health," Bertram M. Brown and James W. Stockdill present a forceful case for participation by mental health professionals, behavioral scientists, and mental health paraprofessionals in the political life of the community, on all those levels where public

policies are determined. Using a case study in program development, they emphasize especially that professionals must understand the mechanisms interacting between social problems and public policy formulations in order to move public policy toward a dominant concern with the quality of life. Whereas it is the very vagueness of mental health definitions and goals that has driven mental health practitioners into practical politics to achieve effective programs, the authors see educated political involvement by mental health practitioners as a practical means toward the achievement of broadly defined goals.

In his chapter "The Community Mental Health Centers Program," Alan I. Levenson has presented straightforwardly the historical background and functioning of that program, and the basic concepts and operational definitions of community mental health centers functioning within that program. After offering practical ideas for implementation of the center approach, he analyzes the challenges and opportunities facing the mental health professional encountering for the first time the necessity for new forms of clinical service, consultative roles, and new administrative responsibilities in the community setting.

The essential ways in which a rural program differs from its urban counterpart, the special problems encountered in the rural setting, and some clear advantages of that setting provide the main subject matter of Hans Huessy's chapter, "Tactics and Targets in the Rural Setting." In addition, Huessy persuasively sets forth principles applicable to mental health programming in any environment, drawn from his experience in the rural setting with its qualities of high visibility of persons and community structures.

In "Woodlawn Mental Health Center: An Evolving Strategy for Planning in Community Mental Health," Sheppard G. Kellam, Jeannette D. Branch, Khazan C. Agrawal, and Margaret E. Grabill detail the development and evolution of the Center's original community mental health program, operating in cooperation with an urban black community on the South Side of Chicago. The Center from its beginnings placed first emphasis on continuous community sanction and participation in policymaking. The chapter follows the authors' model program of intervention (here directed at the problem of adaptation in first grade) through planned stages of assessment, program design, periodic program evaluation, and redesign or refinement based on evaluative measures. The Woodlawn Mental Health Center was conceived and implemented in the early 1960s, and provides a developmental model of the community orientation.

Whereas the previous chapter concentrates on the implementation and followup of a specific program, Sheldon K. Schiff in "Free Inquiry and the Enduring Commitment: The Woodlawn Mental Health Center 1963–1970" has focused on the struggle of the Center to meet community commitments in the face of political obstacles that arose at critical points in the evolution of the Center's original and later programs. Schiff's candid relating of the Woodlawn Center's battle for survival, and his eloquent statement of intensifying personal commitment to free inquiry, the community-professional contract, and democracy raise many powerful issues including that of university-community responsibility.

The concluding three chapters in part IV bring together consideration of research and program evaluation. One chapter surveys research in consultation, a second considers information systems and a necessary data base for program evaluation, and the concluding chapter reviews the area of program evaluation.

Fortune V. Mannino and Milton F. Shore, in "Research in Mental Health Consultation," have written a thorough, integrative chapter reviewing published and unpublished researches and evaluations of consultative practice. It is a symptom of mental health consultation's newness and rapid growth that often common sense has substituted for theory; the requirement grows for goal definitions and empirical studies of high scientific standards. The present authors have critically gathered existing studies for the purpose of adding definition and indicating research needs and directions.

The rapid growth of the community mental health field, with diffusion of care as one of its goals, creates complex problems of systematic information collection and retrieval. To satisfy clincial, management, planning, and research needs of coordinated mental health services, community mental health may utilize modern technological capabilities. In "Community Mental Health Information Systems: The Psychiatric Case Register as a Data Bank," J. A. Baldwin reviews the need for systematic information in the community mental health field, surveys types of data collection systems and their uses, develops the recent concept of the computerized data bank, and treats by example one highly flexible and complete form of the data bank – the psychiatric case register. Baldwin addresses himself briefly to the political and ethical implications of large scale information systems.

As in mental health consultation, an accelerating priority exists for good research and evaluation in more generalized community programs to support community mental health's increased demands for manpower, funds, facilities, and other-agency participation. Bernard L. Bloom, in "Mental Health Program Evaluation," has provided an extensive analysis of the reasons for widespread failure to provide thorough and effective program evaluation, and has critically reviewed several recent program evaluation studies point by point. Bloom closes his chapter and this section with a survey of corrective trends in clinical training, intended to increase the empirical orientation both of university students and of practitioners in the field. He has thus anticipated the focus of the fifth and final part of this volume.

20

Mental Health Consultation

John Altrocchi

"No one, apparently, will object to being called a consultant. The term has prestige value, the quietly unassailable dignity of a hallmark. *Being* a consultant, however, is something else again and not often carried off with 'quietly unassailable dignity.' It is likely to be either a thankless or a most arduous undertaking; the former if we do it poorly, the latter if we do it well (Stringer, 1961, p. 85)."

Mental health consultation has recently become "a popular but misty 'Camino Real' for the transmission of behavioral science understandings to educational settings" (Klein, 1967, p. 403), and to ministers, public health nurses, police, and many other care-giving groups. The federal government has made consultation one of the ten keystones of a community mental health program (Department of Health, Education, and Welfare, 1964). Logistic and manpower considerations are fundamental to this growth in the popularity of mental health consultation in that the major goal is to affect the behavior of many people by working through significant care-givers. Unfortunately, there is only a meager theoretical basis to support consultation techniques and even less evaluative evidence to suggest that they are effective. This chapter will review, analyze, and attempt to integrate existing theory and the varied practices of mental health consultation, differentiating it from related interpersonal methods such as supervision and psychotherapy; and will attempt to differentiate and clarify the various types, roles, techniques, phases, and pitfalls of mental health consultation and to suggest some perspectives for future developments. Chapter 33 by Mannino and Shore will review research methods and findings relevant to mental health consultation.

Many professionals who are involved in community psychology or community mental health are called consultants. They may be called or may call themselves consultants by administrative fiat, or in order to clarify status, or for other considerations, rather than because they consult. Furthermore, in his consultant role a mental health consultant may appropriately perform other functions besides consultation, such as teaching or intervening clinically with a patient. Thus this chapter will focus on what mental health consultation is and on what mental health consultants do rather than on who is called a mental health consultant.

WHAT IS CONSULTATION?

"Consultation or something akin to it has been practiced since the first time one man turned to another for advice or counsel" (Maddux, 1955, p. 1424).

The term consultation has a long and honored history but has been used in a wide variety of ways. A very old meaning is that of one physician asking another to evaluate the former's patient in order to make treatment recommendations (Bindman, 1966). In England the term refers to almost any professional activity carried out by a specialist physician (Caplan, 1964). Similarly, many patients in the United States are referred for psychiatric or psychological consultation rather than for psychiatric evaluation or psychological assessment. In these situations the consultant acts as an expert technical specialist who evaluates. Since other terms, such as those used above, are and can easily be used for such activities, it is clearer not to use consultation to describe them. Nevertheless, many will continue to do so. Some confusion is avoided, however, because such activities are rarely, if ever, referred to as mental health consultation.

A more recent, quite different use of the generic term consultation has developed among applied behavioral scientists, especially students of group and organizational processes, to refer to their attempts at planned social change in industrial organizations, educational systems, or communities (Gibb & Lippitt, 1959). In this kind of consultation, the consultant tends to initiate consultation contacts, sees himself as a change agent and trainer, and tends to collaborate with the consultees in research which has as one of its aims the promotion of change within the system in which the consultee is operating. This kind of consultation usually concerns restraints to creative change and development that reside in or are reinforced by the organization, group, or social system (Bindman, 1966; Klein, 1964). Once again some confusion is usually avoided because such consultation is not usually called mental health consultation. Nevertheless, this consultation approach merits careful consideration by those involved in community psychology and community mental health.

A third general meaning of the term consultation evolved in industry and especially in public health (Croley, 1961; Gilbert, 1960; Maddux, 1955; Siegel, 1955; Towle, 1950). This trend has provided the primary background for current theory and practice of mental health consultation, primarily because of Caplan's influence. We will adapt Caplan's (1964, p. 212; 1970, p. 19) definition of consultation by broadening it slightly to include consultation that directly involves more than two people and that involves people who may not be professionals. Thus consultation is here defined as *an interaction between two or more people—the consultant or consultants, who are specialists, and the consultee or consultees, who invoke the consultant's help, within the consultees' usual work or professional functioning, in regard to a current work problem with which he or they are having some difficulty and which he or they have decided is within the consultant's area of specialized competence.* The work problem

involves the management of, treatment of, or relationship with one or more clients or associates of the consultee or consultees or the planning of a program for the benefit of such clients or associates.

Several features of this definition of consultation should be noted. Expanding Caplan's original definition beyond the one-to-one relationship is appropriate because so much consultation is carried on in groups and because principles of mental health consultation with groups (Altrocchi, Spielberger, & Eisdorfer, 1965) are generally consistent with principles of individual mental health consultation (Bindman, 1959; Caplan, 1964, 1970). The broadening of Caplan's definition to include nonprofessionals as possible consultees is less grounded in established practice but is based on recently increasing interest among community psychologists in working with informal, nonprofessional gatekeepers, care-givers, or agents, such as bartenders or beauticians, who may occupy crucial positions in informal social networks, who often mediate between the general population and formal health resources, and to whom some people turn in crisis (Caplan, 1964; Kelly, 1964; Reiff & Riessman, 1964). Since principles of consultation with such informal gatekeepers would be essentially identical with principles of consultation with professionals, it seems wise to include both under the same definition rather than trying to develop a new term.

Another noteworthy feature of the definition is that client responsibility remains clearly in the hands of the consultee:

The definition of consultation is further restricted to that type of professional interaction in which the consultant accepts no direct responsibility for implementing remedial action for the client, and in which professional responsibility for the client remains with the consultee just as much as it did before he asked the consultant for help. The consultant may offer helpful clarifications, diagnostic formulations, or advice on treatment; but the consultee will be free to accept or reject all or part of this help. In other words, the consultant exercises no administrative or coercive authority over the consultee (Caplan, 1970, pp. 19–20).

There is probably no more powerful message than this in definitions of consultation, no more frequent shoal on which consultants in training flounder, and no aspect of consultation about which even the most experienced consultant must frequently warn himself. Allowing consultees to retain entire responsibility conflicts somewhat with the consultant's experiences in supervision and administration; with the consultant's often accurate inference that he may be technically better able than the consultee to handle certain of the consultee's problem clients; and with needs for power, control, and self-aggrandizement which any consultant may occasionally find influencing his behavior. Nevertheless, in a very real way, the long-range goal of consultation is to work toward the time when consultation will no longer be needed.

This crucial responsibility feature of consultation is related to a final key feature of the definition:

Another essential aspect of this type of consultation is that the consultant engages in the activity not only in order to help the consultee with his current work problem in relation to a specific client or program but also in order to add to the consultee's knowledge and to lessen areas of misunderstanding, so that he may be able in the future to deal more effectively on his own with this category of problem. It is this educational aspect of consultation that makes it a community method, since its goal is to spread the application of the specialist's knowledge through the future operations of those who have consulted him in relation to current problems (Caplan, 1970, p. 20).

This quotation makes the primary goal of consultation clear—to affect many people by working through key care-givers. This goal is often part of a public health approach to community problems—the attempt to decrease disorders and increase effective functioning in a population. This leads us to the specific area of mental health consultation as one kind of consultation.

MENTAL HEALTH CONSULTATION

Mental health consultation is not an island unto itself; it does not stand alone as a completely new social invention. The fact that mental health consultants are of certain professional backgrounds suggests that the different parent professions have provided a unique backlog of familiar skills and knowledge which are being brought to *new* relationships, but to *familiar* problems of human interaction. . . . Mental health consultation is a sibling in the family of helping relationships and is a close cousin to other forms of interpersonal processes (Klein & Perlitsh, 1964, p. 1).

Mental health consultation developed from the two historical roots of consultation in public health and psychotherapeutic principles, especially those developed by child psychiatric treatment teams for work with parents (Klein, 1964). In a series of papers, lectures, and books culminating in *The Theory and Practice of Mental Health Consultation* in 1970, Gerald Caplan has exerted the major influence in coalescing psychotherapeutic and consultation principles.

Mental health consultation refers to consultation which is carried out by mental health specialists with care-givers, such as teachers, nurses, policemen, family doctors, and clergymen, who play important roles in the promotion of mental health and in the prevention and treatment of psychological disorders. Since community mental health centrally involves interpersonal relations, and mental health consultants have some knowledge about interpersonal relationships, the relationships of the consultee with his clients are more likely to be dealt with in mental health consultation than in other kinds of consultation. Adapting Bindman's (1959) and Caplan's (1970) definitions slightly to include groups and nonprofessional consultees, mental health consultation is defined here as *an interaction between two or more people—the consultant or consultants, who are mental health specialists, and the consultee or consultees, who play roles in community mental health and who invoke the consultant's help, within the consultees' usual work or professional functioning, in regard to a current work problem which is relevant to mental health and with which the consultee or consultees are having some difficulty.*

As was true of the earlier definition of the generic term consultation, this definition implies that the consultee may be a group of one or more nonprofessionals; that the responsibility for the client remains with the consultee; and that a major goal is to enable the consultee to handle similar problems more effectively in the future. This goal does not imply that the consultee should become a junior psychotherapist, although it does imply that he may become more psychotherapeutic. A specific goal is to assist key professional workers or key informal care-givers to become more sensitive to the personal and interpersonal needs of their clients and associates and more comfortable and adept in their relationships with them, *entirely within the consultees' accustomed responsibilities and roles* (Altrocchi et al., 1965; Bindman, 1959).

The specific theoretical base for much of the practice of mental health consultation involves the effects of crisis states on subsequent behavior. It is assumed that members of certain professional groups, such as ministers, physicians, police, welfare caseworkers, school personnel, and public health nurses, as well as many informal gate-keepers, are likely to be called upon or will at least be present in times of personal and interpersonal crises (Caplan, 1964). It is further assumed that such time-limited crises provide particularly important opportunities for psychological growth as well as psychological deterioration. During a crisis a person usually seeks help of some kind and is presumed to be more susceptible to influence than at more stable periods of his life. Crises thus present care-givers with unusual opportunities for deploying their efforts effectively toward preven-tion of psychological disorders and promotion of mental health in a population (Caplan, 1964). Hallock and Vaughan (1956) see mental health consultation as approximating specific prevention, in that consultation is concerned with clients who are currently maladapted to their social environ-ment, who are reacting nonadaptively to stress, and whose functioning may further decompensate if they do not find more constructive means of dealing with stress. On the positive side, mental health consultation can enhance clients' opportu-nities to develop new strengths when they work through a crisis effectively (Hollister, 1967a). A problem with crisis theory, however, is that Bloom (1963) has shown that there are serious difficulties in reliably discriminating crisis states from noncrisis states, so that further refinement of the crisis concept is needed.

A mental health consultant thus assumes that people are involved in networks of interdepend-ency (Klein & Perlitsh, 1964) and he

. . . adopts, so to speak, an 'ecological theory of emotional health' which assumes a dynamic equilibrium (homeostasis) between the consultee and his psychologically relevant environment. Within this framework the focus of interaction shifts from individual diagnosis, sickness, and treatment, to appraisal of situations, health promotion and collaboration. The consultee,

therefore, is not received as a client or patient but rather as a collaborator and co-professional. Similarly the consultant is not viewed as a therapist or the giver of prescriptive advice. Instead, the consultant seeks to assist a co-profes-sional (to) deal more effectively with that segment of the population which he serves, by helping the consultee solve those problems in his work which have mental health implications (Simmons, 1960, p. 2).

It will be seen below that, since most mental health consultants come from individually ori-ented clinical disciplines, they do not always shift their focus to situations and health promotion, but they can do so and often need to do so.

MENTAL HEALTH CONSULTATION AS DISTINGUISHED FROM RELATED INTERPERSONAL METHODS

Mental health consultation is similar in some respects to education, supervision, administration, collaboration, and psychotherapy, but it is discriminably different from each of these other methods. Although a mental health consultant may find himself involved in these endeavors, and others too, it is important for him and the consultees to be clear about what role he is in and what method he is using at all times so as to avoid confusion.

Mental Health Consultation and Education

Clearly one of the goals of mental health consultation is educational—teaching the consultee to handle similar problems more effectively in the future—and the consultant may impart general knowledge or teach specific skills to the consultees. Nevertheless there are major differ-ences between mental health consultation and education (Bindman, 1966). Education tends to emphasize a formal, systematic approach; the teacher usually plans and presents the content material to the student in authoritative fashion; the focus is upon the acquisition of knowledge and skills; and the educator has some administrative and evaluative authority. In mental health consultation the content material is not usually presented from above but usually emerges from discussing the consultees' work problems; the focus is on helping the consultees to solve their current and future work problems as well as on acquisition of knowledge and skills; and the consultant does not have administrative authority and thus does not evaluate or grade the consultees. Despite these many differences, however, modern kinds of democratically oriented education are, in many ways, as close to consultation as to traditional education (Abramovitz, 1958).

Mental Health Consultation and Supervision

Mental health consultation and clinical supervision both involve a person with more knowledge or experience in a mental health field helping and advising one or more other people with a specific mental-health-related work problem, with emphasis on understanding general principles and technical procedures. In supervision, however, the supervisor "oversees" the supervisee's work and he is responsible for work of the supervisee: The supervisor directs and evaluates the performance of the supervisee and they are usually from the same professional discipline. In contrast, the mental health consultant is not responsible for the consultee's total work performance and should remain relatively nonevaluative. Often the consultant and consultee are from different disciplines. The key difference is that the supervisor is responsible for the supervisee's work and training, while the consultant is an outside resource person, who is called upon to provide something which the host staff can not provide (Bindman, 1966; Rieman, 1965).

The status of many mental health consultants added to the authority of their ideas, however, often implicitly gives them most of the emotional authority that is ordinarily possessed by a supervisor (Klein, 1964). Thus a case conference for a group of social workers led by a psychiatric consultant is often more similar to supervision than to mental health consultation. Finally, the distinction between consultation and supervision is blurred by the fact that modern supervision makes increasing use of consultative approaches in an effort to help supervisees gain greater self-reliance (Klein, 1964).

Mental Health Consultation and Administration

Another source of potential confusion is the tendency of some consultants to assume responsi-

bility for decisions and administrative leadership (Rhodes, 1960). The administrative role includes responsibility for making decisions and promulgating specific policy; and subordinates are expected to follow the administrator's directions. Mental health consultation has a "take it or leave it" quality. The consultant does not make decisions; the consultee has the right to make his own decisions. The consultant may discuss administrative-related problems with consultees or consult with an administrator about administrative problems, but he is promoting confusion and possibly serious trouble if he assumes the role of administrator when acting as a consultant. The difficulty in separating consultation from administration is especially great when the consultant is part of the organization with whom he is consulting, and acutely so if he also has administrative responsibilities in the organization. Mental health consultation appears to work best when the consultant can keep his role free of administrative authority or responsibility, and when he is able to come into the organization from the outside for purposes of consultation (Bindman, 1966).

Mental Health Consultation and Collaboration

In collaboration, two or more people work together to solve a common problem. As a result of mutual discussion and planning, they may reach joint decisions and carry out action together, as in a collaborative research project. In mental health consultation the consultant is more an advisor than a collaborator, and the consultant is not expected to participate in carrying out action that results from decisions reached by the consultee.

Mental Health Consultation and Psychotherapy

The distinction between mental health consultation and psychotherapy has generated the most anxiety and concern among mental health workers and their consultees and this distinction is therefore most important to clarify. Mental health consultation developed in part from psychotherapeutic principles and is similar to psychotherapy in its attempt to increase the effectiveness, sensitivity, and personal growth of consultees by applying interpersonal processes to intellectual and affective learning; but there are some crucial differences (Altrocchi et al., 1965; Bindman, 1966): Consultation emphasizes educational goals rather than modification of a disorder. The psychological contract in psychotherapy usually involves an agreement by the patient to infringements on his customary privacy, but in consultation the consultee has a right to expect his own privacy to be respected (Caplan, 1970). Furthermore the implicit contract in consultation (Caplan, 1964; Parker, 1958) allows the consultee complete freedom to apply what he learns or not as he sees fit, whereas in psychotherapy the patient is not usually led to believe that he has that much freedom. In mental health consultation, in contrast to some kinds of psychotherapy, transference is minimized, reporting of dreams is never encouraged, resistance is usually not interpreted and is respected as much as possible, and defenses are often supported. Finally, the central distinction is that the content focus of mental health consultation is on the work problems rather than on the personal problems of the consultee: Even consultees' affective reactions to their clients' problems, if they are discussed at all, are discussed only in relation to the consultees' current work problems with the clients.

Some methods of consultation, such as the interactional approach proposed by Delaney, Mullan, and Harari (1959), focus on staff interpersonal blocks, and thus fall in between mental health consultation and psychotherapy. It will be invigorating if many such methods are proposed and developed. What is necessary is that mental health consultants and consultees be clear about what they are doing with each other, operate with mutual consent in all phases of their relationship, and avoid sub rosa psychotherapy which can subtly develop when the consultee desires therapy and the consultant is psychotherapeutically oriented. This can be a trap from which all parties find it painful to extricate themselves (Bindman, 1959, 1966; Caplan, 1964, 1970).

TYPES OF MENTAL HEALTH CONSULTATION

There are many ways that mental health consultation can be classified. For instance, there are the direct and indirect methods of dealing with consultee affect (see section on techniques). The use of the term indirect in this context is not to be confused with the term "indirect service," which many mental health professionals use to refer to indirect methods (including consultation) of serving patients and their families. Another relevant dichotomous classification would be mental health consultation in which the consultant serves primarily as a resource person and mental health consultation in which he serves primarily as a process consultant by helping the consultee or group to understand his or their own functioning better (Klein, 1964). One could also classify consultation into crisis or emergency consultation versus continuous consultation; but sometimes crisis consultation progresses into continuous consultation and crises almost invariable emerge and assume temporary priority in continuous consultation. These pairs of terms may be useful as long as they are understood to refer to end points of behavioral continua and not to real dichotomies. However, only the classification into individual and group consultation and Caplan's (1964, 1970) four-fold classification have come into any general usage. Caplan categorized mental health consultation as to the kind of problem dealt with—a case or an administrative problem—and as to focus—the client or program on the one hand or the consultee on the other.

Client-centered Case Consultation

In this kind of consultation the goal is to help the consultee find the most effective way to deal with this client or situation. Educating the consultee so that he may deal more effectively with similar problems or clients in the future is a secondary goal. Thus this kind of mental health consultation resembles the psychiatric case consultation which is familiar to most clinicians. The client or patient is sometimes interviewed or examined by the consultant, either beforehand or with the consultee, because the consultant is being asked to diagnose the client or assess the situation. The focus of the consultation is on how this client can best be helped or this situation can best be alleviated. In the process, consultees often want to refer or transfer the client to the consultant—a natural wish which the consultant usually examines with a jaundiced eye. In client-centered case consultation, the consultant's suggestions are often summarized in a written report. When a consultant meets with a consultee or a group over a period of time, however, and especially when similar problems are presented repeatedly, client-centered case consultation may gradually merge—presumably with open discussion and sanction—into consultee-centered case consultation.

Consultee-centered Case Consultation

Here, too, problems with a client, patient, family, or social situation are the stimuli and provide much of the content of consultation, but the focus is on the consultee's difficulties in dealing with the problems. The goal of educating the consultee to deal with similar problems in the future is primary. Thus the task of assessing the client's problem or situation is secondary and the central endeavor of the consultant is to assess the nature of consultee's work difficulty which may involve lack of knowledge, lack of skill, lack of self-confidence, or lack of professional objectivity (Caplan, 1970). The consultant, therefore, tries to help the consultee remedy whichever of these shortcomings is present. It is this kind of mental health consultation in which most mental health consultants are involved; which has been written about most; which involves the most refined techniques of mental health consultation; and about which this chapter is most centrally concerned.

Problems are often encountered when consultees expect client-centered case consultation but the consultant intends or hopes to carry out consultee-centered case consultation. Such problems can be sidestepped, for a while at least, if the consultant is using indirect methods of dealing with consultee affect (see section on techniques below) and the consultee thus may not become aware of his own contributions to his difficulties with the case. However, when direct methods are used, the consultant is wise to obtain sanction from the consultee or group before launching into consultee-centered consultation.

Program-centered Administrative Consultation

This kind of consultation is similar to client-centered case consultation except that the problem involves administration of a program rather than the handling of a case. Sometimes the program may not even involve mental health. Then the consultation may not technically be mental health consultation, but it can easily be assumed that the effectiveness of the administration of any program has implications for the psychological functioning of those who are administered, or for the social system, and thus for the mental health of the community.

Here the focus is on a particular program, and the goal of educating the consultees for administration of future programs is secondary. Experience in administration is useful for consultants who take on any kind of administrative consultation. The consultant needs to assess the goals of the program, how the administrator is attempting to carry out the goals, the functioning of the institution, and what the specific administrative problem is, often by means of a site visit of several days, concluding with a detailed written report (Chaplan, 1970). As in case consultation, tactical difficulties arise when the problem centrally involves the consultee himself or his relationships with his superiors or subordinates. Then consultee-centered administrative consultation may be appropriate.

Consultee-centered Administrative Consultation

Here the focus is on helping the consultee to become more skilled in administration. This is similar to consultee-centered case consultation except that the problem is administrative rather than clinical. Few mental health consultants, however, know as much about administrative problems as they do about mental health problems. Thus most clinicians who become involved in this kind of consultation are wise to restrict themselves to the interpersonal and group dynamic features of the problem in which they have special competence. Consultation with groups is frequent in these situations and some consultants set up modified sensitivity training or T-group procedures (Klein, 1967) so as to help the staff better understand their group and individual functioning. When the consultant is, in addition, trained in administration, he may offer an especially useful clinical approach to administrative problems—an approach which consultees find different from the help they receive from specialists in their own field (Caplan, 1964, 1970).

Administrative consultation usually must be approached carefully and often involves specific tactical problems because the administrator's poisition makes him particularly sensitive to issues of authority and power. Thus many administrators do not want to appear in need of help and, when they do request help, there is often an implicit warning that if the consultant gives help, this will mean that the administrator is inadequate (Berlin, 1964). Many administrators, therefore, avoid consultation or approach consultation about their problems indirectly—e.g., by means of a case or by means of discussion of a variety of peripheral problems. At such times the consultant should not be tempted into competition or a power struggle, and techniques which help the administrator to suggest his own solutions or to become a collaborator in solutions are especially useful.

Despite the many difficulties involved, administrative consultation often may be needed in ongoing mental health consultation situations in order to maximize the usefulness of case consultation. Changes in consultees arising from case consultation may stimulate needs for administrative changes. Furthermore, administrative consultation is probably the kind of consultation which holds the greatest long-range promise for community mental health. To the extent that behavior disorders and mental health are closely linked to social structure and human ecology, then changes in incidence and prevalence will involve many environmental and social changes, and administrators will be central figures in such changes and in resistance to such changes. Thus mental health consultation can usefully be oriented, at least in part, toward the apexes of power in organizations or communities.

Group and Individual Consultation

The choice of group or individual methods of mental health consultation will depend on many factors including the training and personal preferences of the consultant; whether an individual or an agency requests the consultation; practical considerations, such as whether the members of the agency can meet together at one time without disrupting the functioning of the agency; and the customs and traditions of particular professional groups. For instance, it has usually been found that individual consultation is preferable to group consultation for physicians who are unusually busy and independent and for

whom individual consultation can comprise a modification of the traditional model of a physician referring patients to a professional colleague (Eisdorfer et al., 1968).

Group consultation, in contrast to individual consultation, also has particular advantages and disadvantages (Altrocchi et al., 1965; Caplan, 1970). Group consultation is more efficient in that more cues and hypotheses are available to the consultant and the consultees, more support is available to group members, and more consultees can benefit from the communications of the consultant and the ideas of the group. Handling of affect by means of encouraging shared expression, opposing transference and regression, supporting defenses such as intellectualization, and helping consultees keep some—but not too much—distance from clients can often be accomplished better in group than in individual consultation. Peer group influence is often powerful, not only in terms of contributions of others "in the same boat" and others who have been through the same problems previously, but also in terms of influence on members to see issues in new ways and to try new ways of dealing with problems. Finally intragroup and intergroup communication can be improved by exploring consultees' differing perspectives toward the problem at hand, by identifying and handling cultural stereotypes and prejudices and common theme problems in the group, and by including members of different agencies in the group.

On the other hand, group consultation has some important disadvantages:

. . . (1) attendance at group sessions takes members of the group away from performing their usual services (Kevin, 1963) and requires more coordination of consultees' schedules; (2) problems that involve delicate personal matters, or in which the confidentiality of case material is critical, may be more appropriately dealt with in individual consultation; (3) insecure consultees are often unwilling to expose to their peers' work problems which they might discuss alone with the consultant; (4) group consultation is not as adaptable as individual consultation for meeting individual consultee-client crises; (5) if group cohesiveness is lacking, the case-seminar method of group consultation may not be effective (Altrocchi et al., 1965, p. 133).

Group cohesiveness is an especially important factor for the consultant to assess before he decides on his method. A hostilely divided group is unlikely to make progress in group consultation unless the members commit themselves to resolving their staff problems directly, in which case the administrator might need to be involved and sensitivity training methods rather than consultation methods might be called for. Finally, another disadvantage of group consultation can be added: (6) Indirect consultation methods for dealing with consultee affect (see section on techniques below) are particularly complicated and difficult in a group, as Caplan (1964, 1970) has pointed out, because it is not likely that all members of a group share exactly the same theme interference and some member can almost always be counted on to try to move the group off the theme or towards insight.

It would be ideal for mental health consultants to be able to move flexibly between group and individual methods. Assuming some group cohesiveness, for instance, a group method which involves didactic components (Altrocchi et al., 1965) may be the most useful beginning for a program, especially with a group which views mental health professionals with more than the usual suspicion, such as policemen, or a group which is very didactically oriented, such as school principals. When the consultant becomes respected and trusted in depth, individuals, including administrators, may then want individual consultation on especially ticklish problems. Sometimes as a result of this individual consultation the consultee may become more comfortable in bringing up his problems in a group; and so on. As another example, individual consultation may convince an administrator that the time is ripe for group consultation, one of the results of which is to uncover some other administrative problems for which he wants further individual consultation; and so on. Sensitive, flexible, and creative exploration of techniques, without premature closure, is clearly needed at this stage of development of mental health consultation.

ROLES AND FUNCTIONS IN
MENTAL HEALTH CONSULTATION

In order to prevent psychological disorders and promote mental health in a population or community, mental health consultants attempt to enable consultees to handle client crises better and to function more effectively in the social system so that the consultee and the social system are better able to handle future disequilibria more constructively and are better able to offer the most useful environmental support for the effective development of individuals (Hollister, 1967a; Simmons, 1960). These aims suggest that mental health consultation involves expert knowledge of behavior disorders and mental health; clinical and/or group training skill in bringing about change in consultees; and the ability to work toward the development of the consultee as a key person in the communication network of a changing social system. These necessary functions and the roles ascribed to mental health consultants by writers who have surveyed practices and publications (Altrocchi et al., 1965; Cohen, 1964; Glidewell, 1959; Rieman, 1965) can be summarized in three sets of roles and functions: teaching and training; facilitating communication; and promoting new ideas.

Teaching and Training Roles in
Mental Health Consultation

Most centrally, mental health consultation involves teaching and training of consultees. The consultant has the knowledge and skill of a mental health or social systems specialist and is called upon to transmit appropriate aspects of this knowledge to consultees in order to help consultees solve work problems. The knowledge and skill often involves understanding of personality development, psychodynamics, psychopathology, psychotherapeutic techniques, administrative techniques, and the dynamics of groups and social systems, but often also involves knowledge of referral resources, sources of outside financial support, and grantsmanship (Cohen, 1964; Klein & Perlitsh, 1964; Rieman, 1965). Thus as a teacher the mental health consultant is both *a technical expert and a resource person.*

The terms teacher, technical expert, and resource person, however, do not fully capture the teaching and training roles in mental health consultation because much of what consultees need to learn involves skill in *doing* as well as knowledge. Programs designed to increase action skills in all fields have for a long time implicitly recognized that formal teaching alone does not suffice but must be supplemented by training.

Training includes exposure to action situations, demonstrations of ways of handling these situations, trying out ways of handling them, experiential learning, the opportunity to discuss critically what has been done with a more experienced person, further practice, and then some of these steps all over again. Most mental health consultants are thoroughly familiar with these implicit principles of training by means of their involvement in traditional clinical or group dynamics training. Thus mental health consultation incorporates many features of training, such as waiting until a problem is experienced and verbalized before pointing it out, and focusing on feeling reactions and crises as especially fruitful learning experiences.

Facilitation of Communication

Openness of communication is almost universally seen as central to intervention in psychological disorders and to effective personal, interpersonal, and social system functioning. Thus the mental health consultant often functions as a *communication facilitator.* He may be in the role of facilitating communication (usually indirectly) between intrapsychic components of a consultee's personality in individual consultation. He may attempt to facilitate communication within a consultee group (Altrocchi et al., 1965) or an agency staff (Delany et al., 1959). He may facilitate communication between agencies which were previously competing over a client, a family, or a program (Altrocchi et al., 1965), or between state and local units working on similar problems (Cohen, 1966). And he may find that he is facilitating communication within an entire community or social system (Simmons, 1960).

Cohen (1964, 1966) has pointed out that the mental health consultant is often called upon to play the role of *human relations mediator*, not only between consultee and client but also within agencies and between agencies and higher administrative bodies. The mental health consultant as an outsider can often help with such problems as the frustrations resulting from policy restrictions, feelings of being unappreciated, conflicting goals, and failure to elicit higher level administrative support by facilitating expression of feelings and facilitating communication in general. Thus in some ways he does function in the role of

mediator; but there are decision-making aspects of the mediator role which the consultant should usually avoid. Perhaps a useful way to summarize the role problem is to indicate that the consultant can often be a mediator to the extent that this involves communication facilitation, but he should be wary of being pushed into the role of referee, which may involve making administrative decisions which are outside of and can easily interfere with his consultation role and thus can easily get him into trouble.

Promotion of Ideas and Programs

Cohen (1966) has also pointed out that many mental health consultants, particularly those involved in administrative consultation, function as promoters of new ideas and programs. They tend to be knowledgeable but also creative people who not only respond to requests but also plant seeds and generate motivation in consultees for new and original solutions to problems. They tend to be *catalysts, inspirers, and facilitators*, and many consultants feel that they are more useful in this role than in any other. Certainly the introduction of successful mental health consultation has often been followed by the development of new programs (Eisdorfer, Altrocchi, & Young, 1968). Such attempts, however, often meet with frustration (Cohen, 1966) as new ideas come into conflict with practical considerations or conservative forces.

There is disagreement among community psychologists confronted with the possibility of political action about the extent to which attempts at change should include actual participation in the implementation of new programs or institutions (Bennett, Anderson, Cooper, Hassol, Klein, & Rosenblum, 1966). Promoting new ideas or programs can easily merge into political activism. Many consultants *are* promoters of new ideas and programs and this role is consistent with mental health consultation as defined here so long as the consultant is focusing on planting seeds and developing motivations *in* the consultees, *for* the consultees, and which will be knowingly carried into action *by* the consultees.

One way to accomplish this is for the consultant to bring his role as behavioral science investigator to his consultation. Group-dynamically oriented consultants have been much more active in using their research training to promote new ideas and programs than most mental health consultants have been. Gibb, for instance, points out that consultation, "to be effective, must be a data-gathering enterprise, in which problems are defined, data are gathered, and actions are planned on the basis of the best current appraisal of the data" (Gibb, 1959, p. 3). In mental health consultation, too, research can be conceived not only as a means of knowledge building but also as a means of introducing new practices into consultee systems (Klein, 1964). This need not involve massive research programs but can involve steps such as a proposal to a school principal, "If you like, I could suggest ways in which you can find out whether your students are only spouting back the teachers' ideas to them or are developing ideas of their own." Such a stance by mental health consultants is entirely within the role of mental health consultation as long as, again, the ideas and programs come, at least in part, from the consultees, are for the consultees, and will be carried out by the consultees.

TECHNIQUES OF
MENTAL HEALTH CONSULTATION

"The general principle here, as throughout the consultant's services at all operating levels, is that he *should insistently avoid 'doing.'* Instead he *should teach others to do*" (Towle, 1950, p. 10).

Since one of the roles in mental health consultation is teaching, many consultants find, especially in the early stages of consultation, that such traditional teaching techniques as lecturing or seminar discussion are useful (Abramovitz, 1958; Altrocchi et al., 1965), especially with some groups who expect it such as policemen and school personnel. It is unnecessary to outline such familiar techniques here. Other commonly practiced techniques merit detailed presentation because only a few of them have been presented rather briefly in published sources (Kazanjian, Stein & Weinberg, 1962; Caplan, 1964, 1970).

In outlining techniques, it must be noted at the start that the appropriate choice of techniques will depend on the personality and training of the consultant as well as on the consultees and the type or phase of consultation. For instance, teachers may expect definite answers (Kazanjian et al., 1962) sooner than psychiatric social workers while the latter will normally be more open to discussion of their affective involvement in a case. Furthermore, some mental health consultants would be quite uncomfortable dealing directly with the problem-related feelings of consultees while other consultants would feel uncomfortable not doing so. No two experienced mental health consultants will handle the same problem in exactly the same way.

A key principle underlying mental health consultation techniques is that consultation is based on the authority of ideas and skills rather than on any kind of institutionalized authority: The consultee should be free to accept or reject the advice of the consultant. Yet this ideal is not always easy to maintain:

To be technical there probably are very few cases in which a consultee feels completely free to accept or reject the advice of the consultant, but unless the relationship borders on this it is not consultation to my way of thinking. Too often that which goes under the label of consultation is the soft sell type of program promotion, or subtle supervision, or the indirect exercise of administrative authority . . . or "slychology" . . . I think you can see from this that I don't see consultation as a subtle way to get people to do what you want them to do (Croley, 1961, pp. 39–40).

Thus, even when a consultant is attempting to practice pure consultation, "The authority of the consultant's knowledge, special skill, and professional conscience" (Maddux, 1955, p. 1424) is implicit. Gaupp (1966) has recently pointed out, in fact, that the concept of pure consultation appears to be a myth, that formal and informal power is frequently present in subtle ways, and that it is thus most important for all parties to be very clear about all power factors, a clarity which may often most easily be obtained by dealing, at the very beginning, with the contract and the sanctions involved.

With these provisos in mind, the following suggested techniques can serve as guidelines which will presumably be subject to continual modification and amplification.

Establishing and Maintaining
a Consultation Relationship

1. Preparing the Ground for Consultation. The gap between the ideal and what often happens in mental health consultation is rather large here. Many times it seems that mental health consultants are asked to consult—or sometimes they even arrive without having been asked (Berken & Eisdorfer, 1970)—and immediately start trying to deal with the problems of consultees. In contrast, Caplan (1964) points out that preparing for consultee-centered case consultation may take months or years; that the sanction of the authority figures in the consultee institution must be obtained and maintained, including a written contract, at least in the form of correspondence; and that ground rules of procedure must be mutually understood. Even for less intensive consultation, Caplan's suggestions should not be ignored: The consultant should know who is asking his help and why at this particular time; should obtain and maintain sanction from above; and should continually be alert to hidden motives and agendas of consultees (Charters, 1955). Thus, preparing the ground for consultation must be done continually as well as early in consultation. For instance, a consultant may ask a group, "I wonder if, in retrospect, it is possible that what we have just been talking about is one of the reasons you sought my help?"

2. Confidentiality. It is essential that the consultant clarify confidentiality with all parties involved as early as possible, especially during the period of negotiating the contract. What will be shared with whom and under what circumstances? A frequent arrangement is for a consultant to indicate that, barring exceptional circumstances, he will want to feel free to communicate with the supervisor about the client but not about the consultee (Caplan, 1970). The latter is the area where difficulties most usually arise because supervisors will often be especially interested in how the consultee is handling things. An extreme example is when the supervisor asks the consultant for an evaluation of the mental health status of the consultee. This administrative and supervisory (or "company spy") function is clearly outside the role which the mental health consultant outlines for himself. This area also causes difficulty because consultees are often afraid for a long while that the consultant will report back to the supervisor, especially when the consultant routinely stops by the supervisor's office, as a courtesy, before he leaves.

It should also be clarified very early whether consultation may include discussion of supervisors or administrators. Sometimes, when this issue comes up, the consultant will agree to listen to and try to help the consultee with his feelings about and ways of dealing with the supervisor, but then he needs to observe at least three cautions:

(a) He should not insert, even by implication, his own comments about or evaluation of the supervisor;

(b) He should avoid being pushed from the partial role of mediator to the role of referee (see above on roles) by means of becoming involved in administrative decisions; and

(c) He will need to reemphasize that he will keep the discussion confidential, because an angry discussion by consultees of the failings of an administrator will probably rearouse fears of disclosure in consultees.

All of this becomes very much more complicated in group consultation. In the first place, consultation confidentiality is one-sided (Caplan, 1970). The consultee is free to use the statements and ideas from the consultation in any way he wishes, including discussion with the supervisor. In a group, of course, this holds for all of the group members. Thus it is wise to reemphasize in a group that the members should be bound by the same rules as the consultant—e.g., comments to the administrator about a client are permissable but not comments about the consultee which derive from a group consultation session. Nevertheless, there is the danger, especially in a group lacking in cohesiveness, that a member will report to a supervisor on the statements of another group member in consultation, or on the statements, perhaps transformed a little, by the consultant about the supervisor! Consultation is indeed, like psychotherapy, not a rose garden (Green, 1964)!

3. Establishing the Relationship. As one of the interpersonal helping methods, mental health consultation depends heavily on the relationship between the consultant and consultee. Indirect evidence for this is found in a study by Rieman (1965) which showed that a sample of consultees often listed many personal qualities, such as maturity, security, informality, and humility ahead of basic professional competence as necessary for effective consultants. The exact nature of the best possible relationship between a consultant and consultee, and the techniques for working toward such a relationship, will depend heavily on the personal qualities of each of the participants (think, for instance, of some consultants who can almost never and some who can almost always break through the tensions of a group by means of humor). However, most consultants would probably agree with the following basic orientation:

(a) The consultant should convey that he expects to learn something from as well as give something to the consultee (Eisdorfer et al., 1968; Farson, 1966);

(b) The consultant should show respect for the profession and the professional competence of the consultee (Caplan, 1964, 1970);

(c) The consultant should listen very carefully to the consultee's presentation of the problem, avoiding interfering with the presentation as much as possible, with special attention to indicators of consultee anxiety and concern (Kazanjian et al., 1962);

(d) The consultant should accept the consultee as a person, including, temporarily at least, his weaknesses;

(e) The consultant should show enough warmth and humanness so that the consultee and the client will emerge as human too.

4. Offering Support. Crises about which consultees seek the help of mental health consultants are usually difficult and stressful. Most consultants, therefore, often freely offer support to consultees when they are showing frustration by noting how difficult, stressful, and frustrating the problem is. Some mental health consultants offer support to consultees by sharing with them experiences of their own which have aroused difficulties similar to the ones' the consultee is experiencing. Consultants who work with groups point out how valuable it is to mobilize the support of the group for the presenting member (Altrocchi et al., 1965; Parker, 1958). There is some disagreement, however, about how much support is appropriate. Caplan (1964) has suggested that consultants be cautious in giving supportive reassurance and praise so as to avoid judging the consultee and to avoid emphasizing status differences. Altrocchi et al. (1965), on the other hand, note that judging and status differences are almost always present anyway, and

that a great deal of direct support can be given so long as it implies respect for the consultee and does not suggest that he is unable to profit from anything besides support.

Many of the above suggestions for establishing and maintaining a consultation relationship are summarized in Caplan's phrase (1970, p. 59) "the consultant sits beside the consultee, as it were, and engages in a joint pondering about the complexities of the problem."

Defining the Problem

As in psychotherapy, the problem that is initially described is often not the critical problem that motivated the consultation request, and a good deal of psychological detective work may be required in order to help the basic problem emerge. In addition to using intuitive, clinical, and group sensitivity skills, consultants have developed a number of specific techniques for encouraging consultees to elucidate and define the basic problem:

1. Playing for Time while Gathering More Information. There are probably more elements to the problem than those which emerge right away (Caplan, 1964), so that playing for time is often a very useful maneuver as long as the consultant is not simply evasive. Playing for time may involve not being too quick to answer questions unless they involve simple information which the consultees do not have. Many questions can be thrown back to the consultee who probably has some tentative answers and, if not, may learn from groping toward answers. For instance, the consultant can ask, in response to a question, "What possibilities occur to you?" The consultant also can convert general questions, such as, "What do you do with a child who steals?" into specific questions by asking, for instance, "Do you have a specific situation in mind?" (Kazanjian et al., 1962). This encourages the consultee to relate more information while the consultant learns more about the situation and the consultee.

2. Listening Carefully for the Core Problem or Core Anxiety (Kazanjian et al., 1962; Parker, 1958). Psychotherapeutic training is especially useful here. Most mental health consultants keep alert for signs of anxiety or particularly strong feelings associated with a topic, with a client, or with another person who is involved with the client; avoiding or blocking on central issues, topics, or people; and indirect references to unstated problems. For example in a course in consultation, some members of the class constructed a role-playing situation involving group mental health consultation and asked the professor to play the role of the consultant. During the role playing, several members of the "consultee" group repeatedly implied that a supervisor was always late on Monday mornings. These remarks turned out to be hints that the underlying consultation problem was not exactly the problem that had initially been described—how to deal with alcoholic patients—but involved how to deal with the consultees' alcoholic supervisor. Sometimes the consultant's first clue of consultees' affective involvement is affect in himself. If he notices that he is feeling a little sad or a little annoyed, and if he is confident that these feelings are not intrusions from his personal life, the consultant can suspect that he is picking up this affect from the consultee.

In mental health consultation with groups it is useful to keep alert to the possibility that there is a shared concern, anxiety, or affect.

In each type of profession, the nature of the work tends to attract individuals who, despite many dissimilarities, may share certain personality characteristics. The type of work itself may also engender specific attitudes and arouse anxieties common to many members of the group, regardless of the personal characteristics or neurotic conflicts of any individual member. Consultation serves an important function by identifying the ways in which such shared attitudes or anxieties are interfering with the professional functioning of group members (Parker, 1962, p. 559).

Examples of shared anxieties or concerns which are familiar to many consultants include teachers' anxiety about children who aren't learning or guilt about anger toward children (Parker, 1962); welfare workers' anxiety about disorderliness and sexual behavior; and public health nurses' sensitivity about dirt and anxiety about hostility toward patients who reject their services (Parker, 1958).

3. Asking the Consultee to Define or Redefine the Problem. The consultant can at appropriate

points during the consultation ask this of the consultee. He can even ask who has the problem: "Is this child's behavior harmful to him or is it primarily disturbing to us?" (Rhodes, 1967) The consultant often attempts several times to restate the problem himself: "I wonder if the problem that is bothering us the most isn't. . . ." Although the consultant may notice historical antecedents or unconscious determinants of the consultee's behavior, the consultant's overt statements concerning the problem deal only with the current expression of the problem. This is true even for those (Delany et al., 1959) who carry out consultation in ways most closely related to psychotherapy. Mental health consultation is a here-and-now approach which retains focus on work related problems.

In ways such as those outlined above the consultant and consultee(s) usually can eventually reach consensus on the definition of the mental health consultation problem. The word "eventually" is to be taken literally. Usually the basic problem doesn't become clearly defined in one meeting. Several meetings are often required, and sometimes it may take months. This lengthy process, of course, in no way prevents the consultant and the consultees from working constructively, meanwhile, on more overt consultation problems. For instance, a consultant may help a school superintendent with repeated crises in school desegregation over a period of years before he begins dealing explicitly with the superintendent's own feelings about black people.

Searching for Alternative Actions

As the problem or problems become more clearly defined, the consultant helps the consultee search for alternative actions or new ways in which the situation may be handled. (Other widely accepted terms, which may imply a little more finality, are problem solving, problem solutions, alternative solutions, and problem resolution.) Precise techniques of searching for alternative actions will, of course, depend on whether the consultation is about a case or about an administrative problem; whether the difficulty is due to lack of knowledge, skill, or self-confidence or whether there is a theme interference; and especially on whether the focus of the consultation is on the client or on the consultee. Thus, in program-centered administrative consultation where there is specific knowledge that the consultant can appropriately pass on to the consultee, this information is given straightforwardly without unusual attention to the attitudes of the consultee. In contrast, in case consultation when there is evidence of theme interference, the consultant will judge everything he says as to its relevance to reduction of the theme interference. There are, nevertheless, some techniques which are often found useful in a wide variety of mental health consultation situations:

1. Review of Previous Actions. Since a goal of mental health consultation is to increase the consultee's skill in handling similar problems in the future, it is particularly important that the consultant forego the temporary pleasure of offering advice on alternative actions too quickly without giving the consultee a chance to develop his own ideas (Kazanjian et al., 1962). An enormously important first step, which is easily overlooked, even by experienced consultants, is to ask, "What have you tried?" This simple key question can help the consultant see how the consultee defines the problem as well as what kinds of actions have been tried, and it helps the consultant avoid the embarrassment of proposing a course of action, only to be faced with, "We already tried that!" In a consultation group, the question, "What have you tried?" can naturally be followed by asking the other members of the group what they have tried in similar situations.

2. Formulations of Alternative Actions. A logical next step is to ask the consultee what alternative actions he can think of now. If by now the problem has been defined a little more clearly and the consultee has been thinking about it during the early stages of the consultation, and if he feels comfortable in his relationship with the consultant, then he may already have thought of or may be ready to struggle toward some new ideas. In a group this question logically leads to asking the other members of the group what ideas they have. If the group has warmed up and has some cohesiveness, many ideas will flow freely. Some ideas may be premature, tangential, scattered, or totally unworkable, but, since the problems involved in mental health consultation are often difficult and have usually remained

impervious to repeated attempts at solution, new and creative ideas from the consultees are to be highly valued, even if many of the ideas have to be rejected later. The consultee or group will usually eliminate most of the unworkable ideas themselves, but it is also appropriate for the consultant to do so. He may also offer ideas of his own at this stage, but only if he has given the consultee or group the opportunity to express their own ideas first and only if the ideas the consultant offers are appropriate to the level of skill or the readiness of the consultees. The consultant may then need to play a role in helping the consultee or group to become focused on one or a few workable ideas. Here the consultant's skill in guiding the process of the consultee's or group's focusing on new actions is often more important than his expert knowledge.

3. Facilitating Communication. The consultant can usefully focus on facilitating constructive communication between the consultee and client or among the members of the consultee group. For instance, a teacher described a teenage student who had been needling him, and toward whom he was beginning to act out his anger by avoiding the student. The consultant encouraged more open expression of anger toward the student by the consultee at times when the consultee felt it would be appropriate (Kazanjian et al., 1962). The consultee could also have been asked to explore why he was angry or to reflect or interpret the student's needling as a beginning of facilitating communication between them.

4. Anxiety Reduction. It is apparent that mental health consultation often involves topics that arouse anxiety in consultees. Techniques for reducing anxiety include those which have been found useful in supportive psychotherapy: accepting the consultee's feelings without criticism; pointing out, when appropriate, the near universality of the consultee's reaction; sometimes admitting that the consultant has similar reactions; and encouraging support by the rest of the group in group consultation. Finally, of course, even partial or potential solutions to the work problem at hand will allay a great deal of anxiety which, in mental health consultation, is often related to feelings of failure, fear of failure, or frustration.

5. Shared Anxiety. Parker (1962) points out that when anxiety is shared by members of a consultation group, consultation can serve an important function by clarifying how such shared attitudes or anxieties are interfering with the professional functioning of group members. A group can almost always accept insight into shared anxieties and this may have therapeutic effects on an individual without his having to confront his personal resistances or defenses. For instance, if a consultant helps a group of teachers to realize that they seem to be expecting themselves to be perfect, and then helps them see why this expectation is unrealistic, a particular teacher may experience considerably lessened anxiety over her failure to reach a certain student, even though her own psychodynamic reasons for perfectionism may not have been touched upon at all.

6. Process Focus. For many, but by no means all, mental health consultants, a central feature of consultation is helping the consultee understand the process of consultation (Klein, 1964). For instance, many group consultants, influenced by group dynamics training, attempt at appropriate times to help the consultees see what group processes they are undergoing and hope thus to help them with their intra- and intergroup communication in order to enable them to be more effective interpersonally.

Dealing with Affect in Consultees

In the course of mental health consultation it is quite natural that a wide range of affects become aroused in consultees: anger, anxiety, guilt, sadness, exhilaration, and others—especially anger. It is apparent, however, that there has been some disagreement among mental health consultants concerning the best way to deal with the emotional involvements of consultees in the work problems they present to mental health consultants:

... mental health consultants are not agreed on the best manner in which to deal with a teacher's emotional involvement in a problem. Some focus directly on the teacher's annoyance, anxiety, or other reaction to a particular child, explicitly pointing up the child's effect on the teacher. Others prefer to avoid any direct confrontation on the teacher's emotions, rather dealing indirectly and implicitly with his or her inner conflicts by discussing their upsetting counterparts in the behavior of the child. The direct approach values,

and seeks to promote, psychological insight and emotional openness in the teacher. It assumes that help in accepting one's own personal feelings is an essential aspect of professional development. Those committed to the indirect method, while not denying the desirability of self-awareness, believe that open exploration of an individual's feelings can be threatening and should be done only within the structured atmosphere of psychotherapy. At this juncture, there is no hard evidence in this matter (Klein, 1967, p. 408).

The terms direct and indirect have come to refer to these contrasting methods. Practitioners on both sides have experienced success, as has happened with different approaches in psychotherapy. When this happens in a field, it is likely that the choice of method is determined by variables other than empirically demonstrated effects and that some rapprochement is possible, usually involving refinement of criteria for when to use which method.

There are at least two variables that seem to be related to choice of direct versus indirect methods of dealing with consultee affect: the personality of the consultant and group versus individual consultation. One can observe that some consultants are relatively comfortable in dealing directly with consultees' feelings ("Does it annoy you a little?" "I notice that I am feeling a little sad about this; are you, too?"). Such consultants are usually comparatively open and communicative and must be willing to run the danger of facilitating affect which evolves from personal rather than work problems. For instance, in the group consultation role playing session referred to earlier in which it turned out that there were strong feelings about the alcoholic supervisor, the professor who was playing the role of consultant eventually encouraged the group to express their affect directly. The amount of affect turned out to be too much to deal with thoroughly in consultation, let alone role playing of consultation, especially since a member of the class took it upon herself to play the role of the alcoholic supervisor and walked unannounced into the group! This role playing session had such an impact that the class spent the whole next class meeting discussing it. It became clear that some members of the class had strong, unresolved personal feelings about alcoholics, and these feelings were not resolved in class and probably would not have been resolved in real consultation. It is especially interesting to note that the professor who played the role of consultant concluded that he had gone too far in helping the group to express affect, in part because he found, somewhat to his surprise, that he still harbored some resentment toward a previous associate who had been an alcoholic and who had caused him some personal difficulties. The recounting of this very tense, although quite fruitful, training session may suggest some advantages but also some pitfalls involved in dealing directly with affect in real mental health consultation.

Other consultants are noticeably less eager to deal directly with consultees' feelings. Their behavior is usually sober and controlled and they may not as quickly facilitate spontaneity in consultees. They avoid the danger of facilitating unmanageable amounts of affect, but may miss opportunities for affective breakthroughs which lead to new ideas for action. As an example which is taken from a role-playing training session, like the alcoholic supervisor example above, a role-playing group in a consultation workshop was discussing how to deal with an irresponsible, repeatedly pregnant teenage girl and her multi-problem family. Frustration, annoyance, and anger built up in the consultees but were not dealt with openly by the consultant or the consultees even though several of them were quite aware of their feelings. Soon this group of fully trained mental health professionals decided that the only solution was sterilization and promptly ended the role playing! The experienced consultant who was training them insisted that they role play the whole situation over again with the consultant instructed to try to help the group express their affect more directly. He did, and they did, and then they were able to move on to a very productive discussion of what they could, and what they could not, do for this family.

A second factor that may be related to differential use of direct and indirect methods of dealing with consultee affect is experience in working with groups versus experience in working primarily with individuals. Those who have written most about mental health consultation with groups (Altrocchi et al., 1965; Parker, 1958) have also advocated the direct approach to dealing with affect. Those who have written most explicitly about individual mental health consultation (Bindman, 1959; Caplan, 1964, 1970) have advocated the indirect approach. Perhaps the indirect approach is often more appropriate in individual consultation, and the direct approach is often more feasible in groups. If this observation is supported by other mental health consultants, some of the reasons for the differential usefulness of the two methods in working with individuals and groups may be that groups tend to stimulate affect, can be guided to support direct expression of affect, and yet naturally tend to control such expression by setting limits.

Personality differences and experience with groups or individuals, which lead to preferences for either direct or indirect methods, then can be built upon, of course, by choice of different kinds of training programs and by selective learning of one more than the other. Here will be presented first the argument for direct methods; then tentative guidelines for when to use direct methods and some suggestions for techniques in this section; the next section will present the argument for indirect methods and will then cover the most fully developed indirect method (theme interference reduction).

The argument for direct methods goes as follows. Affect can mobilize or immobilize. When it immobilizes or interferes, bringing it out into the open for discussion can be enormously useful. The assumption is that openly expressed affects can be dealt with better than hidden affects, and sometimes open expression of affect can free or mobilize a person or a group for creative discussions of alternative actions. Thus, as Parker (1958, p. 2) has suggested in reference to group consultation with public health nurses, "When an emotional reaction of the nurse destroys her objectivity about some aspect of her job, that reaction is a suitable subject for group discussion, but the intrapsychic conflict which may have helped to generate the reaction should not be considered. . . "

Needless to say, opening the discussion to emotional reactions is likely to provoke defensiveness in some consultees. The acceptant, undefensive but also unoffensive manner of the consultant can be crucial at this stage. He can also "dispel, explicitly and implicitly, the common fear that pressure to discuss emotional reactions will result in exposure of personal problems to co-workers. In a nonpunitive, noncoercive atmosphere where reticences are respected, defensiveness among participants in group discussions will gradually disappear" (Parker, 1958, p. 3). The consultant can help this process by helping the group set up ground rules and sanctions regarding discussion of affects and personal reactions. Such informal group rules can, at times, be quite tolerant:

Occasionally, when there is sufficient group cohesiveness and confidence in the consultant, a nonshared, but still work-connected, personal problem of an individual consultee may be introduced into the discussion. (For instance, discussion of a child who has been neglected by a working mother may stimulate a public health nurse to share her personal guilt about leaving her young children to be cared for by someone else.) When this occurs, we have observed that the group usually deals with it in an understanding and appropriate manner. With regard to the sensitivity of consultee groups in handling the personal problems of group members, our experiences with a number of different professional groups are consistent with Parker's observation:

"In the ten years of my experience as a mental health consultant, not once has a nurse succumbed to the pressure of anxiety and brought before the group personal matters that were inappropriate in kind or degree (Parker, 1958, p. 18)" (Altrocchi et al., 1965, pp. 130–131).

Tentative guidelines for when to use direct methods are:

1. For individual mental health consultation: When an individual consultee behaves in ways which indicate strong affect, check your diagnostic cues to see whether theme interference, neurotic conflict, or deeply unconscious motivation is involved. If not, and if you feel some comfort in doing so, go ahead tentatively.

2. For group mental health consultation:

    a. When only one consultee in a group indicates affect, check not only for internal problems as above, but also assess the degree to which you think the affect is shared by others in the group. If it is shared, move tentatively ahead. If not, don't, unless the group seems inclined to do so supportively itself.

    b. If the affect is shared but is directed toward someone not present who is also in the organization (e.g., the alcoholic supervisor) or toward someone in the group (e.g., there are two competing cliques in the same group), be careful, and proceed only if there is sanction from all parties concerned to deal with the problem and the affect involved.

    c. When the affect, however, is shared by a significant portion of the group (not necessarily a majority), and probably does not, in your judgment, represent deeply neurotic problems or theme interference (the group's natural reaction can help in this decision) but is directly related to the work problem at hand (this includes strong feelings toward the consultant), these are times to go ahead.

The specific techniques used by many consultants in dealing directly with consultee affect are generally familiar to most clinicians. When it is becoming apparent that consultee affect is involved, the consultant notes or reflects or asks about it generally (e.g., "How does all this make you feel?") or specifically (e.g., "This seems to be a frustrating issue"). If the response is at all positive the consultant seeks to promote general, usually moderate, expression of the feeling; explicitly accepts and supports such expression (e.g., "I see how you feel; I'm sure I would feel the same way," or "It might help you to know that almost everyone in that situation feels just as frustrated and angry as you do"). Often such expression of affect and the acceptance of it will free the consultee or group to move ahead to thinking about alternative actions. If not, the affect may be related to personal problems or hard-to-change situational problems (e.g., an alcoholic supervisor) and the consultant can try to direct the affect into constructive channels (e.g., "Well, it's clear we all have feelings about such a work situation. How can we channel such feelings into constructive action?"). Exactly the same techniques would be relevant if the affect is directed toward the consultant except that, in addition, the consultant is then in a good position to deal directly with any miscommunications between him and the consultees or any mistakes on his part, hopefully with a minimum of defensiveness.

Thus we concur with Parker's observations and can further suggest that such techniques may sometimes be useful with individuals as well as groups:

If the consultant has been successful in creating a group atmosphere which is generally supportive and nonjudgmental of feelings expressed in discussion, nurses will welcome a chance to acquire a better understanding of their own involvements. Under such favorable circumstances, one function of the consultant is to make the nurse conscious of the attitude or feeling that is the real source of her trouble and to interpret it for her. The consultant also tries to help the nurse exchange her feeling of anxiety, or hostility, or guilt, for a renewed sense of effectiveness—of being able to cope with the situation.

Before deciding to discuss the nurse's personal involvement in a particular problem, however, the consultant must consider how far the nurse's conflict is from her consciousness and how ego-alien. It is also worthwhile to consider how useful an emphasis on her own feelings would be in helping her to solve that problem, and how significant the conflict is to her general functioning, or to the functioning of other nurses. Even when there is clear evidence of a nurse's personal involvement in a case, the consultant realizes that anxiety can sometimes be allayed more successfully by inference than by direct discussion (Parker, 1958, pp. 5—6).

Theme Interference Reduction

Working through of consultee problems by inference (i.e., entirely by means of discussion of the client's problems) is the central feature of indirect methods of handling consultee affect. Some of the arguments for indirect rather than direct methods have been implied above. Even when the consultant is quite correct in his assessment of affective involvement on the part of the consultee and the consultant brings up the affective involvement sensitively and tactfully, it is quite possible for the consultee, whether alone or in a group, to become very defensive. Many consultees, of course, are not nearly as open about dealing with their own affects as mental health consultants usually are. Furthermore, as illustrated by the alcoholic supervisor example above, direct methods run a greater risk of arousing amounts of affect which cannot be worked through in consultation, particularly when a large thrust of the affect arises from the consultee's personal life. Finally, as was also suggested by the alcoholic supervisor example, when the consultant is dealing directly with consultee affect, it is more likely that his own biases and personal involvements will influence the discussion.

The most central argument for indirect methods is that, if there is an interfering theme, direct methods may force the consultee to see the client as a test case of his own theme, which might lead him to shut off communication before the theme interference is reduced or to begin discussing his own personal problems. This brings up to Caplan's (1964, 1970) method of theme interference reduction, which is the most detailed, complex, and subtle mental health consultation technique which has been developed thus far and merits separate discussion here.

If the mental health consultation is consultee-centered, and if the consultee's work difficulty is not caused by lack of knowledge, lack of skill, or lack of self-confidence, but may be caused by lack of objectivity, the problem may be an interfering theme,

a symbolic inhibition of free perception and communication between consultee and client and a concomitant disorder of objectivity. This is usually accompanied by some degree of emotional upset in the consultee, ranging from relatively mild tension when he thinks about certain aspects of the client's case (which we call 'segmental tension') to a marked crisis response, in which the consultee's general professional functioning and emotional equilibrium are temporarily upset. The consultee usually ascribes his discomfort to his difficulties with the client, onto whose case he displaces feelings of anxiety, hostility, shame, and depression, which can be seen by the consultant to be partly or even primarily originating in his personal life or in his involvement with the social-system problems of his institution (Caplan, 1964, p. 223).

The separation of the consultee's personal life from his work difficulty is especially respected in this method and the consultant does not investigate the causes of the theme interference. In fact, the consultant actively prevents insight, even to the extent of interrupting a discussion which is tending to focus on the consultee and stopping any discussion of the consultee's feelings about the case by noting briefly that "we all feel this way at times" and quickly saying something about the client.

In most cases of theme interference, the consultee is unaware of the link between his personal emotional problems and his client's difficulties. If he were aware of this, he would be unable to solve his own problems in terms of the client. *The essence of the displacement which defends him in this way from facing his psychological difficulties is that it is unconscious. Hence, it is important that the consultant conduct the interviews so that the consultee will not become conscious of this personal link.* If the displacement is weakened, the consultee's private problems may become conscious, and he may begin to talk about them before he realizes what is happening and with no conscious intention of asking the consultant for psychotherapy (Caplan, 1964, p. 243).

The consultee seems to be defending himself against confrontation with a personal problem by dealing with it vicariously in the client. Thus the consultant can infer the theme by carefully examining its manifestations in the work context. He listens to the consultee's presentation of the problem somewhat as one might listen to a TAT story or a dream—as a projection of the teller's underlying themes and as an indication of the myopia that prevents him from using his knowledge and skill effectively (Klein, 1964). Yet the consultant must, at the same time, talk with the consultee about the manifest content—the client and his problems. He must thus function at two levels simultaneously. He asks questions that may elicit further thematic material and proceeds deliberately so as to make sure that he understands the problem at all levels. Cues which tend to confirm theme interference include undue emotional tension, excessive pessimism of outlook, distorted perception of some aspect of the client, and especially stereotyping or continued oversimplification: e.g., the consultee persistently refers to the child who is aggressive under certain conditions as hostile in other situations despite nonconfirming evidence; or the consultee expresses extreme statements which cannot be literally true—e.g., "This father is like all the others in this neighborhood—he comes home, impregnates his wife, and then leaves" (Caplan, 1964).

Themes can be seen as involving an Initial Category (e.g., "a promiscuous woman," "a retarded child," "an alcoholic father") and an Inevitable Outcome, which is always negative (Caplan, 1970). For instance, the theme may be: "This is a promiscuous woman (Initial Category) and thus her unborn child is destined to receive bad mothering (Inevitable Outcome)." Through many years of exploring, Caplan and his co-workers have decided that it is often not useful, and sometimes harmful, to "unlink" the client from the consultee's theme by showing him that the client does not really fit the Initial Category (e.g., suggesting that the woman is not really promiscuous because she was only having an affair with a man she loved). If the consultant does this, the theme is left intact and the consultee will probably soon find another displacement object among his other clients. Instead, the consultant accepts the consultee's categorization of his client as fitting into the Initial Category and thus implicitly agrees that this client is a test case for the theme. Then the consultant moves slowly ahead to show the consultee that the Inevitable Outcome is not inevitable (e.g., "Let's see if there are some ways that this promiscuous woman can be helped to become an acceptable mother").

If this method is carried out satisfactorily, it should lead to greater objectivity about the client, a weakening of the theme (e.g., "Maybe promiscuity doesn't always lead to bad mothering"), some reduction of tension and pessimism in the consultee, and less likelihood that the consultee will repetitively work out this theme on future clients. All of this is done without encouraging direct expression of the affects involved and without any infringement on the consultee's private life.

It is easy to imagine how complicated it would be to carry out theme interference reduction in a group. For instance, some group member is likely to see through the defensive displacement and remark on it (for instance, "It sounds as if you have a hang-up about promiscuity yourself"). Furthermore, how likely is it that several members of a group will share a similar theme? Caplan and his co-workers are exploring such problems and are working toward a group method which applies indirect techniques to shared displacements about unsolved problems in the social system of an institution (Caplan, 1970).

Rapprochement between Direct and Indirect Methods

There are some signs that many mental health consultants are realizing that one can use both direct and indirect methods of dealing with consultee affect. For instance, Caplan's (1970) most recent work on mental health consultation, in contrast to his earlier writings (e.g., Caplan,

1964), makes clear his approval of dealing directly with the general (as opposed to segmental or theme-oriented) emotional involvement of a consultee with a case: It is natural for a dedicated professional worker who is responsible for a very difficult case or program to become invested in the situation or person, to be concerned and even anxious, and to become very frustrated. In such situations the consultant can fruitfully encourage direct expression of feelings and can even discuss his own feelings, thus using himself as a role model by showing empathy, by legitimizing the open expression of negative affects which result from frustration, and by thus indicating how one can master and channel such feelings.

Furthermore, an increasing number of mental health consultants are learning about and are being trained in Caplan's theme interference reduction method, especially since the publication of his book in 1970 and as a result of increasing availability of sound movies of examples of consultation. Thus it becomes apparent, for instance, that if one watches and listens very carefully (which is hard to do if one is encouraging and dealing with direct expression of affect), themes or fictions can be seen; these often do involve an Inevitable Outcome that does not have to be inevitable; and there are times when these themes can be dealt with quite effectively by indirect methods without the risks of personal disclosures or more emotion than can be dealt with. At this time not only is an exploratory and open attitude needed but so are further detailed comparisons between methods so that we can most fruitfully see what methods work best for what people in what situations.

PHASES IN CONSULTATION

"By sensitive listening and lucid speaking, by concerning himself to understand the consultee's problems and his potentialities, by thinking with him but from a different orientation and out of a different backlog of experience, he can move with his consultee from one new vantage point to another until the consultee begins to gain new perspective, conceive new ideas, and glimpse how they may be suited to his need" (Stringer, 1961, p. 89).

Dividing such movement into phases of the consultation process can grossly fail to reflect the many different aspects of the different types of consultation practiced by many different consultants and, much worse, can lead to undue inflexibility if consultants interpret the phases as invariant. On the other hand, delineating the phases about which many writers agree can help the consultant to be alert to the sometimes fast-changing process of consultation, and thus can help him respond in the most useful ways, especially if he is also alert to surprises which do not fit the usual patterns. Phases do not evolve in a neat and orderly fashion, are not mutually exclusive, but frequently overlap and blend with each other (Kazanjian et al., 1962). There may even be sudden retrogressions. For instance, issues of boundaries and sanctions are usually handled during the entry or beginning phases of consultation, but a new group member or a new and touchy topic may push a group which is deciding on alternative actions to define new boundaries and obtain new sanctions so as to be able to deal with the new member or topic.

Hollister (1967b) has suggested the usefulness of looking at phases of consultation from the point of view of role evolution. A consultant tends to be greeted with overt friendliness and high expectations which cover considerable anxiety and distrust and many misconceptions. He will probably be tested in many ways. If he passes the tests, new opportunities open up, including consultation with higher level administrators. Recognition of the dynamics and course of role evolution may help the consultant tolerate the process with understanding and expedite the process when he can.

It would be possible to focus on phases within single consultation sessions and then focus on phases in an entire consultation process that evolves over a period of years, but there are some similarities between within-session phases and between-session phases. Therefore phases will be discussed here in general terms which can apply to single sessions or long series of sessions.

Entry or Preparatory Phase

The entry of the consultant can usefully be seen as a special case of a more general problem—the integration of a new person or stranger into an existing social system (Glidewell, 1959; Caplan, 1970). The introduction of any unpredictable newcomer, stranger, or alien, especially a consultant who is a change agent and presumably authoritative, raises anxieties about change, power, and dependency. Thus suspicion toward and testing of the consultant is inevitable, no matter how warm the welcome seems on the surface (Hollister, 1967b; Berken & Eisdorfer, 1970). In fact, Caplan (1970, p. 58) has suggested that the consultant should assume that every case and every question early in consultation should be seen as a test of his attitudes, his ideology, and his goals.

It is understandable that consultants, and especially consultants in training, might be tempted to deemphasize such problems, because entering a new consultation situation would be much easier if these problems were not present; but they *are* present. Thus entry is often entry in the dark (Glidewell, 1959) and, even if there is some light, a consultant would be wise to assume that he is at least somewhat in the dark about what is going on and therefore should look constantly for more light. A shorthand way to summarize the recommended stance is that a consultant is wise to assume that the consultee system is a bit paranoid about his entry and it is useful if his attitude, although not his overt behavior, is a bit paranoid too. It is comforting to note, however, that there are reasons to welcome such early problems because they indicate strength in the social system. How difficult it would be to work with an (admittedly hypothetical) psychotherapy patient who never showed any resistance and thus showed little ego strength! Similarly, how difficult it would be to work with a social system (equally hypothetical) that had so little strength (or such malevolent intent) that it immediately opened its arms wide and seemed ready for total embrace and thus ready for total change or disruption.

The problems of entry are easier if the consultee does the initiating than if the consultant or a third party plays an important role in initiating consultation. In either case, however, someone is asking for help for someone. It is optimal if the consultant can start by working with the one who is doing the asking. Thus, if a teacher asks a school psychologist to help with a disturbing child (Rhodes, 1967), the psychologist, if he is acquainted with consultation methods, ideally might want to start by talking with the teacher

because her initiation of the contact suggests that she is the one who is admitting to feeling most disturbed at the moment. Similarly, if the director of a welfare department asks a psychiatrist to consult with his caseworkers about their difficulties with multiproblem families, the psychiatrist might hope to start by talking with the director in some detail about the problem as the director sees it.

Whether or not the administrator is the one asking for help, the consultant needs to work continually toward finding out the reasons that the help is being requested—and toward obtaining and maintaining sanction for his consultation from the administrative authorities as well as from the consultees. It would also help if he could obtain sanction from the informal leaders in the social system, whose endorsement of a new consultation program will serve to allay many undue anxieties (Klein, 1964). A useful technique is to allow the consultee system as much influence as feasible in making arrangements for the consultation. Sometimes the administrator will deputize a staff member to coordinate the consultant's work and often this is a person whose role domain overlaps with that of the consultant—e.g., a school guidance counselor. Needless to say, such a person will probably be a strict gatekeeper until he feels that his own work and status will not be endangered by the consultant (Caplan, 1970).

The working out of arrangements and discovery of who are the informal leaders can be very useful clues in the consultant's first efforts to understand the consultees' social system—the organization's objectives, its methods of accomplishing these objectives, its internal power structure and subculture, and its relationships with other organizations (Rieman, 1965). One can also use other sources such as newspapers or colleagues who know the particular agency, system, or community. One psychiatrist arriving in a community to be interviewed for a job spent his first evening taking a series of taxi rides around the city and finding out from the drivers a wealth of information about what really went on in the city!

As part of making the arrangements which comprise the "manifest content" of entry, the consultant must reach, with the administrators and consultees, at least some tentative decisions about type of consultation. The consultant can begin to show his skill by giving information at this time about the relative advantages of different types of consultation and different types of administrative arrangements (e.g., should the administrator meet with the consultee group?) while at the same time working toward mutually agreeable decisions about these matters, all of which involve the working contract, whether the contract is written or verbal.

From the consultant's point of view, entry is an exciting but particularly anxiety-provoking phase of consultation. One can even say that if a consultant says he is not anxious during the entry phase, he is likely to be repressing. Obviously the consultant should be aware of his anxiety. A few consultants have even found it useful to express their anxiety to consultees, partly as an ice-breaking maneuver. Other constructive techniques include appropriate humor and channeling one's anxieties into data gathering—e.g., finding out more about the consultation request and the consultee's social system, whether by taxi or in some other way.

Beginning or Warming-up Phase

As in many relationships, there is often a honeymoon phase in consultation that occurs while the consultant and consultee are trying to make a good first impression but haven't yet dealt with basic problems (Berlin, 1964). All may be going well on the surface and the consultee may express high expectations to the consultant while at the same time he smolders or complains to his supervisor. To the extent that the consultant can be alert to what is going on underneath the honeymoon behavior, can help the dissatisfactions to emerge, and can deal with them undefensively when they do emerge, the consultation relationship will be strengthened.

Establishing a working relationship is a necessary feature of consultation, especially in the beginning phase. Specific techniques were noted above (p. 489). Cohen (1964) has pointed out that the development of the relationship is also influenced by such factors as the disciplines, sex, age, and theoretical backgrounds of the participants and the auspices under which the consultation takes place. Many consultants have noted and Beckhard (1959) has explicitly stated that consultation involves two parallel and simultaneous agenda

items—the work on the relationship and the work on the problem. Neither can be ignored.

Thus the other feature of the beginning phase—besides the relationship—is defining the problem. Specific techniques for helping the consultee to define the problem have been suggested above (pp. 489—492). Whether one is talking about defining the specific problem in one consultation session or defining the basic problems that emerge after months of hopping from one crisis to another (Klein, 1964), one can speak of the central feature of this phase as data collection. The consultees have most of the data; the consultant helps them see which data are relevant and how; and both together usually define the problem eventually, and often repeatedly.

From the consultant's point of view the beginning phase of consultation is usually much less anxiety-provoking than was his entry into the system, but this phase can drag out for a long time, with many blind alleys, and can become very frustrating. Therefore the consultant needs to resist various manifestations of impatience and undue eagerness to be useful, such as blustering ahead in the relationship as if mutual suspicions were not present; defining the problem for the consultee rather than helping him to define it; assuming that the problem has been fully defined when alternative hypotheses haven't been fully explored; giving information or suggesting alternative actions before hearing the consultees' suggestions; or confronting the consultees with their resistances.

Alternative Actions Phase

This is the heart of consultation. Now that we realize what the problem is, what alternative actions can we devise? As noted above in suggesting specific techniques for searching for alternative actions (pp. 490—492), the consultant needs to make sure that the consultee arrives at his own solution, because he will be the one who carries it out; but the consultant can usefully help clarify the problem, bring in additional data, and restrain consultees' enthusiasm for unworkable alternative actions. This phase of a single consultation session may come suddenly, in a creative spurt. In a well-functioning group, for instance, this phase tends to be characterized by consensus, working together, and new proposals which constructively modify previous ideas. Ideally at this stage, unrealistic perceptions dwindle and new perspectives and insights emerge. This phase in a long series of sessions is likely to involve sudden integration of a number of problems, but when it occurs to those involved that the problems are interrelated—i.e., when a new, more general problem has been defined—the ideas for alternative actions may emerge quickly. If the problem is a large and difficult one (such as underlying racism in the consultees), however, it may take considerable time for the consultees to agree on alternative actions.

Ideally, as with any endeavor which involves a search for new knowledge or generalizable actions, the phase of deciding upon alternative actions is not over until followup information is available to determine whether the plan worked or whether supplementary or new actions are needed. Thus, even in one-shot consultation, a consultant will often want to end the session by suggesting that the consultee check on the results of the alternative actions and let the consultant know how it turned out.

From the consultant's point of view the alternative actions phase often seems quick and exhilarating, but the exhilaration needs to be tempered by the realization that, in mental health consultation at least, more basic problems are probably just around the corner. In research, answering one question normally leads to new questions. In mental health consultation, dealing with one problem normally leads to others.

Termination

Termination of consultation should involve a mutual agreement between consultant and consultee that the need for consultation is over. A single consultation session usually terminates at the end of a specific time interval or perhaps earlier when the consultees can see their way toward some attempts at alternative actions. If the consultation contract involves dealing with crises as they emerge, then the consultant and consultee may want to spend some time at the end of each meeting deciding how subsequent similar crises might be avoided or dealt with more successfully. If the contract involves a long-term consultation relationship, the consultant should be especially alert to signs that a new consultation format is needed or that consultation is no longer needed, because, as in psychotherapy, the long-range goal is for the consultees to be able to function effectively without consultation.

Whether one consultation session or a long series is ending, human relationships end with some explicit or implicit feelings, such as sadness, relief, anxiety, or anger. Whether or not such feelings are expressed openly, they often set the mood or emotional tone of the last few minutes or the last few meetings and the consultant is usually in a better position to notice the mood or emotional tone than the consultee and thus to deal with it if it affects proposed actions or plans for the future. The consultant will have feelings about termination too, especially if his consultation involves an extra source of income, so he must frequently ask himself, "Am I still needed here?"

Farson (1966) has pointed out that, since successful consultation makes the job of organizational leadership more complex, more demanding, and thus more difficult in some ways, it often occurs that an organization is less grateful to the consultant for his help then he might expect. Thus a consultant cannot necessarily judge how successful the consultation has been on the basis of the gratitude expressed by the consultees at the time of termination.

A MENTAL HEALTH CONSULTATION CASE

Mental health consultation can be illuminated by examining a specific example. A few examples have been presented in detail in the literature (e.g., Bindman, 1959; Caplan, 1964, 1970), but most published examples have the drawback that they are presented through the eyes of one observer or participant, usually the consultant. Fortunately, however, Edward Mason in the Laboratory of Community Psychiatry at Harvard Medical School has begun to produce and make available to qualified professionals some sound movies of actual mental health consultation sessions. This laudatory endeavor, which, one hopes, will be extended by other training centers, thus makes available the raw data of examples of mental health consultation so that the same data is subject to different analyses and interpretations.

A case example, which is available to any qualified professional (from Mental Health Training in Film Program, 33 Fenwood Road, Boston, Massachusetts, 02115) is therefore presented here. "An Example of Mental Health Consultation" (Mason, 1966a) is a 44 minute, black and white, 16 mm sound movie of a complete and actual interview. It is an example of consultee-centered case consultation in which the consultant consistently acts in accordance with Caplan's theory of mental health consultation and uses indirect techniques to help a public health nurse deal with the impact of terminal cancer on a family. The content of the interview is summarized in the Discussion Guide which accompanies the film (Mason, 1966b):[1]

On a regularly scheduled visit by the consultant to this public health nursing agency, this nurse had requested consultation with the consultant and had agreed beforehand to the filming and recording. She had met with him on previous occasions and had discussed the case once of Robert G. but now brings up his father, Alphonse, who has had radiation therapy for cancer of the bladder and has been increasingly ill for several years. A recent hospital stay, during which two cordotomies were performed, resulted in incontinence and his being unable to walk. Since returning home, the nurse says he has become "downtrodden and depressed," and Alphonse himself claims he is a "changed man." The other people in the household are Mrs. G. who has been working but is presently taking a vacation to stay with her husband, and three children: Robert, age 20, who works as a beautician and is having problems because of the conflict between his own interests and those of the family; Norman, aged 17, who is in high school and seems to be excused from the family concerns; and Mary, the youngest daughter, who lives in the home and "does nothing" according to mother. The fourth child is a married daughter who lives away from home, but is of considerable help to the mother.

The nurse describes a change in Mrs. G. who had always been the "staff of strength" in the family and who was now yelling when the nurse visited, apparently mostly at her husband. Mr. G. recently was telling the nurse how frequently he had to get up at night and on this occasion Mrs. G. strenuously objected, saying that her husband should not complain that way, that he should not worry and that he would be getting better. The nurse reports that Mrs. G.'s attitude seemed to be that if one doesn't talk about something it will be less of a problem.

The nurse clearly states her "problem" as being a question of how she should react to this situation. She sees the need to coax Mr. G., give him sympathy and understanding, yet at the same time she doesn't want to go against Mrs. G. whom she feels may be threatened by her nursing efforts.

In the following interchange the consultant explores more details of the reaction of individuals in the family and the nurse says she also understands Mrs. G. as being "caught in between." The area of dependency is explored and it is pointed out that Mrs. G. resents her husband's dependency and giving in to his ailments; she feels that she must push him to try, which only makes him react "like a whipped dog." The nurse wonders whether a change of nurses would decrease Mr. G.'s dependency on her.

The doctor points out that Mrs. G. seems to be saying "stay away" but complaining that the children don't care enough. The nurse wonders whether this withdrawing could represent Mrs. G.'s anticipating her husband's death. She adds that families often visit patients in the hospital less frequently as the ill person is closer to death.

The daughter who has been of so much help and so supportive has been described by Mrs. G. as a girl who "could have been a nurse." The nurse adds that the other children are not fulfilling Mrs. G.'s expectations and then seems to block for a bit before she goes on with the discussion of the feelings of the family that "*we* can handle this." She asks, "I wonder if it's me!"

The doctor then says that "they all seem to know he is going to die" and suggests that Mrs. G. may fear that if the family pulls away from him something terrible might happen. He points out that Mrs. G. seems to blame her children for not supporting her but that she doesn't seem to link this with the fact that their father is dying.

The nurse believes that Mrs. G. is trying to say that although it may appear the family doesn't care at times, they really do. She reports that nurses go in daily to change dressings, even though Mrs. G. could do this and in fact does on the weekends, to give Mrs. G. a break.

The doctor points out that there are things that the nurse and Mrs. G. can do and she doesn't have to pull away entirely. In further discussion, the conflict for Mrs. G. is pointed out in her pushing to have her husband perform and her fear of not helping enough. The doctor says to the nurse that one way of dealing with this would be to pull out and the nurse seems to understand that this message applies both to Mrs. G. and to herself as she ends the consultation interview saying "I'll try to keep this in mind." The doctor encourages her to come again to discuss the case after she has seen them further.

Viewers of this film can infer that the nurse was uneasy about anticipating grief and was tempted to withdraw; and that she was uneasy about her relationship with Mr. G. and felt competitive with Mrs. G., all of which may have interfered with her ability to apply her considerable knowledge and skill to Mrs. G.'s grief and Mrs. G.'s temptation to withdraw. One reasonable interpretation in terms of theme interference would be: "All those who take care of a dying man will be blamed when he dies because they did not save him."

From that point of view the consultant accepted the Initial Category and did not try to point out that the theme might include the nurse's feelings, but he worked toward invalidating the Inevitable Outcome for the wife (and thus indirectly for the nurse) by showing that people would realize that even the best care could not prevent him from dying.

The consultant consistently uses an indirect method by focusing on Mrs. G. For instance, even when the consultee asks, "I wonder if it's me!" the consultant stays with the indirect method by refocusing the discussion away from the consultee and onto the family: He says, "They all seem to know he is going to die." A key criterion on which the decision to use an indirect method was based may have been the inference that the nurse was not conscious of her feelings. If so, then, according to the point of view presented above (c.f. Rapprochement), the justification for use of an indirect method is strengthened. On the other hand, some consultants viewing the film suspect that the nurse's feelings were not entirely unconscious (c.f. "I wonder if it's me!"). Such observers see the nurse-consultee as being not only bright, competent, and psychologically minded, but open to recognizing her own reactions and feelings. With a word or two from the consultant, she might easily have expressed some of her feelings, presumably concerning what seems to be a mild, sympathetic grief reaction on her part. If so, critics suggest that the consultee would have left the interview somewhat more relieved and more open to new ways of dealing with the problem without, presumably, having been lured into dealing with the personal reasons and dynamics behind her reaction but, of course,

without reduction of theme interference, if such interference was present. Perhaps, however, it would be unrealistic to expect such openness in a movie. We shall never know, of course, what might have happened.

As is usually true in consultation, it is difficult to tell how successful the consultation was. Indirect evidence is mixed but encouraging. There was an increase in tension in the latter part of the interview and there were some loose ends. On the other hand, at the end of the interview the nurse seems to have a slightly different slant on the problem. She seems to see the temptation to withdraw as understandable but also sees that withdrawal is not the only solution for the mother or herself. She also seems to have a slightly renewed determination to explore other solutions besides withdrawing. Furthermore, the consultant believed and says he saw evidence later that the nurse felt the consultation was worthwhile (Edward A. Mason, personal communication, 1968). In any case, making such case examples available to professionals should hasten the day when issues of technique and method can be more fully clarified.

Like a good teaching device, this film can provoke considerable discussion about what the problem is; whether theme interference is present; and especially about techniques of mental health consultation. Many consultants who are less committed to the indirect method will notice several openings where the consultant might have usefully focused on the consultee and her feelings.

PITFALLS IN MENTAL HEALTH CONSULTATION

It is clear that mental health consultation is fraught with pitfalls. Some crucial pitfalls, such as confidentiality and slipping from consultation into psychotherapy, and many minor pitfalls, such as answering questions too quickly, have been covered earlier. There are some others, however, which warrant separate presentation.

1. The God Complex or the Lure of "I Know." Many people believe that mental health clinicians possess unusual abilities to understand and to influence people. The mental health consultant is often expected, at some level, to be omniscient and omnipotent, to be an oracle, and to have magical solutions (Berlin, 1966; Stringer, 1961). Sometimes such expectations are not recognized by any of the participants until frustrated annoyance with the consultant's inability to work magic, or disenchantment with the consultant's proposals develop. In the extreme, "the silent petition is, 'If you really love us, you will correct things without requiring effort of us'; or 'You really could help us if you wanted to be nice, but you are being contrary and withholding.'" (Berlin, 1966, p. 167). In response to such expectations, it is easy for the consultant to succumb to the lure of "I know," to spout oracular pronouncements, to act like the big doctor in the white coat (Hollister, 1962), and to develop a God complex. Signs that the consultant may be succumbing to such attitudes include hesitating to convey his limitations, assuming expertness in areas outside his own, and feeling that he needs to help the consultee with everything the consultee brings to a session (Kazanjian et al., 1962). Measures which can help the consultant to avoid this omnipresent pitfall include having trainees with him during his consultations (Golann, 1968, has referred to the trainee as a participant-critic), getting constant feedback from the consultees, occasionally presenting his own consultation experiences to colleagues or trainees in seminars. and becoming involved in research consultation or related problems.

2. Satisfying Major Needs of One's Own in Consultation. Clearly one's needs for omniscience and omnipotence will lead to trouble if one tries to satisfy them in consultation. The same is true for a wide variety of other needs, such as the need to have the social system run "my way," the need to be a voyeur, to be liked by everyone, or to please individuals or groups. Berlin (1966) suggests that consultants learn to recognize the temptation, for instance, to please a group, as a sign to move slowly and cautiously. The mental health consultant's role is primarily auxiliary; is unlikely to involve voyeuristic gratifications very often; and is likely to instill anxiety, frustration, and annoyance at least as much as pleasure, in many consultees.

3. Dropping One's Guard. As noted earlier, a guarded underlying attitude on the part of a mental health consultant is useful. Berken and Eisdorfer (1970) have pointed out that one should not be lulled into a false sense of security by overt hospitality which may indicate a cultural-regional pattern which in no way contraindicates the presence of suspicion and testing out on the part of consultees.

4. Dehumanizing. In contrast to psychotherapy, the consultant is once removed from the troubled persons who need help, so that it is easier to see them as objects to work on or do good to (Berlin, 1966). Thus a consultant may be tempted to go along, for instance, with characterizing a delinquent as a criminal and to look for punitive solutions. Useful preventive—or humanizing—measures include keeping involved with individual psychotherapy, and occasionally seeing a client or patient of a consultee so as to return to raw human data.

5. Stepping on Toes. There are a thousand ways of doing this, some involving lack of tact, ill-considered humor, and insensitivity to the different values of the consultees. In addition, a consultant can make recommendations which conflict with administrative policy (Kazanjian et al., 1962) or can, by his very presence, threaten the person within the organization in whose jurisdiction the problem for consultation resides (Charters, 1955). The consultant's presence implies that the organization doesn't have among its members the resources to solve the problem and this may especially threaten the consultee whose expertness is closest to the consultant's. The number of measures which can prevent stepping on toes is about equivalent to the number of ways of stepping on them, but they centrally include tact and knowing the consultee's organization and culture. Even the most knowledgeable and adept consultant, however, will occasionally find that he has offended someone or overstepped a boundary. The best policy then is to recognize one's mistake openly and thus reveal one's humanness and lack of omniscience and omnipotence.

6. Thinking Simply. As noted frequently above, consultation problems and their eventual solutions are often very complex and subtle. When a consultee or a consultant thinks he has found a simple solution, the consultant should search for unverbalized or unseen complexities or subtleties. Caplan (1970) and others suggest that consultation often complicates the thinking of consultees.

Farson (1966) has suggested that training for consultants should include preparing for coping with paradox and an orientation toward change, the future, growth, and authenticity, all of which might help consultants to avoid getting into the habit of thinking simply.

7. Ignoring Negative Feedback. Berken and Eisdorfer (1970) document how an eager trainee or consultant can ignore subtle cues from consultees that things are not going well. Here, of course, ongoing conferences and supervision provide safeguards.

8. Overstaying. As noted above regarding the termination, consultants sometimes have difficulty recognizing that they are no longer needed. Berlin (1966) has suggested that when a consultant notices not only enjoyment but less work-orientation at meetings, more playful exchanges, and less serious problems being brought up for discussion, he should wonder whether these are signs that he is no longer needed.

TRAINING IN
MENTAL HEALTH CONSULTATION

Training in mental health consultation has been developing rapidly in many settings in the last few years and the dearth of papers on training may be coming to an end (c.f. Iscoe & Spielberger, 1970). One problem that has plagued the development of training in psychotherapy but has not seriously plagued the development of training in mental health consultation is professional territoriality. Psychiatrists, clinical psychologists, social workers, psychiatric nurses, and others have all been involved in mental health consultation and have characteristically worked closely together. One early limitation to training was that in Caplan's training programs in the 1950s, professionals were selected for training only after completing their regular professional training plus several years' experience. Such professionals, who were already committed to traditional ways of doing things, were sometimes resistant to training in new approaches. Currently trainees in community mental health range in experience from beginning graduate students and residents to senior professionals (c.f. Caplan's training program for senior psychiatrists).

One current issue concerns the prerequisites for training in mental health consultation. Almost all mental health consultants agree on the usefulness of training as a mental health clinician, especially training in psychotherapy, so that the mental health consultant can understand and deal with unconscious processes, implicit messages, hidden anxieties, and indirectly communicated affects (Altrocchi & Eisdorfer, 1970; Berlin, 1964; Bindman, 1966; Caplan, 1964). One wonders, however, whether such a prerequisite is absolutely necessary for all kinds of mental health consultation, thus leaving no role, for instance, for the social psychologist trained in group dynamics, the sociologist, the anthropologist, or the public health nurse.

Other prerequisites which have been suggested include: (a) training in dealing with parents of disturbed children so that one learns to hear what a consultee is saying about himself in his statements about his client (Berlin, 1964); (b) thorough knowledge of normal and disordered personality functioning; (c) experience in diagnostic use of behavioral cues; (d) some training in group and educational methods; and (e) some training in epidemiology and community organization (Bindman, 1966). It can be seen immediately that even modest exposure to these areas, plus basic professional training, plus training in mental health consultation involves an elaborate and time-consuming program. This has led to post-doctoral or postresidency specialization training programs—i.e., lengthier training—and may eventually lead to earlier specialization training in mental health consultation.

Concerning methods of training, all programs offer, as would be expected, a combination of courses or seminars, reading, and supervised experience. Other chapters in this book and other new books (e.g., Iscoe & Spielberger, 1970) are relevant to designing courses, seminars, reading lists, and different training formats in community mental health. Here we will only touch upon some issues relevant to the experiential aspects of training which otherwise can be too easily ignored.

Cohen (1964) and others have suggested the usefulness of observing the consultee's social system and the consultee in action so that the consultant understands the consultee's functioning and his point of view better. Altrocchi and Eisdorfer (1970) have outlined an apprentice-collaborator model in which trainees begin by observing experienced mental health consultants and gradually work toward semi-independent, supervised functioning. They suggest that training should be included in developing community mental health programs from the beginning; that training in consultation should be spread over the longest calendar time possible (e.g., two days a month for a year rather than full-time for four months, so that some of the early suspicions can be overcome and consultation relationships can be developed in some depth); and that the most appropriate attitude of the consultant-in-training (and the experienced consultant as well) is eagerness to learn from the community.

The development of video tapes and sound movies of the kind summarized above obviously can provide demonstrations of consultation which can be very useful at various stages in training. The author has found group role-playing of consultation to be enormously useful in training in consultation, whether the trainees are beginners or experienced professionals. Two examples of role playing as part of training in mental health consultation (concerning an alcoholic supervisor and a sterilization decision) were noted above in the section on techniques. It should be noted, however, that role playing is anxiety provoking, especially if it involves only two people rather than a group; that considerable skill in using role playing is needed; and that such techniques can be seriously misused.

Finally, Berlin has struck a note that resonates with the experience of many teachers and supervisors of consultation: "I have come to feel that the trainee has mastered consultation practice when he begins to find fun and anticipatory excitement in consultation meetings; and when he follows his intuitive leads to realize the creative possibilities in mental health consultation" (Berlin, 1964, p. 265).

PERSPECTIVES FOR THE FUTURE

There is considerable excitement about mental health consultation. It challenges the best skills of the mental health professional, fits well into a preventive model, and seems to be an efficient and effective expenditure of professional time (Kiesler, 1964). But there are many questions: Does the

enthusiasm of consultants derive in part from status considerations or the opportunity to avoid the frustration of working directly with patients? What values are central in mental health consultation (Abramovitz, 1958)? How much of mental health consultation is art and how much is science? And how fruitfully can the field develop with such a paucity of research data? In addition, there are ideas afoot, some of which have been alluded to, which perhaps can offer some perspectives for the future and thus provide an appropriate ending for this chapter.

1. Nonprofessional Consultees. Community gatekeepers, indigenous nonprofessionals (Rieff & Riessman, 1964), mental health agents (Kelly, 1964), and even parents of problem children (Guerney, 1964) are all potential mental health consultees.

2. New Models. It is intriguing to note that the stance, the approach, and many of the techniques of mental health consultation are remarkably consistent with some features of behavior therapy. It would seem that the preventive field in general and mental consultation in particular would be natural arenas for someone with a behavior modification approach, but few of those prolific writers have turned themselves to the task. Similarly, as noted earlier, application of a group dynamic approach (Gibb & Lippitt, 1959) to mental health consultation would seem to be a natural and useful development. The inclusion of sociological, anthropological, and ecological models is also needed in this field which has been dominated thus far by individually trained clinicians and their theoretical models.

3. Is the Basic Question Changing? Roen (in press) has suggested that the community mental health approach has changed the basic question in psychology from, "What is the nature of man?" to the situational, contextual question, "What happens at the interface of inner man and problem world?" From this point of view, situational determinants may be the most important factors in understanding behavior; and this would again suggest the importance of including social psychologists, sociologists, and their theories and research skills in community mental health. Mental health consultants seem to be asserting that the context of mental health problems is at least as important as the history or the dynamics of the person and are trying to intervene in problems rather than analyze personalities. Roen (1970) points out that community field training experiences may have the most potential for reorienting the field in such directions.

4. Culture Change. Consultees are likely to reflect the present culture, but mental health consultants take issue with the culture in some crucial ways, such as respecting the reality of emotions and emphasizing individually determined morality (Abramovitz, 1958). Thus consultants and consultees have to come to grips with the degree of culture change which is possible and desirable.

5. Politics. Although consultants may push for change in certain ways, mental health consultation is usually oriented more toward conserving than changing the status quo of consultees' institutions and of society (Klein, 1964). As noted earlier in this chapter, to the extent that behavior disorder and mental health are closely linked to social structure and human ecology, then changes in incidence and prevalence will involve changes in social, economic, and political systems. Mental health consultants and community psychologists are seriously divided on the issue of whether they as professionals should remain within their professional role or should become political activists (Bennett et al., 1966). All mental health professionals would presumably agree that mental health consultants should not impose their social philosophies on consultees. Some, furthermore, would say that consultants abnegate their professional role when they intertwine professional and political activities. Others, however, would say that keeping one's professional activities separate from social and political action involves abnegating responsibility for the future of the society and of world civilization. Mental health consultants will be struggling with such issues for a long time, but they are in a position to understand both the need for change and the natural resistance to change, and thus may be useful even in such momentous matters.

Notes

This was originally planned as a jointly authored chapter with Arthur J. Bindman of the Department of Mental Health, Commonwealth of Massachusetts. Although it ended up as a single-authored chapter, I am very grateful to Art Bindman for his expert advice and criticism in the planning and the early phases of writing. Communications with the author should be addressed to Division of Behavioral Sciences, School of Medical Sciences, University of Nevada, Reno, Nevada 89507.

1. Reprinted with permission from Mason (1966b).

References

Abramovitz, A. B. Methods and techniques of consultation. *American Journal of Orthopsychiatry*, 1958, 28, 126–133.

Altrocchi, J., & Eisdorfer, C. Apprentice-collaborator field training in community psychology: The Halifax County Program. In I. Iscoe & C. D. Spielberger (eds.), *Community psychology: Perspectives in training and research*, pp. 191–205. New York: Appleton-Century-Crofts, 1970.

Altrocchi, J., Spielberger, C. D., & Eisdorfer, C. Mental health consultation with groups. *Community Mental Health Journal*, 1965, 1, 127–134.

Beckhard, R. Helping a group with planning change: A case study. *Journal of Social Issues*, 1959, 15, 13–19.

Bennett, C. C., Anderson, L. S., Cooper, S., Hassol, L., Klein, D. C., & Rosenblum, A. *Community psychology: A report of the Boston Conference on the Education of Psychologists for Community Mental Health.* Boston: Boston University Press, 1966.

Berken, G., & Eisdorfer, C. Closed ranks in microcosm: Pitfalls of a training experience in community consultation. *Community Mental Health Journal*, 1970, 6, 101–109.

Berlin, I. N. Learning mental health consultation: History and problems. *Mental Hygiene*, 1964, 48, 257–266.

Berlin, I. N. Transference and countertransference in community psychiatry. *Archives of General Psychiatry*, 1966, 15, 165–172.

Bindman, A. J. Mental health consultation: Theory and practice. *Journal of Consulting Psychology*, 1959, 23, 473–482.

Bindman, A. J. The clinical psychologist as a mental health consultant. In L. E. Abt & B. J. Reiss (eds.), *Progress in clinical psychology.* New York: Grune & Stratton, 1966.

Bloom, B. L. Definitional aspects of the crisis concept. *Journal of Consulting Psychology*, 1963, 27, 498–502.

Caplan, G. *Principles of preventive psychiatry.* New York: Basic Books, 1964.

Caplan, G. *The theory and practice of mental health consultation.* New York: Basic Books, 1970.

Charters, W. W. Stresses in consultation. *Adult Leadership*, 1953, 3, 21–22.

Cohen, L. D. *Consultation: A community mental health method.* Atlanta, Ga.: Southern Regional Education Board, 1964.

Cohen, L. D. Consultation as a method of mental health intervention. In L. E. Abt & B. J. Reiss (eds.), *Progress in clinical psychology.* New York: Grune & Stratton, 1966.

Croley, H. T. The consultative process. In *Voluntary health agency–Meeting community needs.* (Continuing Education Monographs. Vol. 1) San Francisco: Western Branch, American Public Health Association, 1961.

Delany, L., Mullan, H., & ˙ Harari, C. Mental health consultation: Similarities and differences with group psychotherapy. Paper presented at the American Group Psychotherapy Association Conference, New York, 1959.

Department of Health, Education, and Welfare. Community Mental Health Centers Act of 1963. Title II. Public Laws 88–164. Regulations. Washington, D. C.: Author, 1964.

Eisdorfer, C., Altrocchi, J., & Young, R. F. Principles of community mental health in a rural setting. *Community Mental Health Journal,* 1968, 4, 211–220.

Farson, R. E. Paradoxes in consulting with community organizations. Paper presented at the annual meeting of the American Psychological Association, New York, September 1966.

Gaupp, P. G. Authority, influence and control in consultation. *Community Mental Health Journal,* 1966, 2, 205–210.

Gibb, J. R. The role of the consultant. *Journal of Social Issues,* 1959, 15, 1–4.

Gibb, J. R., & Lippitt, R. (eds.) Consulting with groups and organizations. *Journal of Social Issues,* 1959, 15, (Whole issue).

Gilbert, R. Functions of the consultant. *Teachers College Record,* 1960, 61, 117–189.

Glidewell, J. C. The entry problem in consultation. *Journal of Social Issues,* 1959, 15, 51–59.

Golann, S. E. University based training of psychological consultants. Paper presented at the annual meeting of the American Psychological Association, San Francisco, September 1968.

Green, H. *I never promised you a rose garden.* New York: Holt, Rinehart & Winston, 1964.

Guerney, B. Filial therapy: Description and rationale. *Journal of Consulting Psychology,* 1964, 28, 304–310.

Hallock, A. C. K., & Vaughan, W. T. Community organization: A dynamic component of community mental health practice. *American Journal of Orthopsychiatry,* 1956, 26, 691–706.

Hollister, W. G. Some administrative aspects of consultation. *American Journal of Orthopsychiatry,* 1962, 32, 224–225.

Hollister, W. G. The concept of stress in education: A challenge to curriculum development. In E. N. Bower & W. G. Hollister (eds.), *Behavioral science frontiers in education.* New York: Wiley, 1967. (a)

Hollister, W. G. The psychiatrist as a consultant to the school. Unpublished manuscript, University of North Carolina School of Medicine, 1967. (b)

Iscoe, I., & Spielberger, C. D. (eds.) *Community psychology: Perspectives in training and research.* New York: Appleton-Century-Crofts, in press.

Kazanjian, V., Stein, S., & Weinberg, W. L. An introduction to mental health consultation. *Public Health Monograph,* 1962, No. 69.

Kelly, J. G. The mental health agent in the urban community. In Group for the Advancement of Psychiatry (ed.), *Urban America and the planning of mental health services.* New York: Group for the Advancement of Psychiatry, 1964.

Kevin, D. Use of the group method in consultation. In L. Rapaport (ed.), *Consultation in social work practice.* New York: National Association of Social Work, 1963.

Kiesler, F. Whose is the clinical task? Paper presented at the American Medical Association's Second National Congress on Mental Illness and Health, Chicago, 1964.

Klein, D. C. Consultation processes as a method of improving teaching. *Boston University Human Relations Center Research Report,* 1964, No. 69.

Klein, D. C. Consultation process as a method for improving teaching. In E. N. Bower & W. G. Hollister (eds.), *Behavioral science frontiers in education.* New York: Wiley, 1967.

Klein, D. C., & Perlitsh, H. D. Consultation as an instance of the helping process. Paper presented at the annual meeting of the American Psychological Association, Los Angeles, September 1964.

Lippitt, R. Dimensions of the consultant's job. *Journal of Social Issues,* 1959, 15, 5–12.

Maddux, J. F. Consultation in public health. *American Journal of Public Health,* 1955, 45, 1424–1430.

Mason, E. A. *An example of mental health consultation.* (Movie) Boston: Mental Health Training Film Program, 33 Fenwood Road, 1966. (a)

Mason, E. A. Discussion guide for *An example of mental health consultation.* (Movie) Boston: Mental Health Training Film Program, 33 Fenwood Road, 1966. (b)

Parker, B. *Psychiatric consultation for nonpsychiatric professional workers.* (Public Health Monograph No. 53) Washington, D. C.: United States Department of Health, Education, and Welfare, 1958.

Parker, B. Some observations on psychiatric consultation with nursery school teachers. *Mental Hygiene,* 1962, 46, 559–566.

Reiff, R., & Riessman, F. *The indigenous nonprofessional: A strategy of change in community action and community mental health programs.* (Report No. 3) Washington, D. C.: National Institute of Labor Education, November 1964.

Rhodes, W. C. Training in mental health consultation. Paper presented at the annual meeting of the American Psychological Association, Chicago, September 1960.

Rhodes, W. C. The disturbing child: A problem of ecological management. *Exceptional Children,* 1967, 33, 449–455.

Rieman, D. W. Organization, operation, and extension of consultation services–Some administrative considerations. University of Missouri, Columbia, Mo., 1965. (Mimeo)

Roen, S. New requirements for educating psychologists for public practice and applied research. In I. Iscoe & C. D. Spielberger (eds.), *Community psychology: Perspectives in training and research.* New York: Appleton-Century-Crofts, in press.

Siegel, D. Consultation: Some guiding principles. In *Administration supervision and consultation.* New York: Family Service Association of America, 1955.

Simmons, A. J. Consultation through a community mental health agency. Paper presented at the annual meeting of the American Psychological Association, Chicago, September 1960.

Stringer, L. A. Consultation: Some expectations, principles, and skills. *Social Work*, 1961, 6, 85–90.

Towle, C. Closing summary—The consultation process. Paper presented during a workshop at the University of North Carolina, Chapel Hill, 1950.

21

Mental Health Education: Research and Practice

Daniel Adelson and Lawrence Lurie

A core problem for each individual, given his aspirations, capacities, beliefs, and characteristics, is how to make a psychodynamic adaptation with the larger community. How indeed does one adapt to social subsystems, norms, laws, expectations, attitudes, and all the other facets which define a community, so that the person experiences a sense of satisfaction and of ongoing growth and development (Adelson, 1970b, pp. 114–125).

Traditional clinical psychiatry 'and clinical psychology have been chiefly concerned with the "individual" aspects of this adaptation, i.e., with helping the individual have insight into his inner conflicts and resolve these, so he can adjust to the community and its subsystems, which in this view are fairly static.

With the advent of community mental health has come a shift to concern with making changes in the community and its subsystems and with fostering and facilitating group and community processes toward effecting such changes. The community and its subsystems are helped to have more "insight" into the barriers which they may present and are helped towards change or reconstruction so that they make a better "fit" for individuals and groups. In this view social systems are not static, but open to change and growth, as is the individual.

We conceptualize three major foci: (a) the individual, (b) group and community processes, and (c) the community and its subsystems.

Further, we suggest (a) that the particular emphases of clinical psychology have been on the individual, (b) that social psychology has tended toward concern with the relationships between the individual and the group, falling in the interstices between individual and group, and (c) that community psychology has been concerned with the relationships and processes that fall in the interstices between the group and the community. The movement may be seen as one from a more passive and adaptation-oriented position to a stance for a more active demand for social system change, from laboratory-oriented to natural setting-oriented concerns. Explicitly we have shifted from a focus on the individual to a focus on the total community and, implicitly, from a treatment-oriented relationship with patients to collaborative and coordinate education and information and growth and development-oriented relationships with client systems (Adelson, 1970a, pp. 7–28).

From this perspective the definition of mental health offered by Eric Lindemann—"Mental health appears to demand free commitment to an endeavor in terms of objectives shared within a reference group"—takes on special relevance. And the job of mental health education may be seen "as centrally concerned with education for liberty, not in the sense of license and unbridled competition, but in the sense of preparation for free and responsible participation in striving for shared goals (Lindemann, 1963)."

Since the milestone conference, the 1958 National Assembly on Mental Health Education (NAMHE, 1960), there has been considerable movement towards this more active collaborative point of view. It is reflected in major developments since that time in the areas of legislation, research, theory, and practice.

The 1958 Assembly was focused on efforts aimed at ameliorating mental illness and rehabilitating the mentally ill. "The consensus that truly united the members was that efforts to ameliorate mental illness and to rehabilitate the mentally ill were valid and that efforts to prevent mental illness, either by early treatment or by education for better mental health were largely a matter of faith" (NAMHE, 1960). In this connection it may be noted that there was no consensus on a definition of mental health, though all looked to Marie Jahoda's extended definition in *Current Concepts of Positive Mental Health* (Jahoda, 1958).

Some beginning consensus was reached on a handful of principles with respect to mental health education. These principles, which have an intrapsychic orientation, hold that:

Human behavior is caused: it is not random, no matter how bizarre or deviant it may appear. Most actions are complicated and are a product of many causes. By no means are all known.

Human behavior is determined by emotional drives which sometimes compete with rational considerations: human behavior is influenced in part by unconscious motivation, which is relatively refractive to logic and 'will power.' The need to be stimulated and protected is present in all human infants. Furthermore, a *need to be loved and the ability to love,* which begin in early infancy, lead to the need to love which seems a crucial aspect of human behavior (NAMHE, 1960).

These principles are perhaps more to be seen as providing a basic point of view about human behavior rather than providing a set of principles for mental health education. Their focus is the individual. They do not touch on or explore the variety of political, social, economic, cultural conditions which appear related to men's capacities to love insofar as they are reflected in differential rates for mental health and mental illness in different social classes, in different ethnic groups, in disorganized as contrasted with organized communities, in generations experiencing culture change, in different age levels, etc.

Techniques in mental health education were the most popular topic at the Assembly. "The one firm conclusion that all members reached was that we cannot reach all people at all times with simple and coordinated messages for mental health. . . . Goals must be partial and limited and, for this

reason, techniques must also be tailor-made to the specific goal" (NAMHE, 1960). Process as a basic aspect of educating individuals and groups was not considered.

The need for research on techniques emphasized areas of (a) the actual techniques used, (b) the content of what is taught, (c) the audience, and (d) the interaction of the variables.

The conference did emphasize the need for studies of specific issues—including the effects on mental health of a variety of such factors as age, race, religion, years of schooling, economic situation, housing conditions, diet, etc. The need for research into the ways of making more effective use of the alarmingly short supply of psychiatric personnel, and research into the effects of the "organization" in contemporary life, e.g., research on human relations in industry, was also stressed. The 1960s did see the rise of various indirect methods, such as consultation and community organization, for making better use of highly trained personnel through indirect services, and increasing concern with system conditions and system change.

As a result of the conference, Pennsylvania Mental Health Incorporated commissioned James A. Davis to review the research on mental health education. Davis' book *Education for Positive Mental Health* appeared in 1965. It provided the following conclusions with respect to experimental attempts at influencing attitudes and behavior:

1. It appears that there is a continuum in degrees of change from beliefs to attitudes to subjective states to practices. At one extreme, almost all studies of change in information show positive results, while at the other, studies of change in practices show uniformly negative outcomes.

2. The most strategic target areas of mental health education, attitude and subjective-state changes, lie in the middle of this range, where both positive and negative effects are reported.

3. The diversity of studies and measures makes it almost impossible to speculate about the differences between successful and unsuccessful attempts.

4. A key assumption of existing mental health education programs that mass exposure of books, pamphlets, movies, and so on, has a

positive effect on subjective states—has not been and should be studied (Davis, 1965, pp. 136—137).

Davis points up that generalization is difficult often because individual investigators have not followed through on initial findings with systematic and programmatic research. His findings are also presented in a somewhat "atheoretical" fashion which also makes for difficulties in generalization (Adelson & Miller, 1968).

The major event in mental health education, following the Pennsylvania Assembly, was the publication in 1961 of *Action for Mental Health*, the report of the Joint Commission on Mental Illness and Health created through the Mental Health Study Act of 1955. This report laid significant groundwork and background for President Kennedy's historic message of February 1963 in which he stated, "We need a new type of health facility; one which will return mental health care to the mainstream of American medicine, and at the same time upgrade mental health services": and for Public Law 88—164, the Mental Retardation Facilities and Community Mental Health Centers Construction Act of 1963. The President's message was an important mental health education milestone, in itself, and the implementing legislation provides that mental health education and consultation be one of five basic services to be delivered.

While the Joint Commission's report speaks of "action for mental health" it is really almost totally focused on defined mental illness, and tends to circumscribe the job of mental health education to that of providing public information. Thus, its summary of recommendations states that "a national mental health program should avoid the risk of false promise in public education for better mental health and focus on the more modest goal of disseminating such information about mental illness as the public needs and wants in order to recognize psychological forms of sickness and to arrive at an informed opinion in its responsibility toward the mentally ill."

It then goes on to make the following recommendations:

A sharper focus in a national program against mental illness might be achieved if the information publicly disseminated capitalized on the aspect in which mental illness differs from physical illness.

Such information should have at least four general objectives:

1) To overcome the general difficulty in thinking about recognizing mental illness as such—that is, a disorder with psychological as well as physiological, emotional as well as organic, social as well as individual causes and effects.

2) To overcome society's many-sided pattern of rejecting the mentally ill, by making it clear that the major mentally ill are singularly lacking in appeal, why this is so and the need consciously to solve the rejection problem.

3) To make clear what mental illness is like as it occurs in its various forms and is seen in daily life and what the average person's reactions to it are like, as well as to elucidate means of coping with it in casual or in close contact. As an example the popular stereotype of "raving maniac" or "beserk madman" as the only kind of person who goes to mental hospitals needs to be dispelled. We have not made it clear to date that such persons (who are wild and out of control) exist, but in a somewhat similar proportion as airplanes that crash in relation to airplanes that land safely.

4) To overcome the pervasive defeatism that stands in the way of effective treatment. While no attempt should be made to gloss over gaps in knowledge of diagnosis and treatment, the fallacies of "total insanity," "hopelessness," and "incurability" should be attacked, and the prospects of recovery or improvement through modern concepts of treatment and rehabilitation emphasized. One aspect of the problem is that hospitalization taking the form of ostracization, incarceration, or punishment increases rather than decreases the disability. As a matter of policy, the mental health professions can now assume that the public knows the magnitude if not the nature of the mental illness problem and psychiatry's primary responsibility for care of mental patients. Henceforth the psychiatrist and his team-mates should seek ways of sharing this responsibility with others and correcting deficiencies and inadequacies without feeling the need to be overbearing, defensive, seclusive, or evasive. A first principle of honest public relations bears repeating: To win public confidence, first confide in the public (JCMIA, 1960).

What the report makes little reference to is the increasingly weighty evidence of the strong relationship of a variety of social and social psychological factors to mental health and also physical health, and the implications of these findings for any "action for mental health program" with respect to the total community at risk. The core problem of this interdynamic relationship between the individual and the larger community is implicitly referred to by Tiedemann in an appendix in which he sees guidance as the first line of defense against mental illness (JCMIA, 1960). But Tiedemann, writing in 1960, still appears to emphasize the individual adaptation aspect of the problem.

In this chapter we move to the view that both individual adaptation and movement toward social change are two aspects of the same process which the individual carries out through participating in groups which provide a means for his ongoing consideration and resolution of personal, group, and community issues and problems, as well as a base for reaffirmation of belongingness and support. While provision of information remains an important aspect of the mental health education job, even more significant may be facilitation of group and community processes, which on the one hand foster individual self-acceptance, and on the other provide an opportunity for giving insight and perspective on interpersonal and social system factors which are causes of anxiety, conflict, and maladjustment. The differences between this position and that taken by *Action for Mental Health* is indicated by the fact that the index of *Action for Mental Health* makes no mention of the problem of poverty, no mention of prejudice or of racial minorities. Nor does it mention any of the self-help groups such as Alcoholics Anonymous.

In the decade between 1960 to 1970, the view has emerged that social structures as now arranged may be limiting opportunities for growth of vast numbers of people, so that mental health education, insofar as it is concerned with the facilitation of group, community, action/research processes and social system reconstruction and change may be in a focal position for promoting individual growth and the development of positive mental health.

There is much greater concern with effecting changes in community attitudes and norms, with bringing about legislation, and in facilitating group and community processes which will modify social systems towards the end of producing a better adaptation for all members of the community. As mental health education and the mental health educator move into this central position there is

need for conceptual frames of reference, for some practical techniques, and for some knowledgeability about research findings and approaches to the larger community and its subsystems. We turn first to some research studies and findings as providing a base for further action.

RESEARCH

In line with the frame of reference presented above, this section will present research which is concerned both with the larger community's attitudes and beliefs with respect to mental illness and also with approaches to "growth" in core subsystems of the community—family (parents) and the school and the work organization.

In selecting research, we decided also to present relatively systematic and programmatic research as providing the soundest base for practice. By implication Davis' book points up the need for systematic and programmatic studies as does *Action for Mental Health.* Further, we decided to review research at different points on the continuum from change in information to change in attitudes to change in behavior.

Using these criteria we have selected studies of Nunnally, Hereford, French, and Marrow for fuller presentation.

Nunnally—Change in Information and Attitudes of the Community

Perhaps the most systematic series of studies of popular concepts of mental health and mental illness and the effects of the mass media in communicating information about mental health and mental illness have been those of Nunnally and his associates (Nunnally, 1961).

Nunnally investigated both the information, i.e., knowledge of the facts held by the general public, and public attitudes or feelings, where no question of truth or falsity is involved. He found that the average man is not grossly misinformed. He is simply uninformed about many issues. This, Nunnally stresses, is an important distinction since it is easier to supply new information than to convert well-established opinions.

On the other hand, public attitudes are relatively negative toward persons with mental health problems, those suffering from psychotic disorders being held in lower esteem than those with neurotic disorders. While the younger and better educated have more information than the older and less educated, there is less difference in their attitudes toward the mentally ill. By contrast, the public holds moderately high positive attitudes toward mental health professionals, though it places higher evaluations on those who treat physical than on those who treat mental disorders.

The general practitioners, Nunnally and his group found, tend to be "gatekeepers" for the mentally ill with 77 percent saying they treat about half of the mental patients they see. Further, like the general public, the general practitioners tend to have a negative attitude toward the mentally ill and moderately favorable attitudes toward mental treatment specialists, methods, and institutions. Again, the younger, better informed physicians tend to have more favorable attitudes, and are more prone to treat mental problems rather than refer to specialists. This may be explained in part by their questioning of psychiatric treatment though they express high regard for psychiatrists as persons.

In the same series of studies, Nunnally and his associates also report on the problem of information transmission and attitude change. In a study of public interest in mental health topics, they found that mental health topics compete well with other fare in the mass media, but in general, the public interest is centered on the immediate, personal aspects of mental health problems (e.g., what causes them? how can one recognize them?), with rather low interest in broad problems relating to mental health (e.g., the cost of mental illness to the community).

In an additional study, the effects of a number of variables such as anxiety aroused by the message and the degree to which the message provides a solution to a problem were measured. It was found that public interest is raised when messages tend to alleviate rather than increase anxiety and when messages provide solutions to problems. Further, "when a message is anxiety-provoking, more favorable attitude changes develop if a solution is presented than if a solution is not presented."

The variable of certainty also seemed very important. On the basis of their studies they concluded, "The more certainty with which mental health information is stated, the more favorable will be the attitudes toward concepts related to the message." Further, "the destruction of information about mental illness without supplying new information results in negative attitudes toward related concepts." And they conclude, "Even if available information may turn out to be incorrect, it is better to give such information to the public than to withhold it."

Nunnally's conclusion merits full quotation:

In toto our studies show that the factual content of messages is important largely to the extent that it induces a proper emotional state. A message will promote favorable attitudes toward mental-health concepts if (1) the concepts are visible in the message (directly mentioned) or associated with visible concepts (generalization), (2) the message has a high interest value, (3) the message is thought to come from an authoritative source (e.g. university or a psychiatrist), and (4) the message makes the reader feel *secure* by sounding certain, by providing solutions, by presenting an understandable explanation, and by reducing anxiety in other ways. If these content characteristics are present, people will develop more favorable attitudes and will be more open to continued learning about mental health phenomena. If these characteristics are not present, no amount of sermonizing, haranguing, or factual presentation will work; and it would be better not to communicate at all.

Nunnally's research has thus made a significant contribution to cut understanding of the variables which influence the transmittal of mental health information. It seems also by inference to throw further light on the "closed ranks" phenomenon experienced by the Cummings (1957) when they attempted a mental health education project in Canada. For in the face of messages arousing marked anxiety, this community closed ranks on the researcher-educators.

Hereford—Changing Parental Attitudes through Group Discussion in a School Setting

While research has now revealed much about the correlates of successful families (Zimmerman, 1960; Mudd et al., 1965), and successful child-rearing approaches (Hoffman & Hoffman, 1964), we find less positive evidence about successful approaches to changing parental attitudes toward their children and consequent changes in children's behavior. Indeed, Davis concluded that "studies of attempts to modify the child-handling practice of mothers show generally negative effects" (1965). This despite the vast amount of money spent on parent information materials and programs on the problems of child techniques.

Hereford's (1963) research suggests that techniques for modifying parental attitudes do exist. In reporting his findings we will also describe the community organization approach he used, since the process of involving community groups in research, as Hereford did, is a significant aspect of his action-research design and may indeed be a core principle in changing attitudes.

Hereford and his collaborators attempted to accomplish two aims with their research project: "First, to develop and establish in a community a workable method of helping parents with their parent-child relations; second, to evaluate this method in terms of the resulting attitudinal and behavioral changes."

Based on notions of individual growth and self-development, the study was conducted over a four-year period in selected elementary schools in Austin, Texas. The program was a clearly defined educational program in parent-child relations for parents interested in attending such a program.

Underlying the program were five considerations:

1) The method must provide for participation by the parent. This was seen as a first condition for attitudinal change. 2) The method must be feasible. Psychotherapy for all in this sense was unrealistic even if desirable, given the shortage of professionals. 3) The method must be economical—in terms of unit cost per parent—meaning it should work through the presently operating organization, utilize volunteer help fully, and get results in a relatively brief period. 4) The method must be acceptable and interesting to parents. 5) The method must be testable by evaluative research.

It is of interest to review Hereford's concern with and approach to involving the community as well as the specific aspects of the educational program organized for the parents.

Two major organizations were used in approaching the community. The Mental Health Association of Austin-Travis County served as the community vehicle for the educational program and the Austin Community Guidance Center as the local sponsor for the research part of the project.

A research council including representatives from a number of organizations concerned with education in Austin was also invaluable in paving the way for community acceptance as well as providing consultation for both the research and educational aims of the project. Community acceptance was furthered also through having discussion leaders who were already in positions of community leadership. The only opposition came from the Travis County Medical Association out of concern that the program's purpose was therapeutic and not educational. This opposition faded out through the good offices of the director of the Community Guidance Center, himself a psychiatrist, who served as liaison to the physicians.

With respect to the educational program the group discussion method was chosen as providing for both participation and personal involvement and nonprofessional leaders were used. This was a modification of a plan originally developed by the St. Louis Mental Health Association program under the leadership of Dr. Margaret C. L. Gildea.

The use of the nonprofessional leader helps "to place on the participants rather than the leader the responsibility for the program" and this was a key to its success. "The basic requirement for discussion leadership of this type is an outgoing nature, characterized primarily by a genuine interest in the people and sensitivity toward them." Leaders were trained in workshops; and it is of interest that none asked to be relieved or replaced during the four years.

The discussion groups were organized through the various elementary school P.T.A.s with the format of six weekly, two-hour meetings taken over from a study-group format used by the Texas P.T.A. The size of the group was limited to about 15 members. The group met in an informal small room with seats arranged so everyone could see each other. Child care was provided. Films were used to introduce the meetings, one of the major values of the film being in providing a common experiential background as a basis for discussion.

The study provides also two basic lessons with respect to publicity: (a) "attractive, interesting, and repeated publicity is necessary to induce a sufficient number of parents to register for a discussion group" and (b) "publicity must be worded so as to attract the kind of parent able to adapt to, and profit from, a particular approach." The original publicity which focused on major problems tended to attract parents with major problems, and not those who would profit from the kind of discussion-group approach used.

With respect to the research design, the primary hypothesis concerned both parents and children. It was predicted that the parents' attendance at a series of group discussion meetings would result in significant changes in their attitudes and behavior. These changes would be toward greater confidence in the parental role, more insight into the causation of the child's behavior and feelings, more effective communication between parent and child and a stronger feeling of mutual trust. It was also predicted that these positive changes in parents would, in turn, result in better social adjustment for the children, as measured by the sociometric method and by teachers' ratings of classroom adjustment.

To test this hypothesis parents were evaluated through a parent-attitude survey questionnaire and an interview with respect to five scales: confidence, causation, acceptance, understanding, and trust. Children received a sociometric evaluation and a teacher rating. These were administered before the beginning of the discussion and lecture series, and again a week or two after the series finished.

The results showed that the experimental group of parents who participated in the group discussions changed significantly more than any of the three control groups on the causation, acceptance, and understanding scales. However, an interaction with socioeconomic level was noted. The lower socioeconomic parents showed greatest increase in scores and the higher socioeconomic parents actually showed a drop in some score factors, suggesting that socioeconomic status is a variable that should be controlled in future studies.

As regards the children, those whose parents attended discussion meetings improved in their classmate relations significantly more on the basis of sociometric evaluation than did those whose parents were in the control groups though they did not change in their ratings by teachers. The changes in the discussion-group parents, it is suggested, were apparently pervasive enough to influence the social acceptance of these children by classmates. Since the teachers' ratings remained the same, we might offer an alternative interpretation that the result of meeting in discussion groups carried over so that some parents continued as friends outside the discussions, resulting in their children becoming more accepting of each other. More open-ended data, in addition to the scales, on what actually happened as a result of the discussion group might clarify this question.

Hereford's research does demonstrate the possibility of changing both parental attitudes and also the acceptance of other children by their classmates, though how this takes place needs further research. In relation to parent education we should take note of parent effectiveness training based on behavior reinforcement, which appears to be a promising new approach which might be seen within the framework of mental health education. The issues surrounding this approach are expressed in the title of the Skinner book *Beyond Freedom and Dignity*. Bandura, however, sees freedom of choice as not disregarded in this approach (personal communication).

The work of Nunnally, then, points up significant factors which have to be considered when communicating through mass media; while Hereford's work points up a way of working with parents so that parental attitudes can be changed with associated effects on the sociometric ratings of their children.

The Impact of Organization on Work Attitudes and Mental Health

One of the most important subsystems of the community is the industrial organization. Work done with industrial organizations has in large measure stemmed from the Lewinian heritage. McGregor (1960), Likert (1961), Argyris (1964), Bennis (1966), and others have been the leaders in this field. Here we would like to make particular reference to the views of French (1963) who has been particularly interested in relating the implications of this work to mental health and to Alfred Marrow (1967) who has been particularly effective in translating the implications of this work into practice.

The Work of French and Associates

French and his associates have gathered together a wealth of evidence "showing that status in society and in industrial organizations is inversely related to major mental illness, to psychosomatic disease, to physical illness, to interview measures of mental health, and more satisfaction than those in lower positions." (To be sure, the relationship between status level and various measures of mental health is neither consistent nor simple.)

French has also been concerned with the relationship between self-evaluation and evaluation by others and the discrepancy between evaluation of the boss and self-evaluation. For example in one study 82 percent of the men reported that the evaluation of the boss was lower than their self-evaluation. At the same time French has not overlooked personal characteristics and how these influence adjustment.

In drawing the implications of his findings for practice French suggests increasing the power of the low status members in a business organization, and managing organizations so that members are placed in cooperative rather than competitive status relationships. Because cohesive groups can develop strong group pride regardless of formal status in the organization, and because pride is related to increased job satisfaction and productivity and decreased absences, support for self-esteem through supportive styles of supervision and group interaction was recommended.

Where the environment cannot be changed, its harmful effects can be reduced by appropriate selection, placement, and promotion of people to fill certain positions.

What is particularly significant about the research of French and his colleagues, in addition to its demonstration of the major relationship between organizational structure and mental health, is that it is being carried out within the context of rather fully developed social psychological theory, using self-esteem as a cultural variable. Lewin's dictum that nothing is as practical as a good theory merits repeating at this point.

Marrow—The Harwood-Weldon Study

In one of the early experiments on planned change, the principle of working toward change through removing restraining forces (people's fears, misunderstandings, resistances, suspicions) rather than through the use of driving forces only (lectures, orders, independent studies demonstrating need to change methods), was demonstrated (Coch & French, 1948).

In his factories at Harwood and Weldon, Marrow put into practice the implications of the social psychological theory which Lewin, Lippitt, French, and others have been developing.

The Harwood organization was of about the same size (approximately 1,000 employees) and age (about 30 years), with similar products and accounts, as the Weldon organization. They differed, however, in managerial styles. "Where Harwood emphasized and encouraged participative methods in meeting problems Weldon operated under the traditional authority-obedience system" (Marrow et al., 1967).

Thus an opportunity for a comparative study presented itself. A comparison of crucial cost factors found that Harwood, operating under a participative management system, was superior in terms of productivity, performance standards, turnover, waste, general efficiency, and readiness to innovate.

Six months after Weldon became a part of Harwood, the planned changes were begun. In addition to bringing in engineering and production specialists, Harwood employed psychological consultants to measure and interpret employee attitudes and to observe changes over time. A second team carried out a program designed to increase managerial competence, improve interpersonal relations, and introduce employee participation in problem solving and decision making. Two separate groups of psychologists were employed, then, one to do the theoretical, analytic, and interpretative work; the other to engage in active and personal interventions in the organization. Through various questionnaires and other devices, both management and production workers were surveyed. It was found that morale was low and many production workers were planning to seek other jobs. There were many complaints. People faithfully took orders from those above with little opportunity to exercise some authority on their own. Steps for improving attitudes were taken after top management was advised, though during the first year the chief task was to provide Weldon with the technological improvements that were needed.

During the second year a program of sensitivity training for all levels of management was provided. There was an immediate change in morale, managerial competence improved greatly, and supervisors began to deal more effectively with conflict between departments and personal rivalry. Supervisors expressed a greater sense of self-confidence, many referring to the sensitivity training program as among the most important experiences of their adult lives. In addition, staff were helped to resolve their interpersonal problems on a continuing basis through individual counseling, group meetings, and skill training. Both morale and production were improved. Thus, the average earnings of the piece-rate workers increased by nearly 30 percent while manufacturing costs decreased by about 20 percent. Turnover was halved while employee training time was much reduced. The attitudes toward the company were now much more friendly and the organization began to show a profit.

All this was accomplished with no replacements in managerial or supervisory personnel nor was the basic wage structure changed. Increased earnings resulted from better motivation and better management.

In summarizing, the research reported here supports the view that there is a growing body of knowledge available on which those engaged in mental health education can draw in planning programs whether at the level of using the mass media to communicate with the broader community, at the level of work with such core community subsystems as parents in the school, or the work setting. It also suggests, however, that the complexities of any given situation may be such that generalizations with respect to given factors such as techniques, content, and target groups may be difficult. The need is for underlying principles as a framework for guiding practice. The need is also for continuing evaluation of practice against a background of research and principles.

It is of interest that three of the four groups of studies we have covered stem basically from colleagues and/or students of Kurt Lewin. Lewin was a proponent of action-research which, it seems to us, characterizes the studies we have presented. Action on significant problems within the framework of ongoing evaluation is part and parcel of the mental health educator's approach to the community.

CONCEPTUAL FRAMEWORKS FOR PRACTICE

The Framework of Group Development

There are a number of conceptual frameworks which the mental health educator may use as a guide for practice. We wish to call attention here particularly to the frameworks of (1) group development, (2) the dynamics of planned change, and (3) anticipatory guidance. On one method there appears to be almost universal agreement and that is the use of small groups as one of the

principal, if not the principal method for changing attitudes, beliefs, and behavior. In the research of Hereford, J. R. P. French, and Marrow reported above, the group was, indeed, seen as a central method for stimulating growth and development.

Groups have been studied in a variety of ways and their processes and functions have been described in various ways. One of the most useful frameworks for describing ongoing process in the group is that provided by Bennis and Shepard in their "Theory of Group Development" (1961). The theory centers around two major problems found in every group. The problem of control (power), especially in relation to the authority figure; and the problem of interpersonal relations, of self- and other-acceptance, especially in relation to peers. It is postulated that with respect to control, the group moves from dependence, to counterdependence, to resolution of authority issues and assumption of self-responsibility in an interdependent relationship, and from enchantment, to disenchantment, to consensual validation as the interpersonal relations problem is resolved.

In the initial phase, groups tend to look dependently to the leader for directions. In the sensitivity group in which the leader provides few directions the group soon breaks up into two subgroups in an attempt to ward off the anxiety created by this situation, a "dependent" group which continues to look to the leader for answers, and a "counterdependent" group which now challenges the leader at almost every turn. This "authority" problem is most often resolved when the leader is symbolically rejected and then reaccepted into the group as a "resource" person.

The group members having gained a new cohesiveness through the resolution of the authority problem move into the "enchantment" phase, but now find themselves faced with the problem of how much they accept each other, and move into disenchantment. The "disenchantment" phase is characterized usually by major subcliques, the "counterpersonal" and the "overpersonal" who have divided attitudes on the degree of intimacy to be expressed with each other. As problems in this area get worked out the group moves toward understanding and acceptance in the final phase of consensual validation.

What is significant about this theory is that it provides a useful frame of reference for understanding process in task-oriented groups as well as in the more definitely *process*-oriented sensitivity group as has been shown by Edelson (1964) in work with professional social workers and by Kazzaz (1964) in work on a ward at the Fort Logan Mental Health Center. Adelson and Jacobs (1964) have also used it as a framework for understanding mental health consultation with groups. It also serves as a framework for assessing where a group is in terms of its growth, and for some consideration of factors which may be impeding growth.

The theory also has broad implications for work with "power deprived" populations. For, as they move from dependence to assumption of self-responsibility, at least symbolic rejection of established leadership is to be expected. A punitive response may serve only to perpetuate dependence.

Other investigators have used different social psychological (e.g., reference group, roles) and psychodynamic (e.g., ego, self-image, self-esteem) frameworks in describing the work they have done with groups. Thus, MacLennan and Klein (1965) have described a training program for young people aged "16 to 21 years from impoverished backgrounds, for non-professional jobs in human service fields such as child and health care, community organization, family counseling, recreation and education." For this program the youths participate in on-the-job experience, skill workshops, and also in a core group which provides an opportunity to examine job requirements and to learn a basic curriculum.

As MacLennan and Klein point out, "in social psychological terms we may say that in the core group we create a new reference group in which members examine their roles and functions, learn new coping skills and undergo resocialization. Psychodynamically the core group provides an experiential milieu in which the ego is strengthened through changes in self-image, increase in self-esteem, the provision of opportunities for identification with peers and an acceptable adult, the reorganization of mechanisms for dealing with anxiety, the adoption of more adequate and diversified methods of impulse control, the management of interpersonal relationships, and the sublimation of energy in the direction of work. Opportunities for reality testing and the development of competence as ego-strengthening devices are provided in the work experience" (MacLennan & Klein, 1965).

The "group" approach has thus been used in a variety of settings and for a variety of purposes. As Kurt Lewin has pointed out: "fortunately the methods generally called 'group work' permit reaching whole groups of individuals at once, and at the same time, seem actually to be more efficient in bringing about deep changes than the individual approaches" (Lewin, 1948).

The Framework of Dynamics of Planned Change

A core problem for the mental health worker is in facilitation of the "fit" between the individual, with his capacities, aspirations, values, and other characteristics, and the community with its norms, expectations, laws, and regulations. While the mental health educator is of course concerned with helping individuals make a better "fit" with their various groups and community systems, he is particularly concerned in enabling and facilitating changes in community systems so that this "fit" between the individual and society can occur (Adelson 1970b). Thus, the educator needs guidelines for working at these various levels of community system as he attempts to bring about change. Lippit, Watson, and Westley (1958) have attempted to provide such a general theory of planned change which is applicable at four client system levels: the individual, the group, the organizational, and the community levels.

This is a theory of change within the democratic philosophy, and based on the voluntary participation of the client system.

Lippitt and his co-workers have expanded the Lewinian model which includes three aspects: *unfreezing* (if necessary) the present level, moving to the new level, and *freezing* group life on the new level to seven general phases of change process. These are briefly:

1. The client system discovers the need for help, sometimes with stimulation by the change agent.
2. The helping relationship is established and defined.
3. The change problem is identified and clarified.
4. Alternative possibilities for change are examined; change goals or intentions are established.
5. Change efforts in the "reality situation" are attempted.

6. Change is generalized and stabilized.

7. The helping relationship ends or a different type of continuing relationship is defined.

Lippitt et al. suggest that a change agent enters the situation with a particular set of concepts and theories (diagnostic orientation) which provide him with a way of assessing the situation. They provide six such orientations which they see as applicable at all four levels of client system. They divide these further into those which are primarily concerned with internal relationships (intrapsychic, intragroup, intraorganization, and intracommunity) and those which are concerned with external relations (interpersonal, intergroup, etc.) The diagnostic orientations concerned with internal relationships are energy, power, and communication. In connection with energy, the change agent is concerned with how much time and thought is given to unresolved conflicts without movement toward resolution. Examples of core areas where energies may be used unproductively are: relations with authority, e.g., uncertainty about "job description;" relations with peers, for example, the status question of "who cleans the coffee pot;" sense of competence at work, e.g., a teacher caught up with "disciplinary problems" in what should be a learning situation.

In relation to power, the change agent would attempt to delineate whether power is too concentrated in one person or group, or too diffuse. He would assess how much power a group has and the relation between formal and informal power structures. Communication may be looked at in terms of whether there are regular communication channels, whether communication is one way or two way, and where communication is blocked, distorted, confused, or conflicting.

The concepts used for assessing external relationships are those of goals, skills, and strategies, the relationship between internal and external reality. For example the change agent may work to assess with the client whether a goal is limited and achievable, whether the client system is clear about goals, and if a priority system has been set up. Or the change agent may help the client system learn new skills and strategies for producing change, as buzz group sessions and role-playing. (A more radical change agent such as Alinsky might help a client-system plan a strike.)

The relation between external and internal reality may be understood as the client-system's ability to get feedback which will provide a better judgment of external reality. For example, is a homeowner avoiding meetings with a minority neighbor living nearby?

The mental health educator may use any one or all of these diagnostic orientations in his assessment of the client system.

The "closed ranks" research, through its failure, demonstrates the significance of the planned change phases outlined by Lippitt and his colleagues, and also provides lessons about other significant aspects of mental health education. This experiment in mental health education and planned changed was performed by Cumming and Cumming (Cumming & Cumming, 1957; Paul, 1955) in a small community in a western Canadian province. In an attempt to produce a more accepting climate for "former mental patients," an educational program was devised to show that there was a continuum from normal to abnormal behavior. This concept was in direct opposition to the community's attitude that a wide range of behavior could be considered normal, but that once a "breakdown" occurred, then physical, social, and conceptual isolation of the "mental patient" was the best solution. The presentation of this mental health information, which countered a core community attitude, not only produced no change in attitude but additionally a great amount of anxiety and then hostility toward the project. It was concluded that the problem for the therapy-centered educator was bettering the situation of the identified mentally ill, but the community's problem was its own stability and solidarity. The authors' comment on their approaches to mental health education: (a) It is important to analyze the community before entering. The knowledge of the organizations and key people in the community permitted a gradual entry, but lack of knowledge about schisms and particular sectors of the community diminished their effectiveness. (b) Mass media were less effective than group contacts, but organized groups were composed of the better educated and there was difficulty reaching the more poorly educated. Mass media using scare techniques, such as a movie showing an "uncaused" schizophrenic breakdown, were ineffective and resulted in cancellation of other mental health films. (c) The lack of an *action program* reduced the effectiveness of their program. Allying with a community need to build a recreation center, perhaps, would have given more meaning to their education efforts. In this particular instance, the program failed to take into account significant steps in the planned change process as described by Lippitt et al. (1958). It was a program planned independently of the community without relation to its felt needs.

The Framework of Anticipatory Guidance for Life Crisis

A third framework, important as one considers the whole-life strain, is anticipatory guidance. A special approach which has been developed over the last two decades, anticipatory guidance has been adopted by some mental health education programs (Deigh, 1967).

In the course of a lifetime, there are developmental periods which may strain individuals' coping resources to the point of crisis: attending school for the first time, leaving home, getting married, having a child, and retiring. In addition to these, there are other circumstances that will produce crises, such as the loss of a job, illness with perhaps the need for surgery, divorce, drafting into the service, and death of a family member.

The "Anticipatory Guidance" technique is, in a sense, education for crisis. It differs from other educational approaches because the crisis is always in the foreseeable future and anxiety is either present or being allayed by some defense mechanism. Crucial to the method is the individual's developing prior to the event a detailed picture of the future event. If a picture can be produced with the associated feelings while in the company of an empathetic person, then alternate ways of solving the problems and mastering the feelings can be developed. In part these techniques stem from the work of Janis (1958), who has done research on the psychological preparedness of preoperative patients in relation to their postoperative course. He categorized their anxiety levels into high, moderate, and low prior to operation, and found that the patient with the moderate anxiety level tolerated the surgical procedure best. Those with high anxiety showed the most dissatisfaction with the operative staff, postoperatively. Janis then showed that interventions, lowering the anxiety of the high anxiety patient, and raising the anxiety of the low anxiety patient, were effective in improving postoperative emotional stability. He concluded that the work of worrying is facilitated by intervention which conveys a concrete picture of what the patient will himself perceive. Through this process of fantasizing and verbalizing, the individual is able to cope more effectively at the actual time of crisis. Previously worked out reality solutions and moderate anxiety levels permit the individual to face and resolve the crisis. A significant aspect of anticipatory guidance is that the individual's hope and/or self-esteem is raised by the implication that he is important enough to help and has the capacity to master the impending crisis.

Related to anticipatory guidance is the crisis intervention approach, which has been previously developed by Lindemann (1965) and Caplan (1964). Whether this properly belongs within the function of the mental health educator is open to question, but since all individuals go through periods of crisis, the mental health educator should have some understanding of the approach. Lindemann (1965) and Caplan (1964) have pointed out that during such periods of crisis there is a failure of usual problem-solving responses of an individual, followed by an increased susceptibility to change in problem-solving methods. Following the crisis, the methods used, whether adaptive or maladaptive, are again fixed until the next crisis. (A series of nonadaptive solutions to crisis situations are seen as the steps toward mental illness.) The object of crisis intervention, similar to the object of anticipatory guidance is to help the person in crisis choose or develop adaptive, reality-based, problem-solving methods. In this sense, crisis may also provide an opportunity for growth.

MENTAL HEALTH EDUCATION—PRACTICE

Mental health education may be conceived as having two broad goals: (a) Increasing the understanding, knowledge, and capacity of the individual to effectively cope with problems and crises as these arise in daily life and also special times in the life span. (b) Increasing the knowledge, understanding, and capacity of the community and its subsystems—governmental bodies, public and voluntary agencies, such as school, welfare, police, church, hospital—to cope responsibly and effectively with "social problems" through programs of prevention, treatment, rehabilitation, and change.

The mental health educator and those engaged in mental health education use a variety of techniques and approaches in pursuing these goals. Newspaper articles, television and radio programs, movies, pamphlets, lectures—all are used. He also uses a variety of materials in relation to the needs of the particular target group he is approaching. These may range from Spock's book on baby care, to family life education courses, to movies on alcoholism. A great variety of materials is available from such organizations as the National Association of Mental Health and the Mental Health Education Information Center in New York.

Workshops and seminars in which group participation is encouraged have become a major form of education especially among professionals. Three-day "conferences" and weekly evening groups are now common educational formats.

In discussing practice, we would like to return again to the Pennsylvania Assembly conference classification of three components in mental health education: technique, content, and target group.

Technique

In line with research findings on the significance of groups for individual belongingness, change in attitude, as well as personal growth, discussion with mental health educators reveals that there has been an increasing use of small groups similar to the parent groups in Hereford's work (1963) and sensitivity groups as in the work of Marrow (1964). The increasing emphasis on small groups in mental health education is coordinate with the increasing use of small groups in other settings and with other purposes such as psychotherapy groups and the growth of encounter groups and awareness groups. It might be said that with the use of groups there is a movement away from a recipient to a participant model. The mental health educator who recognizes that education is a participative process acts primarily as a facilitator of the group process and secondarily as a resource person with special knowledge.

While the movement toward use of groups appears to be the major thrust in mental health

education over the past decade, the mass media remain an important avenue for reaching the public. Television, radio, and newspapers often carry reports and programs on mental health and mental illness problems. Television has served to acquaint the general public with the purposes and processes of individual and group psychotherapy. It has helped reduce the strangeness and remoteness of emotional illness and the healing process. More recently, television has covered with a sense of immediacy many programs related to drug use and abuse.

The mass media have also served a useful function for informing the public about developing mental health programs. For example, the need for continuity of care and interagency cooperation and gaining public support in developing a community mental health center was the subject of a television program. This program, which provided a demonstration of the various kinds of help needed for a patient and the members of his family, generated support for a projected mental health center in that community. A later program described the work of a crisis clinic, and illustrated the needs it met and could not meet.

Use of mass media has certain associated problems. There is the danger of oversimplification of the therapeutic process. High expectation for cure may be developed by the audience because of the Hollywood endings. Often the impression is left that if only a single factor about the patient's early life could be recalled, then he would be cured.

The influence of television programs apart from those specifically concerned with mental health and mental illness has been investigated, particularly in connection with the effect of violence on children. Eleanor E. Maccoby in *Review of Child Development Research* (Hoffman & Hoffman, 1964) points out that "what a child absorbs while he is being 'entertained,' he uses in the interpretation of his real-life experiences, and in preparing himself for roles that he will play in the future as well as for immediate action. The media may influence moods (for example, produce a mood of pessimism) or transmit pervasive beliefs (for example, that the world is a threatening place), as well as present bits of information or bits of action for imitation." Separate experiments by Bandura, Dovaas, and Mussen all showed that the exposure of children to an aggressive movie resulted in an increase in aggressive play following the film.

Science (1972) reporting on the government document "Television and Growing Up: The Impact of Televised Violence" stated that "conclusiveness proved elusive." Studies for the report had three focuses: The testing at long-term effects of violence, its immediate effects, and the effects of TV on general behavior. Although 7,500 children were studied, the need was evident for further research in identifying characteristics that predispose a child to aggressive behavior; determining what reactions occur at different ages; exploring how the context of violence affects reactions; and identifying what factors other than violence induce aggression. The document summary states: "We can tentatively conclude that here is a modest relationship between exposure to television violence and aggressive tendencies—which operates only on some children." Eleanor Maccoby concludes in a more strongly stated opinion related to public policy that public spirited pressure applied in the interests of children might well be extended to the mass media, though there is a need to guard against censure which would be an abridgement of civil rights.

Newspapers, of course, often play a vital role in the dissemination of information. Stories involving the emotionally disturbed person seem to have increased in recent years. Vivian Eckstein (1968), for example, found that: "Articles on suicide (as indexed in the Readers' Guide to Periodical Literature) appeared at the rate of about eight per year from 1929 through 1937. The number dropped during the years (1940–1944) ranging from one to two per year, varied between five and nine per year during the 1950s and early '60s then rose steeply from a rate of 15 in 1955 to an all time high of 102 in 1966."[1] Needed is research on how newspaper coverage influences the wider public. One may ask whether this increase in number of stories in the journals had a positive or negative effect on the wider public.

Movies and demonstrations followed by audience discussion have continued to be a much used technique in mental health education. Movies aimed at special groups from policemen to mental health professionals have been developed. A number of effective movies showing varied emotional states which are aimed at helping the audience to recognize and accept the illness and inform them of the treatment programs available have also been produced. An example of these movies is "How Are You?" produced by the Nebraska Psychiatric Institute in 1966.

Talks to organized groups remain a much used vehicle for the transmission of mental health information. Some mental health associations and mental health centers maintain speakers' bureaus for these talks. The groups vary from industrial organizations and businessmen's luncheon clubs to parent associations and professional groups such as teachers and physicians.

It may be noted that over the past decade there has been a movement toward the use of mental health consultation as a means of providing effective education. Consultation is characterized by a participant model (see chapter 20). There is a collaborative, coordinate relationship between the consultant and consultee directed to specific problems. One goal of education is providing new perspectives and understanding into problems. Insofar as this depends on a participant model, consultation is becoming one of the major techniques for providing mental health education.

Content

The content of what is taught is related both to the technique being used and to the needs of the target group. The content becomes related to target group in the sense that if the group is defined as parents, then the subject becomes understanding and communication with children. While the educator brings to the group his special knowledge, content often tends to be defined either by the subject that the group asks the educator to speak about or by the questions that are raised at the time the educator is interacting with the group. Content is, of course, also related to the goals of the mental health educator. If the goal is that of encouraging the improvement of mental health facilities and services, the content may be statistics on mental illness and the lack of current resources, while the technique may be a newsletter or talk with a visual aid. If the goal is encouraging employers to hire the "recovered patient," a meeting may be arranged to demonstrate that former patients are articulate and normal in appearance.

Overall, the knowledge that the mental health educator needs to have in order to serve as an effective resource person includes knowledge of child and individual development, information about mental health facilities, who is a candidate for care in mental health facilities, what mental health professionals do, and, as already indicated, a high degree of understanding of group processes, interpersonal relations, and individual attitudes and behavior. He may also be asked to talk on such subjects which range from the use of leisure time and problems of loneliness, to more controversial topics such as drug abuse and the mental health view of capital punishment.

Target Group

There are many potential target groups within the community. In reviewing research, we have suggested such core systems as the family, the school, and the work setting. With so many different groups, however, the mental health educator is faced with the task of setting up criteria to establish priorities, though often the readiness of a group to accept or to seek mental health education may be a determining factor in the selection that is made. Below are outlined some dimensions for determining priorities:

Criteria for Selecting Groups

I. Vulnerability to emotional disorder
   A. Children and their families.
   B. Groups going through developmental crises, e.g., entering school, retirement.
   C. Groups that are about to undergo special stress, e.g., pregnant women, an organization about to lose a director, loss of job.
   D. Groups that have had long-term chronic stress, e.g., inadequate housing, lack of jobs, disrupted home.
II. Power (ability to control change)
   A. Groups that are "establishment" or "power structure" whose understanding and acceptance of mental health education is necessary for their existence, e.g., the state legislature.
   B. Groups that are nonpower and disenfranchised, to whom some increase in control of their destiny becomes an element of self-esteem and improved mental health.
III. Degree of care-taking functions
   A. Groups of professionals or nonprofessionals such as teachers, public health nurses, ministers, police who work with vulnerable people.
      1. Degree of vulnerability of their client
      2. Intensity with which they work with client

Organizational Charts and Discussions Illustrative of Mental Health Education Practice

It can be seen that actual practice varies widely depending upon such factors as the availability of mental health educators, the readiness and sophistication of the community, and what appears to be the most useful approach in a given situation, as well as the priorities listed above.

The following charts and discussions show the organization of mental health education in one large Western city. It can be noted from these illustrations that several organizations are providing mental health education services. These include the mental health association, the community mental health centers, the university school of medicine, the school district pupil services, and mental health professionals in private practice. It may be noted that the mental health professionals in this city appear to have some characteristic relationships with particular "client systems." For instance, psychologists most often work with psychiatrists and educators most often work with public health nurses. Note further that when the client system is a professional in a nonmental health field or a "key person" and "caretaker" in a nonmental health field, he may, in turn, be doing mental health education with lay groups.

Educational System

In line with the foregoing criteria, nursery and Head Start teachers are special target groups for mental health consultation and education since they are working with children who have just started school and who may be from a poor population. The mental health educator asks the group what they might like to discuss or what problems they might wish to share with him. The teachers of a particular group might respond by

TABLE 21–1

Mental Health Education Practice Directed toward an Educational System

Educator	Direct Participating System	Topic or Objective (Content)	Technique[a]	Indirect[b] Participating System
University Community Mental Health Center (CMHC)	Nursery & Head Start teachers	Normal and abnormal child development	Consultation, lectures, Workshops	Parents, children
School District "Pupil Services"	Elementary school teachers	Learning problems	Consultation lectures	Parents, children
School District "Pupil Services"	Secondary school administrative staff	Supervisory and personnel problems regulations (e.g., concerning dress)	Workshops consultation	Teachers, parents, children
School District "Guidance Services" University CMHC	Teachers	Limits and discipline	Workshops consultation	Children
CMHC American Public Health Association	School nurse	"Health" absences and psycho-somatic problems	Workshops consultation	Children, parents, teachers
Mental Health Associations CMHC	School counselors		consultation workshops	Youth, student mental health clubs
CMHC	College academic counselors	Recognition and referral	workshops consultation	Young adult
CMHC	Special education attendance officers officers	Firmness versus nurturing	Consultation	Families, school staff
CMHC	Family life teachers	Sexual problems	Consultations	Mothers
CMHC	Handicapped	Sexual problems	Consultation	Family

[a]The particular technique used will depend on the needs of the client system at that specific point in time and its readiness to use a technique, among other factors.

[b]For the most part these groups are reached indirectly by the mental health specialist through the community client system.

asking the professional to sit in on a class or talk to a particular child in an attempt to have their own observations about normal and abnormal behavior confirmed or discussed, or the teachers may simply describe the behavior of a child or children and discussion takes place without direct observation by the professional consultant.

Teachers may ask how to communicate with parents. The form this may take is an invitation to the mental health specialist to speak to the parent group about child development. Alternatively, the mental health specialist may be asked to sit in on a P.T.A. meeting and discuss it afterward with the teachers, or he may be asked to lead a parent discussion group. Teachers have limited experience in working with adult groups, although they have worked a good deal with children's groups and need help in translating the techniques and identifying the differences in working directly with the two groups. The mental health specialist may choose to work with teachers and parents jointly in two separate target groups, or judging that the teachers would be more effective with the children if they worked comfortably with the parents, he might limit his job to direct contact with teachers only. Many workers who formerly took children on referral are now moving toward group meetings with teachers and parents as a more efficient way of reaching the goal of improved mental health.

The problems that are brought up in the elementary schools are similar to those in nursery school except for more severe behavior disorders and an increased concern for learning problems. Often the P.T.A. will ask for discussions of child development which are led not infrequently by a mental health professional who has a child in that particular school. Another source of speakers for elementary school parent groups are the educators with the local mental health association.

In the secondary schools the number of activities are much more complex as are the interrelationships between mental health specialists and the target groups. The staff groups can be differentiated into administrative staff, which often includes the disciplinary dean, the counselors, the teachers, and the school nurse. Each of these staff members plays an important role in the child's school adjustment. The nurse must decide if a youngster is to be sent home for a stomachache or headache related to a particular class that he is having difficulty attending. The teacher, of course, is concerned with how much the child is learning and how his attitudes and behavior affect the learning of others in his class. The counselor, whose focus is on the academic career and perhaps the vocational direction of the youngster, is faced with trying to tailor an individual program to meet the youngster's ability and wishes. The administrators usually set the tone of the school as either democratic or authoritarian, efficient or inefficient, flexible or inflexible, etc.

The patterns developed by the mental health specialists in the secondary grades are similar to those in the early grades. The school district's pupil services system and the local community mental health services have been most active in providing mental health education and consultation to these diverse groups. The focus usually is on working with the administrative staff, for it is felt that change there would provide major changes at the student level. Our increasing recognition of the influence of the social system on interpersonal relationships and work productivity means that the mental health specialist has to be knowledgeable in areas of administrative and social systems theory as a base for working with administrative staff. On this level the specialist may act as consultant to the principal who may want to discuss a problem that he has in making teacher assignments or about how difficult it is working with some parent. In these cases, one goal of the mental health specialist may be to increase the conscious awareness of the principal's decision-making and problem-solving mechanisms; another goal may be to help develop and objectively examine the central issue so that the best alternative plans can be reached. Still another may be to give the principal greater understanding of the influence of structure on interpersonal relationships, and the various stages in process as problems in interpersonal relations are faced and resolved.

Educational service to secondary schools also includes participation as a member of a group when a particular policy is being set. Issues such as the no-smoking rule, drug usage, or the level of mini-skirt or hair length are discussed. The specialist can contribute his knowledge about human behavior, drugs, or about how student participation in policy making will provide a greater willingness to carry out these policies.

The counselors, whose training and interest in mental health varies considerably and who are constantly dealing with the problem of "how deep" to go into the problems of the youngsters, are approached in several ways. One approach is to provide additional professional education through talks, discussions, and in-service training courses. Another is to provide consultation in connection with the difficult decisions about "how far you can go," when to refer, and when to remain peripheral, and when to be the central figure in helping a child.

In this particular secondary school system priorities are set so that teachers usually are not worked with directly but are provided indirect help through consultation to administrative staff. The teachers, who often feel like the workhorses in the school situation, frequently take university courses related to psychology. Direct exposure to a mental health specialist in the secondary school is more likely if the teacher is working with a special project, such as compensatory education. The teachers generally receive their mental health education through university courses related to psychology. One recent change within the secondary school system has been the development of discussion groups meeting 2-3 times each week, in which counselors, teachers, mental health professionals, and students participate. The mutual education resulting from the variety of orientations of the participants increases the problem solving capabilities of each of the individuals involved.

The nurses, if they work within a public health setting, may receive education and consultation through the health centers from which they work. The degree to which they work with teachers, school counselors, and social workers seems to depend on the nurse herself and on the degree to which the comprehensive family approach is part of the nursing department's philosophy.

One of the mental health education approaches used in working with the students themselves is primarily supported by the mental health association. This includes talks to the student body around mental health as a career, and such topics as the use of drugs and the "generation gap." Mental health clubs have been organized through teacher-leaders. These clubs discuss mental health topics, visit treatment programs, and provide volunteers for parties on the psychiatric ward of

the county hospital and picnics on the grounds of a state hospital.

Within the school system, the "special education" groups are often singled out to receive the most intensive education, consultation, and collaboration, primarily because many of the students they work with are identified as "problems" in some way. Attendance workers, teachers of the physically handicapped and mentally retarded are in this group. These specialists often have a high degree of training in mental health, and much of the work of a mental health specialist consists in being supportive in what often seems a discouraging task.

Lastly, some college sections and departments may seek mental health education, often from their own psychology department, or from private and community mental health center sources. The mental health educator may meet with the academic counselors five or six times a semester to discuss such subjects as mental health agencies available for referrals, how the counselor can help with problems of motivation and inability to concentrate, the psychological problems of minority groups, and ethics for counselors. Another request might be for help in development of "psychological thinking" among student nurses or help discussing personnel problems involved in nursing team leadership. The mental health specialist's response can be a topic-related discussion with specific situations presented which illustrate the topic. Other approaches such as "sensitivity training" for the development of understanding and skill in group dynamics and process, and interpersonal relationships within the group have also been used.

Health System

The health system which has produced many of the practitioners of mental health education is also the recipient of mental health education at different levels. For example, public health nurses participate actively in the mental health education process. As a student, the public health nurse is active in attending lectures on topics such as interpersonal relationships, and seminars such as those supported by the American Public Health Association and NIMH on the "unmotivated" patient. Public health nurses are also most receptive to mental health consultaiton, and in some areas, because of their traditional activities in homes and neighborhoods, have readily partici-

TABLE 21–2

Mental Health Education Practice Directed toward the Health System

Educator	Direct Participation System	Topic	Technique	Indirect Participation System
CMHC	Public health nurses	Anticipatory guidance aspects of death "unmotivated patient"	Consultation workshop	Expectant parents, chronically ill
University Extension Courses	Pediatricians	Bedwetting	Lectures workshops	Child and adolescent, patients & parents
	General practitioners	Working with severely emotionally disabled, anxiety, insomnia, geriatric problem	Lectures workshops, psychotherapy supervision	Adult patients

pated in developing treatment programs for the identified mentally ill. In addition to her "treatment" role, e.g., observing the effects of and the administration of medications, the nurse also acts as an educator. Her teaching role includes interaction with expectant parents and crisis intervention. The nurse's attitudes toward pregnancy and the anticipatory guidance she can offer the parent may be major factors in helping the parent develop a healthy relationship with her child. The nurse's role in the "well-baby clinic" as she asks the mother, "How are you able to manage?" and listens for the answers is that of a mental health educator. In such settings the "back-up" support provided by a mental health consultant may be especially important.

The pediatricians and general practitioners who, within the health system, are the "intake and referral" or "gatekeepers" for so many emotional problems are constantly acting as educators. They are able to tell a person from their experience whether a particular concern is "not unusual" or whether it is something that needs further exploring. They can be reassuring when it is indicated and flag a situation if needed. These professionals usually turn to extension courses provided by the university medical school for further education in interviewing techniques, diagnosis, and supportive psychotherapy. The educators are often the staff of the psychiatric department of the medical school. Additionally, in large hospital teaching centers where there are

TABLE 21–3

Mental Health Education Practice Directed toward the Religious System

Educator	Direct Participating System	Topic	Technique	Indirect Participating System
CMHC Private Psychiatrist, Psychologists Social Workers	Ministers	Marriage, death "Inner city"	Workshops consultations	Congregation

TABLE 21-4
Mental Health Education Practice Directed toward the Industrial System

Educator	Direct Participating System	Topic	Technique	Indirect Participating System
Private and industrial psychologists and psychiatrists	Executive	Power and control	Sensitivity group	Staff of organization
	Professional staff (middle management)	Communication	Sensitivity group and consultant	
		Interpersonal relations	Workshops and lectures	
	Labor			

strong departments of psychiatry, mental health consultation for house staff is usually developed.

Religious System

The church and its ministers have been the focus of a considerable degree of mental health education in recent years. Symposia on "Religion and Psychiatry" which are collaborative efforts between professions have been frequent. Within divinity schools the processes of counseling have been emphasized in recent years. Participation by ministers in mental health oriented subjects has increased greatly, especially among the younger and more recently trained. Participation includes attendance at seminars sponsored by the mental health association or the university or involvement as a group in work-oriented consultation from a community mental health center and participation in sensitivity groups.

The minister's focus is on the unknown and the important rites in the move from one life stage to another. Marriage, parenthood, and death, and most recently, entrance into the armed services and the draft, are among the subjects that his congregation individually and collectively wish counsel on. The minister may seek out the mental health specialist for knowledge and assistance in these areas as well as for help with such special problems as marijuana smoking and on referring a psychotic person to a hospital for treatment.

Industrial System

The work of the mental health specialist within industry occurs at several levels. In the city from which these examples are drawn one level has involved meetings called for executives by the mental health association in order to encourage them to hire the recovered mentally ill. Demonstrations of the articulateness and appearance of former state hospital patients reduce the apprehensions and stereotypes of the employer. Employability of people who were mentally ill is demonstrated by anecdotes and documented by statistics on their success.

Another level has involved interpersonal relationships and organizational effectiveness within industry such as that previously described in the Harwood project. Executives examine the interrelations within their organization with the help of an "outside" consultant. The organization may seek out a management consultant, or an industrial psychologist, or in some cases, a psychiatrist. The formats differ. The top executive may go to a retreat with top executives from other organizations, or he may establish a group of other executives within his organization for discussion of their relationships. An attempt is made to reduce defensiveness so that feelings, ideas, and attitudes toward one another can be more freely discussed. In this atmosphere effectiveness of the organization may be increased in achieving its goals. The use of T (training) groups or sensitivity groups has become a new tool in mental health education in recent years.

With respect to industrial mental health programs, Rex (1967) surveyed a random sample of 250 of the 500 leading industrial corporations.

TABLE 21–5
A Mental Health Educator Practice Directed toward the Governmental System

Educator	Direct Participating System	Topic	Technique	Indirect Participating System
Mental Health Assn. "Boards" of MH-related organization CMHC University	Legislative body	Legislation, approval and financing of MH programs	Committee hearings, research findings, statistics on add'l needs	Constituents
Private Practitioners CMHC	Corrective institutions, policemen	Management of psychotics, handling hostility	Pamphlets, lectures, movies, role playing	Emotionally disturbed, family in crisis
	Prison officers	Limit setting	Group consultation	Prisoners
	Half-way houses	Nurturing versus limit setting	Consultation	Probationers
	Social services welfare	Giving and limit setting, management of difficult client	Consultation, case conferences	Clients, boarding House operators
	Protective services	Civil liberties versus protection	Consultation	Parents, children, adoptive parents
	Social program director	Priority setting	Consultation	Agencies and affected groups

One hundred and eighteen responded. Of these, 86 indicated they did not consider that their organization had a formal mental health program, 21 had an informal program, eight a partial program, and three a comprehensive program. Most companies reported a medical program and implied that both physical and mental health were the responsibility of its medical unit. Of the 118 returns, 101 answered the question whether they employed applicants who had experienced a severe emotional problem, but who were later considered by competent medical authorities to be good employment risks. Eighty-two said they employed such applicants.

Rex's survey also shows that top echelon and middle managers are more eligible for company counsel and assistance than are employees at the lower level in the hierarchy. Finally, of the 118 companies, 77 felt there would be more interest and activity in this area of industrial mental health over the next five years. One respondent said there would be less.

In view of French's findings, noted previously, that there is a greater emotional disturbance at the lower levels, this would appear to be an area of special meaning. However, there does seem to be a growing number of mental health programs in industry. When the central role played by work in terms not only of time but of one's self-identity and self-valuation is considered, this should, undoubtedly, be a major focus for primary prevention.

Government System

Legislators and policy makers come in touch with mental health specialists in a variety of ways. The local mental health association may invite members of the board of supervisors to a luncheon in which a bond issue for the improvement of psychiatric hospital facilities is discussed or the head of the mental health association and the head of the community mental health services may meet with the mayor to talk about current programs and budgetary needs for better programs.

Policy makers are also reached by workshops run by the state department of mental hygiene. To these the county health officers, members of the mental health advisory boards, chairmen of the concerned committees of the P.T.A., Chamber of Commerce members, and county supervisors may be invited. New directions and programs in community mental health may be reviewed or pending legislation reviewed and discussed. Appearances at legislative hearings of the state senate and assembly are made by both private and public groups. The administrators of public mental health facilities, the members of mental health advisory boards, the concerned committees of professional psychiatric, psychological, and social work organizations, the mental health associations, and others all appear with their recommendations.

These groups also give information to the press, television, and radio which reaches the wider public with information on current conditions, issues, education, and new programs. For example, concerns about snake pit conditions, or pride in award winning special mental health programs are relayed to TV, radio, and newspapers.

The contribution to mental health education of the National Association for Mental Health and its state and county affiliates (to education) is inestimable. Mental health associations at all levels play a very special role in educating and informing the public as well as the legislature on current mental health needs and issues. Through NAMH and its chapters, gaps in service are noted and changes in treatment philosophy are initiated and developed. Often the local mental health association may serve as a watchdog of the community mental health program in a particular community. Among the programs of high priority currently are development of programs for children and a focus on community mental health center efforts.

A look at the programs and concerns of one local association in the past year may serve as an example. The association worked toward convincing responsible officials that a physically deteriorated psychiatric ward in the county hospital needed rehabilitating. Programs were set up interpreting what was going on in mental health centers; and the idea was pressed that legislation abolishing commitment procedures was important to local legislative bodies. Programs related to mental health education included courses for teachers and clergymen; and institutes and forums for the public on such topics as "Communication between the Generations"; "Violence in the Cities"; "Encounter Groups"; "Education: The Agony of Change." Help was offered to a mental health youth forum, planned and produced by high school students.

The association also published a newsletter; offered information and referral services; provided speakers to various groups; and met with candidates for the City Board of Supervisors. But perhaps the most outstanding feature of the program of this association—like that of other associations—is a process that goes on every year. This is the bringing together of mental health professionals and interested nonprofessionals. Both volunteer their time, and work together for common goals. Through volunteer service work in such programs as "Fashion Therapy"—initiated and organized nonprofessionals with professional guidance—patients in local psychiatric facilities are helped. At the same time, community members become more aware of local mental health programs.

Governmental agencies, such as corrective institutions and social services, are approached by mental health education in a variety of ways. In several cities the local mental health associations sponsor the mental health sections of the police recruit training course. As an example, in one city, ten hours are devoted to this section which included sessions at the police academy and at the psychiatric division of the county hospital. The course is taught by psychiatrists, a psychologist, a sociologist, and a police officer. It is initiated by the use of the training movie, "Booked for Safekeeping." This movie, produced by Rowland for the Louisiana Mental Health Association, seems to be the most effective in terms of the response of the recruits. Discussion of psychosis with clues to its recognition and management follow with an emphasis on the partial disturbance of functioning and nonpermanency of the symptoms. A pamphlet (NAMHE, 1960) entitled "How to Recognize and Handle Abnormal People" is distributed. Legal procedures are discussed and the code stating conditions under which a police officer can apprehend and detect a mentally ill person is reviewed. During the hospital visit, a patient is interviewed and then recruits visit patients on the ward. These experiences are then discussed in seminar groups.

Another hour entitled "The Police, the Patient, and the Psychiatrist" consists of a lecture viewing the typical circumstances in which police officers are apt to encounter mentally ill persons, emergency apprehensions, alternative methods for handling mentally ill persons, and an interpretation of the function of the hospital and psychiatrists. This is followed by an informal role-playing session conducted by a psychiatrist. The recruits are invited to establish a crisis situation and then staff and recruits act out the situation, following which the situation is discussed by the class. Drugs, deviations, the handling of hostility, and suicide are among the other topics discussed in the course.

In the social service agencies, education programs usually involve case problems with recurrent themes such as "giving-receiving" or how to handle a grossly disturbed and threatening client. This latter problem has come especially to the fore with the trend toward short-term institutionalizations. Patients now in the community often develop a second or third episode of emotional disturbance. Although the patient's total time in the hospital is much less then before, the number of times the community must deal with the process of channeling him to psychiatric facilities has increased and the skill is a difficult one to learn.

Governmental units involved in planning for the physical resources of a community such as city planning departments and redevelopment agencies frequently have problems related to the "human renewal" aspect of their work. The mental health specialist may be asked to sit on advisory boards or act as consultant in relation to these programs. The problems that are brought to him, however, may be technical and limited, such as assistance in writing a pamphlet on moving procedures or help in handling an objecting client. He could make a more fundamental contribution at the policy level, but such involvement might take a great deal of time. This has deterred the mental health specialist from greater involvement, but it is an area which affects a great number of people, and the planners and urban redevelopers do need to be educated on the mental health aspects of their work (Fried, 1963).

Voluntary and Organization System

Mental health education in the "private" sector of the community is frequently done by private practitioners, by the mental health association, and by the mental health center. Consultation to the staff of senior citizens groups and residence houses are on such subjects as how to "involve" the senior citizen in activities, how to structure things for the senior citizen with memory loss, how to deal with cantankerous members, and to what extent protective services are needed. Occasionally the mental health professional is used to lead discussion groups of senior citizens on topics such as relations with the younger family.

Fraternal orders such as the Rotary Club or Lions are frequently audiences for talks and movies. These talks may be on the latest mental health research, the planning of mental health programs and facilities for the community, and community "problems" such as drugs or hippies. Such organizations may provide financial support for research or for gaps in community service. Often they provide volunteers for work in hospitals and in visiting homes.

ISSUES IN MENTAL HEALTH EDUCATION

Functions of the Mental Health Educator

In any developing field, the first issues that are faced are those dealing with the need for and special knowledge of such a specialty, the acceptance of a specialty in the professional community most closely related to it, the differentiation of its goals and techniques from the related professions, the limits of the field, and the methods of analysis, evaluation, and ethical control within the field.

Goldston (1968), in a recent article, has offered a highly differentiated list of mental health education functions which he divides into those

TABLE 21–6

Mental Health Education Practice Directed towards Voluntary Organization Systems

Educator	Direct Participating System	Topic	Technique	Indirect Participating System
Mental Health Association	Senior centers	Degree of involvement with clients	Consultation	Aged
CMHC	Fraternal and social clubs	Financial support for research, volunteer work in hospital, public support for improved facilities	Lectures	Club members

activities that "generalist" community mental health workers should be responsible for and those that would be the specific responsibility of the "specialist" mental health educator who is a staff member of a community mental health center. The functions of the generalist are:

1. *Community organization.* In this connection he quotes Griffiths (1960): "The encouragement and promotion of interaction processes that open channels of communication, widen social participation, emphasize the value of individual worth in decision-making, are forces of no mean consequence in the total mental health picture of a community."

2. *Community analysis.* This would include both epidemiological studies and program analyses, general demographic studies, and surveys of unmet community needs and community expectation as well as assessment of the attitudes and beliefs regarding mental health and analysis of the effectiveness of educational programs.

3. *Identifying foci of mental illness.* In which stress situations such as regulations which humiliate individuals can be identified.

4. *Establishment and provision of mental health consultation.* "Clinical-education" functions in which the staff educates patients and family groups about what to expect prior to admission and discharge.

The special contributions of the mental health education specialists are identified by Goldston as follows:

1. *Professional training.* Planning and participating in training programs that are given to such groups as general practitioners, teachers, clergymen, police, and others.

2. *General education programs.* Developing programs for organized lay groups such as P.T.A. and labor unions.

3. *Consultation to center staff.* Identifying educational aspects in program planning for the mental health center.

4. *Staff in-service education.* Organizing and/or conducting programs for other professions within the mental health center.

5. *Rehabilitation.* Using educational approaches, including resocialization, emotional reeducation, and planned learning experiences (patient clubs and day care).

6. *Mental health education to the public.* (a) Planning programs, giving talks *about* mental health and illness, and (b) educating *for* mental health, that is, how to manage lives better using techniques of ego-strengthening, coping, anticipatory guidance, education, and crisis intervention.

7. *Communications.* Using educational media such as films, pamphlets, television, radio; developing speaker's bureaus; doing professional writing; and public relations.

8. *Career recruitment.* Developing the interest of youngsters in mental health careers.

This helpful listing of functions raises a significant issue. As we look at the different backgrounds of mental health educators, some of whom have been originally trained in public health education, others of whom come with a background of journalism, others with a social work background, it seems to us that performance of all of these functions goes beyond what now can be expected of many currently practicing mental health educators. It seems necessary that the educator in the mental health setting be cognizant of the variety of functions that need filling and at the same time recognize which he is capable of filling, based on his own background.

What then shall be the education of the mental health educator? As noted, some now performing this function have been trained basically as health educators in a school of public health. Others trained in either psychology, psychiatry, social work, or nursing often perform a mental health education function and some actually have the title "mental health educator."

A few specialized programs for mental health educators or mental health information specialists are being established in different schools in the country. Two of these deserve watching because of the different bases from which they start. At Syracuse University, the School of Journalism has started a program for students trained basically as journalists who receive additional training in mental health. A number of their graduates have gone to key positions in different mental health programs in the country. At the University of California, Los Angeles School of Public Health, a specialized program in mental health education has been established. It will be interesting to see what happens to the graduates of these two programs which begin from such different bases.

It appears on the basis of their training that the information specialist should operate more as a public information specialist concerned with developing and transmitting various statistics, materials, information via lectures, newspapers, radio, television, and other news media. The mental health education specialist may be the individual who works more directly with community groups or is trained as an agent of planned change.

In connection with education there is also the issue of the professionalization of mental health education. Some of the techniques which mental health educators may use may produce anxiety and have negative effects. What should the educator do if this happens? What limitations should the mental health educator have on what he does? Should there be a professional "mental health educator" group which through licensing, education, and other means provides the individual mental health educator with a social philosophy and ethical guidelines, as well as stimulation for further growth and development? A quotation from Lippitt, Watson, and Westley (1958) is of relevance.

The change agent simply by virtue of being a change agent commits himself to the responsibility of making intelligent value judgments. He must pass judgments on unproductive and maladjusted problem-solving processes; he must determine standards of efficiency; he must propose ways to improve interpersonal relationships. All these involve the change agent in ethical values. He cannot make consistent decisions about these and other problems unless he relies on a social philosophy.

The Issues of Differential Cultural Beliefs and Attitudes

A major issue for mental health education is the handling of those problems about which we have limited scientific knowledge, different cultural beliefs and attitudes, and limited knowledge of their association with mental health. What should be the goals and objectives of the mental health educator in providing educational programs and materials in these matters? Take, for example, drug usage and sex. Broadly speaking, it seems to us that the educator's first responsibility is to learn the facts about the physical effects of the drugs, the beliefs and attitudes of different subcultures, and the legal aspects, and to share these with the public.

The issue of how and with what segments of the public to share these facts still remains. For example, sex education has only over the past decade been introduced into some schools—and is often the subject of heated debate by communities when introduced. Such questions as whether to introduce at all, and, if introduced, at what age level, and how extensive the information, and

TABLE 21–7

Child-rearing and family life patterns reported to be more characteristic of the very poor	Child-rearing and family life patterns reported to be conducive to successful adaptation to our predominantly middle class society
1. Inconsistent, harsh, physical punishment	1. Mild, firm, consistent discipline
2. Fatalistic, subjective attitudes, magical thinking	2. Rational, evidence-oriented, objective attitudes
3. Orientation toward the present	3. Future orientation, goal commitment
4. Authoritarian, rigid family structure—strict definitions of male and female roles	4. Democratic, equalitarian, flexible family behavior patterns
5. "Keep out of trouble," alienated, distrustful approach to society outside of family, constricted experiences	5. Self-confident, positive, trustful approach to new experiences, wealth of experiences
6. Limited verbal communication, relative absence of subtelty and abstracts concepts, a physical action style	6. Extensive verbal communication, values placed on complexity, abstractions
7. Human behavior seen as unpredictable and judged in terms of its immediate impact	7. Human behavior seen as having many causes and being developmental in nature
8. Low self-esteem, little belief in one's own coping capacity	8. High self-esteem, belief in one's own coping capacity, active attitude
9. Distrust of opposite sex, ignorance of physiology of reproductive system	9. Acceptance of sex, positive sex expression within marriage by both husband and wife valued as part of total marital relationship, understanding of physiology of reproductive system
10. Tendency not to clearly differentiate one child from another	10. Each child seen as a separate individual and valued for his uniqueness
11. Lack of consistent parental warmth and support, abrupt and early granting of independence	11. Consistent parental warmth and support, with gradual training for independence
12. Rates of marital conflict higher, higher rates of family breakdown	12. Harmonious marriage, both husband and wife present
13. Low levels of educational-occupational achievement by parents	13. Educational and occupational success of parents

Note.—Reprinted from Chilman (1966).

through use of which media, and how teachers should be prepared are all related to and may be determined by the attitudes and beliefs of a particular subcommunity.

In relation to such issues, the mental health educator may have the job not only of gathering the available facts, but also of helping a community educate itself with respect to these facts and to evaluate the effects of programs which have been instituted in these areas and in other communities.

It might be suggested that for some of these issues, such as the use of marijuana, mental health education should keep hands off. However, when it is considered that various groups in the community are expressing their opinions about the subject, the need presents itself for a viable community process for considering the problem. Such a program would serve as a guide to legislators, school personnel, and other professionals.

More than in most fields, the mental health messages given can be misinterpreted and misused. The effect of a movie can be quite far from what the planners expected. Indicating that marijuana has dangers associated with its use may excite rather than frighten. Mental health education which encourages a parent to be less punitive may lead him to be overpermissive. Obviously the effect of an educational effort aimed at more than one person is going to wind up having more than one effect. Unexpected effects which were so clearly illustrated by the Cumming and Cumming book (1957) *Closed Ranks* continue to remain a danger in mental health education and need to be guarded against. Most important is the need for systematic and programmatic research so that mental health education can draw on a body of material gathered over time. And this points up again the need for effects to be studied either through pretesting the material with various subgroups of the population or by a series of evaluations as in the work of Nunnally (1961).

Mental Health Education for the Poor

The issue of how to provide mental health education for the poor has come especially to the fore with documentation of the relationship between social status and emotional disorder (see Hollingshead & Redlich, 1950; Leighton et al.,

1963; Srole et al., 1962). The life styles of the poor are different from those of the middle class and the mental health educator should consider the issues raised by the following chart which Chilman (1966) has put together on the basis of research contrasting the family life patterns of the very poor and the middle class in our society.

If this chart is accepted as valid and we place these characteristics within a framework indicative of poor or good mental health—our judgments would probably be to suggest that the middle class characteristics reflect good mental health practices. This is indeed bolstered by studies of parent-child relations (Hoffman & Hoffman, 1964). At another level it is supported by inference by the numerous epidemiological studies which have found an inverse relationship between mental illness and social class.

On the other hand, looked at critically, it provides a polarized or highly distorted picture through the eyes of middle class social scientists of the situation among the poor as contrasted with the situation among the middle class. For is it not true that the middle class today also has a relatively high divorce rate, suffers from alienation, and is having problems in parent-child relations? The mental health educator approaching the poor through the stereotypes of this chart may indeed meet the "closed ranks" phenomenon. While recognizing their poor conditions, the mental health educator, if he is to relate himself to the goals and strivings of individuals and "communities," has to begin with their interpretation of their situation and needs as part of the phases in planned change outlined above (Lippitt, Watson, and Westley, 1958). This approach may provide a much better entry and thus make for a better mental health education job.

In this connection, Gursslin, Hunt, and Roach (1964) have presented material which argues that the content of mental health pamphlets parallels middle class orientations on the one hand and that there is a disjunction between this content and the lower class orientation on the other.

They suggest that the mental health prototype and the middle class orientation or characteristics parallel each other in such areas as adjustment and conformity: "If you're mentally healthy you can get along with other people." (New York State Department of Mental Hygiene, "What is Mental Health?", 1951); problem solving: "They [mentally healthy people] do something about their problems as they arise." (National Association for Mental Health, 1951); the value of work: "Those who have a zest for working . . . may be said to be mentally healthy." (Public Affairs Committee, Inc., 1957); control of emotions: "Don't let your emotions run you—you be the boss." (New York State Department of Mental Hygiene, 1952); planning ahead: "Plan for tomorrow but don't worry about it." (New York State Department of Mental Hygiene, "Mental Health is for Everyday," 1952, p. 10); striving: "Mentally healthy people . . . make use of their natural capacities—they set realistic goals for themselves—they put their best efforts into what they do and get satisfaction out of doing it." (New York State Department of Mental Hygiene, "Mental Health is 1–2–3," 1951, p. 3); and community participation.

In all these areas, then, the mental health message fits the middle class but not the lower class prototype. According to Gursslin et al., they quote social scientists to the effect that, the lower class have "less to lose from nonconformity"; "react with apathy and indifference to their problems"; view work as "necessary in order to obtain money to buy the essentials of life"; "give more direct expression to their emotions, particularly aggressive feelings"; "see no value in planning for long-term goals"; have "limited aspirations," and are less interested in "community betterment" activities.

Having provided this contrast of personal characteristics, Gursslin et al. then suggest that "the mental health movement, whose purpose it is to contribute to personal organization and not necessarily social organization may actually be contributing to the maintenance of middle class social organization but not necessarily personal organization."

Further, they state that the mental health movement is "dysfunctional for the lower class sociocultural structure since it promulgates an ethic which is contrary to some of the central values and orientations of lower class society."

A number of issues may be raised here. First, to what extent do these mental health messages of problem-solving, zest for work, striving, community participation as characteristic of good mental health reflect more universal aspects of good mental health than just being "middle" or "lower class?" Could we not find lower class individuals who show these characteristics? Further, are the protests now heard in the land not related to community betterment, to attempts to solve group problems, to striving for a better life for selves on the part of the "lower class?"

We are thus left with the notion that the messages may touch on aspects of mental health for all classes, not, as Gursslin et al. suggest, just for the middle class. What they may fail to do is point up the larger socioeconomic conditions and context in which people are living which make it more or less difficult to be like what the messages say. It may be suggested, therefore, that a message from Martin Luther King in terms of his identification with the long-term strivings of his people had more influence on their mental health than do the messages contained in these pamphlets. Whether they are dysfunctional is, however, another question, as is the question whether these pamphlets are really read by the lower class at all.

The Issue of Conceptual Frames of Reference and Social Philosophy

Mental health education is faced, especially at this time, with the need to formulate conceptual frames of reference within which it is carried out, and to formulate also its central goals with respect to the community and individuals who comprise the community. We shall suggest that the concept of identity, especially as developed by Erikson, may be a central concept for mental health education in our time. The notions of self-identity and self-acceptance may provide a central base for both theory and practice (Adelson, 1970, pp. 114–125). Three major mental health problems previously referred to, with which the mental health educator is concerned and for which the concept of identity plays a central role, are the problems of the need for minority groups to value their own identity; the problem of identification over the normal life span (becoming a college student or parent); and the problem of changing community reference and membership groups to which one's identity may be closely tied, such as during urban renewal, return from wartime imprisonment, or return from a mental hospital. Some techniques already described in this chapter, such as anticipatory guidance and crisis intervention, may be used to ease these identity changes.

These need further development. The creation of temporary communities or groups to facilitate transitional "identity crises" may be an effective approach. Curle and Trist (1947) used such an approach in easing the move back to wives of returning prisioners of war.

CONCLUSION

We believe, as regards social philosophy, that underlying the work of most mental health educators is the democratic philosophy and the democratic ethic. Lippitt and White have suggested four basic notions in the democratic philosophy which we believe are also related to good mental health. These are freedom coupled with responsibility and majority rule with respect for minority rights. At the core is the dignity of man. This is a philosophy which is neither laissez-faire nor authoritarian in its approach. It is a philosophy of growth, development, and reconstruction. We believe that scientific breakthroughs at the biochemical level which have introduced hopefulness and optimism for the mentally ill have bolstered the more democratic forms of treatment, such as the therapeutic community, and have also made more feasible changes in the laws regarding the mentally ill, providing many more safeguards for the preservation of the individual's freedom and his opportunity to act responsibly even in the midst of stress and turmoil.

In this time of reevaluation of traditional models which have long held sway, of movement into the community, of new forms of therapy, of new transitional facilities, of new careers, and of the rise of self-help groups, and the increasing recognition of community as a source of power, shared destiny, and identity (Adelson, 1972), the mental health educator would appear to have a unique role to play both in interpreting to the public what is happening in the field and gaining their cooperation and participation in the effort to foster individual growth, group process, and community development within a framework of scientific evaluation and democratic values.

Notes

1. The authors wish to acknowledge the contribution of Vivian Eckstein, who collected these data.

References

Adelson, D. Research in community psychiatry. In L. Bellak (ed.), *Handbook of community psychiatry and community mental health.* New York: Grune & Stratton, 1964.

Adelson, D. A concept of comprehensive community mental health. In D. Adelson & B. L. Kalis (eds.), *Community psychology and mental health: Perspectives and challenges.* San Francisco: Chandler, 1970. (a)

Adelson, D. Self-valuation, social valuation, and self-identity: A framework for research in social and community psychology. In D. Adelson & B. L. Kalis (eds.), *Community psychology and mental health: Perspectives and challenges.* San Francisco: Chandler, 1970. (b)

Adelson, D. "Towards a Concept of Community Psychology: The Implications of Cultural Pluralism. In *Man As The Measure: The Crossroads*, Community Psychology Series, Issue I, No. 1, Behavioral Publications, 1972.

Adelson, D., & Jacobs, S. Some aspects of mental health consultation with groups. Paper presented at the annual meeting of the American Psychological Association, Los Angeles, September 1964.

Adelson, D., & Miller, C. G. Review of *Education for positive mental health* (by J. A. Davis; Chicago: Aldine, 1965). *Community Mental Health Journal*, 1965, 4, 101–104.

Argyris, C. *Integrating the individual and the organization.* New York: Wiley, 1964.

Becker, W. C. Consequences of a different kind of parental discipline. In M. L. Hoffman & L. W. Hoffman (eds.), *Review of child development research.* Vol. 1. New York: Russell Sage Foundation, 1964.

Bennis, W., & Shepard, H. A theory of group development. In W. G. Bennis, K. Benne, & R. Chin (eds.), *The planning of change.* New York: Holt, Rinehart & Winston, 1961.

Bennis, W. A. *Changing organizations.* New York: McGraw-Hill, 1966.

Bergin, A. E. Some implications of psychotherapy research for therapeutic practice. *Journal of Abnormal Psychology*, 1966, 71, 235–246.

Burgess, E. W., & Cottrell, L. S. *Predicting success or failure in marriage.* Englewood Cliffs, N. J.: Prentice-Hall, 1939.

Caplan, G. *Principles of preventive psychiatry.* New York: Basic Books, 1964.

Chilman, C. S. Social work practice with very poor families. In *Welfare in review.* Vol. 4. Washington, D. C.: United States Department of Health, Education, and Welfare, 1966.

Coch, L., & French, J. R. P. Overcoming resistance to change. *Human Relations*, 1948, 1, 512–532.

Cumming, E., & Cumming, J. *Closed ranks: An experiment in mental health education.* Cambridge: Harvard University Press, 1957.

Curle, A., & Trist, E. Transitional communities and social reconnection. *Human Relations*, 1947, 1 & 2.

Davis, J. A. *Education for positive mental health.* Chicago: Aldine, 1965.

Deigh, M. The use of crisis theory and crisis intervention techniques in a mental health education program. Paper presented at the 8th Western Division meeting of the American Psychological Association, Los Angeles, October 20, 1967.

Eckstein, V. Unpublished paper, 1968.

Edelson, M. The utilization of group process in social work supervision. Paper submitted as a report to class in group dynamics, Center for Training in Community Psychiatry, Berkeley, California, 1964.

French, J. R. P., Jr. The social environment and mental health. *Journal of Social Issues*, 1963, 19, 39–56.

Fried, M. Grieving for a lost home. In L. J. Duhl (ed.), *The urban condition*. New York: Basic Books, 1963.

Goldston, S. Mental health education in a community mental health center. *American Journal of Public Health*, 1968, 58, 693–699.

Griffiths, W. The public health educator in mental health. *California's Health*, January 15, 1960, 17.

Gursslin, O. R., Hunt, R. G., & Roach, J. L. Social class and the mental health movement. In F. Riessman, J. Cohen, & A. Pearl (eds.), *Mental health of the poor*. New York: Free Press of Glencoe, Macmillan, 1964.

Hereford, C. F. *Changing parental attitudes through group discussion*. Austin: University of Texas Press, 1963.

Hoffman, M. L., & Hoffman, L. W. (eds.) *Review of child development research*. New York: Russell Sage Foundation, 1964.

Hollingshead, A. B., & Redlich, F. C. *Social class and mental illness*. New York: Wiley, 1958.

Jahoda, M. *Current concepts of positive mental health*. New York: Wiley, 1958.

Janis, I. *Psychological stress*. New York: Wiley, 1958.

Joint Commission on Mental Illness & Health. *Action for mental health*. New York: Basic Books, 1961.

Kazzaz, D. The development of a psychiatry team in the light of a development theory. *Journal of Fort Logan Mental Health Center*, 1964, 2, 101–115.

Kornhauser, A. *Mental health and the industrial worker*. New York: Wiley, 1965.

Lee, R. E., & Schneider, R. F. Hypertension and arteriosclerosis in executive and nonexecutive personnel. *Journal of the American Medical Association*, 1958, 167, 1447–1450.

Leighton, D., Harding, J. S., Macklin, D. B., MacMillian, A., & Leighton, A. H. *The character of danger*. New York: Basic Books, 1963.

Lewin, K., & Grabbe, P. Conduct knowledge and the acceptance of new values. In K. Lewin (ed.), *Resolving social conflicts*. New York: Harper & Row, 1948.

Lewin, K. Cultural reconstruction. In K. Lewin (ed.), *Resolving social conflicts*. New York: Harper & Row, 1948.

Lewin, K. (ed.) *Resolving social conflicts*. New York: Harper & Row, 1948.

Likert, R. *New patterns of management*. New York: McGraw-Hill, 1961.

Lindemann, E. Mental health and the environment. In L. J. Duhl (ed.), *The urban condition*. New York: Basic Books, 1963.

Lindemann, E. Symptomatology and management of acute grief. In H. J. Parad (ed.), *Crisis intervention: Selected readings*. New York: Family Service Association of America, 1965.

Lippitt, R., Watson, J., & Westley, B. *The dynamics of planned change*. New York: Harcourt, Brace, 1958.

Maccoby, E. E. Effects of the mass media. In M. L. Hoffman & L. W. Hoffman (eds.), *Review of child development research*. Vol. 1. New York: Russell Sage Foundation, 1964.

MacLennan, B. W., & Klein, W. L. Utilization of groups in job training for the socially deprived. *International Journal of Group Psychotherapy*, 1965, 15, 424–433.

Marrow, A. J., Bowers, D. G., & Seashore, S. E. *Management by participation*. New York: Harper and Row Publishers, 1967.

Matthews, R., & Loyd, R. *How to recognize and handle abnormal people. A manual for the police officer*. New York: National Association for Mental Health, 1964.

McGregor, D. *The human side of enterprise*. New York: McGraw-Hill, 1960.

Mental health is for everyday. (Pamphlet) New York: New York State Department of Mental Hygiene, 1952.

Mental health is a family affair. (Public Affairs Pamphlet No. 155) New York: Public Affairs Committee, 1957.

Mental health is 1–2–3. (Pamphlet) New York: National Association for Mental Health, 1951.

Mortenson, J. M., Stevenson, T. T., & Whitney, L. H. Mortality due to coronary disease analyzed by broad occupational groups. *Archives of Industrial Health*, 1959, 19, 1–4.

Mudd, E. H., Mitchell, H. E., & Taubin, S. B. *Success in family living*. New York: Association Press, 1965.

National Assembly on Mental Health Education. *Mental health education: A critique*. (A project of Pennsylvania Mental Health, Inc. Cosponsored by the American Psychiatric Association and the National Association for Mental Health, Inc.) Philadelphia: Pennsylvania Mental Health, 1960.

National Association for Mental Health Education. *How to recognize and handle abnormal people*. (Pamphlet) New York: Author, 1960.

Nunnally, J. C., Jr. *Popular conceptions of mental health: Their development and change*. New York: Holt, Rinehart & Winston, 1961.

Occupational mental health notes. Washington, D. C.: National Clearinghouse for Mental Health Information, National Institute of Mental Health, Public Health Service, United States Department of Health, Education, and Welfare, December 1967.

Paul, B. D. *Health, culture, and community*. New York: Russell Sage Foundation, 1955.

Paul, L. Crises intervention. In *The clergy and people in crises. Proceedings of an Interdenominational Institute for Clergy*, May 18, 1965, 13–26.

Peck, H. B. Introductory remarks. Group approaches in programs for socially deprived populations. *International Journal of Group Psychotherapy*, 1965, 15, 423.

Pell, S., & D'Alonzo, C. A. A three-year study of myocardial infarction in a large employed population.

Journal of the American Medical Association, 1961, 175, 463–470. (a)

Pell, S., & D'Alonzo, C. A. Blood pressure, body weight, serum cholesterol, and smoking habits among executives and nonexecutives. *Journal of Occupational Medicine*, 1961, 3, 467–470. (b)

Rapaport, L. Working with families in crisis: An exploration in preventive intervention. In H. J. Parad (ed.), *Crisis intervention: Selected readings*. New York: Family Service Association of America, 1965.

Rex, J. D. Survey. In *Occupational mental health notes*. Washington, D. C.: National Clearinghouse for Mental Health Information, National Institute of Mental Health, Public Health Service, United States Department of Health, Education, and Welfare, December 1967.

Ridenour, N. *Mental health education: Principles in effective use of materials*. New York: Mental Health Materials Center, 1969.

Rioch, M. J. Pilot projects in training mental health counselors. In E. L. Cowen, E. A. Gardner, & M. Zax (eds.), *Emergent approaches to mental health problems*. New York: Appleton-Century-Crofts, 1967.

Seashore, S. E. *Group cohesiveness in the industrial work group*. Ann Arbor: Institute for Social Research, 1954.

Srole, L., Langner, T. S., Michael, S. T., et al. *Mental health in the metropolis*. New York: McGraw-Hill, 1962.

What is mental health? (Pamphlet) New York: New York State Department of Mental Hygiene, 1951.

White, R. K., & Lippitt, R. *Autocracy and democracy: An experimental inquiry*. New York: Harper, 1960.

Zimmerman, C. C. *Successful American families*. New York: Pageant Press, 1960.

22

Intervention Programs in Elementary Schools

Murray Levine and Anthony M. Graziano

The direct intervention in elementary schools by mental health professionals, and the educators' adoption of mental health concepts, have become common school practice. A wide range of mental health services are involved, including special programs of both modest and ambitious scale. Clearly, educators and mental health professionals, increasingly aware of the complex interrelatedness of school behavior and nonacademic factors, are broadening their previously circumscribed domains and are moving towards some degree of coalescence for a better-integrated focus on the school child.

This rapprochement of mental health and education is not new. In 1896 Lightner Witmer, responding to an expressed need to cope with school problems, established his psychoeducational clinic at the University of Pennsylvania. The early child guidance clinics, developed in the 1920s, frequently had close ties with the schools. Visiting teachers, in consultation with the clinics, actually carried out treatment programs, and the early clinical psychologist did much more tutoring than therapy.

In the 1920s some psychologists were developing behavior modification approaches to disturbed children. By the early 1930s they had urged that educators adopt behavioral concepts, and emphasized that teachers, with their direct control over school environments, had to recognize their own direct responsibility as major determiners of academic, social, and "emotional" behavior of school children (Gray, 1932; Graziano, 1969b).

The close working relationships between mental health professionals and educators, and the basic idea that the school environment is extremely important in shaping children's behavior, began to fade and the two professions pulled far apart. This occurred partly because of difficulties in the relationships between mental hygienists and school people (Wickman, 1928), and partly because of changing needs and views of practice within the mental health fields themselves (Levine & Levine, 1970). By the 1930s Freudian psychology was eclipsing the earlier psychoeducational focus, replacing it with intense scrutiny of individual psychodynamics. So pervasive was the Freudian influence that the mental health field subsequently assumed an almost complete identification with the medical or psychopathology model and nurtured the polarity between psychopathology and psychotherapy on the one hand, and education and teaching on the other. With their basic assumptions focused on pathology, mental health professionals operated primarily in clinics, hospitals, and residential treatment centers and their work had little direct relevance for schools.

Recently, however, partly because of criticisms of contemporary clinical practices (Albee, 1959; Levitt, 1957; Rosen et al., 1966; Graziano, 1969a) and because of shifts in governmental policies (Osterweil, 1966), attention has returned to the relationships between the mental health profession and the schools (Allinsmith & Goethals, 1962; Cowen, Gardner, & Zax, 1967; Lourie, 1967; Sarason et al., 1966; Withall, 1964). The two professions, it seems, are moving together again, but each with its own assumptions about the nature of its task in relation to the needs of society. That is, the basic social reference group of the mental health profession is the "sick individual" who needs treatment, while for education it is the large groups of relatively unselected school children who must, by law, be educated. For each profession, of course, the assumptions about the reference group help to define its goals and actions. Because the assumptions of the two professions differ, so, too, will their implementations. When these two professions, with their different social reference groups, assumptions, and actions, focus their efforts on the same population of schoolchildren, the resulting interrelations will, at the very least, be complicated. If mental health professionals hope to engage in large-scale, systematic helping efforts, we will have to be more thoroughly aware not only of the issues we initially face in each new program, but also of all of the side effects and unanticipated consequences which we generate.

Professional intervention to bring about more adaptive behavior in school children has taken many forms which reflect various degrees of influence of the two professions. That is, the employment of psychotherapy in a clinic to alleviate school phobias is clearly an action which derives from the mental health profession, with its clinical emphasis on individual treatment. On the other hand, the More Effective Schools program is clearly educational in nature, aimed at bringing about more adaptive or adjusted behavior in many large groups of children. Standing between the two is the special class for emotionally disturbed children which attempts to combine mental health and educational goals within the educational setting. In this chapter a variety of interventive forms reported in the literature will be discussed. All are programs which have been carried out within the schools. The programs are grouped under the following headings which are arranged in order from more purely mental health efforts to those which are clearly educational:

1. Clinical Methods and Social Structure
2. Mental Health Consultation in the Schools
3. Early Case Finding and Secondary Prevention
4. The Employment of Auxilliary Personnel
5. Special Classes for Emotionally Disturbed Children
6. Nonpromotion as a Remedial Policy
7. Mental Health and the School Curriculum
8. Science and Politics: The More Effective Schools Program

The major goal of this chapter, then, is to examine at least some of those predicted and unpredicted results of various forms of mental health intervention in the schools, as reported in the literature. Produced by specific variables which are brought together by different forms of intervention, these results must, of necessity, differ from one form to another. Such multiplicity makes it difficult to examine all of the intervention forms through any single, unifying set of abstractions or evaluative criteria. Therefore our discussions in each of the following sections will to a considerable degree be independent of each other. Where possible, however, we shall also attempt to abstract general concepts which are appropriate to intervention in general, and which will hopefully provide some degree of conceptual unity for the discussions.

CLINICAL METHODS
AND SOCIAL STRUCTURE

Common to all mental health intervention in schools is the problem of entry. The encounter between the mental health and educational professions is nowhere more evident than in the initial stages of establishing mental health oriented services in the schools. We shall describe the problems here but the reader should recognize that in varying degree every program described within this chapter has had to deal with the problem of entry in some form. Whatever its objectives or methodology, a new program which represents change in an ongoing social system will very likely meet some degree of opposition (Graziano, 1969a; Kandel & Williams, 1964). The first problem for the mental health professional, whether he functions as clinician, as case consultant, or as a program consultant or director, is to gain acceptance for his activity in the schools. That there is wide recognition of mental health problems in the schools does not guarantee acceptance for mental health programming. Superintendents of schools and boards of education have their own priorities, and new programs may not be viewed as salutary for the schools, for their budgets, or for the solution of ongoing conflicts of interests within the school organization (Lindeman, 1966). Politically and socially conservative communities have resisted the entrance of mental health programs into their schools (Libo & Griffith, 1966; Condell et al., 1966; Rae-Grant & Stringer, 1964; Schmuck & Chesler, 1967). Within the school, conflicts have been reported with principals (Shearer, 1969; Sarason et al., 1966; Levine, 1967; Rae-Grant & Stringer, 1964), and with teachers (Condell et al., 1966; Iscoe et al., 1967; Matthews et al., 1961; Sarason et al., 1966) around a variety of issues, including the introduction of nonprofessional teacher aides into the classroom (Cowen et al., 1967). Caution, suspicion, resistance to change, feelings about being observed, supervised and "psychoanalyzed," conflicts of leadership, autonomy, roles and values, and differences about what consitutes effective help are all issues that have presented initial and continuing problems. Resistance from within and without the school system, from those with competing interest in mental health activities, has also been reported (Lawrence et al., 1962; Klebanoff & Bindman, 1962). Entrance may be facilitated when the mental health professional manages to develop a relationship with an informal leader who offers entree and acceptance into the school setting or the community (Klebanoff & Bindman, 1962; Libo & Griffith, 1966; Sarason et al., 1966).

Whatever the problem in entry, some large proportion of the difficulties in relationship must be attributed to the ignorance which mental health professionals have of the culture and social organization of the schools, and to their orientation toward the individual case in contrast to the educators' responsibility for large groups of children. There is very little written about the nature of the mental health services from the viewpoint of school personnel; however, some of the views educators have of the mental health worker and his culture are quite devastating (Evans, 1967).

A service is introduced into a school based on assumptions concerning the "cause" of a problem. Mental health theories generally posit that if a child has a problem in school it is because of a preexisting difficulty within the family. This assumption is readily accepted by school personnel because responsibility for difficulty is placed squarely on the child and the parents, and not upon the school. A service may be offered directly to the parents, or the children within the school, on the grounds that early case-finding and early treatment are more effective. Moreover, providing the service within the school itself avoids the stigma of referral to an outside mental health agency. With such a treatment orientation, school personnel cooperate as case finders, but they are excluded from any other form of participation and thus from responsibility for resolving the problems presented by the children who are defined as having the difficulty. The effects of this assumption on the schools is revealed in data showing that the rate of children nominated as in need of help in a school which provided mental health services was twice that of a control school (Byrne et al., 1968).

When mental health personnel accept the basic treatment responsibility, it is assumed that they have the technical competence to deal with the problems presented in the schools. This assumption, however, may ignore many aspects of the schools' social structure, and lead to certain important limitations in practice. Buchmeuller and Gildea (1949) report an attempt to establish parent discussion groups as an indirect means of treating the problems of children who were having difficulty in school. Principals in each of two schools referred the parents. One school referred 18 families accounting for 24 children, and the other 19 families accounting for 20 children. After interviewing the parents, the clinicians invited 14 mothers from the first group and 12 from the second to attend group meetings. Actually six mothers from the first group and nine from the second attended one or more meetings. Less than half of the initially referred group were reached through the approach used. The mothers who attended one or more group sessions had a total of 25 children. Of these 18 (or 72 percent) improved, according to unspecified criteria of improvement. These 18 children who were said to have improved represented 41 percent of the originally referred group. There is no information on the rate of improvement for untreated controls in those schools, so we cannot judge the effectiveness of therapy.

A similar project with approximately comparable outcomes is reported by Peck et al. (1966). Discussion groups were held with parents and teachers of children with early identified "reading disabilities." The project had contact with the parents of only 30 of 60 children identified as having the problem. The parents who participated in the project, at the outset, had children with significantly better reading scores than the remainder of the group. In this study it is clear that reliance on voluntary acceptance of help reached those who were somewhat less in need of help than those who refused to participate. We are not told about other ways in which the parents differed, but just as Buchmeuller and Gildea (1949) discovered, bringing the service into the school still resulted in considerable selection among those who used the service.

A description of problems encountered in trying to establish a group therapy program in a segregated school in St. Louis (Kahn et al., 1951) clearly presents some of the issues. The program entered the school in the usual way. Initially it seemed to have the cooperation of the principal and of the Negro teachers who made referrals. However, only 18 percent of the mothers contacted ever attended the group meetings. It was felt that the Negro parents had a chronic distrust of white authorities, a distrust amply justified if the description of the school is accurate. The distrust was manifested as passive resistance to intrusion by the white authorities.

From the few parents who did participate, the group leaders learned that the Negro mothers refused to accept the assumption that problems originated in parent-child relationships. The referral was experienced by some as a distinct insult. Moreover, the mothers' group was quite heterogeneous socially, and members of the different social classes had difficulty in relating to each other. The white workers reported that the very vigorous emotional expression of some group members was difficult for them to deal with. That the problems transcend the racial issue per se was demonstrated when, in the following year, a Negro psychiatric social worker introduced into the same school encountered exactly the same problems.

Gildea et al. (1958) offer some data and some incidental observations which confirm that one needs to take into account the social characteristics of both the helping agent and the recipient of help in designing a service. First, the group reported important social class differences in child-rearing attitudes, and complex relationships between indices of social class, measures of child-rearing attitudes, and the definition of problem behaviors. The assumption that all social class groups think alike and act alike in relation to their children is clearly not warranted. Second, the research group report incidental observations to

the effect that their discussion leaders felt most comfortable in lower middle class and upper lower class schools. The workers reported an absolute dread of going to work in private schools serving upper middle and upper class families. Workers who themselves came from upper social class backgrounds reported more subjective success in working in the upper class schools. As indicated above, the group experienced almost complete failure in an all Negro school.

These observations suggest the mental health professional ignores himself as a social being. He does not view himself as having a background, nor does he view his clients as functioning within an ordered social system. He seems to approach the problems of functioning in the schools as if he had an objective technique, a "penicillin shot," equally applicable to all clients, and administerable by anyone with the requisite technical training. The mental health professional does not tend to view his own class biases and interests as factors which enable him to function in one social situation but which may cause his failures in another. Graziano (1969a) points out that mental health professionals, while accepting their professional role, do not recognize the importance of their other social roles which can, and do, affect their operation as professionals. Levine and Levine (1970) have suggested that changes in the people entering the social work field had a drastic effect upon the nature of child guidance services. The above observations reaffirm that *what* one does is important, but so is *who* does it, to *whom*, and in what *social setting* he does it. The problem is rather more complex than our individually oriented theories of help make allowances for.

In the reports cited above, mental health professionals moved services into the schools, but basically, the teacher and principal referred cases, and the mental health professional rendered the kind of service he normally provides in the clinic. Except for the physical presence of the mental health worker in the schools, contact between the education and mental health professions was quite minimal. The results, in so far as we can tell, are very similar to what we expect from clinic treatment. The next step was for the mental health professional to attempt to modify his services further by developing a closer working relationship with educators.

MENTAL HEALTH CONSULTATION
IN THE SCHOOLS

While mental health professionals have engaged in a variety of consultative services, the rediscovery of and the renewed interest in consulting methods reflects the urgent need to redistribute professional resources so that social impact is more pronounced. As consultation moves from the periphery to the center of interest, we see more attention given to the theoretical problems of consultation, and to the problems of evaluating consulting help. Consulting methods and models are quite varied, as the writing of Altrocchi and Bindman (see chapter 20), Bindman (1966), Caplan (1963), and Cohen (1964) show. By now, there is an extensive literature on the subject (Bindman, 1965; Golann, 1969; Mannino, 1969) and several detailed descriptions of the activities of consultants in elementary school settings (Bindman, 1959; Newman, 1967; Sarason et al., 1966). Issues concerning the focus of consultation, distinctions between consulting, educational, and therapeutic roles, the consultant's responsibility for dealing with the personal problems of the consultee, and the ethics of the consulting relationship are among the matters under discussion. The degree to which the consultant can or should intervene in a larger social system, even when problems are recognized, is another vital and unresolved issue in the field. Caplan (1959, 1963) has been a pioneer in the development of the theory of mental health consultation, but by and large the theory of consulting practice remains to be worked out.

In this section we shall discuss consulting help given directly to elementary school teachers, the teacher being viewed as a member of the class of "care-givers." Care-givers are those who relate directly to people in a variety of social roles and settings to assist in providing for the general development and welfare of those people. The care-givers generally deal with emotional stress and crises, on a day-to-day basis, whether or not the popular or traditional definition of the particular role includes such a function. Following Scheff's (1966) concepts, the response of care-givers to residual deviance may be critical in determining whether an individual exhibiting deviant behavior enters into a sick role and a deviant career. Similarly, the expectations and the actions of care-givers may be important in shaping more positive behavior from those who are having problems in a given social setting.

It is generally agreed that the previous training of care-givers such as educators was not designed to help them deal with the variety of social, interpersonal, and emotional problems they face. It is also a basic assumption of consulting practice that care-givers can learn to deal more effectively with those problems. Moreover, consulting practice assumes that if a consultee learns to deal more effectively with the problem presented by one case, he will become more effective in others.

Consultants work with individuals and with groups and the techniques and approaches range through the educational, the case study, group discussions, group therapy, and sensitivity training. Initially the school child may be the focus of the discussions, with attempts made to work out the problem or arrive at a plan to deal with the problem in the classroom or within the confines of the school's resources. Many groups have reported that the problems usually involve more than the psychological and educational issues presented by the child. Most often aspects of the social organization of the school and aspects of the teacher's personality are involved in the definition and the maintenance of the problem.

Given the difficulties in initiating and sustaining consulting relationships in the schools, it is not surprising that few formal, systematic studies of consulting programs exist. We have no good controlled study of either the short-term or the long-term effects of consulting efforts. There are a large number of case reports sufficiently detailed to be convincing that the interventions developed through the consulting relationship were causative in the favorable resolution of many individual problems. However, systematic data concerning the kinds of problems which can or cannot be helped, and systematic data concerning the conditions favorable and unfavorable to consulting interventions, are clearly lacking.

Iscoe et al. (1967) and Pierce-Jones et al. (1968) present data concerning the operation of a program in which senior graduate students in school psychology functioned as child behavior consultants in public elementary schools. They discovered, as have other groups, that a full range of clinical problems were encountered within the classroom. About 80 percent of the potential pool of consultees used the service at least once. The group reported that all Negro schools (the project was carried out in Texas) were less receptive to the service than the all-white schools. Kahn et al. (1951), working in a segregated school in St. Louis, reported a similar problem. On the other hand Sarason et al. (1966) found their services were better received in predominantly Negro schools in a Northern core city area than in all-white suburban schools. In this instance the teachers were predominantly white and embattled. Matthews et al. (1961) reported systematic differences between teachers who used the consulting service and those who did not. Iscoe et al. (1967) reported the same.

There is little point in detailing and comparing the characteristics of teachers who do and do not use consultants, because the characteristics of the consultants are not well defined in the studies and thus are not easily comparable. Moreover the situations in different schools are vastly different. It is inconceivable that the young graduate students of Iscoe's study would attract the same kind of teachers that an older Ph.D. would attract in the same setting. Similarly, a white person entering an all-Negro school in a segregated system will have a different significance and a different relationship to teachers than a white person entering a defacto segregated school with a white faculty.

It seems clear that consultation programs, depending upon the voluntary use of the consultant by the teacher, must necessarily involve differences among those who do and do not use the service, and thus do not obviate the problem of providing services across the board. We shall return to this issue again in discussing other therapeutic interventions in the schools.

Iscoe et al. (1967) report that about a third of their consulting requests centered about the teacher's personal and professional anxieties and concerns, and had to do with role conflicts or other difficult interpersonal situations in the school setting. While the program described by Matthews et al. (1961) was more varied in focus and in method, they report a number of important changes in the participating educators. A variety of paper and pencil tests and scales revealed that the educators developed more positive self-perceptions, and that feelings of conflict with administration were reduced. The results also showed positive changes in attitude toward children and cognitive mastery of new techniques for handling problems. Given that Iscoe's group and Morse's group both reported that educators developed positive attitudes towards the consultants, it may be that consultants were able to help the educators to resolve some of their own immediate emotional concerns.

Does the attitude change developed in the consulting relationship carry over and result in changes in classroom practice? Sarason et al. (1966) claim to have noted instances of carryover but well developed, systematic data are lacking. In another context Morse (1967) presents findings suggesting that pupils saw teachers who participated in a consulting program as less nagging and punitive, less anxiety inducing, and as setting firmer limits. Such findings suggest carry-over but much more systematic study is required, particularly since other evidence suggests it is difficult to sustain new practices in educational settings. Long (1963), for example, has reported that graduate students in education, taught life space interviewing techniques, quickly stopped using them once on their own in the school situation. While the techniques were reported to be helpful and effective, the real problems proved to be deeper and more pervasive than the students had anticipated. Moreover older colleagues were unsympathetic and openly critical in some instances. Without adequate support from the institution, from a group, or from supervision many of these new teachers became discouraged and even depressed. While Iscoe's group developed good working relationships with teachers, the full evaluative study showed that teachers did not feel the consultants helped to produce changes in the classroom (Pierce-Jones et al., 1968). Byrne et al. (1968) report similar results for a project using child development consultants in elementary schools. The problem of carrying over and sustaining gains may be more difficult than appears on the surface.

In summary, in some situations mental health consultants can gain entry and can function effectively in that some emotional concerns of the recipients of consultation appear to become resolved. Moreover, there are case reports which suggest that management plans worked out in consulting relationships can help to resolve manifestations of psychological problems in the classroom, although systematic evidence of effects in the classroom are lacking. There is little evidence that consulting methods produce generalized learning in the care-givers and there is no long-range follow-up of individuals treated through consulting methods. There are also consistent reports which suggest that conflicts of role and values are to be expected between mental health and school personnel, and that school people who use consulting services differ systematically from those who do not use such services. The available evidence suggests that the characteristics of the consultant, the nature of the school setting, and perhaps the service offered, interact to determine who will and who will not use consultants. The use of consultants within a school building will not, in and of itself, solve the problem of the delivery of services. Nonetheless, there are sufficient reports of positive experiences despite difficulties to warrant the systematic development of consulting techniques and programs as a vital means of delivering services effectively and efficiently in the life settings in which problems are manifested. Moreover, testing clinical concepts through attempts to implement treatment programs in the life setting will undoubtedly provide an important means for testing the validity and the generality of clinical concepts.

Most consultation programs send a lone consultant to a school, and for the most part the consultant restricts himself to working with the teacher or principal. He rarely engages in treatment of cases himself, although he may assist in referrals to other agencies. A further step involves bringing a mental health team into the schools to provide a full range of services including diagnosis, consultation, and formal and informal treatment of children identified as having emotional problems.

EARLY CASE FINDING AND SECONDARY PREVENTION

The opportunities for preventive work are broad (Bower, 1963), but if one assumes disorder already exists by school age, then an appropriate strategy is early case finding and early intervention. Probably the most carefully executed and sophisticated study of a school based program is that reported by Cowen et al. (1963; 1966; 1967; Zax & Cowen, 1969). The project studied all of the first grade children in a public school reasonably representative of those in its city. A testing battery, ratings by teachers, and interviews with mothers in the first four to six weeks of school led to the "red-tagging" of a child's folder when the problems were judged to be serious.

During the school year the mental health team and the first grade teacher conferred to formulate plans and objectives for working with their children. When indicated, additional consultations or referrals for further help were available. About one third of the population of first grade children were the subjects of such conferences. The conferences were initiated by the teachers but they were largely concerned with the problems of the red-tagged group. An after-school activity program, a series of teacher seminars, and discussion groups with parents were also conducted. The children were followed until the third grade.

The investigators considered the intervention program to be applied to the school as a whole. Therefore, at the end of the third grade, children in the project school were compared with children from two other control schools, for a variety of indices of adjustment. Actually an initial study (Cowen et al., 1963) and a replication are reported (Cowen et al., 1966). We will point up some important problems through examining some discrepancies in outcome between the two studies.

The project was evaluated through a large variety of indices. There were a few significant differences on objective measures taken from school records. Children in the experimental school had better report card grades and a lower discrepancy between measures of achievement and aptitude. There was indication that children in the treated school had better reading comprehension scores and tended to visit the school nurse less often. An unstandardized secret stories test, and some self-report measures were employed with the children. While the stories showed no findings of any consequence, children in the treated school, particularly the girls, reported themselves on the Children's Manifest Anxiety Scale as less anxious than children in the control schools.

While there were few demonstrable changes in parental child-rearing attitudes, there was evidence that the parents were favorably disposed towards the mental health workers. Teachers in the treated school said they felt more comfortable in their teaching roles and they also viewed mental health personnel favorably. These last results are similar to those reported by Matthews et al. (1961), Sarason et al. (1966), and Iscoe et al. (1967). Apparently it is possible to increase the subjective comfort of teachers, at least as they report their feelings. To what extent these reports reflect a demand to respond in a socially desirable direction rather than an actual change cannot be determined. In any event we are still lacking detailed knowledge of how changes in feelings and attitudes are translated into changed practices in the classroom. Testimonial appraisal provides one level of evidence, but such testimonials sometimes show little relationship to other measures of change in a school setting (Matthews et al., 1961).

Teachers also filled out behavior rating scales based on their observations of children's classroom behavior. In the first study, teachers in the treated school rated their children as significantly *more* maladjusted than control school teachers rated their children (Cowen et al., 1963). Glidea et al. (1967) report a similar paradoxical result in their project. In the second study (Cowen et al., 1966), teachers in the treated school, using exactly the same rating scales, now rated their children as being significantly better adjusted than did teachers rating children in the control schools. Cowen et al. (1963) and Glidea et al. (1967) attributed their findings to the educational aspects of the intervention program which increased the sensitivity of their teachers to signs of psychopathology. While such an hypothesis accounts for the first finding, it does not account for the finding of the second study, reported by the Rochester group (Cowen et al., 1966). In the second study the teachers were reoriented to the use of the scales. The results were fed back to the teachers with the consequence that they were made aware of the criteria and their significance (Cowen, personal communication). We note these issues because it is extremely difficult to evaluate a school based program when the teachers are both helping agents and evaluators. In a school setting, observers with a meaningful opportunity to observe cannot be blind with respect to treatment conditions. Measures vulnerable to subjective bias may be unduly influenced by knowledge of the ongoing program. The problems of design are very difficult

in field work, and subtle forms of controls may be very necessary.

In both of the Rochester studies, separate analyses were carried out for the group of children who were red-tagged in the first grade (i.e., judged in greatest need of help). In both studies, by third grade, the red-tagged children were clearly more maladjusted, on a variety of indices, then the non-red-tagged children. Red-tagged children continued to be more poorly adjusted in follow-ups to seventh grade (Zax et al., 1968). While these findings reveal the predictive value of the measures of adjustment, they also force us to raise questions concerning the significance of the findings that children in general, in the treated schools, were better off than the children in the control schools. If the more seriously disturbed children in the study continued to be disturbed, who was helped by the intervention of the mental health team? Cowen (personal communication) argues that intervention slowed a process of worsening adjustment, but the necessary control to settle the issue, a red-tagged group in a control school, was not available in these studies.

Let us report one other finding which reveals the problems which arise from the "illness" orientation of mental health professionals, and then return to the problems raised by the continued poor performance of the red-tagged children. In the earlier study (Cowen et al., 1963), children of mothers who had appeared for interviews and those who had not were compared. The children of parents who had appeared for interviews were brighter on tests, were viewed by teachers as better adjusted in the classroom, and were less anxious on the Children's Manifest Anxiety Scale (CMAS). Based on their interviews with the parents, the *mental health team* rated the children of parents who came for the interviews as *more poorly adjusted* than they rated the children of parents *who did not appear*. They used the available school records in the latter cases.

While there are a variety of interpretations of this finding, an important one relates to the bias diagnosticians have toward finding pathology. Scheff (1966) has argued that the medical model presupposes that it is innocuous to make a diagnosis and it is safer to call false positives than to miss true illness. In the area of mental health such presumptions are open to important questions. In the Cowen et al. studies (1963, 1966), for example, while the red-tagged designation was known only to the mental health teams, it is conceivable that the opinion that these children were disturbed could have been conveyed to the teachers. Sarason et al. (1966) have described the "hands off" phenomenon in schools; i.e., children labeled "disturbed" are avoided by teachers. Phillips (1967) and Cumming and Cumming (1957) have also shown that the labeling of specific behaviors as symptomatic of mental illness results in rejection and increasing social distance from the person so labeled. Moreover, the notion that an individual treated as "sick" enters the sick role, and thus maintains deviant behavior (Scheff, 1966) suggests that early case findings and attempts at intervention from a mental health orientation can produce mental health casualties. We do not know that any such process occurred in the Rochester project, but the fact that the red-tagged children continued to adjust poorly requires explanation. It may be that they actually did better than if they had not been the subjects of special attention, and would have done still better with intervention efforts directed more specifically toward individual problems, but the necessary control is not available. The findings of continued disability permit us to raise the question that early case finding could have perpetuated the children's problems.

We should also note that the Rochester project is a highly sophisticated attempt to evaluate a school-based mental health service. The studies were carefully done, fully reported, and the investigators themselves noted many of the important problems in their design. In subsequent writings Cowen and his associates (Cowen, Zax, & Gardner, 1967) have indicated their full awareness of the limitations of the medical model, and have advanced important proposals for school reform reflecting an institutional change conception to the problem of preventive mental health. We feel the issues need careful explication and study. If we are to contribute effectively to solving today's problems, we must closely examine yesterday's assumptions and reveal their weaknesses in order to proceed more effectively in the future.

THE EMPLOYMENT OF AUXILIARY PERSONNEL

As extensive a program as described in the previous section is expensive in terms of scarce, professionally trained personnel. If schools are to provide adequately for the varied educational needs of children with emotional and behavioral problems and perceptual disorders, and children who come from poverty groups, the 30 percent of all school children characterized by their teachers as having problems in adjustment (Glidewell & Swallow, 1968), then the manpower problem will have to be faced directly. An important source of help is found in the relatively untrained nonprofessional, the subprofessional, and in the volunteer. Such personnel have been used in mental health and social action programs extensively (Bellak, 1964; Heilig et al., 1968; Cowen et al., 1967; Sarason et al., 1966). In recent years, with the advent of behavior therapy, we have seen the further use of nontraditional personnel in other nontraditional roles. Nonprofessionals have been successfully trained in various behavior modification approaches (DeMyer & Ferster, 1962; Davison, 1964; Graziano, 1967; Blackwood et al., 1969). Parents have also been trained successfully as therapeutic agents for their own children (Allen & Harris, 1966; Evans, 1967b; Graziano, 1967; Patterson et al., 1964; Russo, 1964; Walder et al., 1967; Wahler et al., 1964).

Teacher-moms, housewives, retired people, and Big Brothers have been used in one-to-one therapeutic relationships within the school setting. (Wolman & Shelley, 1967; Cowen, 1968; Cowen et al., 1968; Donahue & Reing, 1966). Nichtern et al. (1964) provide a careful and realistic description of the origin, the initiation, and the problems in maintaining such a program with middle class women. Bloomberg and Troop (1964) report similarly for high school students, and Klein (1967) and Sarason et al. (1966) with ghetto youth as the helpers. The nonprofessional helpers are not necessarily accepted readily into the classroom setting (Cowen et al., 1967).

There has been a parallel development in education in the use of paid and volunteer nonprofessionals for a variety of duties. Ford Foundation studies estimated that up to 69 percent of a teacher's day may be devoted to routine activities which do not require professional competence (Foster, 1964). It has been estimated that tens of thousands of teacher aids are putting in millions of hours per year in two thirds or more of school districts (National Commission of Teacher Education and Professional Standards, 1967; New York State Education Department,

1966; National Education Association [NEA], 1967). Many of these aids are supported by antipoverty funds and provide new career potentials for ghetto residents (Reissman & Pearl, 1965; Denham et al., 1967; Graziano, 1965, 1967; Cowen et al., 1967; Sarason et al., 1966; Zax & Cowen, 1969). Indigenous volunteers have been used in preschool programs, sometimes as a form of rehabilitation for those who were themselves school dropouts (Pope & Grump, 1965). Many descriptions of the use of such personnel and the problems encountered are in the literature. While auxiliary personnel have been used for routine duties, and for noninstructional supervisors of corridors, study halls, cafeterias, and playgrounds (National Commission on Education, 1967), Klebaner (1967) states that such personnel typically view themselves as helping children rather than doing things teachers do not like to do.

Nonprofessional aides have served in more direct teaching roles as well. Mothers have been trained as substitute teachers (Bracket, 1967), as relief personnel so teachers could attend conferences (Craymer, 1968), to make up teaching materials (Thornsbley & Barnes, 1966), and to listen to and correct children learning to read (Thomas, 1967). In another study, unfortunately without controls for comparison, 85 percent of 700 pupils taught by 125 volunteers were reported to show substantial gains on the Metropolitan Achievement Test. Parents came in a close second to certified teachers in a comparative study of teaching methods in fifth grade Spanish (Hayman & Johnson, 1963).

Nonprofessionals have not been employed in complete isolation from professional teachers, but the use of nonprofessionals particularly in teaching roles sometimes threatens the professionalism of the teacher, and calls forth resistance. It must also be said there are almost no systematic evaluations of any of these programs, so their ultimate effectiveness remains in question.

However, several writers have pointed out that additional personnel of any variety increase staff to children ratios, and theoretically at least permit greater individualized contacts between adult and child (Byles, 1967; Karowe, 1967; Shipp, 1967).

Cowen et al. (1966) have reported one of the very few systematic studies of the use of college student volunteers in a school program. Recruited from among elementary education majors, and abnormal psychology students, the volunteers worked in an after school educational and recreational program with teacher referred problem children. Overall, there was no measurable effect of the volunteer program on the classroom behavior of the treated children when compared with controls. The program was limited to two months toward the end of the school year. The intervention may not have been sufficiently powerful or prolonged to produce a demonstrable effect. A more detailed analysis of the data revealed that in those instances in which the volunteers spent more time in talking with their children, in contrast to 'running,' there was greater improvement in the children. Cowen et al. feel their experience was helpful in understanding the use of volunteers, and in isolating effective kinds of interventions. In a later study, Cowen et al. (1969) reported improvement in children who had been exposed to college student volunteers in a five-month program.

Project Scranton (Levine et al., 1968) reports the use of student teachers as tutors for ghetto area first grade children identified by their teachers as potential academic failures. Tutoring was incorporated into the student's practice teaching, and was carried out over a full year during the school day. Controls were obtained from the same classrooms as the tutored children. Something approximating random assignment of children to tutored and control groups was achieved by asking the teachers to supply twice as many names of potential failures as there were tutors. Strict random assignment could not be attained because some of the teachers insisted that certain children needed help more than others. Pretests provided evidence of the validity of the teacher judgments in that those who were predicted to have academic problems tested more poorly than those they predicted would show normal progress. Testing was done by a nonprofessional aide, specially trained for this purpose.

As part of the program, the student teachers made home visits, toured the neighborhood, and met representatives of other agencies in the area. They participated in small group discussions with a psychologist and the nonprofessional aide, while the educational aspect of their work was supervised by the classroom teacher and integrated with ongoing classroom work.

Problems of field research were encountered. Some related to the use of volunteers, and some to the high rate of residential mobility in that school (Levine, 1966; Levine, Wesolowski, & Corbett, 1966). At the end of the school year, of 40 children who had at least one tutoring session, only 17 had ten or more sessions and had also been given all the pretests. These 17 children were then compared with 17 control children from the same classrooms matched for age, sex, race, and initial score on the Illinois Test of Psycho Linguistic Aptitude (ITPA). The control was unusually stringent in that half the children had been predicted earlier to make normal progress in the first grade.

Almost all of the children progressed significantly on the ITPA on retest, and the change was about the same in the tutored group as in the controls. A higher proportion of the tutored children ended in the top reading group in their class, and a higher proportion of tutored children were judged to have completed the first grade reading series. These latter measures were provided routinely by classroom teachers for all children, and in this sense constitute "unobtrusive measures." The teachers were unaware until the end of the project that such information would be requested for evaluative purposes.

The Devereux Elementary School Behavior Scales (Spivack & Swift, 1966) were completed by the classroom teachers for all children in their classes at the beginning and at the end of the school year. Seven of the 12 factors of these scales revealed greater improvement ($p = .10$ or less) in the classroom for the tutored when compared to the control children. It was impossible to keep the classroom teachers blind with respect to who was receiving tutoring help, and these results may well reflect some bias due to that knowledge. In general, teachers described tutored children as more competent academically, as having more confidence in themselves, and as viewing the classroom in more benevolent terms. Overt, attention-seeking, disruptive behavior was *not* strongly influenced by tutoring. Given that there was not an overall set to describe tutored children as "good," one can argue the change that was described was real. However, the involvement of the teachers with the project demands that we view these results cautiously.

Some confirmatory evidence for positive change was found in the weekly ratings tutors made of the behavior of their children in tutoring. Over time they reported consistent improvement in their relationship with their children, in the talkativeness and responsiveness of their children, and in the quality of the learning sessions.

As others have reported for volunteers, the student teachers seemed to have gained a great deal from the experience. On an attitude scale, in contrast to a small group of controls, they seemed to maintain favorable views of teaching in the inner city. Their master teachers reported the students were unusually well motivated, that they settled into full-time practice teaching very quickly, and that a better supervisory relationship was established with the students than had been true in the past. Almost all of the anonymously written evaluative reports turned in by the students mentioned benefits to themselves from the experience. However, a disappointingly low number of the students in the project actually sought out inner city positions after graduation. There are many reasons to account for the problem in recruiting, but the failure of the project to bring a significant number of teachers into the inner city provides a sobering lesson.

In summary, it seems clear that untrained people can take on a wide variety of helping roles within school settings, and can function successfully in these roles from their viewpoint, and the viewpoint of others. There is considerable anecdotal evidence that such people can help in managing immediate behavioral and educational problems and in providing services which are subjectively satisfying to themselves and to recipients of their services. There is some evidence that help provided by subprofessional personnel results in more effective performance in the classroom, but systematic evaluations are very few, and the long-range effectiveness of the help so provided is yet to be assessed.

SPECIAL CLASSES FOR EMOTIONALLY DISTURBED CHILDREN

In recent years many writers have asserted that schools, because of their critical and strategic social placement, must assume responsibility for providing educational services for all children, including those with problem behavior, and that they are capable of developing the necessary technology (Graziano, 1969c; Dupont, 1967; Quay et al., 1966; Bisgayer, 1964; Leton, 1964; Haring & Phillips, 1962). Leton (1964), for example, points out that the public school is our only agency "with compulsory obligations and responsibilities to serve the entire population of children" (p. 209). With regard to children the public schools have established precedence for social responsibility as well as political and professional organizations with many well-placed physical units which could serve as neighborhood special-service centers (Graziano, 1969c).

The schools' current involvement in mental health services seems to have developed from the original practice of referral to other agencies, through a period of cooperative mental health educational programs which were operated by clinics and aimed at returning the child to the classroom (Gold, 1967; Bisgayer, 1964; Rubin & Simson, 1960). Later, the schools began to employ their own pupil personnel staff, such as counselors, psychiatrists, psychologists, and social workers (Reger, 1966). There thus appears to have been a trend to greater responsibility by the schools in providing mental health services within the schools, and by school personnel.

Most of the earlier work involved attempts to incorporate traditional disease-entity concepts into the school structure, dealing with specified children as being "ill." Many writers, however, have criticized the mental illness or medical model concepts as being inapplicable to the school setting, and nearly all of these writers argue for a redefinition of tasks, embracing a psychoeducational approach based on psychological learning theory (Stiavelli & Shirley, 1968; Rhodes, 1967; Hewett, 1967; Harris, 1966; Trippe, 1963; Haring & Phillips, 1962; Bower, 1962; Bentzgen, 1962). They argue against the growing tendency for schools to adopt the traditional mental health concepts, pointing out that educators were too readily and incorrectly ascribing children's otherwise unexplained learning disabilities and academic underachievement to "emotional disturbance." That interpretation often led to public policies of exclusion or segregation of children as being emotionally disturbed and requiring specialized extra-academic, clinical services. These and other writers have offered alternative explanations which focus on the school environment itself, rather than internal psychopathology, as the primary agent of stress. Forty years ago Gray (1932) argued for the educational stress to be placed on the external environmental stimuli to underachievement and problem behavior. More recently Bentzgen (1962) has argued that the schools may be creating behavior problems and underachievers because of what he claims is the schools' invalid policy of grouping children according to chronological age rather than developmental level. The schools may be making invalid demands "by superimposing a continuum of instructional stress upon children whose developmental age is below the level of maturity required by assigned learning tasks" (p. 473). It may be, he argues, that many of the children classified as atypical or emotionally disturbed may, in fact, be "demonstrating a symptomatic behavioral response to an instructional setting which is inappropriate, if not inimical to their particular level of maturational readiness for a given learning experience" (p. 474). Bower (1960), Trippe (1963), Quay et al. (1966), Reger (1966), and others have made similar arguments that the nature of the school is significant in creating so-called emotional problems, which should be conceived of in terms of observable events rather than hypothetical constructs. These critics agree that the most fruitful approach may be some type of psychoeducational program in school, rather than referral to outside mental health agencies, and many of them argue for grouping the children into ungraded or special classes.

The apparent growing trend towards use of special classes for exceptional children suggests two significant trends: (1) the schools' assumption of increasing responsibility for exceptional children and (2) a shift from concepts of *treatment* of exceptional children in specialized clinical agencies to concepts of *teaching* them in an educational framework. Thus, society's task with regard to these children is being redefined as an educational task, best carried out within the school framework.

The extent of this shift at present is, however, not clear. Birch (1956) corresponded with school officials in the 50 largest United States cities and concluded that the schools were providing mental health services which "exist in a variety of forms and are on the increase . . ." in this country. In contrast to Birch's conclusion, Dupont (1957), using a questionnaire to state education departments and receiving replies from 35 states, found that only 15 states reported legislation providing for special classes, five states reported screening programs, and 18 reported some treatment provisions. The author argued that schools must assume leadership in developing preventive measures to avoid adult emotional disorders, but that "in 1955 the screening and treatment of the emotionally disturbed child within special education was an extremely haphazard affair" (p. 14), and there was a lack of available treatment facilities, of good screening procedures, and of public acceptance of concern for emotionally disturbed children. Morse, Cutler, and Fink (1964) found that in 1948, 47 of the 48 states reported special programs for emotionally disturbed and brain-injured children, but in 1962 only 30 of the 50 states did. Scheuer (1966) with a 100 percent return on questionnaires to the 50 states and four United States territories, reported that 40 of the 54 respondents had some provisions for special classes. These reports are not directly comparable, and they do not indicate the overall number of special classes or other programs. However, if we accept their reported results as valid and reliable, then the studies suggest that while nearly all states had some special program in the late 1940s, by the mid 1950s there had been a marked reduction in the number of states so involved and by the late 1960s state involvement had again increased but had not retained the high level of 1948. The data are far from conclusive and it is clear that we do not really know how widespread special classes are. The above reports do suggest, however, that at least since the mid 1950s there has been an increase in the number of states involved with special programs.

Another suggestion of change toward greater involvement of the public with problems of exceptional children is the passage of the Handicapped Children's Early Educational Assistance Act, signed into law by President Lyndon Johnson on September 30, 1968. According to Lavor and Krivit (1969), one of the significant features of this development is that it is the first time in history that Congress approved an action exclusively for the education of handicapped children. Previously all congressional action for special education had been passed as riders to other more "important" acts.

From the above discussion we can conclude that (1) there is only indirect evidence for any increase in utilization of special classes, (2) there are few data available concerning the number of special classes or of the children assigned to them, (3) there appears to have been a shift in concepts from the more traditional notions of pathology dealt within a medical setting, to those of special education carried out in the school setting, and (4) behavior modification concepts and techniques seem to be gaining increased attention.

Despite the apparently increased interest in special education, there has not been clear agreement on the conduct, goals, theory, effectiveness, or even desirability of special classes. While many writers agree, as noted above, that schools must accept more responsibility for services to exceptional children, many do not agree that special classes provide effective answers. Reger (1966) argues that the problems presented by children who are so readily labeled as emotionally disturbed are often created by limitations of the curriculum. Removing such children from the general curriculum and placing them into special classes might essentially serve as a way of preventing the needed changes in the general curriculum and thus perpetuating the poor situation. Trippe (1963), also objecting to the disability or illness concepts, notes that convenient segregation of exceptional children, based on disability, "may only serve to influence the teacher to look forward to the day when all classroom problems can be solved by removing the irritants" (p. 403).

Clearly these critics not only caution against the too easy labeling of children as emotionally disturbed but they also question the effectiveness of special classes. Evaluating effectiveness has been a difficult task, too infrequently taken up, and yielding generally disappointing results. The major limitations seem to stem from lack of agreement and clarity on concepts such as definitions of special class goals, the lack of any clear delineation of criteria for selection of children, and the almost total lack of systematic and rigorous research into the effectiveness of special classes.

As discussed above, the first two problems, clarification of concepts and selection criteria, have been discussed by many writers who argue that traditional medical model concepts cannot be usefully translated into educational goals and procedures, and they argue for a major shift towards a psychoeducational, behavioral focus. Reports and reviews by Haring and Phillips (1962),

Quay et al. (1966), Whelan and Harris (1966), Ross (1967), Graziano (1967, 1969d), Hotchkiss (1967), and Stiavelli and Shirley (1968) suggest that the increased specificity of observed behavioral events will hopefully lead to more objective evaluation of the effectiveness of special classes. That is, referring children who are "emotionally disturbed" to special classes may constitute selection of children for undefined characteristics and placement into a vague class situation without techniques and goals which can be readily evaluated.

Several writers (Rhodes, 1962; Leton, 1964; Morse, Cutler, & Fink, 1964; Balow, 1966; Reger, (1966) have described the field as severely lacking in systematic research and evaluation, and as being characterized by ambiguities and confusions in concepts, goals, and approaches. Reger (1966), for example, commented that reports of evaluations of special classes have not been extensive and the results are "thus far not encouraging." Morse et al. (1964), attempting to gather descriptive data on existing special classes, concluded that the field was characterized by confusion over approaches and lack of systematic research. Wilkerson (1966) noted that "currently available research in this field typically reports ambiguous outcomes of unknown or amorphous educational variables (p. 438)." Rhodes (1962), Leton (1964), and Balow (1966) came to similar conclusions.

While many writers describe special education programs (Bisgayer et al., 1964; Knoblock & Garcea, 1965; Lang & Morse, 1966; Quay et al., 1966; Graziano, 1967, 1969a, 1969d), and others discuss concepts and theory of special educational classes (Rubin & Simson, 1960; Bower, 1962; Trippe, 1963; Brendtro & Stern, 1967; Kidd, 1967; Ross, 1967; Towne & Joiner, 1968), there have been few reports which present data which have been systematically evaluated. One such study is that by Haring and Phillips (1962). Focusing on emotionally disturbed, hyperactive, underachieving public school children, Haring and Phillips utilized a structured classroom approach based largely on the earlier work with brain injured children by Strauss and Lehtinen (1947), and Cruikshank et al. (1961). Haring and Phillips hypothesize that the behavior labeled "emotional disturbance" comes about because the children "lack order or structure or definiteness in their daily living at home and at school" (p. 10), and

the program was arranged to provide the necessary structure. Three groups of children were compared: Group I was given a highly planned special class program which included high structure, reduction and control of extraneous stimuli, and planned, orderly presentation or "programming" of material; Group II children remained in regular classes and Group III children were given a "permissive" special class program, based on the general ideas of easing limits, allowing impulse expression for cathartic benefits, and generally proceeding very gently and with low demands with emotionally disturbed children. The results of achievement testing and the authors' own behavioral rating scales showed that the structured group had made significant improvements in academic achievement and in adaptive social behavior both at school and at home. The authors concluded, "Educational procedures used with brain-injured children appear to offer equal advantages to hyperactive, emotionally disturbed children. Apparently principles such as controlled extraneous stimuli, reduced social activities and ordered presentation of the materials to be learned are basic to successful classroom experiences of emotionally disturbed children" (p. 65).

Jackson (1962) discussed a four-year study of 34 emotionally disturbed elementary school children who were assigned to four treatment groups. Group I was a special class of eight children whose mothers attended weekly group counseling; Group II was composed of nine children who remained in regular class and whose mothers also attended weekly group counseling; Groups III and IV were control groups totaling 17 children who were identified but not placed in special classes. Jackson reports that Group I (special class + group counseling of mothers) showed the greatest achievement in grades, while both I and II showed significantly fewer adjustment problems on the teacher-rating instrument than did the control groups. Thus, according to this study, emotionally disturbed children who were placed in special class and whose mothers participated in group counseling, showed greater academic and social gains than those who remained in regular classes, with or without group counseling of mothers.

Vacc (1968) compared academic achievement and social behavior of emotionally disturbed children in regular classes with those in special classes. The Wide Range Achievement Test (Jastak, 1946) showed that the mean gains made by the emotionally disturbed children in special classes were significantly greater than those of comparable children in regular classes; the Haring and Phillips (1962) Behavior Rating Scale was used and indicated similar results, i.e., special class children had significantly greater mean gain scores in adaptive behavior than did comparable children who remained in regular class.

The studies by Haring and Phillips (1962), Jackson (1962), and Vacc (1968), while having some weaknesses in design, nevertheless do suggest that when systematic evaluation is carried out at least some short-term positive effects may be attributed to the special classes.

Another group of studies (Whelan & Harris, 1966; Graziano, 1967, 1969; Hewett, 1967; and Stiavelli & Shirley, 1968), all utilizing behavior modification approaches in relatively structured special class settings in which there was a focus on specific maladaptive social or academic behaviors, show marked improvement in children from baseline levels of behavior. These two groups of studies taken together, one which presents comparisons of special and regular classes, and the other which shows growth from baseline behavior within special classes, suggest that when children described as emotionally disturbed are placed in special classes which are relatively well structured, and in which specific behaviors are focused on, they show academic and social gains greater than children who either remained in regular class or who were in relatively unstructured special classes. Available evidence then, despite its weaknesses, suggests that carefully structured special classes focusing on clearly defined behavior do have positive effects on at least short-term improvement of emotionally disturbed children. As yet, we have no follow-up data on children from special classes. We also have no evidence concerning the problem of stigma and other negative consequences of the special class placement. Clearly the utilization of special classes as the prime form of help for emotionally disturbed children has not yet been clearly verified, but the initial and somewhat exploratory evidence clearly indicates a promising field and the need for more programs and more systematic approaches and evaluation.

Almost all of the forms of intervention we have so far described have involved the identification of certain children as deviant, and the provision of special services for them. Sometimes the services were directed toward maintaining the deviant child in the normal classroom, and sometimes the deviant was isolated in special classrooms. The next programs we shall discuss are educational interventions, based upon educational concepts, and carried out by the educator in the context of the normal operating procedure of the classroom.

NONPROMOTION AS A REMEDIAL POLICY

Nonpromotion as an educational policy designed to deal with academic problems began with the introduction of the graded school system in Boston in 1848. While problems noted then continue today (Snipes, 1965; Humphreys, 1965), the policy continues to be supported by educators, parents, and some developmentally oriented mental health professionals. How effective is nonpromotion as a measure to improve the educational competence of children?

Rates of nonpromotion have been high and continue to be high. Around the turn of the century, there was an average failure rate in all grades of 16 percent (Thorndike, 1908; Ayres, 1909). During the past century there is evidence that the rate of nonpromotion has been decreasing (Lennon & Mitchell, 1955; Larson, 1955; Humphreys, 1965; Loomis, 1965; Josephina, 1961; Saunders, 1941; Ellinger, 1965; Coffield & Blommers, 1956; and Wolf, 1965). Levine and Levine (1970) point out that in New York City, and perhaps elsewhere, about the time of World War I, the problem of nonpromotion was resolved by administrative fiat, on economic grounds, after revelation of the extent of the problem.

While methodological considerations make it difficult to compare studies, if we consider only the lower grades recent studies have suggested that as high as 20 percent of younger elementary school children are retained in grade at least once (Knudsen & Shailer, 1965; Snipes, 1965; Sarason et al., 1966), although there may be a declining incidence over the last 60 years, considering *all* grades. Systematic and standard recording of nonpromotion is not a part of the practice of many school systems, and reliable data on incidence and distribution of nonpromotion are lacking. Since so many children are involved, we hope school administrators or other educational policy makers can be encouraged to keep more readily accessible records.

Educators offer lack of academic achievement as the overriding reason for nonpromotion. Close examination suggests the issues are not quite that simple. Explicit, reliable measures of the attainment of the educational objectives are not available (Bloom, 1963; Bloom et al., 1956; Kearney, 1953; French, 1957; Adams, 1964). A survey of 27 studies over a 20-year period (1925–1945) revealed more than a dozen commonly offered reasons (Lafferty, 1948) for nonpromotion. Heading the list was irregular attendance. Other reasons had to do with low mentality, poor motivation, laziness, poor health, physical defects, poor educational background, incomplete work, failure on tests, and family problems or poor home conditions. Similar results were reported for more recent years by Clark (1959) and Humphreys (1965). The variability, the vagueness, and the arbitrariness of these criteria are obvious. Otto (1951) and Elsbree (1943) are very critical of irregular attendance, for example, as a ground for nonpromotion. Their studies show that 60 percent of students who missed as much as 25 days made up the work and maintained their academic levels.

Educators tend to place responsibility for school failure on the inadequacies and deficiencies of children. Wolf (1965) notes that only five percent of the failures of children were attributed to the inadequacy of the school in providing for the child. Abraham (1960), Gray (1932), and Wolf (1965) all suggest the school may have considerably more responsibility for children's failures. Factors such as inadequate programming, excessive teacher changes and absences, rigid or inappropriate standards of achievement, unsuitable methods and materials, poor teaching and unwarranted prejudices may all contribute to school failure (Knudsen & Shailer, 1965). Russia also has its problem of school failure (Monoazon, 1963; Tokareva, 1963; Kashin, 1966), and Korolev (1962) maintains that the rate of repeaters varies inversely with the quality of teaching. The evidence for such a view is not well developed either in Russia or in the United States.

Knudsen and Shailer (1965) report that boys fail more than girls; Negroes more than whites; and children from broken homes more than from intact homes. These findings suggest that other than considerations of intellectual competence weigh heavily in the decision to promote or not. Clearly a critical reexamination of the bases for nonpromotion is in order since the evidence is strong that simple "academic failure" is not the crucial factor in nonpromotion. Much more is involved including the school's resources and capabilities in providing varied educational programs for those with varied educational needs. We feel it is significant that the literature on nonpromotion contains hardly any discussion of how the educational program should be modified for a child who is required to repeat a grade.

The practice of nonpromotion rests on three major assumptions: 1) Failure to achieve in grade is clearly demonstrated and reliably measured, 2) the reasons for failure are to be found in the limitations of the child, and 3) retention in grade will result in greater subsequent achievement than will promotion for the child who fails a grade.

We have argued above that the first two assumptions are of dubious validity. We shall now examine the third assumption.

Studies dating back to 1911 have consistently challenged the assumption that children who repeat will benefit academically. Keyes (1911) showed that about 21 percent of repeaters showed academic improvement, while 39 percent showed a decrease in achievement their second year in grade. Otto (1954) reported similar findings more than 40 years later. Retained and promoted children of the same mental age showed no difference in academic achievement over a two-year period (Arthur, 1936). Cook (1941) found lower levels of achievement in a school district with a high nonpromotion rate than in a neighboring district with a more liberal promotion policy. Retention in grade does not reduce the variability of achievement levels within given classrooms (Caswell, 1933; Saunders, 1941; Cook, 1941). By the seventh and eighth grades, 80 percent of those repeating a major subject were still not receiving passing grades, and a fourth were actually doing more poorly the second time than the first (Meussen, 1952). Coffield and Blommers (1956) found that promoted low achievers made more progress than retained low achievers, and over time the retained low achievers fell further behind in achievement levels. Otto and Estes (1960) concluded their review of studies of nonpromotion by asserting that grade repetition is of little educational value, and that promoted low achievers made more progress than their nonpromoted age mates.

In recent years, several reasonably well controlled studies have reaffirmed the earlier results. Kamii and Weikart (1963) found that retained pupils had lower IQs, did more poorly on achievement tests, and got lower classroom grades than regularly promoted pupils. The differences in achievement they report between retained and promoted pupils held up even when statistical controls for IQ differences were introduced. They concluded that at the end of elementary school, retained pupils did not gain from the extra year, and in fact they continued to do significantly worse than regularly promoted pupils.

Dobbs and Neville (1967) used pairs of once-retained first graders and never-retained second graders, matched for race, sex, social class, chronological age, mental age, reading achievement, and "type of classroom assignment" at the beginning of second grade. The Metropolitan Achievement tests were administered at the end of two years to measure gains. The promoted group had significantly greater achievement over the two years. They concluded that "Nonpromotion was not an aid . . . (but) was actually a disadvantage to achievement."

The assumption that retention of a low achieving pupil will result in greater academic gains than promoting the pupil is not supported by the available evidence. If anything, retention in grade seems to have negative effects on subsequent achievement as evidenced by poorer performance by retained pupils in the term in which they were retained, and later on as well. Relatively few children improve academically when they are retained.

Although the data are consistent and convincing, there is no study which permits certain conclusions about retention. A definitive study would require that a sample of potentially retainable children be identified, that half be retained and half be promoted, on the basis of random assignment to each condition. The evaluators and their teachers should be unaware of their status. Under these stringent conditions, firm conclusions could be stated. As it stands, the evidence showing that retained children do poorly, even when compared with children of comparable intelligence

and achievement, can be interpreted to mean that teachers are more sensitive to characteristics predictive of poor school performance than are tests. Teachers may be selecting for retention children who will fail in school, and the available evidence may be interpreted as a validation of their judgment. It is clear that retention doesn't help academic achievement, but we cannot say with certainty whether retention is destructive or whether the children who are retained are incapable of progressing in school.

There are a variety of nonacademic consequences and effects of nonpromotion. A child who is retained is labeled a failure. He must live through parental disappointment and beratement, through the teasing of his peers, and through a summer of reminders that he is expected to atone and do better the next time. The following year, he enters as a conspicuous and marginal member of his new class. He is older, probably physically larger than his peers, and he is forced to associate with children he had previously considered his inferiors in status and achievement. Most children probably do not accept the rationale that nonpromotion is to help them. For most, it is likely the action is viewed as punishment for failure. Personality theory would suggest that a retained child could easily internalize a view of himself as bad, stupid, and incapable. Feelings of discouragement and depression attendant to nonpromotion (Ellinger, 1965), and a self-defeating cycle in which the expectation of failure is fulfilled when failure follows upon meagre effort (Heffernan, 1952; Waetjen, 1965; Ellinger, 1965) have been noted in the literature. Since schools attempt to socialize children into age and sex appropriate roles at each grade level, repetition may not only create a sense of failure and discouragement but it may also result in boredom and in a demand for age *inappropriate* responses which can produce a hostile, negative reaction to education and the school system as a whole (Shailer & Knudsen, 1965).

The available research supports the clinical view that nonpromotion may have negative and disruptive consequences for personality development and for social behavior. Sandin (1944) found that nonpromoted children were rated lower socially than promoted classmates by both teachers and peers, even after the eighth grade. Children who had experienced at least one failure in the first eight grades were rated "less desirable seat mates," and as significantly more "cruel," "bullying," and "unfriendly." In the upper grades nonpromoted children tended to remain apart socially from their younger classmates. The nonpromoted children expressed negative feelings about school and many looked forward eagerly to dropping out of school. Morrison and Perry (1956) and Russell (1952) reported similar negative features associated with nonpromotion. Low achieving children who are promoted are more popular than low achieving children who are not promoted, emphasizing the role of nonpromotion, rather than low achievement in producing negative social consequences (Goodlad, 1954). Another consequence of school failure is referral for psychotherapy. School failure is one of the most frequent precipitants of such a referral (Aguilera & Keneally, 1954), with all that referral implies in terms of stigma and a reinforcement of a view of the self as bad and inadequate.

If a variety of negative personal and social consequences flow from nonpromotion, and negative and hostile attitudes are developed in both child and parent (Russell, 1952), then we might expect children to escape from a punishing situation by dropping out. The research fully bears out this expectation. Better than 70 percent of all dropouts have experienced nonpromotion at least once, in contrast to only 18 percent of those who graduate from high school (Robert & Jones, 1963; Hall, 1964). Many other studies confirm these figures (Liddle, 1962; Matthews, 1962; Matika & Sheerer, 1962; Woolatt, 1961, Snepp, 1956; Dreshen, 1954; Anderson, 1953). Gragg (1949) concluded the most significant factor causing dropouts was school retardation created by earlier nonpromotion. Shailer and Knudsen (1965) concluded their review of studies of retention and school dropouts by arguing for the causative role of retention in helping to create the combination of conditions which promote school dropouts.

As is the case with poor school achievement, the negative attitude toward school and the undesirable social traits may have preceded the nonpromotion and may have contributed to the decision not to promote. The available evidence cannot discount this alternative hypothesis. On the other hand, it is perfectly clear that nonpromotion has no therapeutic effect on such undesirable traits. If retention is a measure used to correct undesirable attitudes and traits, then it is clear that the practice misses its objectives by a wide mark.[1]

Since the major assumptions underlying the practice of nonpromotion have been shown to be invalid by some 60 years of research, why does the policy continue in force? There is no research on this important and vexing issue. However, we would like to speculate on some features of the social organization of schools and the emotional demands on the teacher which may contribute to the maintenance of the practice in the face of the accumulated evidence. We shall discuss the issues under three headings: 1) the distortion of readiness concepts; 2) the philosophy of aversive control; and 3) the partial reinforcement schedule supporting nonpromotion.

The readiness concept is based on observations of large individual differences in maturational levels in children of the same chronological age. An immature child is viewed as not ready to do the work of his grade. By being retained in grade, a child is presumably permitted to mature so that he will be more ready to do the work of that grade. The literature does provide support for the view that children who *enter* school at an older age do better than children who enter at a younger age (Halliwell, 1966; Carter, 1956; Baer, 1958; Reinherz & Griffin, 1968). The differences persist, and have been noted even into the third grade (Carroll, 1963).

Because children who first *enter* school at a later age outperform their younger classmates, it does not follow that children who are older because they have failed and have been retained in grade will also outperform their younger classmates who have not failed previously. Children who are older in grade because they have failed are in a different psychological and social position than those who are older because they have started school at a later age. In the former instance becoming overage for grade has been accompanied by severe disruption, while in the latter case a child has begun school with advantages in size and maturity that are provided by additional months of growth. The disruptions attendant upon retention in grade seem to override any possible advantages which might accrue to being an older child in a grade. While delayed entrance into school may have some merit, nonpromotion does not help children to develop and thus to succeed.

A second factor supporting the policy of nonreinforcement may reside in the continued use of aversive control including corporal punishment (Kozol, 1967) in schools in preference to positive reinforcement. Nonpromotion may be viewed as the ultimate punishment when nothing else works to control or modify the behavior of an unruly, uncooperative, or generally vexing child. The ascendancy and the authority of the teacher may be maintained through the retention of the child as the school exercises its control. The threatening and punitive aspect of nonpromotion is clearly revealed when teachers speak of the useful effect retention has as a deterrent in providing an "example" for other children. The educational literature contains no discussion of nonpromotion as a disciplinary measure, although such a function is clearly implied in the argument that the threat of punishment at the end of the school year provides motivation to work to escape the punishment.

Despite a lack of evidence that fear of failure is a necessary form of motivation for school achievement (Otto & Melby, 1935), many educational programs seem to assume the necessity of arousing such a fear if children are to work in school. Nonpromotion as a tactic to arouse fear-of-failure motivation may be retained for that purpose. It may also serve as a form of punishment or retaliation against children who defy the teacher's authority or who fail to validate the teacher's sense of competence by performing as the teacher would like to have them perform. Given the prevalence of the distorted version of the readiness concept, vigorous punishment can be administered freely and in good conscience under the fatuous rationale: "It's for your own good."

A third factor helping to retain the nonpromotion policy may be the partial reinforcement provided by those children who indeed do reasonably well after having been retained in grade. Although promoted low achievers do as well or better than retained low achievers, up to 60 percent of retained low achievers do function at grade level at the end of their second year (Rheinberg, 1968). Unaware of the research literature, teachers draw on their own experiences and the memories of colleagues, the positive cases providing the variable reinforcement which could maintain the practice of nonpromotion. In this respect, teachers behave much as psychotherapists who also point to their improved cases without paying attention to the natural changes to be expected with time.

In summary then, retention in grade is a powerful intervention designed to ameliorate a variety of educational and behavioral problems. Affecting perhaps 20 percent of children in the lower grades, there is no evidence that this intervention attains any of its positive goals and there is evidence the practice may be terribly destructive. Despite 60 years of educational research showing the inadequacies of nonpromotion, it continues. Here seems to be a problem of formidable proportions for those interested in programs in elementary schools. How might one provide other meaningful interventions to help the variety of academic and behavioral problems posed for the schools by children who fail and repeat?

MENTAL HEALTH AND THE SCHOOL CURRICULUM

The ideal of primary prevention is most closely approximated through devising curricula and teaching methods which can be broadly implemented, which maximize individual development and minimize the dysfunctional aspects of schools. While the American educational system and its goals have been the subject of critical debate for the 200 years or more of their existence (Allinsmith & Goethals, 1962), in recent years we have been provided with direct observational studies of classrooms which clearly reveal some of the dysfunctional aspects. Group processes which manipulate through affection and which promote conformity, alienation, extreme competitiveness, fear of failure, and learning to be "stupid," have been described (Henry, 1965). Classrooms are typically teacher centered (Medley & Mitzel, 1963), and passive, receptive attitudes toward learning are encouraged. Recitation tends to call largely upon rote memory, spontaneous manifestations of curiousity are largely absent, and other mental functions receive little practice or reinforcement (Susskind, 1969a, b). Test-anxious children are known to perform poorly under evaluative conditions (Sarason et al., 1960; Ruebush, 1963) but there is little in the typical classroom which takes into account this particular limitation. The research would suggest that the learning efficiency of perhaps a quarter of all children is adversely affected by evaluative conditions.

While teachers are applied psychologists who make important decisions relevant to mental health each minute of the day, they have little formal preparation for this vital task (Sarason, Davidson, & Blatt, 1962). The need for special psychological training for teachers was emphasized by Witmer (1907) and repeated later by Wickman (1928), but there is little evidence that the recommendations have been taken seriously by educators (Koerner, 1963) or by educational psychologists, for that matter.

There have been numerous, if sporadic, attempts to develop curricula and programs in psychological and human relations training within the classroom. Curriculum materials designed to promote personal discussions have been developed and tried. However, evaluative reports suggest the specific curriculum is of little value unless it is implemented by a skillful and sensitive teacher (Group for the Advancement of Psychiatry [GAP], 1951).

Roen (1968) has described a behavioral science curriculum for elementary school children. Taught by a behavioral scientist, it has produced sufficient cognitive learning to enable the children to do as well on a teacher constructed achievement test as either undergraduate or graduate psychology students. Roen also feels that the training of the teacher is a significant factor in the successful implementation of the curriculum. He provides no evidence that such a curriculum produces better mental health either within or outside the classroom.

Ojemann and his associates, working since the 1940s, have been developing a very sophisticated approach to the use of psychological and behavioral science concepts with the schools. Ojemann's program is designed to produce a causal orientation in thinking through specific curricular materials, through the method of teaching, and through influencing the very approach the teacher takes in dealing with the moment by moment events of the classroom. A causal orientation includes the concepts that behavior is caused, that any behavior has a history, that its causes are complex, that the response to a perceived action should be made in relation to an understanding of the cause of the action, and that behavioral events

have future referrants and consequences which require consideration. Ojemann argues that children are now "infected" with a dysfunctional noncausal orientation at home, in school, and even through the content of their textbooks (Ojemann, 1960a; 1963; 1967).

He and his associates have developed curriculum materials and a training course to help teachers use the causal orientation on a day by day basis. The four-week summer course consists of didactic work, observations of classrooms, a form of personal group therapy, and sessions with an experienced classroom teacher who offers specific suggestions for implementing the causal orientation. Relatively few teachers, and the selection of these was not clearly specified, have been so trained.

Ojemann (undated manuscript) reports some evidence that the program improves teacher empathy with children's feelings, and some indication of a change in classroom performance after teachers have been exposed to his program (Ojemann, 1960). Observers have detected a significant increment in the causal orientation of children in classrooms of causally trained teachers in contrast to control classrooms (Ojemann & Snider, 1964). However, the observers may not have been blind to the conditions of the teacher's training.

On paper and pencil tests, causally taught children showed a sharp decrease in the readiness to respond punitively in hypothetical situations (Ojemann et al., 1955). Causally taught children also show more understanding of teacher behavior (Ojemann & Snider, 1963). Construct validity has been demonstrated for a test of causal orientation through its correlations with a variety of theoretically related tests (Muus, 1960; Levitt, 1955; Ojemann, unpublished manuscript). Changes in causality scores are also accompanied by changes in measures of anxiety and personal insecurity (Bruce, 1958; Roen, 1968).

While there is evidence to support the inference that exposure to a causally oriented classroom leads generally to a less anxious, less hostile, more flexible, and more understanding view of the world and one's self, there is no direct evidence that the program is preventive of academic, emotional, or behavioral problems. Moreover, no follow-up study has demonstrated that gains in the classroom situation are maintained over time or generalized. Ojemann's approach, whatever its present deficiencies, is still the closest to a truly preventive methodology we have. By attempting to intervene at the level of the classroom, both in terms of curriculum modification and in terms of teaching methods, he is intervening in a way which promises profound and significant effects. It is our opinion that in this realm of activity lies the greatest potential for the behavioral scientist.

SCIENCE AND POLITICS: THE MORE EFFECTIVE SCHOOLS PROGRAM

In contrast to the relatively small-scale programs discussed above, the New York City More Effective Schools (MES) program was designed as a radical, large-scale intervention to promote the educational competence of children who would otherwise be faced with a disastrous social and economic adjustment in the future. The designers of MES were rightly disdainful of "patchwork." The MES program accordingly affects 21 elementary schools (as many school buildings as there are in many modest-sized cities), 16,500 children, 1,900 teachers, administrators, mental health personnel, and educational consultants, and costs about $15,000,000 annually.

In contrast to other efforts this program was initiated and designed by the educational establishment itself. Representatives of the Board of Education and the Superintendant of Schools, the United Federation of Teachers, and the Council of Supervisory Associations wrote the prospectus for the program. The designers said they also consulted a variety of community organizations including parents, professional and civil rights groups, and school staff in developing the program.

According to an early evaluation, MES was implemented nearly in accord with the original plans (Bureau of Educational Research, 1966). Eventually, a report from the UFT (Schwager, 1967) charged lack of cooperation, hostility, and sabotage of the program, but such charges came around the time the program became involved in contract negotiations between the Board of Education and the UFT and evaluations were questioning the effectiveness of the program.

The falling-out between parties and the subsequent bitter fights about the effectiveness of the program should give pause to those of us academicians who have a naive faith that technically competent research designs will contribute to rational policy decisions. Today educationally relevant research does not take place in a disinterested environment. Important, powerful, and opposing political forces have stakes in the outcomes.

A chronology is in order to help us understand some of the problems. The committee which designed the program was formed in April 1964. It published its report in May 1964, and the program was implemented in the first ten schools in September 1964. Given the summer vacation, planning and orientation time seems short. In October 1965 the administrative staff of the program wrote a memorandum describing its first year of operation. In August 1966, the Center for Urban Education (CUE) published an evaluation of the MES program based on a survey by educational consultants and the preliminary evaluation of some achievement test results. A month later the Bureau of Educational Research published a more comprehensive report concerning implementation, cost, evaluation of components of the program, and achievement test results (Bureau of Educational Research, 1966). In September 1967, CUE (Fox, 1967) published another comprehensive evaluation which permitted consideration of the effects of the program over a three-year period.

For whatever reasons, the UFT and its parent body, the American Federation of Teachers, had publicly committed themselves to the program through obtaining political endorsement of it, organizing a National Council for More Effective Schools, publishing advertising pieces for mass circulation, and introducing the MES program as a demand in contract negotiations with the New York School Board, and in other cities as well. The union commitment came well before any sound evaluation was available, before the Hawthorne effect would have worn off, and well before any long-range effect of the program could have been determined. The subsequent bitter argument about the program was partly sustained because no evaluation had been built into the project initially with agreed upon objectives. Later, when the power and prestige of a union was pitted against the power and the political and financial concerns of a board of education, it became clear that the issue was not the best program with which to educate children, but who stood to gain or lose from the program.

The program itself began with the assumption that schools had not been doing the most effective job because school people have been denied the material and manpower resources to function effectively. In particular, more teachers, more teacher aides, more specialists, and drastically reduced classroom size (maximum of 21 children) were viewed as the critical elements of the program. From the Joint Committee's report we estimate that each 1000 children were to be serviced by 128 personnel, albeit on an extended day and extended week schedule. Enthusiastic and committed personnel were to be recruited for the program, with provision for inservice training. A number of educational innovations—team teaching, nongraded classes, and heterogeneous grouping— were instituted, while new teaching concepts, materials, and supplies were to be abundantly available.

The new *ideas* to be implemented were never made very explicit. The program assumed that professional educators knew what they were doing and needed only to be allowed to do what they knew how to do. Moreover, the assumption that the education profession knew its job but was dealing with too many children who were deviant can be inferred from the emphasis on psychopathology of children and on the provision of mental health, guidance services, and special classes in the schools.

There is further evidence that the planning body assumed the professional competence of the teachers. The question of motivation, for example, was viewed as one of "instilling in pupils the desire to move ahead," with no recommendations concerning changes in *educational* practices which might help to achieve improved motivation. Similarly, although there has been much discussion in the literature about the role of prejudice on the part of educators, low expectations by teachers for the performance of ghetto children, and the cultural and stylistic differences among teachers which promote or retard learning among low income children, the initial planning report does not even mention such issues. The problem of selecting teachers and administrators sympathetic to the program and the children was undercut at once by an agreement which recognized the right

of teachers and administrators to continue functioning in their posts if they so desired. That such issues are touchy and difficult to resolve goes without saying. That they are highly relevant to the success of a program is suggested by Channon's (1967) report of the MES program from an insider's viewpoint.

There is considerable controversy about the success of the MES program in recruiting specially motivated or qualified teachers and in holding the teachers who were in the program. Union sources (Beagle, 1966; Schwager, 1967) claimed that teachers eagerly joined MES schools and voluntarily remained there. Other sources indicated that voluntary recruitment failed (CUE, 1966), that primarily new and inexperienced teachers joined the program (Channon, 1967), and that the low rate of loss in MES schools was about the same as in control schools (Bureau of Educational Research, 1966).

In none of the reports is there any systematic evaluation or description of recruitment, selection, orientation, or training programs for the teachers, nor is there any evaluation of motivation or attitudes of teachers toward their work. Fox (1967) suggests that the program accomplished much less than it could have because the teachers operated in very standard fashion. Sufficient data are not available to test Fox's hypothesis, and it is important to note that there was too little systematic concern for teachers and teaching variables to permit the hypothesis to be tested at all. While we do not insist that the available literature points unequivocally to the central importance of teacher variables, we are emphasizing that the *comprehensive* program developed by professional educators did not even contemplate any evaluation of the relationship of professional preparation or of professional competence or of educational practices to student attitudes and achievement. Educators define the issues as the child's deficiencies and inadequacies and the community's niggardly support, but they did not even begin to consider the educator's contribution.

What did the MES program accomplish? Observers are in general agreement that teacher morale was high in MES schools (CUE, 1966; Fox, 1967; Beagle, 1967; Schwager, 1967), a not insignificant accomplishment. The reduction in the loneliness of the teachers' position was accompanied by some new problems in developing working relationships among all the specialists (Channon, 1967) but these were not insurmountable. The reduced work load (smaller classes, daily preparation period, teacher aides) probably contributed to a greater sense of teacher satisfaction. That teacher satisfaction is related to more effective teaching performance and, further, related to better academic achievement by the children, is an untested assumption.

Parents, observers agree (CUE, 1966; Fox, 1967; Beagle, 1967; Bureau of Educational Research, 1966), are favorably disposed toward the program. However, no really systematic study was undertaken, and the Bureau of Educational Research's survey (1966) was disproportionately weighted with responses from those with children in the kindergarten and prekindergarten programs. There is no good indication of what program features made the parents feel good about the schools. There was no evidence (it was not evaluated) that the community relations expert was or was not valuable to the program. Channon (1967) implies that they were ineffective because of lack of interest in community involvement by principals, teachers, and parents.

An index of parental feeling about the program, and one of the explicit goals of the program, would be an increase in the degree of integration in the schools. So far, at best, there is a weak suggestion that the rates of whites leaving MES districts have been slowed slightly (Bureau of Educational Research, 1966). Any accomplishment along these lines would be of considerable importance, but it is likely that the forces making for an increased concentration of nonwhites in the city are more powerful than any change in a school is likely to influence significantly.

Mobility is another problem characteristic of city schools (Levine, 1966), and an influence on the performance of children in the schools. By the second year of the program, eight of the MES schools showed a decline in mobility rates (Bureau of Educational Research, 1966). While it would be hopeful to be able to attribute the decline to the MES program, data from comparable schools not in MES, and studies ruling out other factors (i.e., changes in urban renewal activity or changes in school boundary lines) are not available.

The available bits of evidence, although far from conclusive, suggest that parents respond favorably to MES. In this day and age of parental hostility toward the schools, a professional program winning parental support is important. On the other hand, if support is achieved through advertising pressure and is not accompanied by sustained accomplishment, the subsequent disillusionment, should it occur, will be all the greater. More thorough evaluation of the degree of parental support and the reasons for it would have been desirable.

Mental health and the guidance services were evaluated only through interviews and questionnaires administered by CUE observers (1966) and by the Bureau of Educational Research (1966). Most assistant superintendants, somewhat smaller proportions of principals, and two thirds of the teachers felt that the clinical services were satisfactory. However there was no evaluation of the precise contribution of these services to the total program. There was simply no provision for the analysis of the effectiveness of these services. They were merely assumed to be effective. Perhaps the fact that a director of guidance helped to formulate MES had something to do with the failure to examine this assumption. This assumption of effectiveness is carried through in the UFT demand that the *total* program needs to be expanded.

Observers (CUE, 1966; Fox, 1967) were in general agreement that MES schools had a pleasant atmosphere with well-maintained discipline and control. Ratings of classroom functioning on a number of dimensions, however, showed no significant differences from control schools. Questionnaires administered to older children about their schools and classrooms also produced no significant differences from control schools. In this instance the social desirability component of the questionnaire is strong and leads one to have doubts about the validity of the instruments. There was no significant impact of the MES program on pupil attendance, but rates of absence for control schools were not presented. If they had increased, while MES schools remained constant, such a finding would have been meaningful, but the evaluators did not choose to examine that. It is a small point, but the lack of systematic attention to the design of the evaluative study might have resulted in obscuring positive results of the program.

Rightly or not, school programs are often evaluated through use of achievement tests. Meeting, surpassing, or failing to meet "national norms" is often the basis for deciding if schools are doing their job. Achievement test scores are front page news and enter into political and social struggles. The UFT, as we shall see, asserted that the MES program is effective because children come close to meeting the amount of academic growth specified by the test norms for the school year. Achievement tests are also big business. Literally millions of tests are printed and sold each year, and the fact that they are sold commercially may enter into the way in which they are constructed and used.

Test results are reported in terms of grade equivalent scores. Authorities, including the authors of the Metropolitan tests used in the MES program, flatly assert that such grade equivalent scores have no precise normative meaning, and can be extremely misleading. Unless norms are developed on the basis of systematic sampling procedures (and achievement test norms are not) the results can have no meaning as national norms. The evaluation of the MES program in terms of the progress made in meeting so-called national norms is entirely misleading. Evaluation of the performance of one group of children against that of a comparable group of "untreated" children is necessary to draw any inferences about the effectiveness of the program.

The Metropolitan tests are normed in the early fall, according to the test manual, and according to Thorndike (CUE, 1966). The test constructors then extrapolate to what children might achieve in a year by assuming that growth of one tenth of a year results during each school month. This assumption is untested. Growth during the year, as measured by achievement tests given in the spring, is composed of real learning plus "school practice" through the school year. Since the test is normed in the fall, shortly after children return to school from summer vacation, the children may be less efficient with school work at that time, having forgotten school work over the summer. Testing over the school year, in the spring, favors a good score for a child not only because he has learned something over the school year, but because he is accustomed to school work, and presumably higher in test-taking ability than he will be at the end of a two-month summer vacation. The

practice of norming in the fall and testing in the spring clearly provides a commercial advantage in that schools which test in the spring can look good on achievement tests. They are likely to meet or exceed national norms. School administrators might well be inclined to buy tests which make the school program appear effective. For purposes of evaluating the MES program, looking at the change from fall testing to spring testing is inadequate and misleading. The comparisons should be made over a full year, fall to fall, or spring to spring.

Another problem involves the relevance of the Metropolitan tests for evaluating the MES program. Achievement tests are used on the assumption that the test items constitute a valid sample of the kind of knowledge imparted during the year. While the relationship between the content of the tests and the New York City curriculum is not specified, we can assume some relationship since one of the authors of the Metropolitan test is Assistant Superintendent of the Office of Educational Research of the City of New York. However, the MES program had as objectives the "invention and refinement of new practices" and the use of new materials, new procedures, and new equipment to meet the needs of socially disadvantaged children. If there was extensive curricular innovation, then one can raise questions about the content validity of the Metropolitan tests for use in the MES program. If there was not sufficient variation in curriculum and method to invalidate the use of the Metropolitan tests, then what was being done differently that could have an effect, except to introduce smaller classroom sizes? That seems a relatively unpromising technique in itself since educational research has long shown no relationship between pupil-teacher ratios and academic achievement. Coleman et al. (1966) is the latest example of such results.

There are some other issues about which the evaluative reports are silent. Not all of the subtest scores of the Metropolitan test are consistently reported. We do not know whether they were not administered or whether they were simply suppressed. For example, Thorndike states that the arithmetic results were less promising than the reading results at the end of the first testing (CUE, 1966). Thereafter, arithmetic scores are not reported nor do they become the focus of attention. We do not know whether alternate forms or the same forms of the test were used in retesting, and if alternative forms were used, whether they were administered in counterbalanced order. We do not know what happens when scores are compared across different levels of the test (primary, elementary, intermediate). Are scores at the upper range of the primary level really the equivalent of those at the lower range of the elementary form? If they are not directly comparable then the longitudinal studies provide distinct problems in interpretation. All of these issues are of some consequence for the interpretation of results. That we have to ask these questions reflects the failure to plan evaluation at the very outset of the project. Had the evaluation been taken seriously, these questions would have been anticipated.

The first achievement tests were administered in October 1964, then repeated in October 1965, in May and October 1966, March and April 1967, and a special testing was conducted in June 1967. Eight control and MES schools were matched for proportions of Negro, Puerto Rican, and white students and for mean third grade reading scores. There was no indication of comparisons along any other dimension. Moreover, no continuing check of population changes was made so we do not know if the MES and control schools continued to be comparable. While these eight schools are the best controls available, their after-the-fact selection and the failure to thoroughly establish their comparability with MES schools again reflects the failure to take evaluation seriously.

The following comparisons between MES and control schools are based on data collected by the Bureau of Educational Research (1966) and used by Fox (1967) and by Schwager (1967). According to our computations of overall results, the MES schools at the outset (in October 1965) averaged 1.1 *months* of grade equivalent scores higher than the average of the control schools. In May 1966, on retest, the MES schools were 1.9 *months* of grade equivalent scores higher than their controls. If we subtract the initial difference from the final difference, we find that children in the MES schools had a net increment of 0.8 *months* of grade equivalent scores over their controls.

According to the manual for the Metropolitan Achievement Tests, one month of grade equivalent score is gained for one additional correct item. At some points in the scale, one additional correct item can mean two months of grade equivalent score, and at still other points, as much as four months of grade equivalent score. The net increase of 0.8 months of grade equivalent scores means an average increment due to the MES program of something less than one more correct item on the achievement test. Such a small difference is well within the range of the standard error of estimate of the test, based on the reliability coefficient reported in the test manual.

Testing for the school year 1966–67 reveals much the same magnitudes of differences. The growth increment attributable to the MES program itself is exceedingly small. No different conclusion can be drawn from Schwager's (1967) presentation of comparisons between MES and special service schools. The actual increments are quite miniscule. For a program which doubles the costs per pupil, halves the usual pupil-teacher ratio, and which has a class size 30 percent smaller than other schools, the tiny net increment is disappointing.

While it is true that MES schools were consistently ahead of control schools, that alone is not conclusive. We do not know if there was any coaching or special preparation for the achievement tests in MES schools. It does not take much coaching or practice to produce small increments on achievement tests. Anstey (1966) has shown that just a few hours of coaching and practice can produce marked improvement on England's very important "11+" test used to separate the academically inclined from the nonacademically inclined. Practice or special coaching for the achievement tests in a small proportion of MES classrooms could easily have accounted for the net increment of MES schools over control schools.

A very critical question about the achievement tests is raised by Fox (1967) under the heading of the Paradox of Normal Progress with Increasing Retardation. Although children gained at or above expectancy for the school year, they were also paradoxically falling farther behind calendar year by calendar year. Despite evidence of gain when measured from fall to spring, those gains are not maintained when the measures are taken fall to fall. Fox (1967) argues that teachers tend to press hard until the spring achievement tests and their effort decreases thereafter. In the following fall a good part of school work is designed to help children regain what was forgotten over the intervening spring-to-fall period.

Given such an hypothesis, Fox (1967) arranged to retest a sample of 218 MES classrooms in June. Depending on the grade level, from 30 to 41 percent of the reexamined classes showed a decrease in score two months later. There was also a great deal of variability from school to school. In three schools all retested classes showed the normal expected increment in score. In 16 schools the proportion of classes showing a decline varied from 16 to 80 percent. In one school, all 13 retested classrooms showed a decline, the median decline being one full year of grade equivalent score.

On the basis of these data, Fox (1967) asserted that there was some consistent factor which inflated achievement test scores in some schools. Schwager (1967) was highly critical of this aspect of Fox's report. He felt the use of strange examiners (inexperienced with ghetto children), poor timing of the tests, and poor motivation of the children resulted in the poor performance.

While there is no way of determining the merits of these two positions on the basis of available evidence, it is clear that the children who have been continuously exposed to the MES program over several years fare only slightly better than children in control schools. Forlano and Abramson's (1968) longitudinal study showed that children continuously exposed to MES do fall behind national norms, but at a rate slower than that of control schools. MES may have had some impact on their educational development, but that impact is modest considering the cost and effort. It is certainly not sufficient to preclude other approaches to education.

The entire controversy reflects the fact that the original proposal had no provisions for systematic evaluation of the program. Perhaps it was because no one had any real interest in the outcome. It is certainly a telling indication that a program involving 16,500 children, 1,700 educators, and $15,000,000.00 annually, did not have any built-in evaluation and sufficient controls. It is characteristic of our public helping agencies that they do not support or use research. Moreover, as Myer (1966) has pointed out, when administrators use research, it is primarily to justify previously held opinions and to prepare reports to funding agencies, not to modify programs accordingly.

The peculiarly monopolistic and yet defensive posture of our public institutions somehow insulates the administration of such institutions from any demand to modify programs in relation to changing needs. At the same time we note that programs become inextricably intertwined with the prestige of the sponsor, and the battleground shifts to the arena of public opinion. In that arena careful and reasoned factual argumentation gives way to shrill pronouncement, distortion, suppression of adverse information, and sheer fabrication when expedient. When the UFT committed itself so early to the program, then no matter what the facts, its representative (Schwager, 1967) had to say, "We are educating disadvantaged youth in More Effective Schools. We must continue. The program must grow. There is no alternative." The research nowhere supports such an absolute and extreme position, and the publication of such a statement in an official organ of the UFT, a position which union leaders may not themselves believe privately (Channon, 1967), does not contribute to the dispassionate consideration of constructive alternatives. However, the case study is instructive in informing the unwary academic researcher that dispassionate and rational evaluation is unlikely in a climate of change and political conflict.

CONCLUSIONS

What is the state of the art? Our examination of the literature suggests that as intervention programs become more specific in goals and in methods, some degree of improvement in the functioning of children in school is observed. Moreover, it seems that many intervention programs can be carried out by auxiliary personnel and nonprofessionals, with but a modest investment of professional time in training and in supervision. Massive programs which simply bring more people into the schools but result in no change in the way in which children are treated in school, produce disappointing results for the expenditures involved. Our examination of the literature also suggests that the next promising avenue for intervention is carefully thought through modifications in curriculum, methods, and, we would add, the organization of the teaching enterprise. However, radical modifications, no matter how well grounded, will undoubtedly encounter the same problems in implementation in the schools that ongoing attempts at intervention have encountered. The fact that children continue to be left back, despite 60 years of research showing such a practice is useless and may even be harmful, shows how difficult it is to achieve change in matters which are deeply a part of how schools are operated. If we accept the view that situational factors are critical, examination and modification of the environment in which children and teachers spend so much of their lives and in which they interact so importantly seems to be the next direction for preventive work in this field.

Note

1. Recently, we have seen the development of ungraded primary schools and continuous progress classes. It remains to be seen whether such innovations will overcome the negative side effects of nonpromotion, or whether they will turn into the same old thing called by a new name.

References

Adams, G. S. *Measurement and evaluation in education, psychology, and guidance.* New York: Holt, Rinehart & Winston, 1964.

Aguilera, A., & Keneally, K. School failure, psychiatric implications. *Journal of Child Psychiatry*, 1954, 3, 88–92.

Albee, G. W. *Mental health manpower trends.* New York: Basic Books, 1959.

Allen, K. R., & Harris, F. R. Elimination of a child's excessive scratching by training the mother in reinforcement procedures. *Behaviour Research and Therapy*, 1966, 4, 79–84.

Allinsmith, W., & Goethals, G. W. *The role of schools in mental health.* New York: Basic Books, 1962.

Anderson, H. A. Early school leavers. *School Review*, 1953, 61, 389–91.

Austey, E. *Psychological tests.* London, England: Nelson, 1966.

Arthur, G. A study of the achievement of sixty grade 1 repeaters as compared with that of non-repeaters of the same mental age. *Journal of Experimental Education*, 1936, 5, 203–205.

Ayres, L. *Laggards in our schools.* New York: Russell Sage Foundation, 1909.

Baer, C. J. The school progress and adjustment of underage and overage students. *Journal of Educational Psychology*, 1958, 49(1), 17–19.

Baker, J. G., & Wagner, N. N. Social class and mental illness in children. *Teachers College Record*, 1965, 66(6), 522–536.

Balow, B. The emotionally and socially handicapped. *Review of Educational Research*, 1966, 36(1), 120–133.

Bayles, B. C. New branches grow on the educational family tree. *National Elementary Principal*, 1967, 6, 16–17.

Beagle, S. Remarks on the New York City more effective schools program to the California State Board of Education, May, 1967. (Mimeo)

Bentzgen, F. A. Interdisciplinary research in educational programming for disturbed children. *American Journal of Orthopsychiatry*, 1962, 32, 473–485.

Bindman, A. J. Mental health consultation: Theory and practice. *Journal of Consulting Psychology*, 1959, 23, 473–482.

Bindman, A. J. The clinical psychologist as a mental health consultant. In L. E. Abt & D. E. Brower (eds), *Progress in clinical psychology.* Vol. 7. New York: Grune & Stratton, 1966.

Birch, J. W. Special classes for maladjusted children. *Exceptional Children*, 1956, 22, 333–337.

Bisgayer, J. L., Kahn, C. L., & Frazer, V. F. Special classes for emotionally disturbed children. *American Journal of Orthopsychiatry*, 1964, 34, 696–704.

Blackhurst, A. E. Technology in special education: Some implications. *Exceptional Children*, 1965, 31(9), 449–456.

Blackwood, R. O., Horrocks, J. E., Keele, T. F., Hundziak, M., & Rettig, J. H. Modifying social behaviors in severely retarded children. In A. M. Graziano (ed.), *Behavior therapy with children.* New York: Atherton, in press.

Blom, G. E., Rudnick, M., & Searless, J. Some principles and practices in the psychoeducational treatment of emotionally disturbed children. *Psychology in the Schools*, 1966, 3, 30–38.

Bloom, B. S. (ed.), Engelhart, M. D., Furst, E. J., Hill, W. H. & Krathwohl, D. R. *Taxonomy of educational objectives.* New York: Longmans, Green, 1956.

Bloom, B. S. Testing cognitive ability and achievement. In N. L. Gage (ed.), *Handbook of research on teaching.* Chicago: Rand McNally, 1963.

Bloomberg, C. M., & Troupe, C. H. Big brothers to troubled children. *National Education Association Journal*, 1964, 53(1), 22–25.

Bower, E. M. Mental health in education. *Review of Educational Research*, 1962, 32, 441–454.

Bower, E. M. Primary prevention of mental and emotional disorders. A conceptual framework and action possibilities. *American Journal of Orthopsychiatry*, 1963, 33, 832–848.

Bower, E. M. How to build on top of defenses. *Contemporary Psychology*, 1963, 8(2), 62–63.

Brackett, P. C. Substitute training at Belmont. *National Elementary Principal*, 1967, 6, 18–22.

Brendtro, L. K. & Stern, P. R. A modification in the sequential tutoring of emotionally disturbed children. *Exceptional Children*, 1967, 33, 517–521.

Bruce, P. Relationship of self acceptance to other variables with sixth grade children oriented in self understanding. *Journal of Educational Psychology*, 1958, 49, 229–238.

Buchmueller, A. D., & Gildea, M. C. L. A group therapy project with parents of behavior problem children in public schools. *American Journal of Pshchiatry*, 1949, 106, 46.

Bureau of Education Research. *Evaluation of the more effective schools program.* (Summary report, P. H. 22–365) New York: New York City Board of Education, September 1966.

Byne, R. H. Seidman, E., Dayton, D. M., Boek, J. K., & Peterson, M. B. *Final Report: The elementary school project.* College Park, Md.: Research Center of the Interprofessional Research Commission on Pupil Personnel Services, University of Maryland, 1968.

Cain, L. F. General problems and administration of programs for exceptional children. *Review of Educational Research*, 1953, 23, 391–399.

Caplan, G. *Concepts of mental health and consultation.* Washington, D. C.: Children's Bureau, United States Department of Health, Education, and Welfare, 1959.

Caplan, G. (ed.) *Prevention of mental disorders in children.* New York: Basic Books, 1961.

Caplan, G. Types of mental health consultation. *American Journal of Orthopsychiatry.* 1963, 33, 470–481.

Carroll, M. L. Academic achievement and adjustment of underage and overage third graders. *Journal of Educational Research*, 1963, 56(8), 415–419.

Carter, L. B. The effect of early school entrance on the scholastic achievement of elementary school children in the Austin Public School. *Journal of Educational Research*, 1956, 91–103.

Caswell, H. L. *Non-promotion in elementary schools.* (Division of Survey and Field Studies No. 4) Nashville, Tenn.: George Peabody College for Teachers, 1933.

Center for Urban Education. *The more effective schools program.* (Evaluation of New York City School District Title I ESEA Educational Projects) New York: Center for Urban Education, August 1966.

Channon, G. The more effective schools. *Urban Review*, 1967, 2, 23–26.

Clark, W. Emotional problems: A major factor in retention. *South-eastern Louisiana State College Bulletin*, January 1959, 16–17.

Coffield, W. H., & Blommers, P. Effects of non-promotion on educational achievement in the elementary school. *Journal of Educational Psychology*, 1956, 47, 235–50.

Cohen, L. D. *Consultation: A community mental health method.* Report of a survey of practices in sixteen southern states, Southern Regional Education Board, 1964.

Coleman, S. S., Campbell, E. Q., Hobson, C. J., McBartland, J., Mood, A. M. Weinfeld, F. D., & York, R. L. *Equality of educational opportunity.* (Supt. Documents, Catalog No. FS 5.238: 38001) Washington, D. C.: United States Government Printing Office, 1966.

Condell, J. F., Anderson, R. C., & Ebinger, R. D. Providing school psychological service through a community mental health center. *Community Mental Health Journal*, 1966, 2, 82–85.

Cook, W. W. Some effects of the maintenance of high standards of promotion. *Elementary School Journal*, 1941, 41, 430–437.

Cowen, E. L. Effectiveness of secondary prevention programs using nonprofessionals in the school setting. *Proceedings of the 76th Annual Convention of the American Psychological Association*, 1968, 3, 705–706. (Summary)

Cowen, E. L., Carlisle, R. L., & Kaufman, G. Evaluation of a college student volunteer program with primary grades experiencing school adjustment problems. *Psychology in the Schools*, 1969, 6, 371–375.

Cowen, E. L., Gardner, E. A., & Zax, M. *Emergent approaches to mental health problems.* New York: Appleton-Century-Crofts, 1967.

Cowen, E. L., Izzo, L. D., Miles, H., Teleschow, E. F., Trost, M. A., & Zax, M. A preventive mental health program in the school setting. Description and evaluation. *Journal of Psychology*, 1963, 56, 307–356.

Cowen, E. L., Zax, M., Izzo, L. D., & Trost, M. A. Prevention of emotional disorders in the school setting. A further investigation. *Journal of Consulting Psychology*, 1966, 30, 381–387.

Cowen, E. L., Zax, M., & Laird, J. D. A college student volunteer program in the elementary school setting. *Community Mental Health Journal*, 1966, 2, 319–328.

Craymer, H. S. Hart, D. Parents take over so teachers can attend a guidance conference. *Instructor*, 1968, 77, 47.

Cruikshank, W. M., & Johnson, G. O. (eds.) *Education of exceptional children and youth.* Englewood Cliffs, N. J.: Prentice-Hall, 1958.

Cumming, E., & Cumming J. *Closed ranks.* Cambridge, Mass.: Harvard University Press, 1957.

Cutler, R. L., Spieth, P., & Wilkinson, M. School and community mental health programs. *Review of Educational Research.* 1962, 32, 476–483.

Davidson, S. School phobia as a manifestation of a family disturbance: Its structure and treatment. *Journal of Child Psychology and Psychiatry*, 1960, 1, 270–287.

Davison, G. L. A social learning theory programme with an autistic child. *Behaviour Research and Therapy*, 1964, 2, 149–159.

DeMyer, M. K., & Ferster, C. B. Teaching new social behavior to schizophrenic children. *Journal of American Academy of Child Psychiatry*, 1962, 1, 443–461.

Denham, W. H., Shatz, E., Felsenfeld, N. S., & Fishman, J. R. High school training for new careers in human services. *National Elementary Principal*, 1967, 6, 22–28.

Dobbs, V., & Neville, D. The effect of non-promotion on the achievement of groups matched from retained first graders and promoted second graders. *Journal of Educational Research,* 1967, 60(10), 472–477.

Donahue, G. T., & Reing, V. A. Teacher-moms help emotionally disturbed pupils. *Nation's Schools*, 1966, 78, 50–52.

Dreshen, R. H. Factors in voluntary dropouts. *Personnel and Guidance Journal*, 1954, 32, 289–292.

Dupont, H. J. Emotional maladjustment and special education. *Exceptional Children*, 1957, 24, 10–15.

Ellinger, B. D. Nonpromotion. A review essay. *Theory into Practice*, 1965, 4(3), 122–128.

Elsbree, W. *Practical suggestions for teaching.* Vol. 5. *Pupil progress in the elementary school.* New York: Teachers College, Columbia University, 1943.

Evans, R. L. On helping. Hamden, Conn.: High Meadows, 1967. (Mimeo)

Evans, R. L. An exploration of treatment systems in group living. Paper presented at the Regional Conference on Residential Treatment, Wallingford, Connecticut, May 1967.

Forlano, G., & Abramson, J. *Measuring pupil growth in reading in the more effective schools.* (P. N. 22–365) New York: Bureau of Educational Research, New York City Board of Education, April 1968.

Foster, R. E. In slow gear. Volunteer teaching aides. *Instructor*, 1964, 74, 136–137.

Fox, D. J. *Expansion of the more effective school program.* (Evaluation of New York City Title I, Educational projects, 1966–1967) New York: Center for Urban Education, September 1967.

French, W. *Behavioral goals of general education in high school.* New York: Russell Sage Foundation, 1957.

GAP. Committee on preventive psychiatry. Promotion of mental health in primary and secondary schools. An evaluation of four projects. Report No. 18, Jan. 1951.

Gildea, M. C. L., Glidewell, J. C., & Kantor, M. B. The St. Louis mental health project: History and evaluation. In E. L. Cowen, E. A. Gardner, & M. Zax (eds.), *Emergent approaches to mental health problems.* New York: Appleton-Century-Crofts, 1967.

Glidewell, J. C., & Swallow, C. S. *The prevalence of maladjustment in elementary schools.* (A report prepared for the Joint Commission on the Mental Health of Children) Chicago: University of Chicago, 1968.

Golann, S. E. *Coordinate index reference guide to community mental health.* New York: Behavioral Publications, 1969.

Gold, J. Child guidance day treatment and the school: A clinic's use of its psychoeducational facility for new programming in the public schools. *American Journal Orthopsychiatry*, 1967, 37(2), 276–277.

Goodlad, J. I. Some effects of promotion and non-promotion upon the social and personal adjustment of children. *Journal of Experimental Education*, 1954, 22, 301–328.

Goslin, D. A. The school in a changing society. Notes on the development of strategies for solving educational problems. *American Journal of Orthopsychiatry*, 1967, 37, 843–858.

Gragg, W. L. Some factors which distinguish dropouts from high school graduates. *Occupations*, 1949, 27, 458–461.

Gray, J. S. A biological view of behavior modification. *Journal of Educational Psychology*, 1932, 23, 611–620.

Graziano, A. M. Programmed psychotherapy: A behavioral approach to severely disturbed children. Paper presented at the meeting of the Eastern Psychological Association, Boston, April 1967.

Graziano, A. M. Clinical innovation and the mental health power structure: A social case history. *American Psychologist*, 1969, 23(1), 10–18. (a)

Graziano, A. M. An historical note: J. Stanley Gray's "Behavior Modification," 1932. *Journal of the History of the Social Sciences*, 1969, in press. (b)

Graziano, A. M. Mental health, psychotherapy and the new therapists. *Journal of Psychiatric Nursing*, March-April, 1969, 69–72. (c)

Graziano, A. M. (ed.) *Behavior therapy with children.* New York: Atherton Press, 1969, in press. (d)

Haffernan, H. What research says about non-promotion. *California Journal of Elementary Education*, 1952, 21, 7–24. Cited in J. M. Wolf, Syndrome of spring: Social promotion. *Elementary School Journal* 1965, 65, 208–216.

Hall, J. *A study of drop outs.* Miami, Fla.: Dade County Public Schools, Department of Research and Information, 1964. Cited in Shailer, T., & Knudsen, D. D. The relationship between non-promotion and the drop-out problem. *Theory into Practice*, 1965, 4(3), 90–94.

Halliwell, J. W. Reviewing the reviews on entrance age and school success. *Journal of Educational Research*, 1966, 59(9), 395–401.

Haring, N. G., & Phillips, E. L. *Educating emotionally disturbed children.* New York: McGraw-Hill, 1962.

Hay, L. Perspectives for a classroom for disturbed children. *Exceptional Children*, 1967, 33(8), 577–580.

Hay, L. The education of emotionally disturbed children. *American Journal of Orthopsychiatry*, 1953, 23, 676–683.

Hayman, J. L., & Johnson, J. T. Parents help educate their children through instructional television. *Journal of Experimental Education*, 1963, 32(2), 175–178.

Heilig, S., Fareberow, N., Litman, R., & Schneidman, E. The role of non-professional volunteers in a suicide prevention agency. *Community of Mental Health Journal*, 1968, 4(4), 287–295.

Henry, J. *Culture against man.* New York: Vintage Books, 1965.

Hewett, F. M. A hierarchy of competencies for teachers of emotionally handicapped children. *Exceptional Children*, 1966, 33(1), 7–11.

Hewett, F. M. Educational engineering with emotionally disturbed children. *Exceptional Children*, 1967, 33(7), 459–467.

Hotchkiss, J. M. The modification of maladaptive behavior of a class of educationally handicapped children by operant conditioning techniques. *Dissertation Abstracts*, 1967, 27(12–A), 4129–4130.

Humphreys, P. The school's concern over non-promotion. *Theory into Practice*, 1965, 4, 88–89.

Hunt, J. T. Special education: Segregation. *Education*, 1957, 77, 475–479.

Iscoe, I., Pierce, Jones, J. Friedman, S. T., & McGehearty, L. Some strategies in mental health consultation: A brief description of a project and some preliminary results. In E. L. Cowen, E. A. Gardener, & M. Zax (eds.), *Emergent approaches to mental health problems.* New York: Appleton-Century-Crofts, 1967.

Jackson, E. H. A four-year project in the elementary school for emotionally handicapped children. *Dissertation Abstracts*, 1962, 23(3), 1073–1074.

Josephina, S. Promotion: A perennial problem. *Education*, 1961–1962, 82, 373–376.

Kahn, J., Buchmueller, A. D., & Gildea, M. C. L. Group therapy for parents of behavior problem children in public schools. Failure of the method in a Negro school. *American Journal of Psychiatry*, 1951, 108, 351–357.

Kamii, C. K., & Weikart, D. S. Marks, achievement and intelligence of seventh graders who are retained (non-promoted) once in elementary school. *Journal of Educational Research*, 1963, 56, 452–459.

Kandel, D. B., & Williams, R. H. *Psychiatric rehabilitation: Some problems of research.* New York: Atherton Press, 1964.

Karowe, H. E. How volunteers can help disadvantaged children. *Children*, 1967, 14, 151–155.

Kashin, N. Problem of grade repeating. *Soviet Education*, 1966, 8, 18–32.

Kearney, N. C. *Elementary school objectives.* New York: Russell Sage Foundation, 1953.

Kelly, E. M. Organization of special classes to fit the needs of different ability groupings. *American Journal of Mental Deficiency*, 1943, 48, 80–86.

Keyes, C. H. *Progress through the grades of city schools. Contributions to education, No. 42.* New York: Teachers College, Columbia University, 1911.

Kidd, J. W. Perspectives for a classroom for disturbed children. *Exceptional Children*, 1967, 33(8), 577–580.

Klebaner, R. P. School volunteers, a new challenge. *National Elementary Principal*, 1967, No. 6, 13–17.

Klebanoff, L. B., & Bindman, A. J. The organization and development of a community mental health program for children: A case study. *American Journal of Orthopsychiatry*, 1962, 32, 119–132.

Klein, W. L. The training of human service aids. In E. L. Cowen, E. A. Gardner, & M. Zax (eds.), *Emergent approaches to mental health problems.* New York: Appleton-Century-Crofts, 1969.

Knoblock, P., & Garcea, R. A. Toward a broader concept of the role of the special class for emotionally disturbed children. *Exceptional Children*, 1965, 31(7), 329–335.

Knudsen, D. An investigation of the social and familial relationships in the life of the high school dropout. Unpublished doctoral dissertation, University of North Carolina, 1964.

Knudsen, D., & Shailer, T. Some social factors to consider in non-promotion. *Theory into Practice*, 1965, 4(3), 99–102.

Kolstoe, O. P. Nature and impact of special methods. *Education*, 1957, 77, 464–467.

Korolev, F. F. Ways and means of overcoming repeating and drop-outs. *Soviet Education*, 1962, No. 2, 51–59.

Kozol, J., *Death at an early age.* New York: Houghton Mifflin, 1967.

Lafferty, H. M. Reasons for pupil failures: A progress report. *American School Board Journal*, 1948, 117, 18–20.

Larson, R. E. *Age-grade status of Iowa elementary school pupils.* Unpublished doctoral dissertation, State University of Iowa, 1955. Cited in W. H. Coffield, & P. Blommers. Effects of non-promotion on educational achievement in the elementary school. *Journal of Educational Psychology*, 1956, 47, 235–250.

Lavor, M., & Krivit, D. The handicapped children's early education assistance act, Public Law 90-538. *Exceptional Children*, 1969, 35(5), 379–384.

Lawrence, M. M., Spanier, I. J., & Dubowy, M. An analysis of the work of the school mental health unit of a community mental health board. *American Journal of Orthopsychiatry*, 1962, 32, 99–108.

Lennon, R., & Mitchell, B. Trends in age-grade relationships: A thirty-five year review. *School and society*, 1955, 82, 123–125.

Leton, D. A. Differential teaching techniques for emotionally disturbed children. *Mental Hygiene*, 1964, 48(2), 209–216.

Levine, M. Residential change and school adjustment. *Community Mental Health Journal*, 1966, 2, 61–69.

Levine, M. Problems of entry in light of some postulates of practice in community psychology. Paper read at the City University of New York Symposium on Community Psychology, June 1967.

Levine, M., Dunn, F., Brechinsky, S., Bradley, J., & Donlan, K., Student teachers as tutors for children in an inner city school. *Child Psychiatry and Human Development*, 1970, 1, 50–56.

Levine, M., & Levine A. Social change and human behavior. Dependency, deviance or diversity? In G. Goldman & D. N. Milman (eds.), *Psychoanalytic contributions to community psychology.* Springfield, Ill.: Charles C Thomas, 1971.

Levine, M., & Levine, A. *A social history of helping services: Clinic, court, school and community.* New York: Appleton-Century-Crofts, 1970.

Levitt, E. E. Effect of a causal teacher-training program on authoritarianism and responsibility in grade school children. *Psychological Reports*, 1955, 1, 449.

Levitt, E. E. The results of psychotherapy with children. An evaluation. *Journal of Consulting Psychology*, 1957, 21, 189–196.

Libo, L. M., & Griffith, C. R. Developing mental health programs in areas lacking professional facilities. The community consultant approach in New Mexico. *Community Mental Health Journal*, 1966, 2, 163–169.

Liddle, G. P. Psychological factors involved in dropping out of school. *High School Journal*, 1962, 45, 276–280.

Lindemann, E. B. Strengthening the relations between the school and the community treatment facility. In R. H. Ojemann (ed.), *The school and the community treatment facility in preventive psychiatry.* Iowa City, Iowa: University of Iowa Press, 1966.

Long, N. J. Some problems in teaching life space interviewing techniques to graduate students in education in a large class at Indiana University. *American Journal of Orthopsychiatry*, 1963, 33, 723–727.

Long, M. J., & Morse, W. C. Special classes with social and emotional problems in the public schools. In Wattenberg, W. (ed.), *Social deviancy among youth. 65th yearbook of the National Society for the Study of Education.* Chicago, Ill.: NSSE, 1966.

Loomis, M. J. Elementary school non-promotion and individual potential. *Theory into Practice*, 1965, 4(3), 85–87.

Lourie, N. V. Orthopsychiatry and education. *American Journal of Orthopsychiatry*, 1967, 37, 836–842.

Mannino, F. V. *Consultation in mental health and related fields.* (Public Health Service Publication No. 1920) Washington, D. C.: United States Government Printing Office, 1969.

Matika, F., & Sheerer, R. Are the causes of dropouts excuses? *Bulletin of the National Association of Secondary School Principals*, 1962, 46, 42.

Matthews, C. V. The serious problem of the school dropout. *Illinois Education*, 1962, 50, 211.

Matthews, W. M., Kipfer, J. K., Morse, W. C., McNeil, E. B., & Cutler, R. C. A research evaluation of an action approach to school mental health. *American Journal of Orthopsychiatry*, 1961, 31, 320–346.

Medley, D. M., & Mitzel, H. E. Measuring classroom behavior by systematic observation. In N. L. Gage (ed.), *Handbook of research on teaching.* Chicago: Rand McNally, 1963.

Meussen, E. J. *A determination of the effect of retardation on students.* Ann Arbor: University of Michigan, 1952.

Millar, T. P. The child refuses to attend school. *American Journal of Psychiatry*, 1961, 118, 398–404.

Monoszon, E. Successful experiment in overcoming failures and non-promotion. *Soviet Education*, 1963, 5, 9–15.

Morrison, I. E., & Perry, I. F. Acceptance of overage children by their classmates. *Elementary School Journal*, 1956, 56, 217–220.

Morse, W. C. Enhancing the classroom teacher's mental health function. In E. C. Cowen, E. A. Gardner, & M. Zax (eds.), *Emergent approaches to mental health problems.* New York: Appleton-Century-Crofts, 1967.

Morse, W. C., Cutler, R. L., & Fink, A. H. *Public school classes for the emotionally handicapped: A research analysis.* Washington, D. C., Council for Exceptional Children, National Education Association, 1964.

Muuss, R. E. The relation between "causal" orientation, anxiety, and insecurity in elementary school children. *Journal of Educational Psychology*, 1960, 51, 122–129. (a)

Muuss, R. E. A comparison of "high causally" and "low causally" oriented sixth grade children in respect to a perceptual "intolerance of ambiguity" test. *Child Development*, 1960, 31, 521–536. (b)

Myers, A. The impact of the evaluation of poverty programs on local institutions. Paper presented at the annual meeting of the American Psychological Association, New York, September 1966.

National Commission on Teacher Education and Professional Standards. Auxiliary personnel. *National Elementary Principal*, 1967, No. 6, 6–12.

Newman, R. *Psychological consultation in the schools.* New York: Basic Books, 1967.

Nichtern, S., Donahue, G. T., O'Shea, J., Marans, M., Curtis, M., & Brady, C. A community educational program for the emotionally disturbed child. *American Journal of Orthopsychiatry*, 1964, 34, 705–713.

Ojemann, R. H. Researches into alterations in the school curriculum for the primary prevention of mental disorders. Unpublished manuscript, undated.

Ojemann, R. H. Sources of infection revealed in preventive psychiatry research. *American Journal of Public Health*, 1960, 50, 329–335.

Ojemann, R. H. The significance of a causal orientation in human development. In Educational Records Bureau, *Keeping abreast of the revolution in education. Report of the 25th Educational Conference.* Washington, D. C.: American Council on Education, 1963.

Ojemann, R. H. Incorporating psychological concepts in the school curriculum. *Journal of School Psychology*, 1967, 3, 195–204.

Ojemann, R. H., Levitt, E. E., Lyle, W. H., Jr., & Whiteside, M. F. The effects of a "causal" teacher training program and certain curricular changes on grade school children. *Journal of Experimental Education*, 1955, 24, 95–114.

Ojemann, R. H., & Snider, B. C. The development of the child's conception of the teacher. *Journal of Experimental Education*, 1963, 32, 73–80.

Ojemann, R. H., & Snider, B. C. The effect of a teaching program in behavioral science on changes in causal behavior scores. *Journal of Educational Research*, 1964, 57, 255–260.

Olshansky, S., & Schonfield, J. Parental perceptions of the mental status of graduates of special classes. *Mental Retardation*, 1965, 3(5), 16–20.

Osterweil, J. School psychology and comprehensive community mental health planning. *Community Mental Health Journal*, 1966, 2, 142–145.

Otto, H. J. Grading and promotion policies. *N.E.A. Journal*, 1951, 128–129.

Otto, H. J. *Elementary school organization and administration.* (3rd ed.) New York: Appleton-Century-Crofts, 1954.

Otto, H. J., & Estes, D. W. Accelerated and retarded progress. In C. Harris (ed.), *Encyclopedia of educational research.* (3rd ed.) New York: Macmillan, 1960.

Otto, H. J., & Melby, E. O. An attempt to evaluate the threat of failure as a factor in achievement. *Elementary School Journal*, 1935, 35, 588–596.

Patterson, G. R., Littman, R. A., & Hinsey, W. C. Parental effectiveness as reinforcers in the laboratory and its relation to child rearing practices and child adjustment in the classroom. *Journal of Personality*, 32(2), 1965.

Peck, H. B., Zwerling, I., Rabban, M., & Mendelsohn, M. Reading disability and community psychiatry. *American Journal of Orthopsychiatry*, 1966, 36, 420–433.

Phillips, D. L. Identification of mental illness: Its consequences for rejection. *Community Mental Health Journal*, 1967, 3, 262–266.

Pierce-Jones, J., Iscoe, I., & Cunningham, G. *Child behavior consultation in elementary schools. A demonstration and research program.* (Report by Personnel Services Research Center) Austin: University of Texas, 1968.

Pope, L., & Crump, R. School drop-outs as assistant teachers. *Young Children*, 1965, 21(1), 13–23.

Quay, H. C., Morse, W. C., & Cutler, R. L. Personality patterns of pupils in special classes for the emotionally disturbed. *Exceptional Children*, 1966, 32(5), 297–301.

Quay, H. C., Werry, J. S., McQueen, M., & Sprague, R. L. Remediation of the conduct problem child in the special class setting. *Exceptional Children*, 1966, 32, 509–515.

Rae Grant, Q., & Stringer, L. A. Design for a new orthopsychiatric discipline. *American Journal of Orthopsychiatry*, 1964, 34, 722–729.

Reger, R. The questionable role of specialists in special education programs. *Journal of Special Education*, 1966, 1(1), 53–59.

Reinherz, H., & Griffin, C. L. The second time around: A study of achievement and progress of boys who repeated one of the first three grades in school. Paper presented at the meeting of the American Orthopsychiatric Association, Chicago, March 1968.

Reissman, F., & Pearl, A. *New careers for the poor.* Glencoe, Ill.: Free Press, 1965.

Rhodes, W. C. Psychological techniques and theory applied to behavioral modification. *Exceptional Children*, 1962, 28, 333–338.

Rhodes, W. C. The disturbing child: A problem of ecological management. *Exceptional Children*, 33(7), 449–455.

Robert, L. D., & Jones, W. L. *The school drop-out in Louisiana, 1962–1963.* (Baton-Rouge, State of Louisiana, Dept. of Education, 1963) Cited in T. Shailer & D. D. Knudsen. The relationship between non-promotion and the drop-out problem. *Theory into Practice*, 1965, 4(3), 90–94.

Roen, S. R. Primary prevention in the classroom through a teaching program in the behavioral sciences. In E. L. Cowen, E. A. Gardner, & M. Zax (eds.), *Emergent approaches to mental health problems.* New York: Appleton-Century-Crofts, 1967.

Rosen, B. M., Weinger, J., Hench, C. L., Willner, S. G., & Bahn, A. E. A nationwide survey of out patient psychiatric clinic functions intake policies, and practices. *American Journal of Psychiatry*, 1966, 122, 908–915.

Ross, A. O. The application of behavior principles in therapeutic education. *Journal of Special Education*, 1967, 1(3), 275–285.

Rubin, E. Z., & Simson, C. B. Special class program for the emotionally disturbed child in school: A proposal. *American Journal of Orthopsychiatry*, 1968, 30, 144–153.

Ruebush, B. K. Anxiety. In H. W. Stevenson (ed.), *Child psychology. 62nd Yearbook National Society Studies of Education.* Part I. Chicago: University of Chicago Press, 1963.

Russell, D. H. Influence of repetition of a grade and of regular promotion on the attitudes of parents and children towards school. *California Journal of Elementary Education*, 1952, 21, 29–41.

Russo, S. Adaptations in behavioral therapy with children. *Behaviour Research and Therapy*, 1964, 2, 43–47.

Sandlin, A. A. Social and emotional adjustment of regularly promoted and non-promoted pupils. *Child Development Monographs, No. 32.* New York Teachers College, Columbia University, 1944.

Sarason, S. B., Davidson, K. S., & Blatt, B. *The preparation of teachers. An unstudied problem in education.* New York: Wiley, 1962.

Sarason, S. B., Levine, M., Goldenberg, I. I., Cherlin, D. L., & Bennett, E. M. *Psychology in community settings.* New York: Wiley, 1966.

Sarason, S. B., Lighthall, F. F., Davidson, K. S., Waite, R. R., & Ruebush, B. K. *Anxiety in elementary school children.* New York: Wiley, 1960.

Saunders, C. M. *Promotion of failure for the elementary school pupil?* New York: Teachers College, Columbia University, 1941.

Scheff, T. S., *Being mentally ill: A sociological theory.* New York: Aldine, 1966.

Scheur, A. L. Certification, teacher preparation and special classes for the emotionally disturbed and socially maladjusted. Report by states. *Exceptional Children*, 1966, 33(2), 120–121.

Schmuck, R., & Chesler, M. Superpatriot opposition to community mental health programs. *Community Mental Health Journal*, 1967, 3, 382–388.

Schwager, S. A new look at MES in the light of the Coleman, racial isolation reports. Reprint from the *United Teacher*, Official publication of the United Federation of Teachers, Local 2, AFL-CIO, 1967.

Schwager, S. An analysis of the evaluation of the more effective schools program conducted by the Center for Urban Education. New York: United Federation of Teachers, November 1967. (Mimeo)

Shailer, T., & Knudsen, D. D. The relationship between non-promotion and the drop-out problem. *Theory into Practice*, 1965, 4(3), 90–94.

Shearer, M. The principal is often overlooked. *Community Mental Health Journal*, 1968, 4, 47–52.

Shipp, M. D. Teacher aides: A survey. *National Elementary Principal*, 1967, 6, 30–33.

Smith, S. A. An educational program for emotionally disturbed children. *Psychology in the Schools*, 1967, 4(3), 280–283.

Snepp, D. W. Can we salvage the drop-outs? *Clearinghouse*, 1956, 31, 49–54.

Snipes, W. T. Promotion and moving. *Elementary School Journal*, 1965, 65, 429–433.

Spivack, G., & Swift, M. S. *The Devereux Elementary School Behavior Rating Scales. A study of the nature and organization of disturbed classroom behavior.* Devon, Pa.: Devereux Foundation Institute for Research and Training, 1966.

Stiavelle, R. E., & Shirley, D. T. The citizenship council: A technique for managing behavior disorders in the educationally handicapped class. *Journal of School Psychology*, 1968, 6(2), 147–156.

Susskind, E. The role of questions in the elementary school classrooms. Unpublished doctoral dissertation, Department of Psychology, Yale University, 1969.

Susskind, E. The role of questions in the elementary school classroom. In F. Kaplan & S. B. Sarason (eds.), *Collected papers of the Psycho-Educational Clinic*, in press.

Thomas, S. L. Listening mothers: Oral language development in first grade. *Instructor*, 1967, 77, 20–21.

Thorndike, E. L. *Elimination of pupils from school.* (United States Bureau of Education Bulletin, No. 4) Washington, D. C.: United States Government Printing Office, 1908.

Thornsbley, J. R., & Barnes, B. Parent aides make teaching aids. *Instructor*, 1966, 76, 173–175.

Tokareva, E. G. Three years without repeaters. *Soviet Education*, 1963, 5, 9–15.

Towne, R. C., & Joiner, L. M. Some negative implications of special placement for children with learning disabilities. *Journal of Special Education*, 1968, 2(2), 217–222.

Trippe, M. J. Conceptual problems in research in educational provisions for disturbed children. *Exceptional Children*, 1963, 29(8), 400–406.

Vacc, N. A. A study of emotionally disturbed children in regular and special class. *Exceptional Children*, 1968, 35(3), 197–206.

Waetjen, W. B. The alleviation of non-promotion. *Theory into Practice*, 1965, 4(3), 117–121.

Wahler, R. G., Winkel, G. H., Peterson, R. F., & Morrison, D. C. Mothers as behavior therapists for their own children. *Behaviour Research and Therapy*, 1965, 3, 113–124.

Walder, L., Cohen, S. I., Breiter, D., Daston, P., Hirsch, I. S., & Liebowitz, J. M. Teaching behavioral principles to parents of disturbed children. Paper presented at the meeting of the Eastern Psychological Association, Boston, April 1967.

Whelan, R. J., & Harris, N. G. Modification and maintenance of behavior through systematic application of consequences. *Exceptional Children*, 1966, 32(5), 281–289.

Wickman, E. K. *Children's behavior and teacher's attitudes.* New York: Commonwealth Fund, 1928.

Wilderson, F. B. A concept of the "ideal" therapeutic relationship in classes for emotionally disturbed children. *Journal of Special Education*, 1966, 1(1), 91–98.

Wilkerson, D. A. Programs and practices in compensatory education for disadvantaged children. *Review of Educational Research*, 1965, 35(5), 426–440.

Withall, J. Mental health in the classrooms. *Journal of Teacher Education*, 1964, 193–199.

Witmer, L. Clinical psychology. *Psychological Clinic* 1906–1907, 1, 1–9.

Wolf, J. M. Syndrome of spring: Social promotion. *Elementary School Journal* 1965, 65, 208–216.

Wolman, T., & Shelley, F. D. Volunteers in the public schools. *National Elementary Principal*, 1967, No. 6, 34–37.

Woolatt, L. H. Why capable students drop out of high school. *Bulletin of National Association of Secondary School Principals*, 1961, 45, 1–8.

Zax, M., Cowen, E. L., Rappaport, J., Beach, D. R., & Laird, J. D. Follow-up study of children identified early as emotionally disturbed. *Journal of Consulting and Clinical Psychology*, 1968, 32(4), 369–374.

Zax, M., & Cowen, E. L. Research on early detection and prevention of emotional dysfunction in young school children. In C. D. Spielberger (ed.), *Current topics in clinical and community psychology.* Vol. 1. New York: Academic Press, 1969.

23

Toward Campus Community Mental Health Programs

Thomas R. Brigante

INTRODUCTION

Many college and university campuses have begun only recently to establish mental health programs. While in the past relatively little attention has been given to the concept of a campus as a community, it appears that there is an increasing readiness for such an orientation. Student cries for a relevant education, their ever-increasing involvement with broader societal problems, the American concern with rootlessness in a mobile society, and the recent expressions of protest on American campuses all support that aspect of a mental health program which is concerned with the creation of a genuine community. Students are less willing to submit to an impersonal educational experience for the sake of future security. Faculty members and administrators are increasingly aware of this fact and consequently are receptive to finding ways of enhancing students' active participation in educational decision-making.

The present chapter examines issues involved in establishing community-oriented campus mental health programs, as well as offering plans for implementing their development. At the outset, we will devote some attention to problems raised by current campus unrest, especially as they relate to the process of social change and to the role of mental health professionals on campus. Next we will consider the possible alternative administrative structures for student services on campuses, with special attention to their relative degrees of desirability. The third section will be focused upon community oriented approaches to campus programs. It shall consider the role of mental health

consultation, the mental health professional's relationships with various campus groups, campus mental health education approaches, and a variety of program innovations which are being increasingly utilized. A subsequent section will discuss issues involved in making fuller use of the human resources now available for campus mental health programs. Within the final section, a five part program will be proposed for strengthening campus mental health programs, based upon a community approach. Some fundamental questions facing educational communities are raised in the concluding section and attention is given to the role of the mental health professional in working toward solutions to these questions.

CAMPUS UNREST, SOCIAL CHANGE, AND THE MENTAL HEALTH PROFESSIONAL

The multiple signs of student unrest on college campuses have created a new urgency for examining colleges as social instutions. Prior to the recent difficulties, higher educational institutions have been strikingly indifferent to studying themselves and making changes based on needs of all participants in the educational enterprise. In a recent address Martin Meyerson (1968), President of the State University of New York at Buffalo, noted that: "The American University in the 20th century has adapted itself to change less than any institution in our society. Educationally, and in certain other important respects, universities today are remarkably similar to the universities at the turn of the century, the pattern for which had been set by Charles Eliot and many others who had leaned so heavily on the Germanic academic centers of the 19th century" (p. 4).

Meyerson further indicated that it is students who have been the conscience of the universities, pointing to the neglected classroom and to the use of professors' energies in pursuing governmental, business, and other activities, sometimes becoming far removed from students' needs. Although many of his fellow presidents would disagree, Meyerson considers it especially valuable for students to have "mocked and taught us to mock the concept of utterly value-free academic existence, which may have been expedient for the man of cap and gown in Bismarck's Germany, who dared not do otherwise, but is hardly the posture for free men."

In this connection, Goodman (1965) has pointed out that students have recently been seeking to extend the concept of academic freedom from *Lehrfreiheit* (freedom of professors to teach according to their likes) to include *Lernfreiheit* (freedom of students to ask for what they need to be taught, and if necessary to invite teachers, including advocates of causes).

The causes of student discontent have been widely discussed and are increasingly well understood. Herein, we are more interested in student discontent as it relates to educational change as well as to change within contemporary American society. In this connection it is of special relevance for us to examine the role taken by the mental health professional with regard to the social change process.

Major causes of unrest can be quickly identified. First, there are the obvious perennial pains of adolescence which have to do with the transition of adolescents to early adulthood. Although this factor is not new, it does need to be noted that many educational institutions throughout the country have still not taken cognizance of the importance of special student needs during adolescence. One concrete manifestation of this fact is the dearth of fully staffed mental health centers on college campuses throughout the country. Many colleges and universities still have no mental health professionals on campus who are exclusively devoted to student needs.

Another source of student unrest is related to our temporal circumstances of living in the 1960s. Relevant here are the successive assassinations of several national heroes, our urban crisis, our increasing awareness of the hypocrisy of neglecting our poor who live in the midst of our affluence, and last but certainly not least the problem of the blacks in American society and of their painful struggle for personal and social evolution. Student reactions to these events have become intertwined with their strong antipathies to the war in Vietnam. The remarks of a student speaker (Thompson, 1969) at Yale's recent commencement may be cited as illustrative:

The war is destroying not one nation but two—the Vietnamese and our own. Our cities are in decay; our universities are in chaos; our poor are hungry. And yet our money and our energies are expended upon war and the perpetuation of war.

Today as we leave Yale a sense of frustration and despair overwhelms us. On some campuses frustration has erupted into a violence which has shocked the American public. And yet the same public silently condones violence abroad in senseless military action killing thousands of Americans and Vietnamese. The connection between the violence here and abroad must be made: the violence at home will not end while the violence abroad continues. The one feeds the other. To understand the frustrations causing violence, however, is not to condone it. The great majority of students would not advocate violent confrontation. But we do demand a confrontation with reason. The death and destruction in Vietnam have not been explained adequately because they cannot be explained. Then why does the war continue? (p. 30)

Students differ in their degree of hopefulness about what can be done with educational institutions and with the larger society itself. The peer group is becoming more and more a society in microcosm as the larger society is seen as irrational, thwarting, and unworthy of allegiance. Some students are becoming increasingly open in their desires to replace the society with their own society. At one extreme a group of students holds the opinion that present society is in a hopeless state, seeks to exist independent of the larger culture, and makes very little attempt to alter or influence standards which are regarded as totally unacceptable guides for behavior as far as any person of integrity is concerned. Another sector of students also manifests considerable disdain toward society values but is willing to participate in a larger society primarily as a way of gaining the leverage needed to change existing societal standards. These students will relate to adults who can help them in implementing their changes of the larger society. For example, if such adults would help them to establish or implement tutorial projects or to work with underprivileged groups, they would interact with adults on a limited basis.

A third large group of students can be considered to be "undecideds." They experience some dissatisfaction with the adult world at large and want the acceptance of their peers but are still confused and unable to make any firm judgment regarding the system in which they were reared. At this point they are dissidents, and to some extent feel caught between adult standards and their own more rebellious peers.

Black power and student power advocates really consist of two groups of students in terms of the analysis which has just been presented. One subsector of black student-power oriented students believes that the power balance must be shifted but that existing institutions can be "saved," whereas the other sector looks at the usurpation of power as one step in destroying existing institutions so that more adequate ones can be built.

Even within the present cursory discussion we cannot neglect to mention student concerns with relevancy and their underlying wishes to be more active participants in the educational process. Students are more and more regarding classroom activites as outside the sphere of their personal interests, and are increasingly willing to follow their personal concerns instead of docilely acquiescing to the existing structure.

Frankel (1968) has presented an excellent analysis of the implications of student power demands. He is willing to assume that not only students but people generally learn more from their experience and invest more in it if they have some power over the way they live and work. He also grants that they tend to be more responsible if they have such power. He further feels that this has not been acknowledged or understood within the context of higher education. But the question then arises as to what the limitations of student power should be. Should students participate equally with professors in selection and promotion of faculty members? Frankel argues against this, saying that such a procedure would be incompatible with academic freedom by exposing the

teacher to the possibility of intimidation. Our definition of academic freedom in this country has excluded all groups but professors from having any formal power over what happens in the classroom. Thus, Frankel argues, since all groups have been excluded there is no reason to justify giving students power that no other group has. He further asserts that students can be just as intolerant and capable of poor judgment as members of other groups and that there is no reason therefore to grant them special powers. He offers a similar kind of argument with regard to student demands for particular courses. If students want a particular course, this is something which needs to be considered but not necessarily granted.

Having suggested the limitations of student power, Frankel then advocates strengthening procedures for consultation between faculty and student groups. He supports a continuing scrutiny of the curriculum and points out how such a thoughtful scrutiny is not compatible with mass meetings, demonstrations, and pressure techniques for getting changes.

Frankel points out that if communication were opened up and students had more contact with administrators and presidents as well as faculty members, the kinds of alliances which were formed might be surprising. He anticipates that students would find more support from deans regarding classroom reform than they would from faculty members themselves simply because deans do not regularly participate in classrooms.

Frankel's attitudes about the university as an organization vis-á-vis other kinds of organizations are especially important to consider in light of student demands for a more democratic set of procedures. Frankel argues that to generalize from industrial or other kinds of organizations to university organization is to ignore the fallacy inherent in reasoning by analogy. Although the university and industrial organization are similar in some ways, they are also different in important ways. The factory product is a corporate product to which individuals contribute, but the university offers many separate individual products for which corporate arrangements simply provide protection and support. In this connection Frankel questions whether the use of a hierarchical form of organization does not constitute an abuse of democracy. He argues that "the egalitarian ideal does not apply across the board in universities any more than it does in any other field where skill is the essence of the issue. To suggest that it should is to make hash of the idea of learning. If there is a case to be made for student participation in the higher reaches of university government, therefore, it is a case that is not based upon *rights*, but upon considerations of good educational administrative practice." This then generates a further question regarding the role of such groups as trustees in the governing of the university. The trustees have long constituted a natural target for students who feel themselves to be puppets on a string and part of a large impersonal bureaucratic structure over which they have no control.

In response to the position advocated by Goodman, Frankel is willing to at least explore what might happen if trustees simply relegated themselves to the role of fund raisers and kept out of everything else. His position is that this would not be a favorable development because trustees do act as buffers of the university against outside pressures.

Although Frankel's view is a more conservative one than Goodman's it certainly does acknowledge the need for certain reforms in the decision-making and power structures of the university. There is certainly no unanimity of opinion, either on American campuses or within the broader society, that there is increased need for shared decision-making and greater power distribution. At this point in history, there is a widely shared view within society that students have gone too far in their demands, and that administrators have been too compliant and conciliatory.

The "No Exit" Theory of Social Change

The process by which social change occurs in a campus context is a continued matter of puzzlement. It is necessary for us to enhance our understanding of this phenomenon for both basic and applied reasons. In attempting to fuse the aims of a mental health program with educational aims and to enlist the cooperation of others on the college campus in developing a community oriented program, attention must be given to the process by which changes are adopted. Without attempting a complete review of existing theories of social change, a few comments are in order regarding the disaster theory of change. As the title suggests, this particular theory proposes that

social changes will occur only after there has been some major calamity which results in a closer scrutiny of the issues leading to the calamity and to consequent changes which might not have occurred in the absence of the given calamity.

Sometimes issues do not need to reach the stage of calamity or disaster before social changes occur. Because of human complexity, individuals and groups sometimes do project ahead and anticipate the possibility of impending disaster if action is not taken. Although the changes which are needed are inevitably resisted, they may come to be regarded as the best of various unsatisfactory alternatives. Decision makers may come to feel that they have no alternative except to change; this we might call the "no exit" theory of change. Even under this circumstance we do observe that some groups anticipate disasters and yet do nothing. Perhaps this is one occasion in which we need to differentiate among various levels of psychopathology in groups and to propose that less healthy groups are more likely to ignore the threat and let disaster happen. Research reported by Leventhal (1967) regarding responses of smokers of varying levels of self-esteem to movies about the hazards of cigarette smoking is relevant in this connection. Leventhal found that high self-esteem subjects were more openly fearful as a result of the threatening movies whereas low self-esteem subjects showed less immediate manifest fear and only indicated their fear at a later time. To ignore real danger is an inappropriate response which is linked to more serious kinds of psychopathology. This too can occur in pathological social systems.

It is sometimes the case that administrative decision-makers come to regard changes as necessary because they will suffer more in the absence of change. For example, student protests on college campuses have generated concerns in administrators about the methods by which the protesting students may be managed. In their assaults upon administrators, students sometimes indicate that administrators do not care, and cite inadequate teacher-student ratios or inadequate student counseling services as illustrative of administrators' lack of concern. This may place the administrator in a dilemma. He may feel frightened by the student protest and take it as an indication of student anger and discontent, but may regard the unrest as a sign that more attention is needed to students' personal lives.

A counseling center may be regarded as having primarily an emergency function for only the most needy students and administrators may not feel prepared or inclined to support broader programs for a wider range of students. However, it may become reasonable to administrators that if student personnel services were more adequate the students might not be so discontented and the likelihood of their continuing to rebel would be lessened. Features of the social system itself also need to be considered in weighing whether administrative decisions will be made in the direction of desirable change or will continue to support an unsatisfactory status quo. In a more open system students may use the student newspaper and methods of public discussion in order to publicize the issues and confront administrators. This in turn might lead to the local community's becoming aware of these issues and to other newspapers' reporting details of the conflict. Since no college which values its standing wants to be regarded as neglectful of its students, their open expressions of discontent may be seen as embarrassing and may cause administrative decision-makers to feel that they might lose "face" by not changing.

In an academic community, an additional factor is that a great deal of premium is placed upon "the truth" and upon "what is right." One of the aims of higher education is typically regarded as development of a certain kind of intellectual and moral integrity. Thus, in a situation of confrontation such as the one being described, administrators may not feel very comfortable in ignoring the issues especially when they are phrased by students as falling within the realms of truth and integrity.

Thus the "no exit" theory of change being described involves broad assessment of both personality and social system variables as well as a specific understanding of system participants' views of the meaning of change and no-change circumstances. The present theory suggests that changes are most likely to take place in social systems when system decision-makers decide that more is to be lost by maintaining the status quo than by changing. Thus there is no alternative but to change.

The Role of the Mental Health Professional

During recent campus uprisings mental health professionals have not been utilized as fully as they might be. Neither have they been consulted regarding possible solutions to problems of campus unrest nor have they thought of themselves in many instances as being able either to provide special understanding in dealing with campus unrest or to suggest changes that would provide more long-term solutions. The fact that campus mental health professionals have been utilized so little in recent campus uprisings raises some fundamental questions both about their ability to make useful contributions and about the way in which they are perceived. First, it needs to be acknowledged that the training and orientation of campus mental health professionals has heretofore been that of counselors to students. Their self-perceptions have generally not been those of mental health consultants. They have not regarded themselves as being able to offer useful consultation regarding structural and administrative arrangements, such as an industrial psychologist might provide to a company with whom he was consulting.

Furthermore, campus mental health professionals have operated from a shaky power base. They have been typically regarded as necessary "company employees" who will deal with student problems about which other people are fearful and uncomfortable. The anonymity of their work has also been a factor in their being so poorly visible and somewhat taken for granted. On many American campuses today administrators consider themselves fortunate that they have a mental health professional at all to counsel students, since many campuses still do not provide even this basic function. Thus, the mental health professional has not perceived himself as possessing the necessary expertise to help with recent campus problems nor has he been perceived by others on campus as one to whom they might turn for special help. Training for campus mental health professionals needs to be thoroughly revamped and it must become much more global and all-encompassing than has been the case in the past.

Since there are such divided opinions about the kinds of changes needed on college campuses at the present time, a further question arises regarding the most suitable stance to be taken by the mental health professional when he is consulted. Do we need to rely on centralization of authority and concentration of power at the top or are new forms of organization and leadership necessary if progress is to be made?

Bennis (1968) has clearly expressed the kind of leadership which this author envisions as being increasingly necessary on college campuses. He describes it as "an active method for producing conditions where people and ideas and resources can be seeded, cultivated, and integrated to optimum effectiveness and growth." Further, the kind of leadership which Bennis' ideal leader would possess includes four important sets of competencies:

1. Knowledge of large, complex human systems;
2. Practical theories of intervening and guiding these systems; theories that encompass methods for seeding, nurturing, and integrating individuals and groups;
3. Interpersonal competence, particularly the sensitivity to understand the effects of one's own behavior on others; how one's own personality shapes his particular leadership style and value system; and,
4. A set of values and competencies which enables one to know when to confront and attack, if necessary, and when to support and provide the psychological safety so necessary for growth.

Past conceptions of leadership have been either too rigidly autocratic or compulsively group-decision oriented. Bennis' model is far more flexible and necessary to meet the challenging issues currently arising on the American campus scene.

ALTERNATIVE ADMINISTRATIVE STRUCTURES FOR STUDENT SERVICES

Prior to formal establishment of a service for helping persons with emotional problems, a variety of informal arrangements may be observed. They may include having a member of the psychology department or someone else on the college staff set aside a portion of his time for work with students. Sometimes the clergyman on campus will do a great deal of counseling. The nature of the administrative arrangements under which mental health services are organized and operated in colleges and universities is, of course, closely related to their programs and problems as well as the institutional structure. There are three formally established types of organizational arrangements in campus counseling or mental

health services. One arrangement is to have a counseling service administratively under the dean of students. An alternative is to have the mental health professionals appended to the student health service, with a psychiatrist directly responsible to the director of student health who in turn reports to the college president. The health service arrangement is more likely to be in existence where the mental health specialist is a psychiatrist rather than a counseling or clinical psychologist. The third alternative seen typically in larger universities has both administrative arrangements existing side by side. Some mental health professionals are organized in a counseling center and report to the dean of students whereas others are in health service and report to the director of health services. When asked to describe how staff members in administrative services differentiate as to when a student goes to the health services and when he goes to the counseling service, three kinds of reasons are typically given. In order for a student to be referred to the health service, (a) he may need drugs; (b) his difficulty may be considered more severe rather than less severe; and (c) some possibility of hospitalization may be envisioned.

Where the director of the counseling center reports administratively to the dean of students, there often tends to be a minimization of the severity of student problems and an effort to keep the mental health professional's function clearly and narrowly delineated. In such a context, a seriously disturbed student is likely to be advised to drop out of school, rather than be treated on campus. Implicit in this particular model of functioning is the assumption that emotional disturbance is threatening and that major emotional upsets thus justify extreme precautionary measures.

The circumstance in which mental health professionals are part of the health service may afford the possibility of greater autonomy and ability to influence the rest of the campus community, if the health service director supports the mental health program solidly and helps to gain sanction for more widespread influence attempts by the mental health staff.

The third pattern described, in which both a counseling center and a psychiatric service exist separately on the same college campus, makes more historical sense than administrative sense. In part, it grows out of the fact that the mental health function has been seen as part of a student personnel function, and as such is relegated to the dean of students. In part, it grows out of a more recently developed set of needs on college campuses to have some provision made for students in acute crises. In these circumstances, it has been commonly assumed by lay administrators that these matters are part of the medical province and that psychiatrists are needed. At best then, the counseling center and mental health service exist in parallel rather than cooperating closely while pursuing some unified plan.

Although all three alternatives are viable and work with varying degrees of effectiveness, it is believed that the most effective pattern is one in which the director of mental health services reports directly to the college president and is autonomous of any control from deans of students or deans of faculty. In this way, he can have more free access to all members of the college campus community and in time may be able to develop a consultative relationship with the college president.

If the mental health professions are complementary, then there is value in having members of various specialties on the mental health staff. In view of the considerations previously discussed with regard to the attitudes of the academic community toward service oriented personnel, it is also important that teaching and research functions of the mental health staff be emphasized. The person selected as director and his staff should be capable of holding an academic appointment and should have some time for teaching, writing, and research. This is important not only from the point of view of establishing lines of communication with other members of the academic community but also in terms of the needs of mental health personnel themselves. Mental health services on college campuses are besieged with requests for student help, and professional personnel can be burdened unduly unless afforded time for a variety of services to the academic community.

Although it is not typically the case, some mental health services also provide help to the faculty members and other members of the community in addition to students. Obviously, consideration needs to be given to this as part of any community oriented plan. If it is not feasible for counseling center staff to offer such service on the college campus, efforts should be made on the part of campus mental health professionals to insure that the college's insurance policy for members of the faculty and administration covers services for help on a private basis for emotional problems. Where it is possible, it is obviously desirable to have some services to faculty and administrative members available on campus for short-term issues and to have insurance policies which will enable these personnel to get help off campus for more long-term problems. Mental health problems on college campuses are often discussed strictly as student problems rather than as pertaining to all members of the community. This is part of a denial pattern which typically exists and which the mental health professional must take some action in changing.

Mental health professionals must take seriously a professional role definition based on the scientist-professional model. In addition to being appointed faculty members, mental health staff members need to be involved in research regarding student problems as well as problems of the community at large. When mental health staff are incorporated into the structure of the academic community in this way, they can best serve the needs and purposes of the administration, faculty, students, and community at large.

COMMUNITY ORIENTED APPROACHES TO CAMPUS PROGRAMS

The task of the mental health professional on the college campus is often regarded by campus administrators as involving only students. Once the mental health professional's role definition has been broadened so that he considers it necessary to work with all institutional participants as part of a total social system, certain consequences for action become evident. These include the necessity of (a) developing consultative relationships with a wide range of institutional participants, (b) understanding possible existing relationships with formal and informal campus groups as well as what might be desirable, and (c) learning to utilize social science findings and methods in approaching large scale campus problems. Within the present section, each of these three issues will be explored in terms of its potentiality for enhancing the scope and effectiveness of the mental health professional's efforts.

Mental Health Consultation

Caplan's (1964) work is a pioneering contribution in the area of consultation. However, his writings generally begin at a point where a contract has been negotiated with a particular agency regarding the manner in which consultation will be conducted. Little attention has been given to the process of preparing members of an institution to utilize consultative relationships, rather than simply making referrals.

Resistance to Consultation

Within higher educational settings, there are established ways of viewing the educational process which do not fit especially well with the development of consultative relationships. For one thing, most participants assume that the goal of the institution is cognitive learning, and that there are a few people around who need to be concerned about nonintellectual functions. In order for mental health consultation to be accepted, this gap must be bridged so that consultation becomes a relevant activity. According to Caplan, respect and trust must be gained if the consultant is to be effective in offering his consultation services. However, at an earlier level, there is a previous kind of trust and respect that must be developed if others are going to entertain the possibility that the mental health professional might be capable of offering any kind of consultation.

Unique Features of the College Setting

There are special ways in which the consultant needs to move based upon the fact that he is in a higher educational context rather than in some other kind of educational or community system. The college professor has much more autonomy than a high school or an elementary school teacher.

Another point of difference is that the consultant in a primary or secondary setting is seen by consultees as having high status but the college professor is less likely to see the mental health professional as a high status expert. The model of consultation derived from public health settings in which psychologists and psychiatrists have consulted with nurses is more likely to be applicable to primary and secondary settings than to the college setting.

Related to these considerations is the matter of the professor's demand for a certain amount of freedom and his insistence that he be able to pursue his search for truth with a degree of detachment from certain day-to-day realities. Although this stereotype of the professor can be overdrawn, it is understood by scholars that they need to protect themselves from becoming fragmented in terms of varying demands being made on them if they are to engage in sustained work within a given area of knowledge. This is necessary to understand in considering the professor's attitude toward the possibility of collaborating with mental health professionals concerning his students. The professor may regard this as an encroachment upon his time rather than as an asset to him. Thus, when mental health professionals offer consultation to faculty members regarding students, faculty members often do not avail themselves of this opportunity.

In a previous article (Brigante, 1965) it was pointed out that both mental health personnel and academicians may develop false perceptions about each other and consequently fail to establish communication. When this occurs, there is no opportunity for mental health personnel to share their goals within the college. Various misperceptions which academicians develop toward mental health programs on college campuses can be enumerated.

1. The mental health program may be regarded as being inconsistent with the goals of education. Sometimes it is suggested that whereas educators seek to help students become autonomous, mental health professonals cater to students' dependency. A related accusation is that educators seek to foster self-discipline whereas therapy and counseling procedures cater to excessive emotionality and a failure to use intellectual resources fully.

2. Another erroneous perception of campus mental health programs is that they are focused upon preparing the student for the educational process, rather than being a central part of the process itself. Specifically, it is assumed that the mental health professional's task is that of helping the student reach the point where he can profit from his education, rather than regarding the self-understanding a student gains in any therapeutic relationship as an aspect of education.

3. In academic communities, where a great premium is based upon the accrual of new knowledge, it is often the case that mental health

personnel are perceived simply as service-oriented "do-gooders." Activities of mental health personnel sometimes conform to this pattern, thus lending some veridicality to the stereotype.

4. On every college campus, many academic and administrative personnel help students with their personal questions. Many of these persons assume that mental health professionals are of the opinion that they have the only legitimate title to deal with human relations problems. Sometimes mental health workers contribute to this perception by defining their roles as experts in such a way as to exclude others who have important contributions to make, rather than including them. This, of course, is both unfortunate and unwise.

5. Another stereotype of the mental health professional is one which depicts him as regarding the campus as a hotbed of psychopathology. Thus, he is seen as regarding everyone as a "case" or as a "potential case." Mass testing procedures used by mental health facilities which focus primarily on psychopathology help to foster such a perception. Another aspect of the same issue has to do with the misunderstanding that mental health professionals work primarily with the emotionally disturbed, underachieving, or low ability subgroups.

6. Academicians sometimes think that mental health professionals regard every problem as reducible to some inner difficulty, generally traceable to the person's past. A psychologist may thus be seen as misunderstanding philosophy, literature, and the arts by considering them to be derivatives of inner difficulties. From the vantage point of developing mutual trust and respect between mental health professionals and academicians, this is an extremely damaging assumption for academicians to make, and for some mental health professionals to corroborate.

The mental health professional's awareness of such stereotypes may contribute further difficulties if he begins to perceive himself as an underdog who is battling the rest of the academic community for "a place in the sun." Thus, he is likely to behave like an underdog, to his ultimate detriment. One consequence is that he may attract and be attracted to fringe members of the academic community, further enhancing his own perception that he it an outsider and generating this perception in others. Also, he may align himself with students against the faculty and administration, and may look to students to represent the mental health cause. On many college campuses today, mental health professionals do find themselves aligned with students and with the fringe members of the campus community. This is related to the fact that their function is perceived as marginal and is regarded with some uneasiness by many campus administrators and faculty members.

Initial Kinds of Consultation

In order to make good use of human resources on the campus and in terms of his own role definition, the community mental health specialist may try to reduce the need for direct help by offering consultation to selected intermediaries, such as dorm counselors. However much sense such a consultation program may make in terms of logistics, the campus setting may present difficulties in its implementation. Other college personnel may bring pressure to bear on the consultant to accept referrals himself rather than expecting themselves to help students with consultative help. The dorm counselors themselves may experience role conflict since they are themselves often graduate students who identify with both undergraduates and full time administrators.

It may be made clear to the consultant that he would not have been consulted in the first place if he were not expected to see the student in question. If no prior contract about the nature of the consultative relationship has been made, the community mental health specialist is not in a very good position at the time when he is coping with the consultee's anxiety about the case to negotiate the contract itself. Further, the person requesting help may be a peer or superior in the hiearchy who has used a referral procedure over a period of years. As an insider rather than a consultant who comes as an expert from outside, the community specialist therefore may well feel greater pressures to accept the referral rather than to try to maintain a consulting relationship.

In the early phases of program development, however, there will be opportunities for case centered consultation. In such instances where it is requested, it is important the consultant check back and get follow-up information about the consultation. It is important in such instances that the consultant freely admit the vagueness of his perceptions where they are vague and not try to make expert pronouncements when he is on shaky ground or lacking information. At first he will be tested with extremely difficult cases, and it is important for him not to fall into the trap of offering magical formulas which promise quick cures.

As confidence in the mental health specialist grows in the community, further requests for consultation may follow in the form of program-centered administrative consultation, and consultation to groups. A dean, for example, may be concerned about revising procedures for picking student upper class sponsors, and may wonder whether there are any more systematic personality evaluations which might be done. At times of crisis, students, faculty and administrators may all be involved in managing a particularly upset student, and the consultant may need to provide assistance to all persons involved. When the persons are themselves in disagreement the consultant must be fully aware of such complexity. It is important that he do extensive enough interviewing without making commitments in any particular direction so that he has some full grasp of the relationships of the persons involved to the point where he does not further add to the confusion. This particular kind of consultation requires a great deal of sensitivity and an ability to make fairly accurate inferences based upon very minimal cues. It is one of the most challenging forms of consultation in that impressions must be gained rapidly and decisions made because of the critical nature of the situation itself.

Relations to Campus Groups

Mayo and Klein (1964) have discussed the need for the mental health specialist to consider carefully the role he takes in each community group according to its particular functions and purposes. In some groups he might find himself a resource person and in others a listener, while in still others a kind of opinion molder or catalyst. In any case he must not slip into the role of group therapist or let others put him into that role when in fact the purposes of the group are other than therapeutic and the persons involved are colleagues.

Although there are no pat rules for the mental health specialist in group situations, some general statements may be made. All that he has learned about human behavior in group situations does have relevance to his assessment of what is happening in community groups in which he is a

participant. He may find, for example, that because of his relatively low status in a particular group, the group is not able to use his expertise in areas where it might otherwise do so. Here, he will need to make a decision about his behavior. In the long run, it is probably better to respect existing structures and the persons who have defined their roles in particular ways if one is ever to gain a hearing.

It is possible, and, in this author's opinion, desirable, to participate in selected public meetings. A chapel talk may allow the community mental health specialist to communicate some of his values without interfering with effective enactment of his professional role. In meeting with parents or alumni who are concerned about issues on campus, he may serve as a mediator between the students and these concerned others. If he does it judiciously, it will be possible for him to express both sides of the issues about which there is controversy when talking to parents or alumni in a way which will enhance their understanding of students' attitudes.

When meeting with faculty groups it is important that the community mental health specialist use the situation to develop mutually good relationships. Since he sees the students in a different context, he may be able to offer insights about their behavior which are not apparent to faculty members. One of the luxuries of the mental health specialist's role is that he does not have administrative or grading responsibility, and therefore may more naturally see students as they are.

Mental Health Education

Attention needs to be given to the way in which education about mental health now occurs on college campuses. Psychology is often linked to mental health in students' minds, and psychology courses are taken as an index of what mental health is all about. Psychologists may be regarded as examples of what mental health professionals are like. Experiences in psychology courses can thus have a generalized effect upon attitudes about seeking help for emotional difficulties. In addition, contacts with other mental health professionals and with counseling centers, even if only for vocational reasons, are always relevant to attitudes established about the entire field of mental health.

Students are extremely curious about what goes on behind a closed door when another student and a mental health professional talk together, if only about a vocational test result. Students often quiz each other at great lengths about initial contacts with counseling center personnel and in many instances make their own decisions about seeking help on the basis of such inquiries.

Experience with mass testing programs is also incorporated in students' perceptions of mental health professionals and of their roles. The kinds of tests given and students' feelings and attitudes about such tests may become linked to a generalized perception of the entire field of mental health.

An effective counseling center is the most powerful means of mental health education on any college campus. In terms of help given when it is sought, and in terms of conditioning people to seek needed help at later times, the effects of a few counseling center contacts cannot be minimized.

Innovative Approaches

Within the broader society, there have been various recent innovations in mental health approaches which are also assuming an important place in campus programs. One of the most significant of these is the encounter group movement. This particular approach includes various powerful appeals to college students. The intensity of interaction and emphasis upon open expression of feelings which are a part of such groups are consistent with college students' values. As is well known, their complaints about the sterility of education are based upon its excessive emphasis upon intellect and a concomitant absence of feeling. Encounter groups are seen as offering a way of enhancing one's sense of personal freedom without use of drugs. In addition, one need not adopt a sick role in order to join an encounter group, in contrast to a therapy group. All of these features of the encounter group movement argue for its increasing importance on college campuses, as well as within the broader society.

Other specific innovations have also begun to assume a place on college campuses. The propagation of suicide prevention centers and hot-lines throughout the country has emphasized the importance of offering twenty-four-hour services as part of any comprehensive mental health approach. On college campuses, students often develop stress reactions which make such services especially desirable. Campus mental health professionals are also increasingly willing to meet with students in dorm lounges, rather than always expecting students to seek help by coming to the counseling center.

One innovative long-term effort to demonstrate the ways in which the public health model can be applied to the study and design of mental health programs on college campuses has been carried out at the University of Florida under the leadership of Barger (1963). One issue concerned the identification of students who have emotional disorders or who may develop emotional difficulties during their college careers. Three methods of identification were explored.

The first utilized clues gained from initial physical examinations of students. Students who had psychiatric histories were routinely seen by a mental health professional before they had completed registration. Second, the Minnesota Multiphasic Personality Inventory was administered to all new students to assess its role as a screening device. If ten percent of the profiles were deviant in a population of 3,000 students, this meant 300 students would immediately be considered as needful of some sort of help.

A pilot study was conducted in which students who had deviant profiles were contacted in order to explore the feasibility of providing help to them at various points in their college careers. It was found within this group of students that approximately one third wanted help; one third came for a single interview but tended to see no problems; and another one third had negative reactions to having been contacted for an interview.

A related study focused on use of Residence Hall Counselors who had been advised of the students who had deviant profiles. Some students responded favorably to being contacted by counselors but many exhibited no difficulties and others turned out to be troubled who did not show deviant profiles.

As a result of these pilot studies, Barger and his coinvestigators expressed skepticism about campus screening programs aimed at early detection. Such efforts are uneconomical of staff time since three people are seen for every one who is actually ready for treatment. In this connection, treatment is typically more rapid and effective when the person is experiencing some degree of distress. Also, a stream of voluntary referrals is likely to fill up staff schedules. A suggested alternative was that efforts be made to establish effective communication networks involving members of the mental health service, the counseling center, the infirmary, the students' residence counselors, the university ministers, and all campus personnel who have some direct contact with students. They suggest that the three most crucial groups are the residence hall staffs, the academic counselors, and faculty members. Based on this particular conclusion, they have tried to increase the sophistication of student advisors by conducting discussions concerned with symptoms of emotional disturbance, operations of the mental health service on campus, and methods of seeking consultation and making referrals.

Early Intervention Studies

Both at the elementary and college levels some research has been carried out in an effort to define the techniques for identifying emotionally disturbed students at time of entry into a particular educational system. At the elementary level, Cowen, Zax, Izzo, and Trost (1966) have conducted a number of studies which give clear indication that such early identification procedures are possible. At the college level, similar studies have also been conducted. In addition to the work of Barger cited earlier, Kleinmuntz (1961) has tried to develop a short form of the M.M.P.I. for identifying potentially disturbed students. Although both these investigators indicate that the use of either one or a combination of techniques make such early identification possible, the more thorny issues arise with regard to the possible use of such instruments in any kind of action program. A study by Spielberger, Weitz, and Denny (1962) generally corroborates the impressions of Barger in pointing to the difficulties of intervening with people with emotional difficulty before they are ready. In Spielberger's study, the American Council on Education Psychological Examination was given together with a modified form of the M.M.P.I. to all entering freshmen at Duke in the fall of 1959. Then, using the M.M.P.I. data in order to derive an anxiety measure, a sample of male liberal arts freshmen with high anxiety scores were offered group counseling. Only half of the students invited actually agreed to participate and only a third of those who volunteered attended a sufficient number of sessions to derive any benefit from the program. The investigators concluded that counseling may not be a generally applicable procedure for the prevention of under-achievement or academic failure. Perhaps the issue does not have to do with the efficacy of group counseling, but rather with the emotional readiness of the students to accept any kind of intervention procedure at that particular point in time. In any case, studies such as this indicate the difficulties which are encountered when actual intervention programs are attempted and thus have a good deal of merit. Future preventive programs need to build on the results of these findings.

In order to analyze the impact of the college environment upon students, several lines of study have been undertaken by the Barger group. One research project has been utilizing the work of Pace (1967) to ascertain ways in which the students evaluate the college context. The investigator's hypothesis is that the ease with which a student adapts to a university setting is related to the degree to which he shares the dominant values, attitudes, and behavior patterns of the campus community. Another line of study is concerned with the issue of continuity from high school to college. Some students find the freshman semester at college especially difficult and the transition between high school and college is perceived as quite abrupt. In this connection, the investigators have tried a combined approach involving an orientation program for students and for parents in an attempt to communicate (1) the concepts of early identification and early intervention, (2) the fact that it is common for the college student to develop needs for help, (3) the nature of the helping resources that are available, (4) the real interests that college personnel have in helping students understand themselves, and (5) some of the common sources of distress and discomfort they might be experiencing.

In the communications with parents an effort was made to enhance parents' understandings of the stresses of college life and of adolescence so that parents might become more alert to signs of difficulty. In implementing such a program, the investigators continue to be troubled by the fears which many students have about the adequacy of the available helping services and the fact that many students are not really sure when some sort of help is indicated.

Regarding the impact of the college environment, other studies reported by Pace are also potentially significant. For example, a study done at the University of California at Riverside was concerned with students' attitudes toward their scholastic. environment as they perceived it. In addition to having 50 students respond to CUES (College and University Environmental Scales) in regular fashion, 25 of them responded additionally by marking items on a five point scale to indicate whether they considered them unimportant and 25 students responded also on a five point scale on a like-dislike basis. Results indicated that students would like an environment in which scholarship and propriety scores were lower but awareness was much higher than the CUES profile actually shows it to be. Thus, they prefer more emphasis to be placed upon concern for societal issues and aesthetic sensitivities but less emphasis upon competitive academic achievement and propriety.

In another study done at Pepperdine College, subjects were asked to respond to CUES in the regular way and then to indicate what their ideal responses might be. Results for the ideal selections depicted a college that would be high on scholarship, awareness, and community scales and moderately high on practicality and propriety scales. The large discrepancies between real and ideal scores on the dimensions of scholarship and awareness were used as basis for discussions by faculty and administrative personnel regarding the nature of the college and its directions. In a third study CUES was administered to incoming freshmen of ten different colleges during orientation week. The results generally indicated that there was a vast gulf between their expectations about the campus environment and the reality. In only two of 50 comparisons were the scores for expected and actual environments within two points of each other and in only nine of the comparisons were they within four points of each other.

In preventing students' immediate disgruntlement regarding the nature of the college as opposed to their expectations, this study certainly has important action implications. Generally speaking, Pace's instrument and the ideas it generates open up new vistas for obtaining quantitative measurements of the nature of campus environments and the exploration of hypotheses regarding these environments. On the basis of the evidence he cites, Pace certainly seems justified in his conclusion that the concept of campus atmosphere is one which is generally buttressed by substantial evidence of concurrent and construct validity.

Attention also needs to be given to the potentialities of an instrument recently developed by Halpin (1966), in his attempt to measure the organizational climate of primary and secondary schools. Called the Organizational Climate Description Questionnaire, it is considered in this context because of its sophistication in theoretical conception and the possibility that with modifications it could be used in assessing the climate of small colleges. The scale consists of 64 Likert-type items which can be administered to teachers and principals in a group setting and requires approximately 30 minutes to take. Test results may be considered in terms of eight subtests, four of which are concerned with characteristics of the group and the other four with the behavior of the leader. On the basis of group and leader characteristics, six climates are able to be identified. They range from the open climate at one extreme which is characterized by functional flexibility, to the closed climate at the other extreme characterized by functional rigidity. The continuum of climates can be described as (a) open, (b) autonomous, (c) controlled, (d) familiar, (e) paternal, and (f) closed. Like Pace's instrument, this measure also is regarded as having exciting possibilities for studying issues related to characteristics of scholastic environments.

EFFECTIVE USE OF HUMAN RESOURCES

It is a relatively new development for campus community members to consider the emotional lives of students in connection with educational aims. Many campuses now have mental health professionals within the campus community and a few show great concern about students' emotional needs. However, there are still many campuses where no recognition is given to the emotional needs of students. In view of the degree of ferment now taking place on American campuses with regard to the lack of student need fulfillment, it is time to consider the range of human resources available to meet these needs.

Since we are interested in campus communities in toto, human resources must be examined with regard to the needs of all campus community members. It may be argued that we have no way of meeting the ever-growing student demands for help, much less the emotional needs of faculty and administrators, as well as all workers in the campus community. In support of this particular position, studies such as the recent work of Weiss, Segal, and Sokol (1965) at Dartmouth College may be cited. These investigators found in an epidemiological study that the number of freshman students admitted between the years of 1958 and 1962 who showed overt emotional disturbance rose from 6.9 percent to 16.2 percent, a finding consistent with the recent impressions of student personnel workers.

It is this author's belief that we are now in a position to set forth a plan which can provide for the emotional growth and development of all campus participants. No broad sweeping increments in mental health professionals will be required to implement this plan, but instead there needs to be a more judicious use of resources already available. For such a plan to take shape, members of the campus community must acknowledge the relationship between intellectual and emotional development, as far as faculty members and administrators are concerned, as well as for students. Thus, the two issues to be considered concern the nature of the plan and the development of the acceptance necessary within a campus community context for members to commit themselves to change.

The present section deals only with the emotional development of students. The conflicts with which college students struggle are primarily manifestations of a developmental process and typically not an expression of emotional disorder. This point of view makes no effort to minimize the extent of the college students' struggles. Many college students typically meet and resolve a variety of emotional difficulties without professional help.

Interactions of the emotional needs of students and attitudes of relevant administrators must be understood. Protests are partly an expression of students' wishes to have their needs fully recognized, rather than playing along with requirements and hurdles in the academic obstacle course. Not only have faculty and administrative personnel ignored students' emotional conflicts but the students themselves have tended to conceal their conflicts unless they became so severe that they no longer could be hidden. In a paper on student alienation, Halleck (1967) has commented on the viewpoint that intellectual development is the province of the professor, but that emotional needs must be handled by another class of specialists. To begin to describe possibilities for change, role definitions of people involved with students must be considered.

The Faculty Member's Role

When faculty members combine vitality and competence in their specialty with an ability to be human, students flock to them. This kind of faculty member is infrequently encountered. There are factors in the faculty members' training as well as forces within their professional lives which contribute to this state of affairs.

First consider the faculty member's experience as a graduate student. Graduate experience is often characterized by sustained periods of isolated work, reduced human contact, uncertain knowledge of one's progress, and often a lack of definite time boundaries to delineate the beginning and end of the process.

Since graduate education is centered upon a kind of intellectual mastery students often adopt obsessive strategies as a way of coping. After a prolonged period of total immersion in subject matter and a lack of training in education and human relations, the graduate student becomes a professor who now occupies a crucial position in the lives of other students. Fortunately, some faculty members do remember their own needs as undergraduates, and try to rise to the challenge of "meeting students where they live." Many do not, however, and simply define the educational process as concerned with cognitive reorganization.

The educational institution may support this definition of the educational process by rewarding faculty members only for demonstrated intellectual productivity regardless of other attributes. Time spent with students is perceived by faculty members as interfering with their own progress within the university.

The College President

The college president's role also interferes with the development of an optimal kind of relationship with students. A large portion of the president's time is spent off campus and in the role of a college representative to the external world. Internal affairs, especially those pertaining to students, need to be delegated if the college president is to cope with his responsibilities off campus as well as within the life of the college itself. As a result, even in a small college setting, a student sees the president as a figure who has no personal meaning rather than as a leader in an educational enterprise with whom one can have some sort of direct relationship. From the college president's point of view his role demands cause him to become out of touch with student culture. As difficulties arise, he may find himself relying more and more on the opinions of his staff members in understanding these developments rather than making his own evaluations.

Trustees

With regard to trustees, the usual situation is for students to have no contact with trustees and to have little appreciation for the vital role trustees play in shaping college policy. As with the president, the lack of contact between students and trustees goes hand in hand with a lack of any basis for being able to develop a consensus regarding college policies and aims.

Student Personnel Workers

Difficulties faced by professional student personnel workers (deans, vocational counselors, dorm counselors, admissions personnel, and others), in their contacts with students, are not the same as those of the faculty member, college president, or trustee. The student personnel worker often is available to really hear the student but he may feel constrained in his response. As an institutional representative, the student personnel worker must be aware of the attitudes of the persons to whom he is responsible. He may feel that he holds varying degrees of responsibility to the student, the administration, the student's parents, and the community outside the college.

This is especially the case where the student's attitudes conflict with those of the administration and the outside world. Like the clergyman who becomes the pastor of a church, the student personnel worker is ill-equipped by his training to cope with the pressures of his role. Graduate training stresses technical expertise rather than learning about power structures, social systems, and influence processes with which the student personnel worker will be coping once he is on the job.

Clergy

In a way, the clergyman on a campus which is not strictly sectarian or the same denomination as the clergyman's affiliation may be able to define his role with more freedom from strictures than members of other disciplines. His concern about spiritual and personal development does not have to be rationalized or disguised. The difficulties he faces may be defined more in terms of resistances from students rather than from administrators or members of the society at large. Students often stereotype clergymen as being outside the province of concerns that they have during their college years. They may see the clergyman as trying to "sell them a bill of goods" about dogmas that they have already rejected. Clergymen on college campuses have become increasingly sophisticated in their approaches to students in ways which enable them to break through these stereotypes.

Physicians

Constraints on college physicians in terms of developing a broader relationship with students may be imposed by the extensive physical health needs of students on campus. As medical care continues to improve and the general sophistication of the population with regard to health procedures increases, college health services report regular increments in requests for physical care. One result is that the physician has much less time to develop the kind of personal relationship with the students that he might prefer.

As is the case with student personnel workers, the training of physicians does not include preparation for developing a "give and take" kind of relationship with college students. In fact, the reliance of the physician upon authority and his structuring of his own role in those terms may impose special difficulties in developing such relationships.

Mental Health Professionals

In some ways mental health specialists are poorly prepared for their role on campus. A broad understanding of social forces which might come from extensive sociological and anthropological training is typically lacking in the background of members of all mental health specialties. The counseling psychologist may be able to communicate effectively with many students but may lack training which would enable him to recognize and cope with students who have major psychopathology and consequently he may tend to deny severe psychopathology where it really exists. The clinical psychologist's difficulties may be somewhat the reverse. He may be alert to psychopathology but not sufficiently responsive to healthy forces within students. For the psychiatrist, short-term work with students may be alien to his background and experience where he has been trained to work intensively with patients over a period of years. He too is more likely to be sensitive to psychopathology and overlook personality strengths. Social workers may be best equipped by training for work with college students. They work comfortably in supportive roles, move easily into relationships with families and other members of the student's social network, and are realistic about the role of social forces in affecting behavior. Their one problem on campuses might be that they typically do not have doctoral degrees, thus providing the possibility for status distinctions between them and campus professors.

Members of the mental health professions generally have no social relationship with the client and live in a community separate from that of the client. Within a college or campus community the mental health professional will confront the student not only in the office but in a variety of social contexts. They may see each other at football games, at a dance, at a play, or may find themselves in a social conversation at a reception. The mental health professional must be comfortable and flexible in his role. At various times, students in trouble may call him at home or may come to his home. The mental health professional must be available on a 24 hour basis if he is to be really effective in serving the campus community's needs.

These considerations suggest that the mental health professional's personal identity must be well crystallized and he must feel so generally secure that he has no special need to hide behind his professional role and to use it as a way of keeping other people at a distance. In a community role, the professional's own neurotic problems become more visible, and their resolution becomes increasingly important if he is to gain respect and win confidence in his program.

The difficulties of the various educational administrators or professionals in being available to students as helping resources has been explained as a derivative of two sets of circumstances. One has to do with the nature of training and preparation they have received for assuming their professional role on the college campus, and the other has to do with the systematic factors in higher educational institutions which produce an attitude that defines the emotional development of students as a low priority issue. The next section proposes a series of possible changes.

A FIVE-POINT PROGRAM FOR CHANGE

If the foregoing assessment of the deterrents to more effective relationships is correct, it also implies directions for seeking remedies. At least five solutions may be suggested as a basis for enhancing the emotional availability of campus personnel to students.

First, changes in the training programs for the various college related disciplines must be accomplished. Grade and high school teachers are required to have direct preparation in teaching whereas college professors are not. At all levels of education, teachers must increase their self-awareness as a basis for understanding others. In many respects the programs continue to emphasize technique rather than a broadening of personal awareness. The same can be said with regard to student personnel workers.

The training of physicians generally includes some broad experience with psychiatry. However, the stress is often upon learning about oneself as a way of understanding others. Unfortunately, throughout the education and service professions, training is largely didactic and fails to emphasize personal growth through individual and group change methods. If we are really to make some progress in this area, increased stress must be placed upon the importance of individual and group therapy, as well as upon other methods such as sensitivity training and experience in attempting to help individuals with varying magnitudes of emotional difficulty. Didactic classroom procedures are not adequate to equip those who assume faculty and other responsible roles on college campuses in accord with the desired model.

The effective teacher must learn how to create a classroom climate which fosters learning. This is not to advocate that everyone undergo intensive individual psychotherapy; rather it *is* proposed that methods such as sensitivity training be available to persons who are entering the field of college teaching and that there be support given to having such persons undertake psychotherapy as part of their preparation for their professional roles where it is needed.

Second, the creation of a new kind of school or training program should be organized for those who aspire to college personnel roles to support the previously suggested step. This would include mental health professionals, deans, college physicians, clergy, and selected faculty members who work especially closely with students, as well as college presidents. The school would be analagous to schools of public health where people from varying specialties come together and receive some common training. One of the most important outcomes of this experience would be to lessen the stereotypes which members of the different groups hold about each other. Stereotypes are one of the most powerful divisive factors preventing campus personnel from cooperating more closely in helping students. Achieving closer cooperation cannot be simply a matter of resolve. It must stem from an understanding about the relation of one's own specialty to allied professional groups. The faculty of such a school would necessarily be interdisciplinary, and student personnel workers who are not trained in social science or psychiatry could learn some of the methods and findings of the mental health disciplines in order to improve the effectiveness of their work. By the same token, mental health professionals would come to appreciate what others in helping specialties have learned by ways other than formal training in psychology or psychiatry. The length of training would be from nine months to a year. Participants would constantly be interacting on projects which would require cooperation in order to achieve maximally effective solutions. Such a training program could be part of a graduate school but would need to be a separate program.

Those who completed the training successfully might be awarded a master's degree in student development.

Third, there is an additional need for special institutes for campus personnel. The National Training Laboratories now offer the opportunity for students and faculty members to constitute a group which may meet together as a sensitivity training group during the summer months. This kind of possibility needs to be more widely available throughout the academic year both on and off campus.

Fourth, there is need for self-study groups to provide opportunities for discussing current campus needs and problems. Although such discussions often go on in an informal way on a college campus, there is generally not any opportunity for the kind of discussion which would lead to some kind of consensus about the college's attitude toward such issues. A current example concerns drugs. There is ample discussion taking place on campuses about drugs but generally no clear conceptions emerge with regard to causes for students' gravitation toward drugs, nor is there consensus regarding the remedial steps to be taken. As a result there is widespread concern about increases in drug use, and a feeling that something needs to be done, but no action actually being taken other than to issue warnings to students.

Fifth, a valuable procedure would be an intercampus exchange system among campus personnel. The purpose of the exchange system would be to develop deeper insight about the nature of one's current social system and the problems which arise by having an opportunity to observe others in similar positions on other campuses. For example, campus "A" might have one of its college physicians go to campus "B" to observe the operation of that campus for a few weeks while campus "B" is doing the same with an observer going from there to campus "A." At the end of the time, the observer might give feedback to campus members about his observations. Experimentation with regard to this kind of procedure might well involve both members of the mental health disciplines and those outside that discipline. Some persons outside the mental health specialties might not be effective in these roles whereas others could make real contributions. The issue is one of utilizing outsiders' perceptions in order to gain insights regarding a social system which is new to them. This might help participants in that system to understand the built-in, shared biases which they have come to mutually ignore.

Consideration also needs to be given to the nature of the professor's role requirements as compared with those of the student personnel worker. The professor advances within the system by virtue of publication, signs of recognition outside of his own institution, and in rare instances as a reward for good teaching. To the dean of students or dorm counselor, responsibility and loyalty to the institutional values are more paramount in determining his advancement. Often ignored is the fact that the training of the student personnel worker is almost identical with that of the professor with the exception that there has been more emphasis upon applied activities. However, the student personnel worker, except perhaps for the college physician, is not oriented as much toward research activities as the professor. The point is that for the student personnel worker there is typically no legitimate outlet for pursuing some kind of research or scholarly activity within the academic context. Also, rewards are not present for social supports in the form of sabbaticals or flexible time schedules. He must keep regular hours and he must do things which are not likely to produce controversy. Over time, he may come to believe that he is a second class citizen and that the institution is made for professors and students. Perhaps this is an instance where difficulties start at the top. The college president is himself overworked and does not have a sabbatical leave, nor does he typically have summers free to pursue his own research activities. This inconsistency between the roles of professors and the roles of other qualified scholars may give rise to discontent, especially in persons with high drive and talent.

With regard to the professor's role, he cannot be expected to take extra time working with students if his promotion and professional rewards are to be based on publications. There must be more institutional supports for working with students and taking a heartfelt interest in them.

CONCLUSIONS

Within the preceding section we have set forth a variety of issues which arise when campus mental health programs are defined from a community oriented viewpoint. Perhaps the most significant issue which has emerged in our discussion concerns the relationship between the goals of mental health programs and the aims of education. At first glance it might *seem* that the only issue of conern is one of effecting a changeover from conventional mental health programs to a community oriented approach. More fundamental is the question: *Can a genuine educational community be established?* Within educational settings, students, faculty, and administrators are often widely divergent in terms of their goals and values. The concept of community implies the presence of shared goals and values, and standards which are accepted by community participants and which form an important bond among them. In the absence of an educational community in the sense to which it is being referred here, a campus community mental health program is a rather empty concept. All community participants must be willing to struggle toward the real value consensus which makes a sense of community possible.

Recent outbreaks of violence on American campuses indicate the formidability of such a goal once discontents are more openly acknowledged and expressed. Now that this has occurred, it is unlikely that higher educational systems will be able to revert to their former status quo. The depersonalization of the educational process, compartmentalization of knowledge, and the separation of the cognitive and emotional components of learning as well as numerous other issues are far too salient and explicit as problems to be ignored any longer.

The task is one of finding ways of involving students, faculty, administration, and trustees in these issues in a way that there can be some movement toward constructive change. Throughout recent conflicts, it has been clear that many participants feel an absence of institutional loyalty to the point where there is no basis for a common bond or a common framework in order to provide some basis for negotiation. Instead, institutional loyalty has been supplanted by allegiance to oneself, or in the case of faculty and administrators, to one's own discipline.

Learning how to build an educational community thus becomes the most crucial problem confronting higher education. Certainly the task goes far beyond that which can be accomplished by any single profession. Community mental health specialists face several disadvantages as consensus builders. These include being an insider, suffering from insufficient knowledge about community leadership and social processes to furnish the scope of understanding needed, and having a general lack of expertise as social change agents. If he is to make a real contribution, the community mental health specialist must have a thorough grasp of the conflicts and compatibilities in value systems among students, faculty, and administrators and the broader American culture. Further, he must learn how to use his role to help create a climate in which value conflicts can become a source of important learning for students. The climate which he is working to create will not support or condone violence nor will it require the suppression of real differences.

In part it becomes a matter of using his knowledge of student attitudes as a vehicle for feeding back to the administration and faculty how students are really reacting to their educational experiences. Students have become increasingly vocal of late, in making their attitudes known. How to respond to their expressed discontents has thus become the issue.

The mental health specialist will buttress his position if he supplements his contacts with disturbed students by becoming knowledgeable about the entire college population. Administrators and faculty members are sometimes inclined to discount opinions of mental health specialists because they recognize that the latter base their opinions upon contacts with only a limited sector of the total college population. Further, the community mental health specialist needs to achieve a position of strength and influence within the campus context so that he may raise issues involving value conflicts within the administration and faculty itself. Generally, he must be one person who stands for the value of utilizing conflict as a force for growth. From this point of view, it is important that he communicate to others that he does not seek to create the kind of campus climate in which conflicts and tensions are absent.

He must also dispel the stereotype that his position is always one that places him at the extreme left of the continuum. If he is really to help the university as a growing institution rather than simply having an allegiance to students, then his own position must be so well worked out that his clarity about issues enables him to wade through a morass of opinions and counteropinions. Perhaps the most central position which he must take has to do with the role of the college in fostering individual development. *The mental health specialist must make it one of his aims to develop a consensus regarding the aims of education so that intellectual and emotional development are regarded as part of one process rather than being disparate or antithetical.* He must not be mousetrapped into placing complete emphasis on emotional development, nor must he compromise by putting excessive valuation on cognitive development, as is so often done within educational contexts. Instead he must take a thoroughly defensible position and represent it in such a way that others are increasingly able to accept it.

In a broader sense he can work toward building consensus by making proposals to educational participants which will foster a broader set of allegiances than to themselves or to their own professional disciplines. In this connection, it has been proposed earlier that a school be established which might be attended by various educational participants in order to study campus problems and the problems of developing real campus communities. Interdisciplinary self-study groups might also be effective, using sensitivity training methods.

As long as the competence of the mental health professional is in question regarding his ability to make a contribution to the solution of campus issues, his attempts to influence will be relatively ineffective. Thus, he must proceed from a solid base of competence. This constitutes a challenge to those educational institutions which attempt to train community mental health specialists.

References

Barger, B. The University of Florida Mental Health Program. In B. Barger & E. H. Hall (eds.), "Higher education and mental health." Unpublished manuscript, 1963.

Bennis, W. G. Post-bureaucratic leadership. *Trans-action*, 1969, 6, 44–51, 61.

Brigante, T. R. Opportunities for community mental health training within the residential college campus context. *Community Mental Health Journal*, 1965, 1, 55–60.

Caplan, G. *Principles of preventive psychiatry*. New York: Basic Books, 1964.

Clark, D. S. Prediction of problem behavior in men's residence halls. Unpublished doctoral dissertation, University of Florida, 1963.

Cowen, E. L., Zax, M., Izzo, L. D., & Trost, M. A. Prevention of emotional disorders in the school setting: A further investigation. *Journal of Consulting Psychology*, 1966, 5, 381–387.

Frankel, C. Student power: The rhetoric and possibilities. *Saturday Review*, November 2, 1968.

Goodman, P. Thoughts on Berkeley. In S. M. Lipset & S. S. Wolin (eds.), *The Berkeley student revolt*. Garden City, N. Y.: Doubleday, 1965.

Halleck, S. Psychiatric treatment of the alienated college student. *American Journal of Psychiatry*, 1967, 124, 642–650.

Halpin, A. *Theory and research in administration*. New York: Macmillan, 1967.

Kleinmuntz, B. The College Maladjustment Scale (MT): Norms and predictive validity. *Educational and Psychological Measurement*, 1961, 21, 1029–1033.

Leventhal, H. Fear for your health. *Psychology Today*, 1967, 1(5), 54–58.

Mayo, C., & Klein, D. Group dynamics as a basic process of community psychiatry. In L. Bellak (ed.), *Handbook of community psychiatry and community mental health*. New York: Grune & Stratton, 1964.

Meyerson, M. Address to the American Association of University Professors. *U. B. Alumni News*, 1968, 5, 4–5.

Pace, R. *Analysis of a national sample of college environments*. Washington, D. C.: Bureau of Research, Office of Education, United States Department of Health, Education, and Welfare, 1967.

Spielberger, C. D., Weitz, H., & Denny, J. P. Group counseling the academic performance of anxious college freshmen. *Journal of Counseling Psychology*, 1962. 9, 195–204.

Thompson, W. M. Commencement address to the 1969 Yale University graduating class. *Life*, June 20, 1969, 66.

Weiss, R. J., Segal, B. E., & Sokol, R. Epidemiology of emotional disturbance in a men's college. *Journal of Nervous and Mental Disease*. 1965, 141, 240–250.

24

Parents as Agents of Behavior Change

Leopold O. Walder and Shlomo I. Cohen
with Dennis E. Breiter, Frank C. Warman, David Orme-Johnson, and Stanley Pavey

INTRODUCTION

It is reasonable to suggest that those who have the responsibility for a job be given access to the technical information relevant to that job. Parents do have the responsibility for guiding the behavioral development of their children. This chapter presents a rationale for and a description of some attempts to provide parents with information about the analysis of human behavior and to guide them in the application of operant principles in parent-child relationships. The parents worked with were greatly concerned by their child's undesirable behavioral development. These parents had become ensnared in mutually debilitating and unpleasant relationships with their children.

We believe, in addition to being helpful to parents of quite deviant children, this operant approach is also useful to parents whose children are "normal." Indeed, it might be expected that, if people were taught before they became parents to employ behavior principles or if consultation were available to parents before serious child-rearing problems appeared, this approach would be preventive as well as therapeutic.

When parents seek professional help, they frequently receive services which are inappropriate to their needs (Bandura, 1962). Too often, therapists search for underlying negative motivations rather than offer parents the technical skills needed to handle their problems with children.[1] When improvement does not accompany the treatment, parents are often awarded diagnostic labels. This diagnostic labeling has at least two major effects.

The first effect of such labeling is that it puts the source of the problem *inside* the client (in his mental illness, in his defective or disturbed personality, or even in his unfortunate learning history) rather than in the interaction between the client and his environment. As Szasz (1961) points out, the behavioral difficulties often referred to as mental illness may be more usefully and ethically considered as problems of living. Among reasons for avoiding the illness or medical model of disturbing behavior is that it turns the professional's gaze toward variables which are relatively inaccessible and therefore relatively unchangeable; the problems are attributed to internal physiological, consitutional, genetic, or intrapsychic variables. The professional is thus diverted from the study of organism-environment relations (or problems of living).

The second effect of diagnostic labeling (in this case of the unhelped parent) is that lack of improvement is attributed to the unchangeability of the client rather than to the professional's lack of ability. In this way failures to help parents and children do not adversely affect the professional's self-assessment. Consequently, the professional is not likely to reexamine his techniques as may be warranted by the results he obtains.

The plight of these parents is reflected in the words of a physician who fathered autistic twins. He stated that the parents reap a harvest of blame but not a seed of guidance. There are writers who have complained that the traditional approach to mental health problems has not been adequate (Astin, 1961; Eysenck, 1952). In recent years two new trends in mental health have emerged. One new trend is the community approach to mental health; a second is the application of operant principles to behaviors relevant to mental health. The compatability of these two trends will be discussed.

Stubbs (1963) has maintained that the dichotomy between treatment and prevention is a false one and represents priorities rather than mutually exclusive categories. In this vein much of what is described in the present chapter can be related to the treatment-prevention continuum.

A basic premise of the community mental health movement is that "mental illness" is related to social stress and that individual breakdowns are actually indices of societal problems. Rosen (1958) and Skinner (1971) emphasize that the social environment and not the individual is the patient. Programs of prevention and treatment, therefore, must focus on both the social environment and the patient in that environment. In the analysis of the social environment, the epidemiologist makes his major contribution by focusing attention on those societal factors which appear to influence "mental health." Once this relevant information has been collected, society can plan systematic programs of primary prevention, the aim of which is to reduce the incidence of mental disorder. A society which is unsuccessful in preventing mental disorder (that is, a society which does not control those environmental factors related to the development of behavioral disorder) must adopt strategies of secondary prevention, the aim of which is to reduce the prevalence of mental disorder by shortening the duration of suffering endured by the already established cases. With a failure to accomplish both primary and secondary prevention, society must turn to tertiary prevention, the aim of which is to maintain the individual in his community as a functioning, productive person. All of the aforementioned strategies have been labeled *prevention* (Caplan, 1964), but it is not difficult to see that each is also a form of *treatment*. Any program of prevention/treatment would be more effective if one could involve and rely on the assistance of a broad range of community resources. Utilization of community manpower resources is a second area of concern to the community mental health movement.

A statement of the manpower issue need not be complicated or long. Put very simply, there has not been and presently there is not sufficient professional manpower to aid those who are in need of the professional's skills. To compound this difficulty it should be noted that until recently there has also been a scarcity of educational programs to give caretaking skills to nonprofessionals. Thus, educational programs for the training of mental health workers are a third area of concern to the community mental health movement. Some recent innovative educational programs are discussed below.

There are many difficulties associated with mental health education. Perhaps the major such difficulty is the lack of definition of mental health. In the past, attempts to prevent mental illness by educating against it and attempts to promote mental health by educating for it have been made. In neither of these types of programs have the concepts of *mental health* or *mental illness* been adequately defined. The difficulty of defining mental health was evidenced by the conclusions in 1958 of the National Assembly of Mental Health Education whose member could not agree on a definition of mental health. Scott (1958) has suggested several definitions of mental illness; these involved (a) exposure to psychiatric treatment, (b) reference to societal norms, (c) reference to a patient's own feelings, (d) objective psychological symptoms, and (e) references to positive striving. Other definitions of mental illness and health have emphasized concepts such as coping with problems of living (Jahoda, 1958; Szasz, 1960 & 1961), creativity and self-actualization (Maslow, 1962; Rogers, 1961), competence (White, 1959), and well-being (Klein, 1960). One can easily surmise from the above that developing a definition of mental health or illness which is acceptable to a broad community of mental health professionals is indeed a difficult task. The variety of definitions stems from the variety of human problems encountered by the diverse clients of the mental health worker. The question remains, can we mount a program of mental health education without first defining the content of such a program? One can see that effectively programs of mental health education would be extremely important in helping to solve the various human problems alluded to in the definitions cited above. It would probably be of great social import to establish programs of education which help to solve the various human problems alluded to in the various definitions of mental health. For maximum effectiveness such programs should reach nonprofessionals and result in a pool of trained manpower who would help to develop and implement broad systematic programs of primary, secondary, and tertiary prevention.

The issues associated with the problems of prevention, treatment, manpower, and education may be summarized in the response to one short but comprehensive question, "*Who* should administer *what* treatment, to *whom*, *when*, and *where*?" (paraphrased from Golann, 1970). We assume that many of the problems confronting us would be solved if a satisfactory answer to this question would be found. Below are some suggestions regarding the issues raised, with the possible answers as to "who," "what," "to whom," "when," and "where."

Manpower

Until this point, most programs of public education have affected few people and have required long periods of time (although considerably less time than accredited graduate training programs). The use of nonprofessionals may be the only reasonable solution to this problem. One can cite programs which train nonprofessionals such as mental retardates (Berkowitz, 1968; Berkowitz, Walder, Thomas, Boyle, & Beach, in press; Whalen & Henker, 1967), elementary school children (Surratt, Ulrich, & Hawkins, 1969), mental hospital patients (Warman, 1969; Janowitz, 1970), high school students and graduates (Cohen, 1969; Vidaver, 1969), and parents of disturbing children (Hirsch, 1967; Breiter, 1968; Hirsch & Walder, 1969). The above training programs were all behaviorally oriented. Guerney (1969) has reviewed a number of behavior modification and client-centered training programs for nonprofessionals.

The use of parents as a particular subgroup of trained change agents is not new. Freud as early as 1909 reported collaborating with Little Hans' father who thereby became a therapeutic agent in the psychoanalytic treatment of his son's phobia (Freud, 1959). Therapists from a variety of psychoanalytic (see Guerney, 1969, pp. 382–388)

and nonpsychoanalytic theoretical orientations (e.g., Dreikurs & Soltz, 1964, and Guerney, 1964) have similarly involved parents in this way.

These published reports of the training and use of nonprofessionals, especially of parents, are almost uniformly positive. The manpower problem is not solved, however, by adopting strategies of tertiary prevention, that is, waiting until a child is in trouble before training the parent. Another way of not solving manpower problems is to attempt primary prevention with public educational programs lacking clear education objectives (see Brim, 1959; Davis, 1963).

One of the requirements for maximizing the effectiveness of an educational program for nonprofessionals would appear to be in the development of a strategy of behavior change which produces relatively rapid, observable improvements in the desired direction and involves techniques which are understood and mastered without long periods of technical preparation. An operant orientation provides well-defined and organized principles to be taught, empirically based explanations of behavioral phenomena, and principles which can be generalized to fit many clinical situations. In short, a behavioral orientation provides valuable therapeutic techniques and material for programs of public mental health education. Thus, a program of public education for mental health might be a course in the principles of behavior. An extensive literature on behavior principles already exists (e.g., Ferster & Perrott, 1968; Honig, 1966) and could be modified with relative ease to be suitable as material in courses for large groups of laymen (e.g., McIntire, 1970; Patterson, 1971; Patterson & Gullion, 1968; Smith & Smith, 1966; and Valett, 1969). The focus on the importance of a behavioral approach in mental health education is not intended to minimize in any way the relevance of this approach to other therapeutic activities.

It was stated earlier that the community approach emphasizes primary, secondary, and tertiary prevention. These emphases stress a number of goals, some of which are: (a) decreasing the frequency of mental illness, (b) educating the general public and the caretakers in ways to encourage mental health, (c) exploiting the total resources of the community in ways to foster mental health, and (d) protecting the integrity of an individual by maintaining him in his community. In the following paragraphs we shall investigate how operant procedures may be used in aiding the accomplishment of the above goals.

To decrease the frequency of mental illness in the community one must have some knowledge of the environmental events which maintain the behavior of persons in the community. Environmental events include those antecedent events which set the conditions for certain behaviors to occur (discriminative stimuli) as well as those events consequent to the behavior (reward, including avoidance or escape from aversive stimuli; punishment, including loss of reward; and no consequence). Changes in the relevant antecedent or consequent events lead to changes in the behavior they precede or follow. Clinical observers have provided us with a fairly extensive catalog of antecedent and consequent events which may be followed by changes in behavior frequently labeled *mental illness*. Such events include moving to a new job, loss of the old job, the death or departure of a loved one, or loss of income, among a host of other personal "crises."

In order to reduce the negative effect of such "critical events" in the environment, at least three alternatives are available. A first is that the environment must be controlled to a degree that eliminates sudden great changes in the setting conditions and/or in the consequences which maintain behavior. The first alternative necessitates a tightly controlled society highly unpalatable to most of us. A second alternative is to develop, through education, a person whose coping behaviors are appropriate and resistent to deterioration. This second alternative suggests an intensive educational program focusing primarily on child-rearing practices. Such an educational program might instruct parents how to arrange a systematic series of changes in the environment relevant to the child's developing behavior. In such a program, the parents would, at first, give much assistance to the child who is trying to cope with a new situation (a "crises") and would gradually fade out their assistance over subsequent crises until the behavioral repertoire of the child would include a class of coping responses highly resistant to deterioration in the face of changes in antecedent or consequent environmental events. There is some experimental evidence (Cohen & Walder, 1971) which suggests that such a program

would be useful. A third alternative is to develop through education a public knowledgeable in operant technology and its application to the building of therapeutic environments. Perhaps an anecdotal retelling of an actual occurrence illustrating the usefulness of public knowledge about behavior would be helpful here.

Mrs. A. was placed in a mental institution shortly after her husband died. Some years later, Mrs. A.'s daughter, Mrs. B., the central person in this anecdote, was faced with a similar situation which fortunately had a different outcome. When Mr. B. died, Mrs. B. was left alone since her daughter, Mrs. C. had, a few years before, married and moved to a new town where Mr. C. was enrolled in a graduate program in experimental psychology. Some months after the mourning period had ended, Mrs. C. visited and observed that the behavior of her mother, Mrs. B., was deteriorating. Mrs. B. did not leave her house much nor did she engage in outside activities. Upon close observation Mrs. C. noticed that relatives visiting her mother selectively supported nonproductive behaviors by intermittently commiserating and bringing food and other basic necessities. When a psychiatrist suggested drugs and institutionalization for Mrs. B., Mrs. C. suggested instead that her mother visit with her and her husband for an extended period. During this visit at the home of family C., Mrs. B.'s daughter and son-in-law embarked on a program to rebuild Mrs. B.'s behaviors. The children did not attend to mourning, to verbalizations relating to the sad state of affairs, or to other self-pitying, depressive kinds of behaviors. Playing with her young grandchild was a particularly reinforcing activity for Mrs. B. and playing with the child was an activity incompatible with self-pitying. The children did attend to more productive behaviors and during the two-month visit Mrs. B. began once again to cook, clean house, go out of the house to shop, and had made sound social contacts. This therapeutic program was completed after Mrs. C and her infant son accompanied Mrs. B. back home and visited with her for two weeks. There Mrs. C. insured that her mother's recently rebuilt behaviors were maintained in her natural environment. Mrs. C. and her infant son returned home after Mrs. B. had gotten a job and seemed, once again, to be behaving in ways relevant to self-maintenance and normal social interaction.

The above case illustrates the importance of disseminating information about behavior to the general public. If not for the active, relevant intervention of her daughter and son-in-law, Mrs. B. may herself have ended up as did her own mother, Mrs. A., in a mental institution. In this case, the onset of deterioration could not have been prevented, but appropriate application of behavioral principles *by people close to Mrs. B.* prevented the insidious development of increased deterioration and, in fact, reversed its development. Had her children been operating under the more usual assumptions which controlled the behaviors of her other relatives, Mrs. B.'s behavioral deterioration may well have run its apparent relentless course. In this case it was seen that operant principles provided techniques for useful intervention by people close to others whose behaviors deteriorated during a crisis. It is reasonable to assume that the techniques applied in this rather extreme case would be useful in many more typical situations and should therefore be made available to the general public. Readers with other theoretical tastes may see principles other than operant at work. Without claiming this to be a crucial experiment one may note that while a more traditional approach was guiding her therapy, Mrs. B.'s behavior (like that of her mother, Mrs. A., before her) was deteriorating. When the operant approach took over, Mrs. B.'s behavior improved in a systematic and durable way.

Perhaps the public school should present this technology to its students. A useful way to "stamp out mental illness" would be then to provide to young adults educational programs emphasizing the application of behavior principles to child-rearing. Such educational programs should be offered no later than in the high school grades. Teaching potential parents how to raise children may well be a major step toward effective primary prevention and would also serve to enlist many laymen in the service of mental health.

In addition, this training in the application of behavior principles could provide useful tools to those already in the caretaking professions. Courses could be arranged for clergymen, policemen, social workers, interested laymen, etc. Such courses would allow for and encourage an interdisciplinary approach to community problems not only by providing a useful technology, but by providing a common language which, up to now, has been sorely lacking. The use of common language and principles would facilitate partnership in building an overall plan for therapy. Because others, such as family and friends, who are relevant to effecting good therapy, would have learned something of the principles of behavior, they could be *actively* enlisted in therapeutic programs. Thus, brothers, sisters, fathers, mothers, aunts, uncles, boy friends, girl friends—anyone who, to some extent, is an important agent in the environment of someone else—could effect changes in that environment and consequently in the behavior ongoing in that environment. Another advantage is that being actively involved in a therapeutic program for a dear one seems to motivate those involved in the program. During several years of working with the parents of disturbing children in ways which required the parents to become actively involved in the therapy of their children, highest praises from the parents related to the fact that an "expert" was finally saying that they could and must do something for their own children. Effective and durable therapy can best be accomplished in the environment within which the behavioral changes are to occur. Such therapy requires that the "patient" be maintained in his environment, and that others in that environment know how to make that situation therapeutic. The "patient" should not be sent away to some institution unless we wish to strengthen the vegetative behaviors appropriate to many institutional environments. Thus, disseminating the knowledge of and employing operant principles facilitates the accomplishment of another goal of community psychology which is to protect the integrity of the "patient" and maintain him within his normal environment.

From the above brief sketch, we see that the role of the mental health worker may change. The mental health worker may become a highly skilled and specialized technician—a consultant. The mental health worker may become an expert in a technology of behavior. Among his main skills and tasks might then be observing behavior and its interaction with the environment, performing functional analyses, and consulting with and teaching individuals who are interested in modifying the behavior of others. If indeed a massive program for educating the general public in behavior principles is accomplished, the consultant's task becomes much easier. Because those with whom the consultant works would have some knowledge of behavior principles, he could rely on them to formulate therapeutic programs and consult with them to discuss such programs before their implementation. In essence, he would be lending his expertise to someone less expert but still relatively competent in the understanding and application of behavior principles. Within a consultative program similar to that described above, much in the way of analysis and planning would be required of the client. After being educated in behavior principles the client would be able to successfully construct a tentative analysis and strategy for problem solving in which he would also be required to actively participate. Such a public consultation-educational program is described in subsequent pages of this chapter.

A BEHAVIORAL APPROACH
TO TRAINING PARENTS

Behaviorists have long been interested in solving human problems. The list begins with Watson and Raynor (1920) and M. C. Jones (1924), includes the work of Dunlap (1932) and Fuller (1949), and today comprises too many authors to include here (see, e.g., Ulrich, Stachnik, & Mabry, 1966). The evidence is fairly clear that behaviorism has generated effective principles for modifying deviant behavior.[2]

Behaviorists tend to adopt the laws of behavior emerging from the experimental psychology of learning which are based on studies of a variety of animals, including humans. It is thus no surprise to find that the field of behavior modification is based upon principles stemming from the work of Pavlov and Thorndike and refined by the work of Hull and Skinner (see chapter 11 in Ullman & Krasner, 1969). The behavior modifier therefore has available well-documented rules for changing the behavior of troubled and troubling people.

A point of departure is that any pattern of behavior including deviance is a member of a very well studied class of events, behaviors under operant control. This orientation provides a powerful analytic tool which in turn yields a powerful therapeutic tool. Therefore, if one is faced with the problem of changing behavior from disturbing to nondisturbing, he may approach it systematically and with some promise of success.

Therapeutic Goals

Clinical psychologists are concerned with behaviors as they occur in the natural environment. In their roles as social and personal engineers (Lanyon & Broskowski, 1969), they attempt to develop, describe, evaluate, and improve techniques designed to effect *durable* changes in the environment-organism interaction such that the new behaviors will be maintained by the natural environment. It is therefore proper to deal with parents of disturbing children (rather than the child himself) because it is the parent who is responsible for the child's environment. If one assumes that a disturbing child is behaving appropriately within his environment (albeit undesirably as judged by the responsible person), then one should attempt to control the person who is responsible for the child's environment and thereby control the child's behaviors.

The approach developed is a blend of behavioral analysis and of consultative psychotherapy. The former emphasizes (a) relevant data and (b) observables, and the latter emphasizes (c) dealing with the problems brought in by troubled people; (d) consulting across the table with them; and (e) changing behaviors occurring in their natural environment. Contrary to usual psychotherapeutic practices, the therapists take responsibility for the outcome in negotiating and implementing a proper contract. An agreement is reached delineating the child behaviors the parents want changed. This, in effect, determines what parental behaviors must be changed, since changes in parental behaviors are a most effective way to alter a child's behavior. Finally, reinforcers for parents must be controlled in order to achieve the necessary changes in parental child-rearing behavior.

The specification of the behavioral goals to be sought remains the responsibility of the parent. When given aid in achieving their stated goals, parents work energetically and effectively toward those goals. The clinician assumes for his role, helping the parent to develop in the child the desired behavioral outcome. The clinician reserves the right to refuse to help a parent to achieve some behavioral goal which conflicts with his own personal ethic.

The attempt to define a behavior problem in objective, behavioral, and environmental terms requires direct observation in the natural environment. Home visits by staff and teaching parents to record their observations in quantitative terms increase the trust placed in verbal reports of parents in the consultation room. These observations include measures of baseline (or pretreatment) behavior as well as terminal (or desired) behavior. Once these observations have been made, the immediate antecedents (or cues) and consequences of the target behaviors are explored.

On the basis of such observations the parents are helped to program the environment of the child to improve his behavior. In general this procedure requires specifying the step-by-step changes in the parents' behaviors and controlling meaningful consequences for the parent to maintain the new behaviors in the parents' repertoires.

Successive Approximations Toward This Method

It is assumed that failure to achieve the behavioral goals for any family is the fault of the professional who claimed expertise and lacked it. This failure is not ascribed to some inadequacy of the parents or the child. Less than complete success with a family provides the stimulus for reexamination and improvement of methods. In this section some of the major successive approximations are described.

The method of teaching behavior control to parents of disturbing children developed out of work with some children in public elementary schools and other children in a center for extremely disturbing children.

The first problems considered included study problems, laziness, hostile behavior, and social skill problems in a public elementary school. The work done was based on two assumptions: 1) All behavior is appropriate to the environment and 2) all behavior can be changed by appropriate environmental changes.

Requests from parents and teachers to work on a child's emotional disturbances led to the following priorities: First, work on improving or developing the "job" skills that the child would need in order to be "successful" in the school environment; that is, change the child's behavior so that he becomes more efficient in obtaining reinforcers from the natural environment. Later, if necessary, work on the "internal feelings." However, once a child was doing well in the classroom, disturbing internal feelings were no longer reported. On the contrary, the child was reported as being happier and feeling better.

The consultant's task was to present constructive steps to the teacher and parent on how to change the child's environment so that the child's behavior would be less aversive to them. The parents and teachers were not blamed for the undesirable behaviors which were occurring, but simply given tools to alter the behavior. It was soon learned, however, that simply presenting steps for changing a behavior was not sufficient to ensure that the steps would be undertaken. Controls imposed on the parent and teacher by the consultant were developed; they will be discussed below.

The treatment of several families whose children were being served at a center for autistic children provided further lessons about this method. One family was composed of a father and two young boys. The child of concern was in residence at this treatment center while his brother lived at home with the father. Consultation was begun with the father in an attempt to teach him how to deal more effectively with his child who was labeled "autistic." The father was a ready-enough student; however, he was with the child only one afternoon every other weekend. It became clear that a basic requirement for this form of consultation was that parents must be responsible for and in direct touch with their child's environment. Perhaps because this principle was not followed, this consultation did not succeed with this parent. Since then we have consulted with parents only if the child was living at home with them.

Experience with another family was similarly valuable to the development of our procedures. We learned that the approach was useful with a very disturbing child, and that parents could be very good therapists for such a child. We also learned that, through parents' producing large enough changes in their child's behavior, diagnostic experts could be persuaded to change their diagnosis. This occurred in this family's case. On the basis of the child's behavioral changes, the child's diagnosis changed successively from (a) autistic to (b) schizophrenic to (c) emotionally disturbed and mentally retarded to (d) mentally retarded. Since the diagnosticians were well qualified, the method used by the parents as therapists might be evaluated as successful with this family. The child then was ready to learn verbal and other academic skills. When we started with this family, their 11-year-old child was exhibiting a number of very disturbing behaviors both at home and at the treatment center. After about three months, a home visit was made by someone who did not know the details of our activities. The report written of the child's behavior at home showed him to be behaving much better at home than at the treatment center. The treatment center staff called in the parents to learn what they were doing. (When the treatment center used the parents' techniques, he also behaved better there.)

Experience with a third set of parents from this treatment center taught us the need for durable control over the parents. They were helped to deal with a number of very deviant and disturbing behaviors (e.g., smearing feces on the father's bedroom furniture). Once some success with the most disturbing behaviors was achieved, however, the parents' interest in further changing their own behavior to reduce less aversive behaviors of the child decreased. From this experience, a set of techniques was developed. These techniques included acquiring control of reinforcers (e.g., money) for the parents so that they behaved appropriately until the new desirable behaviors of the child maintained the parents' new behaviors.

Another family was referred by the treatment center. In this case we found that the parents were not interested in any one behavior long enough for effective consultation with them. In order to remedy this problem the parents were asked for a ranking of the child's behaviors that were of concern to them. The parents were required to bring a list of at least five positive child behaviors to be increased and a list of at least five negative child behaviors to be decreased. Within each list, the husband-wife pair was to rank the behaviors from the most desired to be changed to the fifth most desired to be changed. The parents were then informed that consultation would focus only on the first ranked behavior in each list. The consultation on this behavior was to continue until some improvement was noted, and only then would a new behavior be considered. After some success with each behavior, the parents were given

an opportunity to revise their lists in order to specify the next behaviors for consultation.

As this procedure became more familiar, it was found that the parents (as well as professionals) were quite proficient at specifying negative behaviors, but quite deficient in specifying positive ones. A decision was made not to teach parents how to decrease the frequency of one of the child's behaviors without, at the same time, increasing the frequency of another. An attempt was then made to help improve the parents' specification of positive behaviors. This led to asking pairs of parents, who specified a negative behavior (to be decreased), "What do you want the child to do instead of this negative behavior?"

Attempts at controlling the parents' behaviors were explored. At that time, a major reinforcer which could be controlled was the parents' opportunity to meet with us. Opportunity to consult was manipulated to insure that an assignment (e.g., coming in with a list of five ranked positive and five ranked negative behaviors) would be fulfilled. This completed assignment became the "ticket of admission." Subsequently, completion of any meeting's assignment became the behavioral admission price for the following meeting.

Complications arose. Problems of interpretation developed when the assignment was unclear. Parents would appear with assignments which were ostensibly completed, but not to the consultant's complete satisfaction. This occurred because of the lack of clarity in making the assignment. It did not seem fair to punish the parents when the consultant was at least equally in error. To avoid this situation, an objective assignment checker was introduced to review the assignment for clarity and to ensure that the criteria for a completed assignment were understood. Since this assignment checker had not witnessed the interviews, we were assured that failure to complete an assignment was not due to lack of clarity.

When parents with incomplete assignments were not admitted, another problem arose. Therapists were frequently unwilling to exclude the parents. In essence, excluding the parents from a therapy meeting for one failure was too aversive for the therapist. To solve this problem, a system was developed in which incomplete assignments became the occasion for the parents to earn *debits*. (Parents could earn *credits* for very well-completed assignments.) When a predetermined number of debits had been earned (which were not balanced by enough credits), the parents could be excluded from the meeting or suffer some other undesirable consequence (such as losing some of their own money). Thus the all-or-none aspect of the earlier procedure was eliminated.

A further difficulty encountered, and one still not completely solved, was the therapists' inability to make assignments which were consistent with the parents' current obligations and current behavioral development. There seemed to be no hard and fast rules for solving this problem. Amelioration of this problem seems to require that the therapist be attuned to a number of factors such as the family's size, the parents' obligations and time commitments, their material resources, their educational level, etc.

To facilitate the use of completed assignments as admission to therapy sessions, a simple agenda was devised which served to control both the parents and therapist. It contained the following sequence of items: (a) Assignment from last time, (b) assignment for next time, and (c) free talk.

The assignment from last time was received and approved by the therapist before he proceeded to the next item. If any part of the assignment from last time was incomplete, the therapist assigned debits and attempted to clarify the assignment for the next meeting. He did not lecture or get angry with the parents, but simply imposed the well-defined consequences for incomplete assignments.

If the therapist received and approved the assignments from last time, he (perhaps after awarding credits for work very well done) then proceeded to the assignment for next time. The content of each successive assignment was based upon the overall therapeutic plan for the family and the weekly data on the target behavior. An incomplete assignment would, of course, slow the family's progress but would not result in a complete impasse. Thus the aversiveness of the child's behavior and the possibility of punishment (debits) represented the major motivational factors controlling the parents' behavior. These are both negative. On the positive side are credits, the positive attention from the therapist, and the improvement in the child's behavior, i.e., in the parent-child relations.[3]

The Method as Applied to Nine Families

The following section describes one variation of operant family consultation, as developed during the course of work with about 50 families. This presentation leans heavily upon case notes and reports of the therapeutic process by the operant consultants and their supervisors. The reports were drawn from a recent clinical study with nine families. The goal of the study was to build an operant oriented family therapy with general applicability toward enhancing the behavioral development of children. Included are enough details so others may attempt this method. Both negative and positive comments about the specific techniques and outcomes cited are included. The reader should note that all reports (from parents, from teachers, and from objective raters) strongly suggest that the method is effective in durably improving the behavior of children within a few months.

Selection of Clients

In general, we offered behavioral consultation to families with severe problems concerning a child living in the home. The latest version of this method was offered to nine families, selected from about 40 applicant families who responded to a newspaper article describing our program. The parents were invited to come to our office for interviews to discuss their child. On the basis of interview notes treatment was offered to those with the most severe problems. Some of the complaints of the parents were that their children wouldn't learn, speak, play, or interact in a satisfactory manner.

The participating families had above average incomes (few with income below $8,000, most above $10,000 per year), and above average education (one Ph.D. in the nine families, almost all parents at least high school graduates). The child of concern was between four and 14 years old, typically a boy, and usually the only sib who presented serious developmental problems. The complaints about the child varied from so mild that no diagnostic label had ever been applied to the child to so severe that the most casual and untrained observer would be disturbed by the child's behavior.

Some Preliminaries to the Treatment

When the nine families were invited for treatment, they were told that they were to attend meetings on three consecutive Monday evenings. During these three meetings the contract was established, the problem was defined, and the parents were taught to observe behaviors.

1. *The contract* was established in order to increase our control over the parents' behaviors. This was accomplished by arranging conditions so that not following instructions led to punishment; whereas following instructions led to avoidance of punishment. During the initial screening interview the parents were asked which organizations they preferred and which they did not prefer. The families were also asked to deliver a copy of their most recent United States income tax return. In order to impose punishment, each family was asked to being three checks to the second meeting: one (No. 1 check) to be made out to a preferred organization; a second (No. 2 check) to be made out to a neutral organization; and the third (No. 3 check) to be made out to a nonpreferred organization.[4] Each check was to be written in the amount of .0016 of the total yearly income (as reported in their most recent United States income tax return). The family which reported the lowest income ($9,000) wrote three $15 checks; the family with the highest income ($22,000) wrote three $37 checks.

If the husband or wife did not follow one of our instructions, he would earn one or more debits. When enough debits had been earned, the No. 1 check was to be mailed and the family was to replace it with a No. 3 check; if another check were to be sent, it would be the No. 2 check; it, too, was to be replaced by a No. 3 check; after that, only No. 3 checks would be involved. (In the work with these nine families, three families' checks were sent, Nos. 1 and 2 for two families and a No. 1 for a third family. The debits for these checks were earned by parents' being absent from scheduled therapeutic sessions.)

Each family gave three checks (in the second meeting) only after it had agreed to the conditions of the contract. The conditions of participation (including assignment to one of three treatment groups)[5] were described in a letter handed to each family. The conditions of participation were as follows:

a. Both parents were required to come to all scheduled meetings on time.

b. They were to have completed all assignments.

c. They were to allow video tape recordings to be made in the home.

d. They were to sign requests for information to be sent from us to all professionals who had contact with the child.

e. They were to sign a release allowing properly disguised information about them and their child to be used for scientific publication.

2. Also during the three pretreatment sessions *the major problems of concern to each family were defined*. Each of the nine families filled out questionnaires about the child of concern. They were asked to specify five (positive) child behaviors to be strengthened and five (negative) child behaviors to be weakened. Unless the therapeutic goals include both positive and negative behavior changes, the goals are less likely to be achieved. At least three reasons for this may be cited: (a) weakening or suppressing behavior necessitates extinction or punishment, both of which reduce the child's reinforcements; (b) eliminating a behavior does not insure that the next behavior in strength will be desirable; and (c) strengthening behavior requires the use of a number of procedures (e.g., shaping, chaining, and imitation) which increase the child's reinforcements. Lectures and demonstrations helped the parents to state their complaints in overt behavioral terms.

3. The third function of the three pretreatment meetings was *to teach the parents how to observe behavior*. This was necessary because experience taught us that lay people do not describe behavior objectively. The goals of the first pretreatment meeting were to determine the level of the parents' initial skills in observation and to introduce the basic methodology of accurate observations. The methodology required that observations be *descriptive*, not *interpretative*, and that descriptions of behavior be in *specific* rather than *global* terms. Pretreatment observational skills of parents were sampled by showing a behavioral interaction lasting a few minutes on the television monitor of a video tape apparatus. The parents were asked to record observations on the interaction and read their notes aloud after the viewing. The interaction consisted of a man and a woman sitting next to

each other, both reading. The woman asked the man for a cigarette; the man responded with a grunt. The sequence of the woman asking and the man grunting cycled several times, with the intensity of the woman's request increasing to a shriek; at that time the man finally and begrudgingly gave her a cigarette.

The interaction showed the woman's repeated and relatively simple responses which change in amplitude. The parents' observational responses to the behavioral interaction ranged from very interpretive ("There are deep underlying stresses between them") to highly objective observations ("The woman asked five times with increasing loudness for a cigarette"). The group leader pointed out that the observations by the 18 people present were quite varied (i.e., there was low interjudge agreement among the parents) and that one could not reconstruct what occurred from the more interpretative descriptions. Parents were then asked to refrain from making inferences while observing the interaction a second time. They were told that objective descriptions would lead to a greater agreement among observers and better communication about the observed behavior.

An attempt to control the observational behaviors of parents was made by giving them data sheets containing columns for description of behavior, frequency of occurrence, amplitude, and time of occurrence. Consequently, the homework assignment required parents to redescribe in highly specific terms the five positive and the five negative behaviors and to observe at least one behavior from each category using the provided data sheets.

The results of this assignment (made in the first pretreatment meeting and brought to the second meeting) were that the observations were not controlled by the data sheets as was hoped. Most of the parents described behaviors fairly specifically, but few of them used the frequency or time column as expected. Some parents used the data sheets to write long descriptions of ongoing interactions between the parents and child. This provided us with data to make some interesting, albeit speculative, functional anlyses. For example, family "H" reported that repeated headbobbing of their child was difficult to record because it stopped whenever they paid attention to her. (This suggested that head-bobbing behavior was being reinforced by parents' attention to it, and conversely, that parents' attending was reinforced by a temporary cessation of the aversive head-bobbing.) Although such descriptions of behavior interactions were valuable for other purposes, it became apparent that the data sheets were most useful for simple repetitive behaviors for which frequency, intensity, and duration could be readily measured. Since descriptions of complicated behavioral interactions were useful in planning therapeutic intervention, they were not discouraged.

The third pretreatment session was devoted to shaping parents' talk about specific behaviors. A video tape of two people playing tic-tac-toe was shown. Each parent in turn was required to talk about what he observed. When the parents used abstract or general names of behaviors, they were asked to give specific behavioral examples "illustrating" (i.e., defining) the abstract category. By the end of the session, no parent was interpreting behavior but was describing behavior in specific terms.

After the three week pretreatment period in which the contract had been established, the problem had been defined, and the parents had been taught to objectively observe behaviors, a 12-week treatment period began. The families were assigned to three treatment groups with three families in each group. The staff for each treatment group was a therapeutic supervisor, a group leader, and three individual family consultants. The three husband-wife pairs came to the clinic one evening a week. From 7:30 to 8:30 P.M. these six people attended an educational group meeting; from 8:30 to 9:00 P.M. these six went to another part of the building to socialize (e.g., drink coffee); from 9:00 to 10:00 P.M. each husband-wife pair met in one of three small consultation rooms with an individual consultant; and at 10:00 P.M. the parents left the building. The parents had been told that a therapeutic supervisor and observer-raters were watching and listening to the group and the individual sessions. No attempt was made to conceal visible microphones which led to audio tape recorders. Parents were told that on occasion video tape recordings were also being made.

In addition to the weekly office meetings each individual behavior consultant made at least one home visit a week to watch, react to, and provide feedback about parent-child interactions. Before describing the group meetings and the individual family consultation, the supervision of the treatment staff will be discussed.

The supervisor (a Ph.D. clinical psychologist) met for planning at least once a week with the three individual consultants and group leader of his therapeutic team (advanced graduate students in psychology and counseling). He also met with them in the half hour between the group and the individual meetings. Finally, the team met for a case conference shortly after the parents left.

The group leader, the individual consultants, and the supervisor attempted to establish a colleague relationship with the parents who were told that the goal of the program was to teach them a theory and related techniques so they could solve their child management problems. They were also told that the group educational meetings were designed to teach theory and techniques in general and that the individual consultation meetings were designed to help each family apply the techniques to its specific problems.

The Educational Group. The purpose of the *group meetings* was to give to the parents the skills to analyze complex interpersonal interactions into simplified behavioral paradigms. It was hoped that eventually the parents would be able to deal with their children's behavior problems beyond the specific problems of concern during the 12-week course. The question arose as to whether it was necessary for parents to have a good verbal facility with the terminology of operant psychology if they were to become successful behavioral engineers. It was decided that verbal facility with the terminology of operant psychology would guide the parents when faced with problems with their children. Of course being able to "talk" operant psychology would not be sufficient to produce good behavioral engineers; the parents would have to be trained during the individual sessions and home visits to use the principles they could talk about.

The general procedure was as follows: Group meetings were held once a week for an hour. Parents had a homework assignment to prepare for each meeting and were told that participation in the meeting was contingent on the completion of this assignment. Failure to complete one assignment led to enough debits to send a check. The

class time itself was devoted mostly to discussion of the textual material, the main part of which was Ellen Reese's book, *The Analysis of Human Operant Behavior* (1966). This text was selected because it includes many examples of behavior modification with humans. (A later group has used Holland and Skinner's *The Analysis of Behavior* (1961) because, by the use of objective tests, it was easier to insure that the parents had done their assigned readings.)[6] During the group treatment sessions the parents were taught by the group leader to appropriately use the terms which occurred in the book. The group leader generally used a question-answer format, rewarding successive approximations to the correct definition or use of a term. Other sessions were devoted to showing movies, role-playing of operant procedures, analyzing behavior vignettes (short descriptions of interpersonal interactions), and parents presenting case reports for plans for future development of their child's behavior.

During the group meetings the supervisor observed from behind a one-way mirror and by way of a walkie-talkie reinforced the group leader for his appropriate behavior. Other equipment present occasionally included video tape apparatus and audio recording equipment which was present for all sessions.

In the half hour between group and individual meetings the therapeutic team and supervisor held meetings during which the group leader reported on what had been discussed in the group, on the performances of the various parents. Other members of the team made suggestions and occasionally requested that special instruction on some topic be given to specific parents in succeeding group meetings.

Specific Procedures of the Group Meeting. During the first treatment group meeting the parents were introduced to an operant approach to abnormal behavior. It was stressed that behaviors in themselves are not abnormal, but their relative frequency, intensity, and the context in which they occur determines if they are disturbing to others. From the three lists of five child behaviors to be increased and five to be decreased developed by the three pairs of parents, a general list of behaviors undesirable to the parents was compiled. Examples were gesturing and grunting instead of talking, repeated rocking, and bobbing up and down. It was pointed out that under some conditions the occurrence of these behaviors would be considered normal. Bobbing and rocking, for example, are considered normal during a pop-rock dance—at least while the music is on. What is abnormal about these behaviors is that they occur inappropriately, too frequently, and to the exclusion of more appropriate behaviors. The problem of making abnormal behavior normal thus became increasing the frequency of desirable or appropriate behavior and decreasing the frequency of undesirable behavior in particular situations. Parents were told that the major function of the group meetings would be to teach principles of operant conditioning, a technology for increasing and decreasing the frequency of behavior. They were told that the frequency of occurrence of behavior was determined by the consequences of that behavior and the basic operation of operant reinforcement and extinction was described. As a homework assignment, parents were required to read the first 23 pages of the textbook. They were asked to read at the rate of five pages a day, and for husband and wife to discuss their reading one day a week.

The reading assignment was reviewed in the second treatment meeting. Parents were more proficient in speaking about the text than they were in learning to apply the concepts to extra-text materials. It was necessary to review several times the various schedules of reinforcement, the procedures and terminology of forming a discrimination, the distinctions between escape and avoidance, punishment and negative reinforcement, and to show how they operated in examples other than those in the text.

The Reese book is organized into procedures which increase behavior and procedures which decrease behavior. Parents were required to learn a list of procedures from each category. When the parents had read half of the text, they saw a movie showing behavior modification of autistic children by Lovaas (1966). In a subsequent session they were shown the film, *Behavior Theory in Practice* (Reese, 1965). They commented that it was easier to understand the concepts when they could see what was actually being done, for example, in discrimination training. The movies also proved to be of value as a reference point for tying down abstract concepts during later discussions.

After the movies, three more sessions were devoted to the Reese text and followed by a review. As a homework assignment during the review the parents were required to answer questions on the text and were given instructions to answer one set of questions per day. Some examples of questions are as follows:

1. Pick one of the following behaviors and describe how you would instate self-control: (a) drinking, (b) procrastinating, (c) smoking.

2. What are the steps you would use to shape talking in your child? Give an example with a specific word.

3. How is discrimination accomplished? Define the following terms: Differential reinforcment, differential response, discriminative stimulus.

The technique of writing out answers as a homework assignment proved to be ineffective. When the questions were reviewed in class, the parents frequently faltered. It became apparent that they merely copied answers from the book and were not able to respond appropriately when questions were even slightly rephrased.

One of the later group meetings was devoted to learning shaping skills in a situation resembling the game of charades. During these shaping sessions one person was assigned to be a subject and the other was assigned to be an experimenter. The subject was instructed to earn as many claps as possible, each clap functioning as a reinforcement. A description of the behavior to be shaped was written on a slip of paper and passed among all of the parents except the subject. Each parent had the opportunity to act as the experimenter and also as the subject for different behaviors. These sessions were valuable in getting the parents to dispense reinforcements and in convincing them that reinforcement works.

After completing the Reese text, parents were asked during class to perform a functional analysis of a behavioral interaction. The parents were generally successful in performing functional analyses of behaviors maintained by escape, avoidance, and positive reinforcement; they were also successful in identifying the probable pattern of reinforcement contingencies which were maintaining the behavior.

One of the functions of the group was to give parents special training relevant to their work with the individual consultant. During one group session, for example, one family trying to set up a token economy in the house, was shown how to establish and use conditioned reinforcers. These parents had tended not to pair tokens with primary reinforcers. They were also reluctant to deprive their daugher, so the back-up reinforcers were generally weak. Several examples of conditioned reinforcement from the text were reviewed, and the relationship between deprivation and strength of reinforcers was described. It was hoped that improved control of the child would reinforce the parents' implementation of these procedures. The parents were not successful in establishing conditioned reinforcers until further individual consultation was made contingent upon the development of conditioned reinforcers. The family was then successful in requiring the child to earn tokens to exchange for meals.

During the *last group session* the families reported on projects they had conducted with their children in conjunction with their individual consultants. These reports indicated that parents who showed the slowest rate of progress in the group meetings also did least to modify their child's behavior. Apparent progress with two of the three families was made. One family obtained standard teaching materials from a college of education and was using these materials in conjunction with conditioned reinforcers (tokens) they had established. These parents were using the principles of operant psychology imaginatively to teach new behaviors. The second successful family also acquired teaching aids and was using them in conjunction with conditioned reinforcement. In addition, the father of this family had constructed a program for teaching his child to write numerals. He had drawn outlines of numerals which the child could fill in with a pencil. To fade out the outline, he planned to place a sheet of lined paper over the sheet with the outlines so the outlines were barely visible beneath. This was a simple and ingenious program and another parent requested some of the sheets for his child. Staff behaviors were reinforced by the parents' exchanging materials and ideas. The third family said that they were "going to do about the same thing as always," and they didn't have any specific plans for the future. (It should be noted that there was some improvement in this family, although less than in the other families.)

Contingencies involving the threat of sending checks were effective in controlling parent attendance and promptness. However, the same contingencies did not control satisfactory completion of homework assignments. Our ineffectiveness in controlling this aspect of group participation probably accounted for the slower progress of one of the families. In later groups, we therefore built contingencies which better controlled the completion of homework assignments. These included a point system of debits and credits and a system for objectively evaluating the completion of the homework.

The Individual Operant Consultation Sessions

The following is a case report to illustrate the individual operant consultation sessions concerning one family and their son, Fred (a pseudonym).

Fred's family includes parents both of whom are professionals (the father a Ph.D. in a physical science and the mother an M.A. in social work), and three other children between two and seven years old. Fred is six, the second oldest. The family lives in a comfortable home in a residential suburb of a large Eastern United States city.

Fred's father is away from home most of the day and most of the burden of raising the children has fallen on the mother. Generally, she programs a rest period for the children in the early afternoon, followed by nursery school-type activities. Fred's mother seemed to the individual consultant to be a pleasant woman who works hard with her children in general, and with Fred in particular. She is warm toward the children and usually controls them in a positive fashion, but lacked confidence in her ability to deal with Fred. This changed for the better during her participation in the project.

Fred's father seemed to be well organized, demanding, and straight-forward. He devoted little time to his children, but had definite ideas about ends and the means to accomplish them, as evidenced by his employing procedures to help Fred to learn to count which the consultant suggested would not work.

Fred's History. Fred was born of an apparently uncomplicated pregnancy and delivery. Due to jaundice, a full blood transfusion was required when Fred was four days old. The parents stated that Fred had some difficulty learning to suck and described him as unusually unresponsive during the first year of life, e.g., did not reach out to prepare himself to be picked up and did little rocking in his crib as a baby. They described the child as appearing dull and stiff when held. At times they thought that the child was deaf. They further described him as happier when he was not handled. Close to Fred's first birthday the parents moved abroad for a year. By the age of one, Fred was seen by a specialist in Europe and was described (according to the parents) as "very abnormal." The parents said that Fred began to walk at about the age of 24 months, after returning to the States. He did not imitate; he occasionally put his hands in bizarre positions; and he liked to cling to adults.

Fred's first words appeared between the ages of two and three years. His pronunciation was described as good at first but the rate of development as slow.

The parents described Fred at three years old as "looking through people, seeming to be in a shell, liking to spin objects, and having unusual dexterity in assembling jigsaw puzzles." They also described his insistence on neatness and evenness and that objects not be disturbed. They said that he did not maintain eye contact at any time. Fred had a fear of strangers, noises, and strange objects and he had little speech.

When he was three years and three months old, the child was examined again. One of the conclusions of the examining physician was that there might have been nothing serious behind the limited speech. At that time the child had a vocabulary of 200 words and some sentences. Most of the speech had just recently developed. The examiner concluded that the store of words and the pronunciation of words seemed to be within normal limits of a child three years and three months old, although it was "certainly not advanced." Fred was described as being negativistic about the examination, aloof, self-sufficient, and maintaining no eye contact although the examiner said that Fred did relate to people. The examiner noted some ritualistic mannerisms and described Fred as being socially immature but not "autistic." He concluded that Fred did not appear to show any neurologic abnormality but that perhaps the boy was slightly retarded and the fact that a foreign language was occasionally used in the household might cause the speech difficulties. His recommendation was to have an audiogram on the child made.

At three and a half years of age Fred was put into a Montessori nursery school which he attended for one year. The child (now four years and four months old) was examined once again, this time at a speech and hearing center. Some of the conclusions of that examination were that there was no need for speech therapy and that there was no hearing loss. There were perseverative and ritualistic behaviors, staring, and giggling and these were thought to be attributable to emotional disturbance. Also noted were fluctuations between cooperation and negativism, excessive neatness and order in playing with blocks, and absence of speech. Fred achieved a score of 103 on the Merrill-Palmer Intelligence Test. However, the examiner concluded that the score was probably not really interpretable. One month later, the Leiter Scale was given and an IQ of 100 was achieved. Because of Fred's behavior, the score was accepted with reservations and was considered "an underestimate of the true IQ." The Vineland Social Maturity Scale showed that Fred had a social age of 2.8 years (with a chronological age of 4.4 years). The examiner stated that Fred showed "a generalized behavioral-emotional disturbance, much autisticlike behavior, behavioral disturbance with organic and emotional components is clearly present."

The parents also reported that he was not toilet trained by age four and that he had begun to wander from home. Occasionally the police had to be sent after him. Because of an infection in his ear during the year, an audiogram was not accomplished.

When Fred was four and a half years old he had been seen by a prominent child psychiatrist who concluded that Fred presented typical features of infantile autism, including self-isolation and obsessive desire for sameness. Later that year, the family again moved to another English-speaking country abroad for one year. The child was enrolled in nursery school and it was felt that substantial progress had been made during the year. Some of these improvements described included: the child liked new things; he began to enter games in school; he began to use personal pronouns; and generally his social relationships seemed improved. Also at this time, the parents reported that the child had a craving for salty foods, he seemed to have somewhat below average coordination, and liked to spin things for long periods of time. They described him as being upset when he was interrupted at some activity, and repetitively playing with objects and staring for long periods. They also said that he frequently used an adult's hand to manipulate the environment, e.g., he would take an adult's hand to turn on the television set rather than turn it on himself. During the year abroad Fred was taken for yet another hospital examination. The conclusions of the examiner were that "Fred showed a syndrome of infantile autism, but his disabilities seemed to be lesser than those of most autistic children. Fred's difficulties stemmed from factors within him rather than with the parents and the family background. The main disabililite seemed to be poor language development."

Upon returning to the United States (at age five and a half), Fred was placed in a public kindergarten. The teacher thought Fred was retarded and probably complained, bringing the problem to the attention of supervisors. In the meantime the parents again visited the prominent child psychiatrist. This visit seemed to be in response to the problem that existed in the kindergarten. The psychiatrist concluded that the child "shows the same features of infantile autism, however, there is evidence of improvement." The psychiatrist further wrote that he felt that "a regular kindergarten would be too threatening for the child and would definitely be too much for any teacher to handle." Instead, he suggested that the parents enroll Fred as a day student in a treatment center for autistic children. It also appeared that this conclusion provided justification for the public schools to expel Fred, which was done. He was enrolled then in a private kindergarten.

The parents were assigned to the operant treatment group. At the time of their formal contact with this parent consultation project the complaints of the parents about Fred were: (1) Fred seldom tells what has happened to him, (2) he screams when frustrated, (3) he does nothing for long periods of time, (4) he is less imaginative than his siblings. (5) he lacks good coordination, (6) he wets the bed at night, (7) his speech is poor—poor intonation. He does use the personal pronouns fairly well, but his speech is characterized mostly by requests. The parents also complained that he (8) frequently leaves the dining table. They reported that Fred's recent progress was definitely related to the fact that they were increasing their demands on him. On the initial problem list which each of the parents was required to write as an assignment, they wrote as behaviors to be weakened: (1) undesirable sounds—screams, grunts, coughs, (2) peculiar hand motions, (3) repetitious behaviors such as page turning, finger sucking, looking at and talking about air-conditioners, (4) wandering away from the home, and (5) wetting the bed at night. Behaviors listed by the parents to be strengthened were: (1) speech (of which there was not enough), (2) assertive behavior and asking for help when hurt, (3) attending to his tasks more, and (4) initiating activities.

The broad goals of the operant consultant were: (1) to teach the parents to perform functional analysis of behavior, (2) to teach the parents skills relevant to behavior control, (3) to encourage the parents to record data and increase behavioral requirements on the child, to continually look for new reinforcers, to continually specify new behaviors to be shaped up, (4) to make the parents independent of the consultant in working with their child, and (5) (on the assumption that it would be helpful in achieving the above goal) to shape up effective use of technical terminology. Some of the general techniques used to achieve these broad goals were (1) instructing in data collection and operant procedures, (2) making home visits and home demonstrations, (3) having parents describe what actually occurred in the home and then requiring them to functionally analyze what occurred, (4) differentially reinforcing parent behaviors consistent with the goals of therapy, (5) modeling and role playing in consultation sessions, and (6) constructing assignments which required behaviors relevant to solving the problems specified.

In giving assignments to parents, a number of factors were considered. First the assignments had to be realistic so that parents could be reinforced for successfully fulfilling them. It was usually necessary to give separate assignments to each parent so that the assignments were reasonable in the face of the parent's other commitments.

In the first individual session, the goal of the consultant was to help the parents to specify the problems in usable language. In Fred's case, speech and cooperative play were specified as problems, though neither label is an adequate description of the behaviors to be modified. The assignment from the first session was for the parents to: (1) generate a list of potential reinforcers, (2) list ways to reconstruct the environment to increase the probability of cooperative play, and (3) to make observations and collect baseline data on cooperative play.

In Session Two, Fred's bizarre hand motions were discussed. The technique suggested for decreasing these behaviors was to use Fred's bizarre hand motion as a stimulus signalling a timeout (a mild form of punishment). Home observations revealed that Fred's bizarre hand movements usually acted as a discriminative stimulus (or cue) for Fred's mother to ask him if there were a problem or if something was wrong. During this session the parents named some specific behaviors which they wished to modify. Coloring, use of scissors, and social interaction were specified. Upon further specification social interaction was broken down to increased eye contact. In shaping eye contact, the mother used bits of dry cereal as reinforcers.

In Session Three, discussion focused on the development of adequate reinforcers through the establishment of a token economy. The father accepted responsibility for establishing the tokens as conditioned reinforcers. The parents reported that they bought a buzzer device in the hopes of alleviating the problem of bedwetting.

By the fourth consultation session, establishment of the conditioned reinforcers had begun. Poker chips served as tokens. Initially no behavior was required to earn tokens. A token is placed on the father's fingertips and a backup reinforcer in his palm. The child takes the token. If he does not take the token, it is placed in his hand. The token is then removed from the child's hand and the backup reinforcer is immediately delivered to him. The delay between the child receiving the token and the exchange for the backup reinforcer is established gradually. At the end of the first week the father brought in data indicating that Fred delayed the token exchange for 30 seconds. The father suggested the use of a bank into which the tokens could be deposited, and then removed for the exchange. The behaviors of depositing and removing the tokens helped to mediate the time delay. The mother reported during the fourth therapy session that she was shaping behaviors relevant to identifying letters of the alphabet. She was using magnetic letters on a metal board plus a

phono-visual book from the public school system. During the fourth session the parents stated that they wanted to teach Fred to appropriately say, "Yes, please" in reponse to a question. To achieve this end, we decided to use food at the dinner table. This experiment was straightforward and simple. Fred would be asked, "Would you like X [some food being served for dinner]? Say 'Yes, please.'" When Fred responded, "Yes, please" he would receive the food. A fading procedure was used and within one week Fred responded correctly to "Fred, would you like X?" The parents reported the generalization occurred in that Fred would respond, "Yes, please" appropriately to various other questions.

During week five, work continued on establishing tokens as conditioned reinforcers and the only behavior required to earn a token was to take it from the father's hand. Toward the end of week five, Fred's father required that Fred count tokens in order to earn them. This was a task which made very small demands in the beginning. A token exchange price list was set up so that the token economy would be stable and records could be more easily kept. The parents reported that they purchased a small chest in which the backup reinforcers would be kept in transparent drawers. They further reported that the token economy was being extended into the private kindergarten Fred was attending. The assignment for week six included specifying behaviors that would be shaped with token reinforcement, listing ways to extend the token economy into all parts of the environment, and generating lists of more backup reinforcers.

During Session Six, the father stated that he was teaching Fred to count and that data from the kindergarten indicated that the token economy was being effective. He reported that an observer to the school was unable to pick out Fred as a child different from the others. The assignment for Session Seven was to expand the list of behaviors to be shaped with tokens.

In Session Seven, the parents reported that tokens were being used extensively throughout the household. Session Seven also revealed that Fred had successfully delayed exchanging tokens for up to two days. This occurred during a visit in a distant city over the Thanksgiving vacation. Fred earned tokens in that city, but could not exchange them until having returned home. The father reported that Fred bought a trip to the zoo for the whole family with some of his tokens. Some behaviors specified by the parents to be shaped with token reinforcement were (1) buttoning, (2) lacing shoes, (3) counting, and (4) sitting quietly during a story. Sitting quietly during a story became one of the target behaviors. To shape this behavior the mother reinforced Fred for sitting quietly, listening to a story, and turning the page. The token was delivered to Fred immediately after the page was turned. The schedule of reinforcement was initially one token for each page turned, Continuous Reinforcement or Fixed Ratio of 1 (CRF), but two therapy sessions later tokens were already being programmed, one token for about three pages turned, Variable Ratio of 3 (VR3).

During Session Eight improvements in the eye contact experiment were suggested by requiring a discrimination task. Rather than have Fred "look in Mommy's eyes," he was to verbally report if "Mommy's eyes were open or closed." The goals of this change were to provide a better behavioral criterion for dispensing reinforcement, and to make the task more "interesting."

By consultation Session Nine there was indication that systematic records were not being kept on the token economy and that too many tokens were available in the economy (i.e., there was not enough deprivation).

After a home observation of the new eye contact procedures between Sessions Eight and Nine, the consultant suggested that the mother terminate the eye contact experiment. Some of the problems associated with the eye contact experiment were: (1) the lack of a good criterion for defining the behavior and (2) many child behaviors incompatible with eye contact were being maintained in the experimental environment. The assignment made in Session Nine was for the mother to continue working with Fred on learning the letters of the alphabet. This endeavor seemed to be the most successful thing that was being done. The father was to continue working on counting. Other parts of the assignment were for the parents to work on programs to teach Fred to dress and undress himself and for them to present graphed data on the alphabet work.

By consultation Session Ten, the "Yes, please" experiment was terminated after three weeks of perfect responding by Fred. Also by Session Ten, the father had abandoned his own techniques for establishing counting behavior and adopted some of his wife's procedures using magnetic numbers on the metal board. The parents expressed a desire to teach Fred to write. There was some question about the handedness of the boy. The assignment for Session Eleven was for the parents to graph data relevant to bedwetting and the alphabet; for them to gather materials from a local college of education as well as from the public schools to facilitate Fred's education; to develop programs for teaching Fred how to write; and to continue working with the alphabet.

Fred's father indicated in Session Eleven that he had gotten materials from a public elementary school as well as from a local college of education. He also related some events indicating to the consultant that he had a fairly good understanding of the concepts used and discussed during the consultation sessions. For example, during an experimental session for teaching Fred to count, the father realized that he did not have a supply of tokens with him. Therefore, he used marks on a piece of paper instead of poker chips as tokens and these were later cashed in for poker chips. It was decided to use breakfast as a reinforcer to shape Fred's dressing behaviors. During Session Eleven preparations for postreatment consultation were begun. The final assignment for Session Twelve was to determine the handedness of Fred, continue working with the letters, continue working with dressing, and counting.

In Session Twelve the mother reported that she was going ahead with the alphabet work and had introduced lower case letters from books. She also used flash cards during the learning sessions. In general she kept good data. The data from the handedness experiment indicated that Fred was left-handed. The father reported that he did some work on teaching Fred to write. He also stated he was using materials from the public schools to teach Fred to count.

Throughout the 12-week treatment, some of the backup reinforcers used to establish the tokens as reinforcers were opportunity to look at pictures in a book, opportunity to manipulate things on father's desk, opportunity to watch the washing machine in operation, opportunity to look at the fan above the stove as it operated, opportunity to type on the typewriter, buying a lunch box with tokens, Pepperidge Farm crackers, M&M's, raisins, fancy candy, ice cream cones, cookies, orange juice, a trip to the zoo. Tokens were contingent on Fred's counting, buttoning, having a dry bed, pushing a button to open up the clothes dryer, drawing, washing hands, drying hands, sitting quietly during a story and turning pages, working at the typewriter, not thumb sucking, cooperating with the other children, making eye contact, and putting on knee socks. In general these parents seemed to have benefited from this operant treatment. They acquired some skills in behavior control. They acquired knowledge that would help them specify behaviors and the reinforcers to build them. They seemed to understand the application of techniques, such as shaping, extinction, modeling, and fading.

The major successes with this family were in making progress with alphabet work, having Fred sit quietly during a story, having Fred respond appropriately to requests, and increasing the frequency of a dry bed. These successes may have been improved greatly had there been more opportunity for home demonstrations and home visits.

A particular weakness in this consultative interaction was the lack of clearness of assignments as well as the lack of enforcing the contingencies for incomplete assignments. Had the consequences for poor work been imposed earlier in the series of meetings, more success may have resulted. The problems that existed in the initial phases of consultation were in (1) getting parents to specify the problems in usable terms, (2) getting parents to use adequate reinforcers, (3) keeping good data, and (4) getting parents to perform good experiments with clear, consistent sets of operations.

At the end of the 12-week consultation program the consultant wrote, "Presently the consultant would estimate that the parents have skills relevant to facilitating the behavioral development of their child, Fred. Whether they have the time to work with Fred in the future and how much of their behavior in working with Fred was maintained by coming to consultation sessions on a weekly basis are questions which will be answered in the future. These parents seem quite well prepared to specify problems, to plan solutions, and to use behavioral

concepts to facilitate the progress of their child."

Outcome

Our experience with over 50 families suggests that this method has much promise. Reports from all parents over more than a two-year period have been positive. The work with nine of the families was evaluated by means of objective ratings of before- and after-treatment video tape recordings (Walder et al., 1968; and Merigan & Miller, 1969). It was found that there was a substantial increase in desirable child behaviors (especially at home with the mothers) after operant consultation with the parents but not after a wait-period treatment and not after nonoperant consultation. One limitation is that the rating system, albeit of high reliability, was developed by a friend of behavior modification (Baer & Merigan, 1968).[7]

Standard personality tests (e.g., Holtzman, TAT, MMPI, Sentence Completion) were administered to the parents before and after treatment. They were administered, scored, and interpreted blindly by Hill (1968). She reported much more improved parent test scores after operant consultation than after nonoperant consultation.

The subjective and objective results continue to appear favorable; however, this methodology is not yet a finished, fully evaluated clinical technique. It deserves replication with better trained and programmed staff (both operant and nonoperant), more subjects, from different educational and social backgrounds, another rating system for the outcome tapes, longer term follow-up, etc.

SUMMARY

We have described a program and an orientation which we hope suggests answers to the community mental health question of "*Who* should administer *what* treatment to *whom*, *when*, and *where*?"

Who and to Whom? The answer to "*Who* should administer the treatment *to whom*?" is: one who is responsible for the behavioral development of another and who is skilled in the modification of behavior. The specification, explicit or not, of who is responsible for whom is a most important aspect of any community. Without necessarily approving, one may observe parents being responsible for the "mental health" of their children. Similarly, teachers are responsible for the "mental health" of their students while in the classroom. As assignments of responsibility are accepted, then the *who* and the *whom* have been identified.

What? We have mentioned several of the definitions of mental health, each one relevant to the situation for which is was developed. The *what* of mental health education must deal with the common factors in the various situations which give rise to definitions of mental health. The constant factors in all of these situations are environmental events which precede behavior, the behavior itself, the environmental consequences of the behavior, and the functional relationships among these events. Thus, the answer to *"What* treatment?" is: the methodology of behavior change which is relevant to all of human behavior. The educational task confronting us is not to enlighten the public about mental health or illness, but to educate about the technology of behavior.

When? The best answer to *"When* should the treatment be administered?" is: before the crisis is reached. Those responsible for the behavioral development of others should be constantly structuring environments to foster the development of durable desirable behaviors.

Where? The answer to *"Where* should the treatment be administered?" is: everywhere that it is possible to control the environment in which someone for whom we are responsible functions. This matches the answers to *when*. Only as treatment is continuous and pervasive can it be preventive. Thus the presence of adequately trained parents in the child's environment may make it possible for the parents to fulfill their responsibilities.

Notes

This chapter is specifically dedicated to the late Paul G. Daston. He was a man of honesty, good humor, diligence, and responsibility. We, his colleagues, and the people he served remember him with pleasure and appreciation. We assure the reader that this chapter would be better written if Paul's fine language skills were still with us.

The work with parents of disturbing children reported in the latter part of this chapter was partially supported by a grant from the Agnes E. Meyer Foundation to the Murch Home and School Association and a grant (# 32–30–7515–5024) from the United States Office of Education to the Institute for Behavioral Research. The encouragment of C. B. Ferster is gratefully acknowledged.

1. A recent development by Guerney and his associates (Guerney, 1964; Guerney, Guerney, & Andronico, 1966) offers technical skills to parents in Rogerian play therapy.

2. Rosalind Dymond Cartwright recently (1968) stated, "Altogether for behavior therapy it looks as though it has been a very good year [p. 390]."

3. Two other gains from this method seem to have been (1) the parents having learned a method of controlling behaviors in general (often being pretty good consultants for their friends) and (2) the husband and wife having reported a better marital relationship, perhaps from (a) having been required by us to act in unison with respect to their child and (b) having achieved additional success in their child-rearing endeavors (and thus not blaming each other).

4. This technique was borrowed from Hirsch (1967).

5. The nine families participated in a study comparing types of family therapy. In this chapter we shall discuss only the operant oriented type.

6. The test consisted of ten randomly selected frames from the sets assigned.

7. The rating system was built by Baer and Merigan, not having been informed as to which behaviors concerned the parents or therapeutic staff.

References

Astin, A. W. The functional autonomy of psychotherapy. *American Psychologist*, 1961, 16, 75–78.

Baer, D. M., & Merigan, W. H. A behavioral evaluation of parent-child interaction from video tape recordings. In L. O. Walker (ed.), *Teaching parents and others principles of behavioral control for modifying the behavior of children.* (Final report submitted to United States Office of Education on December 15, 1968, concerning Grant No. 32–30–7515–5024, Project III) Washington, D. C.: United States Office of Education, 1968.

Bandura, A. Punishment revisited. *Journal of Consulting Psychology*, 1962, 26, 298–301.

Berkowitz, S. Acquisition and maintenance of generalized imitative repertoires of profoundly retarded children with retarded peers functioning as models and reinforcing agents. Unpublished doctoral dissertation, Department of Psychology, University of Maryland, 1968.

Berkowitz, S., Walder, L. O., Thomas, J. R., Boyle, M. L., & Beach, T. A. Acquisition and maintenance of generalized imitative repertoires of profound retardates with retarded peers functioning as models and reinforcing agents. *Journal of Applied Behavior Analysis*, in press.

Breiter, D. E. An analysis of deviant child behavior in the home. Unpublished doctoral disseration, Department of Psychology, University of Maryland, 1968.

Brim, O. G., Jr. *Education for child rearing.* New York: Free Press. 1959.

Caplan, G. *Principles of preventive psychiatry.* New York: Basic Books, 1964.

Cartwright, R. D. Psychotherapeutic processes. *Annual Review of Psychology*, 1968, 387–416.

Cohen, S. I., & Walder, L. O. An experimental analog from crisis theory. *American Journal of Orthopsychiatry*, 1971, 41, 822–829.

Cohen, S. I. Report on the Anne Arundel Learning Center. Unpublished report to the Anne Arundel County Board of Education, Annapolis, Maryland, November 1969.

Davis, J. A. *Education for positive mental health.* (Report No. 88) Chicago: National Opinion Research Center, University of Chicago, 1963.

Dreikurs, R., & Soltz, V. *Children: The challenge.* Des Moines, Iowa: Meredith Press, 1964.

Dunlap, K. *Habits: Their making and unmaking.* New York: Liveright, 1932.

Eron, L. D., Walder, L. O., & Lefkowitz, M. M. *Learning of aggression in children.* Boston: Little, Brown, 1971.

Eysenck, H. J. The effects of psychotherapy: An evaluation. *Journal of Consulting Psychology*, 1952, 16, 319–324.

Ferster, C. B., & Perrott, M. C. *Behavior principles.* New York: Appleton-Century-Crofts, 1968.

Freud, S. Analysis of a phobia in a five-year-old boy. In *Collected papers.* Vol. 3, New York: Basic Books, 1959.

Fuller, P. R. Operant conditioning of a vegetative human organism. *American Journal of Psychology*, 1949, 62, 587–590.

Golann, S. E. Community Psychology and mental health: An analysis of stategies and a survey of training. In I. Iscoe & C. Spielberger (eds.), *Community psychology: Perspectives in training and research.* New York: Appleton-Century-Crofts, 1970.

Guerney, B., Jr. Filial therapy: Description and rationale. *Journal of Consulting Psychology*, 1964, 28, 304–310.

Guerney, B., Jr. The utilization of parents as therapeutic agents. Paper presented at the annual meeting of the American Psychological Association, New York, September 1966.

Guerney, B., Jr. (ed.) *Nonprofessionals as psychotherapeutic agents: New roles for aides, volunteers, parents, and teachers.* New York: Holt, Rinehart & Winston, 1969.

Guerney, B., Jr., Guerney, L. F., & Andronico, M. P. Filial therapy. *Yale Scientific Magazine*, March 1966.

Hobbs, N. Mental health's third revolution. *American Journal of Orthopsychiatry*, 1964, 34, 822–833.

Hill, E. F. Evaluation of psychological testing of the nine pairs of parents. In L. O. Walder (ed.) *Teaching parents and others principles of behavioral control for modifying the behavior of children.* (Final report submitted to United States Office of Education on December 15, 1968, concerning Grant No. 32–30–7515–5024, Project III) Washington, D. C.: United States Office of Education, 1968.

Hirsch, I. S. Training mothers in groups as reinforcement therapists for their own children. Unpublished doctoral dissertation, Department of Psychology, University of Maryland, 1967.

Hirsch, I. S., & Walder, L. O. Training mothers in groups as reinforcement therapists for their own children. *Proceedings of the 77th Annual Convention of the American Psychological Association*, 1969, 4, 561–562. (Summary)

Holland, J. G., & Skinner, B. F. *The analysis of behavior.* New York: McGraw-Hill, 1961.

Honig, W. K. (ed.) *Operant behavior: Areas of research and application.* New York: Appleton-Century-Crofts, 1966.

Jahoda, M. *Current concepts of positive mental health.* New York: Basic Books, 1958.

Janowitz, M. Generalization of verbal conditioning in non-talkative hospitalized persons using other hospitalized persons as tutors. Unpublished doctoral dissertation, Department of Psychology, University of Maryland, 1970.

Jones, M. C. The elimination of children's fears. *Journal of Experimental Psychology*, 1924, 7, 382–390.

Kessler, J. W. *Psychopathology of childhood.* Englewood Cliffs, N. J.: Prentice-Hall, 1966.

Klein, D. C. Some concepts conerning the mental health of the individual. *Journal of Consulting Psychology*, 1960, 24, 288–293.

Lanyon, R. I., & Broskowski, A. T. An engineering model for clinical psychology. *The Clinical Psychologist*, 1969, 22, 150–141.

Lovass, O. I. *Reinforcement therapy* (a movie). Philadelphia: Smith, Kline, French, 1966.

Maslow, A. H. *Toward a psychology of being.* Princeton, N. J.: Van Nostrand, 1962.

McIntire, R. W. *For the love of children.* Del Mar, Calif.: CRM Books, 1970.

Patterson, G. R. *Families: Applications of social learning to Family life.* Champaign, Ill.: Research Press 1971.

Patterson, G. R., & Gullion, M. E. *Living with children: New methods for parents and teachers.* Champaign, Ill.: Research Press, 1969.

Reese, E. P. *Behavior theory in practice* (a movie). New York: Appleton-Century-Crofts, 1965.

Reese, E. P. *The analysis of human operant behavior.* Dubuque, Iowa: William C. Brown, 1966.

Rogers, C. R. *On becoming a person.* Boston: Houghton Mifflin, 1961.

Rosen, G. Social stress and mental disease from the 18th century to the present: Some origins of social psychiatry. A public lecture at the Institute of Psychiatry, University of London, July 8, 1958.

Schopler, E. Parents of psychotic children as scapegoats. Paper presented at the annual meeting of the American Psychological Association, Washington, D. C., September 1969.

Scott, W. A. Research definition of mental health and mental illness. *Psychological Bulletin*, 1958, 55, 29–45.

Skinner, B. F. *Beyond Freedom and dignity.* New York: Alfred A. Knopf, 1971.

Smith, J. M., & Smith, D. E. P. *Child management: A program for parents and teachers.* Ann Arbor, Mich.: Ann Arbor Publishers, 1966.

Stubbs, T. H. The risk of false promise on achieving public emotional well-being. *Alabama Mental Health*, 1963 (February-March), 3–6.

Surratt, P. R., Ulrich, R. E., & Hawkins, R. P. An elementary student as a behavior engineer. *Journal of Applied Behavior Analysis*, 1969, 2, 85–92.

Szasz, T. S. The myth of mental illness. *American Psychologist*, 1960, 15, 113–118.

Szasz, T. S. *The myth of mental illness: Foundations of a theory of personal conduct*. New York: Hoeber-Harper, 1961.

Ullmann, L. P., & Krasner, L. A. *A psychological approach to abnormal behavior*. Englewood Cliffs, N. J.: Prentice-Hall, 1969.

Ulrich, R., Stachnik, T., & Mabry, J. (eds.) *Control of human behavior*. Glenview, Ill.: Scott, Foresman, 1966.

Valett, R. E. *Modifying children's behavior*. Palo Alto, Calif.: Fearon Publishers, 1969.

Vidaver, R. The mental health technician: Maryland's design for a new health career. *American Journal of Psychiatry*, 1969, 125, 1013–1023.

Walder, L. O. (ed.) *Teaching parents and others principles of behavioral control for modifying the behavior of children*. (Final report submitted to United States Office of Education on December 15, 1968, concerning Grant No. 32–30–7515–5024, Project III) Washington, D. C.: United States Office of Education, 1968.

Warman, F. C., III. A fading procedure for verbal conditioning of psychiatric patients. Unpublished doctoral dissertation, Department of Psychology, University of Maryland, 1969.

Watson, J. B., & Rayner, R. Conditioned emotional reactions. *Journal of Experimental Psychology*, 1920, 3, 1–14.

Whalen, C. K., & Henker, B. A. Creating therapeutic pyramids: The use of operant and imitative procedures to teach speaking retardates to act as therapists for non-speaking retardates. Paper presented at the annual meeting of the Society for Research in Child Development, New York, April 1967.

White, R. W. Motivation reconsidered: The concept of competence. *Psychological Review*, 1959, 66, 297–333.

Wilson, L. *This stranger, my son*. New York: G. P. Putnam's Sons, 1960.

25

Mental Health Consultation to Community Settings: A Case Study of a Failure to Achieve Goals

Frances Kaplan Grossman and Donald Quinlan

One goal of many community mental health efforts is to influence existing health and education facilities to redefine their task or to broaden the nature of the services they offer (Blanco & Akabas, 1968; Klapman, Moss, Brand, & Boverman, 1968; Sarason, 1967; Sarason & Sarason, 1969). Unsuccessful attempts at accomplishing such changes are probably the rule rather than the exception to a large degree because of the lack of any helpful conceptual or theoretical framework for considering such an endeavor (Sarason, 1967). The development of a framework is itself hindered by the dearth of detailed case material of attempts by clinicians and others to serve as change agents.

Over the past several years, some of us at the Psycho-Educational Clinic have attempted to formulate some ideas about this problem, in the context of our growing experience in a variety of community organizations (Kaplan & Sarason, 1969; Levine, 1969; Sarason, 1969; Sarason & Sarason, 1969).

The consultation described here grew out of the participation of the Clinic in planning and establishing a Regional Center for the Mentally Retarded in which the principles of use of community resources and primary prevention are emphasized in the allocation of the Center's services.

This chapter presents a detailed description of our thoughts and actions as we attempted to introduce several changes into a hospital's method of dealing with handicapped children and their families, with a brief discussion of some of the ideas the authors have found most helpful in our work with organizations.

Because in our description we have focused on our errors and our uncertainties, the change effort may appear unusually naive and consequently the issues may not appear relevant to less flawed efforts. But even if we had committed fewer errors or none at all, the point of this presentation would be the same, to begin to delineate the relevant issues and dimensions. Only when more clarity on these is reached will it be possible to approach systematically problems of technique.

In this chapter, we first describe briefly the Regional Center for the Mentally Retarded, which was the organization trying to bring about some changes in community services. Next we present the philosophy of service of the staff of the center. Then we present in detail our contacts with the hospital, first giving the "case" material from our notes, then presenting our thinking *at that time* about what seemed to us to be the important issues. After this material has been presented, we then comment on the overall endeavor, with the knowledge of hindsight.

OPPORTUNITY FOR PLANNED INTERVENTION

Several years ago, the opportunity arose for us to attempt to influence a community agency and to keep careful records on much of the resulting process. Several members of the Psycho-Educational Clinic (including both authors) were directly involved in the establishment of a new Regional Center for the Mentally Retarded. The Center is committed to the position that the needs of retarded children and their families can be met only through the concerted efforts of all the existing community facilities, yet presently many of these organizations exclude retarded children from their services (Dupont, 1967). Consequently, one major goal of the Center is to influence existing facilities to provide relevant skills and services to all families, including those where mental retardation is a factor. The second step is to help them provide adequate services in those cases where some specialized skills are required, either by our participation with them in discussion of the case, our supervision of their worker on the case, or occasionally our providing directly the services needed.

A second major focus of the Center is its emphasis on prevention, not only of mental retardation itself whenever possible but also prevention of psychological difficulties that follow the birth of a retarded child. Our assumption is that many of the difficulties associated with mental retardation are psychological and social phenomena, often caused by our culture's way of dealing with these families (Farber, 1968; Kaplan, 1969). Thus, for example, when we exclude families with retarded children from the regular health and education services of a community, we exacerbate their already strong sense of isolation and deprivation.

Even when the culture does not in any obvious or immediate sense create the problem, the difficulties are often potentially responsive to cultural, or community, solutions. For example, many families have difficulty meeting crises in an adaptive way, and often their subsequent development is affected negatively by their reaction to the crisis. Farber (1964) describes the reorganization of family relationships and roles that can occur when a retarded child is born that can be detrimental to the potential growth and development of one or more family members. In one of our cases, a mother became so preoccupied with meeting a severely retarded child's multiple needs that the siblings were deprived of normal mothering, the husband felt neglected and displaced, and the family became isolated from relatives and friends. Our intervention was brief counseling, with referral to community agencies for temporary placement to allow some reintegration of the rest of the family during a vacation. There is other evidence that consistent outside assistance during the crisis period can greatly aid the adaptive resources of the family (Caplan, 1960). One aspect of our conceptualization of our job is to begin to understand the predictable crisis points in a family's development, and then to structure into our agency and others the services to assist families in better handling the stress.

The Hospital as a Site for Preventive Intervention

Given this orientation, several of us have long been convinced of the centrality of the physician in either exacerbating or ameliorating the psychological trauma of mothers of young retarded children (Sarason & Doris, 1969). What physicians say and how they say it has been demonstrated to be enormously important to mothers (Stone, 1967). Thus we have had a growing conviction of the need to influence physicians and also to make other services available to mothers of newborn retarded infants.

In addition, we wondered what happened when handicapped children appear in a hospital. For several reasons this seems to be an important place for a mental health consultant. It provides an opportunity to locate some handicapped children not yet known to the relevant agencies and to ensure they are getting adequate services. If there are actual or potential psychological problems in the child or family, the heightened susceptibility to influence created by the crisis of illness and hospitalization might make it a favorable time to attempt an intervention. Finally, we wondered how the aides, nurses, and doctors actually respond to these children and whether their responses exacerbate or alleviate problems related to the handicap of the child. Turner (1966) found that the particular nursing techniques used on a ward, as well as the way the nurses are organized, affected the extent to which the hospitalization was experienced as a crisis by the patient. Ideally, the hospital could play a major role in providing preventive health and mental health programs to neighborhoods in a community, facilitating prompt referrals to the appropriate agencies, and making available its professional expertise and facilities in a variety of ways (cf. Cathell & Stratas, 1967; Turner, 1966).

Given this orientation, when we began to develop the new Regional Center one of the community facilities that seemed to us to be of critical importance in developing any community-wide preventive program was a general hosptial.[1]

There are a number of possible approaches to the consultation which could have been adopted. One tactic would have involved the consultant providing direct service. Eisdorfer, Altrocchi, and Young (1968) have discussed this as a necessary tactic in consultations to areas devoid of mental health services. Where other mental health services are available, such as in the situation described here, the consultant must somehow provide a distinctively different service that is not seen as overlapping present services, yet within the target agency's definitions of the professional role of the consultant. Alignment with the existing mental health facilities was another possibility, but the authors had been led to believe that the Mental Health Clinic of the hospital was, correctly or incorrectly, peripheral to the hospital and not appreciated by the hospital staff. Yet another model for approach would have been to remain on an advisory capacity to the hospital administration and medical board. But our goals, early referrals and structuring of a therapeutic environment in the pediatrics ward, seemed to dictate our consulting at the level of the particular wards involved with children, while keeping in mind the relationships with the administrative levels of the hospital.

The discussion of our failure to achieve goals is not without precedent in the literature on consultation. Cumming and Cumming (1957) detail a lengthy consultation which ended abruptly when the suspicions and fantasies about the "outsider" consultant prevented the continuation of a program that in some respects had moved toward achievement of its goals. Berken and Eisdorfer (1970) provide a more recent example in which a consultation was ended when the consultant unknowingly became involved in a rivalry between two administrators. Both of these examples highlight one of the many problems of a consultant being available and understood by all of the relevant groups which relate to the target activity of the consultant. Particularly because of the "outsider" nature of a consultant, he is a likely target for the fears, suspicions, and mistrust in a complex social system. Our description of a failure to achieve our goals is offered as a concrete

example of the complexity of dealing with a social system that at best can be only partially understood when the consultant enters.

CASE STUDY

Our impression of the hospital in this small (20,000) isolated New England community was that its energies were focused inward and it had little relationship to the community, other than serving sick people who came to it. This hospital, with no university affiliations, was less than 100 miles from four or five large and prestigious hospitals. In the hospital, as in the community overall, we had the impression that although relatively little of the foment that has hit mental health activities in recent years had yet reached it, some of the professionals were beginning to have uneasy feelings about the need for some recognition of the change in the social climate. In the hospital in particular, there was an ambivalence on the part of the personnel, who by and large did not want the hospital to change its rather old-fashioned ways, but were constantly reminded of their lesser standing vis à vis these other facilities.

We faced a problem in presenting ourselves as consultants. Although we were convinced of the need for mental health consultation and had been invited to attempt this by the administrator of the hosptial, we had the dual task of surveying the hospital, an unfamiliar organization, while convincing the medical staff of the need for program innovations, of our competence in planning these changes, and of the effectiveness of the changes we would introduce. Eisdorfer, Altrocchi, and Young (1968) point out the need for a survey of community needs supported by data, in approaching community agencies. We decided to try to assess the likelihood of actually accomplishing some change as we became acquainted with the organization, and hoped that the understanding of the organization of the hospital would proceed quickly enough to allow us to avoid any major pitfalls. We felt that the organization's reaction to a change effort would provide a useful diagnostic tool for future planning. The following "process notes" are adapted from a running diary the authors kept in the course of the consultation relationship.

"Process Notes"

During the first year of the Regional Center's existence, the hospital director, Mr. A., a relatively young man who had recently taken the job, served on a board with the director of the Center. The two of them became aware that they shared some ideas about how health agencies should serve the community. In particular, the hospital director felt strongly the need for the hospital to move out into the community, both physically and psychologically, and to establish a variety of new contacts with people and organizations in it. At an early meeting between the two, they briefly discussed the possibility of the Center's becoming directly involved with the hospital, and set up a more formal meeting time to consider that.

At that meeting were Mr. A., Dr. U., who was the chief of both the obstetrics and pediatrics wards, the chief of nursing, a new hospital planner, and the two potential consultants, the authors. The director of the Center made some opening introductory remarks and described the ideas we had discussed about the important role of a community hospital for services to retarded children. At this time, he explained, we were interested in having the opportunity simply to learn by observing what actually went on in three hospital units: the obstetrics ward, the pediatrics ward, and the emergency room.

We emphasized strongly that we could not know in advance how we might be helpful to them or what relationship might evolve between the hospital and the Center, that we needed time simply to observe and learn the culture and ways of the hospital. We also stated our awareness that having outsiders observing and not serving any well-defined purpose often made people in organizations uneasy and suspicious.

Dr. U. raised a number of questions. Who were we, the consultants? What was our formal relationship to the hospital going to be? And most pointedly, how long were we committed to working with the hospital? We explained that we were members of the Psycho-Educational Clinic that provided consultation services to the Regional Center. We were clinical psychologists by training, and came to the hospital by virtue of our close association with the Center, i.e., in that relationship we were serving as agents of the Center. As for the formal relationship with the hospital, all we could say was that we would very much like the opportunity to observe the day-to-day activities on the three services. It would take a long time before we could know more specifically what our role might be. We could say that we would not be providing direct individual psychological services, such as testing or therapy, except possibly to families of retarded children. In that case, of course, we would be functioning in our capacity as psychologists at the Center and not consultants to the hospital. The length of our commitment depended entirely on what we and the hospital staff could evolve that would be mutually beneficial.

Dr. U. then raised several questions about specific cases, asking whether we might get involved in any of them. For example, he mentioned the case of a girl with an "imaginary paralysis" (i.e., nonorganic) and asked what we would do. We sidestepped the issue, and carefully avoided comitting ourselves to seeing a child or a family individually at this point in our relationship with the hospital. Rather, we repeated our interest in getting to know the hospital as a total setting. Although Dr. U. probably did not understand why we took such a position, he did seem to accept it for the time being. When we asked him what we might observe that in the shortest period of time would give us the best picture of what occurred on obstetrics or pediatrics, he suggested we accompany him and his partner, Dr. I., on their daily rounds. He could introduce us to the nurses, talk with us about cases, etc. We were delighted and readily accepted the offer, making an arrangement to come out for eight o'clock rounds the following Saturday morning. When we asked whom else we should contact, he said there was only one social worker in the hospital. She was new, provided no service to the obstetrics or pediatrics wards, and was mostly occupied filling out forms. He emphasized something we were also aware of, which was the centrality of the nurses in such an endeavor.

When we asked whether there were any handicapped or retarded children in his private practice, he surprised us by saying, "Yes, why don't you come to our office sometime and sit in when we talk with one of the families?"

In discussing the meeting afterward, we were excited and optimistic. We felt we had been given a good entrée into the hospital through Mr. A. and

Dr. U., both of whom we liked and both of whom held important formal leadership positions in the hospital.

Port of Entry Problems

At that point we were aware that this first meeting was a crucial point in the consultation. It was a critical part of what Sarason and his colleagues (1966) and Bennis, Benne, and Chin (1961) describe as the "port of entry"—the characteristic reaction of any setting or organization to an attempt by an outsider to become part of that system. One problem the consultant faces is to assess quickly critical aspects of the culture at the same time as he has to act in that situation. In particular, one dimension of this is to assess where the power is in the organization. The dual hierarchy of the hospital, administrative and medical, made the location of the sources of power more difficult. The initial suspiciousness, mistrust, testing, etc., which manifest themselves in a host of different ways, must be sufficiently dealt with to enable the innovator to develop a relationship with individuals and groups within the organization. Loomis (1961) states that the problem for the consultant is to develop social capital in the system, which can later be used in applying pressure for change.[2] The entry problem is complicated by the fact that organizations have their own culture, which is initially foreign to the outside consultant, and which thereby emphasizes the differences between "insiders" and "outsiders." Unless the consultant is acutely sensitive to the taboos, restrictions, values, etc., of this culture, he is bound to violate many of them and unwittingly make more difficult his acceptance. Both becoming familiar with this culture, as well as allowing the members of the organization to get to know the consultant, so his behavior becomes predictable and hence trustworthy to them, are part of meeting the entry problem (Glidewell, 1961).

We did know that Mr. A was a forward-looking administrator who had a commitment to bringing about some changes and consequently probably viewed us as potential allies. On the other hand, we were aware of his newness to the situation and of the ambiguous and delicate position of any nonmedical administrator in a hospital (Katz & Kahn, 1966). Further, we had learned that the previous administator, who also came to the job

with a strong interest in updating aspects of the hospital's practices, had achieved some of his goals but only at the price of his own job. These factors all made the value of Mr. A.'s support uncertain. After that first meeting, we decided we would maintain at least enough contact with him to keep him informed of our activities, even though he was not directly involved with the wards. There were several reasons for this. It was possible that he was in an influential position in regards to our interest. Whether he were or not, if we kept him informed he would be more likely to be comfortable about the project and would undoubtedly appreciate our acknowledgment of his right and need as chief administrator to be informed. Further, up-to-date knowledge about our activities could protect him in his position if some questions about us arose and possibly could enable him to protect us if he chose to do so.

The critical importance of the backing of a highly placed physician was clear even without any knowledge of this particular hospital (Katz & Kahn, 1966). Dr. U.'s willingness to let us onto the wards seemed to us an enormous first step, and the fact that he would be there to introduce us made the initial problem of becoming acquainted appear much easier. We were acutely aware of the importance of making every effort to establish and strengthen a good relationship with him and his partner, both of whom we thought likely to respond positively.

Equally important in the long run was for us to establish contact with the nursing staff and the aides. Although the chief nurse had said relatively little, what she did say seemed to indicate an acceptance of what we wanted to do and possibly even some positive feelings about it. We did not know how close her contacts with the ward nursing personnel were or how much actual control she exerted over their activities. As in the case of Mr. A., we decided to keep her informed of our activities with the nurses and gradually assess her position as it influenced our project. Periodically, the consultants stopped in her office to keep her informed of progress in the project. She was invited to all of the formal meetings we had with the nurses, and on one occasion she attended.

Thus far we have described our efforts to establish ourselves with the upper echelons of the hospital. Eisdorfer and his colleagues (1968) emphasize the importance of the support of persons of community (and organizational) influence in helping a consultation program overcome resistance. But we felt possibly the most important group for us to develop a relationship with was the nursing staff and aides on the wards, since several of our ideas of how preventive work might be implemented involved this ward staff, who had the most direct contact with parents and children. Most characteristically, with innovative attempts in service agencies, the changes are initiated from "on high" by the designated leader (Sarson, 1969). Equally characteristically, the changes must be implemented by people at a much different organizational level. Sarason and Sarason (1969) described the introduction of new math into a public school system, where the people who would have to teach this subject had no role in the decision to introduce it or in devising the plan for making the transition to it. Consequently these teachers lacked both the understanding of its significance and the motivation to teach it successfully that could have made it a successful innovation. To state this more generally, although entry into an organization must include contact with individuals at the top levels, in order to institute change effectively great attention must be paid to those who, by virtue of their organizational position, will actually carry out or obstruct the proposed plan (Zander, 1961; March & Simon, 1958).

We accepted—much too readily, it turned out—Dr. U's dismissal of the social worker as unimportant to our endeavor. Our readiness to believe him stemmed in part from a laziness that led us not to seek out extra work. More importantly, we did not see our activities as related to those of an administrative social worker, thereby ignoring a principle we knew quite well: that people whose interests are most closely related to the activities of the would-be change agent usually are most threatened by him and consequently most resistant to changes suggested by him. For example, Reding and Goldsmith (1967) found the only resistance to using nonprofessional volunteers as members of the psychiatric consultation team came from the psychiatrists. Eisdorfer and others allude to this by emphasizing the need to respect the patterns of different professions.

Source of Impetus for Change. The entry problem was further exacerbated in this situation, as in many community mental health projects, by the fact that the impetus for the change attempt came as much from the change agents as from the target organization. Thus, to a greater degree than in most situations described by the industrial psychologists, members of the organization had first to be convinced that some change would be desirable for them and their organization before we could begin exerting pressure actually to create change.

How the Consultant Presents his Goals to the Organization. When the primary motivation for change comes from the would-be change agent, a major question arises as to whether and how and to whom his interest in "reforming" the organization should be made explicit at the beginning. A further question is to what extent his actual consulting activities should from the beginning remain directly focused on the system rather than beginning as the more expected individually oriented clinician who over time tries to influence broader aspects of the organization. Dr. U.'s questions to us about individual cases, coming as it did shortly after we had stated our commitment to trying to evolve a new role that would not involve us in direct clinical services, was not surprising to us. We have found repeatedly that when we say we want to focus on helping the system as a whole—or some subsystems of it—rather than focusing on individual cases, the initial reaction of people in the setting is to act as if they had not heard us. The expectations of how a clinician will function are so strong that only repeated discussions and demonstrations of a different role can convince people in settings that we mean what we say. (This is complicated by the strong temptation on our part to slide back into the better defined and more comfortable role of individual clinician.) After that, we must convince them that our focus is sensible, i.e., that we can ultimately be more helpful to them in this way. This is often difficult, because individuals in such settings seldom share our belief that the ultimate answer to the highly limited availability of good clinical services is not more professionals but different ways of solving problems that make better use of resources in the setting itself and of nonprofessionals (Sarason et al., 1966).

We had felt that for us to provide traditional individual clinical service in the hospital would not solve the problems that concerned us. Our time would immediately be consumed by the demand, many of the traditional clinical services would be of dubious value even to those few patients receiving them, and the situation would continue essentially as it had been. Beyond this, we were not then clear as to what role or roles might develop or how we could be helpful, but we had decided to state this conviction at the beginning of our contact. Our decision to avoid traditional contact was later vindicated by the response of the mental health clinic associated with the hospital, which would have been much more difficult to deal with if we had attempted to provide equivalent services.

Several of us at the Psycho-Educational Clinic are convinced that the way entry is gained greatly effects and ultimately limits what can be done in the consultant position later on (Sarason et al., 1966). To cite an extreme example to illustrate the point, a person might gain access to a school on the grounds of giving piano lessions, but the probability that once in he could use his position to change the relationships between the teachers and the principal is very low. In community mental health work this becomes a critical issue. Whether a consultant is sought or initiates the move himself, rarely will an organization be interested in the kind of change he might think best. That is, most organizations that deal in human services define their problems in terms of the deviance of individuals rather than in terms of a need on the part of an organization to change. Levine (1969) cites many instances in which a school seeks help in handling a disruptive child. The school personnel view the problem as inherent in the child, while the consultant might well see it as a problem in the school system itself. If the consultant openly shares his thoughts about the probable need for some organizational change, he runs the risk of being excluded from the beginning. On the other hand, if he presents himself as interested in providing more traditional individual psychological services, he may find himself so caught in his role as individual clinician

that he never effectively will be able to operate in any other way. Further, he opens himself to the possibly legitimate charge of dissimulation in his initial approach. Finally, the consultant's awareness that he is not being open with the members of the organization about his own motives can make his use of himself less spontaneous. This last point, however, is both complicated and controversial. It is by no means demonstrated that it is helpful for a change agent, be he individual psychotherapist or systems consultant, to share with his client every thought or feeling he has in his head, nor is some restraint in this matter dishonesty. The line between discretion and outright manipulation becomes at times fine and difficult to draw.

Several authors argue the opposite position about how early in the relationship the consultant should focus on his ultimate goals. Rosenbaum and Ottenstein (1965) describe a situation in which their direct efforts at promoting a new model of service among a group of community agencies were completely ineffective until they first established contact by providing a more traditional consulting service to them. In the relationship they built up over time, they were then able to influence the services these agencies provided. Blanco and Akabas (1968) describe an intervention into a factory and emphasize the importance of their initial nonthreatening approach, even though the beginning endeavor was very unlike what they eventually hoped to do. Klapman, Mass, Brand, and Boverman (1968) were able to change the way public health nurses served retarded children only after they had clarified an initially ambiguous role and took a more active and in some respects traditional role in organizing services.

We were aware that in the hospital our unwillingness to prove our usefulness by providing traditional clinical services would make our role more puzzling and less obviously useful to the staff for some time, and would consequently prolong the period of time before we would be accepted by the organization. We believed, however, that in the long run this tactic would give our project a greater likelihood of success. In the case presented, our initial goals may seem unfocused, both in this presentation and in fact as they were presented to the hospital. This ambiguity was unavoidable, since our aim was in fact to arrive with hospital personnel at more specific goals.

First Visit

This visit is described in detail to give a picture of how we actually operated in the situation and how the climate and culture of the hospital appeared to us. We arrived together at 8:30 to meet Dr. U., who had just completed his examination of the newborns on the obstetrics ward. He greeted us with the comment: "Let me get this straight so that when I introduce you . . . you're psychiatrists or psychologists." We said, "Psychologists," and he added "So then I'll know not to use some fancy words doctors use, because you wouldn't understand." Nonetheless, he seemed friendly and hospitable. He briefly introduced us to the nurses who were present, then sat and talked with us about the nursery. It is a small unit with only 12 babies at a time. He said birth rates have been falling off. There were no "interesting cases" around at the moment, several premature babies but nothing special about them.

He talked with us about the difficulties he has in working with parents of obviously deformed or defective babies. When asked how and when parents are told of the defect, Dr. U. said they tell the parents as soon as they are certain of the diagnosis. He added parenthetically that it would be better if these children were not born. The mothers become depressed and give the baby superficial care with no real love. The families, in his view, and especially the siblings, lose the love that is normally given to a child. He described his procedure for telling of a defect. As soon as he knows, he tells her about it and asks if she has questions. At this point, often soon after delivery, mothers very seldom ask questions. He returns in several hours to answer the questions the mothers have once they recover from the initial period of shock and upset. He added that it was probably better to tell the father rather than the mother, but you often can't find the father. He felt institutionalization was the best arrangement, because it reduced the trauma of the family.[3] (He was quite clearly aware, however, that early institutionalization was not best for the infant.) We asked what their policy was about recommending institutionalization. He said they tend to make it on medical grounds, and volunteered that such a decision would be more appropriately based on an evaluation of the psychological situation in the family.

When we suggested we'd like to watch his procedures, he let us accompany him while he talked to several mothers of newborns. We went into a room where a woman who was about to go home was waiting for him. He introduced us as "from the state, interested in listening, in seeing how we do things," and then went on to talk with her about the care and handling of this first born child. In response to her many anxious questions, he seemed friendly, relatively sensitive, but also obviously not going to get into any psychological issues. He spent about five minutes with her, and told her to call any time if she had questions.

He went to the office to write some brief notes. At one point the charge nurse came by and he kidded with her and then introduced us to her. When we asked in her presence if it might be possible for us to be notified when a handicapped child was born so we could observe what happens, they both readily agreed. The charge nurse seemed quite friendly. (Dr. U told us later she is a little Napoleon, and we should talk more with her. She obviously runs the nursery.)

We followed him to the pediatric ward and stood around more or less in people's way while he looked at the charts. The charge nurse on pediatrics was there, as were several other doctors and nurses. (At this point, we were not introduced.) Dr. U. took us with him to see several children on the ward, including a three-year-old dying of leukemia. All the while the child was being examined, through the combined efforts of Dr. U. and a nurse, he was screaming and fighting. When Dr. U. decided he needed a second blood sample, he suggested we did not have to stay to watch. We gladly escaped to the hall.

Afterwards Dr. U. came out looking drawn and talked with amazing openness about how doctors try to feel and seem indifferent, but it's no fun sticking a kid who is screaming that you're hurting him. He talked about the difficulty this boy's parents were having coping with his illness and impending death, and that there was no one to help them. He described his attempts to keep the mother from remaining glued to the boy's bedside, and added that although she desperately needed someone to tell her she didn't have to stay, there was also the danger that she would feel guilty later on if she did not stay, so he had to make it just a suggestion. We asked about the boy's brothers and sisters and their reactions. He indicated it had not occurred to him to think about it. (We were aware, though, that he is amazingly sensitive to his immediate patient's problems.) He talked of the boy himself as a spoiled child, as children with terminal leukemia often are, and of the parents neglecting the other children for the time these children are sick. He half suggested we might want to do something with the boy, but generally focused more on what we might do to help the parents. He said doctors often are not the best ones to talk with the parents in such cases because the doctor is too closely associated with the disease in the minds of the parents.

He told us of another case, one, he said, "you really want to help." This was a 15-year-old girl who was probably going blind. No one had told her this and she had not gotten up enough courage to ask. It bothered him—and us—to think of her sitting there, seeing her world get darker and not knowing what was going on. He himself had not told her, he said, because doctors don't like to tell a 15-year-old she's going to be blind. He described it as a kind of unspoken understanding. He emphasized what a nice kid she is—bright, verbal, the kind you really want to help. He would very much like someone to talk with her.

We asked who was available to do this sort of thing. Of all the possible resources we mentioned—student nurses, the community psychiatric clinic, psychiatric residents—none were available now, and there was no social service time available. We said—quite truthfully—that we were strongly tempted to say we would see her, but repeated our belief that in the long run the amount of direct service we could provide was negligible; that the only real payoff would come if we could make better use of people already in direct contact with such patients as this girl, and could get some nonprofessionals involved in being helpful in specified ways.

This led into a discussion of the potential resources available in the community. Dr. U. had fought long and hard to get one social worker at

the hospital, and had finally convinced his more conservative colleagues to support this. She, however, was always busy filling out Medicare and other forms and at any rate was too busy on the adult wards to have any contact with pediatrics. Dr. U. was not sure whether the problem was primarily lack of funds, or that there was no trained personnel available even if funds were found. The local psychiatric clinic had had two unfilled positions for psychiatric social workers for two years.

Our evaluation of this visit was that it had been stimulating and exciting. Rather than our finding a major entry problem as we had anticipated, we found Dr. U. apparently quite open and interested in our approach and already working with problems that were relevant to our interests. We were not then certain whether his apparently quick acceptance of us was due to some unusual circumstances of which we were not as yet aware. We also considered the possibility that he was less accepting than he seemed. Our initial reception was similar to the reaction given to the consultant described by Berken and Eisdorfer (1970). They warn against regarding initial friendliness as acceptance in a culture where cordiality is the norm. Regardless of the specific dynamics of the situation, it was clear that Dr. U. was relatively sophisticated about psychological matters and amazingly in touch with his own feelings that got involved in the practice of medicine. Possibly our availability as listeners at a time of psychological stress around the impending death of the boy facilitated his acceptance of us.

We were beginning to evolve an idea that one way for us to be useful was to mobilize already existing community resources to provide some of the services needed by the hospital. The case of the 15-year-old who was possibly going blind seemed a good instance of the problem. For us to talk with her in the half day a week we could give to the hospital would not in any way deal with the problem of all the other children and families who needed assistance. Further, we were not convinced that she needed a trained professional; a sympathetic and interested volunteer with more time available would probably be of more use, particularly if some supervision were available. We decided to begin to look around for possible sources of volunteers, as well as for professionals who might provide supervision. A secondary value of getting a psychiatrically trained professional to supervise volunteers in the hospital might be to get the hospital and another agency in closer contact with each other. Despite our optimism and plans, though, we had not forgotten the extent of our ignorance about the workings of this institution, and were committed to spending much more time simply getting acquainted before trying to make any major moves.

We were aware that Dr. U. had not introduced us to the other doctors, but were unclear about its meaning or importance. We felt we could not approach the other physicians on our own without appearing to violate the implicit arrangement we had made with Dr. U. to let him be the techincal guide of our project in regard to his colleagues.

During the next several weeks, each of the consultants spent a different morning accompanying the two pediatricians on their rounds. The other partner, Dr. I., proved to be a friendly, alert man in his early 40s. He liked our idea of meeting with parents of newborn retarded children and was particularly favorable to our plan of introducing these parents to other parents with similar problems. He had done this on his own initiative on occasion. He said he would refer any such parents to us.

We continued to be less clear, and inevitably so did the physicians, about our role on pediatrics. They raised again, somewhat indirectly, the possibility of our seeing individual children in the ward, but made no protest when we continued to resist providing individual psychological services.

In an informal discussion with Dr. I. about his view of mongoloid children, he stated a different opinion from Dr. U. He felt these children should not be institutionalized at birth; it's hard to get placements for them, they don't thrive in institutions, and they tend to do well at home. We wondered what implications these different viewpoints had for their joint practice.

Dr. I. also spoke with us about the inadequacies of parents in reacting to the hospitalization and illness of their children. We began to raise the possibility that this might be a point where we could get involved. He also mentioned his involvement as medical director of a local community action program and asked if we were interested in helping. We said we definitely were, and set up a contact for him with the Center's director.

Again, despite the apparent friendliness and interest in our project, and although we were introduced to all the patients' parents that we met, we were less often introduced to the professional staff, and were conspicuously not introduced to the other doctors.

After we had been there for several weeks, we called Mr. A. to say what we had been doing, where our thinking stood at the moment, and how much fun we were having doing it. We said we would keep him informed from time to time on our progress. He was pleased to hear from us, very friendly, and said he appreciated our keeping him posted.

While waiting for Dr. U., who was always late, one of the consultants got into a conversation with one of the nurses in the nursery. The nurse asked the consultant (a woman) if many women were going into medicine these days. The consultant explained that she was not a physician but a psychologist and briefly described our interest in being around the nursery. The nurse laughed and said something like "Oh, like in-service training on the psychological implications of child raising?" to which the consultant could only reply, "yes." The nurse said she was glad we had chosen this particular ward. Later on, she came in with coffee and apple juice for the consultant.

Meanwhile, one of the nurses who had been busy giving PKU tests and washing the newborns came into the nursing office. We introduced ourselves, apologizing for looking over the nurses' shoulders as they were working. When we told her a little about our interest, she became quite friendly and talked about the PKU tests.

During this time, several physicians came in and looked at records, examined infants, etc. We finally introduced ourselves to one whom we knew to be an older pediatrician. He had not heard we were in the hospital, seemed willing to talk with us, and suggested we get all the doctors together and talk with them. He seemed friendly and interested. However, when trying to arrange to get together, the consultants mentioned Dr. U.'s name. Without warning the pediatrician said, "fine" and left, possibly miffed because he had realized that we had been spending time with these two pediatricians. It seemed clear to us at that time that we would have to meet with all the doctors very soon to avoid resentment building up against us.

On rounds with Dr. U. he did introduce us to the nurses in the premature unit, and we all talked and joked while he examined several babies there. When we mentioned to him again our interest in meeting with the other doctors, he agreed it was a good time. He suggested we come to their medical board and describe our project to them.

On pediatrics, Dr. U. suggested we talk with the chief nurse. She did have time to talk and seemed somewhat friendly but reserved. We explained to her briefly who we were and the general thoughts we had about how we might be helpful, and that we thought it very important that we get a chance to explain this to all of the nurses so that they would not feel uncomfortable when we were there observing. She agreed and indirectly let us know that the nurses had felt some discomfort about our observing them when the boy with leukemia was dying. We agreed to a meeting time when she could get as many of the nurses and aides together as possible. We felt we should not observe further on pediatrics until we held that meeting.

In that conversation with the charge nurse, we mentioned that sometimes one can learn things about the relationship between a mother and her child by seeing the interaction when the child is sick, and possibly such knowledge could be used later for some intervention. She agreed, and described a neglected infant on the ward, implicitly asking what we could do in such a situation. We repeated our need to learn much more about the ward before being in a position to help, but added that ultimately we were interested in just such questions.

Contacts with the nurses seemed to be developing well despite some awkwardness about when and how we were introduced. The fact that we had not yet talked with the other physicians, and the suggestion that this might be causing some pique, made it imperative that we attempt to broaden our contacts. Drs. U.'s and I.'s omission in this regard seemed surprising, given their skill in such tactical matters.

This phenomenon, of a group experiencing fear and resentment when another group within an organization seemed closer to some possible

change than another, has been noted by several authors (Bennis, Benne, & Chin, 1961; Jaques, 1961; Oetting, Cole & Hinkle, 1967). As a consultant, at times it feels as if one must be in many different places simultaneously in order to avoid the problem. Lippitt (1961), who discusses the problem from the standpoint of getting trapped into a relationship with one subgroup of the organization, comments: "Getting into contact with the whole client is one of the most challenging skill problems for the group consultant."

Five weeks after the initial contact both consultants attended a meeting of the medical board, in order to be introduced to all the physicians at the hospital. We were introduced by Mr. A. as psychologists at the Regional Center. We briefly described the Center and our interest in the hospital. The only question we were asked by the doctors concerned our relationship to the Mental Health Clinic, which was affiliated with the hospital. We explained that we were intending to contact them and explore with them possible relationships but now we were just beginning to get to know the hospital. We would not be providing overlapping services, we pointed out, and in no sense were in competition with them. We also told them we would like to talk with them in much more detail about their ideas about such services for children.

While at the hospital, we left a message for the chief nurse, inviting her to attend our meetings with the nurses on the two wards.

Thus far we had deliberately, although perhaps unwisely, ignored the Mental Health Clinic. The Clinic had some administrative ties with the hospital, although it was not directly part of the hospital, and was housed in a separate building. They provided traditional outpatient services to children, and were known to have a six month waiting list for all services. In our initial discussion with Mr. A., he had mentioned this group as people we should eventually get to know. The early contacts of several people at the Center with the Clinic had convinced us the Clinic was not a likely resource for us in the community. It seemed to be deeply committed to a traditional model of providing services with traditional lines of authority observed.[4] Secondly, we had no reason thus far in our dealings with the hospital to think the Clinic was involved with the personnel or the patients there.

Following our presentation to the board, we had no way of evaluating the physicians' responses to our comments. We had both been frightened by the awesome task of speaking before more than 50 apparently unresponsive and possibly unfriendly physicians, and were further unnerved by the discussion which just preceded our presentation, focusing as it did on their complaints about having to deal with lower class patients on Medicare, and parking lots. Only time would tell what the actual response to us had been.

Two weeks later, each of us met with one of the nursing groups on the two wards. The chief nurse did not come to either meeting. The nurses were quite friendly and interested, and also rather open in a joking way about raising questions about our interests and role. On the pediatrics ward they quickly moved to talking about individual children and raised the possibility of our making home visits. We said this might be possible when the child was retarded, but pointed out the inefficiency of our trying to provide much direct psychiatric and social work service, since there were two of us and we had relatively little time in a week to give. We emphasized the need for us all to learn a new way for these services to be provided. On their own initiative, they began describing the important and revealing things children say to them, expressed their uncertainty in knowing how to respond, and said how nice it would be if they could talk to someone more trained in this area about their work with parents and children.

At this, with the exception of two aides, they agreed that they would be happy for us to follow them around and observe as they went about their work in order to teach us about the culture of the ward. (The aides, after much coaxing, finally said they would feel very self-conscious being watched. We said we appreciated their telling us and of course would honor that feeling.) We pointed out that this was a new culture to us, and that we would inevitably do some things wrong in that culture, and that it was important for our relationship with them that they tell us when we did. They seemed to appreciate this point. We warned them of the inevitable frustration they would feel to have able-bodied people just standing around and watching when there was

work to be done, but emphasized how important it was for us to wait and learn about things before jumping in. In response to their question, we said we would each spend several hours a week on the ward.

After the meeting, the charge nurse raised some questions about the rough way one of the specialists handled the children. She wondered if we might observe but cautioned us not to mention her name. We said we would see what we could do and reassured her about our discretion.

Overall, we were both surprised and impressed by the easy air of camaraderie among the nurses and aides, and their openness to our ideas. Further, the willingness of the charge nurse to speak to us about a physician seemed to indicate a view of us at least as potential allies. And while we saw clearly the dangers of siding with the nurses *against* a physician, we were also pleased by the trust this indicated.

A meeting with the nurses on the obstetrics ward went equally well, with the nurses there showing a high level of sophistication about the potential uses of psychological consultants. However, they agreed with our view that the relative infrequency of births of defective children made it unnecessary for us to concentrate on this floor.

The good relationship with the nursing staff and aides continued and progressed over the next several months. Contacts with the pediatrics ward focused increasingly on problems arising in the day-to-day patient care. Informal conversation with them gave the consultants a fair knowledge of the relationships among the staff and allowed individual staff members to verbalize their doubts and questions about us. Generally, the nurses, and to a lesser extent the aides, brought interesting and appropriate questions to the consultants: what could they do about a girl who was concerned about medication she was taking to regulate her period? How could they deal with a nine-year-old boy who seemed continually to get hurt in order to get into the hospital, which provided a more pleasant and supportive environment than his disorganized home?

Both consultants found the work interesting and gratifying, and gradually became more active in discussing with the ward staff what they might do in various situations, and how they might think of the situation. There were the inevitable attempts by them to get us directly involved in providing direct services to cases, but they responded well to our insistence on being consultants to them rather than getting tied down by direct service activities.

A few weeks later, the pediatrics ward staff wholeheartedly approved our suggestion that we meet regularly with them for consultation if we could get the approval of the relevant physicians. We used these contacts with the nurses around specific patients as a vehicle for introducing ourselves to a number of physicians. When we asked Dr. U. about expanding the number of physicians we were working with, he advised us to proceed cautiously, to first demonstrate our usefulness with his and his partner's patients and with the patients of the people we had already met. Then, in a number of weeks, he would arrange for us to meet the group of pediatric physicians.

Several aspects of the program began to be clearer to us by this time. As was mentioned, we decided to spend only as much time on obstetrics as we needed to maintain contact with the nurses so that they would get in touch with us when a defective baby was born and would not feel uncomfortable about having us around. On pediatrics, in addition to trying to implement our goal of getting outside agencies and volunteers involved,[5] we had become convinced of the value of our providing group consultation to the nurses and aides to enable them better to handle the psychological aspects of their dealings with parents and children. In the very long run, we hoped to be able to interest psychologically trained personnel from other agencies to take over the consultative role, once its form, as well as its value, was established.

Although we knew a critical next step was for us to begin to be involved with other physicians who had private patients on the pediatrics ward we had to abide by Dr. U.'s decision as to the timing and sequence of our contacts.

A short time later, Dr. I. gave the consultants the names and phone numbers of two families in their practice who had young mongoloid babies and suggested we contact them. He had already prepared them for this call. We followed up immediately, each of us calling and visiting one of the families. We described the Center and its services, emphasizing our availability to them to help with the questions and issues that would periodically arise. Both families responded very positively to this interest and support. They had questions that we were able to answer about their children. When we mentioned a group of parents of young retarded children that we were starting as part of the Center's activities, both families expressed an interest in attending.

We made a point of informing the referring physicians of our contacts with these families, both as a courtesy so they would know what was happening with their patients, and also indirectly to educate them more about how we thought people could be helpful to families with retarded children.

At this point, these referrals that were made long before any major problems developed in these families seemed to us to be the most important result of our contact with the hospital. We felt then, and still believe, that early contact provided the best possibility for preventive interventions. Our willingness to provide direct clinical services to families of retarded children stemmed from our position as psychologists at the Center and not simply as consultants to the hospital. That this distinction might not be clear to the hospital personnel was predictable and would have to be dealt with in specific instances as it came up.

About four weeks after our meeting with the medical board, while making rounds, Drs. U. and I. mentioned some reactions that had occurred after our presentation. We set up a time to discuss this and also to discuss in more detail where the project was heading. Afterwards, "off the cuff," Dr. I. stayed to give us his views on the situation. He said he and Dr. U. had accepted us because they were more progressive and less defensive than most of the other doctors. He agreed with us that the town and hospital were beginning to change but he felt it was a very slow awakening. After we had been presented to the physicians, several had commented to him, "Why do we need them?" and were particularly upset because of a belief that we were associated with a regional board, which was a state group trying to bring medical services under regional planning and control. Despite our explicit disclaimer that we had any relationship with this group, our affiliation with the state-supported Regional Center brought with it the taint of state control and socialized medicine. Dr. I. felt that once we had our feet well in the door, and as the other physicians saw us being useful to himself and Dr. U., they gradually would come to accept us.

He seemed to convey the idea that as far as he was concerned we had already proved our worth. However, he also made it clear that he did not believe a direct approach by us to the other physicians would be a good way to proceed.

He started talking more generally about how one goes about getting a change accepted in the hospital, and recalled with obvious enjoyment some of the fights he and his partner had waged and won. The most recent was a program that allowed parents to stay in the room with their child in pediatrics as long as the parents would help with the child's care.

We again felt excited about the conversation, feeling that it greatly clarified the situation for us, since the unquestioning acceptance we had felt so far was literally too good to be true. Now at least we knew where the opposition would come from and could better cope with it. The fact that we first heard some weeks afterwards about reactions to our presence at the medical board did not surprise us, nor were we surprised that the reactions had not been apparent to us at the time. We were more impressed than ever with the need for great care about any involvement with the patients of other physicians until we had won their support.

Two weeks later, at this meeting with the two doctors, we reviewed for them the three parts of the project, which was more defined than previously: 1) We wanted to contact as many pediatricians as possible to explain in detail our thoughts to try to get referrals of newborn mentally retarded children. 2) We wanted to begin to meet regularly with the aides and nurses on pediatrics. 3) We wanted to continue to explore the possibilities of volunteers and other help from various community resources.

Dr. U.'s response was surprising to us. He said we could begin to explore potential community resources without any difficulty. Consultation with the nurses would meet with more obstacles from the physicians but he felt we could continue meeting with them while the obstacles were negotiated. But contacting the physicians would provide the most difficulty, since our presence had been questioned by a number of them at the staff meetings. Several, for example, had asked whether we had been seeing any of their patients without their knowledge. (He had assured them we had

not. Actually, in going the rounds with the nurses, we had been in the rooms of some of their patients, which step, according to hospital protocol, constitutes "involvement.")

Would it be possible, he asked, for us to write out a more substantial outline of what we were doing to present to the rest of the medical staff? Specifically, he wanted to know what services we would be providing to the hospital. Both doctors seemed to be in the position of having the consultants as proteges, and it was necessary for us to produce visible services or a tangible program to justify their support. They suggested we try to get formally approved as consultants by the hospital administrator and then the medical board.

In further discussing the situation, the two doctors suggested two other pediatricians who might be amenable to our ideas and services. They were less optimistic about other specialists who deal with children, such as the orthopedic surgeon, who they felt gave little thought to the psychological implications of having a child in the hospital. We discussed a possible procedure to minimize potential problems in our contacts on the ward. They suggested that when we or the nurses identified a problem, we should avoid any direct contact with the child until we had contacted one of them, and that they would then get in touch with the relevant physician. They could introduce us then to the doctor and pave the way for our getting in touch with the child. They felt we could talk with the nurses about anything or about any patient they brought up, but we ourselves were leery of the possible dangers involved even in that as long as the other physicians were viewing us with some suspicion.

The meeting ended on a friendly, almost conspiratory, note. Dr. I. recounted the remark of one of his colleagues most opposed to us. The man had been outraged, and sputtered to Dr. I: "Why, I haven't even seen their credentials!" to which he had replied, "I haven't seen yours either." He reported with some glee that his comment had not been appreciated.

An overall pattern that seemed to be repeating itself at this meeting was an initially pessimistic or doubting position taken by Dr. U., followed by a discussion, during which he became increasingly enthusiastic about what we had in mind and optimistic about the probability of our surmounting the potential barriers in our path. However, we took the meeting as a clear indication of the need to move very slowly and carefully in regard to the physicians.

An issue that was becoming blurred in our minds, as well as in the nurses' and doctors', was again the one of direct service *versus consultation.* When we talked directly with a child, we were ourselves falling into the trap of direct clinical services. The one justification we had for this was that one learns something important about an organization when one tries to provide a service (Sarason & Sarason, 1969). Eisdorfer and others (1968) cite the use of clinical skills as an important means by which the clinician-consultant demonstrates his utility. However, we felt we could equally well have learned by staying with our decision to provide a service to the ward staff, rather than directly to individual patients. But our periodic uncertainty about our competence as consultants, combined with pressure from the hospital staff, occasionally led us into the more familiar role of individual clinician. In retrospect, this exacerbated the confusion of the hospital personnel as to our role and made us seem in direct competition with the Mental Health Clinic.

Two weeks later, one of us contacted Mr. A. and described the program to him. He was friendly and supportive but indicated there were some misgivings about the project. Several people had expressed concern to him that we were providing services that overlapped with others already available in the hospital. He suggested we contact the Mental Health Clinic and the hospital social worker. He said he would ask around about what would be the legal means of making us official in the hospital, to make our position less vulnerable. We talked in some detail about our discussions with Drs. U. and I., and he said he might drop in on the meeting with the Clinic.

We immediately set up a meeting with the Clinic. We contacted Mrs. T., the social worker, and told her we had not talked with her previously because we were still just getting acquainted with the hospital. But now things seemed a little clearer, and we would like very much to meet with her. She seemed very friendly on the phone, said she had been waiting for us to call, and did want to get together. She agreed to come to the meeting with the Clinic staff.

A few days later, during the week preceding the meeting with the Clinic, one of us—unaware of the conversation with Mr. A.—became involved with a boy who was a behavior problem on the ward. In a discussion of the situation with the nurses, the decision was reached to contact the family's welfare worker. The consultant was then referred to Mrs. T.'s office, accompanied by one of the senior nurses. Mrs. T. greeted the consultant and the nurse with great friendliness and called the appropriate worker for the consultant to speak with. She mentioned the meeting arranged with the Mental Health Clinic and expressed regret that we had not been able to talk with her before this. She offered the use of her office for our work and asked to meet with the two of us at our convenience.

The following week, both consultants attended the meeting with the Clinic, which included, four staff members of the Clinic—two psychologists, two social workers—and the head of the Clinic, a psychiatrist, Mrs. T., and Mr. A. Initially the group was openly hostile and challenging, asking such questions as, "Why do you think we need your services?" We responded in a nonhostile but also not intimidated manner, explaining that we were not going to be providing direct clinical services except to retarded children and their families and in no way were we competing with the other clinicians or groups for patients.

When they questioned our interest in providing emergency consultation to the pediatrics ward, implying that this fell within their domain, we asked if they would be available to handle such problems, if the nurses requested it. They replied, practially in unison, no, they were already overburdened with their regular appointments.

From that point on in the meeting, they seemed more concerned that we not give them more work to do than that we take away their patients. They also seemed somewhat reassured by our repeated comments that our project was not a criticism of their activities but a supplement to them. We emphasized that the kinds of problems we would be dealing with would not involve the children for whom psychotherapy was indicated.

The situation with the social worker was somewhat different. She seemed to be a somewhat sugary, hysteric woman. One the one hand, she kept saying she was already doing all the things we were talking about, such as consulting with the nurses on pediatrics. On the other hand, she kept excusing herself for not having done these very things by saying she had too much else to do. Her position toward us wasn't entirely clear, but we noted in our diaries that we should make a point of working more closely with her. We did learn at that meeting that more was going on about cases we have been involved with than we had realized, e.g., that other social work agencies were actively involved. This reminded us once again that simply because one does not see something in an organization does not mean it does not exist and have an active influence.

We left after an hour or so, apparently on civil terms with everyone and with the agreement to keep in touch with the Clinic. The head of the Clinic suggested we attend a monthly interagency meeting and took our addresses with the promise that he would send us a notice of the next meeting. (He did not follow through on this.) We also set up an appointment to talk with Mrs. T. the following week.

One of our reactions to the meeting was that the Clinic probably would not block our activities in the hospital, and in fact probably was not in a position to do so, since they were under critical attack themselves from the hospital for not providing more service. However, we still wanted to establish friendly relations with them if possible and ideally to convince them to take over some of our activities in the hospital at some future time. We were beginning to sense the extent to which our presence, and our disregard of her, had threatened and angered the social worker.

The next week the two consultants met with Mrs. T. in her office. In the context of a cordial and overly social approach, and repeatedly denying any hostility towards us, she was extremely critical. She stated many objections to our presence and indicated—or more accurately, tried to deny—her fury that we had not contacted her earlier. During this confusing and difficult meeting, she also described to us her difficulties in working with what seemed to her to be a hostile hospital staff. From our perspective, her position in the hospital was made more difficult by her extremely passive approach to her job. She repeatedly stated her belief that social workers have to wait for the physician to ask before they say anything, that one only provides service if it is

requested both by the patient and the physician, etc. Again, after reassuring the consultants that their services were needed and how pleased she was to have us, she asked that all of the activities of the project be coordinated through her office, in terms that implied that we become an ancillary of the Social Service Department.

Up to this point in the meeting, we had been apologetic about not contacting her sooner, repeatedly stating that the only reason for the oversight was that we had not known of her interest in and involvement with pediatrics, and generally tried to placate her. (Generally, this seemed to have absolutely no effect on her.) However, when she wanted all referrals to come to her first, including minor issues the nurses might want to discuss, and including all retarded children, we told her that although we could understand her anxiety about us, in order for us to maintain the independence of the project we could not work within that rigidly defined framework. However, we said we would like to talk with her further about it.

At this she became more emphatic about coordinating our work through her office, pointing out that much of what we were doing would ordinarily be called social work. For the moment, she said, she was very very busy. However, if we discovered a need for more social workers, there would be, of course, more social workers placed in the hospital.

After the meeting, we attempted to figure out how we had gotten into this predicament. We had been told, both by Dr. U. and later by the pediatric ward staff, that the one social worker in the hospital was too busy to provide any services to the pediatric ward. Yet the social worker was extremely threatened by our presence, furious at our disregard of her, and insistent that she was already doing everything that needed to be done. It was obvious to us now that we had made a serious error in not contacting her sooner, regardless of what she was or was not doing for pediatrics. The fact that our activities could be in some ways related to social services meant that we should have introduced ourselves to her at the same time as we had to the nurses and aides.

The situation was further complicated by several factors. We had real ideologic disagreements with her about the nature of social and psychological services, e.g., about the question of waiting for a question before providing help. We felt a more active stance was often more productive and at times prevented more serious trouble from developing.[6] This difference of opinion would ordinarily not have been difficult for us to deal with had it not been for the fact that her personality was peculiarly provocative to both of us, which made it much more difficult than usual to maintain a consistently friendly, or at least neutral, position.

Finally, we felt we could not accept the restrictions she was trying to place on us and still maintain the goals of the project. We were aware that we were drawing a line that would necessitate a show of power on both sides and that it could result in the death of the project, but the issue seemed important enough to justify that. We have given some thought to alternate responses to the social worker's feeling of being threatened. We could have attempted to convince her of our strategy of approach, but at the time and in retrospect this did not seem an easily done task and would have seriously diverted our energy. We had been led to believe she herself was quite tentatively accepted by the hospital staff, and alignment with her, we felt, would have gained us little in our ability to influence the rest of the hospital. Although we initially viewed our failure to mollify the social worker and deal with her feeling of being threatened as one of the turning points of the consultation which led to our failure, we are more convinced of an alternate interpretation. Our failure to convince the medical board of the value of the consultation coupled with their mistrust of a state-affiliated agency, and their general lack of appreciation of a mental health intervention either by us or by their own Clinic was, we believe, the crucial point that led to the eventual end of the program. Had the medical board been generally favorable, Dr. U. and others would probably have been more active in assisting our reconciliation with the social worker, and she, in turn, would have been more able to accommodate her own role if she had perceived this would have been viewed favorably by her superiors (cf. Sarason et al., 1966). Nonetheless, one of the pitfalls of a change-oriented consultant may well be impatience with mental health professionals over views that are more generously treated when they are perceived in other professions.

A brief meeting with the pediatric nurses revealed a difficult and unsatisfying relationship between the ward and Mrs. T., a set of conflicts into which the consultants had stumbled. The nurses said Mrs. T. did not provide any social work services to the pediatric ward, and the nurses resented her physical presence on the floor (her office was on pediatrics). Further, as we suspected, the kinds of things we had been doing were entirely different from the type of services she offered anywhere in the hospital.

We contacted Mr. A. to let him know of the recent developments and mentioned—both kiddingly and apologetically—that we thought he had an angry social worker on his hands. In a much more guarded manner than usual, he said he had just spoken with her and did not feel she was angry. He felt she had a number of real concerns about what was going on and he thought we ought to clarify in writing in detail what it was we were doing. This seemed at first a suggestion, but it became increasingly clear it was an order: before we could do more in the hospital, we had to first put in writing our plans and then meet with Mr. A. and Mrs. T.

We were quite angry by this time. In reflecting on the situation, it seemed comparable to the resistance maneuvers and attacks of an individual psychotherapy patient. But we did put together a document describing our activities and the philosophy behind them, as well as our proposal, similar to the one we had discussed with Drs. I. and U., for a more permanent arrangement with the hospital. We also notified all concerned that we would postpone our next trip to the hospital until our position had been clarified.

When the description was completed, we called Mr. A. to tell him it was in the mail. He was again friendly, said he would be on vacation for a month but if he had any comments on our plan, he would give them to Mrs. T. before the scheduled meeting the following week.

Mrs. T., on her own initiative, arranged to have a social worker from the Clinic, the assistant hospital administrator, and Dr. U. as chief of pediatrics at the meeting. Although neither of us knew these people were coming, we were glad to have them, since our only personal difficulties had been with Mrs. T., and we thought we might all stay cooler with their moderating influences. Mrs. T. opened the meeting by questioning the adequacy of our written description but Dr. U. took over the meeting. He suggested we go through the proposal paragraph by paragraph, and as we began, he and the assistant administrator asked for clarification, information, etc.

Dr. U. surprised us by being extremely cautious, although not unfriendly. He seemed to be conveying two messages. On the one hand, he seemed to be saying that he was having enough difficulty with the people he was responsible for in his role as chief of pediatrics to make it doubtful whether it was worth it for him to fight to keep us in the hospital. On the other hand, he was giving us advice as to how we could manage to surmount the political difficulties blocking our way. He suggested several times that we focus on the problem of unwed mothers, since this was of concern to him and would be, he thought, an acceptable research project to the hospital staff. He was clearly defending the status of the hospital social worker, saying we should work through her and agreeing with her that we should spell out in much more detail what we were up to and why.

The assistant administrator admonished us for what seemed to him also to be a vague, nonspecific plan, but also made it clear that he appreciated our position of having to deal with a threatened and hostile staff. Of all the participants, he seemed most aware of the possibility that under the onslaught we would simply abandon the project, and he clearly did not want that to happen, at least until Mr. A. returned from vacation. He said explicitly at one point that he knew Mr. A. was very much interested in this kind of project, and that we certainly should not make a decision to leave without discussing it with him.

Mrs. T. insisted throughout that no matter what we mentioned as a possible service, she was already doing it, doing it well, and that we should only trust her and have confidence that she was doing it well. She repeatedly focused on her position— which she insisted was the only legitimate social work position—that you wait until a family asks for help before you intervene. She worried that we were smothering families with services and pointed out how rich the town was in services. (This sounded like nonsense to us but we tried hard not to respond with the rage we felt.) We again gave our arguments against this position, more for the benefit of the others than for her, since she was

too angry and frightened to respond to rational arguments by this point.

Although the interpersonal and group dynamics were by far the most demanding of our attention, several interesting content points were raised. The assistant administrator responded to our emphasis on flexibility with an argument about the hospital's need for clear structure and stability. We agreed that structure is helpful for efficiency, and indeed that a degree of it is essential, but pointed out that too much structure defeated any possibility of innovation. This seemed to clarify the problem somewhat for us all, as we began to see the problem of balancing these two somewhat contradictory needs.

Another position on which real differences of opinion existed was that we held different views of the future. The hospital staff argued that if only they had more money, they could have more professional staff and everything would be taken care of. We stated our belief that there will never be enough trained professionals to hire, no matter how much money is available, and reminded them of the existence of several unfilled psychiatric social worker positions at the Clinic. Furthermore, professionals are often unsuccessful in their efforts to be helpful. We feel there exists an enormous need to evolve new ways of functioning that can be more helpful to more people but that require no increase in professional staff. Although this was clearly an unaccustomed mode of thinking to them, it did clarify for us all what we were trying to accomplish and what the differences of opinion were.

After several harrowing hours, we closed the meeting with the agreement that we all needed to think about the project and to talk about it with Mr. A. when he got back. They wanted us to rewrite the project, again being more specific, but we would not agree to this at this time. We said our willingness to rewrite it again depended upon whether we thought there was any possibility of things working out to our satisfaction, and at this point, this was in doubt.

Once the heat of the meeting wore off, several factors separated themselves out. Dr. U.'s ambivalence had been present before. Given a strong demand for support from the social worker, whom after all he placed in that position over much opposition from his fellow physicians, his need to protect her was understandable. He could not have done anything else.

Then, too, the hospital staff agreed with each other that they felt our proposal much too broad and nonspecific. To them, this signified possible confusion on our part, and it was too vague for them to be comfortable. Initially, we had difficulty understanding why they thought it vague, since to us, coming as we did from a very unstructured and unspecified academic milieu, the proposal was already uncomfortably detailed.

This relates to the last point, which is the conflict of interest between the hospital assistant administrator's need for structure and our insistence on a great deal of flexibility to allow us to create a new style of service. The rigidity of hospital structures has been noted before (Katz & Kahn, 1966) and this particular one was no exception.

Our initial reaction to the meeting, however, was totally dominated by our rage at the abuse we had had to silently accept from Mrs. T. We felt at the time that she was responsible for our difficulty and that we might have prevented the problem by contacting her in the beginning.

A month later we met with Drs. U. and I. to see what move they thought we should make. They began with what felt like a frontal attack on us. Dr. U. said how disappointed he had been by our proposal, how general it had been, how we had been here for "a year or so" and hadn't seemed to have learned anything they didn't already know. In general, they seemed to be arguing in the following points: 1) Everything is being done by the social worker already; 2) we had been impolitic in the way we had gone about things; and 3) you can't function in a small town New England hospital in the same way you do in a thriving university hospital. To the first, we simply said that if that was the case, we had no basis on which to talk. They then retreated from that position but pointed out that since our previous discussion, Mrs. T. had in fact begun providing regular social work services to pediatrics. They were not sure what had brought about this change, since previously she had said she did not have the time to do this.

To the question of our being impolitic, we said as always we would be happy to change our approach if that were the main problem, but the question for us now really revolved around the extent to which they were willing to support us. If they were not, we had no possibility of succeeding and were prepared to withdraw. We discussed in this context the conflict between their need for structure and clarity and our need for flexibility.

The longer the discussion went on, the more positive Dr. U. again became, until by the end, both were quite positive about their interest in backing us up. (Dr. I. had never been hostile.) Dr. U. ended by reminiscing about the fights he had had that involved hospital politics. The final agreement was that we would write a short, specific, conciliatory proposal in which we would repeatedly state our admiration for the present social work department. Drs. U. and I. would look it over, and if they thought it acceptable they would present it to the medical board.

We sent them a new written proposal after several weeks, and never received a response to it.

We began to understand the vacillation in Dr. U.'s position as a response to strong and conflicting pressures. As we saw it, he had a genuine interest in the kind of changes we were proposing and, further, he liked and respected us. On the other hand, he was an important part of the medical community and had administrative responsibilities, both of which obligated him to deal with, and placate, his colleagues and subordinates. In addition, the pressures came not just from our project but from all the innovations he and his partner had supported and were still defending against the conservatism of the hospital. We had not been able to provide enough force on the side of change to support him against these counterforces. Bennis, Benne, and Chin (1961) state that only by providing a positive force to balance opposing forces can a change agent produce change.

What began to be clear to us was that although Mrs. T. had made things unpleasant for us, she was really a distraction from the main issue, which was the difficulty in convincing the other physicians on the medical staff. If we had had strong support from them, the social worker's complaints would not have been heeded, particularly since she herself was in a very marginal position in respect to the physicians.

Even in retrospect, given our awareness from the beginning of the importance of the physicians and given our attempts to establish contact with them, it is not clear that we could have done things differently and thereby been successful. The single most important rule about influencing a medical community is probably the need to have physicians do it, or at least strongly support it (Cathell & Stratas, 1967), and this we had done to an extent as great as we could. So we probably could not have begun without the support of Dr. U., yet once tied to him, we had to accept his counsel as to how to approach the other doctors. Finally, he very well could have been right that a direct approach on our part to his colleagues would have been fruitless.

Postscript: June, a Year Later

In trying to write about our adventures with the hospital, we became curious about the point of view of Drs. U. and I. We first talked with Dr. I. about it. He was very friendly and glad to talk with us, although he had little to add to what we had known or surmised. In his view, two critical factors influenced what happened. Mrs. T.'s decision to provide services to the pediatrics ward had occurred around the time of our project; he wasn't sure what caused her to change her mind about this. Secondly, we had come at a time when the physicians were particularly defensive about the state proposal for regionalization of medical services, and were consequently more resistant than usual to any innovations, particularly coming from a state agency.

Dr. U. agreed to talk with us as well, although he sounded somewhat reluctant on the phone. He then came 45 minutes late, having forgotten about a dentist appointment, and was extremely contrite about keeping us waiting. Despite this apparent ambivalence, he seemed to talk openly with us. His view of the situation was not greatly different from ours or from what his partner had said. He felt Mrs. T.'s protests had played a major role in the difficulty and felt he had been in error in the beginning in not seeing the importance of her role to our project. He did feel her sudden willingness to provide services to pediatrics was probably in response to our presence.

He felt she was providing good prompt service to pediatrics now. We pointed out that there had been only one referral in nine months to the Center and expressed our doubt that they had seen

only one retarded child in all that time. He could not remember any others but acknolwedged that there must have been several. So from the standpoint of adequate referrals to the Center, no progress had been made. In this context, he mentioned something we had not known. What had threatened Mrs. T. most of all of our activities had been our work with the families of the young mongoloid children, which from our perspective had been the most rewarding and successful aspect of our work. Dr. U. added that these families had all found their contact with us very helpful.

He agreed that the threatened regionalization of medical services had made the physicians much more resistant than usual to any change, and the fact that we had come when this reaction was at its height worked against us.

The last factor he mentioned related to the problem of the physicians' fears and fantasies about us. He said he and Dr. I. were always a little confused about exactly who we were and where we came from. They knew we had affiliations with the university and hospital nearby but were not sure if we were on a grant or what. They wondered if our vagueness was because we were trying to use up grant money without any real idea of what we wanted to do. He then began to elaborate on the relationship between the university hospital and their own. Essentially he described a long history of seeming—and possibly real—snobbishness and indifferences on the part of the university hospital, and threat, envy, and dislike on the part of the small-town physicians. The degree of affect in his monologue, as well as the fact that he talked for some length about this, made clear the strong feelings involved, and suggested that our associations with the university had also entered into his own ambivalence toward us and our project.

We parted on friendly terms.

The fact that Mrs. T.'s strongest reaction had been to the one aspect of the project that we were most pleased about raised the possibility that nothing we could have done about winning her over would have been successful. That is, given her objections to our activities that were a central aspect of the Regional Center's services to the community, it is unlikely she would ever have accepted our role as consultants in the hospital.

Probably the most important issue, as we mentioned, was the apprehension of the physicians in response to the pressure towards regionalization, which also occurred in the context of their having to learn to live with Medicare. Drs. U.'s and I.'s confusion about us, and the resentment against our university and the hospital it represented were also striking, and reminded us again of how different can be the cultures and attitudes of different settings. Although consciously we knew it not to be the case, implicitly we had assumed that they, like us, live in a world where having people wandering in and out doing strange things is commonplace and certainly no cause for alarm. Although we had defined ourselves and our positions several times to them, we had not remembered clearly enough that such definitions and clarifications need to be made repeatedly.

DISCUSSION AND CONCLUSIONS

Before considering several of the issues already raised, another question is how one evaluates such a project. In terms of our explicit goals, we failed. The hospital failed to continue to refer retarded children and their families to the Center and they did not make mental health consultation available to the ward staff on pediatrics and they made no other important changes in their style of functioning. On the positive side, the social worker did begin providing the traditional social work services to pediatrics, which she had not done previously, and as a reaction to her increased work load, was able to convince the hospital to hire another social worker to assist her.

Possibly more important than that are the long-range effects of such pressure on the hospital. We discovered afterwards that we were part of a series of attempts by several progressive service organizations in the community to influence and update hospital practices. The visiting nurses had tried for a number of years to get the hospital to refer patients who needed continuing nursing support or supervision, rather than simply sending these patients home without even advising them of the availability of nurses. After years of negotiation, this very small change had been rejected by the medical board. During and after our efforts, the visiting nurses then tried to get permission for one of their nurses to go into the hospital to expedite referrals. This proposal had been debated for the past two years and looks now as if it might eventually be accepted. Since the

Center had good relations with the visiting nurses, we would expect close cooperation on referrals of retarded children from them. Perhaps only by maintaining consistent pressure for change on such an organization does change eventually occur.

Issues Raised by the Experience

As consciously aware as we were of many of the problems of dealing with an organization as a client, a number of pitfalls were nevertheless encountered, and a number of mistakes were made. Although it was tempting to attribute the failure of the program to personalities, its ultimate fate more likely stemmed from our inability to influence the conservative and powerful group of physicians. Regardless of its overall success or failure, a number of issues were raised by the case material, and while no definite solutions can be given, the questions perhaps can now be defined more clearly.

Perhaps the broadest and most critical one is how does one get to know a new setting. One characteristic of the organization that seems extremely important is its culture, i.e., its implicit rules and traditions that govern the relationships within it. Another is the locus of power within the setting and particularly the influence as it relates to the project the consultant has in mind. The same question can be asked in its negative form: what individual and/or groups in the setting are in a position to be able to block any proposed innovation or to otherwise defeat it?

Related to the questions of power and influence are those relating to the potential support available in the setting. Particularly when the impetus for change comes from the outside, the identification and assessment of potential or actual allies from within is critical. Again, this involves assessing not only those individuals' or groups' commitment to the change but their ability to influence the organization in respect to it. How a consultant comes to know a setting so that he can answer these questions is greatly complicated by the fact that whatever he does within the organization in order to learn about it will be interpreted by the organization as part of its assessment of him. For example, if a consultant were to devote his early contacts with a community agency such as the hospital to watching and asking questions, such as about power in the agency, it would greatly influence the agency's perception of him and their willingness to trust him. Because of this problem, the question of whether to begin by fitting into the more traditional service model or whether to totally avoid that role is critical.

In the case described, our decision was to eschew the traditional role of clinical psychologist from the beginning and instead to focus on the other ways of providing service and potential changes in the way the hospital functioned in respect to handicapped children. Although this decision did undoubtedly increase the suspiciousness of us and the ambiguity of what we were doing, it did keep us from getting tied up doing direct service activities. In this instance, it also made us less of a threat to such groups as the Mental Health Clinic, which did provide direct psychological services. The degree of openness with which a consultant states his aims cannot be prescribed. The · consultant's estimate of the openness of the organization to change, and the anticipated effects of such a direct statement must be assessed. It is well to keep in mind that the consultant's aims may change as he works with the organization. Whatever the consultant states as his goal, it is best that he state it in such a way that he does not confine himself in the remainder of the consultation.

During the six months of watching and looking and talking to people in the hospital, we found that although the director had enough power to bring us in initially, the real power in respect to our project lay with the physicians. Possibly the director and the ward nurses could have blocked the project if they had opposed it but their support was not powerful enough to override the physicians. Dr. U. himself was in a somewhat similar position. He had a great deal of power, by virtue of his long standing position in the hospital and the respect held for him, but he had been using this influence repeatedly to prod his conservative colleagues to change. It would have taken an unshakeable conviction on his part of the value of our project to enable him to have won out over the resistance of the other doctors and even then the outcome is doubtful.

We learned, to our surprise, that the nurses were also potential allies, along with the director and Drs. U. and I. However, the value of such support has to be evaluated in respect to the probable force of the opposition in order to assess the likelihood of success. Had we been aware of the history of this hospital's long standing resistance to even very minor changes, we might have decided not to attempt an intervention at this point.

This experience highlighted again for the authors the necessity for appreciation of the complexity of organizations. This complexity, stemming in part from the intricate interrelationships of parts, is aptly portrayed by Chin's (1961) analogy of a model composed of rubbed bands and paper clips: movement at any point affects the entire structure. One consequence of this interrelatedness for a consultant is the importance of making contact with each of the relevant component parts and keeping all of them sufficiently informed of the change efforts as they progress. A second principle that we actively struggled with is the need to avoid becoming identified with one group within the structure (Bennis, Benne, & Chin, 1961; Jaques, 1961; Oetting et al., 1967). In this regard, particular attention might be paid to groups and individuals who are insecure in their relationship to it. In other words, these are people whose role and importance have not yet been clearly defined for themselves or for other members of the organization. In the hospital project, a serious error was committed by overlooking the relatively new social worker, who had been dismissed by a member of the more established group in the hospital. This example illustrated clearly that there is much more to be learned about an organization than the formal structure would suggest, both in the informal relationships and in the unwritten and unspoken culture of the organization, in the taboos on what one says and does. We note that we selected the model of consultation to a particular area of the hospital as one of a number of possible tactics for effecting change of the organization. Other possible approaches could have been to begin with the most powerful group in the hierarchy, the medical board. Another approach would involve organizing the community to bring outside pressure for change. The specific goals we had for introducing preventive measures in the care of children led us to choose the consultant-clinician approach. The organization of community pressure to apply to the hospital continues as part of the long-term overall approach of the Regional Center.

A final question we must raise is whether it is possible for a self-invited consultant to influence an organization such as a hospital to adopt a more community oriented method of providing service. One possible answer is that mental health professionals can no longer ignore such organizations if they are to attempt seriously to provide preventive mental health care. After our experience, we take a more cautious position: that such efforts can be successful if timed correctly to meet an organization ready for change, with persons of influence sufficiently committed to change to ride through the turmoil that inevitably arises when the stability of an organization is threatened. Whether or not to undertake a particular consultation attempt also depends in part upon the minimal goals that are acceptable to the consultant. There are undoubtedly many situations in which the most beneficial effect of a consultation can be to get the rubber bands and paper clips moving around, to sensitize the organization to the pressures the community will undoubtedly exert to effect needed change.

Notes

Frances Kaplan Grossman was formerly at the Psycho-Educational Clinic, Yale University.

1. The Psycho-Educational Clinic staff has worked in a number of Centers in several New England states. All names and identifying characteristics of the individuals involved have been changed to protect their anonymity.

2. The similarity between this process and the initial stage of psychotherapy is striking. In both situations, natural resistance to change can only be overcome by means of a relationship with the change agent.

3. He probably was aware that the Center's philosophy and commitment was to find alternatives to early institutionalization of all but the most severely retarded children.

4. In retrospect, we had learned that this was an oversimplified description of the Clinic.

5. Actually, we had begun to get a local psychiatric facility involved with us in the hospital. However, because this did not seem to play a central role in the ultimate outcome, it is not described here.

6. It has been our experience that all such endeavors have at least one crisis point early in their development, and how that crisis is resolved has important consequences for the potential development of the project. Prelinger (1967) has noted a similar phenomenon in his work with individual psychotherapy patients.

References

Bennett, E. M., & Kaplan, F. A way of thinking: Mental health professionals in community programs. *Community Mental Health Journal*, 1967, 3(4), 318–324.

Bennis, W. G., Benne, K. D., & Chin, R. (eds.) *The planning of change*. New York: Holt, Rinehart & Winston, 1961.

Berken, G., & Eisdorfer, C. Closed ranks in microcosm: Pitfalls of a training experience in community consultation. *Community Mental Health Journal*, in press.

Blanco, A., & Akabas, S. H. The factory site for community mental health practice. *American Journal of Orthopsychiatry*, 1960, 38(3), 543–552.

Caplan, G. Patterns of parental response to the crisis of premature birth. *Psychiatry*, 1960, 23, 365–374.

Cathell, J. L., & Stratas, N. E. Mobile psychiatric consultation-education for primary physicians. *Community Mental Health Journal*, 1967, 3(3), 226–230.

Chin, R. The utility of systems models and developmental models for practitioners. In W. G. Bennis, K. D. Benne, & R. Chin (eds.), *The planning of change*. New York: Holt, Rinehart & Winston, 1961.

Cumming, E., & Cumming, J. *Closed ranks: An experiment in mental health education*. Cambridge, Mass.: Harvard University Press, 1957.

Dupont, H. Community mental health centers and services for the mentally retarded. *Community Mental Health Journal*, 1967, 3(1), 33–36.

Eisdorfer, C., Altrocchi, J., & Young, R. F. Principles of community mental health in a rural setting: The Halifax County Program. *Community Mental Health Journal*, 1968, 4(3), 211–220.

Farber, B. *Family: Organization and interaction*. San Francisco: Chandler, 1964.

Farber, B. *Mental retardation: Its social context and social consequences*. Boston: Houghton Mifflin, 1968.

Glidewell, J. C. The entry problem in consultation. In W. G. Bennis, K. D. Benne, & R. Chin (eds.) *The planning of change*. New York: Holt, Rinehart & Winston, 1961.

Hersch, C. The process of collaboration: A case study. *Community Mental Health Journal*, 1967, 3(3), 254–258.

Jaques, E. Social therapy: Technocracy or collaboration. In W. G. Bennis, K. D. Benne, & R. Chin (eds.) *The planning of change*. New York: Holt, Rinehart & Winston, 1961.

Kaplan, F. College siblings of retarded children. Unpublished monograph, Yale University, 1969.

Kaplan, F., & Sarason, S. B. (eds.) *The Psycho-Educational Clinic: Papers and research*. Boston: Massachusetts State Department of Mental Health Monograph Series, 1969.

Katz, D., & Kahn, R. L. *The social psychology of organizations*. New York: Wiley, 1966.

Klapman, H. F., Moss, M. H., Brand, D. L., & Boverman, H. The search for retardation interveners: A family and community approach through public health nursing. *Community Mental Health Journal*, 1968, 4(5), 363–367.

Levine, M. Some postulates of community psychology practice. In F. Kaplan & S. B. Sarason (eds.) *The Psycho-Educational Clinic: Papers and research*. Boston: Massachusetts State Department of Mental Health Monograph Series, 1969.

Lippitt, R. Dimensions of the consultant's job. In W. G. Bennis, K. D. Benne, & R. Chin (eds.) *The planning of change*. New York: Holt, Rinehart & Winston, 1961.

Loomis, C. P. Tentative types of directed social change involving systematic linkage. In W. G. Bennis, K. D. Benne, & R. Chin (eds.) *The planning of change*. New York: Holt, Rinehart & Winston, 1961.

March, J. G., & Simon, H. A. *Organizations*. New York: Wiley, 1958.

Oetting, E. R., Cole, C. W., & Hinkel, J. E. A case study in community agency visitation. *Community Mental Health Journal*, 1967, 3(1), 45–48.

Prelinger, E. Some recurrent problems in brief psychotherapy. Unpublished manuscript, Yale University, 1967.

Reding, G. R., & Goldsmith, E. F. The nonprofessional hospital volunteer as a member of the psychiatric consultation team. *Community Mental Health Journal*, 1967, 3(3), 267–272.

Rosenbaum, G., & Oteenstein, D. From child guidance to community mental health: Problems in transition. *Community Mental Health Journal*, 1965, 1(3), 276–283.

Sarason, S. B. Toward a psychology of change ·and innovation. *American Psychologist*, 1967, 22, 227–233.

Sarason, S. B. *The creation of settings. Changing patterns in residential services for the mentally retarded.* Washington, D. C.: President's Committee on Mental Retardation, 1969.

Sarason, S. B., & Doris, J. *Psychological problems in mental deficiency*. (4th ed.) New York: Wiley, 1969.

Sarason, S. B., & Sarason, E. K. Some observations on the introduction and the teaching of the new math. In F. Kaplan & S. B. Sarason *The Psycho-Educational Clinic: Papers and research* Boston: Massachusetts State Department of Mental Health Monograph Series, 1969.

Smith, E. R. Current issues in mental health planning. *Community Mental Health Journal*, 1966, 2(1), 73–77.

Stone, N. D. Family factors in willingness to place the mongoloid child. *American Journal of Mental Deficiency*, 1967, 72(1), 16–20.

Turner, R. J. Social structure and crisis: A study of nursing organization and patient adjustment. *Community Mental Health Journal*, 1966, 2(4), 285–292.

Warren, R. L., & Hyman, H. H. Purposive community change in consensus and dissensus situations. *Community Mental Health Journal*, 1966, 4(2), 293–300.

Zander, A. Resistance to change—Its analysis and prevention. In W. G. Bennis, K. D. Benne, & R. Chin (eds.) *The planning of change*. New York: Holt, Rinehart & Winston, 1961.

26

Psychological Consultation in a Maximum Security Prison: A Case History and Some Comments

Edward S. Katkin

This paper will describe an attempt to develop a program of psychological consultation within the walls of a maximum security prison—a program that set out to provide clinical service, and which found quickly that the very definition of such service was beyond discovery. Specifically, this paper will discuss the circumstances which led the project staff to the conclusion that "service as usual" was impossible to deliver, and to the corollary conclusion that the delivery of "legitimate" consultative service required a deep involvement in the administration of the institution, and thence the politics of the institution, and thence the *Realpolitik*. Before proceeding, perhaps a review of the context in which the consultative program was initiated is in order.

In the spring of 1968 the New York State Department of Corrections and the New York State Education Department entered into an agreement whereby the Education Department, with the support of the Rehabilitation Services Administration of the federal government, would provide funds and personnel to initiate a demonstration program in vocational rehabilitation in a large upstate maximum security prison. Specifically, the services offered by the consultative team were restricted to one cell block of the prision which had been devoted to the project. The client population for the demonstration project consisted of approximately 80 physically and/or emotionally handicapped inmates selected from among a total prison inmate population of 1700. The program, to be carried out by the Division of Vocational Rehabilitation (DVR) of the State Education Department, was conceived as

a demonstration program of service and research. The service aspect of the program consisted of the identification and evaluation of handicapped inmates resulting in the development of vocational rehabilitative programs which would enable these handicapped inmates to strive towards more satisfactory adjustment after parole or release. For those inmates who would not be eligible for release, more satisfactory vocational adjustment to the prison environment was also considered a legitimate goal. The project was also to provide competent research to evaluate the extent to which such an evaluation program facilitated eventual vocational rehabilitation.

In the course of establishing this program within the prison institution a variety of personnel from different backgrounds were called together to function as a team. Directing the program was a rehabilitation counselor with many years of experience in prison settings in the Southwest. Working with this director was a project coordinator recruited from the correctional system itself. In addition to these two administrative leaders the project employed a full-time rehabilitation counselor, a full-time parole advisor, a full-time school teacher who was able to provide educational instruction from first grade through high school for the inmates on the project, a full-time industrial arts teacher whose responsibility was to evaluate the vocational skills of the clients selected for the project, and a full-time service unit advisor whose primary function was to act as administrative liaison between the inmate and the institution and who often served a role of "camp counselor" to the men. In addition to these full-time personnel, the project employed two half-time clinical staff psychologists (both of whom were advanced graduate students at the nearby State University), two half-time research psychologists (also graduate students), and a part-time supervisory consultant, a faculty member in clinical psychology at the same State University (the author).

In the summer of 1968 the Department of Psychology of the State University was contacted by the DVR project director and requested to enter into a contract with the project whereby the State University would provide graduate student interns for the project and supervision of these interns from the University staff. The contract indicated that the psychologists would be expected to provide relatively traditional clinical services, much the same as might be expected at any mental institution or hospital. They would be required to administer intelligence tests, projective tests, and objective personality tests to clients, with an eye toward contributing to the total goal of evaluating them for vocational rehabilitation. In addition, the psychologists would be encouraged to provide psychotherapeutic service, both individual and group, for inmates on the project who seemed capable of benefiting from it. The prison environment appeared to have potential as a particularly interesting internship setting for students in that the DVR project director was eager to have the consulting psychologists experiment with new techniques such as behavior therapy, encounter groups, and T-groups. There was the additional attraction for the psychologists that there would be essentially no medical or psychiatric supervision and the possibilities for freedom in providing psychological service seemed much broader than they are at the usual hospital setting.

Thus, with a naively exaggerated sense of doing good and unbridled optimism, the graduate students and the author entered the prison in the fall of 1968. The optimism faded rapidly. Operating within the structure of the prison institution at the same time that one tried to operate within the framework of the traditions of DVR and of clinical psychology proved to be an unusual and almost impossible experience for the staff psychologists, primarily because the apparent mission of the corrections institution appeared to

be at complete loggerheads with the mission of the rehabilitative and clinical institutions. Whereas the ethic underlying the rehabilitative approach is founded upon the recognition of each man's individuality and worth and the systematic attempt to encourage individual growth, the correctional tradition, quite to the contrary (notwithstanding official pronouncements from wardens), is founded upon principles of uniformity for administrative orderliness and safety. These principles of uniformity demand equal treatment for all inmates regardless of individual needs and/or differences, for the prison institution and its traditions are structured so that the overall security of the prison complex must precede any consideration of individual need, whether of inmates or of staff. While this approach maintains the highest level of security with a minimum of distress or overt disturbance it often appears to force the prison institution into an abdication of its rehabilitative responsibilities.

In the pages to follow we[1] will briefly describe our attempts to provide traditional service as psychodiagnosticians, psychotherapists, and research psychologists. We will then try to explain some of the reasons why this traditional service orientation failed and we will describe the emergence of a changed role for the staff pscyhologists, a role of institutional consultant and evaluator. We will describe a broadening of our own horizons and the realization of the importance of coming to grips with the new culture and new traditions of the institution to which we were called; and we will present some opinions concerning the role of a clinical consultant in an institution whose values and traditions are diametrically opposed to those from which he operates. Finally, we will try to relate our experience in this consultative program to certain general principles and postulates of community mental health practice elucidated by Levine (1967, 1969) and thereby extrapolate from our experience in this particular maximum security prison to the experience of clinical consultants to "alien" institutions in general.

SERVICES PROVIDED

Under the terms of our agreement with the project and the project's agreement with the prison, the consulting psychologists were to provide the institution with research services as well as psychodiagnostic and psychotherapeutic services. At the very beginning of the project, therefore, a program of research was designed, and mechanisms were established for evaluating the total project over a three-year period. Such information will be available in future reports. It should be reported however that the following description of the problems met in providing diagnostic and therapeutic services applies equally well to the research function of the consultants.

Psychodiagnosis

Personality Assessment. Psychodiagnostic evaluations were attempted in a manner quite similar to the traditional psychodiagnostic role of the clinical psychologist in a mental hospital setting. That is, evaluations were requested from other staff members with specific administrative needs in mind, such as parole evaluation or suitability of personality for certain vocational placements. Occasionally a psychodiagnostic evaluation was requested specifically by an inmate on his own initiative. In general, an evaluation involved personality and intellectual assessment utilizing traditional projective and objective tests as well as "standard" clinical interviews. However, personality tests administered under conditions of imprisonment in a maximum security setting do not yield the same kind of results a clinical psychologist is used to seeing. The results of such personality assessments, therefore, were difficult to evaluate within our intuitive and/or actuarial framework.

Unlike the mental health setting, the prison atmosphere is one of severe suspicion and interpersonal instrumentality; test results indicating significant psychopathology might result with equal probability from deliberate falsification or fear of negatively affecting one's parole board. It became apparent to us also that the nature of prison life rendered many of the assessments we used as inappropriate. Inmates in a maximum security prison are under continual observation and have virtually no privacy. They live in a cell which is open to public view. The cell contains their toilet facilities, washing facilities, and bed. Consequently, an inmate must learn to be subject

to scrutiny not only during his waking hours and sleeping hours but he must learn to adjust to being scrutinized during bowel movements, urinations, and masturbations. At any time of day or night the constantly patrolling uniformed guard may be staring in at the inmate. Dozens of times during his daily life the inmate makes direct eye contact with his patrolling guard. Dozens of other times while his back is to the corridor he hears his guard passing by, stopping, looking at him, and continuing. The inmate develops a permanent awareness of being observed and scrutinized. How then does a clinical psychologist interpret the Rorschach test of a newly arrived inmate in which there is apparent paranoid content such as eyes staring at him? How does the clinical psychologist interpret the TAT response of an inmate who describes the hero as feeling that he has no private life, that he is always being watched, that people are out to get him? It is too simple to conclude, as we might in a mental health setting, that these are pathological signs. Conversely, it is also too simple, and probably misleading, to conclude that these are signs *simply* of the situational context in which the inmate lives.

These may be extreme examples, and perhaps overdrawn; but how does one interpret clearcut signs of hostility when expressed by a man who has been living in a six foot by eight foot cage for ten years? How does the psychologist deal with the fact that almost all inmates tested show psychopathic spikes on the MMPI? Can the penal system be so perfect that it is imprisoning only psychopaths? Or it is more logical to conclude that the prison itself is augmenting and sharpening psychopathic trends in all its inmates? And finally the psychologist begins asking himself what is normal and what is abnormal for a man living in a cage? And how do these criteria relate to the criteria and norms which we have come to understand in the outside world?

In addition to these conceptual and interpretive restrictions the staff psychologists found themselves faced with severe restrictions on their actual administrative responsibilities. In hospital and clinic settings the mental health specialist is accustomed to being the central figure in a patient's schedule. Hospital routines are presumed to be secondary to the doctor's scheduling of diagnostic and therapeutic sessions, and the "doctor" becomes accustomed to the notion that the institution is organized around his services. Not so in the prison! The inmate is scheduled according to the mandates of "security." If the hospital is "doctor centered" then the prison is "officer centered" or more appropriately "security centered" and the mental health specialist had better accommodate himself. For instance, inmates are only available for testing and interviewing during certain prescribed and limited daytime hours. The prison routine is relatively inflexible and no exemptions are made for the psychologist who is in the midst of an important interview. Not only do meal schedules interfere with the work at hand but inmates are locked in their cells several times a day for security counts. These factors necessitated a choice, where possible, of psychological tests which did not require extensive time for administration. Early in the life of the project, we tried to circumvent these difficulties by asking inmates to take certain objective tests, such as the MMPI, back to their cells for completion. This plan failed. First, the fear of self-incrimination which is so prevalent among inmates tended to invalidate almost all such tests. Second, inmates have asked other inmates for the "correct" answer to these tests and more often than not inmates have asked prison personnel for such answers and received them. It is likely that most of the MMPI profiles obtained from inmates under such conditions were in fact group profiles jointly contributed by fellow inmates and officers. And finally there was a perceived stigma associated with being selected for testing. No inmate wanted to risk being labeled "psycho."

Vocational Testing. Vocational rehabilitation efforts traditionally require some standardized evaluation of client interests, aptitudes, and motivation. It is natural that a project such as the DVR project in this prison would expect the psychologists to provide such service. However, just as in the general area of personality assessment, a number of problems were encountered in attempting to administer vocational testing to inmates. Disingenuousness, apprehension, and basic distrust clouded the interpretation of results. Furthermore, individual testing turned out to be somewhat more difficult than had been expected because inmates felt stigmatized when chosen for vocational evaluation just as they did

when selected for personality assessment. Consequently the staff developed a standard test battery which was routinely administered to all inmates served by the DVR project when they were selected for the project. This standardization approach was successful in two ways. First it allowed inmates to take these tests in a routine manner which freed them from stigma and second it enabled the staff psychologists to schedule evaluation meetings with all of the inmates as an aid to their placement in the project. These evaluation meetings provided an opportunity for initial counseling contact with selected inmates without the stigma many inmates felt either in attempting self-initiated counseling sessions, or in being selected out in the earlier manner.

Psychotherapy

Individual. At the outset of the project, a variety of inmates were seen in individual therapy both in formal sessions and informal consultations. These psychotherapy sessions were useful for two purposes. First, for some inmates they provided essential support which facilitated adjustment to the prison environment and helped them to develop greater self-understanding. Second, and importantly for the therapist, the sessions provided an enormously important opportunity to acquire an understanding of the prison environment from a different perspective than might otherwise have been obtained. This new perspective, it was felt, enabled the clinician to work in the system with far greater understanding of his impact on the population.

Group. At the beginning of the project the staff psychologists entertained the notion of group therapy as a viable alternative to individual therapy. The thinking of the psychologists was quite traditional. Group therapy could accommodate a larger number of inmates in the same time as individual therapy, and could maximize the effectiveness of the small psychological staff. However, group therapy was unable to be carried out with any degree of effectiveness. First of all the logistics of getting 8 to 10 inmates in a room with a therapist without correctional supervisory attention were difficult. The security considerations of the prison required correctional officers in the therapy sessions. The presence of this "security force" made it very difficult for the inmates to talk openly or freely about their problems for fear (realistic) that their comments might be taken directly to the warden. In addition to the fear which inmates have of the correctional staff, the problem of effective group therapy was complicated further because the inmates would also have to trust the psychologists. This, we soon discovered, was far from likely. Irrespective of the high opinion we had of ourselves and of our integrity, we were for all intents and purposes nothing more than plainclothesmen to the inmates. Much to our surprise, in the inmates' eyes we were about as distinguishable from the correctional officers as the Vietcong and the "loyal" South Vietnamese must be in the eyes of a G.I.

We did little to help ourselves in our initial announcement of the availability of the sessions. Our aim was to begin the group therapy sessions by billing them as self-help rap sessions for any inmates who were interested or curious. To bring this to their attention we posted a notice on the cell block bulletin board side by side with various notices from the warden, deputy warden, hall captain, and various other correctional administrators. That was mistake number one. To compound this grievous error we referred to the inmates in the notice as "prisoners" (mistake number two), as yet unaware that the men reject emphatically the notion that they are anybody's captive. We learned later, from a sympathetic lifer, that the men are inmates, but *not* prisoners. We were in trouble but we were learning.

Attempts at group therapy were complicated further by yet another unexpected development. Not only were the inmates inhibited by the presence of correctional officers and unwilling to trust the plainclothesman-psychologists, but they were equally afraid (for equally valid reasons) to deal openly with their fellow inmates. The prison culture is riddled with informers, extortionists, blackmailers, and a variety of other unsavory characters, against whom the average inmate is constantly on guard. The possibility of lessening one's defenses in a group therapy situation, and opening oneself up to possible attack is quite intimidating, and rightly so. In a prison group therapy session there is no way for the men to hide from each other between sessions, no

community for them to slip back into anonymously. What we did not know until we started is that it was unreasonable of us to expect these men to play by our rules!

Behavioral Therapy and Milieu Therapy. Some attempts were undertaken to deal with individual psychopathology through the use of systematic desensitization and environmental manipulation such as "token economies." But they have been largely abortive. The problem of milieu therapy in this setting appears to be that it is difficult to make effective *environmental* changes within the confines of defined security.

Summary Comments. The successful use of therapy in all of its forms seems less likely in the maximum security environment than in most other settings. The reasons for this pessimistic outlook stem from the fact that the inmate culture weighs against the successful utilization of therapeutic services, and the corrections culture (in addition to creating its own obstacles) reinforces this aspect of inmate culture. Inmates have learned from repeated unfortunate experience that they cannot trust other inmates or staff members with confidential information. The use of selected inmates as informers, and the explicitly stated policy of all officers that they are duty bound to inform, seriously inhibits an inmate from divulging highly personal information to others. This lack of confidence (which is eminently realistic and sensible under the circumstances) surely interferes with the development of effective, mutually trusting therapeutic relationships. It is difficult if not impossible for an inmate to believe a staff psychologist who claims to offer complete confidentiality.

In the case of milieu therapy the flexibility required is not available within an institution insisting upon unformity of treatment. In addition, the degree to which new behaviors developed in prison would generalize or carry over to the outside world is reduced by the absence of opportunities for follow-up therapy on the streets. Thus, before six months had passed the psychologists became aware that their traditional approach to diagnosis and therapy was considerably less than optimal in the setting. Standard procedures did not seem to fit the requirements of the institution and attempts to develop nonstandard procedures were thwarted either by the inmates' resistance or the institution's inflexibility. We had jumped into the fire too hastily and it was time now to climb back into the frying pan and try to gain a greater understanding of our immediate surroundings. Consequently the consultants spent a great deal of the next six months evaluating the institutional factors which affected inmate behavior as well as staff behavior.[2] The purpose of this evaluation was, hopefully, to enable us to plan new programs which would be effective *within the limits of institutional restrictions*. However the notion was not ruled out that the evaluation might lead to the conclusion that these institutional restrictions and some institutional structures might have to be renovated.

INSTITUTIONAL EVALUATION

The Perceived Role of the DVR Project in the Prison

The contract under which the DVR project was established indicates that a variety of rehabilitative strategies including environmental manipulation would be carried out; yet, the experience of the staff psychologists indicated that the corrections authorities who approved this contract either never read it closely or never took it seriously, for there was little institutional cooperation in the accomplishment of these stated goals. For example, an inmate suffering from gross obesity related to physical and emotional isolation had been granted informally the privilege of an open cell door at times when other inmates were given the privilege of going to certain specified jobs or spending free time in the yard. The obese inmate, who could not work and could not exercise in the yard because of his physical condition, nevertheless requested that he be granted his hour of freedom simply by having his cell door left open. The staff psychologists decided to use this potential freedom as a reinforcement for a weight-loss program that the inmate needed desperately for his future medical safety; the extension of this privilege was discussed with a correction officer on the block and the privilege was granted. However, within a week the privilege already granted was repealed due to "orders" and the need for "security," and the inmate, feeling betrayed, rejected further approaches from the

psychologist. An attempt to find out where the orders came from and what the security question was resulted in complete failure. The fact that the inmate in question was a virtual invalid, incapable of moving, and therefore a nonexistent security risk never entered into the final decision. There is simply a prison rule that an inmate must be either locked in his cell or locked out of his cell; the possibility of his remaining in the cell with the door unlocked during "free" time was never considered. This example is not meant to document the attitudes of the correctional institution but merely to reflect through one instance the notion that the institution perceives its responsibilities solely in terms of stated security rules and that these security rules are not readily bent, stretched, or modified in the interests of the rehabilitation of an individual inmate's emotional problems.

After a series of instances of this nature, in which a psychologist requested minimal environmental change in order to facilitate emotional rehabilitation of an inmate, and in which the psychologist met with no success, a direct confrontation was made with the prison authorities concerning the stipulation in the DVR contract which called for "environmental manipulation." The institution, through the warden, indicated that environmental manipulation obviously could be allowed only within the limits of defined security. Psychologists countered that the limits of defined security eliminated any and all environmental manipulation and that this must have been clear to the warden at the time he accepted the project; these minor disputes were not easily resolved.

Later it was discovered that the DVR project had been foisted upon the prison largely at the pleasure of the administrative hierarchy in the state capital, who felt that such a project would lend "class" to the prison and to the New York State system. The warden, for his part, had not been eager to welcome us to his house. The decision-making process which resulted in the placement of the project, then, was related to considerations of administrative prestige seeking and institutional competition between the State Education Department and the State Corrections Department at the highest levels. The project itself and its success or failure were never taken very seriously by the upper administration; the placement of the project within the prison was seen in Albany as a means for providing opportunity for upper administration to give talks to professional and nonprofessional groups about the state's interest in the vocational rehabilitation of inmates. In short, everybody in the state capital was happy as long as nobody at the prison rocked the boat. The staff psychologists could easily have fit into this pattern by acting as ballast in that boat, seeing inmates for superficial therapy and continuing to give projective tests irrespective of their value. What the psychologists did, in fact, was compromise; they agreed among themselves to continue to provide the services requested while actively and discreetly lobbying and using whatever powers of argument and persuasion they had to change some of the prison regulations.

Initial Attempts to Modify the System

The first such attempt to modify the structure was a proposal to the warden that weekly training groups (T-groups) be established for purposes of enabling interested members of the DVR staff (including correctional officers) to improve their relationships with each other. Essentially what was being proposed was a modified form of sensitivity training for all members of the staff. The psychologists hoped that by asking for a weekly staff meeting in which both uniformed and nonuniformed personnel could participate, channels of communication might open up and some of the walls of hostility between the correctional and rehabilitative staff might break down. This plan was rapidly undercut. First, the warden decreed that corrections officers would not be allowed released time in which to participate in such groups. Second, the warden ordered that the groups could only be attempted if attendance was mandatory for all members of the project, incredibly even for those officers for whom no time would be provided! Either of these restrictions alone would have impeded the effectiveness of the group; together they rendered the operation useless. Furthermore, these restrictions, coming as they did from the correctional authority rather than from the DVR authority, emphasized the open fact that the DVR project was being denied responsibility for developing its own programs. This was just one example of how the imposition of superior correctional authority

on a specific psychological program proposed by the DVR project sabotaged an operation.

Upon reflection, we discovered that there were numerous other incidents which could serve to illustrate the destructive imposition of correctional authority upon the rehabilitative function. Our awareness of these new incidents was mind-expanding at first because of our gradual understanding that the areas in which the imposition of such authority affects the inmate's psychological life are more often than not those areas which psychologists do not normally recognize as their province. That is, the institution interfaces with the mental health of its inmates in areas that neither the institution nor most psychologists traditionally would consider to be a psychologist's business.

For instance, constant censorship of inmate reading material is carried out, often by men who have no awareness of the ability, interest, or need of the inmate, nor any understanding of the literature being censored. Thus, black inmates from urban ghettos are denied access to relevant black literature, because white rural censors find the material in some sense "foreign." Books containing common obscenities are censored although the majority of correctional employees themselves can be heard using the same profanities in their common speech. The critical point here is not the merit of the literature in question; rather it is the damaging assumption by the authorities that the inmate is to be protected from himself at all times and denied the simple human dignity of choosing for himself what he will read. This, we began to realize, is inimical to positive mental health.

The denial of political literature to inmates is particularly at odds with the stated aims of a rehabilitative model which strives to train men for reentry into society as alert, active good citizens. The denial is even more insidious when one recognizes that for some minority group members constructive political activism can become a viable alternative to criminal activity. Such denial of access to responsible literature often serves to force the inmate to develop his interests through less reliable "unofficial" political education groups among the prison population, and it reinforces his belief that the institution as a representative of the greater society desires to keep him uneducated. Again, the rules are based on an egalitarian treatment model . . . since political reading will make a rabble rouser out of one man it may make a rabble rouser out of any man; therefore, no man shall read political material. And again, these regulations are inimical to positive mental health.

The failure to deal with differences among inmates and the continual failure to recognize that inmates can be treated as men of individual character serves to provide an uniquely sterile environment for a project devoted to individual self-development. Often this environment acts to deprive men of simple and even trivial privileges. For instance, no inmate may carry into his cell an object of great value for fear that this object will either be stolen or become a source of currency in illegal trade; thus, a prisoner had to place his expensive watch in custody for the duration of his sentence. Since his sentence was from 20 to 30 years, he chose to give the watch to an inmate friend who was soon to leave; but gift giving is denied (because sometimes for some men it is associated with illegal operating) so the watch will remain unused for 20–30 years.

The uniform application of rules and regulations has a similarly devastating effect upon the interpersonal relationships of the staff members and the inmates. For example, staff members are warned never to do a favor for an inmate no matter how slight. Do not even give him a cigarette if he wants one. Why? Because doing a favor is against the rules and the inmate knows it; thus, once you perform the favor you are subject to blackmail on the grounds that you have broken a rule. The idea that you would not be subject to blackmail if giving the cigarette were not against the rules seems to carry no authority as an argument because this argument, of course, implies that the institution must trust the judgment of its officers to discriminate reasonable from unreasonable requests. Thus, the system tends to infantilize its own staff members by reminding them constantly that they are to follow rules literally—that they are not to be trusted with decision-making ability at any level.

Our initial observations were disquieting, and at first we were convinced that the underlying reason for the preservation of such institutional rigidity was simply that nobody had thought to change things. We were, once again, wrong and naive. Discussions with various members of the staff indicated, further, that we were mistaken in the notion that we alone had discovered these phenomena. Members of the correctional establishment were not unaware of the effects of the rules on the inmates and on the staff; they *were* aware, and they felt it necessary to run the institution in this manner. The cornerstone of their argument was that the traditional correctional approach actually protects the inmate, for as long as officers are required to act by rote and are prohibited from treating the inmate as an individual, they are also prohibited from discriminatively abusing inmates they do not like. From our point of view this justification can be derived only from a system in which the inmate has no mechanism whatsoever by which to have his grievances redressed. If inmates could obtain such a mechanism, and if it were handled well, then the officers could be left to use their discretion in dealing with the men. The rebuttal to our position was that the inmates could not be trusted to use such responsibility judiciously. Thus, we return to the nucleus of the entire system: no person, whether he be staff, professional, or inmate can be trusted!

What are the implications of functioning in a system based upon mutual distrust, spying, confidence breaking, and fear? The primary result is the development of extraordinary skepticism among inmates and to a large extent among the officers. Thus, when a project such as ours presented its credentials to the inmate population they did not expect it to be serious; they just suspected that they were being "conned" again. to a large extent their expectations came true, because many of the promises made could not be carried out in the context of the prison rules. For instance, many inmates discovered upon entering the project that their idle time increased rather than decreased. They discovered further that actual training programs often waited until after parole while they waited on the project with little or no personal gain. They discovered also that the project was held suspect by the correctional authorities and the officers assigned to it were often rejects from other blocks.

Inmates discovered further that they were being discriminated against by some members of the prison staff because of their affiliation with the DVR project. As tension between the rehabilitative personnel and the correctional personnel mounted the inmates became the victims of displaced aggression. Simple requests for privileges were kicked back and forth between the DVR office and the Corrections office in petty jurisdictional disputes while the inmate waited for an answer. Medical services offered by the prison hospital (administered entirely independently of the DVR project) seemed suddenly to deteriorate. Apparently the knowledge that the DVR project had a budget line for outside medical consultants influenced the prison physicians to resist offering medical service to DVR inmates. The rate of inmate complaints about poor medical service increased consistently as the project continued, and most of these complaints were seen as entirely valid by the rehabilitation counselor whose responsibility it was to investigate them. The medical staff and the corrections staff interpreted formal complaints from the DVR staff as a combination of paranoia and trouble-making. At about this time, the consulting psychologists tried to withdraw somewhat from the immediate stresses and strains of the situation and attempted to analyze the role demands placed upon the various staff members and inmates involved in the life of the project, hoping that this analysis would indicate appropriate directions for future input to the system.

A Role Analysis of Participants in the Project

In the course of observing the daily functioning of inmates, correctional officers, and higher correctional authorities, it became apparent that each member of the prison community perceived himself within a clearly defined role. Therefore, it became possible to some extent to analyze the social interactions in the prison setting in terms of the role definitions and the role expectations afforded to the people occupying various positions in the prison.

Starting from the top, the warden's role is defined primarily by the State Department of Corrections to whom he is responsible. The role he plays for them is that of efficient chief administrator. To fulfill this role expectation the warden concerns himself with a variety of administrative responsibilities such as the average daily cost of feeding a man, the average yearly expense for heat, and the costs for maintenance of the concrete. In addition, the warden is expected to preserve order. A prison with no disturbances or internal violence is a good prison. There is little evidence that the role definiton of the warden includes reducing the recidivism rate (that is for the parole department to do), teaching skills that are in demand outside the prison, or creating an environment conducive to human development.

The correction officer, who is the interface between the inmate and the system, fills a role which is also defined primarily by those above him. The officer's role, as defined by his superiors, includes the task of dispensing rewards for behavioral expressions of conventional values on the part of inmates. These rewards include block jobs and their associated privileges; but "rewarding" is not extended definitionally to include encouraging or anticipating good behavior. An officer's role is not in any way defined as "assistant to the rehabilitative venture"; the correctional officer is told simply that he guards! The implications of such a job definition are extensive and distressing: a guard is alert but not relaxed; he is responsible for blaming and/or punishing but he is not receptive; he relates to inmates only on the basis of administrative rules; therefore his authority depends on his position, not on his competence; he makes no decisions on the basis of consistency with an overall goal.

An inmate's behavior must be directed toward satisfying the expectations both of his peers and the staff. An interesting facet of his role in the institution is that a variety of community members holding different values concur with each other in their anticipation of inmate behavior, although for different reasons. For example, the correctional officer may expect inmates to gamble because he knows they "intentionally try to get away with everything." The DVR staff member similarly expects gambling from the inmate since "he can't help but want to gamble" in such an oppressive situation. The inmate subsequently encounters expectations which are shared by officers and DVR staff, then generalizes that all prison employees are alike.

The inmate must also behave in accord with the expectations of other inmates. While this peer pressure also is exerted by staff members upon each other, the existence of such pressure is clearest among the inmates. Consequently, just as it is considered bad form for a staff member to befriend an inmate (for fear that his authority will be weakened) it is considered equally bad form among inmates for one of them to befriend a staff member (for fear that he may be seduced into acting as an informer). Consequently, an inmate achieves esteem among his peers in proportion to the degree to which he is viewed as unfriendly or hostile to the staff.

Since the inmates, as we mentioned before, do not discriminate easily between the correctional staff and the rehabilitative staff, it follows that they display equal aloofness toward members of both categories of staff. Recognition of these factors explains in part the reluctance of most inmates to "take advantage of the service" being offered to them by the "good guy" psychologist; ironically we found ourselves being victimized by the inmates through essentially the same social processes that serve to victimize them.

Members of the DVR project defined their roles as essentially different from those of the officers. Yet the inmate, from his perspective, did not perceive the difference and the warden, from his perspective, did not want to perceive the difference. This conflict between the DVR worker's self-definition and the definitions imposed on him from below and from above often led to friction between him and the institution. For instance, the project director respected his staff's ability to use discretion in drawing a distinction between their rehabilitative function and their custodial function; consequently correctional authorities, who did not display such respect, felt compelled to warn DVR workers about the dangers of being "conned" into breaking rules. As might be expected the rules most likely to cause polarization between correctional officers and rehabilitation workers are usually those which the rehabilitation workers deemed least dangerous if violated and potentially harmful to inmates if enforced. For example, the reading of sexual literature and magazines is seen as dangerous by officers *because* it is outlawed; but the DVR staff may see it as a source of constructive tension reduction. Any resolution of such conflicts which arise as a result of the rehabilitation worker's lapses of rule enforcement and the correctional officer's prohibitions must come through the warden, who in turn *must be convinced that no negative consequences will follow his actions*. Naturally, under a situation where the warden perceives his role as stabilizer of the orderly status quo, decisions favoring the status quo predominate.

Given this basic structure in which pressure always flows towards preservation of the status quo, what is the proper role for the clinical consultant? The consultant entered the project as the agent of the institution, requested to fill a prescribed role, that of diagnostician and therapist. Yet, the consultant also was the possessor of a professional role as an agent of the inmates. Within the prison the conflict between these roles seemed unusually exaggerated. Whereas the mental health ethic prevailing in our culture labels the hospitalized as "sick," the prevailing societal code labels the imprisoned as "evil." This is especially so in those states (including New York) which provide specialized institutions for the "criminally insane"; for by definition, the inmates who are *not* "criminally insane" are just plain bad. In attempting to define his own role in this setting, therefore, the psychologist found himself in conflict between his role as agent of the inmates whose needs and rights he must serve, and as agent of an institution which perceived the inmate as unworthy of help and for whom the needs of the inmate were at best a nuisance.

And yet the needs of the institution (to preserve order and increase efficiency) and the needs of the inmate (to develop along socially and vocationally acceptable lines) need not be entirely incompatible. Our plan was to present our views emphasizing the compatibility of the two models to the correctional administration with the hope of influencing them at the local level to allow the DVR project sufficient freedom to attempt to demonstrate that modification of the existing structure would be advantageous to the prison and to the inmates. We kept in mind, however, our observation that the local administration functioned in accordance with the role expectation perceived to emanate from higher state authority, and that it was possible that no changes would be allowed unless pressure for them was perceived to come from the state. In that case, we had already begun to plan possible techniques for approaching the higher administration in Albany to plead our case.

RECOMMENDATIONS TO THE INSTITUTION

Proposals

Our first suggestion was that the tenuous state which existed between the correctional and rehabilitative organizations could be improved only by changes in the role expectations created by their respective job definitions. Significant changes in the formal demands upon both positions were recommended: correction officers should acquire responsibilities which, to begin with, allow them to refrain from retarding rehabilitation; rehabilitation staff should acquire responsibilities for enforcing those rules they can support (i.e., assume some of the unpleasant but necessary burdens of the officers). We proposed also that the demonstration block provide for the inmates a model of what an effective society can be. We suggested that a milieu based upon mutual trust (which must be constantly demonstrated, not just talked about) be established. This milieu should offer graduated degrees of freedom and responsibility as rewards for constructive behavior. In short, we proposed an attempt to carry out what was described in the original description of the project—milieu therapy. The block, it was suggested, should guarantee each inmate complete freedom from informers, freedom from duplicity, and freedom from being prejudged because of past behavior. It should provide the inmate with free access to other people in the block without fear of being trapped or "conned." The block should demonstrate the rudimentary principles of democracy and encourage the men toward self-government of their affairs, training them in principles of responsible, rational bargaining with the authorities. It should entrust to the officers the responsibility for making daily decisions concerning responses to prisoner requests, thereby increasing the responsibility of the officer and placing the prisoner face to face with his keeper in a mature confrontation. Naturally the block should enable all factions within it to develop methods by which their grievances may be heard by disinterested third parties. It should encourage education in civic affairs and politics as well as in vocational development and it should recognize the essential humanity of its inmates by allowing unrestricted private correspondence and regular conjugal visits.

What the clinical staff suggested is that the risks involved in such an undertaking were worth taking. It was likely, we believed, that the number of inmates who would create serious problems in such an environment would be far outweighted by the number who would demonstrate growth and change toward more constructive living. Eventually such a milieu should provide *internal* correction for the troublemaker (i.e., inmate judiciary), relieving the institution from some of its current policing responsibility.

The first obvious problem facing the psychologists, if such recommendations were accepted, was the establishment of conditions within the prison environment conducive to the changing of antisocial behavior on the part of the inmates and substitution of new behavior patterns conducive to the demands of society both inside and outside the prison. To these ends we proposed that the DVR block itself become an experimental unit in which prisoner behavior could elicit either rewards or punishments from the staff; for these purposes the staff was described both as civilian and uniformed staff. The essence of the program was to give immediate reinforcement to inmates for their total behavior, not just for isolated aspects of training and development; as inmates are processed through the project their success or failure should not only be evaluated but rewarded. Inmates demonstrating clear-cut effort, motivation, and achievement in educational training situations should be reinforced with some increased financial stipend. The prison environment currently makes this impossible because of the uniform regulations governing remuneration for all inmates. Although the institution recognizes some financial rewards for certain specific jobs it does not recognize financial rewards as reinforcement for successful rehabilitative efforts. In general what we recommended was a type of "token" economy program for the demonstration block in which specific tasks would be described for the inmates and limited goals established for them with reinforcements built in as they achieved those goals.

As the end of an inmate's prison term approached we envisioned more substantial rewards. For instance, an inmate who had consistently earned rewards and demonstrated great progress in his own personal, intellectual, and vocational rehabilitation could be allowed, during the last months of his sentence, to leave the prison and become involved in a work-release program. This type of arrangement used as a reward would give the inmate the freedom to compete on equal terms with other members of society and would give him the sense that the institution respects him and entrusts him to take care of his own destiny.

The risk involved in such a program seems quite minimal since the inmate will be released in a few months and returned to society anyhow; under these circumstances it would be foolish for him to abuse his leave privileges and endanger his imminent release.

Inmate Morale

As part of our overall proposal to the institution, we suggested also that inmate morale was essential to effective functioning of the project and that at least minimum steps should be arranged to improve morale on the block. We proposed competitive recreation programs on a year round basis with prizes for winners and a general purpose music room in which a phonograph and tape recorder might be available, so that inmates could satisfy their musical interests more adequately than they could with the limited radio services available. Also we suggested that a block newspaper or newsletter be developed using existing facilities and incorporating *all* members of the block into the activity. Again "all members" of the block implied staff as well as inmates, civilian as well as uniformed. Along the same lines we suggested establishing for the inmates a library which they could operate by themselves outside the current limits of the prison imposed censorship.

A therapeutic milieu should be one in which the inmate feels that the personnel are truly concerned with his development, not merely with his imprisonment. We suggested that all staff on the project, both correctional and rehabilitative, dress in civilian clothing. There is reason to believe that the blue uniforms present in such abundance within the prison establish a barrier between the inmate and the correctional staff; *and equally importantly add a barrier to communication between the correctional staff and the rehabilitation staff.* Inmates in prison systems generally have strong conditioned responses to the sight of blue uniforms and it is difficult for them to accept the notion that a man in blue is concerned about their development. It is easier for them to conclude that the man in blue is concerned only with their arrest and imprisonment. A total therapeutic milieu should free the inmate as well as some of the staff members from stereotyped responses and should provide an environment in which people can deal with each other free of such artificial barriers. Finally, we suggested a regular program of legal counseling in which law students from surrounding universities would be invited to meet with inmates on their requests, to give them sensible advice about their legal status with respect to potential appeals or misconvictions.

The Politics of Implementation

The proposals were greeted with something less than enthusiasm and it became readily apparent that the warden was dissatisfied with the input he was receiving from the clinical staff. Rather than minding their business and going about their day-to-day activities, certain members of the rehabilitation project had instead presumed to offer suggestions for "radical" change in institutional policy. The general response to these proposals for change was one of total silence and apparent inattention. It became apparent that the warden was not responsive to suggestions from below, and that even minor changes in the system would be impossible to achieve unless the "system" directed him to start selling new and different products: that is, rehabilitation instead of detention. After discussion among the project director and various members of the DVR staff, a tentative and optimistic conclusion was reached that the higher authorities in the state would be willing to accept our viewpoint as long as we talked about trying it exclusively with the small number of inmates assigned to our project. Our job now was to convince the state authorities of the virtue of allowing us to try, and to convince them to communicate to the warden that no negative consequences would result from allowing us more freedom within the prison.

Consequently the project director, through the state Office of Education, attempted to schedule a high level meeting with the Commissioner of Corrections, the State Director of Rehabilitation, the warden, and concerned members of the project staff to hammer out the dispute concerning the proper role of the DVR project within the prison. But repeated attempts to schedule such a meeting were met with delaying tactics. After months passed without a meeting, it became increasingly clear that the rehabilitation project had one of three choices concerning its future role in the prison. One choice was simply to fold up our tent and steal away admitting that there was no conceivable way within this context to carry out the mandate of the project. A second alternative was simply to capitulate to the system, go through the motions, take home our salaries, and provide the semblance of service requested by the institution. This alternative, admittedly, was appealing because it would minimize conflict and maximize ease, but would result inevitably in failure for the project and any future projects of this sort. The third position, which was tentatively agreed upon by the majority of staff members, was to force some sort of confrontation through the exercise of what little political power we had.

This plan was carried out in the following manner. The project director made clear his sense of dissatisfaction and impotence to the funding agency in Washington which had underwritten the project from the beginning, emphasizing to the funding agency that little progress was being made and little support was being offered. It was also made clear that it was unlikely that the demonstration project could succeed under the current conditions. Needless to say, the funding agency notified the state Office of Education that it was placing the entire demonstration project on probation and if there were not some significant change in the nature of the project within a six month probationary period the entire project would be terminated. The Department of Corrections, as we mentioned earlier, was eager to maintain the project if for no other reason than the prestige and the potential financial benefits it derived from "overhead." The prospect of an abrupt termination of funds and severing of the project was sufficient stimulus to cause the Corrections Department to schedule a meeting at the Commissioner's office within a relatively short period of time. The application of pressure had opened the door.

The meeting, which included the Commissioner and depty Commissioner of Corrections, the warden, the project director, and the chief psychologist (the author) was often acrimonious but nevertheless constructive. Sometimes functioning as a purely cathartic session, sometimes as a constructive problem-solving session, and sometimes as a sensitivity training group, the meeting wound down finally to a mutual agreement that the rehabilitation project would be given considerably more autonomy in the future and allowed to

experiment with a variety of programs. A crucial factor in the meeting was the insistence by the Deputy Commissioner that the warden need have no fear of negative feedback if some of the attempted innovations failed. The Deputy Commissioner agreed to assume administrative responsibility for the changes that might take place in the DVR project, and continually reminded the warden that he was "safe." As a gesture of his interest in shifting the emphasis from security to rehabilitation the Deputy Commissioner proposed that the warden, the DVR project director, and the chief psychologist take a trip, at state expense, to a highly respected state institution specializing in the rehabilitation of the "criminally insane." The Deputy Commissioner suggested that a few days of observation of its innovative program which emphasizes independence and self-government among inmates would be profitable for all of us who had been involved in the present conflict. The trip was made, and all indications are that the warden, if not convinced of the wisdom of the different methods, at least understood the message from his chief that he was expected to allow some changes to be made.

Those programs which the warden agreed to implement immediately included the establishment of a block newspaper to be printed on a weekly basis and handled mutually by inmates and all staff members. In addition, the warden agreed that a token economy program could be established on the block as a demonstration project, and agreed to allow the project necessary flexibility for changing rules and regulations to meet the needs of the token economy situation. Group counseling sessions without a security force were set up for all the inmates on the block. The DVR project director was allowed to initiate a weekly "gripe" session in which the inmates could come together in a town meeting and air any and all grievances freely.

Some of the proposals which had been made were summarily rejected for reasons often unique and entirely unpredictable to us. For instance, the suggestion that officers wear civilian clothes instead of uniforms was vetoed on the grounds that it would cause a crisis with the union. Once again we came up against an entirely new nuance which defied normal expectation. It seems that officers receive a special clothing allowance for the purchase of uniforms and that the union argues strongly during collective bargaining for relatively liberal allowances. The purpose, of course, is for the union members to receive an allowance considerably larger than they actually need for purchase. To establish a prison block in which uniforms were not required would be a threat to the union's ability to gain some extra funds for its members.

Nevertheless, the result of the applied pressure was generally positive. The second year of the project began with a renewed spirit. The inmates' morale was increased somewhat upon the observation that the project staff had in fact accomplished something on their behalf and was able to make the institution bend at least some of its rules towards rehabilitation needs. The morale of the staff members themselves improved tremendously at the recognition that their efforts had been rewarded. The relationship between uniformed officers and rehabilitation staff also seemed to improve. Part of this seems to stem from the fact that the rehabilitation workers, having tasted just a small bit of political power, no longer felt completely intimidated by the uniformed men, and conversely the uniformed men, recognizing that the civilian employees indeed had some power, gained newfound respect for them. Let us not be deceived into thinking that a revolutionary and utopian project emerged. The project continues; it stumbles; and there are day-to-day frictions between correctional and rehabilitative men. The group counseling programs are only marginally successful partly because of the reasons outlined during our discussion of psychotherapy and partly because they are so new to the inmates and to the staff that they have not had an ample opportunity yet to work into the prison routine. The block newspaper, on the other hand, has been an unqualified success. Both the inmates and the staff members derive an enormous sense of pride from the production of the paper, and there is tremendous desire to participate either as writer, editor, printer, or collator of the paper. It has contributed substantially to group morale. Unfortunately, at this point most of the improvement in project life seems to be centered primarily around morale. It is still unclear whether the project in fact is facilitating the vocational readjustment of the men on it, and it is unclear whether or not such a project can. To this end, the empirical research mentioned earlier is being conducted.

SOME COMMENTS UPON THE PROBLEMS OF ENTRY INTO THE MAXIMUM SECURITY PRISON SETTING AND A CONCEPTUAL FRAMEWORK

In reflecting upon the course of events that followed our entry into the prison setting it appeared that most of our difficulty derived from two sources: our inadequate preparation for the task of dealing with the institutional problems unique to the prison and our inability to come to grips with the question of whom to serve.

Inadequate Preparation as a Source of Trouble

It seems almost absurd to have to say that a professional who is inadequately prepared for his job is likely to fail at the task; yet, it is not unlikely that many psychologists need to have this fact stated explicitly at a time when the demands and pressures for the extension of services to the community are increasing rapidly. The crucial problem here is that there is a wide gap between the job for which most professional psychologists were trained ten years ago (and more) and the realities of the responsibilities they will be asked to assume in extending their services to new settings in the community. Graziano (1969) has described the excruciating difficulties encountered even when attempting to provide innovational service within a rather standard setting for mental health workers; the problems seem even more monstrous when one moves to a setting such as the prison where mental health workers are truly foreign agents.

Our failure was not just a failure to anticipate the problems! It was also a personal failure of attitude—a belief that existing knowledge and existing skills were sufficient to cope with whatever difficulties may have arisen. It was a homely example of professional "arrogance of power," and unfortunately may have resulted in a temporary worsening of the entire situation. By the time we became aware of the need to *treat* the institution and its administrators rather than to fight it, it was almost too late to save the situation. By the time we learned to diagnose the organizational ills and learned to negotiate successfully within the system itself we were almost out of the professional ball game. By the time we recognized what was happening to us we were almost nothing more than an unpleasant entry in the institution's memory bank. But we gained a reprieve at the last minute, and we now have to work double time to alleviate difficulties created by past mistakes. At the beginning of the project we would respond to many daily annoyances with the phrase "incredible" followed by a sigh of exasperation and a lingering angry feeling. Now we have learned that the correct response is "entirely credible but how, and why and what can we do about it?"

Who Is the Client?

Clinical psychologists usually are clear about whom they serve—they are hired by patients in distress and charged with the responsibility of relieving that distress; or they are hired by an institution and requested to relieve the distress of the inmates of that institution (although as is obvious, conflicts emerge in mental hospitals also). Functioning in the community, and specifically in a maximum security prison, the situation was entirely different. The institution saw us as its agents, whose responsibility was to serve it; dealing with inmates was merely incidental to the task.

The psychologist's job was complicated further by the institution's implicit belief in "intrapsychic supremacy" as the primary determinant of deviant behavior. "Intrapsychic supremacy," as Levine (1967) discusses it, is the notion that deviant behavior can be attributed almost exclusively to intrapsychic disturbance or psychodynamic disequilibrium. In a prison setting this doctrine leads to the conclusion that the social deviance which resulted in imprisonment and any subsequent social deviance within the prison may be attributed in large part to an inmate's intrapsychic disturbance. This enables the entire correctional institution (police and penal) to conveniently kick the ball to the psychologist, neatly absolving itself from major responsibility for understanding the deviance as an outgrowth of social forces, and more importantly, relieving the institution from any guilt that might bloom amidst the outrageously high recidivism rates. The high incidence of recidivism, incidentally, serves to reinforce strongly the doctrine of "intrapsychic supremacy," being interpreted as evidence that some guys are just plain bad.

To the extent that he feels that the problem is larger than the limits set by the intrapsychic life of the inmates and includes also the setting in which the inmate finds himself and the nature of the treatment which he receives from the institution, the consultant finds himself in severe conflict with the institution which has hired him as an agent. In the prison situation, for example, what are the implications of helping an inmate adjust to living in a cage and adjusting to 20–30 more years of social isolation and sexual deprivation? Helping an inmate adjust to these conditions is helping him to become pathological by normal criteria.

A Conceptual Framework

A psychologist adhering to the standards by which he was trained inevitably finds himself in some disagreement with the system for which he is working. As Levine (1969) has pointed out in a discussion of school consultation, the

disagreements, the problems, the conflicts come about when the consultant finds himself, for example, identified with the child in the school situation and in marked disagreement with the way in which the problem is being handled in the setting. The anger and the distress that such a position elicits in the caretaker, teacher, or principal comes about only in part because of the implied or stated criticism of these people. It also comes about because the consultant may be viewed as having broken a contract. He is no longer supporting the caretakers in the institutional setting in their judgment of what constitutes a problem. But in fact he has aligned himself with the opposition to their judgment (p. 3).

If we substitute in Levine's statement "inmate" for "child," and "warden" for "principal," "teacher," or "caretaker" we can see the extraordinary generality from the school situation Levine describes to the prison consultation program.

Levine (1967) has presented five postulates of practice in community psychology. It is our intention at this point to demonstrate how these five postulates, generated from consultative experience with educational institutions, can be easily applied to the prison setting. Levine's experience with school situations was the source of these postulates. Our experience in the prison setting is a test of their generality. To the extent that community consultants develop programs in varieties of institutional settings the generality and validity of these five postulates can be continually tested.

Postulate One—A Problem Arises in a Setting or in a Situation: Some Factor in the Situation in Which the Problem Manifests Itself Causes, Triggers, Exacerbates, or Maintains the Problem. Levine originally developed this postulate to deal with the obvious consideration that most people, including psychologically disturbed and even psychotic people, act differently in different situations. Some children respond well to one teacher but not to another teacher. The most common example we all remember from school is the way a group of well-behaved school children can suddenly become unmanageable and rowdy when a substitute teacher replaces a regular teacher. This first postulate is hardly controversial in the context of normal psychological work, and it must be obvious that it is considerably less controversial in dealing with the majority of criminal cases. Very few people ever wind up in prison (or even get processed by penal systems) for deviant behavior which does not involve acting out against some other person or property. Thus, the very definition of the client in the prison setting is a deviant individual who has been identified as deviant in some specific situational setting. The definition of deviant behavior within the institutional setting even more clearly reflects the verity of this postulate. An inmate who becomes excessively introspective in the prison situation is often seen as a model prisoner; the inmate who responds "badly" to the inflexibility of prison rules or who cannot cope with the radical shift from freedom to encagement is often defined as the "crazy" inmate. The psychologist then is required or requested to provide service for this "intrapsychically disrupted" individual who never showed signs of this type of disturbance before his imprisonment.

Postulate Two—A Problem Arises in a Situation Because of Some Element in the Social Setting Which Blocks Effective Problem-Solving Behavior on the Part of Those Charged With Carrying Out the Function and Achieving the Goals of the Setting. In other words, when the social system of deviant control or conflict resolution is ineffective for whatever reason, the behavior for which it is ineffective is defined as a problem. In the case of crime, this postulate is almost definitional. The entire common law structure represents society's essential attempt to define acceptable limits of deviance. Our laws are considered the limits; when they are violated, deviance is defined. Yet, despite the common law, the penal code, and increasingly sophisticated police tactics, we are faced with a continual increase in violations of that law, and an unceasing determination on the part of some violators to repeatedly thwart all efforts to deter them. Surely, "some element in the social setting . . . blocks effective problem-solving behavior on the part of those charged with carrying out the function and achieving the goals of the setting."

Levine deduces from his second postulate that a consultant called into the system must necessarily learn something about the system, and that in order to intervene effectively he must take into account variables related to the social system. As we have already seen it is clear that appropriate consultation to the prison system could be carried out only after we did learn a great deal about the social system and after we began to take into account variables related to it.

Postulate Three—Help, to be Effective, Has to be Located Strategically to the Manifestation of the Problem, Preferably in the Very Situation in Which the Problem Manifests Itself. To the extent that all help in a prison consultative program must be done inside the prison this postulate appears to be self-evident; however, it is not. Let us look again at an example from the school system and compare it to the prison. Levine suggests that in the school system there is a tendency to deal with deviants by getting rid of them in some way. When a child is identified or labeled as disturbed or mentally retarded the teacher tends to feel incompetent, and thus avoids dealing with the child and refers him for psychological or psychiatric aid. In the prison system exactly the same situation occurs and is handled in one of two ways. When a corrections officer labels an inmate as incorrigible, or crazy, or assaultive, he either sends him into isolation or calls the psychologist and says "cure this crazy person." The concept of locating help strategically to the problem in this situation implies that the correction officer himself must begin to assume certain responsibilities for more flexible responses to deviant behavior within the institution. Furthermore, the correctional officer must learn to discriminate, to the extent possible, between situationally determined and intrapsychically determined problems and must begin to define his own role not purely as a custodial agent but as a rehabilitative agent.

Postulate Four—The Goals or the Values of the Helping Agent or the Helping Service Must be Consistent With the Goals or the Values of the Setting in Which the Problem is Manifested. It is obvious that this postulate, if adhered to, restricts severely the utopian goals of a prison consultant since it is almost fundamental that the goals or values of the helping agent in such a setting are not likely to be consistent with the goals or values of the setting in which the problem is manifested. Levine states "the community psychologist may have to decide whether or not he can conscientiously support the goals of a given setting even though he may feel that he can be of help in that setting in a technical sense" (1967, p. 8). The *reductio ad absurdum* of this point arises when a clinical consultant is asked to help the Ku Klux Klan or the American Nazi Party with their interpersonal and organizational problems so that they can become more effective. The community psychologist in such a situation may either refuse to accept such responsibility, or he may simply capitulate and offer such service, or he may do as we have attempted to do in the prison setting: use whatever skills, powers, and pressures he has at his disposal to attempt to reconstitute the organization and direct its goals differently. There is nothing in the fourth postulate which prevents the community consultant from working with the institution to bring the values and goals of the institution into a higher degree of consistency with the values and goals of the agent.

Another deduction from postulate four is that the consultant may strive to help the institution bring its stated goals and its actual practices into closer alignment. For instance, social critics of the schools (Kohl, 1967, 1969; Kozol, 1967) have pointed out that although the stated goal of school systems is to educate, their actual practices often turn out to be a combination of baby-sitting and disciplining. Similarly while the prison system purports to be a rehabilitative agent its actual working concern is exclusively with security. There is nothing in the fourth postulate which prevents the community consultant from working with the institution to help bring its current practices into closer agreement with its own stated goals and objectives.

What we are suggesting here is perhaps a controversial position in that the community consultant is being asked to impose his values on the setting rather than to simply adopt the values of the institution which hires him. The tradition of scientific psychology has been one of value-free orientations; as the clinical psychologist moves into the community he may find that to remain value free is to unnecessarily blind himself and to restrict his total effectiveness in the situation. It is crucial for his effective functioning that the community consultant understand his own value system and project it in such a way that the agents with whom he has to deal have an honest and reliable view of his value system.

Postulate Five—The Form of Help Should Have Potential for Being Established on a Systematic Basis Using the Natural Resources of the Setting, or Through Introducing Resources Which Can Become Institutionalized as Part of the Setting. This postulate formalizes the consultant's view that settings should be able to take care of themselves and furthermore that they should be able to use their own resources and personnel in providing this help. Levine has pointed out that the "role of the community psychologist in these instances is in helping to identify the problems, helping to develop solutions which are meaningful within the structure of the setting which has the problem, training the workers, if that is indicated, and helping to institutionalize the solution as a means of dealing not with a single problem, but with a class of problems" (1967, p. 9). Broadly speaking, our attempt to influence the Corrections department towards redirecting the warden's activities and changing its message to him was a step toward "introducing resources which can become institutionalized as part of the setting." The single most powerful resource in the institution is its staff; proper use of that staff in a systematic attempt to establish a rehabilitative environment is more useful than the imposition of such activity by outside consultants.

When we arrived at the prison for the first time we were not sure what to expect. Basically, we adhered to an oversimplified view of Goffman's

(1961) notion that an institution is an institution is an institution; consequently, we mistakenly suspected that previous experiences with V.A. hospitals, state hospitals, community clinics, and private practice would serve us well in dealing with the problems of a maximum security prison. It did not take long to realize that we were unprepared for the challenge; and it did not take long to realize that the true essence of Goffman's point was that if we were to function effectively we would have to deal effectively with the individual institution as a client as well as with the inmates as clients. In order to do this we had to learn (often the hard way) to understand *its* needs, *its* values, and *its* potentialities for change. As any conscientious therapist does, we are still learning.

Notes

I am indebted to Mr. Charles Van Boskirk for sharing his wisdom with me and to Professor Murray Levine for his encouragement and guidance in the preparation of this paper.

1. The "editorial we" used frequently throughout this paper is more than a writer's conceit; more often than not the "we" refers to me and two indefatigable graduate student-interns, Mr. Emory Hill and Mr. Michael Moses.

2. It should be noted that at this time we became acutely aware of our severe inadequacy of preparation for the task at hand and sorely aware of the hubris manifested in jumping into a new professional context without consulting what turned out to be a voluminous literature on the problems emerging before our eyes. Of particular importance to us and to any members of the reading audience who may find themselves in our footsteps in the future are books by the American Correctional Association (1959), Cleaver (1967), Conrad (1965), Cressey (1961), Fenton, Reimer, and Wilmer (1967), Kesey (1962), Menninger (1968), and Solzhenitsyn (1963). In addition much was gained from studying papers by Kelly (1966), Graziano (1969), and especially Levine (1967, 1969). Alas, most of our formal education took place after we were neck deep in the "real world."

References

American Correctional Association. *A manual of correctional standards*. New York: American Correctional Association, 1959.

Cleaver, E. *Soul on ice*. New York: McGraw-Hill, 1967.

Conrad, J. P. *Crime and its correction*. Berkeley: University of California Press, 1967.

Cressey, D. R. *The prison: Studies in institutional organization and change*. New York: Holt, Rinehart, & Winston, 1961.

Fenton, N., Reimer, E. G., & Wilmer, H. A. *The correctional community: An introduction and guide*. Berkeley: University of California Press, 1967.

Goffman, E. *Asylums: Essays on the social situation of mental patients and other inmates*. New York: Anchor Books, 1961.

Graziano, A. M. Clinical innovation and the mental health power structure: A social case history. *American Psychologist*, 1969, 24, 10–18.

Kelly, J. G. Ecological constraints on mental health services. *American Psychologist*, 1966, 21, 535–539.

Kesey, K. *One flew over the cuckoo's nest: A novel*. New York: Viking, 1962.

Kohl, H. R. *36 children*. New York: New American Library, 1967.

Kohl, H. R. *The open classroom: A practical guide to a new way of teaching*. New York: New York Review, 1969.

Kozol, J. *Death at an early age: The destruction of the hearts and minds of Negro children in the Boston public schools*. Boston: Houghton Mifflin, 1967.

Levine, M. Some postulates of practice in community psychology and their implications for training. Paper presented at the University of Texas symposium on Training in Community Psychologist, Austin, Texas, April 1967.

Levine, M. Problems of entry in light of some postulates of practice in community psychology. Unpublished manuscript, Department of Psychology, State University of New York at Buffalo, 1969.

Menninger, K. *The crime of punishment*. New York: Viking, 1968.

Solzhenitsyn, A. I. *One day in the life of Ivan Denisovich*. New York: Praeger, 1963.

27

An Innovative Approach to the Treatment of Adolescent Delinquent Boys Within a Suburban Community

Milton F. Shore and Joseph L. Massimo

The history of the development of mental health services for children was originally very closely tied to the area of crime and delinquency. One of the pioneers in the field, William Healy, was the author of a well-known work on delinquent youth (Healy, 1915). In fact, one of the first child guidance clinics in the country was named after Judge Baker of the juvenile court who had been instrumental in developing mental health services for children out of a court setting. Over the years, however, fewer and fewer mental health professionals have been involved in working with delinquents and criminals. As a result, much of the work with antisocial youth has either been under the aegis of the correctional system (such as the juvenile courts and the training schools) or left to sociologists whose areas of interest are social problems within the broad social context. Unable to get well-trained mental health personnel, public agencies have often been forced to employ young, inexperienced mental health workers. Sociologists, on the other hand, not trained in the setting up and delivery of services, have for the most part limited themselves to delineating the variables within social disorganization and group structure that they feel would relate to delinquent behavior and its origins.

Recently, as mental health professionals, sometimes by choice, sometimes by necessity, have become more and more concerned about the current social issues, there has been a revival of interest in the possible contributions clinically trained professionals can make to the understanding of criminal and delinquent behavior and its treatment. This revival, however, has necessitated "an agonizing reappraisal" of many of the assumptions upon which much clinical work had been based. This, in turn, has generated some new ideas and new directions for mental health programs.

DEFINING THE AREA

In 1966 the Children's Bureau (United States Deparment of Health, Education, and Welfare, 1966) revealed that at the existing rate, one of every six male youths would be referred to juvenile court for a delinquent act (other than a traffic offense) before his 18th birthday. At that time, although they represented 13 percent of the population, the 11- to 17-year-old age group had one half of the total arrests in the country, with the highest number of arrests for any age occurring between the ages of 15 and 17.

The most recent statistics (United States Department of Justice, 1969) indicate that while arrests for *all* criminal acts increased four percent in 1968 over 1967, adult arrests increased some two percent, while arrests for persons under 18 years of age increased ten percent. The trend from 1960 indicated that the arrest of persons under 18 years of age had doubled while the population growth for the group during that time had shown a rise of only 25 percent. A study of rearrests and repeaters over a five-year period revealed that the largest number of repeaters rearrested were in the under-20 age group (72 percent of those under 20 when arrested the first time were rearrested within five years).

While descriptive statistics can be criticized in many ways and the analysis of the data challenged, there is no doubt that antisocial behavior has risen greatly over the last decade and that it continues to grow at an alarming rate, especially amongst youth.

One of the problems clinicians have found almost insuperable in their attempt to deal with delinquency is the complexity of defining the area itself. Juvenile delinquency is so intimately tied to social values and the social context that it is often difficult to determine even the nature of the problem. For example, recent work on undetected delinquency has found that 90 percent of youth admit acts that, if discovered, could be labeled delinquent in a particular context, and lead to correctional measures by society. In reality, it is often well-nigh impossible to know whether or not a given act is delinquent. States have different laws regarding delinquency, and many of the activities of youth labeled delinquent are not classified as crimes when committed by adults (stubborn child, wayward child, running away from home) although deliquency is often defined as the commission of an antisocial act by an individual below a certain age. In addition, sociological factors so subtly interweave in a variety of ways so as to make any simple attempts to delineate the causes almost impossible. As a result, appropriate programs of intervention are extremely difficult to set up.

In an attempt to clarify the area, there have been recent attempts at developing some typologies of delinquency (Rubenfeld, 1967). From these typologies appropriate methods of social and individual intervention have been planned (Palmer, 1965). Palmer has not only developed ways of classifying delinquents and ways of treating them but has even attempted to select individuals who can best work with each particular category of delinquent.

The need to view the total social context and understand the relationship of individual behavior to this context can best be illustrated by the experience of the authors in their effort to set up a program for aiding delinquent adolescent youth. The program was developed within a suburban middle class community where there were many opportunities for employment and recreation. The school system was considered one of the most flexible and forward-thinking in the country: mental health and remedial education services were available to all students who were having academic difficulty. The social milieu was one that encouraged adult interest in youth and attempted to foster the health development of the young people in many different ways. Jobs were available for young people. The police did not feel under pressure and were extremely amenable to a variety of ways of handling antisocial problems. For example, the police had on their own developed many alternatives to booking a child for an antisocial act so that the youth would not get a police record. These alternatives included talking informally to the child's parents, driving the child in the paddy wagon to show him what it was like, or even informally booking the youth then having him sit for a while in a jail cell to show him what a police station was like without in reality formally carrying through the procedure. Tolerance for deviance in the community was extremely high with many opportunities for help from a variety of social agencies.

However, despite all the positive elements in the community, there remained certain youths who when they became adolescent either dropped out or were suspended from school for antisocial activity and poor school performance. It was clear from the histories of these youths that they were totally unable to avail themselves of the resources within the community and that their families seemed alienated and isolated from the total social milieu. Most of these youths were from a lower social economic status, with their fathers employed as laborers, truck drivers, gasoline station attendants, refuse collectors, factory workers, and maintenance men. However, unlike many families of lower social economic status living in the inner city, these families had a certain degree of cohesiveness with mother and father usually living together, very little mobility, and usually regular, stable employment by father. Also unlike many urban settings, youth activities rarely took place within a gang; there were few opportunities when the boys left school for them to find a position of high status among their colleagues. As a result, dropping out of school merely served to isolate the boy further from the community, often alienating him even from his friends who were frequently able to function in some marginal way within the school setting. It was our belief that considering these many factors within the community, the problems these antisocial youths manifested were more those of individual psychopathology than those which arise from sociological causes, and that individual treatment would, therefore, be the treatment of choice. However, individual treatment of antisocial youth has often been found to be extremely unsuccessful; many clinicians have continued to be discouraged by the negative results obtained from classic clinical studies such as that in Sommerville and Cambridge (Powers & Witmer, 1951). It was clear that new things had to be done. But what?

DEFINING THE TASK

The innovative program for adolescent delinquent boys described here was guided by three general principles: (1) Something had to be done about the area of delinquent behavior, and the clinician has a unique and important contribution to make in this regard; (2) traditional clinical approaches to the area have not been successful and new clinical approaches were needed; (3) anything new that was undertaken should be based on firm, theoretical, and empirical foundations and include careful evaluation so that whether any changes occurred could be determined, the dimensions of the change understood, and these changes then related to the process of normal growth and development.

Two advances in clinical theory over the last decade gave rise to the optimism which generated our program for antisocial youth: ego-psychology and crisis intervention. Ego-psychology has broadened the motivational focus of traditional clinical theory to include the adaptional aspects of behavior. This had led to greater concern with the relationships between inner needs and the social environment culminating in psychosocial theories such as that of Erikson (1959) and in greater specification of the general social milieu (Cumming, 1962). Ego-psychology, with its focus on structure, has indeed brought about a rethinking of many of our psychotherapeutic techniques, especially those for psychotics, borderline psychotics, and character disorders.

The recent work on crisis intervention (Parad, 1965) had added to our clinical tools by increasing our awareness of new opportunities for psychotherapeutic intervention. Times of crisis are characterized by severe disequilibria caused either by internal changes (physiological changes of adolescence, for example) or external events (for example, death in the family, natural disasters, or the loss of a job). These crisis situations have been found to have been especially opportune times for helping people whose chronic adjustment problems have frequently been characterized by minimal degrees of distress or anxiety. Appropriate interventions during these crisis times have, in fact, been found to have a major effect on the individual's total adjustment.

The ego structure of the character-disordered delinquent with severe academic problems who comes from lower socioeconomic classes has often been described as present time-oriented, focused primarily on nonverbal expression and on motor activities, concrete in thought, impulse-ridden, low in frustration tolerance, and very limited in capacity for delay (Rubenfeld, 1967). Any program geared toward helping these youths would have to take account of these characteristics. The customary psychotherapeutic techniques which focus primarily around insight obtained through verbal discussions in an office setting on a once-a-week basis have not been found to be appropriate for this group. Likewise, a service that focused only on distinct areas such as remedial education, vocational assistance, or psychotherapy would be meeting only some and not all of the needs of these youths, since they had profound problems in all three areas.

The therapeutic program that was planned was aimed to reach the adolescent deliquent boy during a crisis point. It was also felt that the boy would be amenable to the three elements of vocational assistance, remedial education, and psychotherapy, if these were presented by one person who would administer that aspect of the program most appropriate for the youth at a given time rather than dividing these services into different departments and among different people, as has been customary in the past.

The crisis situation was identified as that of having dropped out of school or having been suspended from school. No matter how much denial takes place, leaving school permanently, we felt, would be a crisis for these youths and their families (whenever a boy is suspended from school or drops out, his parents are notified in writing by the school). This crisis, we felt, was even more acute in suburban areas where gang structures are loose and where the youth has no alternatives that would offer him personal satisfactions. To take advantage of this crisis situation, the therapist obtained the boy's name from the supervisor of attendance of the school within 24 hours after he had left. The youth was contacted immediately and offered the opportunity to meet any place, and any time, to discuss any aspects of help, particularly if by chance he was interested in finding a job. Each of the boys agreed to talk with the therapist about employment possibilities since employment is always seen by these boys as an idealized step toward getting all the things they might want. The boys were met on street corners, in restaurants, or in an automobile, rather than in a formal office. The general philosophy and details of the technique are explained in Massimo and Shore (1967). Although the therapist had some awareness of employment opportunities within the community (as described in Shore & Massimo, 1966), most of the time the therapist went out to business establishments to explore job opportunities with the youth. In this way, both the therapist and the boy were able to better understand the educational requirements that would be necessary in order to undertake a certain job. Using the job as an entrée, the therapist would discuss with the boy necessary academic requirements as well as personal problems that might interfere with his work. Initially, the focus was on job-readiness. As the boy was placed in a particular job, the focus was then changed to performance on the job and personal problems that related not only to the job, but also to other aspects of the boy's life. In line with the characteristics of the boy's adaptive styles noted above, the therapist had no office, appointments were not scheduled, and the therapist was available any time of day (day or night).

Employers who had hired the youth were not expected to act as therapists. The youth was to learn to handle the employment situation as a reality situation. The only request that was made of the employers was that when a youth was doing poorly on the job, or had to be fired, the employer contact the therapist so that the therapist could work with the boy around the concrete issues of what was happening, thus using the concrete situation for therapeutic work.

Each boy found a job, and other services appropriate to his needs and interests were planned. The therapist was available to help the boy purchase clothes, open a bank account, visit probation officers, appear for a job interview (he always accompanied the boy to his first job interview), and obtain a driver's license. At no point were the boys urged to return to school unless they chose to do so on their own. It was found that the focus on the realities of the job served two purposes—it helped maintain the necessary distance between the therapist and the boy, since closeness is often extremely threatening to these youths unless taken in small doses; and it offered an opportunity for the youths to develop skills which would be useful in advancing to higher levels of occupational status.

This comprehensive vocationally-oriented psychotherapeutic program lasted ten months. All the boys in the program were told of the program's duration. Although formal termination took place at the end of the ten-month period, the boys were told that if any difficulties arose they could come back for further help. Only one boy decided to keep informal contacts with the therapist for a year. How all elements of the program—job placement, remedial education, and psychotherapy—were integrated into a unified program can be seen in the following case:

Mark, age 15, was thrown out of high school in his sophomore year because of his overt hostile, destructive behavior. He was not only preoccupied with violence but participated in any physical fights that he heard about. Although considered above average in intelligence, he did nothing academically in school and was failing all his subjects. His provocative behavior in school included placing firecrackers in the ventilating system of the school and scaring the students. Mark was reading at about the fifth grade level. He also had participated in a variety of remedial services and counseling services in the school. He attended remedial and counseling sessions once or twice but then would not appear. He was in trouble with the police, having been put on informal probation for drinking and later on formal probation for car theft.

Mark's mother would probably be diagnosed as a borderline paranoid schizophrenic. His father, also a seriously disturbed person, was an outstanding draftsman who had not done well financially despite his education. Mark's father left the family when Mark was nine years old. Two years later the divorce was finalized. Mark was the oldest of four children in the family.

The initial interview revealed that Mark's destructive impulses were so overwhelming that he could only talk about his desires to destroy anything and everything. The intensity of Mark's destructive impulses did not permit adequate handling of his conflicts at the beginning. The therapist, therefore, sought to attempt to redirect Mark's hostile behavior into more constructive channels and see if that would work.

As occurred in each initial interview, the focus was on jobs that were not only available if the boy wanted to work but which were in some way related to his personal needs. For example, after some discussion with the therapist, Mark realized that he might be interested in working with a construction company that did some housewrecking. Since this job was not one of the jobs known to the therapist, Mark and the therapist looked through newspaper advertisements and visited firms where Mark was immediately employed as a helper in demolishing houses, hopefully in this way directing some of his destructive impulses into more constructive channels.

The therapist spent many hours discussing housewrecking with Mark. Mark related intimate details of demolition and destruction. The therapist and Mark also attended stock car races. One day the firm decided to move a house that was slated for destruction. Mark was angry that he did not have a chance to destroy another house. It was this event that led to discussion around Mark's life and dedication to destruction and some of the causes behind his destructive behavior. It was in this discussion that Mark began to show some interest in cars and thought of a job in an automobile salvage company where parts and cars were saved prior to the total destruction of the car. In addition, Mark was able to get extremely dirty in the salvage job, something which gave him a great deal of pleasure.

In this auto salvage job, Mark did very well. He continued to enjoy going to scenes of death and destruction in order to obtain the wrecked cars. As his performance on the job improved, Mark was given more responsibility. This required telephone calls, reading auto parts books, and writing orders. It was at this point that remedial education became important and the therapist and Mark worked on spelling and reading. Because of Mark's high intelligence, he was able to learn rapidly.

Meanwhile, the therapist humorously interspersed remarks about Mark's anger and continued to explore the reasons behind Mark's anger. However, it took a great deal of time before Mark was able to handle his feelings and before he was able to adequately deal with some of the questions the therapist asked.

Following his job in salvage work, in the eighth month of treatment, Mark became interested in body mechanics work. This required further involvement in terminology, catalogs of body parts, and other academiclike pursuits. The therapist and Mark visited body shops to find out the necessary requirements for a body mechanic job. Mark learned to handle an oxyacetylene torch. It was during this period that the therapist was also able to inroduce Mark into some areas of chemistry and gaseous mixtures.

It was only after some nine months of treatment that Mark was able to talk about some of the origins of his rage. As a young boy he remembered having a tree house which after having been carefully built was completely destroyed by some boys in the neighborhood. He also talked about his father and his anger at this father for leaving the family. His one positive memory of his father was how his father had built their house and how Mark and his father together had built a wall around the house. Mark was able to recall these many events in bits and pieces as he and his therapist worked around concrete situations.

During the three years following treatment, Mark took a correspondence course from the Department of Education for the State of Massachusetts and completed his high school equivalency for a diploma. He has had some minor traffic violations, but none serious enough to place him on probation. He has married. For some four years, Mark has held one job with a firm as an auto body man. He has consistently been pleased with his job, as his skills and his wages have progressively increased.[1]

EVALUATION

Although it is mandatory that any new program set up to bring significant personality change be subjected to careful evaluation, few such evaluations have been reported in the clinical area despite a marked increase in the number of new programs. One of the reasons may lie in the great difficulties inherent in doing evaluative studies. Suchman (1967) in his major work on evaluative research quotes a Public Health Service report: "Evaluation of mental health activities is necessarily difficult. It must cope with the influences of numerous variables, consider the validity of those basic assumptions upon which mental health relies at the present time, and take into account the personal beliefs and attitudes of both the evaluators and those whose activities are being evaluated" (page 20). Suchman also comments that although there have been many exhortations that better evaluative research be done, few researchers have attempted to analyze the source of the difficulties in doing evaluative research, or have helped set forth guiding principles or procedures to deal with some of the problems.

The evaluation of comprehensive vocationally-oriented psychotherapy for the adolescent delinquent boys was totally separated from the psychotherapy itself. The individual who collected the data was in no way involved in the treatment process, and the person who evaluated and rated the material was in no way aware of either the goals of the study, the details of the psychotherapeutic process, or the ways in which the data were being collected. In this way, it was hoped that any biases that frequently interfere with the evaluation of clinical programs would be lessened or even eliminated.

Four questions were asked in the evaluation of this therapeutic program: (1) How effective was comprehensive vocationally-oriented psychotherapeutic treatment in bringing about change? (2) If there was any change, were the changes specific or general? (3) Was any change that occurred maintained after treatment? and (4) How did any change that occurred compare with that which might be expected in normal development?

In addition, it was hoped that some questions relevant to clinical issues might also be answered, such as the relationship between responses on projective tests and overt behavior, the role of the stimulus in projective testing, and the relationship between the various aspects of projective tests, various cognitive functions, and intelligence. In addition, could one gain some insight into the personality structure of antisocial youth as compared to youth who were not involved in the antisocial activity?

Three levels of personality functioning were evaluated: (a) The overt behavioral level—job histories, marital status, and involvement with legal authorities; (b) cognitive level—academic achievement in many areas; and (c) attitudinal variables.

Overt behavior was evaluated descriptively. The number of jobs held, length of time, reason for leaving, and salary level were all used to gain a general picture of job history. Legal status was judged by the relationship between the boys and legal authorities—on probation, awaiting a hearing, or awaiting sentencing, as well as the reasons for the association with legal authorities. Because of the complexities in the area of evaluating overt behavior, quantification was extremely difficult. In evaluating antisocial behavior one must always be aware that a boy who has been identified as "bad" by police authorities would easily be recognized and often be accused of further antisocial behavior even though he may not have indeed participated in such behavior. Since no adequate quantitative measure of these dimensions was available, descriptive tables were used for comparisons.

Cognitive functioning was measured by using standard achievement tests (Metropolitan Achievement Test) in the four areas—reading, vocabulary, arithmetic fundamentals, and arithmetic problems. Different forms of these tests were administered; all these tests were administered individually.

Attitudinal dimensions were selected which were considered to be most important to change if there was indeed a personality change in the youth with antisocial problems. The dimensions selected were attitude toward authority, self-image, and control of aggression. Questions arose as to how these areas could be measured in youth who were characteristically hostile, defensive, and clever in avoiding their real feelings, sometimes even presenting a much more favorable picture than was present in reality. It was believed that the most appropriate technique would be projective tests. The total testing situation was to be seen conceptually as a stimulating situation with certain task demands. How these task demands were handled would be analyzed both structurally and through content analysis. This analysis would be a measure of the adaptational aspects of ego functioning. Certain projective tests were not considered, either because they were too complex in their stimulating demands, or because they were measures of such depth that any major changes within the ten-month period could not be anticipated. Thematic pictures, i.e., pictures to which thematic stories were to be given, were selected as the most appropriate measure.

Recent work on thematic tests has shown that the stimulating characteristics of the picture about which a person is asked to tell a story are of great significance in determining the quality and form of the final product. This concept of stimulus value was used in the evaluation. Pictures were selected which might elicit reactions in the three areas in which we desired change—self-image, control of aggression, and attitude toward authority. The pictures from a variety of tests as well as pictures especially designed for other research on thematic processes were presented (a total of some 35 pictures) to three clinical psychologists who were asked to select those pictures that would most probably elicit stories in the three personality areas of interest. Five cards were chosen for each area, pictures on which the three judges had total agreement.

The boys were tested three times—at the start of the program, immediately after the program, and three years after the program had ended. On the first testing, in addition to the projective and achievement tests, each boy was given an individual intelligence test (Wechsler Adult Intelligence Scale [WAIS] or Wechsler Intelligence Scale for Children [WISC]). Only boys aged 15 to 17 with an I.Q. of over 85 who revealed no overt psychotic functioning or brain damage were selected for the study. Each boy also had to have been on probation at least once and had to have dropped out of school. Ten boys were selected at random for the treatment program and ten boys were not given the program (they were told the testing was being done merely for school and city records).

The first judgments of change were global ones. In an effort to determine if the program was successful, thematic stories of each individual and all groups (treated and untreated) were paired and randomized. A clinical psychologist who had had many years of experience with projective techniques, but who was in no way connected with the development of the project, was asked on the basis of criteria derived from analysis of the literature on thematic material to make a judgment as to whether the story which was numbered "2" showed marked deterioration, slight deterioration,

no change, slight improvement, or marked improvement over the story numbered "1". For the final analysis, the scale was collapsed to a three-dimensional scale of deterioration, no change, and improvement. Each boy received a positive (improvement) or negative (deterioration) score for the total variable derived from the direction of a majority of his five stories (the one "no change" score was included as deterioration because of the directional nature of the hypothesis). Chi square analyses were then done to determine the differences between the treated and untreated groups over the ten-month treatment period.

The results revealed marked improvement in the treated adolescent delinquent boys. The improvement occurred in all three dimensions—overt behavior, cognitive functioning, and attitudinal areas (Massimo and Shore, 1963). A noticeable reduction in involvement with police authorities occurred in the treated group while the untreated group showed continued involvement with legal authorities (two untreated youths were institutionalized within the ten-month period). The treated boys also showed more stable work histories with fewer job changes resulting from being fired or quitting. The academic changes in all areas—vocabulary, reading, arithmetic problems, and arithmetic fundamentals—were highly significant with the untreated group showing no change in cognitive skills over the ten-month period while the treated group advanced an average of two grade levels. As noted above, significant attitudinal changes (as measured by thematic stories) also took place in the areas of self-image and control of aggression (attitude toward authority changed in the predicted direction, but not significantly). This improvement continued when the boys were retested on follow-up two or three years after treatment was terminated (Shore & Massimo, 1966). The untreated group consistently showed deterioration during that time, with the discrepancy between the two groups widening over the three-year period.

A question of major importance upon which much of the analysis of the attitudinal functions depended was whether or not the three dimensions selected for study (self-image, control of aggression, and attitude toward authority) were indeed relatively autonomous aspects of personality functioning or whether the changes that occurred were merely measuring three aspects of the same area. A factor analysis (Shore & Massimo, 1955) revealed that the changes in the area of self-image, control of aggression, and attitude toward authority were indeed separate and independent (they loaded on separate factors). The changes in self-image were found to load on the same factor as the changes in all four achievement tests, I.Q. loaded on a separate factor. Therefore, changes in self-image were very closely tied to changes in achievement but were independent of changes in control of aggression and attitude toward authority.

In order to explore those elements of personality structure that contributed to the overall change, scales were developed to analyze different dimensions on the thematic stories. Guilt, object relations, perception of roles, temporal perspective, and productivity—all these were measured prepost and follow-up and were correlated with behavioral measures of change, changes on the achievement tests, and the initial I.Q. level.

Another question that arises is whether the various measures of ego-functioning (object relations, guilt, perception of roles, etc.) were also separate areas of functioning or whether they might be so strongly intercorrelated that there was little significance in looking at these separate areas. Intercorrelations between these areas and analysis of the thematic stories showed that only certain variables could be measured on certain cards. Changes that occurred were also independent. For example, the measurement of guilt was only possible on control of aggression cards because so few stories on the other cards dealt with the area of guilt (Shore, Massimo, & Mack, 1964). Verbalization was found to increase only on stories on the control of aggression cards and not to any of the other two areas (Shore & Massimo, 1967). Object relations changes were greatest on the self-image cards (Shore, Massimo, Kisielewski, & Moran, 1966; Shore, Massimo, Moran, & Malasky, 1968). Because these various areas seemed to elicit separate kinds of responses, it appeared indeed that separate dimensions of personality functioning were being measured.

Not only were self-image, control of aggression, and attitude toward authority found to be separate dimensions, but they also seemed to change in specific order. Both during the ten months of treatment and from termination to follow-up, the order of change was consistent.

Changes in self-image seemed to be a prerequisite to changes in the other two areas. Following changes in self-image, the next area of change was control of aggression. The area that changed the least, perhaps because of the nature of the adolescent process itself, was attitude toward authority (Shore, Massimo, Moran, & Malasky, unpublished paper).

Other findings were of special significance. The treated delinquents showed a significantly greater increase in orientation toward the future than the untreated delinquents (Ricks, Umbarger, & Mack, 1964). Verbalization increased significantly in areas stimulated by aggressive material and seemed to serve as one mechanism by which control over antisocial behavior was being developed (Shore & Massimo, 1967). The learning problems in these adolescent delinquent youth were found to be related more to the socialization process and the rejection of socialization by these boys than to the neurotic interactions that are often found in many learning problems (Shore, Massimo, Kisielewski, & Moran, 1966). Acceptance of passivity was not an important aspect of the treatment process. Successful change was directly related to redirecting the high energy level that these youths seem to have into more socialized channels rather than reducing their activity level (Shore, Massimo, Kisielewski, & Moran, 1966).

Comparisons with nondelinquents of the same age, same intellectual level, and same socioeconomic status who were followed and retested after a ten-month period, revealed that chronic delinquent adolescents are qualitatively different in their interpersonal way of relating to the world (Shore, Massimo, & Moran, 1967). The antisocial youths seem to be more aware of other people: that is, although they give stories of exactly the same length, the stories involve many more activities and much more talk about people's interactions. The nondeliquents, on the other hand, use many more adjectives and elaborate a great deal more. These results suggest that part of the cognitive structure of chronically antisocial youths might be an increased sensitivity to opportunities for manipulation and self-gratification from others, something clinicians have commented on.

Further analysis of the changes occurring over a ten-month period in the *nondelinquent* adolescents showed no consistent group changes, but individual variability which averaged out when the nondelinquents were viewed as a total group. In contrast, the group of treated delinquents consistently showed improvement in all areas, while the untreated delinquents, as a group, had clearly deteriorated (within three years, two of the untreated group had already been incarcerated in an adult criminal institution).

A recent five-year follow-up study of the treated and untreated delinquents (Shore & Massimo, 1969) showed that the untreated delinquents were consistently in trouble with the law and had very unstable work records. Only one of the ten untreated delinquents made any effort to return to school. Most treated delinquents, on the other hand, showed consistent, stable work records (only two of the ten are unemployed) with three of the ten having minor infractions with the law. The results suggest that successful psychotherapeutic intervention at one stage in the developmental process may be successful in helping individuals cope with later developmental issues. A revealing finding during this five-year period was that those in the untreated group who had had contact with the usual rehabilitative agents of society (training schools, reformatories, and state hospitals) showed no reversal in the deterioration that was taking place. Such a finding adds additional support to the need for finding new and innovative ways of intervening with groups that are major social problems.

Implications

There is little doubt that the community mental health movement will have a major impact on our clinical activity. Likewise, clinicians can make a significant contribution to the directions that the community mental health movement takes. Community mental health implies greater concern with significant social problems and greater efforts to bring to bear our clinical knowledge in these areas. As a result of our involvement in new areas, many changes will have to take place in our agency structure and in our treatment techniques. It is important that these changes be based on solid, theoretical, and empirical foundations. It is also important that the changes that take place be carefully evaluated so that the forces that operate to bring about change can be clearly understood. It is only then that adequate social policy decisions can be made.

The program for adolescent delinquent boys in a suburban community described above attempted to reach the so-called unreachable youth. It was based on a philosophy similar to that which has formed the core of federal programs aimed toward helping youth in the lowest socioeconomic groups—the Neighborhood Youth Corps, the National Job Corps, and the Youth Opportunity Program. It demonstrated that a program combining job placement, remedial education, and intensive psychotherapy in a flexible framework can be successful in bringing about major changes in adaptation.

The rising concern about major social problems and the limited mental health manpower have highlighted the need for new personnel in the mental health field. In fact, many gifted people have been found who are especially talented in working with antisocial youth, although they have minimal specialized training. One of the problems has been to clarify what needs to be done and in what manner. The study described above tried to answer this question. The challenge now is to see whether or not highly talented, indigenous workers can be trained to perform the functions listed above under adequate supervision. Some explorations in this area are currently being undertaken.

One of the major features of the above program was its challenge to traditional professional models and roles. In order to do new things, theoretical, technical, and administrative changes are required, with experimentation in many different directions. The clinician is the most appropriate one, not only to suggest new directions in the area of service, but also to see that changes in mental health services are not based on fads and fashions, but on firm foundations that contribute significantly both to the solution of the social problems and to the science of individual and group behavior.

CONCLUSIONS

The field of community mental health has many dimensions. It includes the reconceptualization of psychological functioning within a social context with the establishment of new theoretical models from which hypotheses for testing will be derived. It also involves a rethinking of our current models, broadening their scope to include an understanding of social phenomena and their relevance to personality development and functioning. One result of this new focus has been the greater involvement by mental health professionals in devising new and often creative ways of viewing the mental health aspects of major social problems such as poverty and antisocial behavior. The ultimate development of the field of community mental health, however, is dependent on the planning, implementation, and evaluation of specific programs developed within a community framework. It is only to the degree that the field is able to develop a discrete body of knowledge based on empirical evidence and actual experiences that it will be able to develop its own identity and have a significant impact on social policy.

Note

1. This case is reprinted in slightly revised form from M. F. Shore and J. L. Massimo, "The Alienated Adolescent: A Challenge to the Mental Health Professional," *Adolescence*, 1969, 4(13), 19–34, and is used with permission from Libra Publishers, New York.

References

Cumming, E. *Ego and milieu.* New York: Atherton, 1962.

Erikson, E. Identity and the life cycle. In *Psychological Issues, No. 1.* New York: International University Press, 1959.

Healy, W. *The individual delinquent.* Boston: Little, Brown, 1915.

Massimo, J. L., & Shore, M. F. The effectiveness of a vocationally oriented psychotherapy program for adolescent delinquent boys. *American Journal of Orthopsychiatry,* 1963, 33, 634–643.

Massimo, J. L., & Shore, M. F. Comprehensive vocationally oriented psychotherapy: A new treatment technique for lower class adolescent delinquent youth. *Psychiatry,* 1967, 30(3), 229–236.

Palmer, T. Types of treaters and types of juvenile offenders. Unpublished paper, CPPCA Conference Workshop, Sacramento, California, 1965.

Parad, H. (ed.) *Crisis intervention: Selected readings.* New York: Family Service Association, 1965.

Powers, E., & Witmer, H. *An experiment in the prevention of delinquency.* New York: Columbia University Press, 1957.

Ricks, D., Umbarger, C., & Mack, R. A measure of increased temporal perspective in successfully treated adolescent delinquent boys. *Journal of Abnormal and Social Psychology,* 1964, 69, 685–689.

Rubenfeld, S. *Typological approaches and delinquency control: A status report.* (Public Health Service Publication No. 1627) Washington, D. C.: United States Government Printing Office, 1967.

Shore, M. F., & Massimo, J. L. Comprehensive vocationally oriented psychotherapy for adolescent delinquent boys: A follow-up study. *American Journal of Orthopsychiatry,* 1966, 36, 609–616. (a)

Shore, M. F., & Massimo, J. L. The mobilization of community resources in the out-patient treatment of delinquent adolescent boys. *Community Mental Health Journal,* 1966, 2(4), 329–332. (b)

Shore, M. F., & Massimo, J. L. The course of psychotherapy in adolescent delinquent boys: Implications for a theory of treatment changes. Unpublished paper. (c)

Shore, M. F., & Massimo, J. L. Verbalization, stimulus relevance, and personality change. *Journal of Consulting Psychology,* 1967, 31, 423–424.

Shore, M. F., & Massimo, J. L. Five years later: A follow-up study of comprehensive, vocationally oriented psychotherapy. *American Journal of Orthopsychiatry,* 1969, 39, 769–774.

Shore, M. F., Massimo, J. L., & Mack, R. The relationship between levels of guilt in thematic stories and unsocialized behavior. *Journal of Projective Techniques and Personality Assessment,* 1964, 28, 346–349.

Shore, M. F., Massimo, J. L., & Mack, R. Changes in the perception of interpersonal relations in successfully treated adolescent delinquent boys. *Journal of Consulting Psychology,* 1965, 29, 213–217.

Shore, M. F., Massimo, J. L., Mack, R., & Malasky, C. Studies of psychotherapeutic change in adolescent delinquent boys: The role of guilt. *Psychotherapy: Theory, Research and Practice,* 1968, 5(1), 85–89.

Shore, M. F., Massimo, J. L., Kisielewski, J., & Moran, J. K. Object relations changes resulting from successful psychotherapy with adolescent delinquents and their relationship to academic performance. *Journal of the American Academy of Child Psychiatry,* 1966, 5, 93–104.

Shore, M. F., Massimo, J. L., & Moran, J. K. Some cognitive dimensions of interpersonal behavior in adolescent delinquent boys. *Journal of Research in Crime and Delinquency,* 1967, 4, 243–248.

Shore, M. F., Massimo, J. L., Moran, J. K., & Malasky, C. Object relations changes and psychotherapeutic intervention: A follow-up study. *Journal of the American Academy of Child Psychiatry,* 1968, 7, 59–68.

Shore, M. F., Massimo, J. L., & Ricks, D. A factor analytic study of psychotherapeutic change in delinquent boys. *Journal of Clinical Psychology,* 1965, 21, 208–212.

United States Department of Health, Education, and Welfare, Children's Bureau. *Juvenile court statistics 1965.* Washington, D. C.: Superintendent of Documents, United States Government Printing Office, 1966.

United States Department of Justice. *Uniform crime reports for the United States 1968.* Washington, D. C.: Superintendent of Documents, United States Government Printing Office, 1969.

28

The Politics of Mental Health

Bertram M. Brown and James W. Stockdill

INTRODUCTION

Politics is the resolution of social forces. Our subject is the politics *of* mental health and not politics *and* mental health. We therefore are not concerned with politics and mental health in the sense that the healthier, more mature individual may bring more objectivity to his political choices, but rather, we are concerned with the politics of mobilizing society's scarce resources for the support of mental health programs. Mental health has to be political in part because mental health cannot be precisely defined. The fact that mental health professionals do not have a precise enough conceptualization of the problems in their field to clearly define goals, tasks, and priorities results in mental health political battles on three fronts: (1) Mental health professionals and interested citizens must speak to legislative appropriations committees at all governmental levels in dramatic and large numbers of voices to get their share of the pie, because they are unable at the present time to present a logical case in modern economics cost/benefit terms; (2) within the professional mental health community, arguments rage between the supporters of the traditional "medical model" or concentration on illness and those who see mental health in the much broader context of man and his total environment and the quality of life; and (3) in the community, particularly as the supporters of the broader view of mental health win out, there are many jurisdictional conflicts with other social agencies and between levels of government.

Even if the amorphous boundary issue were not present, mental health would still be political because mental illness treatment programs are still largely supported with federal, state, and local government dollars. The mental health department with the state hospital system is often the biggest employer in the state government and has the largest payroll. As early as 1967, states employed 320,000 persons to treat the mentally ill and retarded (Schnibbe, 1967). The states in 1967 invested 2.34 billion dollars in the treatment of the mentally ill and retarded (Schnibbe, 1967). This is big business. Big business means big politics, and thus, mental health must hold its place in the political arena.

MOBILIZATION FOR PROGRAM SUPPORT

The basic dimension of mental health program politics has to do with the management of power and the allocation of resources. In the contest for scarce resources, the key question is which experts and social forces will win out? Equally important to this qualitative issue is the quantitative one—what resources can be made available to solve the human and social problems that comprise the domain of mental health?

History

Our historical section is brief because we are not seeking to develop a historical model but only to give some perspective to the current politics of mental health.

The concentrated political effort to gain a greater share of public resources for the care of the mentally ill in this country began in 1841 when an outraged and determined Dorothea Dix first visited the Massachusetts State Legislature. She carried on her campaign with state legislatures across the country until her death in 1887. The modern community mental health movement began in 1908 when Clifford Beers appealed to concerned citizens by describing his own experience in mental hospitals in his book *A Mind That Found Itself*. Subsequently, Beers founded the Connecticut Society for Mental Hygiene which became the National Committee for Mental Hygiene in 1909 and has long since developed into the National Association for Mental Health.

The passage of the Mental Health Act in 1946 brought a national perspective in the sense that the federal government now recognized and supplemented the previously initiated citizen and state government efforts. It was this Act that made the establishment of the National Institute of Mental Health possible. The national Congress responded again in 1955 with a resolution that led to the establishment of a Joint Commission on Mental Illness and Health. This Commission conducted the first nationwide study of the extent of mental illness and made its final report, "Action for Mental Health," in 1961. We need not detail the extensiveness of its work, but would like to highlight the comprehensiveness of the social forces that were engaged in this endeavor and paid such handsome dividends in the political arena in 1961 and 1962.

There is no doubt that cooperative activity between organizations varying from the American Legion to the American Psychiatric Assocation, between the American Public Health Association and the American Medical Association, was, at times, difficult. But it is because of the very extensiveness and comprehensiveness of the organizations and forces involved that the report had major attention.

At the start of its work in 1956, the Joint Commission had to define how comprehensive its studies would be. Many important areas were left out by lack of time, by conscious design, or by other factors. The area of great future significance that was separated and left out of the Joint Commission's work was that of mental retardation. Another area of specific interest to this group that was not covered in depth was services to children. Plans were made at that time to have the National Institute of Mental Health fund a technical project on planning in mental retardation to be carried out by the American Association on Mental Deficiency. This Association was to develop a parallel program and fill in the area of mental retardation.

The mental retardation program had great initial difficulties in getting underway and while it produced outstanding work in the field, it never gathered the comprehensive social force that characterized the Joint Commission on Mental Illness and Health. However, the technical material produced respectively by the Technical Project and the Joint Commission are roughly comparable in size and scope.

With the election of President Kennedy, mental retardation took on national significance. Simultaneously with the publication of the final report of the Joint Commission, the President became concerned with the need for a national program in mental retardation. Following a review of the situation, he appointed a distinguished Panel on Mental Retardation. President Kennedy's awareness of the Joint Commission's work was brought dramatically and graphically to our attention, for during the preparation of the early drafts of material for the President's Panel on Mental Retardation he asked, "What is the relationship between our proposed work in retardation and the Joint Commission report?" It was this question that led to a careful historical review of the early days of the Joint Commission and its decisions relative to mental retardation.

From the fall of 1961 to the fall of 1962, two simultaneous activities ensued. One was the appointment by the President of a Cabinet-level committee to study the Joint Commission report and to propose federal action; another was the work of the Panel on Retardation. Both these sets of endeavors were studied, analyzed, and integrated by the White House staff in the winter of 1962–63, culminating in the President's Message to Congress of February 1963 on Mental Illness and Mental Retardation.

Two separate bills—one for mental health and one for mental retardation—were proposed and later fused in part for political purposes. The combined law (P.L. 88–164), now known as the Mental Retardation Facilities and Community

Health Centers Act, was signed by the President on October 31, 1963. Thus began the real national political mobilization for support of community mental health programs.

Some Concepts of Mobilization

Two models, the "elitist" and "pluralist," are frequently used by political scientists to describe community or organization power structures. Elitism indicates the domination of the decision-making process by a few. The pluralist model indicates that political power is distributed among various groups and strata of the community. There is no question that for the national mental health effort and more and more on an individual state and local community basis the power structure is pluralistic. Because of this, mental health action agencies at all levels of government must carefully mobilize public and governmental support for their budgets, policy interests, and legislative proposals.

The effective agency will be the one that has mastered the political culture of its state or community and thereby provides program leadership and support regardless of its organizational location in the bureaucratic hierarchy. It is an absolute necessity to understand the state and each major community's political influence system and to know how to function effectively with it. Given the degree of pluralism present today this is not an easy undertaking.

The basic difficulty in getting increased legislative support for mental health is usually not a negative attitude or stigma but indifference and ignorance. In the lower houses of state legislatures and the national Congress there is a significant turnover which creates a continuous need for education from state and federal administrators. Of course, what motivates those legislators *that have a high interest* in mental health is always an important factor. Some may be motivated by mental illness or mental retardation in their families; others may be seeking mental health facilities for their districts. The manner in which problems and new program proposals are described to legislators is of critical importance. Problems relating to direct services and bricks and mortar, such as direct services in community mental health centers, are not very difficult because they have the advantage of being comprehensible to the layman and are fairly easily introduced into the legislative process. That is, they can easily be placed in a format which a legislative body can act upon. However, problems relating to indirect services or which require research, education, or training approaches are much more difficult to formulate into requests for legislative action. Both legislators and mental health professionals tend to become frustrated in communications in these areas. Legislators deal best with specific facts, problems, and requests and not so well with generalized concepts. In order to meet mental health program needs, legislators need something concrete that can be put into draft legislation and debated.

However, in few states are the legislators in the forefront of the policy determination process. The governor's position has generally been strengthened and he is more and more responsible for legislative and policy leadership. State and local agencies, therefore, must develop procedures for having an effective and continuous relationship with the governor's office.

The lay community organizer is invaluable for developing local program support. But it is often the case that voluntary agencies themselves are hamstrung with communications problems.

The business community can be made an active force in supporting mental health. For example, on a national level, the NIMH has worked effectively with the national organization and local chapters of the Junior Chamber of Commerce.

As a general rule we feel that professional groups tend to function most effectively in the political system as "veto" groups (Connery, 1968). This means they normally have to be won over or balanced against each other so that they do not block efforts to bring about needed change. Although they do not usually provide much innovation or initiative for change themselves, they can be powerful forces in assuring either the success or failure of political efforts to achieve program change.

In relation to public opinion in general, the mental health *leader* seeks to develop it rather than follow it. If the current public view is beneficial he uses it; if not, he tries to change it. If the mental health administrator has valid program data with political punch or crunch, he should use it by getting it out to the newspapers or other proper channels. If his motivations are honorable and not personal there would seem to be nothing wrong with intentionally generating anxiety in order to bring about program improvement and increased allocation of resources. The angry, outraged professional, particularly the M.D., can be very effective with the public and with politicians. If genuine, why shouldn't this anger be used to achieve needed program action? The good administrator in any program seeks to optimize program effectiveness and therefore keeps pushing on. The mediocre administrator seeks only to satisfy.

The Current Mental Health Power Structure

In a pluralistic power structure, whenever a problem or issue becomes widely felt among the people—when it becomes a public problem—all of the power groups—citizen, professional, and governmental—come into play. The games they play and the music they make are clearly political.

The current power structure, in relation to the national mental health effort, can be described by taking a hypothetical program development situation in relation to the NIMH and outlining some of the external forces having an effect on reaching a program decision. The persons and organizations affected by the NIMH and their relationships to it form the power structure for the hypothetical or simulated program decision-making situation.

The hypothetical situation is an attempt by the United States Department of Health, Education, and Welfare to achieve increased legislative authority and appropriations to conduct a greatly expanded research and education program at the NIMH on the problem of narcotic addiction and drug abuse. The schematic diagram (see Figure 28–1), based on a model developed by Anthony Downs, outlines the various groups that might conceivably be relevant to this issue in their roles as "sovereigns," "suppliers," "allies," "rivals," and "beneficiaries" (Downs, 1967). We hasten to point out that, depending on the situation, the various elements may find themselves in different roles but, in any event, they take a position as part of the power structure.

The Sovereigns

As the sources of legal authority over the bureau, in this case the NIMH, the United States Congress and the Department of Health, Educa-

tion, and Welfare (as an agent of the President) are the sovereigns. These are the powers which must be influenced by all the other organizations shown on the diagram in relation to the hypothetical situation described above. The relation strength of these two sovereigns will vary and cycle. For example, there is general agreement that much of the credit for mental health's sound national legislative base of the 1960s can be attributed to the leadership of legislators Fogarty and Hill. However, their era is over. One strategy which must be adopted is to forego the temptation of extolling the leaders of the past at the expense of the present and to actively and positively support new executive and legislative leaders without comparing their performance to the days of Fogarty and Hill and other golden eras.

The Suppliers

As the receivers of research grants and contracts, the universities, hospitals, research firms, and foundations will be the suppliers of new knowledge about narcotic addiction and its causes. As potential suppliers, these organizations will also act as external origins of political pressure and information feedback mechanisms.

The Allies

As Downs has stated, "any persons or organizations willing to support the bureau in some conflict can be considered its *allies* insofar as that conflict is concerned" (p. 46). Some potential allies of the NIMH in relation to the hypothetical question are listed on the schematic diagram. The membership of these organizations obviously overlaps with the membership of the organizations shown as *suppliers*. Individuals who are also suppliers can act much more overtly as political supporters of the bureau in their role as members of allied organizations than they can as suppliers. The list of potential allies will vary with the program in question. In relation to other types of problems, organizations such as the following may also enter into the mental health power structure: American Medical Association, Society of Biologic Psychiatrists, Psychiatric Research Society, Western Inter-State Commission on Higher Education, National Council of Community Mental Health Center, the Urban Coalition, local governments, and the developing organizations of subprofessional mental health workers.

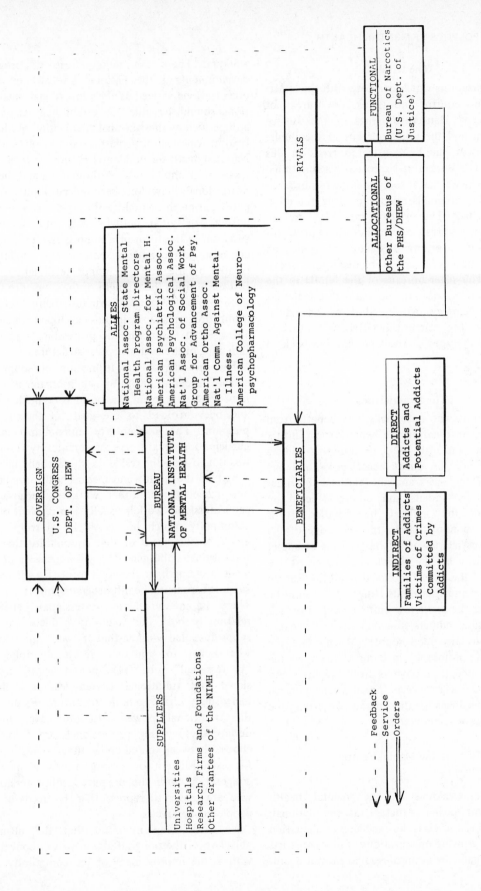

Fig. 28–1. The power structure. From Anthony Downs, Inside Bureaucracy. A RAND Corporation Research Study. Copyright © 1967 by the RAND Corporation. Reprinted by permission of the publisher, Little, Brown and Company (Inc.) and the RAND Corporation.

The Rivals

As organizations which compete with the NIMH for program control and funds, the Bureau of Narcotics and Dangerous Drugs of the Justice Department and the other bureaus of the Public Health Service can be considered rivals in this situation. The Bureau of Narcotics is a functional rival in the sense that it too is seeking resources to develop new programs relative to drug addiction and drug abuse. The rivalry is intensified by the fact that one bureau approaches drug problems from a law enforcement standpoint while the other approaches it as a medical and social problem. The sister bureaus of the NIMH in the Public Health Service are allocational rivals in that any *new* programs sought by NIMH provide added competition for scarce U.S., DHEW health resources. Both types of rivals provide feedback to the sovereign.

The Beneficiaries

The persons who potentially will benefit from the program in question are beneficiaries. In this case addicts and drug users, or potential addicts and users, are the direct beneficiaries and the families of the users and the victims of crimes committed by addicts and others affected by addicts are the indirect beneficiaries. It is interesting to note that in this case one of the indirect beneficiaries of NIMH (victims of addict crimes) might be the direct beneficiary of the programs of the chief functional rival, the Bureau of Narcotics and Dangerous Drugs. Or it could be argued that the strict law enforcement approach actually causes addicts to commit crimes because it eliminates any legal source. At any rate the difference in philosophy in terms of the approach to the beneficiaries is obvious. Both the direct and indirect beneficiaries can provide an external source of feedback to the bureau concerning the effectiveness of its programs.

Gaps or Flaws in the Mental Health Power Structure

A major weakness in the mental health establishment power structure at the national, state, and local levels is the exclusion or alienation of the fast growing organizations of new careerists and other para- or nonprofessional mental health workers. There are many areas of program development at the national level where these organizations as well as the professional organizations should be allies of established leadership groups such as the National Association of Mental Health, American Psychiatric Association, and the National Institute of Mental Health. This did not develop in the 1960s. Although mental health professionals have long sermonized about citizen participation in mental health programs, when the citizen or layman actually gets into the work situation in the form of a nonprofessional worker and also gets organized, considerable anxiety is created by the threat of nonprofessional control. Instead of using the strength of these organizations to improve the power structure behind mental health programs, a rivalry has developed which has also created fissures in the professional organization wing of the current power structure.

The increase of the utilization of subprofessionals in mental health and their organization for improving their own situation has coincided with and been attuned to the goals of the poverty program. The concept of maximum feasible participation on the part of community residents was not lost on the residents who actually became a part of the health and mental health system as new careerists and other workers. Because the subprofessional worker usually is a resident of the community which he serves, he is truly more aware of the needs of that community than his professional colleague. This awareness should be made a strength in the total effort for increasing support for mental health programs, but it has not. There is an unrealistic professional belief in relation to both the inner-city resident and the subprofessional worker that if "we" don't know what is best for you then we are not doing our "professional" jobs. The mental health professional and traditional citizen leaders will be increasingly challenged in the future. Fissures in the traditional power structure have already developed as young professionals are forced to choose between maintaining their identity with the establishment or seeking a new identity in cooperation with the organized subprofessionals who are closer to representing the needs of the people being served.

We must keep in mind that the ultimate objective of the political action we are concerned with is the improvement of the community; the approach—to be effective—must contain shared values rather than disparate elements. However, in the case of the gulf of misunderstanding between the professional and subprofessional mental health worker, it is one in which the change some men seek is the change other men fear.

In their own organization and uprising for political power, mental health aides have not only sought to improve their income and working conditions but in the process have attempted to demonstrate how hospitals and other facilities can be run more efficiently and effectively. This was the case in the rebellion of the Kansas mental health aides in June 1968 when they took administrative control of Topeka State Hospital and demonstrated their own model of how a ward should be operated. The aides were trying to demonstrate that in addition to their own self-interest, they were more concerned about effective patient care than were their professional supervisors (Efthim, 1968). When the subprofessionals have achieved their immediate goals (particularly that of career ladders), and it is not the subprofessional against someone else but the subprofessional for better services and advancement, perhaps there can be a unification with the more traditional elements in the mental health power structure to provide a more effective mobilization of effort for mental health resources.

From the practical standpoint of pure political strength, perhaps the greatest advantage of bringing subprofessional organizations into the power structure is that this could serve to bring the whole union movement into the mental health system more effectively than has been done in the past. The total labor and trade union movement is beginning to be a powerful force in demanding more and better mental health services in the market system. Of course, the subprofessional and general union involvement also provides a much better link to general community involvement. For the more traditional elements of the power structure to warrant the assistance of the subprofessionals in seeking more and better mental health services, they must of course also be willing to accept changes in the basic nature of services and accept the rights of the workers and the community in program development and assessment. Also, there can be no question that the act of involvement itself—involvement in community work and involvement in political action for the support of this work—can be a valuable form of prevention. As Cesar Chavez (*Tempo*, 1968) has said:

One of the most beautiful satisfying results of our work in establishing a union in the fields is in witnessing the workers bloom—the natural dignity coming out of a man when his dignity is recognized. Even some of the employers are seeing this point. Workers whom they previously had treated as dumb members of a forgotten minority suddenly are blooming as capable, intelligent persons using initiative and showing leadership (p. 5).

Mental health new careerists and other subprofessionals have now organized themselves in conjunction with community residents in a number of cities around the country in order to effect desired changes in community programs. The mental health professionals and traditional mental health organizations must seek a new humility and learn to work effectively with this new force in developing support and resources for mental health programs.

ORGANIZATIONAL PROBLEMS AND RELATIONSHIPS

Jurisdictional Problems

Mental health agencies represent only one of many types of interest groups involved in the struggle for political power and authority. Inasmuch as they all have ethical goals for the use of power—to benefit the aging, children, alcoholic, addict, delinquent, or retarded—at times these various groups or advocates may well find ways to cooperate in order to help the population, which is the target of their common concern. But even under such optimal conditions, autonomy will remain a source of conflict. To the extent that the various groups are concerned primarily with hierarchical position and jurisdictional power, there will be chronic and intense bureaucratic battles. Accordingly, these relationships with other agencies in the human service field must be taken into account by those concerned with the development of comprehensive mental health programs. These jurisdictional problems are inherent in the definition or lack of definition of mental health.

As mental health programs have become more community oriented, the probability of conflicts with educational, welfare, and other related state organizations is increased. Community mental health is so ill-defined that its implementation may well appear to be empire building that threatens jealously guarded functions performed elsewhere. Agreed upon definitions are lacking. For instance, are the problems of alcoholism, mental retardation, or geriatrics most closely related to mental health, public health, education, or welfare? Despite the trend toward unifying mental health activities in a single department, the splintering off of mental health activities is also growing.

Jurisdictional lines between agencies become fuzzy at all levels of government. If the welfare department wants to attack causes of dependence rather than merely provide for dependents, it might move into mental health, mental retardation, rehabilitation, employment counseling, and job training fields. Education will move toward providing special classes for the emotionally disturbed and the retarded. Corrections will identify mental illness or retardation as a cause of social misbehavior and attempt to treat it to avoid mere incarceration. All these programs are competing for the same tax dollars. Consolidation of departments through the development of human service agencies may to some extent solve some of these coordination problems.

Of course, the real concern is not that there is a lack of administrative neatness to prevent duplication, but that some people with real needs may not be served at all because they fall through the cracks between specialized agencies that have no common focal point of administrative leadership and decision making. Examples of actual jurisdictional problem areas are presented below to highlight key issues and controversies.

Alcoholism is a multifaceted problem which has evoked the interest of diverse disciplines, ranging from anthropology to zoology. The relationship of alcoholism to mental health is equally diverse. Clinically, it is seen as an effect and/or cause of mental disorder or emotional problems. Administratively, at the state level, alcoholism programs may be either independent of or under the aegis of a mental health agency. Programmatically, alcoholics may be specifically forbidden or actively encouraged to utilize a variety of mental health services, such as general hospitals, in-patient psychiatric services, and out-patient psychiatric clinics. Legally, the alcoholic may be considered mentally disabled and, like the psychotic and mentally retarded, not responsible for his criminal behavior. Or, on the other hand, he may be subject to special laws, governing such matters as commitment and treatment.

In areas where mental health has jurisdictional authority over alcoholism but no investment there may be a clear gap in service for alcoholics. On the other extreme there may be two separate systems, one under mental health, the other under alcoholism, but neither providing one full range of services needed by an individual.

Mental retardation provides a second example. President Kennedy's historic message in 1963 to Congress on "Mental Illness and Mental Retardation" begins with a brief introductory section which addresses itself to the common concerns of mental illness and mental retardation, followed by two distinct sections: "I. A National Program for Mental Health," and "II. A National Program to Combat Mental Retardation." Clearly, this orientation provided impetus for the formal expression of the separatist view of mental illness and mental retardation. In fact, however, the historic roots of this schism run deep, reflecting long decades of neglect of mental retardation by psychiatry. This neglect becomes particularly apparent when it is contrasted with the recent success in effective program development in mental retardation due primarily to the active political efforts of lay organizations. In any event, the complexity of the current relationship between mental health and mental retardation is evident at many levels.

At the federal level, administrative responsibility for various aspects of mental retardation resides in several of the constituent agencies of the Department of Health, Education, and Welfare. In contrast, mental health responsibility is, for the most part, centralized in the National Institute of Mental Health. There is considerable variation in the administration of mental retardation programs at the state level. In some instances, departments of mental health bear the major responsibility for mental retardation programs; other states maintain separate mental health and mental retardation departments. Again, there are variations in local programs which may discriminate for or against services to the mentally retarded. In general, however, even in programs designed specifically for the retarded, such as child-centered diagnostic clinics, a significant proportion of the patient population is not retarded but manifests emotional or psychological problems.

At the clinical and conceptual level, the question of whether mental retardation can ever exist without concomitant emotional problems is a continued source of controversy. There is no question, however, that mental retardation represents a significant mental health program for the family.

Finally, perhaps the overlap between these areas is demonstrated most clearly by the fact that the same personnel—psychiatrists, psychologists, social workers, and educators—are involved in the diagnosis and management of both problems.

The underlying issues inherent in the definition of mental health vis-à-vis mental retardation are similar to those discussed above with regard to alcoholism. In brief, professional and lay groups which have organized independent mental retardation programs object to mental health sponsorship on the grounds that the problems of mental illness (health) are different in certain essential respects from those associated with mental retardation, and/or because of their desire to preserve the critical aspects of visibility, autonomy, and the political growth potential of their own programs.

Public Health Versus Mental Health

The irony of the relationship of mental health to public health programs is perhaps best illustrated by the frequently asked question, "Why shouldn't mental health be brought back into the mainstream of American medicine." The irony results from the fact that what is meant by the "mainstream" is usually the activities of state public health departments. However, public health is not synonymous with the "mainstream" or with *health*. It is only one aspect of a broad spectrum of which mental health is also a part and mental health is most frequently the bigger part.

As has been pointed out elsewhere (Schnibbe, 1967):

To give you a comparative picture of the significance of *mental* health and *public* health, take for example the state of Illinois. In the biennium period July 1, 1965–June 30, 1967 the budget for the Department of Mental Health is $307,612,674. For the same period the budget for the Department of Public Health is $59,357,963. The *mental* health budget is seven times the *public* health budget. This ratio generally holds true throughout the country (p. 10).

The development of state mental health authorities as independent of public health began in 1947. There are now independent mental health authorities in 40 states or territories. Some are completely separate from public health while others are subsumed under umbrella agencies along with health programs. Many observers have made the argument that the best mental health programs have been developed by the totally separate mental health authorities. However, the major point we want to make here is clearly that we are dealing with the interaction of *two* major systems of health planning and services. Mental health has virtually become viable by its independence. In addition to being a practical program reality, this is a political reality.

It is unrealistic, therefore, to consider mental health as being subsumed under public health for planning purposes as was done with the passage of the Comprehensive Health Planning Act (P.L. 749). From a historical standpoint, "No public health planning, for example, has ever equalled in the extent or in the public participation and support, the results achieved in the comprehensive mental health planning which has gone forward in every State of the Union in this decade" (Yolles, 1969, p. 12). However, in many states, the agency designated to head the comprehensive health planning effort will be the State Department of Public Health. This means new political competition and challenge for mental health. One of the great difficulties in partnership for health is that it is both so bold and so weak considering the complexities of the task before it. It is bold in that it touches the planning organizational dimension of everything under the sun, and on the other hand it comes in with money muscle of miniscule proportion compared to the nature of the systems on which it is trying to have impact. These small amounts of money for planning will mean that once more the competition will be keenly felt between public health and mental health.

While politically the state public health departments have more clout with the Federal Department of Health, Education, and Welfare, mental health serves the *people* more directly. If there is to be a system of health that means anything to the people who need help, the state mental health officials must cash in on their power with the people to offset the public health power with the federal bureaucracy. Only together can public health and mental health serve the people well. And together means equal status for mental health.

Federal-State-Local Relations

Federal, state, and local partnership in mental health was placed on firm footing through the comprehensive mental health planning effort undertaken by every state under the stimulus of federal support. In 1963 and 1964 Congress appropriated a total of $8.4 million to NIMH to support statewide interagency comprehensive mental health planning. This planning effort involved all states, and almost every community in the nation, and required the active participation of more than 25,000 citizens, both lay and professional. The final reports of this planning effort became available in the fall of 1965. This nationwide review of each state's needs and resources and the close involvement of thousands of professionals and lay citizens in planning mental health services lent invaluable force to future mutual federal, state, and local efforts.

This model for federal, state, and local cooperation became of particular significance with the making of the first construction grants under the Community Mental Health Centers Act. No longer were the state governments almost solely responsible for public mental health care. To meet the requirements for obtaining financial assistance for a construction grant, state government now had to work in cooperation with both local and federal governments. However, this same federal program of financial assistance for the development of community centers which became the catalyst for federal-state-local cooperation, also has the potential for creating state-local frustrations and new political maneuvers. This frustration can be due either to the nature of what has been called the federal government's "initiate-and-abandon" tactics relative to state matching programs or to the vagaries of the federal legislative and budget process.

We feel that it is these potential problems of the future rather than the successes of the past with which we should be concerned in a book such as this.

As has been reported by Schnibbe (1967), the federal government (executive and Congress) has in recent times initiated programs, promised and authorized extensive federal participation on a matching basis with the states, and then reduced the appropriation or cut the allocation or in effect partially abandoned the program. To a certain extent this has been true of the Community Mental Health Centers' program.

Due to the economic squeeze, appropriations committees of Congress have in recent years seldom met the funding levels set by the program authorizing committees. On the executive side, changes in national administrations, whether there are changes in party or not, mean that new people in key positions must be educated to the problems of mental illness and to the commitments the federal level has made to the mentally ill.

Of course, federal-state-local problems relative to mental health grant programs must be seen within the total context of the crisis surrounding the growing magnitude of the totality of federal grant programs. As Brown, Sirotkin, and Stockdill have reported in another paper (1969): "The possibilities of Federal-State government friction grew larger in keeping with the burgeoning funds, people, and policies involved. Grant-in-Aid programs had grown from 15 million dollars in 1920 to 15 billion dollars in 1965, to a projected 50 billion dollars in 1975. Obviously, it became necessary to improve administrative and political handling of these affairs" (p. 646).

This growing number of federal grant programs led state and local mental health administrators and leaders to wonder "who is it most productive to relate to at the Federal level?" It became obvious that there was more money for mental health services in the Medicare and Medicaid programs than in NIMH. The Office of Economic Opportunity was also into the mental health scene in a big way. Federal-state-local relationships grew much more complicated. Each new federal program had its own regulations and requirements for states and localities to interpret and follow.

It was this growing proliferation of programs

and their regulations, related appropriations problems, related appropriations problems, grants administration problems, and confusion of political responsibility which led to the support of new ideas such as block grants and revenue sharing on the part of local, state, and some federal officials. These concepts of program financing can effect the support of mental health services along with all other so-called categorical programs. In relation to health and mental health the "Comprehensive Health Planning" program was probably the forerunner of the block grant concept. And in 1968 the President's Advisory Commission on Intergovernmental Relations recommended a revised system of federal aid to states and cities which included block grants. In relation to such areas as education and to a great extent health, the Commission recommended that the proliferation of project grants should be consolidated into block grants.

The critical question is *"what is the block grant concept and how might it effect mental health programs and the people who administer them and the population they serve?"*

Block grants are intended to encourage maximum state coordination and permit the states and localities to set priorities and operate programs with a minimum of federal regulations, guidelines, and directives. The attraction to state governments is the flexibility to spend money as they want to in the general area of concern such as special education or vocational rehabilitation. The supposed advantage at the federal level is the lumping together of federal project grant programs to provide simplified administration. The Comprehensive Health Act, for example, purported to consolidate 16 separately administered programs and encouraged states to develop plans, establish priorities, and coordinate local activities. The Law Enforcement and Criminal Justice Assistance Act passed in 1968 also employs a block grant approach and is therefore intended to provide maximum state and local control over law enforcement with minimum federal interference.

What are the political implications for mental health programs? With a block grant approach in relation to federal funds, more decisions will be made in the states and not at the federal level. Blocks grants *do not* necessarily mean that more decisions will be made at the local level where the

people are directly served. The important question is how well would state mental health administrators do in competition with other programs for funds in the potential health block? What would be the political lineups relative to establishing priorities? Mental health programs would be competing with older state programs whose accomplishments may be less significant but more easily measured and translated into quantitative terms. Those responsible for mental health programs would have to be prepared to provide the best possible program justification in the medium demanded. Will they do as well at the state level as national administrators and leaders have in the competition for federal funds? The state program administrator would have to be even more of a politician than in the past in order to develop and maintain grass-roots support for his block or his share of the block. He who can rally the most citizen support might well be the most successful.

With block grants, a change in governors may be more disruptive than it normally would be in terms of program continuity. The Office of the Governor rather than federal agencies would be responsible for setting the priorities.

The federal role might well have to be expanded in the area of evaluation and standard setting. Better criteria and indicators for measuring success or failure of programs would have to be developed. We in mental health would have to provide clearer evidence that people are really being helped.

Block grants could result in even more vertical functional alignment of political forces as opposed to competition between governmental levels performing the same function. The competition would be increased between program areas at the same governmental level rather than between federal, state, and local levels. For example, mental health professionals at all three levels in the federal system might become even more closely affiliated in order to protect the interests of the mentally ill. This would be particularly true if indeed mental healthers continue to see themselves as dealing with man in a broader social context than do the professionals in other fields.

We in mental health may be forced to better define the universe of mental health and reevaluate our whole basic purpose for existence. Depending on the nature of block grants, interrelationships with other state agencies such as corrections, alcoholism commissions, public health, vocation rehabilitation, etc., would be more critical than ever.

One of the dilemmas resulting from the trend toward grant consolidation is what we like to call "State Mental Health Authority Schizophrenia." This schizophrenia results from the fact that governors are continually asking for consolidation of separate federal grant programs into single state block grants. Yet the strength and vitality of the national and state mental health programs has been based on autonomy and resultant visibility. These conflicting interests result in schizophrenic behavior on the part of state mental health officials who try simultaneously to represent their governors and their own programs. Their conflict is further complicated by the fact that block grants can also influence organizational changes in the states such as the amalgamation of public health and mental health departments. This has serious implications for mental health because state experience has shown that autonomy provides a favorable environment for the development and flourishing of a vigorous mental health program (Brown et al., 1969, p. 649).

Also on the federal-states relationships horizon is the concept of revenue sharing. The direct redistribution of federal tax dollars to states and localities rather than more federal project grants, grants-in-aid, or block grants may become the major fiscal experiment of the '70s. We mention it here because the concept of "no strings attached" revenue sharing could result in a loss of visibility of programs for the mentally disabled and thereby also result in a reduction of resources to meet the needs of the mentally disabled. If this fiscal concept is implemented, it is obvious that the major responsibility for insuring a commitment to mental health problems and programs will rest with state and local agencies rather than with national organizations.

Another type of organizational relationship is one which is fairly new to the field of intragovernmental relations. This potential point of friction is between state executive branch bureaucracy and staff of the state legislature. This dilemma has resulted largely because of increased strenghtening of professional staffs in some state legislatures. The principal reason for

this conflict is the difference in the values, interests, and constituencies of the two decision-making groups, and the fact that state legislatures having their own professional staffs are no longer as dependent on the professional bureaucrat in the specific program area. While the professional bureaucrat is trying to maximize professional values in the decision-making process, the professional representing a legislative committee may be trying to maximize grass-roots citizen values. "This creates a new challenge at the Federal level; namely, how do you bring state executive and legislative staffs together when they may be at odds concerning such programs as mental health. Time spent by Federal officials in developing better relationships with state executive branch representatives may well be wasted time if it is the legislative professional staff that swings the power in developing new program legislation" (Brown et al., 1969, p. 650). In concluding this section on federal-state-local relationships the point that must be made clear is that regardless of the emergence of block grants and other new developments, the extent to which the state level fails to measure and meet *local* needs will inevitably determine the extent to which all federal agencies may be compelled to work and plan directly with the local level.

A Systems Approach

In the above sections, we have discussed several of the jurisdictional and organizational problems which effect the politics of mental health. Because of these problems, mental health has a great need for a systems approach to administration and planning. Stripped of the fancy terminology of systems technology, a systems approach means simply the analytical framework which makes it possible to perceive things in relation to each other and to the whole.

The following steps have been described as being inherent to most systems analyses:

(1) A comprehensive definition of the environment within which the program or system to be studied will function,

(2) a detailed program or systems description, including its various hardware/software subsystems and components,

(3) a statement of the system's or the program's objectives and performance criteria, and

(4)· a definition of alternative ways to meet the system's or program's objectives and performance criteria (Smith, 1968, p. 7).

For mental health and other social services the system is the community at large. In the context of mental health and politics, a systems approach means that each of the political variables in a community (whether it be the local, state, or the national community) must be considered in relation to each other and to their totality. Too often in the past, the mental health political system has contained almost solely the mental health service, research, and training agencies; professional organizations; and some well-meaning middle class citizen organizations.

The application of a systems approach can break down some of the invisible barriers which now present the interaction of certain groups who should and could be working cooperatively toward the development and improvement of mental health services and the total system of human services of which mental health is a part. Mental health services have to be developed in parallel with health and educational services. Poor health and educational services will have their impact on the mental health of the populations they serve. A system approach will now allow mental health to deal only with direct individual treatment. A systems approach will now allow mental health to or in other words, one must conceptualize the end product or change he is trying to achieve in the population he serves. Thinking in this way will allow mental health professionals to rethink and reshape their professional roles; it has, in fact, led many to seek an active interaction with politicians, educators, judges, and lay leaders in a total community approach to local mental health problems. A systems approach results in the early recognition that many mental health problems can be solved only when other basic social and economic problems are solved.

A systems approach will lead to the recognition that it is impractical to always think in terms of using state jurisdictional boundaries in developing mental health services or the political support for mental health services. More consideration must be given at both the state and federal levels to coordination with the growing number of interstate or regional bodies. "These regional bodies have resulted from the obvious recognition that problems do not end at the state line and that

they cannot be solved at the National level. There is clearly a great need for interstate regional planning and more intrastate regional planning through consolidation of local governments. In applying a systems approach to intergovernmental considerations these regional bodies will be given more consideration" (Brown et al., 1969, p. 654).

The local mental health administrator should use a systems approach in considering interaction with other local, state, and federal agencies and with citizen and professional groups. In the first approach, nothing should be considered to be outside the system—all variables must be considered.

POLITICAL PSYCHIATRY

The Definition

In order to avoid responding to social change and social policy with either complacency or aggressive misdirection, there is a crucial relationship betwen public policy formulation and psychiatry and the other behavioral sciences and professions which we in the mental health field must recognize and understand. It is this relationship which we are calling "political psychiatry." Historically, mental health has been mandated by public policy to care for those in institutions where the quality of life was at its lowest ebb and interaction with the community outside the walls of the institution was limited. But as the mental health specialist leaves the shelter of the treatment setting and indicates a desire to interact with the power structure of the community, he emerges into an extensive arena of conflicting and competing interest groups. Typically, the outreach activities of the community mental health professional include extensive interaction with a wide variety of governmental structures and agencies at federal, state, and local levels; liaison with diverse lay and professional organizations; and to an increasing degree, contact with the mass media. These activities may be administrative, financial, or purely political in nature.

To the extent that these outreach activities are motivated by a desire to rally community support behind specific mental health programs in the competition for scarce resources, or to rally support behind a mental health approach to general community problems, the activities are political. The manifest interest or content of these activities is behavioral and clinical; the political aspects are inherent in the arena or medium through which public policy is developed. Looked at in this way, political psychiatry is an essential ingredient of community mental health—a blending of the practice of the clinician with the recognition that many of the problems identified in this practice cannot be solved or even approached in the isolated clinical arena but that they must be illuminated in the much broader political arena. By accepting this political action responsibility, the mental health professional does not claim omnipotence relative to all community problems. He is assuming the role of a community catalyst, attempting to bring his perception, gained through working with the problems of individuals, to bear on common community needs and problems. How well the mental health professional succeeds in applying his special experience and skills will depend on the sophistication of his participation with others in the community who are also trying to effect public policy. One thing is certain, however; if the goal of mental health is really the alleviation of human suffering, then the mental health practitioner must not be timid about selecting the political arena as a major focus of his effort.

We think we have made a case for the serious utilization of the term "political psychiatry." Politics is known as both an art—witness the well-known definition of politics as the art of the possible—and as a science—witness the profession of political science. And both politics and psychiatry deal with arenas complex and compelling, leading to successful practice more often described as art than science. Our case for the terminology will be further clarified by the following section concerned with the transitory state of mental health programs.

Mental Health Programs in Transition

The 1960s was a decade of transition in which we witnessed basic changes in the traditional systems of treatment of mental illness and in the role of the individual care-giver. With the development of community mental health programs more was required than merely clinical science and technology and facilities planning and administration. Consideration by the mental health professional now had to be given not only to the patient's social setting but also to the political setting in which the programs themselves were developing and operating. "The success of a mental health program is no longer simply a function of the clinical skills of the program staff; the success of the program is equally dependent on skills in coping with, adapting to, and sometimes even changing the local political, social, and economic environment" (Brown and Levenson, 1968, p. 117). Many psychiatrists and other mental health professionals must undergo a considerable change in attitude in order to assume expanded responsibilities for participation and coordination with citizen and other government groups in the task of planning for the needs of a population group where they live. It has been said that "negotiation" may be the key concept in this new role. "The psychiatrist-participant negotiates with others as his peers about spheres of influence and the sharing of authority and responsibility" (GAP, 1968, p. 893).

The Federal Community Mental Health Center Program has been in large part responsible for stimulating and maintaining these new concerns on the part of psychiatrists and other mental health professionals. The development and operation of a community mental health center requires that its professional staff become deeply involved in the political life of the community and at the same time the center itself is the means for developing this community involvement. For example, in many community mental health centers there is both a great need for and the means for becoming involved in community action programs relative to poverty conditions. There is no question that a coordinated community attack on poverty has major mental health relevance; however, the mental health worker's contribution will depend on his effectiveness as a collaborator in the community political process and not directly on his professional training.

If the mental health professionals are to be effective collaborators in the political process, rather than be used by it, then some basic in-depth training in such fields as the legislative process, political theory of municipalities, and community organization is needed. Some schools of social work and community psychiatry courses have included the study of the congressional processes, or, on a more practical level, the study of the legislative process in their own state capitals or city councils. More of this type of training is needed, for in today's complex world the game goes to the one who is not only courageous but also thoroughly trained in the technical skills and moves of political structures and social engineering.

There are concerns in many professional groups that mental health care in transition has grown too diffuse. Although few modern mental health professionals would argue that mental health should deal only with the classically defined mental disorders, many would feel more comfortable if some boundaries were drawn, and drawn somewhat short of the popular phrase "to deal with the total quality of human life." However, we do not feel that this boundary delineation is either realistic or desirable! When an individual practitioner or a center joins a community, it must take that community as it is and deal squarely with what is there.

There can be no predetermined set of problems or complaints that will be dealt with exclusively. When mental health care givers assumed a community base, they necessarily assumed responsibility for at least having a concern for broad programs of social reform requiring political action such as antipoverty programs, urban renewal, juvenile delinquency, educational processes and opportunities, and racial and sexual equality. More specific moral issues which must increasingly be both courageously and politically faced on the firing line are such things as the unrealistic penalties for the possession of marihuana, legal restrictions on abortion, and family planning.

In particular, population and family planning involve public policy matters ranging from the "real politik" of international power to laws specifying permissible sexual behavior of individuals. The mental health field may have much to offer, it may have very little—but *not* to participate in the determination of public policy in this area is an abnegation of responsibility on all levels, as citizen, as a professional, and as specialist in human relations.

It is more than coincidence that the psychiatrist stands in the eye of the hurricane of controversy around abortion. He knows the problem at the practice level but has done little to translate this knowledge into enlightened public policy. He treats the mother with postpartum psychosis and he may treat the abused or neglected child; but, he leaves the shaping of laws that deal with these problems to others.

Violence is another political issue because it causes divisions in society, rocking the boat, alarming the American people. Mayors are ranked by how well they can keep the lids on in their cities. Through the drama of presidential commissions, this has been one more of the issues in which the nation's mental health professionals are involved. The mental health field can play an important role in helping America solve the problems of violence and aggression by adding the insights of behavioral science and the clinical knowledge we have in these areas.

As political psychiatrists we must keep one foot in science and clinical practice as we enter the political ring. When the National Institute of Mental Health was asked to contribute to the Kerner Commission investigations, they had to make a hard-nosed analysis of the relative knowledge they possessed. They found that behavioral science research could provide a base for basic understanding, and for effective action which must rest on such understanding. However, many of its insights run counter to intuitive popular opinion and for this reason result in controversial new approaches. For example, much that is known about crowd processes can be used to prevent or ameliorate a situation otherwise prone to develop into a full-blown riot. More importantly, at the level of prevention, there is important, useful information about the nature of the system which stimulates social unrest and leads to mass violence. While much research remains necessary, the current behavioral science knowledge, if properly utilized, can make a major contribution to some of the most pressing domestic problems of our times.

The President's charge to a National Commission on the Causes and Prevention of Violence, in the wake of the assassination of Senator Kennedy, also included a call to utilize the knowledge of medicine, sociology, and psychology.

Dr. Henry Brosin, at the time he was president of the American Psychiatric Association, said clearly that our intent as mental health professionals—or as political psychiatrists, as we might be called—is not to assume the role of healer for all of sick society, but rather to make what contributions we can to the molding of public policies that affect our concerns. Dr. Broslin said: "While our society is totally not sick, it is not bright, either. We can solve this problem without becoming either utopian or authoritarian. We can do better. And we can start by tackling the problems of dependent segments of our population—the alcoholics, the drug addicts, the deviates, the criminals . . . . " (Brown, 1968, p. 8).

Dr. Brosin's statement implies that mental health professionals can make important contributions to social problems by working harder in the clinics, the laboratories, the hospitals, and the mental health centers. It also implies, however, that there are important tasks in the public arena.

Community mental health in transition has to join forces with other politically active agencies and contribute what force and experience it has to lobby with the power structure of the communities in developing political and financial answers for many of the social and moral problems of the day.

The Future

What will be the role of the mental health professions in the future ferment of public policy development? It seems clear that in the '70s there will be growing opposing public pressures and demands from those who are protesting social injustice and from those who are disturbed by the seeming social disorder caused by the protesters of social injustice. Will the mental health professions be there to lead in the resolution of an explosive clash of social values? Or will the mental health field continue its abnegation of responsibility in many of the very areas that have helped create the bubble of pressure that is about to burst?

Public policy is developing, but is far from fixed, in relation to such social problems as poverty, hunger, abortion, the draft, crime, birth control, the right to good health care, drug abuse, racism, alienation, and war. We must look in turn at each of these areas and see what we can or cannot do. One thing is certain: the mental health field cannot pull its head back into the safe turtle shell of the medical model.

Perhaps one approach is to ask what do we know from clinical practice about personality and character disorders, and their relationship to the social environment process, that should be vigorously fed into the policy process. As one of the authors (Brown, 1968b) has stated in the past, "While it is blatantly grandiose to presume that psychiatry will make all the poor rich, the bad good, the intoxicated sober, the unhappy happy, it *is* fair to ask what we can contribute to these

compelling human hopes" (p. 39). The pace and nature of social change is complex and awe inspiring. But insofar as man can control his own destiny he must try. The one arena for hope in the creative influence of social change is the making of public policy. The role of mental health in the future must include insuring that public policy moves from an overriding concern with power and matters material to a dominant concern with the quality of life.

The point is that social problems interact with public policy formulation, and it is the mechanisms of this interaction which the mental health professions must understand and influence. Problems beget policy as surely as policies help create the problems in the first place. It is in relation to this axis between problem and policy that we must work. The development of legislation and the law is a major arena in which practice and policy interact. As in the past we have seen the walls of prejudice against the mentally ill come tumbling down through changes in and the development of new laws, we must now see that other laws change and we must help to change them. Means of influence may be as direct as legislative testimony or as indirect as private contributions to political parties. Where the nature of the problem is such that we can make a contribution, we should not follow but provide leadership to assure that social policy is changed in a real way.

In summary, politics is people at their worst and at their best and psychiatry is a field that attempts to understand and help people to develop from their worst to their best. If political psychiatry had not evolved naturally, someone would have had to invent it. We will watch with great interest and concern for its coming day in the sun.

SUMMARY

We have tried to point out that the politics of mental health has many dimensions. Basically, politics and mental health must be partners because mental health manpower and services are still provided largely with public funds and politics is the watchdog of public funds. The sides of the mental health power structure may vary depending on the issues in the power struggle. We illustrated this with a model way of looking at the power structure and struggle around a single hypothetical issue at the national level.

Community mental health can be viewed as a political model. The basic objective is to establish a relationship with and between groups in and out of the power structure. The community mental health center must become part of a network of political and economic forces in order to exist as a social institution.

Mental health professionals must learn to operate in the free-swinging, interest laden, public forum. If they are going to apply their training and skills most effectively, they must learn to be citizen participants, practical politicians, and responsible leaders. Because they have already developed the political clout—and in the interest of more relevant programs—subprofessional employees must be a part of the formal political power structure. They are in many ways closer to and therefore more conscious of the needs of the people being served.

A significant dimension of professional practice in the future will be in the realm of program and policy development at community, state, and national levels. The 1970s will see an intense and more constructive concern with social issues and a burst of public pressure and demand for programs concerned with the antisocial disorders. Mental health professionals must be able to respond to this concern in the public arena. As long as the definition of mental health remains flexible, there will be organizational and jurisdictional problems. Therefore, those with leadership responsibilities in mental health must push forward on many fronts, i.e., education, corrections, public health, and welfare.

The politics of mental health requires active federal-state-local relationships and a sound basis for these relationships was developed through the comprehensive mental health planning program of the early '60s. We see the concept of "block grants" as the most significant development on the horizon of intergovernmental cooperation. Indeed, if this concept envelopes mental health programs, it may well create new frictions and realignments in the power struggle of program support.

It has been said (Turnbull, 1968) that "holding on to political power is like a juggling act: it requires constant attention to an orbit of rapidly-moving objects (called in politics blocs of voters), and even a momentary lapse can bring the performance to a confused and embarrassing end" (p. 9). To avoid the "momentary lapse" a systems approach is required to consider all the "rapidly-moving objects" in the political orbit. In order to develop specific strategies, techniques, and skills and maximize the potential of mental health programs, their interrelationships with all human services must be considered. Mental health in the '70s must be cognizant of and willing to take public positions on all environmental factors affecting the quality of life.

In conclusion, it can be said that in view of the dependence on influence and support from political leaders, for the mental health system to hold itself above politics would be a luxury it can ill afford. On the other hand, a warning may also be in order: a chauvinistic approach to politics by mental healthers, i.e., mainly for the glory of the chase, can also be costly to the cause. The one clear guideline to keep in mind is that social change is going to be a continuing process in this country, and that our charge in mental health is to participate effectively in the political response to this change, so that we may develop programs which will adequately meet the needs of *all citizens.*

Note

Work on this chapter was performed by the authors as private individuals and not in their capacities as officials of the National Institute of Mental Health. The chapter was prepared in 1969 for inclusion in the present volume.

References

Brown, B. The program politics of violence. Paper presented at the Eighth Symposium—Psychiatry for the Physician on Violence and Aggression, Belle Mead, New Jersey, The Carrier Clinic, November 6, 1968. (a)

Brown, B. Psychiatric practice and public policy. *American Journal of Psychiatry*, 1968, 125, 2. (b)

Brown, B., & Levenson, A. Social implications of the community mental health center concept. In *Social psychiatry*. New York: Grune & Stratton, 1968.

Brown, B., Sirotkin, P., & Stockdill, J. Psychopolitical perspectives on federal-state relationships. *American Journal of Psychotherapy*, 23(4), October 1969.

Committee on Preventive Psychiatry. *The dimensions of community psychiatry*. New York: Group for the Advancement of Psychiatry, April 1968.

Connery, R. H., & contributors. *The politics of mental health: Organizing community mental health in metropolitan areas*. New York: Columbia University Press, 1968.

Downs, A. *Inside bureaucracy: A Rand Corporation research study*. Boston: Little, Brown, 1967.

Efthim, A. We care in Kansas: The nonprofessional revolt. *The Nation*, August 5, 1968.

Schnibbe, H. Mental health politics: A new state-federal competition. Paper presented at the annual meeting of the Alabama Association for Mental Health, Montgomery, May 17, 1967.

Smith, R. The systems approach and the urban dilemma. Staff discussion paper 101, Program of Policy Studies in Science and Technology, George Washington University, July 1968.

Tempo. The Church's economic force at work for social justice. Huntington, Ind.: National Council of Churches, October 15, 1968. (Quotation by C. Chavez)

Turnbull, J. Washington comment. *Tempo.* Huntington, Ind.: National Council of Churches, October 31, 1968.

Yolles, S. F. The state of the institute. Paper presented at the annual conference of State and Territorial Mental Health Authorities, Washington, D. C., January 10, 1969.

29

The Community Mental Health Centers Program

Alan I. Levenson

The community mental health center represents a new approach to the care of the mentally ill. The Federal Community Mental Health Centers Program, administered by the National Institute of Mental Health, provides support for the construction of mental health center facilities and also for the initial staffing of center services. The federal program was established in 1963. In that year the Congress passed the Community Mental Health Centers Act, Public Law 88-164, which authorized funds for the construction grant aspect of the program. Staffing grants were authorized by an amendment passed in 1965, and the authorization for both types of grants was extended and expanded by legislation passed in 1967 and 1970.

BACKGROUND

The origins of the community mental health center can be traced to two sets of factors. One was a growing sense of public and professional dissatisfaction with previously existing mental health facilities and programs. The other was the development of new methods and approaches for the provision of mental health services.

Both the inadequacies of the old methods and the potentials of new approaches were clearly evident by the end of World War II. The war itself focused attention on the extent of mental illness in the United States. Of approximately 15,000,000 men examined for their fitness for military service, 12 percent were rejected for neuropsychiatric causes; and these neuropsychi-

atric rejections accounted for 40 percent of all selective service rejections (Menninger, 1948, pp. 281–283). In addition to the large number of men found mentally unfit for the armed forces, increasing numbers of persons were being admitted to neuropsychiatric hospitals. By the mid-1940s more than 450,000 patients were hospitalized in large public mental hospitals (United States, 1966).

Although psychiatrists in private practice cared for some of the nation's mentally ill, most of the mentally ill were relegated to long-term custodial care in large, overcrowded, and understaffed public institutions, and many went without any care. The records of the Selective Service System demonstrated the inability of these institutions to meet the nation's needs, and, in addition, public discussion revealed the inability of most of these hospitals to provide a socially acceptable level of patient care (Deutsch, 1948).

The years during and just after World War II were thus of great significance for the developing sense of dissatisfaction with the nation's mental health services. These same years also made it clear that alternative approaches were available. The war years, for example, demonstrated both the effectiveness and the practicality of short-term treatment for mental disorders. Previously the emphasis had been placed almost exclusively on the long-term care of chronic conditions. Now it became clear that acute psychiatric casualties could be treated and restored to active duty by the use of short-term treatment methods. Moreoever, it was learned that these brief methods were suitable for, and in part dependent upon, treating the patient close to the site of the precipitating trauma. Psychiatric services were provided close to the front lines, and, as a result, it was not necessary to isolate the patient geographically or socially from the setting in which his disorder began (Ginzberg, 1948; Glass, 1955).

Translating this military experience into civilian practice was a relatively straightforward process. Conceptually, at least, the parallels were clear. Just as the psychiatric battle casualty was treated near the battlefield, the civilian mental patient was to be treated close to his home; and just as the mentally ill soldier was kept in contact with his unit and its continued fighting, the civilian patient was to be kept in contact with his family, his job, and his friends.

Operationally, this type of civilian mental health service required the availability of treatment resources within the patient's own community. To meet this need a growing number of local general hospitals opened psychiatric units. By 1965 there were several hundred psychiatric units in general hospitals, and over 80 per cent of them were established after 1947 (Glasscote, 1965, pp. 4–5). The creation of these general hospital psychiatric units was a very important step in the development of the Community Mental Health Centers Program. In addition to establishing a trend toward community care, these units also have proven to be community focal points for the organization of individual community mental health centers.

Two additional factors contributed directly to the growth of general hospital psychiatric units and thus indirectly to the community mental health movement. One of these was the introduction of the tranquilizers and related psychotropic medication. These drugs added significantly to the available short-term treatment resources. In addition, they made it possible for ward staff to control the hyperactive and destructive behavior which some mental patients presented. The drugs thus enabled the mentally ill to be more readily accepted for admission to general hospitals.

The second additional factor was a changing attitude toward mental illness among the general public. Mental disorder gradually began to lose some of the social stigma that had previously been associated with it. The mental patient began to be more readily accepted within the community, and

concomitantly, less need was felt for isolating him in a far distant institution. This community acceptance was essential for the growth of general hospital psychiatric units, and the still greater acceptance which has developed more recently has been essential for the establishment of local community mental health centers.

Specific Steps

It is against this background that there occurred the specific steps leading to the Community Mental Health Centers Program. In 1955, aware of the need for action, the Congress enacted a Mental Health Study Act. This Act established the Joint Commission on Mental Illness and Mental Health, and the legislation charged the Commission with a mandate to "survey the resources and to make recommendations for combating mental illness in the U. S." The Commission spent five years in its analysis of the problems of mental illness in terms of manpower, facilities, and costs. The final report of the Commission was published under the title *Action for Mental Health* (Joint Commission, 1961). Although the Commission recognized the unmet needs of the chronically mentally ill, the report also clearly emphasized the needs of the nation in regard to acute mental disorder. For the chronically ill it was recommended that all existing state hospitals be gradually reduced in size so that eventually none would be larger than 1,000 beds. Moreover, it was recommended that these hospitals be coverted into centers for the long-term care of all types of chronic illness, including mental illness.

The recommendations regarding acute mental illness focused on the need to develop a variety of resources in every community. The authors of *Action for Mental Health* proposed that there should be "a full-time mental health clinic available to each 50,000 of population" (Joint Commission, 1961, pp. 262–263). Such clinics were envisioned as serving both adults and children with both short-term and long-term outpatient services. In addition, the Commission recommended that community general hospitals of 100 beds or more accept mental patients for short-term hospitalization. Finally, in regard to the provision of local services, the report proposed that the mental health clinics offer not only diagnostic and treatment services but also that they serve as a "headquarters base for mental health consultants . . . . " (Joint Commission, 1961, p. 264).

Action for Mental Health thus clearly outlined a program of locally available mental health services. Moreover, it set this local service in the context of a network of regional and statewide services. These latter were seen as providing long-term and intermediate length inpatient care. The community resources, on the other hand, were charged with offering inpatient care on an acute basis as well as outpatient services and aftercare.

The report of the Joint Commission was the first step. Three years later the federal government responded to the Commission's proposals with a program to support comprehensive mental health services operated on a local basis. In February 1963 President John F. Kennedy sent to the Congress a historic document. His message on mental illness and mental retardation proposed a "national mental health program to assist in the inauguration of a wholly new emphasis and approach to care for the mentally ill" (Kennedy, 1963, p. 3). His proposal was a federal program to support the development of a new type of local mental health facility, the comprehensive community mental health center. Although this message did not specify the details of the Community Mental Health Centers Program, it did identify the principal features of the mental health center concept. For example, mention was made of such matters as the emphasis to be placed on local resources, the need to combine existing elements of service into coordinated programs, and the significant role to be played by community general hospitals in the establishment of individual centers.

The President's Message was followed in October of 1963 by the passage of the Community Mental Health Centers Act (Public Law 88–164). The act authorized a program of grants to assist communities in the construction of facilities for their community mental health centers. The President's Message had also called for a program of grants to assist in the initial staffing of the centers. The Congress, however, did not authorize this aspect of the program until two years later. Now both forms of federal support are available to help communities mount their own programs. The administrative procedures and the grant mechanisms are different for the two parts of the program, but the conceptual framework is identical for both.

THE CONCEPT OF THE COMMUNITY MENTAL HEALTH CENTER

The implementation of the Community Mental Health Centers Program has provided a response to President Kennedy's call for a "bold new approach" to the problem of mental illness (Kennedy, 1963, p. 2). The newness is apparent in the concept of the center itself, for the center provides not only a new mechanism for giving service but also a new way of thinking about the care of the mentally ill. The basic concepts of the community mental health center model are accessibility of service, comprehensiveness of program, and continuity of care.

The first of these, accessibility, is of fundamental importance. The establishment of a community mental health center means that services are made available on a local basis. Needed care can be obtained without requiring the patient to travel far from home. Treatment can be had without compounding the problem by placing the patient in unfamiliar surroundings. Moreoever, the patient's family can be involved in the treatment process and personal ties and normal living patterns can be maximally maintained. To achieve accessibility careful attention must be paid to the geographic location of the community mental health center. It is not enough, however, simply to place the center at a centrally reachable point within the community. It is equally important that the center's buildings also be planned in a way that will promote access to them. High fences and impenetrable walls may have been appropriate features in the design of 19th century asylums, but they are hardly appropriate for today's mental health center. The design of the center must make it inviting in appearance and must lie in harmony with that of the community's other buildings. In addition to its geographic and design aspects, the concept of accessibility also has important temporal implications. To be truly accessible, the community mental health center must make its services available not only *where* they are needed but also *when* they are needed. Operationally, this means that the center must function on a 24-hour-a-day, seven-day-a-week basis. Morever, it means that services must be available at all times for new patients, not simply for patients who are already on the center's rolls.

Whereas the concept of accessibility calls for ease of access to needed services, a second basic community mental health center concept relates to the nature of these services. This is the concept of comprehensiveness. In an early paper on the Community Mental Health Centers Program (Brown, 1964), it was pointed out that comprehensiveness is not only a key principle of the Program's operation, but it is also a principle which in and of itself sets a number of specific requirements. Basically, to be comprehensive, a community mental health center must meet the range of services. It is not sufficient for the center to offer a single or even a limited range of types of care, no matter how proficient the staff may be in delivering that care. A single patient during the course of his illness needs a variety of services, and any group of patients with a variety of illnesses must likewise have different services available at any single time. Moreover, at any time in a single community there will be patients of all ages and they will come from a variety of social settings.

In terms of the variety of the services to be made available to achieve comprehensiveness, the community mental health center must meet the needs for preventive, diagnostic, therapeutic, and rehabilitative services. In this sense, the comprehensiveness of the center enables it to offer help to the patient in all phases of his illness. To achieve comprehensiveness in terms of the variety of illness to be dealt with, the center must meet the needs of patients with situational reactions, neuroses, psychoses, and character disorders. In this sense the center's comprehensiveness makes it available to patients regardless of their diagnostic classification. To achieve comprehensiveness in terms of meeting the needs of the entire community, the center must be able to serve the young as well as the old, it must cooperate with other local service agencies, and it must be available both to those who can pay for services and those who cannot. In this sense the center's comprehensiveness makes it responsive to the community as well as to the individual patients.

The third basic concept of the community mental health center model is continuity of care. In essence, continuity relates to the coordination of the several services made available by the center. Coordination, however, is an organizational and administrative matter. Continuity of care, on the other hand, places the coordination in the realm of individual patient services. Continuity of care means that the community mental health center does more than offer a range of services. It requires that these several services function as a unified program. It requires that the staff of the center maintain a concern for the patient in all phases of his illness; and, what is perhaps even more important, it requires that the staff pay particularly close attention to the patient's needs during those transitional periods when he moves from one type of service to another.

A PUBLIC HEALTH APPROACH

As described above, the concept of the community mental health center is based upon principles of good clinical practice. The center is designed to meet the needs of patients who need care. In addition to these clinical roots, the origins of community mental health centers also rely heavily upon principles of public health practice.

One of these public health principles is implicit in the center's emphasis on comprehensive care. Another important component of the center's program is prevention. A public health approach emphasizes prevention as a basic aspect of any health service program. For the public health practitioner, prevention is a tripartite matter. First, it implies primary prevention—the reduction of incidence of new cases of illness. Second, it implies secondary prevention—the reduction of prevalence of disease through such efforts as early case finding. Third, it implies tertiary prevention— the reduction of long-term sequelae of disease through active rehabilitation programs. The community mental health center very clearly shows a public health orientation in its commitment to all three phases of preventive service.

In addition, the community mental health center shows its public health origins in its commitment to serve a specific community. The provision of service for a designated community is very much a part of public health programs. Moreoever, a public health approach requires that the center assume responsibility for the mental health services in the community. The center becomes a primary locus of service for the community it serves. The center need not be the only provider of service in the community, but it does have to be the focal point to which all residents of the community can turn for help and around which all the community's providers of mental health services can organize a coordinated program.

Assuming responsibility for its community means that the mental health center makes itself available to everyone who lives in the area. Moreover, it means that the center must develop a program which is specifically responsive to the needs of its community. Certain basic services are essential to any community and thus must be offered by every mental health center. Communities will vary considerably in the extent of their needs for these services, however; and communities vary even more in the nature and extent of their needs for specialized service programs. For example, the community mental health center must offer services to young and old alike, but a community of young families and growing children will need an extensive program for children, while a center serving a "retirement village" will have to place proportionately more emphasis on its geriatrics program. In like manner, every center must stand ready to serve the alcoholic, but in a community with a high rate of alcoholism the center must be able to develop a highly specialized program dealing with all aspects of this particular problem.

OPERATIONAL DEFINITIONS AND FEDERAL GUIDELINES

Given the origins, philosophy, and goals of the Community Mental Health Centers Program, the operational form of the individual center is readily determined. In essence the community mental health center is a locally based and broadly developed program serving a defined population. It is comprehensive in its range of services; it is readily accessible to the people it serves; and it provides an organizational framework which assures continuity of care.

Catchment Areas

A basic component of the operational center concept is a definition of the community served. Sociologists and urban planners have offered a wide variety of definitions for the term community (Howe, 1964). Some of these definitions have focused on demographic data; others have been based on geography; and still others have been expressed in terms of abstractions regarding a shared sense of identity and common ideals. Certainly each of these approaches is important in describing and understanding the community served by a community mental health center. It seems most pertinent to define the population first, however, in terms of its size. For operational purposes the size of the community is of critical importance. In the development of the Federal Program, it was anticipated that if the population served were too small it would be inefficient to develop a full range of services. On the other hand, if the population were too large, then it would be impossible to maintain the degree of organizational unity needed to assure continuity of care. Moreover, as is described below, an important part of the community mental health center's function is based on its close interaction with other service resources in the same community, and efforts to serve too large a population preclude this kind of cooperation.

The optimal size of the population must then be carefully determined. For the Federal Community Mental Health Centers Program, this population, the community served, is designated the "catchment area," and the acceptable catchment area is defined as one with a population of 75,000 to 200,000. The term catchment area itself was chosen to express the center's function of gathering in all those in the community who need care. The quantitative limits placed on the operational catchment area concept were chosen to achieve the necessary balance between the demands for operating efficiency on the one hand and continuity of care on the other.

Essential Services

A second aspect of the community mental health center that requires an operational definition is the service program itself. As noted above, a goal of this program is comprehensiveness. The center must offer care for all in the community who need it; and, moreover, this care must be appropriate to the stage and nature of the patient's illness.

In order to meet these responsibilities each federally supported community mental health center is required to provide five essential services. Four of these services are direct clinical activities designed to provide for individual patient care. The fifth is indirect and designed to extend the impact of the center on the community and its residents. Taken as a group, the five services cover the full spectrum of preventive, diagnostic, therapeutic, and rehabilitative services.

The five essential services of the community mental health center are inpatient care, outpatient care, partial hospitalization, emergency services, and community consultation and education. The selection of these five as essential elements can be readily understood in terms of the recent history of mental health services in this country, and the stated philosophy and goals of the community mental health center. Together they enable the community mental health center to utilize the best features of existing programs while at the same time developing both new methods of care and a more effective system of delivering this care.

The inpatient care offered in community mental health centers is primarily short-term and inter-mediate length care. Most patients are admitted for periods of several weeks to several months. For many other patients the period of inpatient care may be even shorter. A few days of hospitalization is a not uncommon experience for patients in some community mental health centers, while on the other hand, some patients may remain on inpatient wards for a year or more.

The principle clearly is one of flexibility rather than adherence to using an inpatient unit in a particular way. The flexible programming is in large part possible because of the availability of the other services offered by the center. The patient who is hospitalized for only a few days, for example, may then be transferred to a day hospital program.

In order to meet the requirement of partial hospitalization services, the community mental health center must offer a day hospital program. In addition, it may also provide a night hospital program. The day hospital enables a patient to receive the benefits of a multiple-activity and milieu therapy program while at the same time maintaining a place in his family by living with them at home. The night hospital provides a patient with a supportive environment and active treatment while he maintains his contacts at work or at school. Both types of partial hospitalization offer alternatives to full-time inpatient care. Thus both can be of great help to the patient who needs

hospital-based services but who does not need to spend all of every day in the hospital while obtaining these services.

For some patients partial hospitalization follows full-time hospitalization on the inpatient service. For others admission is provided directly to the partial hospitalization program instead of to the inpatient service. Similarly, the outpatient service can be used as a followup to inpatient care or it can provide for a patient who has never been hospitalized. In addition, for some patients the use of the community mental health center is best conceptualized as long-term outpatient care which is punctuated by periods on the inpatient service in the day hospital.

The essential point is that the development of a variety of services makes it possible for each patient to receive care in the way which is most appropriate for him at any given time. This flexibility is further enhanced by the round-the-clock availability of emergency services. The concept of emergency service in the community mental health center has dual meaning. On the one hand the provision of emergency service means that the center is available to its community at all times. In this sense, the emergency service concept implies the designation of a primary contact point for patients and their families. Through its emergency service, the community mental health center can be contacted by phone or in person by active and potential patients. In addition to this administrative meaning, the emergency service idea also has a clinical meaning. The concept of emergency service includes the provision of both diagnostic and treatment services on an immediate basis. For a few patients no more than a single emergency contact will begin a treatment program which involves a variety of other center services. In either case, an active program of diagnosis and therapy is at least begun with every emergency visit to the center.

In addition to these four direct services, the community mental health center provides mental health consultation and education as a fifth required service. Consultation is an indirect mental health service in that patients and potential patients are helped through the assistance provided to other care-givers in the community. Mental health consultants work with clergymen, teachers, policemen, probation officers, and other commu-nity service personnel. Each of these care-giving professionals is responsible for helping people who are in trouble and/or people who are experiencing periods of normal developmental crises. Each of the care-givers can be helped in his work by the mental health professional who, as a consultant, can aid him in understanding his client and can further assist him in understanding aspects of his relationship with his client as they pertain to mental health.

The consultation program of the community mental health center is a principal focus of the center's efforts at the prevention of mental illness. In its various forms, mental health consultation is a means by which the center applies primary, secondary, and tertiary prevention techniques. Mental health consultation represents an approach to primary prevention when the consultant assists teachers in reducing the stresses of classroom work; it is secondary prevention when the consultant aids the teacher in the early identification of disturbed students who are in need of definitive treatment; and it is tertiary prevention when the consultant helps the teacher to facilitate the classroom adjustment of a disturbed child for whom participation in school activities has a rehabilitative (or "habilitative") function.

The five essential services—inpatient care, outpatient care, emergency service, partial hospitalization, and community consultation and education—constitute the basic program required of all community mental health centers participating in the Federal Program. In addition to these basic five, there are five other services which the centers are encouraged to provide. These are specialized diagnostic programs, precare and aftercare services for patients in state hospitals, rehabilitation services for patients reentering the community, training programs for professional and nonprofessional personnel, and research and evaluation programs designed to further the effectiveness of the community mental health center as a system for the delivery of mental health services. To be truly comprehensive in terms of offering a full range of service, the community mental health center must provide all ten services.

Just as the catchment area concept provides an operational approach to the identification of the specific community being served, the lists of essential services and additional services provide an operational approach to the implementation of comprehensive care. The third basic goal of the community mental health center, continuity of care, has also been defined operationally for purposes of the Federal Community Mental Health Centers Program. Specifically, it is required that participating centers provide for the movement and flow of patients, staff, and records among the several services offered. In order to assure this interchange, the center must develop a mechanism which guarantees that patients who are eligible for one service are eligible for all others as well; it must guarantee that staff members who care for patients via one of the services can care for them in all the others; and it must guarantee that records of patient care provided on one service are available to staff members on the other services whenever the patient is transferred.

THE FEDERAL PROGRAM

In order to promote the development of community mental health centers throughout the country, the Congress has authorized a program for the support of both the construction of center facilities and the initial staffing of center services. The original goal of the Federal Program was stated to be the establishment of 2,000 community mental health centers. As was noted above, the construction support was authorized by legislation enacted in 1963, and the staffing support was authorized by an amendment adopted in 1965. Together, the staffing and construction grants made by the federal government are of great importance in the creation of individual centers. The two grant support activities are administered by the National Institute of Mental Health as complementary pieces of a total program for the promotion of community mental health services.

In many respects, the administration of the staffing and construction grant mechanisms are very similar if not identical. Eligibility for both types of grants is defined by the same set of program requirements. In order to obtain a federal grant for either construction or staffing, a center must offer at least the five essential services which were discussed above. In addition, the center must serve a designated catchment area with a population of 75,000 to 200,000 (or a catchment area with a population size outside these limits if a special exemption has been obtained). Moreover, both staffing and construction grantees must provide for continuity of care in terms of arrangements for the transfer of patients, staff, and information.

The programmatic requirements are thus identical for both construction grant applicants and staffing grant applicants. In terms of the operational mechanics of the two types of grants, however, there are a number of significant differences.

A basic difference stems from the fact that the construction grants are awarded through a state-oriented formula grant mechanism while the staffing grants are awarded on an individual project grant basis. Operationally, the formula grant approach means that a specific amount of money is allocated to each state in each fiscal year. (The allotment made to each state is determined by a formula based on both the size of the state's population and its per capita income.) Communities within each state then compete for a share of the state's allotment. Funds allotted to one state are available for use by a community in a second state only if the governors of the two states agree to an interstate transfer of funds to the second state.

An essential ingredient in the administration of the construction grants is the development by each state of a plan for the construction of centers throughout the state. The plan is prepared and administered by the state agency designated by the governor to be responsible for the construction of community mental health centers in that state. In many states, the state mental health department has been given this responsibility; in others, it has been given to the state's public health department since this is the agency responsible for other statewide health facilities construction. In either case, the state plan is a master guide for the state's development of community mental health centers. Federal regulations require that the plan divide the state into planning regions and that the extent of mental illness and related social problems be documented for each region. In addition, the plan must identify the resources already available within each region to meet its mental health needs. On the basis of the extent of mental illness, the extent of related problems, and the availability of service resources within each region, the state planners must assign each region a priority ranking for the construction of community mental health

centers. This rank list in essence identifies the intrastate priorities for the use of federal construction funds. The state agency administering the plan must approve each fundable application for a construction grant; and the state approvals must be consistent with the state plan in that approval must be given first to a fundable application submitted from the highest priority region. Review and approval of any construction application by the National Institute of Mental Health can come only after the application has been reviewed and approved by the responsible agency in the applicant's state.

Unlike the construction grants, staffing grants are awarded through a project grant mechanism. Since the staffing grants are not awarded on the basis of a state allocation formula, the competition among applications is on a nationwide rather than a statewide basis. Applications are reviewed and approved by the National Institute of Mental Health individually rather than by state. Each state is encouraged to use its proportionate share of the total amount available; but if one state does not use its full share, the funds can be awarded to an application in a second state without invoking the mechanism of a formalized interstate transfer.

It must be pointed out, of course, that even though the staffing grants are made through a project grant mechanism rather than the formula grant approach, statewide planning and state agency participation are still essential components of the program's operation. Applications for staffing grants are carefully reviewed for their consistency with the state plan for the construction of community mental health centers. This consistency is especially important in regard to the geographic placement of proposed centers. Moreover, state agency evaluation is required for each staffing grant application. In the case of the staffing grants, however, the responsible agency is always the state mental health authority (rather than being a health facilities construction authority as it is for the construction grant applications in some states).

In addition to this difference in administrative mechanism, the staffing and construction grants differ also in the level of federal support. In the case of the construction grants, the federal share is a variable one. Nationally, except for centers serving designated poverty areas, the federal grant provides between one third and two thirds of the cost of community mental health center construction. For each state, a specific percentage of federal matching is set within this range. The maximum percentage for non-poverty catchment areas is determined on the basis of the size of the state's population and its per capita income. In the course of developing the state construction plan, the responsible stage agency has the option to elect any federal matching percentage up to this maximum.

The staffing grants, on the other hand, provide a standardized percentage of federal matching for centers in all states. The 1970 amendment to the Community Mental Health Centers Act (Public Law 91–211) provides for federal staffing support for a total period of eight years. During this period, the level of federal matching decreases progressively. Initially, for centers serving non-poverty areas, the federal grant can pay 75 percent of eligible staffing costs. This percentage is applicable for the first two years of the grant. During the third year the federal grant pays a maximum of 60 percent of these eligible costs. The federal share then drops to 45 percent for another year and then drops to 30 percent for a final four years.

Initially, when the Community Mental Health Centers legislation was first adopted, these percentages for staffing and construction support were applied to all grants. With the passage of the 1970 amendments to the law, however, higher levels of support became available to centers serving designated poverty areas. Qualifying poverty area centers can now receive construction support at a level of up to 90 percent of eligible construction costs. Staffing support for these poverty area centers begins at 90 percent for two years, drops to 80 percent for the third year, becomes 75 percent for the fourth and fifth years, and then continues at 70 percent for the final three years of federal support. Designation of a catchment area as a poverty area is based upon the percentage of resident families whose income falls below the poverty level as established by the Social Security Administration.

It is important to note that the eligible costs covered by a staffing grant are *not* the total operating costs of the center. Instead they are certain personnel costs involved in the operation of new services offered by the center. The eligible personnel costs are now defined as the salaries and related fringe benefits for all personnel except those whose duties can be considered to be of a housekeeping or minor clerical nature.

It should also be noted that the staffing grants can assist only in meeting the personnel costs of new services offered by the center. A grant cannot be made to support the provision of a service which the center or its constituent agencies has previously been providing. Moreover, federal funds cannot be used to support an expansion of such a previously existing service. As specified in the federal regulations, grant funds may be used for services which are new in that they (1) have never previously been offered by the community mental health center or by any of its constituents or predecessors, or (2) have been offered previously but only on a pilot basis for no more than nine months, or (3) are offered by the center in a form which was not previously available, or (4) are offered by the center to a new population which did not previously receive them from the constituents or predecessors, or (5) represent a new type of service offered within an existing unit.

The Individual Centers

Although both staffing and construction grants are awarded on the basis of identical program eligibility requirements, the two types of grants are awarded independently. Thus, a community mental health center can elect to seek either a staffing or a construction grant, or it can choose to apply for both types of grant funds. Moreover, if the center administrator decides to apply for both types, he need not do so simultaneously. Both types of grants can be awarded concurrently, but it is more common for a center to apply for staffing and construction support in different years. The decision on the timing of these applications is clearly determined by the individual developmental requirements of the center. Some centers have sought staffing funds for assistance in initiating a program and have delayed the construction of new facilities until the program was well underway. In other cases, the sequence has been reversed. These latter centers have first sought construction assistance for facilities needed to house new center services, and only when the building was complete did they need funds for staffing support.

The flexibility in the use of the federal grant funds is an important feature of the national Community Mental Health Centers Program. Such flexibility is essential since the goal of the program is the establishment in each community of a center which is uniquely tailored to that community's needs. Efforts to achieve this uniquely suited program in the community are evident also in the variety of organizational patterns adopted by different communities. The basic program is determined by the requirements that there be at least five essential services, specific provisions for continuity of care, and a specifically designated catchment area. Within these broad guidelines, however, there is wide latitude for the establishment of a program and organizational structure for a single community mental health center.

Community mental health centers differ widely in regard to their programs. All provide at least the five essential services, but the nature of these services takes many forms. In some centers the dominant theme is direct patient care; in others it is the indirect consultation service. In some centers inpatient and outpatient services are emphasized; while in others day care is the principal direct service. In some centers the staff is composed largely of professionals; in others it includes large numbers of nonprofessionals who are participating in a "new-careers" training program.

In addition to their program variations, there is also much variety in regard to organizational patterns. In this connection is it important to point out that the establishment of a community mental health center need not involve the creation of a new agency. Moreover, even when federal construction funds are involved, the establishment of the center need not involve the erection of a new building housing all the center's services. Instead of representing a totally new agency or a single centralized facility, the creation of a community mental health center more typically represents the consolidation and coordination of a number of already existing agencies. Each of these agencies provides services which together comprise the total center program. Staffing grant funds are typically employed to add services which were previously unavailable, and construction grant funds are used to provide facilities for new and/or expanded services.

Because of the variety of approaches available for organizing a community mental health center,

it is hard to identify a perfectly typical pattern. There is, however, one organizational arrangement which provides the most common basic model. This is the general model of two existing agencies joining together to establish the center program. In this simplest version of a "multiple-agency-center," the two participants are usually a general hospital and a mental health outpatient clinic. Both agencies may be operated under public auspices; both may be voluntary institutions; or one may be a publicly supported unit while the other is a nonprofit corporation. Whatever their corporate structure, however, they participate in establishing the center as equal partners.

In terms of program responsibilities, the two agencies share the requirement for providing the five essential services. The general hospital is the site and provider of the inpatient service. In addition, the hospital's emergency room is the locus of the center's 24-hour-a-day emergency service. The clinic, on the other hand, provides the outpatient services as well as the center's community consultation and education program. The fifth service, a day hospital program, can be operated by either participant. In some cases the partial hospitalization service is located at the general hospital, either in conjunction with or distinct from the inpatient unit. In other cases, the clinic operates the day hospital while the general hospital provides partial hospitalization in the form of a night hospital.

The establishment of a "multiple-agency-center" requires careful attention to program planning and community organization. Such planning efforts are essential whether the center involves two agencies or many. (Indeed, efforts at planning and organization must be emphasized even if the center is being developed and operated by a single agency.) It was noted above that statewide planning is of considerable importance for the administration of the Federal Community Mental Health Centers Program. A concern for planning at the local level is of equal importance for the establishment of an individual center. Moreover, it must be noted that this planning must be directed at a variety of issues. Community participation and the organization of local mental health resources are both major considerations. In addition, the local planners must make maximal use of the mental health resources available outside the immediate community. Of particular importance in this regard is the relation of the center's program to the state hospital which serves the community. Finally, it is important that the planners develop their program so that it is optimally related to the total spectrum of community services. Health and social welfare services must be considered as carefully as are the mental health services, for in developing a community mental health center it must be remembered that center's range of services is but one segment of the total human services network.

THE MENTAL HEALTH PROFESSIONAL AND THE COMMUNITY MENTAL HEALTH CENTER

For all mental health professionals, the community mental health center offers a variety of new challenges and opportunities. Within the setting of a community program, the professional has the means of continuing his clinical work with individual patients and groups. In addition, he shares with his professional colleagues the possibility of providing these services in a way which brings him into very close contact with the community at large. As a result he can work with a variety of other community service agencies and he can extend his own effectiveness by working through these agencies. The mental health professional's role as a clinician is not a new one. On the other hand, the role of mental health consultant is new for most staff members of the community mental health center. Working indirectly through other community care-givers is a new approach. Rather than working with the patient himself, the mental health consultant must focus on the needs and problems of another professional, and he must enable his consultee to be one who provides service for the patient. The consultation approach calls for new techniques. It differs from both psychotherapy and supervision. Moreoever, effective consultation calls for a new professional attitude. The consultant must see his consultee as a professional equal, and he must regard himself as a hidden partner in the care-giving process (Caplan, 1964, p. 29; Kazanjian, 1962).

This change of attitude on the part of the mental health consultant is required in other aspects of community mental health center operations as well. The traditional approach of the mental health professional is an independent one; he functions as an individual in his work with a patient or client. In the community mental health center, on the other hand, professionals are likely to function as members of a term rather than as individuals. Moreover, the team is likely to function in relation to a specified geographic pattern of the catchment area rather than in relation to a specific type of service unit.

The team approach makes new demands upon all the mental health professionals. Equally significant demands are made by the presence of new types of mental health workers. The nonprofessional or technical personnel who are supported by federal staffing grants represent new forms of mental health manpower. Roles must be created for them within the structure of the community mental health center, and as these new roles are established, the functions and positions of established mental health professions must be accordingly modified. Tasks which were performed only by professionals are now handled by nonprofessionals, and the professionals must assume responsibility for new tasks which are created both by the presence of the new types of staff members and by new organizational structure of the center.

Many of these new responsibilities fall under the general rubric of administration. Whatever its organizational form may be, a community mental health center presents a variety of new administrative challenges. The unification of multiple services in a single functional program is but one reason for needing a new approach to program management. The coordination of independent agencies requires a special kind of administrative skill; and the utilization of new types of manpower adds further responsibilities to the work of the center administrator.

In addition to their clinical and consultative functions in community mental health centers, mental health professionals of all disciplines have taken on a variety of administrative roles. The federal regulations for the Community Mental Health Centers Program specifically state that the administrative leadership of the center may be placed in a person with a background in any of the mental health professions. Although medical responsibility for each patient must be vested in a physician, program responsibility is in no way restricted to a single professional group. Already a number of centers have named nonphysicians to be their administrative directors, and it can be anticipated that, as additional centers are established, still more of them will do so.

The new forms of clinical service, the consultative roles, and the new administrative responsibilities all require skills which have not been customarily included in any mental health professional curricula. Some of the staff members of community mental health centers have been able to obtain specialized training prior to assuming center positions. For most, however, the situation continues to be one of on-the-job experience and inservice training. The latter constitutes an important function of any community mental health center. As was noted above, training and education constitute one of the ten services of a comprehensive center program. The training activities of a center must be oriented to the needs of all the staff members, whatever the nature and level of their previous training may be.

THE FUTURE

The Community Mental Health Centers Program is still in its early growth stages. In the years to come it can be anticipated that the program will be further developed in size while the community mental health center concept is further refined in operation.

With the addition of more centers and more services, there will also be developed new methods in the provision of these services. The community mental health center represents a new approach to the organization and delivery of mental health services. As an organizational framework for the provision of these services, the center also provides a setting for the development of new techniques of mental health care.

Already the center has begun to serve as a focal point for creating new mechanisms in financing and administering mental health services. In addition, it provides the opportunity and the stimulus for creating new approaches both to

treatment and to prevention. The origins of the community mental health center lie in the experience of earlier efforts to care for the mentally ill. The future of the center lies in its capacity to provide both a quantity and a quality of care which these previous approaches could not achieve.

References

Brown, B. S., & Cain, H. P. The many meanings of comprehensive. *American Journal of Orthopsychiatry*, 1964, 34, 834–839.

Caplan, G. *Principles of preventive psychiatry*. New York: Basic Books, 1964.

Deutsch, A. *The shame of the states*. New York: Harcourt, Brace, 1948.

Ginzberg, E. Army hospitalization, retrospect and prospect. *Bulletin of the United States Army Medical Department*, 1948, 8, 38–47.

Glass, A. J. Combat psychiatry and civilian medical practice. *Transactions of the College of Physicians*, 1955, 23, 14–23.

Glasscote, R. M., & Kanno, C. M. *General hospital psychiatric units*. Washington, D. C.: Joint Information Service, 1965.

Howe, L. P. The concept of the community: Some implications for the development of community psychiatry. In L. Bellak (ed.), *Handbook of community psychiatry and community mental health*. New York: Grune & Stratton, 1964.

Joint Commission on Mental Illness and Health. *Action for mental health*. New York: Basic Books, 1961.

Kazanjian, V., Stein, S., & Weinberg, W. L. *An introduction to mental health consultation*. (United States Department of Health, Education, and Welfare, Public Health Service) Washington, D. C.: United States Government Printing Office, 1962.

Kennedy, J. F. Message from the President of the United States relative to mental illness and mental retardation, Washington, D. C., February 5, 1963. (88th Congress, First Session, Document No. 58)

Menninger, W. C. *Psychiatry in a troubled world*. New York: Macmillan, 1948.

United States Department of Health, Education, and Welfare, Public Health Service. *Patients in mental institutions—Part II, States and county mental hospitals*. Washington, D. C.: United States Government Printing Office, 1966.

30

Tactics and Targets in the Rural Setting

Hans R. Huessy

Much of what we propose as new and original in community mental health today can be found in the literature of the 19th century. In 1864, for example, the Association of Medical Superintendents of American Institutions for the Insane resolved that: "The large states should be divided into geographical districts so that hospitals could be placed nearly in the center of them and thus be accessible to all persons living within their boundaries and available for treatment. . . . All state, county, and city hospitals shall receive persons in their vicinity, whatever may be the form or nature of their mental disorder" (Hurd, 1916). Neither is concern for provision of mental health services to rural areas a recent phenomenon (see Ebaugh & Lloyd, 1928; Rademacher, 1931; Cameron, 1948; Sloman, 1948; Maddox, 1953). History's relevance is apparent but the rapidity with which its lessons may be forgotten is highlighted by a recent report on development of mental health services in Wyoming (Daniels, 1967), which made no mention of a similar extensive program in the same area between 1949 and 1953 (Stubblefield & Herrold).

The title of this chapter suggests a clear division between urban and rural and implies that this difference should greatly affect the organization of a mental health program. It must be kept in mind, however, that the distinction between urban and rural mental health programming is sometimes artificial and inadequate, because urban and rural areas often share particular problems and characteristics, and within each there is a wide variation in setting and in the requirements for mental health programs. The authors of the previous chapter on urban settings have worked in an area which was a ghetto of a large metropolitan complex. They would be the first to admit that the ghetto is no more typical of the urban condition than is the rural farm community typical of all rural settings. In the Midwest and New England, rural settings contain farm communities separated by only three miles, and individual farms within easy walking distance of each other. Such settings may foster a fairly high level of social interaction with only thinly scattered examples of rural poverty. In the rural South, on the other hand, there may be overwhelming poverty throughout a whole township, complicated by a serious racial problem and by rigid boundaries. The Rocky Mountain area furnishes rural settings involving ranches spaced five or ten miles apart, villages 30 to 40 miles apart, where social isolation, rather than concentrated poverty, constitutes a serious problem. Finally, a rural area such as the Navajo Reservation in Arizona and New Mexico is plagued by poverty, maximum geographical dispersal, comparative social isolation, and culture conflict. Clearly, these rural areas are as different from each other as the urban ghetto is different from suburbia or Fifth Avenue in Manhattan. Clearly, moreover, no one rural mental health program can hope to handle all the different rural problems.

People often have rather romantic ideas about the country, ideas which go so far as to assume that rural areas do not have the same kind of mental health and social problems that city areas have. Statistics do indicate that the worst ghetto areas, in which there is extensive social disorganization, do produce a much higher rate of social breakdown than other parts of our cities or rural areas. But, except for these very disorganized areas, the incidence of most emotional disorders is the same whether we look at a city, a suburban area, a town, or a rural village. Certainly some of the difficulties especially created by a city, such as the social and racial segregation in school systems, can be avoided in many rural areas, where there is usually one school which serves all the children in that area regardless of race or economic status. This does reduce the social ostracism of the poor and of minority groups, and makes it easier for members of a lower class family both to aspire to and to achieve a higher level of living. (This does not, obviously, entirely apply to the rural South.) It is also true that in rural Vermont, for instance, delinquency rates are definitely lower than they are in urban areas. One major explanation for this may be that one is very well known in a small town and, therefore, likely to be recognized and apprehended. With the greater availability of automobiles, however, this rural benefit is disappearing because young people can travel to another town where they are unknown and where, therefore, it is safer to engage in criminal activity. It should be remembered, furthermore, that rates of reporting are highly difficult to interpret—an apparently high delinquency rate may be due to a lenient judge who favors probation for first offenders and is seen as someone to turn to for help, while a low delinquency rate may be due to a strict judge who invariably metes out jail sentences, causing officials to handle cases in informal ways to keep them out of court. We cannot, in other words, state with absolute certainty that rural delinquency rates really *are* lower than urban rates. It is only in northern rural areas, where middle and upper middle class members predominate, that the problems of cities with large inner city populations do not occur.

Recently Eisdorfer, Altrocchi, and Young (1968) attempted to delineate some principles for community mental health work in a rural setting. A total of 20 principles were presented and discussed—all of them, however, also applicable to an urban setting. Their "Principle 2," for instance, states: "The support of community leaders is crucial for the development of a mental health program. While a key individual may play the central role in starting a program, he must depend upon the support of other community figures for long-range development." Similarly, their "Principle 3" states: "An accurate appraisal of community needs and attitudes, supported by data, is extremely helpful in approaching community agencies, especially those with fiscal responsibility." It seems clear that the "support of community leaders is crucial" for the success of any mental health program, anywhere, and, likewise, that "an accurate appraisal of community needs and attitudes" is an essential basis for any mental health program, be it urban or rural. This author, on the other hand, believes that there are aspects of mental health programming which are peculiar to a rural setting. For this reason, this chapter is divided into two parts: the first part describes factors specific to rural programs, while the second summarizes principles which are probably applicable to mental health programs in any setting.

ESSENTIAL FACTORS WHICH DISTINGUISH A RURAL FROM AN URBAN PROGRAM

In the first place, there is a tendency for rural communities to underestimate their mental health problems. The statisticians at state headquarters contribute to this because their figures frequently indicate fewer admissions from rural areas. Studies have shown, however, that admission rates are directly related to geographical distance from a state hospital. Admission statistics mislead because they reflect this fact (Weiss, Macaulay, & Pincus, 1967; Zubin, 1961; and Odegaard, 1956). For this reason, a more extensive educational effort may be required in rural areas before they will be ready to support the needed program.

Even if the rural area is convinced of the need for a mental health program, the rural area, unlike the urban area, will have difficulty obtaining professional mental health personnel. Improved travel and communications systems are rapidly changing this picture in some parts of the country, but geographical isolation, professional isolation, and distance from specialized services are still some of the basic obstacles for professionals working in a rural mental health program. Area staff meetings are an excellent way to provide appropriate professional stimulation and force the participants to keep abreast of developments as they prepare their presentations.

Once professional personnel have been obtained, there is still the problem of the social visibility of the professional. The professional in an urban setting can be a private individual—his life outside the mental health center is his own. In a rural setting, however, whether he lives in the community or only visits on an occasional basis, his extraprofessional activities will be watched and will play a role in the community's evaluation of his professional competence. Slight lapses of social judgment can prove disastrous. The professional who is a "character" can create real difficulties for a small town mental health program.

There are further ramifications of this problem. If the professional in a small town wishes to engage in private practice, he must realize that the community is likely to feel cheated. There is a tendency to assume that private (expensive) care is good, while public (cheap) care is poor. The opposite may actually be true—a professional is likely to be at his best during regular clinic work hours, while on his own, private practice time, he is likely to be distracted and exhausted. He must, nevertheless, be prepared to deal with this public prejudice.

A major obstacle to rural mental health programming, however, is the tendency for state administrative staff to try to duplicate, in the rural areas, the same kinds of services that they provide in urban areas. Since many states are dominated by urban areas, federal legislation tends to discriminate against rural areas by attempting to impose the urban pattern on the rural situation. Thus, we might find a small town 100 miles away from its main medical resources being supplied with a wide variety of specialty clinics on a one-day-a-week to a one-day-every-two-months basis. Applied to mental health, you might find a mental retardation clinic one day a month, an alcoholism clinic one day a month, a child guidance clinic one day a month, a learning disability clinic one day a month, an aftercare clinic for psychiatric patients one day a month, and a psychiatric treatment clinic for adults one day a month. Each of these clinics would be staffed by different professionals, each of these professionals spending at least four hours of his day's time traveling to and from this town. A closer

look at these types of services will reveal that they are definitely second-rate, and not because the professionals are doing a second-rate job. Rather, there is a total lack of continuity—community follow-up of clinic recommendations is very haphazardly carried out, and the patient in acute need has to wait too long. These same criticisms can be leveled at many large city clinics but the contributing causes are somewhat different. The clinic, furthermore, is often not integrated with the community. It is obvious, finally, that providing professional services by these means becomes ridiculously expensive, since the high-priced professional whose services are so difficult to obtain is being paid mostly to travel over the highways.

Which brings us to one final problem in rural mental health programming—financing. Many states have passed grant-in-aid laws for mental health programs based on the law passed in New York State in the early 1950s. This law requires that a specified percentage of mental health financing come from local sources. In New York State, mental health programs are organized on a county basis and the counties are expected to provide the local finances. Since New York State has strong county government, this presents no problems. A similar law passed in Vermont has created difficulties. Vermont has no county or district government, only town and state government. Since any area suitable for a mental health program includes many independent towns, perhaps as many as 50, all of which transact their business on the same town meeting day once a year, raising the local financing through town taxation would require getting all 50 towns to act on such a request on the same day. Since this is virtually impossible, it has meant that local financing has depended on annual fund drives, a very uncertain foundation for a service agency. Professionals needed for mental health work spend much time raising the moneys to pay their own salaries. As a result, many agencies have signed contracts for service to school districts. Unfortunately, there may be some constitutional questions about this method in some states, depending on the laws relating to state aid to education. Any state mental health law should provide some realistic method for achieving stable financial support in a rural area. If a mental health district is identical to the limits of a governmental unit, then this unit can assume responsibility for local financing. In rural areas this is almost never the case.

Although it may seem from the above discussion that the problems facing a rural mental health program are formidable, there are certain advantages, especially for the professional, inherent in a rural mental health program. For instance, rural programs, as indicated before, most frequently start on a part-time basis. Although a full-time service is undoubtedly better than a part-time service, the part-time service does continually force the professional to examine and question his methods, because they cannot be applied in the same way as in a full-time operation. The professional must improvise and adapt to the very real limitations he encounters and, in so doing, he finds that less expensive and less extensive methods than he has been taught can achieve results which seem to at least equal the results of his usual methods.

In a truly rural setting, moreover, the patterns of formal organization rarely interfere with cooperative client-centered action. The local representatives of any agency are few in number and are usually known to all other agency representatives, often on a first name basis. Local interagency cooperation is, therefore, much easier in a rural setting. One does not have to work one's way up and down urban administrative hierarchies and, when appropriate, policies set in some distant central office are circumvented by one or another agency for the sake of the common purpose.

Another advantage of the rural setting is the opportunity it provides to work within a smaller area. In a rural program, the standard community mental health center catchment area of 200,000 people becomes unrealistic because of geographical factors, i.e., the distance between client and services is still too great. Community mental health centers propose to achieve continuity of care of the psychiatric patient by coordinating the organization of all psychiatric services, perhaps even placing them all in the same building. Despite this laudable effort, the patient is still transfered from worker to worker, each using a different psychiatric consultant. On paper, the patient has had continuity of care, but in actuality, he has experienced discontinuity. In a rural setting, the opportunity is available to work with a much smaller catchment area and a genuinely coordinated and continuous kind of care is possible. As

the patient works with his aftercare worker, his vocational rehabilitation worker, and, perhaps, his welfare worker, a consistency of approach is feasible because the same psychiatrist consults with all three workers. The Office of Economic Opportunity has already learned to reduce the size of population groups served by its new health centers. Rural mental health experience points in this direction. Continuity of care cannot be provided by a table of organization. Some one of the caretakers must have continuous responsibility or there will be no coordination of care. As psychiatric consultant to a rural clinic, I have referred patients to the state hospital, personally intervened there to have them referred to vocational rehabilitation, then dealt with them as the psychiatrist for vocational rehabilitation, the psychiatrist in the community clinic that was supplying aftercare, and the psychiatric consultant to the Welfare Department. In the usual urban setting, at least four psychiatrists would have invested time to study the case, to form an opinion, and make a plan. Would the four opinions and plans be identical? Very unlikely. In our rural setting, the same psychiatric opinion and plan was brought to bear on the patient's care repeatedly through a variety of agencies. Care had both continuity and consistency. The efforts of different agencies were easily coordinated. A higher quality of care with a lesser amount of psychiatric time was achieved. The rural clinic may be in an excellent position, therefore, to demonstrate the optimum population size to be served by any one clinical team.

Along the same lines, our experience has shown that one psychiatrist can be directly responsible for the work of 12 to 15 co-workers. As soon as this number is surpassed, supervisors and administrators, i.e., second-level management, become essential. Rural programs increase the feasibility, in other words, of running programs which do not require the introduction of second-level management. The introduction of second-level management makes personal and continuous care more difficult to provide, besides making any unit of care more expensive. The need for conference time for intraagency communication goes up very rapidly as increased size demands the introduction of second-level management. Many care-giving agencies, from medical clinics to school systems, have felt the impact of growing size: increased rigidity and lessened adaptability, decrease in personalized service, and increases in cost per unit of service. Admittedly, there are also gains: better competitive position for hiring, greater varieties of specialized services, more extensive supervision of inadequately trained workers. Rural programs, then, might be studied to provide guidelines for escaping the problems of size, and to suggest ways of combining growth with flexibility.

One of the real assets of the rural mental health setting is the comparative ease of doing research (Rees, 1967). Evaluation of results is far simpler, as the population is more readily delineated, and follow-up through cooperation with other agencies, whose workers one knows by name, is easy and does not require elaborate agreements and coordination of hierarches (Kiesler, 1968). The young man eager to make his mark can demonstrate a new approach to a problem, study the effect of a technique, or investigate an epidemiological factor much more simply and with a great deal less money if he uses a rural situation rather than an urban one. In our large training centers, moreover, the student in a mental health discipline seldom gets a chance to be genuinely on his own, to carry full responsibility without the immediate availability of more experienced back-up personnel. The opportunity to assume the full responsibility which a rural program may offer him allows for a kind of growth and development which should greatly improve his training experience. Finally, the exciting opportunities for the community psychiatrist in the rural situation are documented in a recent book by the writer (Huessy, 1966).

As indicated, the rural area is ideal for research purposes, but not only because of the greater freedom and flexibility it affords. If some of the clinic staff, professional or secretarial, is of local origin, it is surprising how much historical data will be available to the clinic before the client ever sets foot in the door. This will include a fairly clear picture of the family's physical setting and much information about the extended family, information which is often extremely difficult to obtain in the usual clinic.

The small close-knit community has further advantages—mental health professionals who work and live in a rural setting have a new and sobering experience not commonly available to their urban colleagues. Their clients do not disappear from sight when the case is closed. At social occasions, in the local paper, in the school their children attend, at the local supermarket, and in many other settings, professionals will continue to encounter or hear about their former clients. This provides an automatic evaluation of their work and continually checks their diagnoses and predictions. The 16-year-old girl who dropped out of treatment, against our advice, after two interviews, appears in the paper because she made the Dean's List at a nearby college. The family for whom we predicted a career of instability achieves stability and success in running a roadside restaurant. Our successfully treated 10-year-old acting-out child hits the papers as a delinquent. The couple we helped to work through their separation is reunited. The boy we helped ease out of high school wins a medal for heroism. Once again, a rural setting forces the mental health professional to take a long, hard look at his own work.

Having explored some of the advantages and disadvantages of the rural mental health setting, we might now turn to a discussion of strategies—that is, ways in which we can maximize the advantages and minimize the disadvantages of the rural setting. The drawbacks of the traveling specialty clinics have already been mentioned. If, instead, a town could establish an all purpose clinic which would have at least one full-time local staff member, a much higher level of service could be given. The town could avoid the specialty clinics, which usually do not know about each other's cases and might, conceivably, be providing four different services to members of the same families without any coordination. An all-purpose clinic would be cheaper, moreover, since if the traveling professional can stay overnight, the travel time will be greatly reduced. Coordination of social and health services is sufficiently important to warrant the possibly lower level of expertise that an all purpose clinic might provide. This shortcoming can be minimized by backing up the traveling professional with easily available telephone consultation from the nearest medical center. A limited demonstration of this method was used in our work with family physicians to increase their role in the care of major psychiatric problems (Huessy, 1963).

Modern urban community mental health programs utilize the process of consultation extensively. The professional talks with other types of professionals such as school teachers, public health nurses, general practitioners, probation officers, welfare workers, ministers, etc., who themselves are involved in helping people with problems. By giving help to these other professionals, their effectiveness is increased and the number of clients who have to receive direct services from mental health professionals may be reduced. In a rural program, however, it often becomes necessary to design these kinds of programs along different lines. In a city, it is easiest to meet first with school teachers, then public health nurses, then ministers, etc. In a rural community, it is often better to meet simultaneously with all the different people involved in giving care. This automatically provides communitywide integration of effort and makes available all information known about any client (Townsend, 1966).

Long ago, a series of papers based on the experience of the traveling clinics in Colorado questioned many of our standard psychiatric clinic practices (Thaler, 1950; Coleman & Switzer, 1951; Hopple & Huessy, 1954). Referral to a once-a-month traveling clinic in a small town may set in motion a therapeutic process which has, as its focal point, the actual contact with the traveling mental health professional but where the technical details of this contact may play only a minor role. The referral of a problem child in a rural school subtly changes the attitudes of teachers, parents, and social workers toward the problem case as they jointly examine the situation for possible contributing causes and begin to view the child as in need of help rather than as a problem or nuisance. This change in perspective may be the most important part of the therapeutic process. It is necessary to begin with the scheduled clinic, but the therapeutic process may actually have run its course by the time the expert from the city sees the patient. "On the surface it would seem that such a treatment procedure must be doomed to failure. Yet, it has been our experience that it meets with fairly good success in cases that would ordinarily be considered short-term treatment cases in the usual child guidance clinic where mother and child are seen by separate therapists on a weekly basis" (Coleman & Switzer, 1951).

The traveling mental health clinic is a special type of rural service described in detail in a number of publications (Daniels, 1967; Ebaugh & Lloyd, 1927; Hubbard, 1956). Suffice it here to point out that experience over the years has shown the need to have a professional residing in the community as a permanent member of the team.

This need not be a mental health professional. In most cases it has been a welfare worker or a public health nurse. The traveling clinic teams described in the above papers consisted of psychiatrists and psychologists.

When the days of a traveling clinic are over and a full-time local service has been established in a rural area, it becomes necessary to establish regular links with still further outlying villages. The need for truly local integration and follow-through soon becomes evident, yet obviously would not justify full-time clinic team members in each of these villages. In Vermont, surprisingly, we have had no difficulty finding various professionals living in the area who are delighted to work with the clinic on a part-time basis. In three counties, we are building an active program around nonworking or retired nurses (Huessy, 1969c). One finds former social workers, teachers, nurses, occupational and physical therapists, none in a position to accept full-time work but many eager to help part-time. It is often possible to identify child welfare workers, public health nurses, or other professionals who have developed real skills in certain mental health endeavors because for so long there was no one to help them or for them to hand the work over to. Such people are not competitors; one should capitalize on their talents, support them in their work, and give them due recognition. All these people become local coordinators and crisis handlers, always with the clinic available for immediate back-up help. The same resource may supply specialty services which do not warrant a full-time employee. One looks around, in a rural setting, to find what skills are available, and develops the program accordingly (Hamann, 1968; Huessy, 1969b).

Many rural areas are not of a sufficient size to warrant the establishment of branch offices of other agencies. This allows the community mental health agency to coordinate many other auxiliary services under its aegis, either through the use of visiting specialists from other agencies, or by contracting with other agencies to provide these services for them. These other professionals are provided with a genuine multidisciplinary setting in which to work with broad professional association and immediate consultation available. Planning for the client is more readily coordinated. This method also reduces the duplication of administrative costs. Here again, the rural program may be able to develop patterns of efficient service coordination which then could have value for urban settings as well.

One of the requirements of current community mental health center legislation is to provide for partial hospitalization. This is a treatment modality developed in urban settings. With the lack of public transportation available in rural areas, the feasibility of partial hospitalization becomes doubtful and group homes may offer a better option. Instead of attempting to duplicate existing facilities, an activities program for exhospital patients can be conducted in a local nursing home. The tone and morale of the nursing home is improved while something close to partial hospitalization can be achieved. Since nursing homes are to be found almost everywhere, either a traveling worker or a local part-time worker can set up a program in any village with a nursing home. The nursing home does not carry the stigma of a "mental health" facility, and care is likely to be more personalized than in a state hospital setting. Personalized care is a major ingredient of the current community mental health boom. The rural areas are the best place to test out the benefits of this personalized care, since for any given population it can be implemented much more easily than in an urban area.

As mentioned at the start of this chapter, mental health problems in a rural area are often underestimated because of the low number of admissions to the state hospital, which in turn is due to the extreme distance of prospective patients' homes from the hospital. To what extent, then, should the in-patient facilities of the state hospital be brought to the rural area? How small can these units be? Rands (1960), in describing a rural program in Saskatchewan, laments the lack of in-patient beds, implying that the program would be even more successful in the reduction of hospitalization and recidivism if such beds were available in the immediate area. A home treatment service, however, might be more appropriate. Since the geographical proximity and easy availability of in-patient beds increases utilization rates (Weiss et al., 1967), we may be defeating ourselves. The development of in-patient facilities in small towns has generally not affected the rates of admission to the state hospitals from such towns. The use of available in-patient facilities for a difficult case is often so much easier for the psychiatrist. The more difficult hospitalization is, the more likely he will be to find some way to avoid it. Our own experience in Vermont has been that as in-patient facilities become more easily available they are utilized for patients who previously were not being hospitalized. Mental health programming faces a genuine dilemma here. We wish to reduce the number of patients being hospitalized, yet simultaneously promote easier entrance into hospitals and the availability of psychiatric beds closer to the patients' home. How can we program effectively to achieve these purposes? When I receive an emergency call while eating supper, and in-patient care is easily available, I will be tempted to use this resource. If no in-patient facility is available, I have no choice but to go out and perhaps resolve the crisis in a few hours with a home visit. Methods of financing and availability of in-patient beds have dramatically influenced patterns of medical care outside psychiatry. How can we make certain that the care of the psychiatric patient will be determined by what is best for the patient? In many teaching centers the assumption seems to be that high quality hospital care is always something good. Yet, numerous studies indicate that we should exert considerable effort to prevent the hospitalization of the psychiatric patient. We might, perhaps, learn from the Clarinda Plan, an Iowa hospital in which patients were distributed on an ecological basis, according to the geographical areas and sociocultural units in which the patients lived outside the hospital. This plan provided continuity of treatment for the patient, reassurance for the family of the patient, decentralization of hospital structure, and utilization of the community resources for reintegration of the patient into the community (Garcia, 1960; Beckenstein, 1964). Perhaps a state hospital, regionalized along the lines of the Clarinda Plan, would better serve the needs of a rural area than a multitude of small in-patient units with too easy accessibility. The state hospital can provide some specialized services which the small unit cannot. And the chronic patient is still with us as shown by the experience of the Fort Logan Mental Health Center in Colorado (Kraft, Binner, & Dickey, 1967). How to arrange for the best of both worlds? It is clear that we are not ready to promote "the" pattern of rural mental health care. We need to try many patterns, with documented results, to compare and combine. Easy access to in-patient care seems like an obviously worthy goal. Ease of hospitalization and the prevention of hospitalization are both accepted goals of mental health planning. Yet, they work against each other and typify how inadequately we have thought out our premises and purposes. In our aftercare demonstration (Vargish, 1966), a number of patients would have been hospitalized had local beds been available to us. I am not prepared to say whether the use of such beds would have provided the patients with better care.

Dr. Chunilal Roy, in a recent article, summarized his experience with a rural mental health team in Saskatchewan as follows: It is easier to use volunteers effectively, easier to hear the community, and easier to identify community leaders—and with special training for new roles he achieved a 50 percent reduction in the admissions to the state hospital.

Two other strategies might be mentioned, with special reference to the professional working in a rural mental health setting:

1. The professional who engages in private, as well as public, practice will, as already indicated, be faced with public suspicion that his private work is better than his public efforts. This can be partially overcome by having the private work done on the same model as the public work. By using the various mental health professionals in the same way and perhaps even renting the clinic space, private work can be used as an effective way for the psychiatrist to publicly show his genuine confidence in his co-workers and in the public methods.

2. The training value of experience in a rural clinic has already been elaborated. However, some teaching programs in mental health disciplines have recognized this value, but are not willing to let the trainee have this experience over a long enough period of time. Stability of professional staff over time is important for the success of any mental health program. If a training center abuses a rural program in this regard it will do serious harm. The trainee, moreover, cannot appreciate what the rural program has to offer him unless he works in it for a sufficient length of time. One day a month for a year teaches more than two weeks full-time (Kern, Jacobson, & Hess). It is the changes through time which can teach him

the most. Contact over a one-year period seems minimal to us.

I would now like to offer some general observations based on my experience in rural settings—the common weakness of mental health programs is their indefinable goal of improving the community's mental health. In the future we must plan programs with specific measurable goals: to reduce recidivism amongst former state hospital patients (Vargish, 1966); to reduce the dropout rate of high school students; to facilitate the early diagnosis and treatment of reading disabilities (Huessy, Twellman, & Walter, 1967; Rabinovitch, 1959); to reduce the incidence of neurological damage to the fetal and neonatal nervous system (Rogers, Lilienfeld, & Passamanick, 1955; Prechtl, 1960; Huessy, 1967); to reduce the high incidence of physical and psychological illness among the bereaved (Rees, 1967). Unless we specify our goals, we become preoccupied with our beliefs, techniques, and favorite activities without continually being challenged by our results. We use the community to meet our needs and do not meet the needs of the community. We develop no realistic basis for establishing priorities for judging which mental health dollar shows the greatest payoff, and someday we will be called to account. Frank Kiesler in northern Minnesota has been developing an "Event-Reporting System" which in time may help us overcome this problem (Kiesler, 1968).

In our appeals for support we have either promised prevention outright or strongly implied it. Yet, only recently have we learned to mount valid programs of secondary and tertiary prevention. Most of the evidence in the field of primary prevention points to a need for action by others than mental health professionals (Eisenberg, 1962). Public health, obstetrics, and pediatrics are the areas for action. We can highlight the needs, but for results we must rely on many others. Social welfare and rehabilitation must be our partners, as must education. Here we must work among equal partners, being humble about the limits of our knowledge and skills.

To digress slightly, one of the most puzzling aspects of our work with family physicians was that many of the acute cases about which we were consulted disappeared from sight. These cases had been evaluated as representing chronic maladjustment and requiring long-term supportive care.

Neither the original physician nor another physician nor a social agency was found to have further contact during the period of our project. This experience has been duplicated in urban round-the-clock clinics, in military psychiatry (Glass, 1953; Hausman, 1967), and disaster studies (Tyhurst, 1958). There seems, in other words, to be a "crisis point," and if one can intervene at this point, the patient may, in spite of dire predictions to the contrary, require no further help. Crisis theory holds that minimal intervention at this point will have a maximal positive impact. A large percentage of these "crisis disorders" get well even without intervention. Our original theories, however, offered no explanation for this phenomenon. Again, we must be humble and flexible. It has been both easy and popular to heap blame on others and to forget that our own house is not in such excellent order, with its divisive theoretical conflicts and a preference for belief over scientific evidence. We have handed out a great deal of advice to other professions—for instance, to pediatricians on matters of child-rearing—which we now realize is not valid (Redl, 1962). Redl's presidential address to the American Orthopsychiatric Association implies that only a lack of funds is keeping us from major successes. I am not that optimistic.

The second pervasive shortcoming of mental health programs consists in our justifying our failures with our good intentions. Quality is established by requiring high levels of training for staff members, good record keeping, extensive conferencing, and, often, adherence to standard patterns of therapy. This type of "quality" plus our good intentions is assumed to assure a "good" program. In the early part of World War II, the United States mounted the most extensive and expensive psychiatric treatment program for our military casualties. It was designed by "experts" and executed with enthusiasm and good intentions. Its failure was monumental—not only militarily but also for the individual casualties, many of whom were unnecessarily turned into lifelong pensioners (Glass, 1953; Hausman, 1967). I would subscribe to the five principles of parsimony recently enunciated by Dr. William Hollister at the annual meeting of the American Public Health Association in 1967. They are: (1) the least disruption is the first choice of treatment; (2) the least separation from family and job will be sought; (3) the least expensive treatment will be used first; (4) the least extensive interventions will be used first; and (5) the least trained intervenors will be used first.

"High quality treatment" applied at the wrong time or in the wrong place is not only useless, but can be severely damaging. Our choice is not alone between having a beneficial effect or having no effect, but between having a beneficial or a negative effect.

The psychiatric education of the family physician is a popular activity for which extensive financial support is available. Our experience (Huessy, 1963) in working with family doctors convinces us that individual direct contact and freely available consultation via telephone is a better way to invest one's energies than in seminars and lectures. The physicians' recollections of the classroom were not favorable and when special lectures were offered they declined. Many of the doctors who can be reached with an individualized and personal program would never participate in a formal educational program.

In community mental health work, we hopefully utilize all sorts of local resources. If the psychiatrist believes that the therapeutic use of such resources is a second- or third-rate method of treatment and that by far the best method would be direct treatment by him only, then he should not be in community work. To expect respect, cooperation, and hard work from other professionals, while making it clear that they are doing a second-rate job, is unrealistic. Since a good community program depends on the enthusiastic cooperation of many, its continued operation will depend in good part on the extent to which the psychiatrist believes and can convince his co-workers that they are doing a first-rate job. I happen to be convinced that professionals in other disciplines and nonprofessionals can do things I cannot do as well or even cannot do at all.

In working in a therapeutic community we came face to face with the limitations on professional human relationships imposed by an individual's training and professionalization (Huessy, 1966, 1969). In some ways it seems akin to bureaucratization. Routines, techniques, regulations all combine to keep distance between the professional and his client. It must be so, particularly in the helping professions, for no one could withstand the stress of being completely involved on a personal level with all of one's clients. The amateur, the volunteer, the part-time aid, the indigenous helper, all can contribute something the professional cannot provide. They can respond spontaneously without professional limitations. Mental health programs must find ways of combining the best of professional skills with these irreplaceable skills of the nonprofessional. Gerald Caplan, in a recent presentation (Caplan, 1968), describes his program in which widows help other widows through the crisis of bereavement. He emphasizes that it is essential not to profession-alize these workers. He feels training would decrease their effectiveness. The professional is needed to determine the needs, to find new avenues of possible prevention and intervention. The nonprofessional, however, constitutes one of the major resources available for meeting these needs. Many professionals feel threatened by the idea that an untrained person can do something he, the professional, is incapable of. This is unfortunate. Freud's most productive analytic ventures occurred when he was a nonprofessional as far as psychoanalysis is concerned. This melding of the professional discipline, technique, and theory with the spontaneity, warmth, and intense compassion of the nonprofessional is essential for the running of a good mental hospital or community program. It is our most promising frontier. Perhaps this is why the established psychiatrist experiences such excitement when he ventures into new fields in community psychiatry. Perhaps, also, the reason the community psychia-trist has some tendency to move on to even newer programs is that in this way he, too, has the opportunity to experience the enthusiasm, spon-taneity, and commitment of the nonprofessional, for in these new ventures he is a nonprofessional.

The psychiatrist in a community program is like the conductor of a symphony orchestra. He conducts people whose instruments he cannot play, but whose skills he respects and can evaluate critically. He is essential to the overall functioning, and there are a few jobs which only he can do, but there are many more jobs which can only be done by others. Warmth, compassion, and caring are the qualities essential for helping people. Professional training teaches us to keep these qualities under control, to keep our distance. We must learn to use nonprofessionals, who have no such restraints and inhibitions, to supplement our professional skills. Kiesler's rural mental health program in northern Minnesota is built completely around consultation and education. Dr. Kiesler and his staff offer no direct patient services outside the consultation model (Kiesler, 1968).

Hot arguments rage as to who must be the administrator of a mental health program. There are certain responsibilities only the psychiatrist can assume, but administration is not one of them. In any program, administrative duties should be carried out by whomever has the best talents for this very special task. Much practical mental health is known to other workers. The consultation process has been highly developed in other fields and in community organization we are late-comers.

Community mental health never deals in perfection. Regardless of the quantity of staff or money, there are certain givens in any situation. The capacity to adapt to these, to accentuate the positives and find ways around the negatives, is the trademark of the successful community mental health worker. One of these givens is the personality characteristics of the staff. Rather than planning a program and then trying to hire the staff to carry it out, it is wiser to build the program around the special assets of the various staff members available. This is especially true in rural areas, where the number of representatives of any particular discipline will obviously be small. Another given is the stage of development of the other social agencies in the area. The mental health worker must adapt to them, not the other way around (this is not, however, meant to imply that the mental health worker does not help other agencies upgrade). In the consultation program, the style of consultation must fit the consultee rather than the predilections of the consultant (Huessy, 1966).

If a community mental health program achieves one of its goals, namely, to alter another agency's attitudes toward mental health problems, it must be prepared to alter its program to fit the new reality. Many exciting programs have died because they froze into a pattern which became useless when some original purposes had been achieved. Here again, the specifying of program goals is most helpful.

A recent article (Crawshaw, 1967) pokes fun at the political activities a clinical mental health worker becomes involved in. If we believe in social change, and social change requires leadership, then who is better qualified to offer this leadership? Major public health advances of the past were brought about through the leadership of devoted public health professionals. Admittedly, mental health professionals in the past and present have clamored for some very questionable programs but this does not excuse us from promoting what we believe in. We should only remain sufficiently humble to remember that our expertise is limited to matters of mental health (Cruikshank, 1968). In rural areas, the mental health worker may be the first to formulate a local need and his agency may play a major role in bringing this need to the community's awareness. To improve its own functioning, the agency may be actively involved in developing a new program, and hand it over to another agency once the service is organized.

Unfortunately, many exciting programs are built around one individual, and when he leaves, the whole program collapses. Such an event does not invalidate the program—it only highlights the fact that not all mental health professionals are trained to work in this type of program and that not all are temperamentally suited for this type of work. Enthusiasm and leadership are essential ingredients for any successful public program. These qualities are personal rather than professional.

Finally, a few words about the concept of complementary programming. "Whenever meeting the needs of the ill can be combined with meeting the needs of the well, you have a more lively and creative service than when you are only meeting the needs of the ill" (Huessy, 1966). College students have a need for meaningful and purposeful participation in their communities; children in these communities need older companions (Mitchell, 1966). Translated into a program, one can use student volunteers as companions to children in need of relationship supplementation. Young Americans need opportunities for constructive risk taking and meaningful service—other social groups need enthusiastic helpers. Translated into programs, we have the Peace Corps and Vista. Any program which genuinely meets the needs of both the giver and the receiver will be more stable over time and will maintain its essential qualities more easily, particularly the personal involvement and enthusiasm of the participants. Foster grandparents,

volunteer work in hospitals, the tutorial program for deprived children—all share this common factor of complementary planning, the needs of two divergent groups being met by service to each other. Our era has tended to meet identified needs through hired professionals alone. Professionals move on, or their interests change. Such qualities as involvement, caring, and commitment are not for hire. Complementary programming offers one way of making these qualities available to the clients of a mental health program.

References

Beckenstein, N. The new state hospital. In L. Bellak (ed.), *Handbook of community psychiatry*. New York: Grune & Stratton, 1964.

Buell, B., Beisser, P. T., & Wedemeyer, J. M. Reorganizing to prevent and control disordered behavior. *Mental Hygiene*, 1958, 42, 155–194.

Cameron, E. Child guidance services in semi-rural and neglected areas. *American Journal of Orthopsychiatry*, 1948, 18, 536–540.

Caplan, G. Widows for widows. A presentation at the Inter-University Forum, University of Vermont, May 1968.

Caplan, R. (in collab. with G. Caplan) *Environment & mental disorder: A history of psychiatric concepts and methods in nineteenth century America*. New York: Basic Books, 1969.

Coleman, J. V., & Switzer, R. E. Dynamic factors in pscho-social treatment and traveling child guidance clinics. *Mental Hygiene*, 1951, 35, 386–409.

Crawshaw, R. Political psychiatry, Part II: Tactics. *Medical Opinion and Review*, 1967, 3(5), 40–51.

Cruikshank, N. H. How to win friends and influence legislators. *American Journal of Orthopsychiatry*, 1968, 38, 67–75.

Daniels, D. N. The community mental health center in the rural area: Is the present model appropriate? *American Journal of Psychiatry*, 1967, 124(4), 32–37. (Supple.)

Ebaugh, F. G., & Lloyd, R. The role of a mobile clinic in the educational program of a state psychopathic hospital. *Mental Hygiene*, 1927, 2, 346–356.

Eisdorfer, C., Altrocchi, J., & Young, R. F. Principles of community mental health in a rural setting: The Halifax County Program. *Community Mental Health Journal*, 1968, 4, 211–220.

Eisenberg, L. Possibilities for a preventive psychiatry. *Pediatrics*, 1962, 30, No. 5.

Garcia, L. B. The Clarinda Plan: An ecological approach to hospital organization. *Mental Hospital*, 1960, 11, 30.

Glass, A. J. Psychiatry in the Korean campaign: Historical review. *United States Armed Forces Medical Journal*, 1953, 4, 1563.

Halleck, S. L. Community psychiatry: Some troubling questions. In L. M. Roberts, S. L. Halleck, & M. B. Loeb (eds.), *Community psychiatry.* Madison: University of Wisconsin Press, 1966.

Hamann, W. A. Mental health in the Northeast Kingdom. *SK&F Psychiatric Reporter*, 1968, 41, 21.

Hausman, W., & Riock, D. Military psychiatry—A prototype of social and preventive psychiatry in the United States. *Archives of General Psychiatry*, 1967, 16, 727—739.

Hopple, L. M., & Huessy, H. R. Traveling community mental health clinics: Their extratherapeutic aspects and functions. *Mental Hygiene,* 1954, 38, No. 1.

Hubbard, O. Alaska's flying mental health clinic. *Mental Hospital*, 1956, 7, 7.

Huessy, H. R. Increased use of the family physician in the aftercare of state hospital patients. *American Journal of Public Health*, 1963, 53, 603—608.

Huessy, H. R. Yankee ingenuity in low-cost programs. In H. R. Huessy (ed.), *Mental health with limited resources.* New York: Grune & Stratton, 1966. (a)

Huessy, H. R. Spring Lake Ranch—The pioneer halfway house. In H. R. Huessy (ed.), *Mental health with limited resources.* New York: Grune & Stratton, 1966. (b)

Huessy, H. R. Exciting possibilities for secondary prevention. In H. R. Huessy (ed.), *Mental health with limited resources.* New York: Grune & Stratton, 1966. (c)

Huessy, H. R. Mental health consultation in varied settings. In H. R. Huessy (ed.), *Mental health with limited resources.* New York: Grune & Stratton, 1966. (d)

Huessy, H. R. Twellmann, W. *Leseschwache Schüler*, August Bagel Verlag Dusseldorf, 1967. (a)

Huessy, H. R. Study of the prevalence and therapy of the Choreatiform syndrome or hyperkinesis in rural Vermont. *Acta Paedopsychiatrica*, 1967, 34, 130—135. (b)

Huessy, H. R. Beyond the halfway house. *Journal of Hospital and Community Psychiatry*, 1969, 20, 147—149. (a)

Huessy, H. R. Satellite half-way houses in Vermont. *Journal of Hospital and Community Psychiatry*, 1969, 20, 147. (b)

Huessy, H. R., Marshall, C. D., Lincoln, E., & Finan, J. L. The indigenous nurse as crisis counselor and intervener. *American Journal of Public Health*, 1969, 59(11), 2022.

Hurd, H. M. (ed.) *The institutional care of the insane in the United States and Canada.* Baltimore: Johns Hopkins University Press, 1916. (As quoted from the *Journal of Insanity*, 1894.)

Kern, H. M., Jr., Jacobson, W. E., & Hess, J. B. The inductive method—A report of four years' experience in continuing education. Paper presented at the 123rd annual meeting of the American Psychiatric Association, 1967.

Kiesler, F. Building an event-reporting system. In *Community mental health.* San Francisco: Jossey-Bass, 1968.

Kraft, A. M., Binner, P. R., & Dickey, B. A. The community mental health program and the longer-stay patient. *Archives of General Psychiatry*, 1967, 16, 64.

Leighton, D. C., Leighton, A. H., & Armstrong, R. A. Community psychiatry in a rural area: A social psychiatric approach. In *Handbook of community psychiatry and community mental health.* New York: Grune & Stratton, 1964.

Maddux, J. F. Psychiatric consultation in a rural setting. *American Journal of Orthopsychiatry*, 1953, 23, 775—784.

Mitchell, W. E. Amicatherapy: Theoretical perspectives and an example of practice. *Community Mental Health Journal*, 1966, 2, 307—314.

Ødegaard, Ø. The incidence of psychosis in various occupations. *International Journal of Social Psychiatry*, 1956, 113, 302—311.

Page, M. Rehabilitating the multi-problem family. In H. R. Huessy (ed.), *Mental health with limited resources.* New York: Grune & Stratton, 1966.

Prechtl, H. F. R. The long term value of the neurological examination of the newborn infant. *Child Neurology and Cerebral Palsy, Little Club Clinics in Development Medicine (Oxford)*, 1960, No. 2, 69—74.

Rabinovitch, R. D. Reading and learning disabilities. In, *American handbook of psychiatry.* Vol. 1. New York: Basic Books, 1959.

Rademacher, E. S. Clinical psychiatric service on a part-time basis, its advantages and disadvantages. *Mental Hygiene*, 1931, 15, 81—86.

Rands, S. Community psychiatric services in a rural area. *Canadian Journal of Public Health*, 1960, 1, 404—411.

Redl, F. Crisis in the children's field. *American Journal of Orthopsychiatry.* 1962, 32, 759—780.

Rees, W., Dewi, M. B., & Lutkins, S. G. Mortality of bereavement. *British Medical Journal*, 1967, 4, 13—16.

Rogers, M. E., Lilienfeld, A., & Pasamanick, B. Prenatal and paranatal factors in the development of childhood behavior disorders. *Acta Psychiatric* (Kbh.), 1955, Supple. 80, 99—102.

Roy, C. Paper read at the World Mental Health Assembly, Washington, D. C., November 1969.

Sloman, S. S. Problems of giving child guidance in neglected areas. *American Journal of Orthopsychiatry*, 1948, 18, 541—542.

Stubblefield, R., & Herrold, D. Personal conversations and participation.

Thaler, M. The role of a psychologist in a traveling psychiatric clinic. *Mental Hygiene*, 1950, 34, 219—227.

Townsend, M. Barre Parents Club—Consultation service. In H. R. Huessy (ed.), *Mental health with limited resources.* New York: Grune & Stratton, 1966.

Tyhurst, J. S. Research on reaction to catastrophe. In I. Gladston (ed.), *Panic and morale.* New York: International Universities Press, 1958.

Vargish, F. A community after-care project. In H. R. Huessy (ed.), *Mental health with limited resources.* New York: Grune & Stratton, 1966.

Wedel, H. L. Characteristics of community mental health center operations in small communities. *Community Mental Health Journal*, 1969, 5, 437—444.

Weiss, P., Macaulay, J. R., & Pincus, A. Geographic location and state hospital utilization. *American Journal of Psychiatry*, 1967, 124, 637—641.

Zubin, J. (ed.) *Field studies in the mental disorders.* New York: Grune & Stratton, 1961.

31

Woodlawn Mental Health Center: An Evolving Strategy for Planning in Community Mental Health

Sheppard G. Kellam, Jeannette D. Branch, Khazan C. Agrawal, and Margaret E. Grabill

In the United States, the design and implementation of mental health services have historically limited access to service to two specific groups of people. The first, severely disturbed individuals, have received help mostly through the state hospital system, one of the oldest socialized medical programs in this country. The greater percentage of these individuals have been poor, partly because the limited financial resources of the poor precluded other alternatives. The second group has included mainly those people able to afford private, individual out-patient care—the upper middle and upper class sectors of society (Davidson, 1967; Hollingshead & Redlich, 1958).

This state of affairs has left a population vastly larger than either of the aforementioned to suffer a dearth of mental health services. As the plight of these people has worsened, particularly in our urban centers, both the American public and mental health professionals have begun to exert pressure for innovations in mental health practice. Since the early 1950s and on through the 1960s there has been a groundswell of public support to do something about this prevailing gap.

In response to growing public awareness, mental health professionals are struggling with the challenge to develop a wider diversity of services which emphasize the importance of the social system to the individual's sense of identity and self-esteem. In some instances this has led to community-based programs located in or near the social contexts in which people's troubles occur. In the process of determining priorities and gaining ongoing sanction for programs, some mental health professionals have also assumed more

intiative in developing links with local community citizens.

In our view, intervention should be intimately related to the processes which occur in social contexts in the community. Thus, the targets of intervention are not restricted to individuals or families as in the case of the clinic setting. On the contrary, any aspect of the social field processes related to the individual's sense of well-being can be subject to intervention. In school the classroom is a major social field and the teacher, the peer group, the family, the administration of the school, or even the curriculum can receive the attention of the intervention process.

Such a social system view of intervention requires, however, more than mental health skills. Other health, education, and welfare workers, who are under increasing duress because of the general failure to meet human needs, may also ascribe to such a view. Indeed our own experience, based on systematic studies and clinical impressions, raises the question as to whether our focus ought to be on mental health as a speciality or on an integrated human service system that seeks to approach mental health through institutional processes which are more consciously and purposefully concerned with the breadth of human need.

This chapter will examine this and other issues that have come to our attention during our years of work in a mental health program that was begun in 1963 in Woodlawn, an urban Negro neighborhood on the south side of Chicago. The 1960 United States Census Bureau figures, gathered four years prior to the start of the Woodlawn program, set the population of this

711

community at 81,000. Our base has been the Woodlawn Mental Health Center, a facility of the City of Chicago Board of Health. Additional funds have been granted by the State of Illinois Department of Mental Health, with research and training functions being supported also by the University of Chicago Department of Psychiatry.

This discussion of the Center's program development reflects our thinking during the years when the notion of independent community-based mental health services was still to us a viable idea. What was then the most avant-garde conception of mental health has evolved with startling speed. Many mental health professionals, including ourselves, have moved over the last several years from the concept of mental health centers to comprehensive health centers and from there to serious consideration of the neighborhood human service system (Daniels, 1969).

THE CONTRACT WITH THE COMMUNITY

In 1963 the staff began its work in Woodlawn with the strong belief that community mental health needed new strategies operating from new institutional bases that would provide avenues for reaching people in need, and facilitate effective contribution by the community. One of the major problems facing health, education, and welfare professionals is the development of ways of relating more closely with the communities they serve. Agencies need to move closer to the social contexts in the neighborhood. To do this the neighborhood and the agency must negotiate a contract in which the citizens exercise their role by sanctioning agency involvement in the neighborhood, by collaborating with the agency in priority setting, and in planning and participating in the carrying out of services.

The Neighborhood Agency Council Model

Several models for local community participation have been developed over the years. One of the oldest is the neighborhood agency council. The idea was to bring together the variety of agency professionals in a community to establish common goals, collaborative procedures, and coordinated services. Occasionally one or two citizens from the neighborhood were invited to join the council and provide some representation for the consumers of

the services offered by the professionals. In smaller rural communities where agency professionals live in and identify with their community, this model may be more effective; in the urban community, however, the inclusion of a few citizens in the agency organizational structure generally produced negligible results. The citizens most often felt excluded from the basic agency organizational structure and had no structure of their own within which to operate. A very basic lack of this model was the absence of any real definition of the powers of the consumer in policy-making.

The Retail Store Model

Another attempt to bring agency and community closer together is the retail store model. In recent years some programs have been located in store-front facilities on the main streets of the neighborhood they serve, presumably to bring services within easy, convenient reach of the citizens. Nonprofessional community people may serve as counselors, group therapists, or in other roles designed to involve the community in the program. This model offers no formal or informal contract between the community and the agency. Such a strategy suggests that the mental health needs of the community may be defined by determining the categories of need in which the most demands for help occur. When programs are planned on this basis, the community is left little opportunity to participate directly in the process. If the citizens do not like the selection of services offered or feel a need in an area where no services are provided, the likely alternatives are (1) not to use the services or (2) to protest through demonstration or picketing. In the 1970s, with the unrest growing out of the concern over citizen participation in agency policy-making, the lack of a structure for ongoing negotiations with the community makes it quite improbable that professionals could gain access to the main social fields of the community for programs of prevention.

The Volunteer Board

Agencies which utilize the volunteer board model must rely on advertising in the neighborhood that any citizens interested in taking part in planning of services should come to community meetings held by the agency. Often no criteria of membership are defined and no serious investigation is made to determine whether the various citizen groups in the community are represented. Such boards are often constructed by agency professionals who generally have not been successful in attempts to find and engage with community leadership. The citizens who attend may or may not have the right to speak for others in the community, and large groups within the neighborhood may vigorously contest the validity of such a board.

The Elected Community Board

From time to time citizen boards have been elected by majority vote. This method has great appeal to middle class professionals who often feel the election is an essential characteristic of the democratic process. In large urban areas where there is a strong political machine, such a method may give tremendous advantage to machine candidates, thus eliminating the neighborhood independent leadership. The experience with this kind of board in Philadelphia and elsewhere suggests also that only small percentages of citizens actually vote in such elections (Clark & Hopkins, 1968).

A Community Board Composed of Citizen Organization Leaders

The board composed of community organization leaders, while not free of problems, is the model we have found useful in supporting our efforts in community mental health programming in Woodlawn. This model recognizes the already existing leadership of community organizations. Each community organization delegates a community representative who is empowered to represent that organization's view on the board. In our view this method is most likely to afford representation of the broadest range of community aspirations and opinions.

The Community Board in Woodlawn

The evolution of the Woodlawn Mental Health Center board began in 1963 after a commitment of support had been obtained from the City of Chicago, the State of Illinois Department of Mental Health, and the University of Illinois Department of Psychiatry. The three psychiatrists[1] who would become the Center's co-direc-

tors approached Woodlawn's community leaders to discuss the possibility of coming to Woodlawn to establish, with the community, a community mental health center. We made it clear from the beginning that we would not come to Woodlawn unless they, as the community's established leadership, offered their support.

Considerable discussion ensued. Very specific questions of trust were raised by the leadership, especially the question of why three white doctors wanted to become involved with the Woodlawn community. After a good many reservations had been voiced about the placing of a community mental health center in their neighborhood, these citizen leaders finally agreed to provide the support we needed to begin our work.

A watchdog committee was appointed by The Woodlawn Organization, an especially strong, influential confederation of smaller political and social groups in the community. We welcomed the watchdog committee since it gave us our first structure through which we could engage with the community. In the many conversations we had with members of the committee and other community organization leaders, we were able to emphasize our belief that we needed community support for any programming we might undertake, and that as professionals our first commitment was one of service to the community.

The watchdog committee compiled a list of Woodlawn's community organizations, and representatives from these organizations joined together to form an advisory board. The major problem confronting the new board was defining its powers. This issue revolved around the board's role in choosing program priorities in dialog with the Center staff; the board's collaboration in planning programs; the board's communication of the community's concerns to the staff; and the role of the board in providing community sanction for programs (Kellam & Schiff, 1968).

Choosing the first program that the Center would develop was tremendously important in defining the role of the board on one hand and that of the staff on the other. While the staff was a source of technical information, both the board and the staff realized that the ordering of program priorities is largely an issue to be decided by the community. Whether a program for children is more or less important than one for acutely disturbed adults is a decision most rightfully made by the community citizens—even though the technical information offered by the staff and the availability of resources must be taken into account. Social values, then, become a primary determinant in this kind of decision-making process, and when a service facility is supported by a board comprised of various community organization leaders, the advantage is clear. Board members can return to their own organizations for open discussion of not only priorities but proposed program plans. Thus, any necessary modification and, in fact, a kind of formalized community approval can take place before programs actually begin.

After lengthy discussion with the staff and the community, the Woodlawn Mental Health Center board finally made the decision to develop a program of prevention and early treatment for the community's first-grade children. Board members continued to attend various community organization meetings and meetings of parents and teachers to explain the program, answer questions, and enlist full support for the program. In many cases, board members were vigorous, effective troubleshooters when issues arose in the schools or in the community that threatened the program's survival. There is little doubt that their continuing efforts were fundamental to the introduction and ongoing operation of the program in Woodlawn's 12 elementary schools.

The community board has been the stable foundation on which programs have been built at the Woodlawn Mental Health Center. There has been a distinct evolution of the board's relationship to the staff, to the organizations from which the board members originally came as representatives, and the community at large. Though the board began as an informal advisory board, over time a constitution and by-laws were developed, board leadership was assumed by an elected chairman, and board members became increasingly involved in the intimate workings of the Center itself.

The problems that remain for the board to consider and resolve have to do with the degree of strictness with which staff and board should be separate and have separate roles; how to maintain a board membership which truly reflects the diversity of community populations to be served; and the degree of involvement the board should have in the internal functioning of the Center. These problems are no less critical now that we are beginning to be concerned with planning new comprehensive neighborhood human service systems than when we considered community mental health the function of an independent agency.

Once the community board is established, the next step is to define a strategy for community-wide mental health programming. The strategy that was implemented in Woodlawn may be simply depicted as consisting of the following steps:

(1) selection of total subpopulations in the community for which programming is to be planned after sufficient community involvement has occurred;

(2) selection and development of methods for conducting periodic community-wide assessment of the mental health needs of the specific subpopulations for which programs are to be designed;

(3) following the initial assessment of needs, development of intervention programs which range from direct services in strategically selected sites in the community to programs aimed at strategic aspects of the social system;

(4) reassessment of mental health needs following programming, with adequate care to provide the control populations necessary for systematic, specific measures of impact; and

(5) redevelopment of programs in the light of clinical experience and measured impact.

In the long run, such measures of need and impact may present opportunities for combined programming across professional disciplines, with a number of different professional agencies using the same measures for planning and evaluation.

As we briefly describe the experience with this strategy as it was applied to the Woodlawn School Mental Health Program of Prevention and Early Treatment, it should be remembered that although this program was based on measures of mental health need and was essentially a mental health program carried out in collaboration with the schools, it did not achieve the degree of agency synthesis we have suggested as optimum. This appears to be part of the work which now confronts us.

ASSESSING MENTAL HEALTH NEED

Our strategy required that community mental health programming deal with specific definable subpopulations of a total community whose boundaries are clearly delineated. Woodlawn's boundaries have been precise and stable for a number of years so this criterion was easily met. Our collaboration with the board on the issue of setting priorities had early produced a commitment to develop community-wide mental health services for young children. First graders are the youngest total subpopulation accessible in the community, i.e., the youngest age other than birth at which names and addresses are known. In addition, first grade marks a point of major transition in a child's life course—his first legal step out of the family on his own. Thus the strategic social field in which to develop community-wide programs for first graders appeared to be the school—specifically the first-grade classroom.

What Is Mental Health?

In several ways, criteria for mental health are more important to the program developer working in the community than for the professional working in the traditional clinic. In the latter case, it is the patient who finds his way to the clinic, and this in itself is a primary selection criterion, however inadequate. As a result, this kind of clinic is concerned primarily with the people who come for help rather than the entire population in need in the community. The program developer in the community, however, must be concerned with the total population; therefore he must define selection criteria more specifically than the traditional self-selection method allows.

The Woodlawn first-grade program required a specific, operative definition of mental health which would permit us to make qualitative and quantitative measures of mental health. The aim to develop a community-wide prevention program added a still more complex issue to this already knotty problem since the preconditions—whether in the system, the child, or both—of later emotional difficulties need also to be identified.

Even though in recent years traditional clinics have tended to include a few family members or significant others in their consideration of a patient's problems, community programs must be based on the characteristics of the social system as well as important characteristics of the individual person. In fact, help may be most strategically directed at the social system, or particular aspects of it, in addition to or instead of the person in need.

Generally, mental health clinicians and investigators seeking definitions of mental health or mental disorder have approached the task using one or both of two basic views as sources: first, that of social adaptation, social mastery, or the adequate functioning of an individual in a social role; and second, the sense of well-being, self-esteem, or self-confidence of the individual. Upon superficial examination, these two views may seem contradictory. If an individual is socially well-adapted, can we assume he is experiencing a sense of well-being? Indeed is adequate social performance even compatible with a sense of well-being when social performance requires a degree of conformity and restraint?

If we consider the nature of these two dimensions of mental health, the social adaptive view implies that mental health involves a degree of acceptance by society of one's behavior, i.e., adequate performance in some sense equals good mental health. The second view, a sense of personal well-being, suggests quite a different source of definition, namely the individual himself. The societal view has a legal and social power which cannot be denied and certainly represents an important contribution to the definition of mental health. The individual view, on the other hand, must be considered equally important. Empirical studies of the relationship between these two dimensions are vital to the general problem of defining mental health. This need has been cited in an article by Blum in which he states the value of such research and carefully analyzes the problem of defining criteria of mental health and illness (1962). On the basis of this discussion it could be argued that such research is fundamental to the development of community-wide programs of prevention and early treatment, and we will discuss several such studies later in this chapter.

When intervention is a goal of program planning as it was in Woodlawn, the social adaptive view is no more likely to lead to effective programming than the individual patient-oriented view; alone, neither facilitates systematic intervention. In combination, however, these two major areas of criteria should allow intervention to be conceived of as directed primarily at the *social system*—a view which allows us to consider the individual, as well as his total social and interpersonal network, as potential areas in which help might be given.

In approaching the assessment of the social adaptational status of first graders or any other subpopulation in the community, several background concepts are helpful. All the individuals in a community are passing through various stages of life. Each stage of life is intimately related to three or four basic social fields such as the family, the classroom, the peer group, and so on. In each social field a natural rating process is carried out by the *natural raters*. The parents in the family, the teacher in the classroom, the foreman on the job, and one's social peers are all examples of natural raters.

In a sense, natural raters function to transmit to the individual, through a variety of social institutions, certain goals of the social system. As part of this process, the natural raters in a social field define the tasks each individual must perform in pursuit of system goals. In addition, the natural raters judge each individual's performance of these tasks, either formally or informally. One's teacher and one's foreman make formal judgments. The judgment of peers or parents is usually informal but nevertheless quite important. These judgments represent the social system's view of the social adaptational status of the individual.

In accord with these background concepts, we proceeded to examine the natural rating process that goes on in the first-grade classroom. We first determined the tasks required of the children in the social system of the classroom. We then developed procedures to obtain systematic ratings of how well each child was performing in the role of student in the judgment of the natural raters (Kellam & Schiff, 1967).

ASSESSING THE CHILD'S
ADAPTATIONAL STATUS

The first-grade teachers in Woodlawn's 12 elementary schools (nine public and three parochial) were contacted through the District Superintendent, the archdiocese office, and each of 12 principals. The teachers were asked what major tasks first-grade children face when they enter the new social field of the classroom. On the basis of the teacher responses, we were able to construct five scales representing the major social tasks required of the child by the system. A sixth scale was added relating to the overall adaptation of each child to first grade. These six scales were:

(1) Social contact, (2) authority acceptance, (3) maturation, (4) cognitive achievement, (5) concentration, and (6) global adaptation.

The scales were constructed so that they could be used to assess various aspects of each child's social adaptation to the role of student. Students were to be rated by their teachers on a four-point scale with zero being the only adapting rating and one through three representing mild to severe maladaptation. Assessment was planned to take place in standardized interviews with the child's teacher several times in first grade and periodically thereafter. This procedure was called Teacher's Observation of Classroom Adaptation (TOCA). In the context of the life course-social field concept, the teacher is the natural rater of the child in the classroom and thus provides the system's view of his social adaptational status as a student. As our educational system is constructed, the child must succeed in the view of his teacher if he is to achieve a good school record. She is the legally appointed judge of her students despite the fact that she may be sensitive or insensitive, fair or unfair in her assessment.

In the fall of 1964, soon after the development of the assessment instrument, the first ratings were made of all the first-grade children in Woodlawn. The teacher interview, conducted by a member of the Center staff, was characterized by an open-ended, yet structured format. Initial conversation was devoted to any concerns the teacher might have about the program, her students, her school, or whatever. Then the interviewer recorded the teacher's ratings of each child in her class.[2]

Validation procedures were carried out to see if these numbers we called ratings meant anything. A series of comparisons were made of various a priori characteristics of the child. For example, children who had had kindergarten were compared to children who had not had kindergarten; girls were compared to boys; children who had changed schools within Woodlawn between kindergarten and first grade were compared to those who had not; and children who were repeating first grade were compared to those who had attended kindergarten the previous year.

The comparisons indicated that our ratings were valid gross measures of social adaptation. Children who had not had kindergarten appeared to their teachers to be more shy and more globally maladapted. Boys were more maladapted than girls on all scales except social contact. Children who had changed schools between kindergarten and first grade were rated more maladapting on all scales except social contact.

Of most interest is the proportion of children who each year were having difficulty in one or another of the social adaptation categories. Table 31–1 contains the results, for control schools only early in first grade of these assessments over the course of four years for each scale. (In order to provide a group against which to evaluate the intervention program, six of the 12 Woodlawn schools were designated as control schools. See discussion on page 722). Consistency in the prevalence rates of each adaptational scale from year to year is indicated by the narrow ranges across the four years. The number of children having trouble was a strong factor in the design of the intervention program.

Over the four year period covered by Table 31–1, about two thirds of Woodlawn children were assessed as having mild, moderate, or severe problems in their early efforts to accomplish one or another of these tasks. When we assessed these children's social adaptational status again in third grade, we found that early mastery in school was significantly associated with the child's future adaptation. These data were useful as we sought to investigate the children's sense of well-being, a major criterion of the concept of mental health we are considering.

Assessing the Child's Sense of Well-Being

We devised several procedures with which to assess each child's sense of well-being. One procedure involved the direct observation by clinicians of the children in a standardized play setting; in another the mother's observations were used to derive a measure of the child's psychiatric symptom status; in a third, the child was asked to rate himself on two aspects of his sense of well-being, sadness, and nervousness. Each of these methods was kept independent from the others so that we could study their interrelationships.

While we refer to these methods as ways of measuring symptoms, they do not fully warrant such an assumption. We use the term symptom provisionally until sufficient empirical research has been done to establish whether what we measure should indeed be called symptoms. In addition to

that caveat, no one of the methods should be thought of as an adequate clinical screening method of psychiatrically disturbed children. They are considered separately here for purposes of study.

In the direct clinical observation (DCO), teams of clinicians made symptom ratings based on traditional categories of psychiatric symptomatology. They observed a 50 percent random sample of Woodlawn first graders in which there were equal numbers of boys and girls. As shown in Table 31–2, children rated symptomatic by clinicians using the DCO procedure numbered far fewer than those who were rated as socially maladapting by their teachers (refer to Table 31–1). The frequency rates are fairly consistent across the two populations that were studied, the 1964–65 and the 1966–67 first graders. Five different community-wide assessments were made, one early in first grade for both populations, one at the end of first grade for both populations, and one at the end of third grade for the 1964–65 population.

Although the results were consistent from one population to the next when the same procedure was employed, the percentage of symptomatic children varied widely from procedure to procedure. The results of the mother's symptom inventory (MSI) illustrates this point. The inventory consisted of 38 behaviors often considered symptoms by clinicians (Lapouse & Monk, 1958). It was administered to two large populations of mothers of first-grade children. The sampling procedure for these two interviews is described on page 723.

In Table 31–3, the behaviors are arranged under 13 general category headings. The behaviors were suggested by the work of Conners who originally validated most of them for Negro children of the same age living in a neighborhood similar to Woodlawn (1967 and 1970). Table 31–3 indicates the percentage of children rated by their mothers as "not at all" exhibiting these behaviors and the percentage rated as exhibiting these behaviors "pretty much" or "very much."

The frequency rates are again remarkably consistent from the 1964–65 population to the 1966–67 population. However, the percentage of children who were rated as exhibiting each behavior ranges broadly, although generally the

TABLE 31–1

Teachers' Observations of Classroom Adaptation Made
Early in First Grade–Control Children Only

Percentage Ranges Across Four Years*

Scales of Adaptation (ranked by percent adapting)**	0 = Adapting within minimal limits	1 = Mildly maladapting	2+3 = Moderately or severely maladapting
Authority Acceptance	71.4–75.3	10.7–14.1	10.6–18.0
Social Contact	68.3–73.7	14.6–18.0	8.3–15.8
Concentration	57.6–64.0	16.7–22.0	14.0–25.6
Maturation	56.8–63.0	18.3–21.6	15.7–24.9
Cognitive Achievement	52.0–58.1	20.9–28.5	15.0–22.6
Global Adaptation	31.1–38.8	36.5–42.8	21.3–32.3

*Populations for these studies include all of the children in the six Woodlawn control schools early in first grade in 1964 (N=944), in 1965 (N=863), in 1966 (N=737), and in 1967 (N=732). The total number of children enrolled in first grade decreased each year in intervention schools as well as in control schools.

**The rank order of these scales for percent adapting was the same in each of the four years.

frequencies are much higher than those obtained using the DCO procedure.

In a third procedure, psychiatric symptoms were assessed on the basis of self-ratings by third-grade children who were administered an instrument called the "How I Feel." The study population consisted of groups of 20 children chosen randomly from the total class population of each of 44 third-grade classrooms in Woodlawn. The total was 752 children. Table 31–4 shows the percentage of children who indicated that they felt nervous or sad, and again we observe the distinctiveness of these frequency rates from those of the other procedures. One must remember, however, that "How I Feel" was administered to third graders, not first graders.

As we commented earlier, it is also important to remember the conceptual problem involved in

TABLE 31–2

Percentage of Children Rated Symptomatic by *Direct Clinical Observation*

Symptoms	Early in First Grade		End of First Grade		Third Grade
	1964–65 N=1000	1966–67 N=1080	1964–65 N=1000	1966–67 N=1120	1964–65 N=1350
Flatness of Affect	1.0	1.1	0.4	0.9	1.3
Depression	1.5	0.6	1.2	0.8	0.4
Anxiety	2.8	2.4	3.4	1.8	0.8
Hyperkinesis	1.7	0.7	1.3	1.5	0.9
Bizarre Behavior	2.9	1.3	2.4	1.8	1.0
Global	6.9	4.6	6.4	4.9	3.9

TABLE 31—3

The Frequency of Symptoms among First-grade Children as Reported by Mothers
1964—65* and 1966—67** Control School Children Only

Mother Symptom Inventory Items Grouped by Symptom Clusters	Percentage of Children Reported Having Symptoms "not at all"		Percentage of Children Reported Having Symptoms "pretty much" and "very much"	
	1964—65	1966—67	1964—65	1966—67
EATING PROBLEMS				
Picky and finicky about food	38.55	37.10	23.91	27.42
Underweight	73.41	69.17	5.27	5.88
Overweight	90.46	91.91	1.45	1.73
TROUBLE WITH FEELINGS				
Lets himself get pushed around by other children	47.30	51.43	16.22	15.89
Keeps anger to himself	66.85	72.48	7.12	6.84
CHILDISH OR IMMATURE				
Clings to parents or other adults	61.26	64.04	12.36	11.63
Sucks thumb	82.24	86.51	10.66	9.36
FEARS				
Afraid of being alone	61.04	60.44	10.90	12.52
Afraid of new situations	73.70	73.48	2.19	3.23
Afraid to go to school	94.59	92.47	1.08	1.80
Afraid of people	91.53	89.29	0.54	1.82
TOILET PROBLEMS				
Wets bed	85.40	84.89	8.54	8.82
Runs to bathroom constantly	76.78	80.96	6.29	4.80
Has had accidents with bowel movements in the past year	88.22	89.21	2.46	2.16
Wets self during the day	95.26	95.84	1.12	2.35
NERVOUS HABITS				
Picks at things such as hair, clothes, etc.	71.04	73.35	6.56	7.52
Bites or picks nails	76.58	78.46	6.06	6.82
Chews on clothing, etc.	84.47	84.74	3.54	4.66
SAD AND WORRIED				
Cries and sobs for unexplained reasons	76.22	79.75	7.57	5.02
Worries about illness and death	80.93	84.20	4.63	5.20
Looks sad	70.30	74.69	3.00	3.77

TABLE 31–3 (*Cont.*)

Mother Symptom Inventory Items Grouped by Symptom Clusters	Percentage of Children Reported Having Symptoms "not at all"		Percentage of Children Reported Having Symptoms "pretty much" and "very much"	
	1964–65	1966–67	1964–65	1966–67
COMPLAINS OF SYMPTOMS EVEN WHEN DOCTOR FINDS NOTHING WRONG				
Stomachaches	56.87	54.68	6.05	6.84
Headaches	69.21	66.43	4.90	4.46
Aches and pains	82.97	84.05	2.75	1.62
Loose bowels	87.36	87.34	1.92	1.24
Vomiting	84.25	82.94	1.66	1.08
SPEECH PROBLEMS				
Doesn't speak clearly other than stuttering	74.10	76.52	5.79	5.56
Stutters	85.05	88.63	2.45	2.52
SEX				
Plays with own sex organs	85.95	85.38	4.95	6.24
Involved in sex play with other children	92.33	93.06	2.19	1.95
MUSCULAR TENSION				
Twitches and jerks, etc.	83.78	89.39	4.59	1.62
Muscles get stiff and rigid	91.83	93.51	1.63	1.26
Body shakes	95.68	96.04	0.81	1.08
SLEEP PROBLEMS				
Restless or awakens at night	81.59	78.84	3.57	4.34
Has nightmares	83.20	78.32	2.44	2.55
BIZARRE BEHAVIOR				
Says wierd, odd, or strange things	79.61	80.60	3.58	3.03
Looks stony-faced	86.92	84.79	1.36	1.43
Has weird, odd, or strange movements or looks	89.86	89.84	0.54	1.07

*Children in control schools from early to end of year (N=370).

**Children in control schools from mid-year to end of year (N=562).

interpreting ratings of all these kinds of behaviors as psychiatric symptoms. Can a child who rates himself as sad be considered symptomatic on the basis of such a rating? Do such behaviors as being picky and finicky about food have the same meaning as, say, ratings of anxiety by a clinician? Obviously we are discussing a broad variety of behaviors, some of which have been related empirically to being a psychiatric patient while others have a tradition among clinicians of being considered symptoms. And, of course, one of the basic reasons for the problems in defining a symptom is that we are still struggling with the question of what psychopathology is. This last question requires that more empirical research be done into the interrelationships among such

TABLE 31–4

Frequency Distribution by Percentage of Self-ratings Made by
Third Grade Children on Two *How I Feel* Questions

How I Feel *Questions*	Almost not at all	A little	Pretty much	A lot	N*
I Feel Nervous	31.8	36.3	16.8	15.2	752
I Feel Sad	35.6	34.5	14.9	14.9	750

The population consisted of groups of 20 children comprised half of girls and half of boys who had been randomly selected from each of the third-grade classrooms in the 12 Woodlawn schools.

*The N's are different because two of the children did not respond to the "I feel sad" question.

symptom measures as are now available, including those involving more intensive psychiatric examination of individuals. It requires also that empirical research be done into the relationships between psychiatric symptoms—measured in a variety of ways—and the process of social adaptation.

In this regard our research appeared to be simpler when we were concerned with studying the 1964–65 first graders by the DCO procedure than it does now that we have had a chance to replicate these studies with the 1966–67 first graders. The results of concurrent studies carried out on the 1964–65 population of first graders indicated a significant relationship between being rated symptomatic by DCO and being rated as maladapting in the classroom on the social contact and global scales at the beginning of the year, and on the authority acceptance, concentration, and global scales at the end of the year.

If we look at this relationship longitudinally, children in the 1964–65 population who had difficulty mastering the social adaptational tasks of first grade early in the year were also more likely to be rated symptomatic at the end of the year than were children who began first grade adapting. However, in replicating these studies we have found this relationship to be more complex than we had imagined. The results of the early DCO-TOCA concurrent studies in 1966–67 were very similar to those of the 1964–65 study, in that children found to be symptomatic early in first grade were having difficulty in the areas of

social contact and maturation. On the other hand, in the end-of-year study, the concurrent relationship disappeared. We found no relationship between being assessed as symptomatic by a clinician and being assessed as maladapting by a teacher at that time—and just as unfortunately, no clear explanation as to why the relationship disappeared. The mother symptom inventory and the "How I Feel," however, do reveal significant relationships between social maladaptation and being symptomatic. We are still analyzing these data in hopes of further clarifying this relationship.

Even though the relationship between symptoms and social adaptation appears to be a very complex one, where it occurs—at least with the procedures we have used and the populations we have studied—this relationship is almost always in one direction. Symptoms are associated with social maladaptation, not social adaptation. We can say, then, that thus far there appears to be a relationship between psychiatric symptoms and the failure to adapt socially, though this relationship still needs to be clarified by using other methods of assessing symptoms, other study populations at other stages of life, and by study of other communities.

The Results of Assessment as a Basis for Planning Intervention

Early results indicated that large numbers of first-grade children were maladapting, and that these children were more likely to be symptomatic than were adapting children. The population of maladapting children thus appeared to be a strategic population for intervention.

Accordingly, Woodlawn's 12 elementary schools were divided into two matched groups on the basis of the prevalence of maladaptation among the first-grade children in each school and other criteria such as the financial resources of the families and the size of the enrollment in each school. By flipping a coin, one of these matched groups was designated control schools and the other intervention schools. While systematic, periodic assessment was to be carried out in all 12 schools, only the six intervention schools were to receive the intervention program in first grade. This plan would enable us to compare various assessments of children in the intervention program with those of children in the nonprogram control schools.

Evaluating a Program of Prevention and Early Treatment

The intervention program was the result of the decision by the Center's board to ask the staff to program for first graders. Program design was based on the life course-social field concept described earlier and the results of early assessment. The first-grade classrooms were chosen as strategic social contexts in which to intervene. The goals of intervention were seen to be the strengthening of the child, classroom, school, and family characteristics which might impinge on the child's adaptational status and his sense of well-being. In addition, the program was explicitly designed to involve in the intervention process not only the child and his family but the teacher and the school as a social system as well. The program was directed by Sheldon K. Schiff, M.D., and the details of its operation are described elsewhere (Schiff & Kellam, 1967).

The essential element of the program was a series of weekly classroom meetings involving all of the children in first-grade classrooms in intervention schools, the teacher, and a mental health staff person. As we measured the program's impact over the years, the character of the meetings changed, moving from a small group of maladapting children meeting in the same classroom where the rest of the children carried on regular work at their seats, to a total class meeting that included both the adapting and maladapting

children. Later on, with additional measures of impact and study, the parents of the children were included also in these meetings.

The weekly class meetings focused on the child's sense of confidence in trying out and mastering the first-grade tasks expected of him. There was an effort to catalyze the development of the class's group identity in order to promote a sense of membership and accomplishment on the part of each student. Increasingly the teacher was able to run the classroom meetings and the active role of the mental health person diminished. This transfer of the leadership function from mental health person to teacher was encouraged since we had a fundamental interest in building the program into the institution of the school.

In addition to the weekly classroom meetings, there were also weekly staff meetings and, occasionally, parent meetings were held. Staff meetings were devoted to interstaff issues such as role definition, the degree to which the teachers could bank on the support of the administrative staff, and critical analysis of the clinical process that went on in classroom meetings. Difficult behavioral problems were discussed and planning for day-to-day modification of the program also occurred in staff meetings.

Since 1964 we have used the assessment of social adaptation to measure the baseline and outcome status of children in the intervention schools as compared to those in control schools. Psychiatric symptom assessments, achievement and intelligence test scores, and grades have also functioned as criteria of impact.

At the end of the first year of the program, teacher assessments revealed that children in intervention schools were less adapted and had become significantly worse than control school children. Later experiments and long-term follow-up showed this to be due most likely to a change in standards of the intervention school teachers. For the next three years, the teachers' assessments of the social adaptational status of children in the intervention schools showed improvement over the course of first grade when compared to those of control school teachers for their students.

In regard to the other measures of outcome, at this stage in the analysis of this data there does not appear to have been measurable short-term or long-term impact on psychiatric symptoms. In third-grade follow-up of those children still in

Woodlawn public schools, intervention appears to have some impact on grades, particularly in the area of language arts although we have not completed analysis of these results.[3] While achievement tests revealed a minimal impact in language, the most consistent impact appears to have been in intelligence test performance.[4]

Figures 31–1 and 31–2 compare changes in IQ scores between first and third grades for the 1964–65 and 1966–67 public school children when control and experimental groups are classified according to first-grade IQ. Results for the 1965–66 population are not shown but are included in the summary comments that follow.

There was a general tendency for IQ performance to decrease between first and third grade except for children who were low performers in first grade. Keeping this in mind, we can now examine the impact of intervention. In general, children who experienced intervention showed significant benefit in IQ performance. We find that intervention children who were high performers on first-grade IQ tests showed less drop in performance than did similar control school children. Intervention children who were low performers in first grade showed greater improvement in performance than did similar control school children. It is also worth noting that the form of the test administered in third grade appears to influence whether performance gets better or worse (see Figure 31–2).[5]

Program changes were made periodically on the basis of the assessment and our clinical impressions. This intimate relationship of assessment/program design/evaluation/redesign should be a basic principle of community mental health and, in our view, should be equally useful as we turn our focus to the development of a new neighborhood human services system.

While measurable impact appears to have been achieved it has been modest. It is evident that we must consider other factors and be open to other kinds of intervention in support of first-grade children going through a critical period in their school career. An important source of information in this regard are the families of the first graders.

Family Life and Adaptation to School

In 1965 and 1967, extensive interviews were conducted with the mothers or mother surrogates of first-grade children that enabled us to make community-wide studies of family life.[6] The 1965 interviews were conducted by one group of interviewers and the 1967 interviews by another. In 1965, 863 interviews were conducted, a 50 percent sample of the mothers of first graders. The 1965 sample was random except for the condition that the child had been rated by his teacher early and at the end of first grade. The sample thus represents first-grade children who were in any of the Woodlawn schools throughout the 1964–65 school year. About 15 percent of the total population moved out of Woodlawn, and these children were not part of our study population. In 1967 we attempted to contact the mothers of all the first-grade children; 1,392 interviews were completed out of the total of 1,691. The remaining children were not found by home visit.

By means of a detailed interview schedule, we investigated such factors as family constellation, child-rearing practices, health history of the child, the mother's health history during pregnancy, socioeconomic status of the family, and the political and social attitudes of the families.

Each interview schedule contained approximately 200 precoded questions organized into two major categories: (1) the child's relationship to his family and (2) the family's relationship to the community. In addition, six subcategories were formed, applicable to both major categories, that represent various aspects of family functions and characteristics. The relationship of the subcategories to the major categories is shown in Table 31–5. This organization provided a broad view of family characteristics. The six categories were taken from an eight-category grid constructed by Harold Lasswell to compare social systems in terms of human need satisfaction (1959).

Many of the factors we investigated were significantly related to the child's adaptation to school. These are summarized in Table 31–5 according to the categories described above. Among other things, it seems to be very important that the mother be healthy during pregnancy; that the mother not be the only adult in the household; that the mother feel hopeful about her ability to influence her child's future; and that the family have someone to whom they can turn in time of trouble. Since these are associated apparently with social adaptation—probably through complex

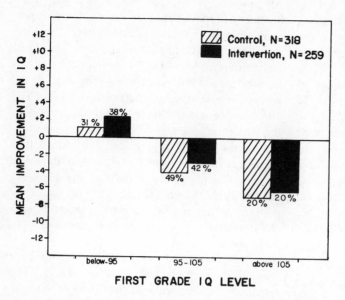

Percentages represent the proportion of Control or Intervention
children in each IQ level.

*Fig. 31—1. First cohort (1964—65). (Mean improvement
in IQ from first to third grade distributed by first grade IQ
level.)*

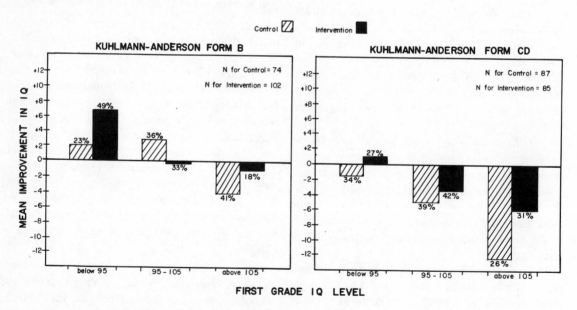

Percentages represent the proportion of Control or Intervention
children in each IQ level.

*Fig. 31—2. Third cohort (1966—67). (Mean improvement
in IQ from first to third grade distributed by first grade IQ
level.)*

TABLE 31—5
Family Characteristics Related to Child's Better Adaptation to School*

	Child/Family Characteristics	Family/Community Characteristics
Affection	Mother was not the only adult in the household Time and attention a child received Amount of confiding a child did with the adults in the household	Length of time the family had been in their geographic location Had someone to turn to in time of trouble** Belonged to social and/or political organizations
Wealth	Space, toys, and clothes a child had	Family income above $5000 Husband in family was main earner† Main income came from source other than welfare** Families owned their homes†
Well-Being	Child was not rated symptomatic by mother	Mother seldom felt sad and blue, or nervous and tense Mother had good physical health during pregnancy**
Respect	Confidence and respect a mother felt for her child's ability and competence	(See Wealth above)
Decision-Making	Clearly defined rules set by the parents which were not overly restrictive or permissive	Parents were registered to vote in preceding election† Parents were leaders in social groups in the community
Value Orientation	Mother's (1) hopes and (2) expectations that her child would go to college Mother felt influential in her child's future	Mother felt civil rights could best be obtained by nonviolent demonstration rather than by violence, or by a stay-out-of-trouble position**

*These findings are based on two-tailed t tests significant at the $p < .05$ level. Unless otherwise noted, results cited were significant for both the 1964—65 and 1966—67 interviews.

**The double asterisk indicates results based only on 1966—67 interview because question had not been asked in 1964—65.

†Results based on 1966—67 interview. Relationship did not occur on 1964—65 interview.

interrelationships—they are also examples of the kinds of concerns we feel should be within the scope of the intervention processes. They suggest further that our approach to the problem of adaptation in first grade has been indeed piecemeal, and that interventions other than those within the traditional purview of mental health seem indicated also and should be carefully considered.

DISCUSSION

The outline for the development of a community mental health program presented in this chapter involved a strategy that places primary emphasis on establishing ongoing community sanction and participation in policy-making. Secondly, this strategy concerned the development of a community-wide system for the periodic assessment of specific subpopulations in the community, one that would yield basic information for program development. The third step was to plan an intervention program for a total population based on the assessment of both qualitative and quantitative characteristics of need. The strategy's fourth stage called for the evaluation of the program by means of periodic reassessment of need in the total subpopulation. Finally, as the last step, the intervention program was refined in light of the kinds and quantity of impact achieved by the program.

The initial baseline assessment made on the first-grade population of Woodlawn revealed that extremely large populations of children were having difficulty mastering the job of first grade. Subsequent reassessments showed further that many of these children, particularly if left without intervention, remained unsuccessful in school at least as far as third grade. Measures of the program's impact revealed benefit to IQ performance, little impact on third-grade achievement test scores, and short-range benefit in the teachers' assessments of the children's social adaptation to school.

A major implication of these results is that it is possible to follow the strategy we have outlined and achieve measurable impact over several years. There is also a major significance in what was not achieved. A mental health program which enhances the intelligence test performance and general social adaptation of first-grade children is not sufficient to eliminate the problem of maladaptation among these children. In reference to the difficulties which remain, systematic studies of the correlates of social maladaptation suggested that the help of a variety of other professional disciplines is needed to deal with the overall issue of social maladaptation. In addition, we must examine broader aspects of the social system in the neighborhood and in the larger community with a view toward eliminating those aspects of our total social structure that help to generate the conditions for social adaptational failure.

In terms of human services, it seems clear that without a coordinated, broad-scale response from across the human service disciplines, these children will continue to fail at their attempts to master school in uncomfortably large numbers. Such coordination is, of course, impeded by the professional jurisdictional struggles which too often characterize any efforts to synthesize. In addition, the limitations that result from narrow training of professionals and the professional's lack of expertise in engaging with communities in their new role as policy-making partners serve to make progress toward coordination even more difficult. Nonetheless, it has become increasingly clear that the gaining and maintaining of community sanction through citizen participation at both the policy-making and operational levels of human services is absolutely critical for the success of community-wide programs.

ACKNOWLEDGMENTS

This facility could not function without the support and active participation of the people of Woodlawn. The Woodlawn Mental Health Center board has been fundamental to the work of the Center.

The support of the Chicago Board of Health, Murray C. Brown, Commissioner, and its Mental Health Division, Dr. Thomas McGee, Director, have been invaluable in this work.

We are grateful also for the support given to us by the Chicago Board of Education and Dr. James Redmond, General Superintendent of Schools; Dr. Curtis C. Melnick, Area A Associate Superintendent; Dr. Donald Blyth, Superintendent of District 14; Mr. Michael R. Fortino, Superintendent of District 21; and Rt. Rev. Msgr. William E. McManus, formerly Superintendent, Roman Catholic Archdiocesan School Board.

The entire school mental health program of study and intervention has depended on the strong support and active collaboration of the faculties of the 12 Woodlawn elementary schools. This report is one of the products of this collaboration. The authors and the staff of the Woodlawn Mental Health Center are grateful to the faculties for their help in this partnership.

The direction of the first-grade intervention program and the training of school and mental health staff associated with this program were the primary responsibilities of Dr. Sheldon K. Schiff until June 1970. Dr. Schiff and the senior author shared responsibility as codirectors of the Center until April, 1970. Mrs. Jeannette Branch, formerly Chief of Children's Mental Health Services at the Center, assumed the position of Director July 1, 1970. The third member of the original team of codirectors, Dr. Edward H. Futterman, left the Center in 1965. Dr. Futterman shared with us the trials and problems of the Center's formative period and made an important contribution to its development.

The staff of the Woodlawn Mental Health Center responsible for clinical services to the community while this research was being conducted has been and remains crucial in the development and evolution of the Center. The authors would like to acknowledge the contribution made by Mrs. Doris Van Pelt, M.A., Staff Psychologist, Woodlawn Mental Health Center, in the analyses of these data. For help in the organization and clarification of this paper, we are indebted to our publication unit and especially to Mrs. Loretta Hardiman, Editor.

In the founding and early organization of the Center, Dr. Melvin Sabshin, Head of the Department of Psychiatry, University of Illinois College of Medicine, gave active support and guidance.

Notes

The assessment and evaluation of the Woodlawn Mental Health Center School Mental Health Program is supported at the time of this writing by:

Public Health Service Research Grant Number 5 RO1–15760, National Institute of Mental Health. A five-year grant which began in 1968.

State of Illinois Department of Mental Health Grant Number 17–322, Psychiatric Training and Research Fund. A two-year grant which began in 1968.

Maurice Falk Medical Fund Grant. A three-year grant, which began in 1968, to support publication of scientific work.

Research Scientist Development Award Grant Number KO1–MH 47596, National Institute of Mental Health. Awarded to the first author in 1970 for a five-year period.

1. Edward H. Futterman, M.D., Sheldon K. Schiff, M.D., and Sheppard G. Kellam, M.D.

2. Mrs. Branch was in charge of this process throughout the course of these studies.

3. Parochial schools did not administer IQ tests or achievement tests in first and third grades, and their academic grades were not arithmetically comparable to those of the public schools and were therefore not included in these results. Parochial school data will be analyzed separately.

4. The sixth edition Kuhlmann-Anderson test of mental maturity (IQ) was administered to the public school first- and third-grade students in 1964–65 and 1966–67 and to the public school first-grade students in 1966–67. These tests were given by the public schools under the supervision of Blanch B. Paulsen, Director of Bureau of Pupil Personnel Services, and Elmer M. Casey, Director of Evaluation and Pupil Studies Bureau of Pupil Personnel Services, The Chicago Board of Education.

5. The third-grade students in 1966–67 were given the seventh edition Kuhlmann-Anderson test of mental maturity which was administered by testers and proctors hired and supervised by the Woodlawn Mental Health Center. Half of these classes, randomly chosen, were given Form B and half were given Form CD of the Kuhlmann-Anderson test.

6. The National Opinion Research Center gave technical consultation in devising the interview schedule and was responsible, under Dr. Kellam's supervision, for conducting the interviews with the mothers in their homes. This study has profited greatly by having Paul Sheatsley and the senior staff of the National Opinion Research Center available for consultation.

References

Blum, R. H. Case identification in psychiatric epidemiology: Methods and problems. *Milbank Memorial Fund Quarterly*, 1962, 40, 253–288.

Clark, K. B., & Hopkins, J. *A relevant war against poverty*. New York: Harper & Row, 1968.

Conners, C. K. Symptom patterns in hyperkinetic, neurotic and normal children. Baltimore, Md.: Johns Hopkins University School of Medicine, 1967. (Mimeo)

Conners, C. K. Symptom patterns in Hyperkinetic, neurotic and normal children. *Child Development*, 1970, 41, 667–682.

Daniels, R. S. Health: A human service component—A model. In E. N. Williams (ed.), *Delivery systems for Model Cities*. Chicago: University of Chicago Press, 1969.

Davidson, H. A. The double life of American psychiatry. In H. Freeman & J. Farndale (eds.), *New aspects of mental health services*. New York: Pergamon Press, 1967.

Hollingshead, A. B., & Redlich, A. C. *Social class and mental illness*. New York: Wiley, 1958.

Kellam, S. G., & Schiff, S. K. Adaptation and mental illness in the first-grade classroom of an urban community. In *Psychiatry Research Report No. 21*. Washington, D. C.: American Psychiatric Association, 1967.

Kellam, S. G., & Schiff, S. K. An urban community mental health center. In L. J. Duhl & R. L. Leopold (eds.), *Mental health and urban social policy*. San Francisco: Jossey-Bass, 1968.

Lapouse, R., & Monk, A. An epidemiologic study of behavior characteristics in children. *American Journal of Public Health*, 1958, 48, 1134–1144.

Lasswell, H. D. Strategies of inquiry: The rational use of observation. In D. Lerner (ed.), *The human meaning of the social sciences*. New York: Meridian Books, 1959.

Schiff, S. K., & Kellam, S. G. A community-wide mental health program of prevention and early treatment in first grade. In *Psychiatry Research Report No. 21*. Washington, D. C.: American Psychiatric Association, 1967.

32

Free Inquiry and the Enduring Commitment: The Woodlawn Mental Health Center 1963-1970

Sheldon K. Schiff

The changing values of the academic market place, the increasing reliance on governmental and private funds—both of which suffer from transient popular priorities—plus the growing demands of government and industry for the expertise of university scientists and "experts" have reduced the number and the vitality of long-term, innovative research projects. This trend has resulted in a paucity of teachers who have had first-hand experience in designing, initiating, and carrying out such projects.

Today's pursuit of grant funds has almost eclipsed scholarly curiosity and contributed to an overemphasis upon the entrepreneurial aspects of grant applications. University departments tend to encourage short-term projects which have limited value but will lead to rapid publication of results (Ashby, 1965; Caplow & McGee, 1958; Cronbach & Suppes, 1969; Jencks & Riesman, 1968; Levi, 1969; Taylor, 1959). Grant proposals most likely to be funded are those which define single, short-term, circumscribed studies. Academic rewards for the successful "grants man" are now universally recognized. Consequently, it is not surprising that graduate students and junior faculty members decide that the short-term project represents a more appropriate pursuit than the long-term study.

Certainly, many such studies are useful because they allow one small question to be answered fully. However, only through long-term study is there opportunity for gaining a deeper understanding of a problem's dimensions and for possibly discovering, as a result, that the basic problem is not what it was originally surmised to be.

Of all the difficulties associated with sustained inquiries, the most obvious and frequently reported are those of getting established. These have been well described in the past (Aberle, 1950; Demerath, 1952; Festinger et al., 1948; Merton, 1947; Sewell, 1949). Developing interest in community mental health programs in the late 1950s and the host of programs created by the new legislation of the 1960s (Public Law 88–452, 1964; Public Law 89–10, 1965; Public Law 88–164, 1963; Public Law 89–105, 1965; Public Law 89–97, 1965; Public Law 90–248, 1967) have added a number of dramatic reports of the early efforts at professional involvement in communities (Cumming & Cumming, 1957; Gildea et al., 1957; Glidewell, 1959; Kellam & Schiff, 1968; Klebanoff & Bindman, 1962; New York Times, 1966).

But what happens when an investigator finds that his view of the original problem is changing as the nature of the problem is better understood? What happens when a change in approach requires additional funding support? What are the problems in seeking new sources of funding and the renewal of funds for ongoing study and program development? More importantly, what are the unique dilemmas which a community-based academic investigator encounters as a result of his university affiliation? Particularly, what is the impact of this institutional affiliation upon his professional contract with the community in which he works?

This chapter will explore what happened after our entry into Woodlawn, an urban black community of 81,000 people on Chicago's South Side. As mental health professionals, our goal was to establish a community mental health center that would effectively serve the community and provide a base for developing a field laboratory in community psychiatry. Our entry into the community was accompanied by a commitment on the part of the three codirector psychiatrists[1] to remain there for at least five years and develop during this time community mental health programs based on the needs of the residents and on priorities established in collaboration with the community (Kellam & Schiff, 1966; Kellam & Schiff, 1968).

These two key elements of our initial professional commitment to Woodlawn—its long-term nature and requirement of community participation—form the backdrop for the problems we have encountered over seven years. It is also the background from which the source of these difficulties can be more clearly understood.

EARLY DEVELOPMENT OF A LONG-TERM, COMMUNITY-BASED MENTAL HEALTH PROGRAM

From its beginning in 1963, the Woodlawn Mental Health Center has been a service facility of the City of Chicago Board of Health, and has maintained an academic institution affiliation.[2] The university ties offered the program and the codirectors the unique resources of scholarship and academic prestige without which our innovative efforts could easily have foundered or been dismissed as nonprofessional, political social action.

During the early months of the Center's development, we were constantly involved in community meetings concerning such issues as the site for the Center. This early exposure to the community revealed the presence of a pervasive concern on the part of the community residents as to the true extent of our accountability to the community. An important test of our accountability was their role in determining the first program priorities.

Despite its heterogeneity in terms of socioeconomic class and other characteristics, the Woodlawn community was most concerned about the future of its young children. Community citizens asked specifically about the prevention of mental illness in children and programs for insuring the children's future success.

Basic to their concern was the fact that nowhere in the community was there a context in which the children's true abilities were being addressed—let alone realized. The almost total lack of communication between parents and schools at that time left the parents feeling remote from an educational system which they considered unresponsive to the needs of their children.

The advisory board made it clear, in the discussions which then followed and which preceded our first grant applications,[3] that it had no interest in a program which: (a) involved only a small number of children; (b) looked only at problems defined in esoteric professional terms; (c) was in any way condescending; or (d) was oriented to conditions not typical of the Woodlawn community.

Subsequently, the basic principles of the intervention program design were decided upon in collaboration with the advisory board.[4] The program would: (1) involve the total population of first-grade children; (2) be carried out in the first-grade classrooms of the community's schools; (3) focus on the key influences affecting the child's successful transition to first grade: his teacher, his school, and his family; (4) be carried out ultimately by the teachers and other school personnel; (5) data collected would be regarded as medically confidential records; (6) the information would be available for future investigators, but the advisory board would screen all materials prior to publication.

The rationale for the choice of first-grade children, and the random division of Woodlawn's 12 elementary schools into two matched groups of schools—six intervention and six control schools—have been described elsewhere by the author and his colleague (Kellam & Schiff, 1967; Schiff & Kellam, 1967).

THE PROGRAM BEGINS

In 1964—65, when we first introduced the program of prevention and early treatment into the six schools selected for intervention, we decided to forego any systematic parent involvement. In this initial year, the basic program design in each of the six intervention schools was a half-hour Classroom Group Meeting and a one-hour School Staff Meeting each week for 12 weeks beginning after January.

In the Classroom Group Meetings, the teacher and psychiatrist met with 10 to 12 children selected by their teacher because they were not adapting as well to school as the teacher thought they were capable of doing. The focus of the discussion was how the children could utilize their capacities best in view of the importance of first grade. The teacher was supposed to lead the group discussion, but after teaching the psychiatrist to talk to the children, the teacher allowed him to be "boss."

In the School Staff Meetings, which were held at lunch hour, the psychiatrist met with the principal, assistant principal, adjustment teacher, and the *first-grade teachers only*.

Our clinical experiences during Year I demonstrated that this basic early program design was both feasible and successful and that adding parent involvement would not overwhelm our resources. Faculty attitudes caused us to approach this program modification gingerly—and with the board's assistance.

Program Modifications in Year II

In Year II, the Classroom Group Meeting was modified to include the entire class in the discussion and all the children were encouraged to discuss any individual or group problems, including those involving their teacher. The teacher took the initiative as group leader. As indicated in Figures 32–1 and 32–2, there had been positive changes in the teachers' attitudes toward the Classroom Meetings and the program.

The School Staff Meeting retained its original structure, but the school personnel were more interested and there was less skepticism. Questions about group technique in the Classroom Meetings dominated our conversations, while the question of parent involvement was rarely raised and seldom pursued.

It must also be noted that we mental health professionals were not without our own concerns about direct involvement with parents.

Initially, when we had indicated that there would be no parent participation in 1964–65, the teachers had expressed serious doubt about whether or not the program could affect the children and produce any real change without involving the parents. However, in Year II, we found that many teachers now felt that the new Classroom Meeting design had accomplished so much that involving the parents was unnecessary.

Indeed, they also expressed their concern about how fruitless and even risky any attempt to involve their students' parents could become. In the opinion of some teachers many of the parents in the Woodlawn community could cause considerable chaos in the school and upset the children and themselves. Furthermore, the teachers held that conducting the Classroom Meetings was all the responsibility they could assume, since they were not trained for such involvement with parents.

On the other hand, the advisory board, while listening with interest to the favorable reports of program outcome, remained focused on our original intent to involve parents when it was programmatically appropriate. To the board, the success of Year I and the early experiences with the new Classroom Meeting design meant that parent involvement was now appropriate. Finally, they directly requested us to get busy designing parent involvement for later in Year II.

The mental health professionals and the school faculties, bolstered by the support, attendance, and prodding of the advisory board, began the first of a series of evening PTA-type parent meetings. Before long, parents freely expressed their dissatisfaction with the typical auditorium meeting characterized by anonymity and dominated by one or two articulate people. The parents were interested in talking directly to their child's teacher in the classroom, together with the parents of his classmates. As a result, it was decided to hold the Parent Meetings in the classroom during school hours, with the children present.

One such meeting, of one and a half hours' duration, was held in Year II, with all parents meeting together with their child's teacher and the principal, assistant principal, adjustment teacher, and psychiatrist. About 270 of the 1,000 children had a parent in attendance.

Program Developments in Year III

By Year III, the number of Parent Meetings was formalized to three—each of one and a half hours' duration and held at a time of report card distribution. However, it became clear that the parents' preference for more personal encounters with their child's teacher and his classmates' parents was now extended to include involvement in the Classroom Meetings. This desire reflected not only their general parental interest but also the fact that the children's reports of what occurred at these meetings had piqued their curiosity.

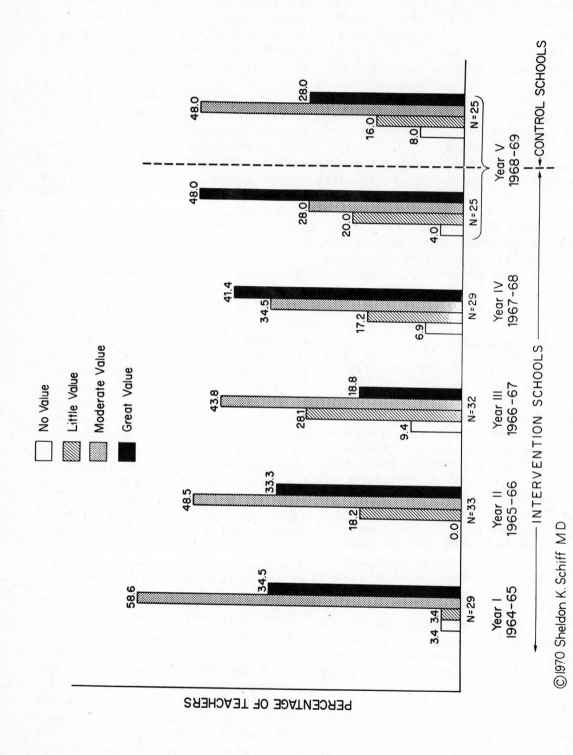

Fig. 32–1. Response of teachers to: "How valuable has the mental health program been?"

© 1970 Sheldon K. Schiff M D

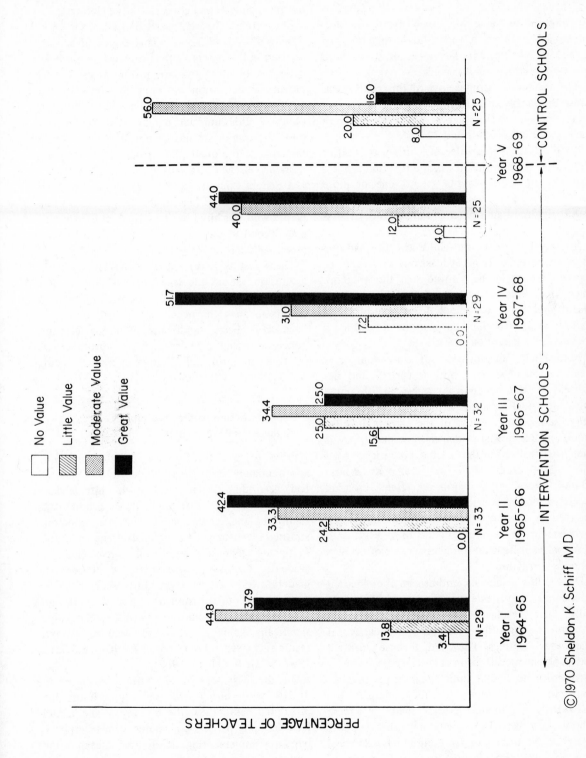

© 1970 Sheldon K. Schiff MD

Fig. 32–2. Response of teachers to: "How valuable have the classroom meetings been?"

Suggestions by the children, the silent demands of the parents, and our own escalating understanding of the value and feasibility of the idea, convinced us that parents should indeed start attending the Classroom Meetings, and so the third program modification was made.

The teachers' attitudes toward this change was more universally questioning and negative than we had experienced in either of the prior program years (see Figures 32–1 and 32–2).

At the three Parent Meetings this year, 600 of the 1,000 children in the six intervention schools had one or more parents attend one or more meetings. At the Classroom Meetings, 360 of the 1,000 children had a parent in attendance at least once.

Seventy percent of the children (700) had one or more parents attend at least one Classroom or Parent Meeting in the 17 weeks of the program. More than 800 parents visited the 30 first-grade classrooms in the six schools for a total of 1,560 parent visits for the purpose of attending a Classroom or Parent Meeting.

Fortunately, the district superintendents and school principals were both surprised and delighted at the program's success in obtaining unusually high parent attendance. The most immediate positive effect of the parents' involvement was felt by the principals. For many, it was their first realization that such a potential existed for their school—and for them as school administrators. They began to attend program meetings more frequently and displayed a keener interest in learning the techniques for parent involvement. As a result, in the third year, each principal identified the program as part of his own school's curriculum.

Despite the principals' enthusiasm about parent attendance, they made no effort to deal directly with their teachers' skepticism and obvious discomfort regarding parents' attendance at Classroom Meetings. They did, however, protect this program modification. The teachers' requests to discontinue it and limit the parents' involvement to Parent Meetings failed, despite the infrequent but intense efforts made by some school faculties. The uncompromising support given to the principals by their immediate local superiors was also essential to this first test of parent participation in Classroom Meetings.[5] In addition, the board members protected and facilitated the parents' entry into these meetings out of a fundamental concern for the children.

The extent of parent participation is shown in Figures 32–3 and 32–4.[6] This degree of success realized in this aspect of the program had not been expected by the program professionals—mental health or education—or even members of the advisory board. The method by which the program obtained this unusual parent involvement—not only in terms of attendance but more importantly in terms of the quality of participation—has been described elsewhere (Schiff & Turner, 1969).

A School Community Representative was added to the School Staff Meeting in Year III. This was a parent who was hired by the school on Elementary and Secondary Education Act funds (ESEA) and was usually a former PTA president.

These results have served to alter a very basic assumption about the willingness of parents in a community like Woodlawn to become involved in efforts to meet the needs of their children. They have also been significant in refocusing my concerns about the training of professionals engaged in providing human services (Schiff, 1970b; Schiff, 1970c; Schiff & Turner, 1971).

Implementation of the Program by the Schools in Year IV

Prior to the fourth year of the program, approximately 2,800 first graders in six schools had been directly involved in the intervention program. Periodic evaluations have produced a significant and growing body of evidence demonstrating the program's beneficial effect upon the first-grade children's successful performance as students. Follow-up assessment of these first graders two years later in third grade revealed strong signs of continued impact, despite no further program exposure, with demonstrable significant gains in their third-grade IQ and reading-achievement test scores (Kellam & Schiff, 1967; Schiff & Kellam, 1967).

On the basis of this evidence, we began to discuss with our board and the schools the program's next phase—the training of the school faculties and parents to assume direct responsibility for implementing the program in each of the six intervention schools.

In Year IV, we tested the feasibility of this plan. In all but two of the six schools, mental health

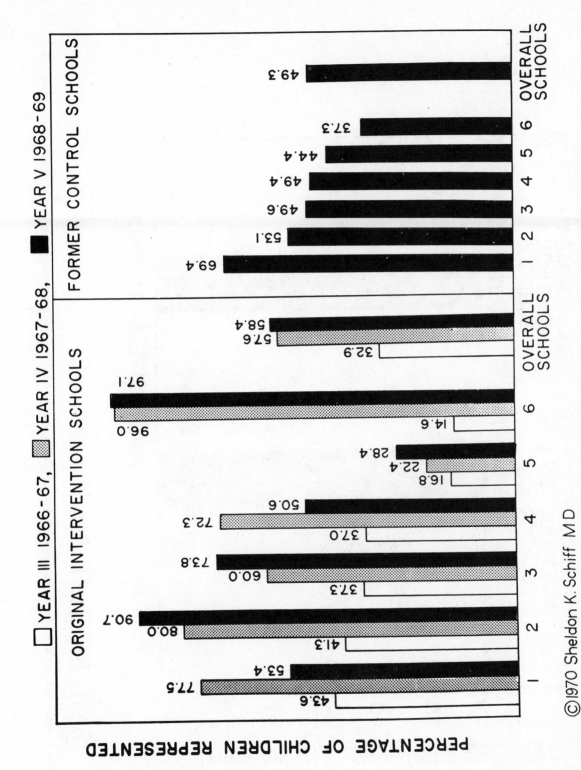

© 1970 Sheldon K. Schiff MD

Fig. 32–3. Percentage of children represented by parents attending classroom meetings.

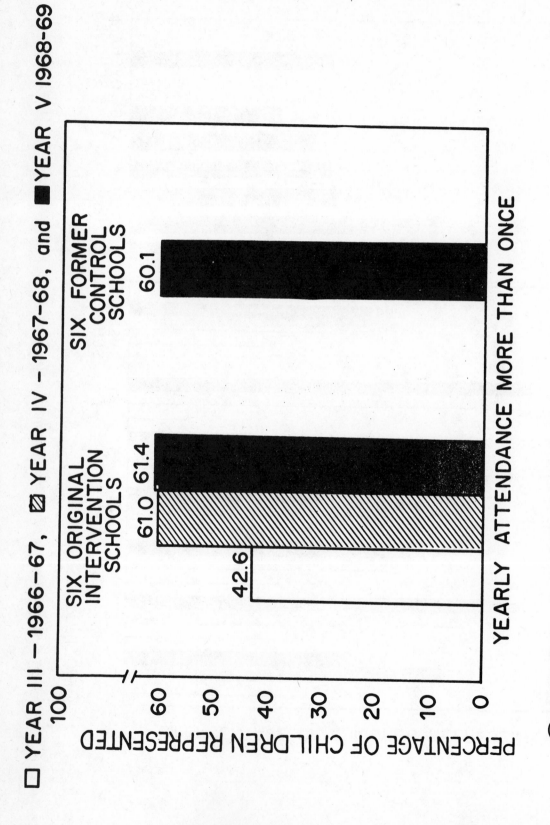

Fig. 32—4. Percentage of children whose parents attended classroom meetings two or more times among parents who attended classroom meetings.

professionals reduced their attendance at all program meetings to every other week, in general, but in a few cases attended only when requested by the teacher to assist with some special problem. School faculty members planned most of the schedules and increasingly assumed direct responsibility for most program procedures. The principal or one of the administrative staff was present at each Classroom Meeting in all but one school.

The School Staff Meeting was the one meeting the psychiatrists attended with some regularity. It was planned that this year, this meeting would be the key training context. This goal was only partially realized.

The assumption by the school faculties of primary responsibility for the program resulted in a greater than usual number of innovative program ideas from the teachers. For example, in several schools, the scheduled Parent Meetings were held for an hour, but then all the parents were invited to spend the remaining time in a Classroom Meeting with their children. Thus, those parents who had been reluctant to attend Classroom Meetings were included in them. The many ideas tried out by the teachers—while not always successful—gave a new vitality to the program.

Even though teachers had initially experienced extreme discomfort at the presence of parents in the Classroom Meetings, by the end of Year IV they had moved to a more positive attitude (see Figure 32–1 and 32–2), despite the fact that parent participation had increased markedly over the previous year, 1966–67 (see Figures 32–3 and 32–4).

The role of the School Community Representatives evolved considerably this year. They displayed more initiative and began to work with the Community Mental Health Worker from the Center. The initial home visits made by the Center staff were placed under the primary aegis of the School Community Representative in each school. In one school, the School Community Representative taught and supervised those first-grade teachers who wished to make home visits.

The gains reported in regard to the childrens' improvement this year were similar to those found in Year II. Although less than in Year III, they were nonetheless significant (Kellam, Schiff, & Branch, 1968; Kellam, 1969).

A report prepared by my colleague, Dr. Kellam, of the results of periodic assessments showed: (1) an increasing program effectiveness each year

by the time of the year-end assessment and (2) the persistence of these significant gains as much as two years later (demonstrated by follow-up assessments at the end of third grade) (Kellam, Schiff, & Branch, 1968).

Primarily on the basis of these results and following a number of meetings with both the Center's community board and the schools, the decision was made to introduce the program into the six former control schools in the next school year, 1968–1969.

Obstacles to the Program's Entry into the Control Schools in Year V

This year the direct responsibility for the program would not be that of the Center's mental health professionals. School Mental Health Teams of parents and educators from the six original intervention schools would receive further intensive training in order to successfully introduce the intervention program to the parents and faculties of the six control schools unfamiliar with the program. The responsibility for the development of both the training program and the teams was the author's.

The obstacles we encountered in 1968–69 as we began this most critical period in the program's history fall into distinct categories. While these categories overlap, they nevertheless can be defined as: (1) professional—those major conceptual and technical problems associated with the development of the training program and teams; (2) community—those problems involving opposition to the teams from certain community factions; (3) university—those political and fiscal difficulties related to the program's academic base.

Professional Obstacles

Parent participation and leadership were considered vital to the success of the Classroom Meetings and to the successful transfer of program implementation to the school staffs. How to effect a working alliance between teacher and parent was thus a primary concern.

The School Mental Health Training Program was designed to develop effective collaboration of parents and teachers within a team structure and to teach them the basic mental health principles and the specific techniques that had been developed in the intervention program over the previous four years (Schiff, 1970 c; Schiff & Turner, 1971).

Few training programs provide joint training for professional students from different disciplines; fewer, if any, attempt the joint training of professionals and nonprofessionals where serious questions of trust and dignity between the professional and nonprofessional must be resolved. Once out of training and in the schools, the team would face a wide variety of obstacles, some more direct than others. All, however, had to be met and overcome if the program was to survive.

If successful, we were sure this collaborative design would provide an unusual potential for further innovation in the intervention program. Since in each school the team would be comprised of teachers and parents from that school, the design was bound to be more creative than that from detached consultants less familiar and less directly committed to that specific school context.

The two training teams were each led by administrators from former treatment schools who had each been assigned first-grade teachers and School Community Representatives from the original treatment schools. The roles of the team members were to train their counterparts in the control schools in the program techniques. In addition, seven Community Mental Health Workers strengthened the teams' development in their role as the Center's technical "experts."

Candor and Status Problems. As this transition year moved through the final stages, we saw many difficulties arise. Videotapes of group meetings made during previous years of the school program permitted close examination of problem relationships.[7] How can professionals and parents talk to each other? How straight can a teacher be with a parent? How straight can a parent be with a teacher? These were the fundamental questions raised throughout the course of the training program. The fundamental problem was that of trust. Parents felt a severe sense of alienation from the teacher who was, after all, a professional. Professional "trade unionism" was a real and dangerous threat to an honest, close relationship between a well-meaning teacher and an interested and concerned parent.

The issue concerned the degree to which a teacher could be candid with a parent. This involved recognizing the parent's intrinsic worth as a team member because of her potential for unique and essential contribution. The yardstick by which the parents gauged the teacher's honesty was the explicit expression on the part of the teachers of full understanding of the nature of the contractual relationship between teacher and pupil. Once the parent felt the teacher recognized the danger facing the child and herself should the teacher abrogate their trust relationship, a foothold was established for a team relationship. Unfortunately, the teachers also retained many professional biases with regard to working with nontraditional professionals. Very early they expressed great concern about divulging "professional confidences." Through continuing discussion, their feelings were identified as a reflection of the image they had developed of their professional role—particularly vis-à-vis parents.

Politics and the Nonprofessional. There has been a good deal of evidence of late which has emphasized the difficulties resulting from the ambiguities of the nontraditional professional's role. Of most concern has been the tendency of the nonprofessional to become politicized. In our experience, however, and that of others, it is the professional and his pejorative view and use of the nonprofessional that has been the source of these difficulties (Roman, 1969; Schiff, 1970a). The nonprofessional requires a dignified and specific role involving functions other than those which the professional no longer wishes to retain.

Opposition from the Control Schools' Faculties: Team Leaders—Principals' Relationship. There were inevitable difficulties surrounding the fact that the teams were replacing the Center professional who had served as the mental health consultant and trainer in the six intervention schools. These problems were most acute for the two coordinators in their relationship to the principals of the new schools. Several principals expressed specific displeasure, commenting that after expecting to have access to a psychiatrist on a regular basis, as had their colleagues in other schools, it now appeared that they would not have a psychiatrist but two women as mental health consultants—neither of whom were even principals.

Each of the six principals was given his choice of which of the two coordinators would work in his school. Despite the fact that each of the coordinators had, in most cases, a prior relationship with each of these principals, the choice of each principal would be respected over and above the personal choice of a coordinator. This strategy proved to be useful in permitting the principals some sense of control as the teams began their work in the schools, and preserved everyone's dignity without undercutting roles.

Opposition from the Control-School Teachers. The control-school teachers, who were an important group of trainees, presented many roadblocks to the teams. Initially, the teachers were reluctant to accept the teacher-trainers as having any special skills in the area of mental health. Neither were they willing to accept the coordinators as having any role other than "experimental" in the shool system.

This general attitude of the teachers toward the program was patently evident early in their relationship with the teams. In those schools where black militant separatism was prominent, it became very serious. Black team members, especially the coordinators, were accused (though rarely explicitly) of being "Uncle Toms" trying to implement a "white program." Meetings were held for the purpose of creating community distrust of the school program on a racial basis and efforts were made to mobilize parents to block the program's entry. The consistent support of members of the Woodlawn Mental Health Center board was critical to the resolution of these problems.

Parents on the team were largely excluded from the negative criticism of control-school faculties. This immunity was a singular recognition of the teachers' isolation from the parents of the children they taught and from a community of which they were not residents. On the few occasions when a team parent actively intervened with a militant teacher, the usual tactic was to speak first as a parent and then as a team member.

Community Obstacles
The Woodlawn Organization (TWO)

Most unexpected of all the obstacles which threatened the school Mental Health teams' progress were those directed at the program by The Woodlawn Organization (TWO). Shortly after our initial arrival in Woodlawn, TWO presented the codirectors with their first community crisis (Kellam & Schiff, 1966; Kellam & Schiff, 1968). Public charges of "race bias, bypassing Negro

psychiatrists," and inability to "relate to the community" were made by TWO against the three psychiatrists after our arrival in Chicago in 1963. This provided us with the first and most important personal and professional test of our ability to engage in a new kind of crisis situation and learn from those confronting us and from the events themselves.

During the next four years, this organization had come to be a major and important source of the Center's community support.[8] TWO's president, the Rev. Arthur Brazier, was one of the Center's early community advisory board members. Attorney Lawrence W. Carroll, chairman of what is now the Woodlawn Mental Health Center Board, since its constitution was passed in November, 1968,[9] and the present assistant treasurer of TWO, was one of our first board members.

The Rev. Thomas H. Ellis, one of the early founders of TWO and also one of the first advisory board members, has also been one of the few board members whose children have been involved in the program. His observations as a parent of the program's benefits to his children and their classmates—as well as the parents involved—were unusually persuasive to both teachers and parents of the program's value.

Reflecting on his role during the 1968—69 school year, The Rev. Mr. Ellis commented on a University of Chicago telecast in the summer of 1969:

I have fought more battles for this community health program, I think, than anybody, simply because I have known more about it as a member of the board who is accessible within the context of controversy. . . .

Recently when we expanded our program there were those who were suspicious, especially those who were of the more militant stance who knew nothing about the program and were suspicious of the two doctors who were white. . . . They [the Center staff] actually called on me to inform the people [about the Community Board's role in developing the program].

It wasn't an easy task. . . . Our [the Center board's] confidence has been quite extensive because we knew at this point that we were basically in control of the program.

The Rev. Mr. Ellis went on to describe his personal efforts to resolve the difficulties with TWO:

I remember during the controversy I had to call Rev. Brazier about one staff member who had gone in opposition to the program on this same bit of these two doctors being white. . . . At first he didn't know a thing about it and he couldn't believe that it was one of our staff men. I had been informed that it was.

I really became angry about it, largely because we had worked on this program for approximately seven years. I told Rev. Brazier in no uncertain terms on the phone that I was not going to sit idly by and allow someone to shoot this program down the drain after we had worked seven years on it. And he says, 'O.K., Reverend, if you feel like this, then this is the way it is. Certainly I'm with you on it.'

The basic facts are that the board really runs this program because nothing is really done apart from the board and the board's consent.[10]

Since that time, TWO, a former University of Chicago antagonist whose past struggles with its famous academic neighbor were well described by Silberman (1964), has become a collaborator with the University of Chicago in a host of service programs and real estate projects (Chicago Tribune, 1970; The Observer, 1970; Woodlawn Booster, 1969; TWO-UC Enter, 1969).

University Obstacles

When we made our first site visit to Chicago in winter of 1962, Woodlawn was still engaged in bitter conflict with the University of Chicago over the community's future. To the neighborhood residents' dismay, the University of Chicago's announcement of its expansion plans in 1960 was an ominously familiar prelude to the conversion of Woodlawn into an academic land quarry from which the University could mine real estate parcels as it needed them.

However, it became very clear that our University of Illinois affiliation would be short-lived; rapid changes were occurring in the University of Chicago's relationship to Woodlawn. The early efforts of a few faculty members to persuade the University trustees and administration to work *with* TWO, rather than against it, gained pragmatic support from other developments, among which was the fact that we were able to get along with TWO and yet carry on our work without compromising our purpose.

The "South Campus" conflict was abruptly settled (Colley, 1968; Snow, 1968; Woodlawn Booster, 1964),[11] and a number of collaborative TWO-University of Chicago service and study programs were being contemplated. A major experiment in public education, an educational research institute, a child health center, a social service center, and other projects all were in the early planning stages or being readied for funding and implementation.

The University of Illinois was becoming more involved in developing health services for its own surrounding neighborhood. The University of Chicago's attitude toward Woodlawn, with the change in the University of Illinois' tie to Woodlawn, ended our affiliation with the University of Illinois. I became a member of the University of Chicago faculty in July, 1966.[12]

Since then, however, certain developments in the neighborhood, as well as changes in the structure and function of TWO and in the climate of the University, have unexpectedly resulted in mutually conflicting goals. The most pervasive conflicts are reflected in questions asked by the children, parents, and teachers with respect to the yearly decrease in the student population, the university's role in certain community efforts (which for most of the parents appear to support a militancy felt primarily by black professionals and an occasional parent) and finally the university's ultimate goal in providing services, and to whom.

Fiscal Obstacles

Two formidable fiscal obstacles threatened the successful introduction of the program's group meetings into the former control schools. The first and most immediate was the need for additional funds to support the training of the school mental health teams upon which this responsibility would rest directly. The second was the mounting difficulties we began to encounter with the administrative policies and procedures of the University of Chicago, the fiscal agent for my grant funds.

Four letters and supportive documents intended to initiate private foundation support were sent off in the summer of 1968. Efforts were also made to enlist the assistance of the University of Chicago's considerable resources.

Initially, considerable and impressive "spadework" was done by Professor Julian Levi following a meeting we held in July 1968 with our chairman's prior knowledge and sanction. At that meeting, Professor Levi described those resources most likely to prove immediately rewarding. He also provided a working list of potential contributors compiled by his staff. Unfortunately, these efforts were aborted when, following a summary report of potential sources of immediate funds, a memo from my chairman alerted the university and myself that these efforts were in conflict with other departmental funding needs from these very same sources.

Happily, the letters to the private foundations were more successful. After a site visit, two of the four private foundations awarded the total amount requested, but for only one year. They both viewed the function of their grant awards as leading to longer-term support by one of the larger foundations.

The other two foundations raised questions. One made a significant contribution by directing the author's attention to a number of issues that had been either ignored or only partially addressed. The need for the Chicago Board of Education to begin assuming some financial and administrative responsibility for the implementation of the school program was one such issue. It was proposed also that the University of Chicago assume some responsibility for conducting the School Mental Health Training Seminars.[13] Following a letter responding to these questions, this grant was awarded.

The other foundation's request for clarification centered upon its need for more evidence of the intervention program's effectiveness. Such evidence clearly existed (Kellam & Schiff, 1967; Kellam, Schiff, & Branch, 1968). A site visit was scheduled by the foundation in May 1969. The results of more extensive data analysis carried out by Dr. Kellam and his evaluation section during the ensuing eight months were now available (Kellam, 1969). At this point, questions concerning program effectiveness could be more fully answered than for most community mental health programs or current psychotherapies.

Furthermore, the school mental health teams were now ending their program-period involvement, after a nine month program. The skeletal curriculum outline described in my initial grant request was now more substantive in ideas, materials, and techniques. More critically, curriculum development as a field of a study and as it pertained to my efforts to formulate an innovative joint training program was better understood.

Many of the obstacles described earlier for both the training program and team development had been largely overcome. The training program's library of video tapes of both the team's participation in the control schools' group meetings and the training seminars themselves represent a data bank of almost all the major technical obstacles encountered. The parent attendance this year—though not direct proof of the training program's effectiveness—was greater and more intense than ever before (see Figures 32–3 and 32–4).

During the site visit, the psychiatrist reviewing the application visited the school program in progress, viewed video tapes of the training and teams, and clarified those questions remaining about evidence of effectiveness. The visitor requested that a new and more comprehensive application—with supporting documents—be submitted within the week.

One week after this revised application was mailed, the president of the foundation wrote Dr. Kellam that the application had been rejected because there was insufficient "solid evidence to the efficacy of your program."

In the summer of 1969, the three foundations which had granted one year's financial support in 1968 were again approached, since the availability of federal as well as state monies was then greatly reduced. All three renewed their support for an additional year on the evidence of the results of the year's work.

Concerned with the program's need for more long-term stable funding, one foundation helped us contact a staff member of a large and well-known foundation. Although the initial contact with the larger foundation was very encouraging, it became less so after a scheduled site visit was canceled because of other commitments, with a request for "additional evidence of effectiveness." I referred this latter request to Dr. Kellam. The end result was a denial of funds on the basis of other funding priorities.

The Chicago Board of Health and the University of Chicago. Requests made of the Mental Health Division, City of Chicago Board of Health, to assume the burden of funding the salaries of the school mental health worker staff were no more successful. This was surprising, since from its beginning the school mental health program had been proudly identified as primarily a city agency. Dr. Eric Oldberg, President of the Chicago Board of Health and Professor and Chairman of

Neurosurgery, University of Illinois School of Medicine, had noted on the occasion of the Center's open house, "The Center is the first effort of its kind in the country that is run by a metropolitan board of health" (Chicago Tribune, 1964). In the text of the 1965 Budget Statement, Mayor Richard J. Daley had stated:

In September of this year, the Woodlawn Mental Health Center was established and is a primary community mental health resource. With the assistance of community agencies an initial program has been developed to identify and provide treatment for those first grade children who appear to be having trouble in reaching their full potential.

This program will be concerned with approximately 2,000 first grade children in Woodlawn, including children in parochial as well as public schools.

In addition, a program for family group therapy for children in elementary schools is now being planned. Also psychiatric consultation for the civic agencies in Woodlawn is being instituted. This program—being directed by three psychiatrists who are assistant professors at the University of Illinois College of Medicine—is attracting nationwide comment and is serving as a model for similar programs in other cities.

Shortly after the change in the Center's affiliation from the University of Illinois to the University of Chicago, increasing friction developed between the Chicago Board of Health and our new academic base. While the specifics of this controversy embraced a host of picayune mutual grievances and unfortunate *ad hominems*, the core centered upon a growing struggle with regard to the ownership rights of the Woodlawn Mental Health Center. Each new newspaper article or university publication which seemed to attribute the Center and its work singularly to the University of Chicago increased this friction (Beadle, 1968; Dunbar, 1967; Moore, 1967; Walker, 1970; Woodlawn Mental Health Center, 1968).

One result of this was the peremptory "firing" of the Center's codirectors—Dr. Kellam and myself—from the Board of Health for two days. It also contributed to our inability to transfer some of our service staff salaries to the Board of Health.

It was support given our work by three private foundations,[14] together with the federal funds provided by my five-year NIMH grant awarded in 1964, which allowed the work described in this chapter to continue.

Fiscal Administrative Difficulties. In an earlier publication (Schiff, 1970a), it was reported that the kind of fiscal administrative difficulties described at Lincoln Hospital (Roman, 1969) were being more frequently encountered by the Woodlawn Mental Health Center staff. These difficulties reached critical proportions when it was discovered that expenses incurred by my colleague or myself were frequently and indiscriminately charged to the other's grant account.

We both commissioned a certified audit of our accounts but were informed these accounts were inauditable and could not be certified because of an inadequate internal control system. Our accountants advised us to settle whatever differences in charges existed.

Following the completion of the accounting firm's report, and together with the members of the executive and grievance committees of the Center's community board, who were awaiting the report with some concern, the codirectors settled the differences. It was mutually agreed that more than $17,000 was owed my grant accounts and would be transferred from Dr. Kellam's grant to mine. The recovery of this sum of money and the internal voucher system developed for the Center by the accounting firm were almost as important to the program's continued existence as the new monies acquired.

Not unlike the difficulties at Lincoln Hospital, members of the school mental health teams, consultants, and occasionally full-time Center staff encountered frequent delays and errors in salary payments. Rental payments were withheld, with the result that some important landlord services were restricted. Administrative staff found themselves increasingly frustrated by red tape and counter-directives from the University business and administration offices.

Efforts to have University procedures clarified in some systematic fashion were never fully realized, even though this was recommended by the accountants' final report.

The future director of such a program is admonished to be more informed about the nature of his responsibilities and those of his fiscal agent.

THE OUTCOME

The foremost criteria of program outcome have to do with the questions: Have the children benefited from this work? Has it been of any value to the parents? What effect has it had on the teachers? Has it had any impact on the schools and the community? In two previously published accounts, it was reported that with each successive year the percentage of children found to be successfully adapting to first grade was higher in the treatment schools than in the control schools (Kellam & Schiff, 1967; Kellam, Schiff, & Branch, 1968).

Both of these earlier publications reported that the first discernible effect of the program was a change in the teachers' view of the children. In the course of the first year they acquired a new appreciation not only of their students' true abilities but also of their own professional capacities. As a consequence, their ratings of the children reflected this higher expectation of the children and themselves and were therefore less favorable.

If no future follow-up had been undertaken, we would have been left with no evidence of any direct program benefit to the children as a result of our efforts in 1964–65. Certainly, as Becker described so well in the early 1950s (Becker, 1952) and, as has been suggested by more recent studies (Rosenthal & Jacobson, 1968), the change in teacher attitude is not without benefit for the child. It was, however, not measurable at that time.

However, long-term follow-up of these children at the end of third grade reveals that this first year's change was not solely one of revised teacher attitudes. Analysis of the reading achievement scores two years later, of this first year's group of first graders in third grade, indicates that the children did indeed benefit. When their reading scores were compared with those of the children in the control schools, this group showed a gain of two months (Kellam, Schiff, & Branch, 1968).

The results for the second year revealed that there was an increase of seven percent in the children rated by the teachers as adapting.[15] Two years later, the results of a follow-up evaluation demonstrated significantly greater improvement

for the intervention children on all the six scales of adaptation (Kellam & Schiff, 1967; Kellam, Schiff, & Branch, 1968; Kellam, 1969). This suggested that the change in the Classroom Meeting had been helpful.

The third program year resulted in the greatest gain. This was the year that parents became regular participants in the weekly Classroom Meetings, and that Parent Meetings during school hours were formalized. This year there was a gain of eight and a half percent in the number of adapting children. Moreover, the results of the two-year follow-up evaluation revealed for the first time significant gains in the IQ test scores of the intervention-school children.[16] In addition, significant gains were also found in various parts of the reading achievement tests administered by the Chicago Board of Education. (Kellam, Schiff, & Branch, 1968; Kellam, 1969).

It is important to note that the program this year was received by the teachers with a qualified and often explictly negative attitude. The pervasive impact of this negative attitude is strongly suggested by the fact that, for the first time, no gains were found in the third-grade children's rating (Kellam, 1969). (The third-grade teachers were part of the intervention-school faculties but not part of the intervention program itself.)

The results of Year IV in which the teachers assumed more direct responsibility for the program, are equally important. Significant gains were found in the children's adaptation. While these were less than the previous year, they demonstrated that teachers and administrators trained in the program's techniques could, with the parents' participation, effectively implement this program (Kellam, Schiff, & Branch, 1968).

This year there was a striking reversal in the teachers' attitudes toward the program. Yet, despite the teachers' more positive views toward the program in Year IV (see Figures 32–1 and 32–2), Year III showed stronger results for the children.

In Year V, the program was operating in 48 first-grade classrooms in 12 schools; 25 of these were in the seven former control schools, 23 in the six original intervention schools. The success of the teams in gaining entry to all of the former control schools and effectively implementing the program in each of them in the face of all the obstacles is indicated by our data. Despite the fact that in the 1968–69 intervention period four fewer Classroom Meetings[17] were held, and despite the fact that 11 of the 12 schools carried out the program without the direct, regular involvement of the Center psychiatrist in the meetings (one of the original intervention schools required the Center psychiatrist's regular participation because of long-standing problems), parent attendance in the six former control schools was much better than it had been in the six original intervention schools during the third year of the program. This was clearly the result of the intensive effort of the School Mental Health Training Teams.

In 1968–69, 49 percent of the children in the former control schools had a parent attend at least one Classroom Meeting in *12 weeks*, whereas in 1966–67 only 33 percent of the children in the six intervention schools had a parent attend once in *17 weeks* (see Figure 32–4). In that year more than half of the parents who did attend came to only one meeting. In 1968–69, however, more than half of the parents who attended in all 12 schools came to two or more meetings (see Figure 32–4).

In 1968–69, 1,007 visits were made by parents to the 25 first-grade classrooms in the six former control schools. Over all, 2,207 visits were made by parents to the 48 first-grade classrooms of all 12 schools. Such results are a tribute to the effectiveness of the School Mental Health Training Teams in working with the faculties.

In 1968–69, 57 percent of the children in the six former intervention schools had at least one parent attend a Classroom Meeting in the *12-week* program period, as compared to only *33 percent* in the *17-week* program period during 1966–67, the first year of parent participation.

Despite one month less of program this year, the new program schools (former control schools) had greater parent participation than did the six former intervention schools in 1966–67 (see Figures 32–3 and 32–4).

THE PROGRAM'S FUTURE

Results such as these, together with the School Mental Health Training Teams' success in over-coming many serious obstacles, have persuaded other school systems here and abroad to consider the intervention program.[18] The first step in this direction was taken by the Chicago Board of Education at the conclusion of the School Mental Health Teams' work in the control-schools in 1968–69. Two new full-time positions were fully funded by the Board of Education and tested during this past 1969–70 school year. These positions are based on the role functions developed in the training program and implemented by the School Mental Health Teams.[19]

The Chicago Board of Education was sufficiently impressed with the effectiveness of the teams' functioning to support the submission of a three-year proposal written by the author in conjunction with the two Team Coordinators for a Title III, ESEA grant to fund the program throughout Area A, a division of Chicago which includes about 250,000 children. This grant application was approved with a budget of $145,000 for the 1970–71 school year.

A rural farming community, predominately white and ethnically diverse, has contracted to replicate the program thoughout their school system. Its neighboring small city is interested also. Their willingness to participate in all the necessary evaluative procedures will permit comparison of the program's effectiveness and pertinence for this very different population and locale.

THE COMMITMENT TO FREE INQUIRY AND CHANGE

After reviewing the many obstacles which arose at critical points in the evolution of this community mental health program, one might ask why I did not beat a secure and dignified retreat, protected by having fulfilled at least the five-year term we had contracted for with the community.

Reluctant to relinquish all I have learned during these past years, unwilling to be constrained in the process of inquiry, and equally hesitant to indulge in thoughtlessly provocative inquiry, I have had to choose an appropriate way to continue my work and accept any possible consequences of this choice.

In many ways, the program's ongoing demand upon us was no less directed to change—both personal and programmatic—than it was to the children, parents, and teachers. For, learning to pursue with the child the possible impediments to his progress is not part of most mental health curricula, which focus predominately on working with adults. The real core of the program—an enduring commitment to free inquiry—became indistinquishable from a commitment to change.

Child and Parent Commitment. For the children, the changes to be wrought very often involved relinquishing a safer, more dependent position and assuming new personal obligations and commitments of their own. The tasks of relating not only to his peers but also to his parents and teachers are not always easy, and the child who does not immediately succeed at them cannot simply be dismissed as incompetent.

For parents the road is no easier. Recognizing their parental responsibilities is difficult. We were fortunate, however, that in Woodlawn we were working with a group of parents who have seldom had the luxury—more common among affluent families—of engaging in duplicity to disguise the self-interest motivating their behavior.

The exigencies of survival for the mother with several children and a tight budget leave little time for anything beyond caring for her family. The difficulties she encounters in day-to-day living too often become inexorably defeating. Although little recognized, these daily combats for a dignified family survival appear to strengthen the Woodlawn parents' comparatively straightforward interest in their children's future. This constant engagement with the "nitty gritty" realities of existence is a fundamentally honest struggle whose raison d' être is the present and future well-being of their children.

The Professionals' Commitment. A teacher's involvement with the child's welfare is necessarily less personal. The professional criteria which teachers learn to apply, the contractual nature of their profession, and the often confounding need for professional validation all serve to limit their interest in the child. In some instances, particularly those common to the urban ghetto school, the educators' true basis for being interested is frequently a masked one—unacknowledged and "concealed" even from their own awareness (Becker, 1952; Becker, 1960).

As for the mental health professional and the local service program director in the school and community, their stake in the child's welfare is even more specialized and hence more constricted and distant. In this group, the tendency to serve professional self-interest becomes more prominent and the seduction of professional recognition and other rewards more difficult to resist. Neither current trends in professional training nor current yardsticks for professional advancement gives hope that this trend will be reversed.

The opposition our program encountered from the black middle class professionals was the result of professional self-interest, often in an exaggerated form. This was just one example of a host of confrontations and demands to be found in a profusion of newspaper reports (Black's Attack, 1969; Collier, 1968; Fraser, 1968; Health and Community Control, 1970; New York Times, 1968a,b,c,d; Sizemore, 1970). These published accounts help to explain the suspicion with which the black professional is viewed by the ghetto resident. It is better understood by considering Myrdal's analysis of the self-serving function of the black middle class's appeals for racial solidarity.

He suggested that "upper-class Negroes find it necessary to instigate a protest against caste on the part of Negro masses as a means of averting lower class [Negro] opposition against themselves and to steer it instead against the white caste" (Myrdal, 1962, p. 767). He asserts that the preaching of race solidarity is, in fact, a vehicle for the upper class Negro to assert his leadership over his less fortunate but more numerous brothers. Myrdal's concluding sentence may well be ominously fulfilled by current circumstances; in it, he notes that the function of such appeals is social mobility within "the race," not integration within the larger American society.

The attitudes found by the Kerner Commission among the ghetto residents of Newark and Detroit after the riots strengthens Myrdal's view of racial solidarity. More than 71 percent of the self-reported Newark rioters agreed that "Negroes who make a lot of money are just as bad as white people." This finding was repeated in Detroit with over 50 percent in agreement. In addition, 60 percent of those who participated in the Detroit riots of 1967 were opposed to exclusively black civil rights groups (Report of the National Advisory Commission on Civil Disorders, 1968, p. 76).

Myrdal, while acknowledging the need for all Negroes to experience a positive respect for their origins and a dignified and proud sense of group identification, is uncompromising in his presentation of the self-serving function of the middle class Negro's appeal for racial solidarity.

Despite the objections of the faculty, which were made strictly on a racial basis, the parents, whose principle concern was their children's future, were not deterred from their involvement. When black teachers or black community organization staff spoke for "community control" of the schools, they were reminded—on occasion explicitly, but more frequently by the impressive parental attendance at the program meetings—that for the parents "community control" did not mean the right to hire and fire their children's teacher or doctor on any criterion other than professional ability. For the Woodlawn parent, like all parents, wants the best professional service available.

Woodlawn children and parents have traditionally had little share in decision making. The eagerness of both to involve themselves openly in the Classroom Meetings revealed an intense desire for democracy.

The professional employed as a policy-maker or advisor to government agencies is at least as removed from the service recipient as teachers, mental health professionals, and local service program directors and more likely to allow self-interest to conflict with his job. Indeed, recent evaluations of the contributions of such professionals to programs developed from the hopeful legislation of the 1960s—Headstart (Semple, 1969), OEO (Clark, 1969; Lowi, 1969; Moynihan, 1969), and Medicare and Medicaid (Eaton, 1969; Lyons, 1970)—strongly suggest that self-interest was predominant.

The Kerner report revealed that in Detroit only 30 percent of the $12.6 million of OEO funds was actually received by the poor persons for whom it was intended; in Newark, only 44 percent of $1.9 million reached the poor, and in New Haven, only 42 percent of $2.3 million (Report of the National Advisory Commission on Civil Disorders, 1968, p. 80). It appears that any benefits of these programs accrue largely to the professionals and middle class employees who dispense and administer the new social programs—not the service recipients.

Change and the Status Quo. Professionals and institutions are either change-oriented or committed to the status quo. For example, the pediatrician and elementary school teacher live continually with the hope of constructive change in children and are, by profession and experience, very much committed to optimism about the life continuum.

By contrast, the law and the courts serve the citizenry through their foundation in tradition and precedent. Thus, it must be recognized that labeling an individual institution or policy as either change-oriented or status-quo-oriented does not automatically indicate that it is either harmful or beneficial.

It is unfortunate that the mechanisms for implementing changes in the law are laborious and costly in time, money, and personal investment. It is more unfortunate, however, that the solutions to many of society's problems are assigned priorities based upon the criteria of time, money, and the willingness of individuals to contribute their efforts. It can be catastrophic when one has to go through a lengthy, costly process to change and improve education for children. Resistance to change in social service agencies, and worst of all, in the university, is tragic.

Academia and Politics. With disturbing frequency, the university and the professional political administrative advisor seem indistinguishable in function and indeed in person (Boffey, 1969; Boffey, 1968; Boffey & Nelson, 1968; Carter, 1969). Rarely are academics who voice dissenting opinions to the current political posture appointed to these posts. In fact, evidence of the systematic exclusion of such academics from advisory and policy-making functions has caused grave concern in scientific circles (Boffey & Nelson, 1968; Nelson, 1969a,b; Washington Post, 1969).

President Eisenhower, in his Farewell Address, warned the nation of "the danger that public policy could itself become the captive of a scientific and technological elite" (Eisenhower, 1961, p. 421). Recently, Supreme Court Justice William O. Douglas, in a series of essays underscoring the vitalizing function of dissent in a democracy, pointed to the threat to such dissent posed by the university's role in the military-industrial complex (Douglas, 1970). A former advisor to President Johnson repeated this warning as she struck out at the "academic-industrial complex" (Reilly, 1970). Senator J. William Fulbright voiced his concern with the readiness of scholars to "accept existing public policies . . . as if [their] proper and only function were to devise the technical means of carrying these policies out" (p. 42). Fulbright concludes his remarks on the changing role of the university by strongly warning against the increasing tendency of the university today to conceive of itself as nothing more than "the servant of the party in power" (Fulbright, 1966, p. 42).

Describing the current power base and constituency of the Republican Party, Kevin Phillips (1969) notes the existence of a university-governmental complex in his book *The Emerging Republican Majority* but describes it as a positive development. The support given former Harvard Professor Daniel P. Moynihan's pejorative assessment of the capacities of the poor citizen—an assessment as based on the failures of the community programs of the 1960s and supported by the opinions of such academic "rear-echelon" experts as Banfield (1970) and Lowi (1969)—is perhaps most indicative of this coalition.

Clearly, there are many questions still unpursued and unanswered with regard to why such programs as OEO, Headstart, and Medicare have "failed" (Clark, 1969; Moynihan, 1969; Semple, 1969). The assignment of major culpability to the ghetto citizen's incapacities or the overwhelming complexities of the problem may be regarded as one more example of the politically self-serving needs of universities, government administrations, and industry (Anderson, 1970; Carter, 1969; Reilly, 1970; Walsh, 1969).

Evidence does exist that inexpensive, properly conceived and implemented programs based on a sustained commitment can work. The Woodlawn Mental Health Program is one example. Such pragmatic evidence is in direct conflict with the published judgments of such academics as Banfield, Lowi, and Moynihan, whose lack of direct and continuous programmatic involvement with the residents of such neighborhoods renders their analyses vulnerable to the criticism of "ivory

towerism." Even more germane to today's academic climate of short-term studies is the criticism that their conclusions represent a premature synthesis of insufficient data collected over too brief a period of time. For certainly both the "benign neglect" memo of Moynihan (Kihss, 1970) and Banfield's argument that incompetence and lack of will—not discrimination—are the major reasons why black ghetto residents fail to get ahead (Banfield, 1970) are seriously challenged by our success in Woodlawn in helping the children and involving the parents in an effective community mental health program.

Even more pertinent than the political implications of such "scholarly" works is the recent controversy on university campuses concerning the propriety of a "political recess" for faculty and students prior to election time for the purposes of electioneering. The concern that such institutional action is the first step toward the destruction of free inquiry is shared by a surprising number of academics (Friedman & Stigler, 1970; Kurland, 1970; Lowi, 1970; Rheinhold, 1970) and has caused some concern with regard to the university's tax-exempt status. This is one more reason why the university-community obstacles that threatened the program in Woodlawn require additional scrutiny.

If the university, out of a valid concern that its ability to pursue the truth is threatened by current political pressures, decides to protect its traditional values by itself becoming politicized, then its unique raison d'être as the one neutral social institution dedicated to the pursuit of truth will be destroyed. On the other hand, the future of the university is no less imperiled if curriculum, teaching methods, and contexts are believed to be as immutable as the idea of free inquiry and change is considered suspect.

It is now seven years since I came to Woodlawn and, with my colleagues—and later the Center board members—developed the Woodlawn Mental Health Center.

My early commitment was to pursue—in collaboration with the citizens of the community—the development of meaningful mental health programs whose effectiveness would be carefully tested. In retrospect, this commitment was a limited one, restricted in time and parochial in its almost exclusively professional concerns.

My commitment today is a stronger one than in 1963—but it differs in ways which I could not have predicted initially. In the process of carrying out my work, I now discover that new obligations and interests have become new commitments, as the origin and nature of the obstacles encountered have become better understood. These new commitments are to people—first and foremost to children—and to the concept of democracy.

From my experience in the schools of Woodlawn, I have been learning from the best teachers of all—the children, with the help of their parents and the school faculties—how inadequately I had viewed children, with respect to their rights and potentials, in the past. This growing understanding of childhood has developed into a new and different commitment to the welfare of children—both as a professional and as a parent.

I have discovered what Socrates labored to teach so long ago: that "both in the time when [a child] is a man and when he isn't, there are to be true opinions in him, which are awakened by questioning and become knowledge. . . . For it is clear that through all time [a child] either is or is not a man" (Warmington & Rouse, 1956, p. 51).

Similarly *I* have learned to respect the honesty and abilities not only of the children but of their parents as well.

I have also gained a better understanding (along with a sense of caution) of those repressive and threatening forces which prevent these qualities from being manifested and exercised.

Despite the possible termination of my work in Woodlawn, I am now more strongly committed to the concept of a community-professional contract that is not based upon any right of sovereignty of professions, institutions, or political or corporate structures.[20] Rather, such contracts must represent a commitment more identified with the ancient Greek ideal of the community as a teacher of virtue—a concept which held that only within such a community is moral, human, and hence professional, behavior possible. It is no longer feasible for any individual or group—or any institution—to establish professional or social contracts with the community based upon interests and rights that set them apart from society. Certainly, the demands for "community control"—particularly in communities like Woodlawn—authored largely by black middle class professionals, are quite Hobbesian in rationale. The "community" in these cases is invariably defined in a self-serving fashion by those who would do the "controlling."

My awareness that the self-interests of some individuals and institutions are conceived as unique and apart, and that the consequences of this view are unfortunate for individuals and society, has grown during the past few years with the progress of my work and my own professional development. It has been only within recent months, however, that I have realized how related these phenomena are to my work and to me personally. For it is now quite clear to me that the innovative professional work which I originally came to Woodlawn to develop has its taproots in the soil of democracy. Clearly, my professional work is completely dependent for its existence, both now and in the future, upon the presence of a democratic system of government.

It would be tragic if the current political obstacles to the program's existence in Woodlawn finally are successful in depriving the children and parents of its well-demonstrated benefits—benefits which the parents acknowledge but are powerless to fight for openly because of their vulnerability and historic disenfranchisement. In a democratic community, this program could not be so pervasively obstructed.

ACKNOWLEDGMENTS

The ability of the author to maintain his long-term commitment in the face of the obstacles described in this chapter is dependent upon the unusual support and encouragement of his family and staff. Miss Luise Smyre, the author's Administrative Assistant, Mr. Douglass T. Turner, Associate Director of the training program, Mr. Tedwilliam Theodore, Audio-visual Specialist, and Miss Dianne Dickson, Research Specialist and their staff continue to demonstrate rare conviction in this work and loyalty to the author under uniquely trying circumstances.

The work presented in this chapter is part of a project of intervention and study begun in 1963. Both this project and the Woodlawn Mental Health Center were products of the efforts of the author and his colleague, Dr. Sheppard G. Kellam, who, until recently, shared coequally in its development and accomplishments.

The author is grateful to the Woodlawn Mental Health Center Board for having provided him the opportunity to enjoy the most personally satisfying and productive years of his professional career. Neither the program developed and described in this chapter nor the Woodlawn Mental Health Center itself could have been possible without the Board's initial singular honesty of purpose and concern for their children.

The Honorable Richard J. Daley, Mayor of the City of Chicago, and the Chicago Board of Health have provided this program and the author with important support. The author is also grateful for the assistance in the program's early years of Dr. Harold Visotsky, formerly Director of the State of Illinois Department of Mental Health, and Dr. Melvin Sabshin, head of the Department of Psychiatry, University of Illinois College of Medicine.

The author is appreciative of the support given this work by the Chicago Board of Education, Dr. James Redmond, General Superintendent of Schools; Dr. Curtis C. Melnick, Area A Associate Superintendent; Dr. Donald Blyth, Superintendent of District 14; Michael R. Fortino, Superintendent of District 21; and The Rt. Rev. Msgr. William F. McManus, Superintendent Archdiocesan School Board.

The work presented is largely supported by USPHS Research Grant R01–MH 14–807, from the National Institute of Mental Health as well as grants from the Wieboldt Foundation, the van Ameringen Foundation, the Field Foundation, and the Maurice Falk Medical Fund.

Notes

1. Edward H. Futterman, M.D., Sheppard G. Kellam, M.D., and the author. Dr. Futterman left the project after its first year in Woodlawn. Until recently, the directorship of the Center has been shared by Dr. Kellam and the author.

2. The Center was affiliated with the University of Illinois Medical School, Department of Psychiatry from July 1, 1963, through June 1966. Since July 1966, it has been affiliated with the University of Chicago Pritzker School of Medicine, Department of Psychiatry.

3. A grant from the State of Illinois Department of Mental Health Research and Training Authority, DMH No. 17–322, awarded for a three-year period beginning July 1, 1964 (Principal Investigator: S. G. Kellam, M.D., and coprincipal Investigator: S. K. Schiff, M.D.); and a grant from the National Institute of Mental Health 5–R01–MH–14807, awarded for a five-year period beginning January 1, 1966 (Program Director: S. K. Schiff, M.D., and Codirector, S. G. Kellam, M.D.).

4. Woodlawn Mental Health Center Board Constitution, adopted November 21, 1968, gave the board the added responsibilities of consent as well as advice.

5. Dr. Curtis C. Melnick, formerly Superintendent of District 14 and now Area A Associate Superintendent, Chicago Board of Education, provided crucial support to the program during this period.

6. The program of prevention and early treatment has been carried out during the last semester of school for the first five program years. It was begun after the January mid-year assessments and terminated in late May or early June of that same year. This early program termination was to allow sufficient time for the end-of-the-year assessments and data gathering. In the first program year, 1964–65 only 12 weeks of Classroom Meetings were held.

7. Signed statements of permission to videotape and audiotape the program's group meetings for educational and training purposes were requested from the parents of all involved children, school faculty, Center staff, and visitors. In those rare instances when these were not obtained from the parents, their children were excluded from that particular meeting.

8. In Year III, 1966–67, members and staff of TWO provided the Center with valuable assistance in one school by making home visits and encouraging parents to attend the program meetings despite the extreme hesitancy and negativism of the school faculty.

9. Attorney Carroll replaced one of the codirectors, Dr. Sheppard G. Kellam, as chairman following the Board's adoption of its constitution. As Attorney Carroll stated during a University of Chicago telecast in the summer of 1969, "We (the Board) came together . . . with a mutual respect that got ever greater . . . to the early extent that we never had a (permanent) chairman–(but) a chairman protemp. We had all chiefs and no indians."

10. Rev. Thomas H. Ellis, verbatim comments on University of Chicago telecast "Perspectives"; July 23, 1969; Chicago, ABC, WLS-TV, Channel 7. Reprinted with permission.

11. Two and a half months after its appointment, the Subcommittee on South Campus of the University of Chicago published the first report of its studies of the problems of "relocation and demolition in South Campus." While the University is described in this report as "a concerned neighbor . . . [and] a concerned academic institution, the report defines its role with regard to the future of the South Campus areas explicitly: 1) it is clear that the authority and responsibility for relocation and demolition in South Campus rest with the Department of

Urban Renewal [City of Chicago] and not with the University."

It is of some interest to note that with the exception of Dr. Sheppard G. Kellam, then Codirector, Woodlawn Mental Health Center, the membership of the committee included no faculty member whose academic work was based in Woodlawn and intimately linked to this community's future.

12. In our letters requesting the transfer of our grant funds from the University of Illinois to the University of Chicago—mine to the National Institute of Mental Health and Dr. Kellam's to the State Department of Illinois Division of Research Service—the following reasons were given and were accepted to complete the transfer:

The change is being brought about because of the increased commitment on the part of The University of Chicago to the mental health of the local communities around it, including Woodlawn. The University of Chicago faculty feels that the work we are doing, which is partly described in this Grant, is of basic importance, and has asked us to come on to the faculty of the Department of Psychiatry in order to be a nucleus of that Department's growing clinical training and research commitment to the mental health problems of the community of Woodlawn. We have discussed this transfer with Dr. Harold Visotsky, Director of the Department of Mental Health, who has given his heartiest approval. Dr. Melvin Sabshin, Chairman of the Department of Psychiatry of the University of Illinois, is encouraging this transfer in order to facilitate these developments. . . . Dr. Daniel X. Freedman, the new Chairman of the Department of Psychiatry of the University of Chicago, is strongly supporting the transfer as part of his new commitment to the community of Woodlawn. The Acting Chairman of the Department, Dr. Robert Daniels, is fully supporting the transfer and is available for consultation with you, if this is at all necessary.

We have discussed this transfer with our community Advisory Board, made up of twenty-two community leaders from Woodlawn, who are supporting this transfer in the interest of enhancing the mental health resources available to the community of Woodlawn.

13. The listing of the school mental health seminar in the University Time Schedule resulted from this suggestion as did a request for rent-free classroom space which was provided the next year.

14. The Field Foundation, Chicago, Illinois; The Wieboldt Foundation, Chicago, Illinois, and the van Ameringen Foundation, New York, New York.

15. The adaptation rating scale administered to the teachers by Mrs. Jeannette Branch, M.A., formerly Chief of Children's Mental Health Services, and from which their results were obtained is described in two earlier publications, together with the assessment method used to evaluate the program's effectiveness (Kellam & Schiff, 1967; Kellam, Schiff, & Branch, 1968).

16. This year the long-term follow-up was more extensive, including independent tests, testers, and procedures employed by the Woodlawn Mental Health Center, rather than relying entirely on those administered by the Board of Education.

17. In 1968—69, the number of meetings was reduced to an average of 12 in each school because the third-grade follow-up evaluation was in progress. With the exception of the program year, 1964—65, when only 12 weeks of Classroom Meetings were held, in each of the next three successive years, there were 17 weeks of Classroom Meetings during the program period.

18. Within recent years, the school intervention and training program, as a result of the increasing wide recognition it has received (Alinsky, 1967; Beadle, 1968; Bliss, 1968; Dunbar, 1967; Smith, 1968; Strunk, 1969; Woodlawn Mental Health Center, 1968), has been requested to provide consultation to a number of school systems, mental health authorities, and private groups both nationally and in other countries as well.

19. Mr. Douglass T. Turner, Associate Director of the training program, and his staff have been indispensible to both the intervention and training programs' achievements. The work of Mrs. Lauretta P. Naylor and Mrs. Frances C. Carroll, the first two Team Leaders in 1968—69, and now Area A Mental Health Team Coordinators, and the parents and educators of the teams, have also been essential to the program's achievements.

20. Since this chapter was first submitted for publication some months ago, the emergence of more formidable and hazardous university-community obstacles resulted in the removal of both Dr. Kellam and myself from our seven-year tenure as codirectors of the Woodlawn Mental Health Center and assigned the position of "psychiatric consultant."

Shortly after that, I, my staff, and my operations were physically removed from the Center and Woodlawn and relocated at our new university offices in the Windermere Hotel. Dr. Kellam continues to work at the Woodlawn Mental Health Center.

References

Aberle, D. F. Introducing preventive psychiatry into a community. *Human Organization*, 1950, 9, 5—9.

Alinsky, S. D. The poor and the powerful. In *Psychiatric Research Report No. 21: Poverty and mental health.* Washington, D. C.: American Psychiatric Association, 1967.

Anderson, J. Elite educators being used to push corporate causes. *Chicago Daily News*, February 5, 1970.

Ashby, E. On universities and the scientific revolution. In A. H. Halsey, J. Floud, & C. A. Anderson (eds.), *Education, economy, and society; A reader in the sociology of education.* Glencoe, Ill.: Free Press, 1965.

Banfield, E. C. *The unheavenly city; The nature and future of our urban crisis.* Boston: Little, Brown, 1970.

Beadle, G. *The University of Chicago: Report of the President.* Chicago: University of Chicago Press, 1968.

Becker, H. S. The career of the Chicago public school teacher. *American Journal of Sociology*, 1952, 57, 470—477.

Becker, H. S. Notes on the concept of commitment. *American Journal of Sociology*, 1960, 66, 32—40.

Blacks attack psychiatry for ignoring ghetto needs. *Psychiatric News*, 1969, 4, 4.

Bliss, B. Insight. Psychiatry's "numbers game"; Thousands of children diagnosed as mentally disturbed, are kept from treatment by shortage of trained workers. *Chicago Daily News*, April 30, 1968.

Boffey, P. M. Scientists in politics: Humphrey group outshines Nixon's. *Science*, 1968, 162, 244–245.

Boffey, P. M. The Hornig years: Did LBJ neglect his science adviser? *Science*, 1969, 163, 453–458.

Boffey, P. M., & Nelson, B. NSF directorship: Why did Nixon veto Franklin A. Long. *Science*, 1969, 164, 406–411.

Butts, R. F., & Cremin, L. A. *A history of education in American culture.* New York: Holt, Rinehart & Winston, 1953.

Caplow, T., & McGee, R. J. *The academic marketplace.* New York: Basic Books, 1958.

Carter, L. J. University of Texas: On the way up–But politics still intrude. *Science*, 1969, 164, 1150–1154.

Chicago Tribune. Modern mental health center serves Woodlawn: City sponsors psychiatric facility. October 11, 1964.

Chicago Tribune. TWO has high hopes for area development. May 7, 1970.

Clark, K. B. *Relevant war against poverty: A study of community action programs and observable social change.* New York: Harper & Row, 1969.

Collier, B. L. Ocean Hill crisis endangers peace in city's schools. *New York Times*, November 26, 1968, p. 1.

Cooley, B. TWO meetings: Students score Woodlawn policy. *Chicago Maroon*, May 10, 1968.

Cronbach, L. J., & Suppes, P. (eds.) *Research for tomorrow's schools: Disciplined inquiry for education.* (Report of the Committee on Educational Research of the National Academy of Education) New York: Macmillan, 1969.

Cubberley, E. P. *Public education in the United States. A study and interpretation of American educational history.* (Rev. ed.) Cambridge, Mass.: Houghton Mifflin, Riverside Press, 1947.

Cumming, E., & Cumming, J. *Closed ranks: An experiment in mental health education.* Cambridge, Mass.: Commonwealth Fund and Harvard University Press, 1957.

Demerath, N. J. Initiating and maintaining research relations in a military organization. *Journal of Social Issues*, 1952, 11–23.

DeTocqueville, A. *Democracy in America.* (Ed. by J. P. Mayer; trans. by G. Lawrence) Garden City, N. Y.: Doubleday, Anchor Books, 1969.

Douglas, W. O. *Points of rebellion.* New York: Random House, Vintage Books, 1970.

Dunbar, R. Woodlawn experiment: Adapting in first grade. *Chicago Sun-Times*, January 22, 1967.

Eaton, W. J. Medicaid a "disaster"–Egeberg. *Chicago Daily News*, July 9, 1969.

Eisenhower, D. D. *Public papers of the presidents of the United States. Dwight D. Eisenhower, 1960–61,* (Containing the public messages, speeches, and statements of the President, January 1, 1960, to January 20, 1961) Washington, D. C.: United States Government Printing Office, 1961.

Ensign, F. C. *Compulsory school attendance and child labor; A study of the historical development of regulations compelling attendance and limiting the labor of children in a selected group of states.* Iowa City: Athens Press, 1921.

Festinger, L., Cartwright, D., Barber, K., Fleischl, J., Gottsdanker, J., Keysen, A., & Leavitt, G. A study of a rumor: Its origin and spread. *Human Relations*, 1948, 1, 464–486.

Fraser, C. C. Community control here found spreading to the field of health. *New York Times*, March 9, 1968, p. 42.

Friedman, M., & Stigler, G. Address to members of the faculty, University of Chicago, May 9, 1970.

Fulbright, J. W. *The arrogance of power.* New York: Random House, Vintage Books, 1966.

Futterman, E. H., Meltzer, M., & Schiff, S. K. A study of delinquents in groups. Unpublished manuscript, Yale University Dept. of Psychology, 1959.

Gildea, M. C. L., Domke, H. R., Mensh, I. N., Buchmueller, A. D., Glidewell, J. C., & Kantor, M. B. Community mental health research: Findings after three years. Paper presented at the 113th annual meeting of the American Psychiatric Association, Chicago, Illinois, May 13–17, 1957.

Glidewell, J. C. The entry problem in consultation. *Journal of Social Issues*, 1959, 15, 51–59.

Health and community control: An interview with Roy Innis. *Social Policy*, May-June, 1970, p. 68.

Jencks, C., & Riesman, D. *The academic revolution.* Garden City, N. Y.: Doubleday, 1968.

Kellam, S. G. Woodlawn school mental health program of study and intervention: Assessment and evaluation. Unpublished manuscript, Woodlawn Mental Health Center, 1969.

Kellam, S. G., & Schiff, S. K. The Woodlawn Mental Health Center: A community mental health center model. *Social Service Review*, 1966, 40, 255–263.

Kellam, S. G., & Schiff, S. K. Adaptation and mental illness in the first grade classrooms of an urban community. In *Psychiatric Research Report No. 21: Poverty and mental health.* Washington, D. C.: American Psychiatric Association, 1967.

Kellam, S. G., & Schiff, S. K. The origins and evolution of an urban community mental health center in Woodlawn. In L. Duhl & R. Leopold (eds.), *Mental health and urban social policy.* San Francisco: Jossey-Bass, 1968.

Kellam, S. G., & Schiff, S. K. Adaptation to first grade and family life. Paper presented at the 122nd annual meeting of the American Psychiatric Association, Miami Beach, May 9, 1969.

Kellam, S. G., Schiff, S. K., & Branch, J. D. The Woodlawn community-wide school mental health program of assessment, prevention and early treatment. Paper presented at the Midwest Annual Regional Conference, Reports from the Rockton Conference, Rockton, Illinois, September 29-October 1, 1968.

Kiessler, F. More than psychiatry–A rural program. In M. Shore & F. Mannino (eds.), *Mental health and the community: Problems, programs and strategies.* New York: Behavioral Publications, 1969.

Kihss, P. "Benign neglect" on race is proposed by Moynihan. *New York Times*, March 1, 1970, p. 1.

Klebanoff, L. B., & Bindman, A. J. The organization and development of a community mental health program for children: A case study. *American Journal of Orthopsychiatry*, 1962, 32, 119–132.

Kurland, P. B. U. S. universities—Can they survive? *Chicago Today*, June 11, 1970.

Levi, E. H. *Point of view: Talks on education.* Chicago: University of Chicago Press, 1969.

Lowi, T. J. *The end of liberalism; Ideology, policy and the crisis of public authority.* New York: Norton, 1969.

Lowi, T. J. An open letter to Edward H. Levi, President, the University of Chicago. May 27, 1970; June 13, 1970.

Lyons, R. D. Medicare study in senate seeks urgent reform. *New York Times*, February 9, 1970, p. 1.

Merton, R. K. Selected problems of field work in the planned community. *American Sociological Review*, 1947, 12, 304–312.

Moore, R. Child health tops Woodlawn recast. *Chicago Sun-Times*, July 6, 1967.

Moynihan, D. P. *Maximum feasible misunderstanding; Community action in the war on poverty.* New York: Free Press, 1969.

Myrdal, G. With the assistance of Richard Sterner and Arnold Rose. In *An American dilemma; The Negro problem and modern democracy.* 2 vols. New York: Harper & Row, Harper Torch Books, 1962.

Nelson, B. HEW blacklisting issue ignites again. *Science*, 1969, 166, 357. (a)

Nelson, B. HEW: Finch tries to gain control over department's advisory groups. *Science*, 1969, 164, 813–814. (b)

New York Times. Community balks aid to retarded. December 26, 1966.

New York Times. Bronx health units shut after revolt. March 7, 1968, p. 74. (a)

New York Times. City health service protested in Bronx. March 5, 1968, p. 9. (b)

New York Times. Head of Ocean Hill District Board and teacher are arrested in school. November, 27, 1968, p. 1. (c)

New York Times. 23 seized at sit-in in Lincoln Hospital. March 21, 1968, p. 35. (d)

Phillips, K. *The emerging Republican majority.* New Rochelle, N. Y.: Arlington House, 1969.

Public Law 88–164. Mental Retardation Facilities and Community Mental Health Center Construction Act of 1963. 88th Congress, S. 1576, October 31, 1963.

Public Law 88–452. Economic Opportunity Act of 1964. 88th Congress, 2nd Session, S. 2642, August 20, 1964.

Public Law 89–10. Elementary and Secondary Education Act of 1965. 89th Congress, 1st Session, April 11, 1965.

Public Law 89–97. Social Security Act amendments of 1965. July 1965.

Public Law 89–105. Mental Retardation Facilities and Community Mental Health Center Construction Act amendments of 1965. 89th Congress, H. R. 2985, August 4, 1965.

Public Law 90–248. Social Security Act amendments of 1967.

Reilly, J. Betty Furness hits "university-industrial complex." *Chicago Sun-Times*, May 22, 1970.

Report of the National Advisory Commission on Civil Disorders. Washington, D. C.: United States Government Printing Office, 1968.

Rheinhold, R. Poll recess is rejected at Harvard. *New York Times*, June 9, 1970, p. 39.

Roman, M. Community control and the community mental health center: A view from the Lincoln Bridge. Paper presented at a National Institute of Mental Health staff meeting on Metropolitan topics—Dilemma of community control: University and community relations, NIMH, Washington, D. C., November 21, 1969.

Rosenthal, R., & Jacobson, L. *Pygmalion in the classroom.* New York: Holt, Rinehart & Winston, 1968.

Schiff, S. K. Community accountability and mental health services. *Mental Hygiene*, 1970, 54, 205–214. (a)

Schiff, S. K. A proposal for the education of minority medical students. *Medicine, on the Midway*, 1970, 25, 25. (b)

Schiff, S. K. Training the professional. *University of Chicago Magazine*, 1970, 62, 8–14. (c)

Schiff, S. K., & Kellam, S. G. A community-wide mental health program of prevention and early treatment in first grade. In *Psychiatric Research Report No. 21: Poverty and mental health.* Washington, D. C.: American Psychiatric Association, 1967.

Schiff, S. K., Theodore, T., & Turner, D. T. The "mirror-within-a-mirror" process: Conceptual and technical issues in the use of television as a curricular aide, in preparation.

Schiff, S. K., & Turner, D. T. Parent participation in a community-wide school mental health program. Paper presented at the 46th annual meeting of the American Orthopsychiatric Association, New York, April 1, 1969.

Schiff, S. K., & Turner, D. T. The Woodlawn school mental health training program: A community-based university graduate course. *Journal of School Psychology*, 1971, 9:292–302.

Semple, R. B., Jr. Head Start pupils found no better off than others. *New York Times*, April 14, 1969, p. 1.

Sewell, W. H. Field techniques in social psychological study in a rural community. *American Sociological Review*, 1949, 14, 718–726.

Silberman, C. B. *Crisis in black and white.* New York: Random House, 1964.

Sizemore, B. Educational leadership for the black community. *The Observer*, February 26, 1970.

Smith, M. B. The revolution in mental-health care—A "bold new approach"? *Trans-action*, April 1968, 19–23.

Snow, B. University integrity not to be trusted in community relations. *Chicago Maroon*, May 10, 1968.

Strunk, B. B. New approaches for schools: Helping the disturbed child. *School Management*, 1969, 13, 53–64.

Taylor, D. W. (ed.) Education for research in psychology. *American Psychologist*, 1959, 14, 167–179.

The Observer. Programs for '70. April 30, 1970.

TWO—U C enter new housing venture. *University of Chicago Magazine*, 1969, 62, 30.

Walker, W. L. The University of Chicago and its community. *University of Chicago Magazine*, 1970, 62, S–7.

Walsh, J. Universities: Industry links raise conflict of interest issue. *Science*, 1969, 164, 411–412.

Warmington, E. H., & Rouse, P. G. (eds.) *Great dialogues of Plato*. (Trans. by W. H. D. Rouse) New York: Mentor Books, 1956.

Washington Post. Editorial: Blacklisting for the fun of it. October 11, 1969.

Woodlawn Booster. Dispute rages over site of mental health center: Race bias charged. December 18, 1963.

Woodlawn Booster. Review of 1963 via top ten local news stories. January 1, 1964.

Woodlawn Booster. TWO U of C set up $15 million for Woodlawn—Money to be used for redeveloping the area. December 2, 1969.

Woodlawn Mental Health Center. *Medicine on the Midway*, 1968, 24, 1–4.

33

Research in Mental Health Consultation

Fortune V. Mannino and Milton F. Shore

Mental health consultation can be viewed as a major, if not the major technique and focus of community psychology, community psychiatry, and community mental health. There are several reasons for this popularity of consultation among mental health professionals: (1) it is a means of influencing large segments of a population through contact with relatively few significant individuals; (2) it is a means of extending mental health principles to other community service professionals, thereby broadening the community service base; (3) it is a way of developing the mental health potential of various kinds of community programs which have mental health relevance; (4) it is helpful in dealing with the professional manpower shortage, since it is a very efficient use of scarce professional time; (5) insofar as it deals only indirectly with the client system, it has a natural linkage to "primary prevention"; and (6) due to increased specialization plus the phenomenal outpouring of professional knowledge and information, there is a continuous need for expert advice if only to maintain an adequate standard of competency in various fields of practice. Consultation is able to fill this void.

As a professional activity, however, consultation is considerably broader than the mental health field. Its participants include professionals from a variety of disciplines, including psychology, education, social work, behavioral science, psychiatry, nursing, medicine, public health, and business and management. In a recently completed reference guide to the consultation literature, 646 articles were entered and classified, representing the writings of these various groups (Mannino,

1969). As might be expected, the articles reflect the tremendous diversity of opinions and practice in the consultation field. In a previous chapter, Altrocchi and Bindman have reviewed much of this literature in order to define consultation and to clarify the various roles, techniques, methods, and practices of consultation. The purpose of the present chapter is to review the published works and a number of unpublished doctoral dissertations in the area of research and evaluation in consultation[1] in an attempt to classify the material in terms of major areas studied, critically analyze the research in each area, summarize the findings, and point to needed directions of research in future studies. The chapter is organized in terms of the system developed to classify the research areas studied: (1) empirically derived classification and typology; (2) program analysis (administrative evaluation); (3) research related to general areas of consultation practice; (4) research on the process of consultation; and (5) research on the outcome of consultation.

EMPIRICALLY DERIVED CLASSIFICATION AND TYPOLOGY

A major difficulty for anyone who attempts to work in the area of consultation is coming to grips with the many diverse activities included under the consultation label. Although there have been several attempts to classify these activities into orderly categories, these have been mostly based on personal experience, clinical practice, or a general intuitive feeling for what is going on in the field. Nevertheless, these approaches should be mentioned insofar as they have served to facilitate communication and comparisons of different experiences. Probably the approach which has had most popular usage is that of Caplan (1963) who classified consultation on the basis of problem and focus into four categories: (1) client-centered case consultation; (2) consultee-centered case consultation; (3) consultee-centered administrative consultation; (4) program-centered administrative consultation. Other classifications include the three category scheme of Haylett and Rapoport (1964): (1) client-centered consultation; (2) consultee-centered consultation; and (3) program-centered consultation; and the six "models" of consultation mentioned by Bindman (1966): (1) the medical model, (2) the resource model, (3) the intramural model, (4) the counseling model, (5) the process model, and (6) the group approach or consultee-trainer model. As noted above, none of these approaches has been derived from empirical data.

The only attempt utilizing field research methods to develop an empirically-derived conceptual classification and typology of consultation has been the study of consultation to child care agencies conducted by the Behavior Science Corporation (McClung, Stunden, & Plog, 1969) for the Center for Studies of Child and Family Mental Health of the National Institute of Mental Health. This group used structured and open-ended questionnaires as a basis for interviews with 86 consultants and 92 consultees, representing 18 mental health facilities located in ten sites throughout the United States. The data were analyzed first by site; the total were subsequently reduced and collated. As a result of the analysis of these data, sufficiently consistent patterns of operations were established from which a conceptual scheme arose which contained descriptions of seven types of consultation. These were seen as mutually exclusive and exhaustive: (1) client-centered case conference consultation—this type of consultation is directly parallel to the traditional medical model; (2) client-centered staff development consultation—uses a discussion of the client of the consultee for the purpose of staff development and training; (3) agency-centered staff development consultation—focuses on the intrapersonal and interpersonal problems within an agency; (4) agency-centered program development consultation—focuses on aiding the administration

of an agency in originating, planning, and implementing programs; (5) community-centered mental health consultation—focused on community groups and boards relative to the planning of community mental health activities; (6) community-centered behavioral science consultation—focuses on community and governmental organizations for the development of programs beyond a specific mental health area, such as urban renewal; (7) behavioral science consultations on national and international problems—focuses on the resolutions of problems and the generation of decisions in areas of broad social concern having a national and international impact.

In addition to these seven types of consultation the authors also derived a group of 18 parameters which described the techniques and the philosophy of each type of consultation and which served to differentiate one type from the other types. Four of the parameters were considered definitive rather than descriptive. These included contact with the client, degree of consultant's responsibility for case disposition, direction of the consultant's responsibility, and degree to which the consultant was willing to permit his involvement in the personal processes of the consultee. According to the authors any type of consultation can be differentiated from any other by the use of these parameters. Examples of the more purely descriptive parameters are: frequency of consultation sessions, time period allocated for consultation, professional background and training of the consultant, the status relationship between the consultant and consultee, and the criteria used to measure the effectiveness of consultation. These parameters are said to provide an exhaustive description of the relevant variables which determine how consultation will be carried out.

Whether one agrees or disagrees with this conceptual classification and typology, it is nevertheless the only one to date that has been developed empirically. It is, therefore, worthy of careful study and evaluation since its value is not only to the practice of consultation but also to training and to research.

PROGRAM ANALYSIS

One way of attempting to understand the workings of consultation programs is through quantifying some of the activities that occur during consultation and then to translate these into some general principles. These could include pictures of who is seen in consultation, for how long, what kind of consultation is done, etc. This statistical picture of consultation can be used in two ways: (1) it can merely reflect the actual course of the activities of a consultative service; or (2) it may be used to attempt to monitor the service and to be fed back into the organization to try to change directions of consultation services. Two major studies have been reported.

Iscoe, Pierce-Jones, Friedman, and McGehearty (1967) and Pierce-Jones, Iscoe, and Cunningham (1968), as part of a larger evaluative study on consultation in schools, have also included a general program analysis.[2] They are interested in identifying the kind of children that are the target for consultation, the differences in the schools that ask for consultation, how the schools use consultation differently, whether more experienced teachers use consultation more than less experienced teachers, the kinds of problems that concern the teachers most, the relationship between time and the problems brought to the consultation, the characteristics of those that use the consultation service and those who do not use it, and the suggestions consultees have for improving the service. Findings from this study indicate that the consultation was widely used by the teachers—80 percent used the services one or more times. Range of usage was from zero to 22 consultations, with the median number being two. Seventy-two percent of the children consulted about were boys and 28 percent were girls. Approximately 58 percent were in grades one to three while the remainder were in grades four to six. Rated on a seven level scale of emotional handicap, 34.3 percent of 903 consultations centered about children who were judged to display "moderate" to "severe" behavior disturbances. The majority (65.7 percent) appeared to be relatively minor problems. There was no evidence that a child would be consulted about more or less frequently depending on the rated severity of his disorder, or that teachers who consulted more or less frequently differed in the average emotional handicap rating of the children consulted about. The main concern of teachers was that of seeking from the consultant confirmation of a decision already made. Findings from a questionnaire which dealt with assessment of the consultation

services indicated that the consultation service was well known to the teachers, that consultants were accessible, and that teachers could usually find free time for consultation. Teachers generally viewed the consultations very favorably. They saw consultants as most helpful in identifying children's problems, facilitating the understanding of children's problems, conveying greater knowledge of human behavior, and confirming teachers' own judgments. Areas in which consultants were viewed as least helpful were: enhancing communication with the principal and others about children, providing ideas which were discussed with other teachers, helping the teacher with a more realistic view of self. Out of nine pupil personnel services, teachers gave consultation a relatively low value ranking among other services. Special education and remedial reading received the highest value rankings.

Griffith and Libo (1968) classified various aspects of their consultation service (through daily logs) and quantified the frequency of direct service, case conferences, and individual consultations. In looking at what was done over time, three stages were identified in setting up a program of consultation: (1) the initial courtship period in which the purpose is to set up the consultation and get it started. Enthusiasm is high; (2) the retrenchment period. Fewer contacts, but efforts are made to develop these few contacts in meaningful ways; and (3) the consummation period where sustained and increased contacts develop and are related to specific tasks identified for the consultation.

Although program analysis is very important for making determinations about such factors as quality control and cost and efficiency of operations, one should be careful not to consider such studies as evaluative studies. The danger of confusing such monitoring activities with evaluation of consultation is very great and may lead to a preoccupation with numbers with very little understanding of what has been achieved. A description of the service, the use of staff time, and types of problems dealt with are of great value to administrators, but they rarely answer whether or not a program has achieved its goals. The latter is the job of evaluative studies. An excellent example of this is the study reviewed above by Pierce-Jones et al. Although the program analysis revealed that the consultation program was widely used and was viewed as being helpful by the teachers, the evaluative part of the project (which will be reported below) indicated that the consultations had no significant effects on the teachers' attitudes or orientations.

STUDIES OF CONSULTATION PRACTICE

Many efforts have been made to classify and organize the various experiences occurring in consultation. The analysis of the actual practice of consultation has led to the delineation of areas such as roles and activities of the consultant, the roles and functions of the consultee, selection of the consultant, personal characteristics of the consultant, characteristics of consultees, problems for which consultation is sought, and an analysis of those aspects that lead to a successful or unsuccessful consultation.

Efforts to begin to define the area of consultation are not limited to the mental health field or to medical settings. Consultation in educational settings as well as in business management have much to offer in clarifying similarities and differences of consultations in various settings. However, despite certain similar practices in mental health to areas of business and education, there are also some important differences.

Roles and Functions of the Consultant

An examination of the roles and functions of consultants from various fields of practice shows a wide range of activities and responsibilities covered under the consultation label. Unfortunately, the goals and objectives are not usually made explicit in most of the studies, making it difficult to determine the importance or relevancy of the described roles. One important point is apparent, however. The most narrowly described role-functions are in the area of medical-psychiatric consultation. As psychiatrists and other mental health workers move into community mental health work and function as mental health consultants, there is a broadening of their roles so that the consultants begin to function more like educational, business, and nursing consultants. This is not to say that they have similar goals or that they use the same or similar techniques in carrying out their roles. It does mean that their

psychiatric concerns are accompanied by an ever widening array of nonpsychiatric and nonmedical concerns, such as curriculum development, administration, or program review. This suggests many areas of mutual concern between the mental health consultant and the consultants in these other areas. Despite the fact that these consultation activities have been treated as separate endeavors in the literature, it may indeed be that as consultants, professionals in all areas can learn from one another how to be of assistance in their common efforts. For example, the educational consultant who is an expert in curriculum building may be of immense help to the mental health consultant who finds himself involved in curriculum procedures. Similarly, the mental health consultant might help the educational consultant better understand some of the emotional and psychological dimensions involved in curriculum building. Likewise, the management consultant's expertise in organizational areas may be of special use to the mental health consultant involved in organizational consultation.

A review of some of the roles of consultants found in these studies may clarify these issues. To avoid repetition, the description of roles and functions from several studies have been summarized in Table 33—1. (The authors have taken the liberty in some cases of converting lists of functions or methods into role descriptions.)

A few comments about these role-functions seem appropriate. First, as we have already noted, many of the role-functions listed in Table 33—1 are often considered as nonconsultation in that they include direct service (diagnosis and treatment) as well as indirect service. Another element to note is the inclusion of administrative, regulatory functions in some of these descriptions. Such functions are considered incompatible with consultation by many in the field. Yet we find consultants performing such tasks under the consultation umbrella. Hence, at this point it seems clear that there is a need in the field to define what is and what is not included in consultation practice. Only then can we have any expectations of applying specific methods in a conscious manner.

Another important dimension of the study of the consultant's role is that of differentiating it empirically from the role of the supervisor who has similar functions. Kindelsperger (1958) was able to effectively do this by constructing two

TABLE 33–1
Consultation Roles[1]

Psychiatric[a]	Mental Health[b]	Nursing[c]	Education[d]	Business and Management[e]
Case Problem Solver	Resource Person	Policy Formulator	Helping Teacher	Management Surveyor
Teacher	Program Reviewer	Developer of Methods and Procedures	Educational Leader	Planner
	Program Promoter	Assister in Content and Emphasis of Special Area Programs	Evaluator	Decision Maker
	Innovator	Program Planner	Public Relations Person	Personnel Expert
	Teacher-Trainer	Analyst of Agency Needs	Liaison Officer	Efficiency Expert
	Human Relations Mediator	Analyst of Community Needs	Change Agent	Marketing Specialist
	Supervisor	Evaluator	Counselor	Labor Relations
		Researcher	Expert	Manufacturing Specialist
		Program Coordinator	Administrator	Operations Expert
		Nursing Service Provider	Curriculum Specialist	Financial Planner
			Program Developer	Specialist in Office Procedure
			Program Coordinator	Organizational Specialist
				Advisor

[a]Parker (1958) [b]Cohen (1964)   [c]Gilbertson and   [d]Malkin (1965)   [e]Dobson (1962)
FSAA (1953)   Williamson (1952)   Banister (1962)   Seney (1963)
Aikin (1959)   Gordon (1952)   Anton (1964)
                                                     Savage (1952)
                                                            (1959)

[1]See also a study by Frist (1965) who describes major roles and task functions of the Community Extension Specialist.

instruments, a case inventory that consisted of concepts of the supervisor role and consultant role and a case instrument which consisted of 18 actual work situations. Each case was drafted with two solutions, one as defined in the "case inventory" and the other as exemplifying inappropriate behavior. The case instrument was given to eleven matched pairs of consultants and public assistance workers. Responses established a convincing differentiation between the roles of consultant and supervisor.

Selection of the Consultant

Despite the obvious importance of selecting the right consultant for a particular job, very little work has been done in this area. One reason may be the lack of clarity as to the job description of the consultant. The main approach used in three studies which dealt with this area was to search for sources of information that would be useful in making a decision as to whether a consultant should or should not be hired. In management consultation, Dobson (1962) found that the sources of information used to select consultants came through associations with activities different from consultation. For example, sale solicitations, business acquaintances, personal contacts, and general recommendations. What was used to select the consultant was experience with similar problems, reputation for successful service, prestige, method of approach, and the effectiveness of the ability to solicit sales. Similar findings were noted by Watson (1958). Anton (1964) in education found four factors: personal knowledge of the consultant's ability, general professional reputation, previous working relationships, and recommendation by county school officials as influencing the selection of the consultant. All but "general professional reputation" were found to correlate highly with effectiveness of the consultant. No studies were found in the mental health area which dealt directly with the issue of selection.

Personal Characteristics of the Consultant

Two problems arise in defining the personal characteristics of the consultant. One is to determine the characteristics or traits that are related to the performance of the particular kind of activity, and the second is to determine whether those who have these traits are indeed successful in performing that activity. Most of the research has been done in the first of these areas.

In educational consultation Savage (1952) mentioned that cooperativeness, emotional stability, and personal adjustment were important for a successful consultant. Anton (1964) points out that a pleasing personality and the ability to inspire confidence are necessary elements. To this list, Downing (1954) added permissiveness, since he felt that a dictatorial personality was not conducive to good consultation. Within the business field, Tatham (1964) mentions traits such as modesty, assuredness, sensitivity, and tactfulness. Dobson (1962) listed ability to gain confidences of the client, analytical mind, ability

to generate enthusiasm for new ideas, patience and tact, and confidence in his own work.

In the area of mental health consultation Robbins and Spencer (1968) found that consultants more than consultees stated that the mental health consultant should be "friendly" or "personable." Mannino (1969) studied perceptions of behavior believed to. be most beneficial in the consultation process. His findings were the reverse of those by Robbins and Spencer, i.e., consultees rather than consultants described such behavior as "sympathetic," "helpful," "cordial," "pleasant," "receptive," "friendly," "interested," and "sensitive" as the behaviours of the consultant that were seen as beneficial to the consultation. Even though there were distinct differences in subjects and methodology in these two studies, further research is needed to adequately understand the conflicting findings. Erickson (1966) states that the consultant should have the capacity to be permissive and not to impose his own ideas. He should be able to give, share, and relate effectively to people.

It is not clear from these studies how many of these traits are specific to consultation and how many are characteristic of a constructive interpersonal relationship of any kind, such as in teaching, clinical work, supervision, or even personal friendships. None of the studies have actually evaluated these traits, nor has any attempt been made to relate them to the selection or training of consultant. It is indeed possible that other than some general traits related to human warmth and awareness of interpersonal behaviors, certain specific skills may be needed to perform consultation tasks. It may be, therefore, that a combination of skills and certain interpersonal characteristics will be found to be most relevant to the selection and training of individuals for practice in the area of consultation.

Characteristics of Consultees

Another area of study, largely neglected, is the characteristics of consultees which facilitate the consultation process. Are some consultees able to make better use of consultation than others and is this related to certain of their personality characteristics? Only one study (Kline & Cumings, 1955) focused on this aspect of consultation. These authors compared two groups of public health nurses whose reactions to a mental health consultation program were clinically different—one group performing much better than the other. The objective was to determine if there were any distinguishing differences between the groups which might be related to prediction of performance in a mental health education and consultation program. Comparisons were made on the Allport-Vernon-Lindzey Study of Values, the Otis-Self-Administering Test of Mental Ability, The Conservatism-Radicalism Opinionaire, Mental Hygiene Ratings, and a scale for evaluating an inservice mental health and consultation program. The authors found that the more productive nurses had higher intelligence, higher theoretical, social, and aesthetic scales on the values test, and were less conservative in attitude. It appeared that the productive nurses also were more interested in knowledge than in moral issues and were more concerned with aesthetic and social aspects of their own behavior than with the minute practicalities of everyday living. They also seemed more capable of dealing with conceptual impressions and were capable of extending their thinking into broader generalization areas as well as in specific applications. It was concluded that the results point in the direction of being able to predict nursing reaction to mental health education and consultation.

Problems for Which Consultation is Sought

One of the most obvious features of the field of consultation is the confusion as to what is expected from the consultation. It is only when the field has been clearly defined that one is then able to set goals and determine the kinds of training necessary to carry out certain activities. The empirical way of setting such goals is to inquire as to what is wanted from a consultant. However, one must be careful, for frequently what is verbally stated as wanted is not necessarily the problem to which the consultant should address himself. Bearing in mind this limitation, certain studies have been done that have attempted to summarize the problems around which consultation is sought. Many of these problems vary by discipline and by the type of consultation (case consultation versus program consultation). In a survey of management consultation, Samaras (1961) states that as one begins to get specific, the problem areas cover a very wide range. The areas

most often listed in management are: production, sales, finances, new products, management assistance, profit improvement, improved methods, and greater efficiency. Seney (1963) indicates that executives use business consultants to advise in seeing, defining, and solving specific management problems in the organization, direction, planning, and control of the operation.

The educational consultant, in a study by Savage (1952), works primarily in the areas of finance, teacher recruitment and training, building and grounds, public relations, curriculum construction, improvement of instruction, and reorganization of school districts. In the area of public health, nursing consultants are called upon to render assistance in policy formation, development of procedures and methods, to assist on content and emphasis in a specialized area program, as well as consulting in relation to the whole program (Gilbertson & Williamson, 1952).

In a study related to consultation with nursery school personnel, Knisely (1964) found three levels of problems: simple practical problems arising from lack of knowledge and experience; interpersonal relationship problems such as family relations and child adjustment; and hierarchial problems—roles, conflicts between individual and groups.

Macht, Scherl, and English (1968), in mental health consultation to the Job Corps, found that the problems in which consultants were involved included individual case-focused problems, problem areas in the center program (such as group living, leisure, and orientation programs) and problems related to general program issues (such as limit setting, discipline, and communication). In her study of psychiatric consultation to family service agencies, Aikin (1957) listed the main problems for which consultation is sought as: (1) cases in which advanced knowledge beyond that of the case worker was needed regarding the psychodynamics and personality organization of the client; (2) cases needing advice regarding the health or pathology of a client; (3) cases in which there is suspected psychophysiological illness or psychopathology; and (4) cases with obvious or suspected psychopathology for confirmation of a tentative diagnosis and psychiatric examination or referral. It is clear that in Aikin's situation the focus was on case-centered psychiatric consultations. In studying her consultation with public health nurses, Parker (1958) found that the major problems presented were: dilemmas encountered by the nurse in some aspect of her work, and case material presenting a specific problem typical of a group of similar problems.

The problems for which consultation is sought range from broad organizational concerns, through concerns around programs, to concern with an individual case. To a large extent the discipline, background, and experience of the consultant determine the kinds of problems about which he is consulted. In mental health, however, there is a variation and often confusion, with lack of clarity, as to whether one is at one point case or patient oriented or at another point more involved with program and organizational issues. The question arises as to whether one can define these clearly in the mental health area or whether or not the two are naturally combined, as in the Macht et al. (1968) study where both were necessary.

Uses of Consultation

An important aspect of consultation is how it is used or not used by consultees. Unfortunately, it appears that consultants and administrators of consultation programs take too much for granted that if consultation programs are made available, consultees will avail themselves of the services. Two studies show that this is not necessarily true, but that there are factors which interfere with the use of consultation by community groups. One study by Mannino, Rooney, and Hassler (1970) investigated the effect of geographical distance on the use of a mental health facility as a contact source for referrals and consultation. Their findings showed that not only is distance a definite factor in the use of a mental health facility as a contact source for referrals and consultation but that there are substantial differences among the community professionals' use of the facility because of the effect of distance. For example, agency-centered professionals were more likely to use the facility for clients who resided at relatively great distance from the facility than were more autonomous professionals such as medical practitioners and clergymen. In another study, Selzer and Benedek (1965) made a mail survey of attorneys and found that they used psychiatric consultation sparingly. Deterrents cited were expense to clients, clients' resentment of being sent to a psychiatrist, and psychiatrists' unavailability as well as lack of interest in legal matters.

Another way of studying use of consultation is to compare consultees who have used consultation differently, to determine if they also differ on some other dimensions relevant to the consultation. Using this approach, Mannino, Rooney, and Hassler (1967) made a comparative analysis of two groups of clergymen around their use of telephone consultations. A group that had made frequent telephone contacts was compared with another group that had made only single contacts, to see if there were any differences in the way they presented and described their clients' problems. It was expected that the group that had made frequent contacts over a period of time may have been influenced in some way by the mental health professionals with whom they consulted. No significant differences were found.

Successful and Unsuccessful Consultations

Some efforts have been made to determine the factors which facilitate or hinder the effectiveness of the consultation. For the most part, however, these are reports based upon judgments made by consultants and consultees and are intuitive in nature. Dobson (1962), in a study of the reasons why businessmen fail to benefit from consultation, interviewed both consultants and consultees. He reported that: (1) the consultant was unqualified and the businessman was uncooperative; (2) the consultant's suggestions were not accepted; (3) the consultant failed to adapt his ideas to the specific situation in the firm; and (4) the consultee was impatient. In line with the interest of management, Dobson stated that the success of consultation is ultimately measured through lower costs or increased profits.

Tatham (1964), in another study of management consultation, states that the following factors facilitate success: (1) the client (consultee) must see the need for help and cooperate with the consultant; (2) the work should be divided into phases so it may be evaluated frequently; (3) the ideas of the consultant must be "presold" in the client organization; (4) the consultee should be frank in volunteering information; (5) cordial, personal relationships are crucial; (6) the client should raise questions about the consultant's report; (7) the consultant's suggestions should be implemented. Samaras (1961) stated that in management consultation greater satisfaction was expressed for the consultant's objectivity, introduction of new methods and ideas, planning for future activities, and problem solving ability. On the other hand, unsatisfactory results came from poor selection of the consultant, poor management structure within the firm, unsuitable consulting techniques, and the overselling of the consultants and what they were able to do.

In consultation within an educational setting, Savage (1952) points out that the most successful consultants are those who are acquainted with the superintendent, are able to clarify and define problems, can follow up the service, and are able to evaluate their work. As with all other studies, if the consultant's suggestions were carried out, the consultation was seen as successful. One cannot be clear, however, as to whether or not this phenomenon is circular because if there is enough trust to carry out the consultation adequately the chances are that the consultation will be successful. On the other hand, if this trust does not take place then the consultation may tend to be viewed negatively. Savage also indicated the reasons for unsuccessful consultations. He stated that the unsuccessful educational consultations mostly fall into the human relations category; that is, personality conflicts, friction, preconceived notions, action based on insufficient information, the hostility of the administrator, and general apathy on the part of consultant and consultee. He noted a tendency on the part of the consultants to blame the local situation on other people rather than to assume personal responsibility for the effectiveness of their work.

Macht et al. (1968) investigated the conditions that facilitated or hindered mental health consultation in the Job Corps. In a questionnaire given to 97 psychiatrists who were consultants in the Job Corps, the consultants were asked to list the factors that they felt facilitated their work with center directors, counseling staff, and resident worker staff. Rank-ordered by frequency the responses were: (1) staff interest in psychiatric consultation; (2) positive response of staff to psychiatrists; and (3) center director's interest in psychiatric consultation. In exploring the conditions that hindered the work of the consultant, the factors most frequently mentioned were: (1) no hindering conditions; (2) poor communication between staff members; and (3) negative responses to psychiatrists.

Mannino (1969) in studying consultation to a family agency did not use a forced-choice questionnaire, but had the consultees and consultants rate the degree of occurrence of selected characteristics believed to be beneficial to the consultation, and then related these to judgments made regarding the degree of success of a specific consultation. These findings revealed that while consultants and consultees tended to use the same criteria in judging successfulness, the consultants were more likely to characterize these criteria in terms of being able to tie together the material discussed into a final summary. Consultees on the other hand appeared to characterize success in terms of presenting pertinent information for discussion, clarifying the problem, and coming to grips with the possible solutions.

It is not clear from all these studies what success and lack of success really means. There are as such no general measures of success. It would appear that the criteria for success must be based upon specific goals of a particular consultation. Once such criteria are developed one could explore the relationship of a number of variables to the stated criteria of success. At this point, however, it is extremely difficult to specify goals and methods in a clear fashion.

STUDIES OF CONSULTATION PROCESS

Evaluations of the consultation process deal with the events which characterize the course of consultation. They include factors which lead to progress in consultation as well as factors which impede progress, and focus upon variables which best describe the events that transpire during a consultation.

There are basically two methodologies that have been used for studying the process of consultation. One is the use of data derived from the perceptions, attitudes, or opinions of the participants. How do the participants in consultation see what happens and what do they identify as the elements of change? In this approach data collection takes place after the consultation and consists of two main sources: (1) primary data collected specifically for the research; (2) secondary data collected for other purposes, such as case records. In some studies, various combinations of these methodologies are used.

A second methodology for studying the process of consultation has been to analyze the actual behavior manifested by the consultant and the consultee during the consultation situation itself.

Interaction analyses and participant observation have been utilized.

Studies Utilizing Primary Data

Tetreault (1968) attempted to identify certain general characteristics of the consultation process. The technique used was a questionnaire given to 25 school social workers. It was found that the school social workers saw as their objective appealing to the consultee's affective needs rather than their cognitive and educational concerns. Four casework techniques were identified—sustaining procedures, ventilation, clarification, and direct influence. A significant association between the choice of a particular technique and the phase of consultation was found.

In a narrative study of consultation in small manufacturing companies, Tilles (1960) attempted to identify certain phases in the consultation problem solving process using the reports of the consultant, and the client, and his own experiences. He sees the stages as: (1) recognition and statement of the problems requiring the attention of the consultant; (2) the ability to quantitatively evaluate the seriousness of the problem; (3) knowledge of the relevant cause and effect of relationships; (4) the formulation of alternative solutions; (5) the selection of a particular alternative; and (6) putting selected alternatives into effect. How the consultant gets involved in these areas, he states, determines the specific relationship which has to be worked out by the company and the consultant.

Cumings and Kline (1953) studied the process of consultation in a mental hygiene consultation program for nurses using a perceptual approach. Each nurse was interviewed and given a rating scale on 16 major aspects of the program. The program lasted two years. The most satisfactory parts of the program as seen by the nurses were the individual case conferences, the opportunity for individual participation, the general flexibility in relating to the consultant, and the efforts made to stimulate interest in mental health. The greatest dissatisfaction was seen as topical content, the teaching abilities and communication techniques of the consultant, group conferences, lack of well defined program goals consistent with public health nursing needs, and the lack of objective measures of achievement within the program.

Another study of the process of consultation as perceived by the consultee was that of Lippitt (1959). Lippitt studied the effectiveness of a workshop in a school of nursing as reflected in a questionnaire filled out by the consultees following two five-day workshops. Thirteen of the 14 members of the group answered the questionnaire. Most of the respondents felt that self-development and self-change took place as a result of the workshops. Most negative responses revolved around the domination of an authority person in the group. A majority of the members of the group was disappointed that the consultant did not use his own authority to handle this situation but let the group work out their own ways of handling the relationships.

Knisely (1964) used consultant records as well as questionnaires given to the consultees and other officials to evaluate the effectiveness of a consultation program to nursery schools. The primary focus of her analysis was on problem solving activities. She found that the problems moved through six phases: (1) who the problem was presented to; (2) who the problem was presented by; (3) steps by the staff to solve the problem prior to the consultation request; (4) consultant's formulation of the problem; (5) action suggested by the consultant to alleviate the problem; and (6) the outcome of the problem. The questionnaire results led to the description of consultants' behaviors and were confirmed by an interview with the 15 people who were given the questionnaire. The consultant was seen as: (1) making specific suggestions and giving information; (2) interpreting and clarifying behavior; and (3) supporting adequate function and roles of the consultee.

Mannino (1969) asked both consultants and consultees immediately after a consultation to discuss what they considered as the helpful and nonhelpful aspects of the consultation process. The study was done with a family service agency and utilized a questionnaire as the main source of data. The views of the consultants and consultees were then related to the perceived success or lack of success of the consultation. The findings revealed that the responses of the consultants and the consultees appeared to be a function of their respective roles which in some respects were similar to the roles of the patient and therapist in psychotherapy. The consultee placed considerable emphasis on the personal, emotional experience the consultation provided. This was labeled as an affective component of the consultation. Both parties emphasized the cognitive component which was manifested in the technical help given in regard to evaluation and understanding of the case and the help given in regard to treatment. The consultant, however, placed more emphasis on the development and maintenance aspects of consultation, which were labeled as the relationship component.

As noted earlier, the success of a consultation was also seen differently by consultants and consultees. The consultants were more likely to characterize success in terms of being able to tie together the material discussed in a final summary. The consultees, however, characterized success in terms of presenting pertinent information for discussion, clarifying the problem, and coming to grips with solutions.

Biggers (1965) studied 23 cases from rural communities that did not have local psychiatric facilities. She obtained her data through interviews. She found that one of the negative aspects of the consultation service was recommendations to agencies that could not be carried out because of limited resources in their own communities. This area of unrealistic recommendations was also one of the nonhelpful aspects mentioned by the consultees in the study by Mannino (1969).

Studies Utilizing Secondary Data

Parker (1958) reports a study based on impressionistic materials she had collected in consulting with nurses over a number of years. She classified the problems into three general groups: (1) problems of understanding and handling of cases; (2) dilemmas encountered by the nurse in some aspect of her work; and (3) case material presenting a special problem representative of a group of similar problems. The nurse, she felt, primarily sought consultation for support and clarification of her nursing role. Parker saw the goals of consultation as falling into two major categories: (1) emphasis on influencing the process or content of group thinking, and (2) reduction of individual or group anxiety. By emphasis on influencing the process of group thinking, she

mentions demonstrating methods of solving a problem, attempting to expand the scope of thinking and to break down stereotypes, widening intellectual horizons and changing attitudes, and pointing out the aspects of a nurse's involvement which impede her objectivity. This seems to be primarily a cognitive goal. In attempts to relieve individual or group anxiety, she sees relief of guilt over emotional reactions, reduction of the threat to the nurses' status of sensibilities, relief from conflicts over jurisdiction, and conscious avoidance of the nurses' status of sensibilities, relief from conflicts over jurisdiction, and conscious avoidance of the nurses' involvement where such would contraindicated. The discussions with the nurses fell into seven general categories of activity: (1) exploration by the group of the observable patient behavior or symptoms. The consultant helped in interpreting the meaning and implication of the symptoms; (2) exploration by the group of individual nurse's feelings and their effect on a specific problem; (3) exploration by the group of factors involved in assuming responsibility for a problem; (4) suggestions for management; (5) discussion of general principles of public health nursing functions, common reactions, duties, and policies; (6) handling of anxiety or hostility; and (7) the delivery of abstract information.

Another study which dealt with the consultee's perception of the process of consultation in which case records were utilized was conducted by Aikin (1959). She studied the provision of psychiatric consultation to two family service agencies. Aikin, similar to other studies, found that the consultant functions primarily as a teacher; offers suggestions that are generalizable to other cases, maintains a certain objectivity, identifies the degree of health of the client, and discusses long-term treatment goals. This educational function shows itself, Aikin believed, through: (1) the formulation of the client's personality structure; (2) formulation of the client's functioning; (3) specific recommendations for treatment; (4) identification of the actual problem; and (5) formulation of the prognosis. However, the other side of consultation, namely the affective elements, especially in the worker-client relationship, also were mentioned as important factors that were discussed and served to sharpen the caseworker's understanding of the implication between herself and the client.

Observations of Actual Behavior

Only two studies have used the method of observing and analyzing behavioral interaction of consultants and consultees. In both studies, the actual behavior analysis was used in combination with other techniques such as questionnaires and interviews.

Tiedeman (1968), in studying psychiatric consultation within a medical setting, saw the primary problem as that of the psychiatrist-consultant working toward defining a place on a medical ward different from that of the medical internist. In his sociological study, Tiedeman was interested in those factors in hospital organization as well as the attitudes of the internist that affected the proper function of the psychiatrist-consultant on the ward. Through participant observations and interviews he found that consultants went through a complex process of developing and clarifying their tasks. Differences between the internists and consultants centered around three areas: (1) How much educating should the consultant do for the medical staff? (2) How active should the consultant be? and (3) Which of the cases were the ones that required consultation? He found that consultants responded to the demands of the ward situation on the basis of the legitimacy of the defined tasks, the practicality of the tasks, and how committed the consultant was to the consultation.

The only study in which ongoing consultations were observed and tape recorded for the purposes of research was that of Robbins and Spencer (1968). These authors dealt with health department personnel as consultees and observed 35 ongoing consultations. In the early part of consultation the consultee uses most of the time. giving out information. This stage was called the "expositional stage." In the second stage or middle stage the consultant becomes active by interpreting and clarifying and bringing perspective to the problem. This stage is the "reactive stage." The last stage was less easily identified but the impression gained was that what was occurring was summarizing, making decisions, and making future commitments. In addition, 26 consultants ranked various characteristics of consultants and related these to the consultant's actual behavior in conferences. The results suggested that the perceptions of the consultant do influence his behavior and could be sources of conflict if they diverge from the perceptions of the consultee.

In summary one could say that process research in the area of consultation is still in the beginning stages. Most of the research on process amounts to describing the variables that are involved. Little has been done to associate the variables with success of consultation, and as yet there has been no research into the process of change itself, i.e., the elements and characteristics of change in the consultee which are set in motion as a result of the consultation.

OUTCOME STUDIES IN CONSULTATION

Studies of outcome are essentially studies of goal achievement and are naturally dependent upon being able to clearly define the goals one sets out to accomplish. In the area of mental health consultation this is an extremely difficult undertaking. What is it that one expects to change through consultation? It would appear that there are at least three major areas of outcome that can be measured. First, there is the immediate objective of effecting change in the knowledge and skills of the consultee so that he will be more effective in his work with the clientele he serves. Second, there is the long range objective of bringing about positive change in the client group itself. Finally, there is what might be spoken of as an intermediate goal—that of effecting change in the institutional structure, or the system, aimed at improving the mental health components of its services and activities. One might approach an evaluation of outcome by focusing on one or more of these levels in the same study, as will be seen in the materials presented below.

Outcome Studies of Changes in the Consultee

A few research studies have attempted to identify the changes that occur in the consultee. One of these studies (Teitelbaum, 1961) evaluated the effect of consultation on teachers who were newly appointed to the New York City schools. One hundred and twenty pairs of teachers were matched on a number of relevant variables and assigned to 40 special schools (also matched) for lower class black and Puerto Rican children. Each consultant worked with 15 experimental teachers on the handling of these children. Monthly logs were completed by both the teachers and the consultants, and rating forms were completed by the principals on the degree of teacher growth. The results indicated that the teachers who were given the consultation (experimental group) became more confident in their ability to function and showed significantly greater professional growth.

Dorsey, Matsunaga, and Bauman (1964) did a detailed study of consultation to public health nurses over a five-month period. They did not have a control group. The public health nurses met as a group with a psychiatric team consisting of psychiatrist, psychiatric social worker, and psychiatric nurse to discuss cases. Very careful evaluation of change took place with six techniques used: (1) process notes of the consultation; (2) an evaluation of the sequences of the referrals over time; (3) anecdotal observations of the psychiatric team; (4) before and after self-ratings (interpersonal checklists); (5) before and after ratings of the effectiveness of the course (special scale); and (6) the review of the notes by a nonparticipant observer as to the understanding of the cases and changes in the understanding over time. The findings were statistically significant. There was increased awareness on the part of the nurse of family involvement and family interaction in the cases described at the end of consultation, as compared to before. The nurses also showed a greater emphasis on prevention. The nurses, after the course, were closer to the mental health view and also seemed to have a better idea as to why they were referring cases. The greatest effects resulting from the course, as reported by the nurses, were in the areas of nursing knowledge, nursing practice, and attitude toward patients. The least effect of the program was in professional relationships, private and social life, and the attitude of the patients toward the nurse. A review of the cases presented to the nurses toward the end of the course, when compared with the beginning, showed greater understanding of the case. Although the interpersonal checklist was used to obtain a picture of change in the self-image of the nurse that might be induced by the program, this was not found to occur. Thus, the nurses' skill in early case findings, the ability to utilize more effectively a psychiatric consultation, and the further ability to integrate the results

into improved understanding were clearly demonstrated.

Mariner, Brandt, Stone, and Mirmow (1961) report a two-year project on psychiatric consultation consisting of group discussions with counselors, administrators, and public school teachers, most of whom volunteered for the program. The aim was to increase their awareness of the influence of motivation and other aspects of personality dynamics on learning. They used a test of "psychological-mindedness" to evaluate the effectiveness of the program and a rating scale to determine whether or not the program was received favorably. The "psychological-mindedness" test showed a significant increase at the end of consultation when compared with the beginning. The rating scale indicated that the participants felt the discussions were stimulating, meaningful, and beneficial to their work. However, there were no groups tested who were used as controls.

One of the very few studies of consultation using a clearly formulated conceptual framework was done by Friedlander (1968), who studied the effect of three separate consulting styles on the organizational development and functioning of groups. His view of the consultant was very close to that of group leader and included, among other roles, leading sensitivity training sessions. His outcome measure was a questionnaire developed from open-end interviews that was factor analyzed and covered six general areas: group effectiveness; leader approachability; mutual influence; personal involvement and participation; intragroup trust; and the worth of the meetings. There were three general styles for operating the three groups. One consisted of a sensitivity training session. A second included a minimal amount of preliminary work followed by a training session with emphasis on active, conceptual, analytical work-related problems. A third used a training period similar to the second group, but also had an extensive relationship with the consultant prior to and after the training session. The third group improved its effectiveness to a greater degree in all six areas than any of the other groups. Hence it was the group with the combined program that had the greatest impact and led to the belief that organizational meetings of either sensitivity training or task related activity are not as effective as when there is extensive prework and follow-up in a continuously, carefully thought out, long-term program. Even though more consultant time is needed in this arrangement the payoff appears to be considerably greater and therefore worth the effort. Implicit in the findings is the belief that even had the sensitivity group and the analytical work problem group been given the same amount of time as the combined program, the results would not have matched those of the combined program.

A major study of a two-year mental health consultation program in Texas was reported by Iscoe, Pierce-Jones, Friedman, and McGehearty (1967) and Pierce-Jones, Iscoe, and Cunningham (1968). The mental health consultation was in a school setting and seen as inservice education designed to improve the skills of the teacher and encourage her use of school resources. Two major areas were evaluated: changes in the teachers (consultee) and certain elements of program functioning. Fourteen schools were offered the consultation service and 14 were not. The measures used to evaluate changes in the teacher, many of which were specifically designed for this study, include: (1) Dimensions of Teachers' Opinions—110 items designed to measure teachers' orientation to child behavior; (2) Need-for-Assistance Scale—50 items identifying classes of problems which school personnel need help in managing; (3) Behavior Classification Check-list—92 item scale designed to determine what a child does in the classroom and how much it irritates the teacher; (4) What-Is-an-Ideal-Pupil Scale (Torrance, 1964)—comparing responses of teachers in this group to other geographical areas; (5) Child Attitude Survey—a survey of teachers' attitudes with regard to aspects of child behavior; (6) Assessment of Consultation Service—questionnaire given to determine how much was known about the consultation service and how much it had been used; (7) School and Community Survey—to determine the teachers' perception of the interaction of the school and community at the beginning and at the end of the academic year. In addition, other data collected were biographical data on the teachers and consultant report forms in which an objective reporting device was used to get demographic data and identify the nature of the consultant—consultee relationship, the origins of the case, the way the case was handled, and the general assessment of the problem.

A "quasi-experimental" design was used to test two general hypotheses: (1) consultation will produce significant change in experimental teachers' mental health orientation over and above any change occurring in control teachers; (2) differential use of consultation within the experimental group will be associated with differences in measures of the teachers' mental health orientation. Both hypotheses were tested with analysis of variance procedures. The results disclosed lack of statistically significant differences which would support either hypothesis. The only statistically significant finding of the study was an increase in rapport between consultant and consultee which occurred between the beginning and the end of the consultation program.[3]

Outcome Studies of Change in the System

Only one study was found which dealt specifically with change in the system. Although it is far removed from the mental health area it is included as an example of this particular focus.

Foster and Hartman (1959) attempted through "voluntary" consultation to dietary and personnel administrators in 33 general hospitals to raise the quality of dietary services using a checklist of 51 items dealing with dietetic administration. They evaluated the hospital before and after the consultation program. They also tried to compare the voluntary consultation with consultation services given by state agencies and by private service firms. (The authors indicate that voluntary consultation was seen as lacking the financial involvement through fees of the private service firm, and the sanction of licensing implied by governmental regulatory agencies.) Although there was no control group, the authors felt that the consistency of the changes suggested more than circumstantial evidence of the program's value. They also concluded that voluntary consultations were at least as effective as those given by state agencies or private firms.

Outcome Studies of the Effects of Consultation on the Client

Several studies have attempted to evaluate the effectiveness of consultation on the client. Ginther (1963) and Payne (1964) in similar studies tried to evaluate the effectiveness of two different methods used by science consultants in elementary schools. The criterion of change was improvement in the student's achievement tests. Two groups were used, one where the science consultant worked only with the teachers in planning the unit, and the second where the consultant talked to students directly once a week and the regular teacher followed up the consultant's work during the remainder of the week. In the first study, the author found that there was greater learning in the students when the consultant worked only with the teacher. In the second study (Payne, 1964) neither method had any advantage over the other in terms of student achievement. These conflicting results may have been due to two differences in the studies: (1) in the second study the roles of the teachers were reversed from the first study, i.e., the teachers who originally worked only with the consultant in the planning of work now followed up the consultant after he worked directly with the students, and vice versa. This may have had an effect on teaching effectiveness, particularly if one role was preferred over the other; (2) in the first study the subject matter content was "light" and in the second it was "electricity." Hence, there may have been a change in the complexity of the subject and in the teachers' familiarity with it.

Chapman (1966) did a follow-up study to determine the subsequent performance of enlisted men who had received what he called "unit group mental health consultation." This unit group consultation was consultation in which mental hygiene technicians were functioning as consultants to unit commanding officers in the United States Army and assisting the commanding officers in coping with behavior problems presented by enlisted men under their command. The study attempted to determine the subsequent performance of the 316 enlisted men. Six to 12 weeks after the consultation, the military performances of these men were reported as satisfactory or better in two thirds of the cases. The technique described was midway between consultation as it takes place in a mental health profession and direct service. No control group was used in this study.

Hunter and Ratcliffe (1968) did a one year follow-up of cases seen in mental health consultation at a community mental health center. The consultee was asked to rate whether the social adjustment or symptomatic behavior was better, the same, or worse at the end of the consultation than upon referral. The aim was to base the rating on the client's observed behavior toward people in his environment; family members, peers, friends, or caretakers. Despite the lack of checks on reliability the data showed that the distributions of the outcome (better, same, worse) were not significantly different from the results of direct clinical service: fewer than 10 percent were rated "worse." Although further research is needed to substantiate this finding, as the authors point out, the results are encouraging. For if consultation is found to be as effective as direct clinical services, the advantages of consultation are clear in view of its being less expensive, as well as a more efficient use of scarce professional manpower.

In a college setting, Bolman, Halleck, Rice, and Ryan (1969) set up a consultation program that consisted of group meetings between house fellows in university dormitories and university psychiatric and psychological counseling faculty, aimed at increasing the house fellows' sensitivity to problems in the dormitory. The experimental dormitory contained 567 women and 567 men, mostly freshmen and sophomores. A dormitory which was not given this service was used as a control. The effects of the program were measured by comparing academic performance, number of visits made to a variety of campus service agencies, withdrawals, and dropouts. No significant differences were found.

Eisenberg (1958) reported a study of what he termed psychiatric consultation to the welfare department. The specific nature of the consultation was diagnostic. Highly skilled mental health personnel were employed to determine the diagnosis of the child but the treatment was left to others in the agency. The clinical staff that had done the diagnostic (with the psychiatrist as head of the team) was available to the social workers who were carrying out the program to help in determining strategies for treatment. Forty-eight children were studied during the first year. A comparison was made of the outcome of the cases where the treatment plan was not followed as compared to where the treatment plan was followed. The results showed that the number of cases that improved was significantly greater for those in which the plan was carried out. Despite certain limitations in measurement, such as the imprecise clinical distinctions between the categories "improved"–"unimproved," the authors were extremely impressed by the significance of this combination of direct and indirect service.

The Effects of Consultation
on a Combination of Elements

A few studies have attempted to study multiple aspects of the effects of consultation. Some have studied the consultee and the client, some have attempted to study all three elements—consultee, client, and system.

Townes, Lytle, Wagner, and Wimberger (1968) studied the effectiveness of brief, intensive, diagnostic evaluations of children done by a mental health team. Twenty-seven cases referred by general practitioners were seen by the diagnostic team and recommendations made. A questionnaire was then sent out to the referring physicians and to the parents (father and mother separately) to determine the effectiveness of the program. Ninety-five percent of the physicians who returned the questionnaire felt that the program was helpful, although they felt it was least effective in teaching techniques for handling the child and his parents. A large number of parents found the diagnostic consultation helpful. The parents' report of the degree of assistance to the child was independent of the child's age, the family's socioeconomic status, or the presenting symptoms. The parents felt that the consultations were less helpful to the child than to themselves, and that they wished for more information on etiology, what to do with their child's problem, and where to go within the community. The child was not seen independently to see if there indeed were any changes in him. Rather, the information was obtained from the parents. No independent measures were taken of either the practitioners' handling of cases or the possible changes in the parents. All questions focused on whether or not the service was perceived by these individuals as being helpful. No control groups were used. A secondary finding, inconsistent with the feeling of being helpful, was that over half of the patients never returned to the physician for further treatment after they were seen for diagnostic evaluations, despite the need for further help, and 37 percent received no treatment elsewhere in the community.

Trione (1967) studied the feasibility of using school psychologists as inservice consultants to assist the teacher by helping her assume an attitude of psychological exploration and reduce any of the tensions that were present in the classroom. Nine classes were given consultation and eight classes were not. The students were matched in each of these classes by IQ. Two evaluative measures were used. Changes in the students were measured by the California Achievement Tests given before and after the program. Posttreatment results demonstrated significant differences between the experimental and the control students in the expected direction. A 60-item test was used to evaluate changes in the teachers (consultees). This Guidance and Reading Scale was constructed by the author to study the teachers' attitudes toward guidance practices and the knowledge of reading principles and teaching methods. The results showed that the experimental teachers earned significantly higher scores than a control group. Hence, there was increased awareness in the teacher of guidance and reading principles and an increase in her knowledge and confidence with new reading techniques. These results seem to reflect the systematic and intense efforts through interviews to encourage the teacher to make her own evaluations in the light of new knowledge, rewarding any new attitudes aimed at understanding the psychological reasons for specific student's behaviors, instead of seeing them as personal threats or willful and vicious attempts to disrupt the classroom.

Schmuck (1968) reported a very careful study of the effects of consultation on classrooms, teachers, and students. His is one of the very few studies to test a series of hypotheses. The consultants (mental health personnel) who, unfortunately, had little experience with consultation to teachers, attempted to assist teachers with classroom coping through small group discussions, visits to the classroom, and individual conferences. All contacts were problem oriented and centered around classroom processes and how the teachers might improve group interactions within the classrooms. The consultants were assigned one to a school for half a day each week for 15 weeks. Forty teachers (in the experimental group) received consultation, and 20 teachers from another school did not (controls). The problems around which discussions were focused were primarily problems of self-esteem, learning difficulties, and interpersonal problems.

Schmuck evaluated the changes in the teachers (the consultees), changes in the students (the clients), and the changes in the classroom (the system). Changes in teachers were determined through anecdotal materials and through four questionnaires. The questionnaires focused around the conceptions teachers had of themselves as teachers (through writing ten phrases), ways of categorizing students (through classifying given cards with students' names on them), the teachers' conceptions of positive mental health in the classroom (writing about an open-ended fictitious situation in which various elements varying from the physical to the psychological would be mentioned), and an analysis of 44 situations presented in dialogue about problems in the classroom and their resolution. Anecdotal material indicated that the teachers at the end of the program were better able to ask each other for help and use each other to talk over problems, trade materials, and respond to the new ideas. They developed a strong group feeling with a new sense of challenge and interest. Also reported was a greater differentiation of standards and attitudes and greater leeway in accepting students' behavior with more interest and ability to deal with individual differences. The questionnaire results revealed significant changes in the experimental teachers' perceptions of self as teacher, their cognitions of mental health categories (greater realization of the emotional problems and their diversity), and better views on how problematic situations in the classrooms could be handled. There was no significant change in the data on categorizing students when the experimental teachers were compared with the controls.

The students in both the consultation and comparison groups were given four questionnaires to determine whether group processes in the classrooms changed and whether their attitudes toward school and self improved. These four questionnaires covered: (1) the students' perceptions of the informal group processes in the class (12 questions); (2) attitudes to school and self-esteem (through incomplete sentences); (3) sociometric scales on friendships and helping relations and their own status in the group; and (4) students' attitudes of academic work and school in general. No improvement was found in any of the students' areas as a result of the consultation. Group processes also were unaffected by the consultation process. Thus, cognitive and attitudinal changes did occur in the teachers but it was clear that there were no accompanying behavioral changes, changes in the classroom group processes, or the students' attitudes. Schmuck's study brings up a very important issue. What is the relationship between cognitive and attitudinal change in teachers to actual behavioral changes in relation to students?

In one of the most comprehensive studies in the field, Cutler and McNeil (1964) evaluated the effectiveness of a three-year consultation service to a group of Michigan public school personnel. The consultation program aimed toward helping teachers handle classroom problems better and improve the mental hygiene atmosphere of the school. This was done through a series of intervention techniques: group and individual meetings related to general questions in areas such as aggression in schools, work with a staff on a homogeneous group of underachievers, a seminar for special services personnel on their roles and functions, a group meeting with school personnel around sixth-grade transitional problems and their relationships to adolescents, executive training programs for principals on personnel practices and other aspects of executive roles and functions, contacts with parent groups, consultation on curriculum, consultation with special groups on demand, and participation in teacher-child and teacher-parent conferences (in the whole program, children were seen only once or twice). It is clear this was an intense program covering many levels of functioning of the school. Parents, children, teachers, administrators, and special service personnel were given questionnaires to evaluate the effectiveness of the program. The teachers, administrators, and special service personnel (N−200) had seven forms—Personal Data Sheet, Content Orientation Scale to basic mental health concepts, Leary Interpersonal Checklist, a questionnaire on problems and the handling of the classroom, a 36-item Sentence Completion Test on attitudes toward children and the staff's role, Classroom Procedures Scale (to tap the authoritarian-permissive dimension of teacher behavior), and a validity scale adapted from the MMPI. Parents (N−100) were given a series of general questions, items from the Parent Attitude

Research Instrument (PARI), and the Leary Interpersonal Checklist to rate themselves and what they felt the teachers were like. Children in the fourth, fifth, and sixth grades were divided into experimental groups (N–47) and control groups (N–98) and were given four tests: A questionnaire on how often things happen (work demands, classroom climate, and pupil satisfaction), multiple choice items about school (peer relations, reactions to teachers, and pupil satisfaction), a semiprojective technique on classroom attitudes and feelings toward classmates, and a rating scale on attitudes toward specific and school-related activities. There were no control groups for teachers or parents. However, a special group of ten teachers, eight special services personnel, and six administrators were identified as being more intensively exposed to the consultation program and were compared to the larger comparable group.

The major analysis of the data on teachers and other school personnel consisted of a series of "t" tests between pre- and posttest measurement on 43 relevant variables. Out of the 43 variables, 16 showed significant change in the expected direction. Significant improvement was noted in the staff's understanding of personal relationship with colleagues and in their self-described overall effectiveness. Results of the Interpersonal Check List ratings were interpreted as showing that the teachers seemed to have a somewhat stronger, more assertive, and forceful view of themselves and that important improvements had taken place in terms of a reduction in the disparity between their self and ideal self-ratings, leading to the conclusion that greater general comfort and self-satisfaction had been achieved.

In regard to the group of "Intensive Participants" it is not clear how much greater their exposure was to consultation than the larger group. There was a shift made in the second year of the program in which an additional man day of consultation was provided and attention was directed solely to a single elementary school. Apparently, it was from this latter school that the Intensive Participants were drawn. The pre-post method was also used in analyzing the data from this group as well as comparisons made with the larger group. It is difficult to determine what results are statistically significant since only means are presented in tabular form and levels of significance are not consistently presented in the narrative. However, the authors were pleased with the results and concluded that the intensive participants did benefit substantially more than the larger group, particularly in terms of increased flexibility in their relationships with children, increased openess in interpersonal relationships, and their proneness to judge fewer children as serious classroom problems.

For the parents, 56 variables were analyzed with the use of the pre-post measurement and 12 showed significant positive change. The results indicated a decreased emphasis on "Deification of Parents" and "Breaking the Will" and "Intrusion into Private Lives of the Children." There was greater strength in their relationship with their children, with less emphasis on comradeship and sharing. It was believed that these changes reflected a more mature parental role. The parents felt better able to influence the school and were more convinced that the school was doing a better job. They participated more in the school and read more about mental health and school related materials.

The comparison of the experimental group of children with the control group on 19 variables revealed that the controls showed a total of 12 negative changes, five positive changes, and two variables remained the same. The experimentals showed 12 positive changes, five negative changes, and two variables remained the same. However, four of the positive changes in the controls were statistically significant compared to only two statistically significant positive changes in the experimentals. Hence, the conclusion that teachers who participate in the program produce children whose responses are much more positive than those who do not is based on directional changes rather than on changes that are statistically significant.

In addition to these changes the study also made some suggestions relative to consultee characteristics and the use of consultation. They report, for example, that a key time to provide consultation to teachers is in the early years of their careers. Their findings showed that the younger, less experienced teachers are more likely to change—they are more highly motivated, less certain of techniques to use, and more susceptible to change than the older, more experienced teacher.

Although in these outcome studies much of what passes under the label of consultation is not spelled out or differs widely from one situation to the next, still the evidence as presented appears to indicate that "consultation" does have a positive effect in many instances. Unfortunately, there are no reported studies of the effect over various time intervals. As already indicated, there remains a great need for more theoretically based research in which relationships among identified variables can serve as predictors of outcome. Despite the fact that a number of theoretical schemes could furnish a useful orientation to consultation, i.e., crisis theory, ecological theory, small group theory, organization theory, systems theory, etc.—none of these have gained wide acceptance at this time.

Table 33–2 attempts to summarize the outcome studies reported in terms of scope of study, area of study, and design.

CONCLUSIONS AND RECOMMENDATIONS

The natural evolution of a new area of service activities seems to take place in two stages: First, the problems are directly related to practice with a beginning effort to tie the practice to some new theoretical views. There is a great deal of discussion and clarification of what is done which leads to the development of scientifically oriented clinical evaluations. Second is the effort to begin to structure what is done much more carefully and to evaluate the activity in an objective fashion integrating ideas from anecdotal materials and case studies. This then leads to more highly sophisticated efforts at trying to understand the phenomenon and to link it more solidly to empirical foundations. Hypotheses are tested through experimentation, with control and comparison groups used. Consultation has evolved in this fashion. The literature is replete with examples of consultation activities in various fields. But only recently have there begun to appear empirical studies and only very recently have these studies begun to reach scientific standards.

Inherent in the evaluation of consultation are some highly complex problems. Research in psychotherapy has been going on for many years and still poses many difficulties. Research in consultation contains many of the same problems of psychotherapy research plus some added difficulties of its own. The reasons for this are several. For one, the goals of psychotherapy can be narrowly defined and made quite specific. Consultation, however, not only has ill-defined goals, but still struggles with basic nomenclature differences, even as to what does and does not constitute consultation. At the present time trying to compare descriptive reports of consultation programs is painfully difficult because there is so much diversity in the field. Another major problem is the target group in consultation. In psychotherapy, the therapist works directly with the client in whom he is trying to effect change. In consultation, however, the consultant may never see the client, for he works primarily through an intermediary agent. The system of linkage between the intermediary agent and the client needs to be demonstrated.

Although there are several theoretical approaches which might be applied to consultation practice, e.g., crisis theory, systems theory, etc., for the most part consultation practice continues to be dominated by a common-sense approach. Procedures and methods used vary from consultant to consultant with little consistency in any aspect of consultation practice. Some conceptual progress has been made in defining different types of consultation, but as yet these new definitions have little application in either research or training.

The research that has already been done has been noticeably lacking in any effort to conceptualize the variables studied. Few of these studies have had any hypotheses which they have attempted to test. Many of the studies lack simple scientific elements such as control groups. Although many studies ostensibly seem to be investigating the same elements, the findings which occur are difficult to compare because of differences in terminology, unclear specification of what was done, differences in methods of measurement, etc. One of the most noticeable lacks in the field is any effort to replicate studies. As yet, only one study, and that was in the field of educational consultation, has been replicated. Not only are there no replication studies, but few studies in consultation even refer to other previous studies.

One of the purposes of this review, therefore, as was stated at the beginning, is to try to define the area so that people are clear as to what is being

TABLE 33–2
Outcome Studies

Author	Date	Kind of Consultation	Controls Used	Positive Effect Reported in:		
				Consultee	System	Client
Eisenberg	1958	Psychiatric	Yes	–	–	Yes
Foster & Hartman	1959	Dietary	No	–	Yes	–
Mariner, Brandt, Stone, & Mirmow	1961	Psychiatric	No	Yes	–	–
Teitelbaum	1961	Educational	Yes	Yes	–	–
Ginther	1963	Educational	Comparison Group	–	–	Yes
Cutler & McNeil	1964	Mental Health	Yes	Yes	–	Yes
Dorsey, Matsunaga, & Bauman	1964	Mental Health	No	Yes	–	–
Payne	1964	Educational	Comparison Group	–	–	No
Chapman	1966	Mental Health	No	–	–	Yes
Pierce-Jones, Iscoe, & Cunningham	1968	Mental Health	Yes	No	–	–
Trione	1967	Psychological	Yes	Yes	–	Yes
Friedlander	1968	Behavioral Science	Yes	Yes	–	–
Schmuck	1968	Behavioral Science	Yes	Yes	No	No
Townes, Lytle, Wagner, & Wimberger	1968	Mental Health	No	Yes	–	Yes
Hunter & Radcliffe	1968	Mental Health	Comparison Group	–	–	Yes
Bolman, Halleck, Rice, & Ryan	1969	Psychiatric	Yes	–	–	No

–*indicates not applicable to particular study

studied, how they might conceptualize the material, and how they might either use what has already been done or develop new methods for measurement. For example, it is unclear at times in the consultation research whether the investigator is attempting to study the process of consultation, the characteristics of the consultee, or the effect of the consultation. Multivariate studies would indeed be in order with efforts to study the different levels of change and their relationships to other variables. These multivariate studies could try to determine such issues as how experienced consultants differ from inexperienced consultants in their effects, whether different disciplines have different effects, and whether different kinds of consultations produce different effects.

One of the major notable features of the research up to this time has been the focus on large-scale studies with wide use of attitudinal measures and other broad measuring instruments. There is a critical need for depth studies in consultation with subtle sophisticated measures of change that can attempt to delineate what is going on in the consultation process and help not only to see if changes occurred but what might be some of the elements in bringing about such change. This means multidimensional studies with specific measures related to the goals of the program.

Herzog (1959) has written a book on evaluative research that has become a classic in the field. Those who are attempting to undertake an evaluation of the outcome of consultation should read the book very carefully. Consultation offers an opportunity for some very creative and innovative research. The significance of the field will be increasing over the next few years. It therefore becomes necessary that careful consideration be given to ways of evaluating the area so that it can have a solid empirical base and indeed become a significant area of intervention in the mental health field.

Notes

This chapter appeared in slightly different form as Public Health Mono. No. 79, U.S. Public Health Service Publication No. 2122.

1. Studies in the area of medical-psychiatric consultation are not included here since an excellent review of this research is contained in the series of articles by Lipowski (Lipowski, I, 1967; II, 1967; III, 1968).

2. For a more complete review of this study see page 768.

3. Additional findings from this study can be found in the Program Analysis section.

References

Aikin, D. Psychiatric consultation in the family agency. Unpublished doctoral dissertation, University of Chicago, 1957.

Anton, T. A. Outside specialists and school districts. Unpublished doctoral dissertation, University of Southern California at Los Angeles, 1964.

Bannister, R. E. The role of the elementary consultant in Iowa. Unpublished doctoral dissertation, University of Nebraska Teachers College, 1962.

Biggers, M. The use of mental health consultation in rural areas. *Smith College Studies in Social Work*, 1965, 36(1), 81–82.

Bindman, A. J. The clinical psychologist as a mental health consultant. In L. E. Abt & B. F. Riess (eds.), *Progress in clinical psychology*. New York: Grune & Stratton, 1966.

Bolman, W. M., Halleck, S. L., Rice, D. G., & Ryan, J. L. An unintended side effect in a community psychiatric program. *Archives of General Psychiatry*, 1969, 20, 508–513.

Caplan, G. Types of mental health consultation. *American Journal of Orthopsychiatry*, 1963, 33(3), 470–481.

Chapman, R. F. Group mental health consultation—Report of a military field program. *Military Medicine*, 1966, 131(1), 30–35.

Cohen, L. D. Consultation: *A community mental health method. Report of a survey of practice in sixteen southern states.* Bethesda, Md.: Southern Regional Education Board and National Institute of Mental Health, 1964.

Cumings, R., & Kline, M. V. A study of the learning characteristics of public health nurses in relation to mental health education: A preliminary report. *Journal of Psychology*, 1953, 36, 195–200.

Cutler, R. L., & McNeil, E. B. *Mental health consultation in schools: A research analysis.* Ann Arbor: Department of Psychology, University of Michigan, 1966.

Dobson, J. T. The possibilities and limitations of management consulting as an aid to small business. Unpublished doctoral dissertation, University of Florida at Gainesville, 1962.

Dorsey, J. R., Matsunaga, G., & Bauman, G. Training public health nurses in mental health. *Archives of General Psychiatry*, 1964, 11(2), 214–222.

Downing, M. R. A study of certain factors involved in the effective utilization of the services of educational consultants. Unpublished doctoral dissertation, University of Virginia, 1954.

Eisenberg, L. An evaluation of psychiatric consultation service for a public agency. *American Journal of Public Health*, 1958, 48, 742–749.

Erickson, M. H. Consultation practice in community mental health services. Unpublished doctoral dissertation, University of Southern California at Los Angeles, 1966.

Family Service Association of America. *Practice in the use of purchased psychiatric consultation in 17 private FSAA member agencies.* New York: Author, 1953.

Foster, J. T., & Hartman, J. A project in voluntary consultation for hospitals. *Public Health Reports*, 1959, 74(7), 607–614.

Friedlander, F. A comparative study of consulting processes and group development. *Journal of Applied Behavioral Science*, 1968, 4(4), 377–399.

Frist, R. J. A study of state extension specialists' functions and tasks in program development in Indiana. Unpublished doctoral dissertation, University of Wisconsin, 1965.

Gilbertson, E. C., & Williamson, E. M. The consultation process in public health nursing. *Public Health Nursing*, 1952, 44, 146–147.

Ginther, J. R. Achievement in sixth grade science associated with two instructional roles of science consultants. *Journal of Educational Research*, 1963, 57, 28–33.

Gordon, D. E. A study of the functions of consultants— With special reference to cancer nursing. *Nursing Research*, 1952, 1(2), 41–42.

Griffith, C. R., & Libo, L. M. *Mental health consultants: Agents of community change*. San Francisco: Jossey-Bass, 1968.

Haylett, C. H., & Rapoport, L. Mental health consultation. In L. Bellak (ed.), *Handbook of community psychiatry and community mental health*. New York: Grune & Stratton, 1964.

Herzog, E. *Some guide lines for evaluative research*. Washington, D. C.: United States Government Printing Office, 1959.

Hunter, W. F., & Ratcliffe, A. W. The range mental health center: Evaluation of a community oriented mental health consultation program in northern Minnesota. *Community Mental Health Journal*, 1968, 4(3), 260–267.

Iscoe, I., Pierce-Jones, J., Friedman, S. T., & McGehearty, L. Some strategies in mental health consultation: A brief description of a project and some preliminary results. In E. L. Cowen, E. A. Gardner, & M. Zax (eds.), *Emergent approaches to mental health problems*. New York: Appleton-Century-Crofts, 1967.

Kindelsperger, W. L. Differentiating the role of child welfare consultant from the role of public assistant casework supervisor. Unpublished doctoral dissertation, University of Chicago, 1958.

Kline, M. V., & Cumings, R. A study of the learning characteristics of public health nurses in relation to mental health education and consultation. *Journal of Social Psychology*, 1955, 42, 43–60.

Knisely, S. Consultant services to community nursery schools. Unpublished doctoral dissertation, Teachers College, Columbia University, 1964.

Lipowski, Z. J. Review of consultation psychiatry and psychosomatic medicine: I. General principles. *Psychosomatic Medicine*, 1967, 29(2), 153–171. (a)

Lipowski, Z. J. Review of consultation psychiatry and psychosomatic medicine: II. Clinical aspects. *Psychosomatic Medicine*, 1967, 29(3), 201–224. (b)

Lipowski, Z. J. Review of consultation psychiatry and psychosomatic medicine: III. Theoretical issues. *Psychosomatic Medicine*, 1968, 30(4), 395–422.

Lippitt, G. L. A study of the consultation process. *Journal of Social Issues*, 1959, 15(2), 43–50.

Macht, L. B., Scherl, D. J., & English, J. T. Psychiatric consultation: The Job Corps experience. *American Journal of Psychiatry*, 1968, 124(8), 1092–1100.

McClung, F., Stunden, A., & Plog, S. *A study of the theory and practice of mental health consultation as provided to child care agencies throughout the United States*. Vols. 1, 2, & 3. Panorama City, Calif.: Behavior Science Corporation in cooperation with the Center for Studies of Child and Family Mental Health, National Institute of Mental Health, 1969.

Malkin, S. The role of the elementary science consultant. Unpublished doctoral dissertation, Teachers College, Columbia University, 1965.

Mannino, F. V. *Consultation in mental health and related fields: A reference guide*. Washington, D. C.: United States Government Printing Office, 1969. (a)

Mannino, F. V. *An experience in consultation as perceived by consultants and consultees*. Adelphi, Md.: Mental Health Study Center, National Institute of Mental Health, 1969. (b)

Mannino, F. V., Rooney, H. L., & Hassler, F. R. Distance and the use of the mental health clinic by community professionals. *Mental Hygiene*, 1970, 54, 73–78.

Mannino, F. V., Rooney, H. L., & Hassler, F. R. A study of clergy referrals to a mental health clinic. *Journal of Religion and Health*, 1967, 6(1), 66–73.

Mariner, A. S., Brandt, E., Stone, E. C., & Mirmow, E. L. Group psychiatric consultation with public school personnel: A two year study. *Personnel and Guidance Journal*, 1961, 40(3), 254–258.

Parker, B. *Psychiatric consultation for nonpsychiatric professional workers*. (Public Health Monograph No. 53; Public Health Service Publication No 588) Washington, D. C.: United States Department of Health, Education, and Welfare, 1958.

Payne, A. Achievement in sixth grade science associated with two instructional roles of science consultants. *Journal of Educational Research*, 1964, 57, 350–354.

Pierce-Jones, J., Iscoe, I., & Cunningham, G. *Child behavior consultation in elementary schools: A demonstration and research program*. Austin, Texas: University of Texas Press, 1968.

Samaras, J. The use of management consultants in small manufacturing firms. Unpublished doctoral dissertation, Harvard University, 1961.

Savage, W. W. *Consultative services to local school systems*. Chicago: Mid-West Administration Center, University of Chicago, 1959.

Schmuck, R. A. Helping teachers improve classroom group processes. *Journal of Applied Behavioral Science*, 1968, 4(4), 401–435.

Selzer, M. L., & Benedek, E. Lawyers' use of psychiatry. *American Journal of Psychiatry*, 1965, 122, 212–213.

Seney, W. *Effective use of business consultants. A research study and report prepared for Financial Executives Research Foundation*. New York: Financial Executives Research Foundation, 1963.

Tatham, L. E. *The efficiency experts: An impartial survey of management consultancy*. London: Business Publications, 1964.

Teitelbaum, D. I. An evaluation of an experimental program of assistance for newly appointed teachers in certain elementary schools of New York City. Unpublished doctoral dissertation, New York University, 1961.

Tetreault, J. M. Informal consultation: Social work activity with the elementary school teacher. *Smith College Studies in Social Work*, 1968, 39(1), 85–86.

Tiedeman, G. H. Psychiatric consultation in a medical setting: Intra-professional differentials and resolutions. Unpublished doctoral dissertation, University of North Carolina, 1968.

Tilles, S. An exploratory study of the emerging relationship between the executives of small manufacturing companies and their consultants. Unpublished doctoral dissertation, Graduate School of Business Administration, Harvard University, 1960.

Torrance, E. P. *What is an ideal pupil?* Minneapolis: Bureau of Educational Research, University of Minnesota, 1964.

Townes, B. D., Lytle, C. E., Wagner, N. N., & Wimberger, H. C. The diagnostic consultation and rural community mental health programs. *Community Mental Health Journal*, 1968, 4(2), 157–163.

Trione, V. The school psychologist, teacher change and fourth grade reading achievement. *California Journal of Educational Research*, 1967, 18(4), 194–200.

Watson, W. K. The use of management consultants by the United States Air Force. Unpublished doctoral dissertation, George Washington University, 1958.

34

Community Mental Health Information Systems: The Psychiatric Case Register as a Data Bank

John A. Baldwin

Control by means of feedback loops occurs ubiquitously in nature. Whether physicochemical or biological phenomena are considered, the self-regulation of dynamic systems by means of internally generated forces is encountered. The more complex the system, the more sophisticated the control mechanisms. In the higher forms of biological systems the capability has evolved of indirect control through the medium of information about system status rather than by direct use of system forces, yielding vastly increased possibilities for subtlety and finesse in controlling behavior. Man at least, among the animals, has learned to apply the principle of control through the use of information to social organizations, and has developed the ability to use the awareness which information brings to control purposefully the behavior of organizations.

As in every organizational endeavor, the need for information in the community mental health field has grown in parallel with its development. This need stems directly from its function as the means of controlling mental health through understanding, detecting, preventing, and treating mental ill-health. Information is required for all these purposes and in addition, for the planning, management, and evaluation of the community mental health organizations themselves. It is the object of this chapter to examine some of the types of information required to fulfill these purposes and some of the methods by which it may be obtained. A brief review of the need for systematic information in the community mental health field is followed by a discussion of types of data collection systems and their uses. The recent

concept of the data bank is developed and the main part of the chapter treats of one form of data bank in detail: the psychiatric case register.

THE NEED FOR SYSTEMATIC INFORMATION IN COMMUNITY MENTAL HEALTH

When most serious mental illness was the exclusive responsibility of the custodial mental hospital and only a tiny fraction of minor illness was treated, mainly by private resources, there was little need for complicated systems for reporting its occurrence. It seemed reasonable to assume that the inmates of mental institutions represented nearly all mental illness so that there was no interest in a wider epidemiology. The concern of epidemiologists was in any case limited to the pressing but soluble problems of infectious diseases. Such research as was undertaken could be adequately based on mental hospital populations without risk of drawing erroneous conclusions from unrepresentative samples. The planning and management of such institutions was a relatively simple matter, being dictated mainly by the availability of funds. Indeed, the detection, incarceration, and care of the insane was as much a legal and lay problem as a medical one.

The gradual development of therapeutic methods, the relaxation of rules governing entry into and release from mental institutions, and the appearance of outpatient clinics and acute treatment facilities in general hospitals in the first half of the century, particularly the period from 1930, accompanied the realization that mental illness was more widespread than had been supposed, was not always severe enough to warrant hospitalization, and was apparently treatable in a proportion of cases. Although the importance of ecological factors had long been appreciated, it was not until after World War II that interest in the social aspects of health and illness burgeoned.

Today the movement is away from the mental hospital as the major resource for the care of the mentally ill, towards the development of complex patterns of services more closely related to the patient in his community. Outpatient services; day and night patient services; hostels of various kinds; treatment units for special conditions like alcoholism, for particular age groups like adolescents, or for particular therapies; home-visiting services for evaluation, treatment, and follow-up, and many other innovations have wrought a revolution in treatment, but they have also created their own problems in management and planning, in the distribution of resources, in the detection and estimation of a community's illness, and in the study of the course and outcome of disorder. In the pursuit of treatment a patient may enter care through many different agencies, may pass through several different services, may be subject to a wide variety of presumed therapeutic influences and may pass out of care, usually after a few weeks or months, without ever leaving his home or even his work environment. The patient is no longer captive.

In this situation it is more than usually necessary to have the right kinds of information available for clinical care, for planning and administering the services, and for research. In essence, the *clinical need* is for a cumulative record of the patient's main personal, social, and clinical features, including both physical and psychological histories, and a complete statement of previous treatment, which is readily available, at least in summary, whenever and wherever he appears with a request for help. It should not be necessary to waste patient's and staff's time spending hours quizzing and evaluating a patient anew, just because he has not been seen in that particular facility before, though last week he was in the one next door. For *management* there should be available complete, reliable, and up-to-date information about the functioning of the services in terms of the patients who use them, the types and

facilities which provide it. Management of mental health services, whether privately or publicly financed, must be on business lines, with proper attention to the most effective distribution of scarce resources. The need for overall *planning* of service provision and development becomes more pressing as the diversity and complexity of services grows so that both wasteful duplication and inadequate coverage are minimized. The need for extensive information is perhaps most apparent in this area and in *research*, where the data must relate to the population at risk of entering the services as well as to the patients and the available resources. Demographic and sociological information on the population at risk may sometimes be supplemented by attempts to measure directly the extent of untreated morbidity by community surveys and kindred techniques, despite the inadequacy of methods of detection and estimation. Yet only when valid and reliable methods of measuring morbidity have been devised will it be possible to evaluate the effect of the community mental health services on the level of psychiatric morbidity with assurance; in the interim, reliance must perforce be placed upon estimation of changes in patients over time in the presence and the absence of well-defined therapeutic procedures.

It is obvious that all these divers needs for information cannot be met all at once and everywhere at the same time. Nor is it necessary that they should be, since for many purposes, particularly in research and planning, generalization from adequate samples is more reliable, more efficient, and more economic. Yet in other respects it is desirable that a skeleton of basic data should be generally available for the provision and evaluation of clinical service, and for the conduct of research appropriate to the local situation and the interests of professional staffs. It is no coincidence that the growth of demand for systematic information for these objectives has been paralleled by the development of the conceptual and technological capability to fulfill it.

TYPES OF INFORMATION SYSTEMS FOR COMMUNITY MENTAL HEALTH

The universe from which data are obtained, the kinds of information, how it is collected, and what is done with it after it has been collected, ought always and in all circumstances to be dependent exclusively on the purposes for which it is required. Thus, the first question which must be asked whenever systematic data collection is envisaged is: "What use will be made of these data; what questions will they be required to answer?" Once the purposes have been decided, the second question is: "What data are required to answer these questions and in what form will it be necessary to organize them in order to answer the questions?" When the necessary data have been satisfactorily defined, the final question should be asked, "Can these data be obtained with sufficient reliability by means of the methods and resources available?" Submission to this harsh discipline will pay dividends far in excess of normal market returns. It will often be found that surprisingly little information is required if it is of high quality and pertinence and if the purposes are precisely enough defined. With a little ingenuity, sufficient capacity for rearrangement can often be incorporated to allow multiple purposes to be combined with only minor additions, but the temptation to substitute quantity and diversity for quality and relevance should be strenuously resisted. These old-fashioned homilies on good research practice apply equally to general data systems designed to meet the many needs of modern community mental health.

The Universe and Its Record. The universe is the class of units from which the input to the data system is drawn. The data about each unit can be referred to as a record. The universe from which the input to the data system is to be selected will usually be a group of *persons*, either patients or the general population. The most common clinical need is for a record on the individual which brings together information about a wide variety of his characteristics and experiences. For management and planning there is usually less interest in an individual-based record than in records dealing with *events, transactions,* and *processes* in which the person is one characteristic of the record rather than its basis. The primary concern is likely to be as much with the number of admissions, referrals, interviews, tests, treatments, etc., as with the number of persons admitted, referred, interviewed, tested, treated, etc. This difference is important, but the two types of record are not mutually exclusive since the characteristics of the individual and the events which happen to him may be contained in a person-based record and, provided arrangements are made for retrieval, may be sorted, counted, or manipulated in other ways. It is less easy, though not impossible, to use an event-based record system to obtain data about individuals. It requires a means of linking together the records pertaining to an individual, which must be some item in the record which identifies the individual wherever he appears in the system. The difficulty of incorporating links of this sort and the obverse difficulty of constructing processable individual-based records like the medical record has been an effective obstacle to developing practical data systems serving both types of universe until very recently. The immense power of manipulation of complex records inherent in modern data processing and computing systems has removed the technical objections, but most reporting systems in community mental health, and indeed, in the health field generally, were conceived well before this technological revolution and so are based exclusively on one kind of record or the other.

An even simpler type of universe is often used for management and planning, based on *organizations*, such as the hospital or clinic, or some arbitrary unit like a census tract. Records for this kind of universe contain more general data such as numbers of beds, doctors, patients in a hospital, etc., or numbers of people, dwellings, etc., in a census area. This type of record is quite satisfactory for grosser managerial and planning operations and has the advantages of simplicity and economy over more complex approaches. The task of compiling the record can often be dispersed to existing resources in the organizations themselves, where the information is more readily available and is likely to be collected for local purposes in any case. The task of processing the data is simplified since the number of records is drastically reduced. Nearly all local and national governmental data systems in the health field begin with this type of record, and it still forms the main source of planning data. It is obvious that this approach can provide counts of each item in the record, which may be of events or individuals according to design, but the drawback is that once the design is settled, nothing can be obtained by manipulation beyond what was originally envisaged. For instance, if there are no person counts, counts of persons are unobtainable even for single units, and if person counts are included there is still no way of knowing if the same persons appear in more than one organization. The reward of simplicity is economy; the price is inflexibility. On the other hand, a data system based on persons or events can yield organization-based records provided only that the organizations are identified in each person or event record.

For many types of research, especially clinical, evaluative, and epidemiological, person-based records are required, though event records will serve others, such as most operational research. Yet such is the diversity of data requirements for research that other universes may be called for, such as the family or the household. In principle, records based on this type of unit can be derived from person records if the necessary linkage information is incorporated, but in practice it may be extremely difficult to achieve reliable rearrangement because of defects in the available data. Fortunately, many national systems for recording vital statistics (births, deaths, and marriages) contain sufficient information to permit family relationships to be derived and some of the most important research in population genetics has been carried out on these records. There is great scope for research on large populations of human groups in community mental health and if the appropriate linkage information can be incorporated, it is quite practical using general data systems.

Types of Record. There are two basic types of record—cross-sectional and longitudinal. The most common type of record is *cross-sectional*, that is, it contains data about persons or events at a specified point in time. In practice the assumption is often justifiable that the data are also valid at other points in time. Many items, like the sex of the individual, are extremely unlikely to change, while others, such as his address, may change rather unpredictably. Cross-sectional records are satisfactory for most purposes, are relatively easy to construct and manipulate, and the data they contain are usually much more easily obtained than longitudinal record data. Cross-sectional records can, of course, be used to obtain descriptions or analyses of members of the universe at particular points in time, and repeated at different times they provide information about trends in the universe. To a very limited extent they can sometimes be used to infer changes over

time in specified members of the universe but this is always a hazardous procedure and resort must usually be had to some form of longitudinal record.

The *longitudinal* record contains data about persons or processes valid over specified time periods. In practice it is usually composed of data collected on each member of the universe at intervals, the assumption being made that changes did not occur during the intervals. This type of record is generally much more difficult to compile since it involves more sophistication in data collection. It is also much more difficult to manipulate and methods of analyzing longitudinal records are not yet sufficiently developed to yield their full potential. Longitudinal records are unnecessary for most purposes but are essential if it is desired to monitor changes in individuals or processes over time. The clinical record is a good example, and the better cohort studies are based on longitudinal records rather than repeated cross-sections or adaptations of cross-sectional record systems. Longitudinal records can be used to provide cross-sectional data without difficulty and to this extent are more flexible. Again the reward of complexity is flexibility.

Types of File Organization. A collection of records may be referred to as a file and the capability of the data system is as much dependent on the organization of the file as it is on the structure and content of the records which compose it. The two chief types of file are the static and the cumulative. *Static* files are record systems constructed on a once-for-all basis with no intention to add to them or change them in any way. This type is the most common, and nearly all research projects are based on static files of information collected for the purpose of the project only. Many governmental data collections are organized in static files and the periodic national census is a good example. Data are collected and input to the system once only and if it is necessary to repeat the exercise a fresh static file is generated even though the same members of the same universe may be included. For most purposes static files are entirely adequate.

Cumulative or dynamic files are designed to be modified by the addition or removal of specified data by the process of updating. Updating may be a fairly simple procedure where only new records are being added, as with many cumulative files of event records such as admissions to hospital. But where modification of existing records is involved, as is usually the case with longitudinal records, the procedures may be complicated in the extreme and involve linkage decisions based on both identification of records and ordering of temporal sequences within records. So central is the concept of linkage in record structure and file organization that data systems are sometimes classified according to whether linkage is involved or not. Unlinked files are called indexes and linked files are called registers.

Cumulative file organizations are clearly more flexible and capable of providing a much wider variety of descriptions and analyses of the universe than static files, but as usual they incur penalties in greater complexity at all stages from data collection through the updating procedure to manipulation. Cumulative records and cumulative files are necessary for some purposes, and the clinical record based on the unit system of "one patient one record" is again a classical example. Static files can obviously be derived from cumulative files, and the practical utilization of cumulative files often involves the extraction of a group of records for duplication and construction of a static file as a subset for particular purposes. In respect of file organization, as with person units and longitudinal records, the more sophisticated the data system, the more complicated, expensive, awkward to use, and difficult to maintain it becomes. Yet it is sometimes necessary to accept and try to overcome the difficulties, and the payoff in flexibility and yield may, on occasion, justify the investment. The feasibility of linkage and large files has been improved enormously by computer manipulation and in some countries even the national censuses are being linked to form a rather gross and crude form of longitudinal person record organized as a cumulative file.

The Choice of Information System. An information system of one sort or another is required today wherever patients are seen in any numbers and wherever effort is made to provide systematic service to a given population. No clinical service can be considered satisfactory which does not construct usable records on its patients and on its own work. The question is now rarely whether an information system of any kind is desirable, but how extensive it should be, what purposes it should serve, and what form it should take.

In most situations the only requirements are for a clinical record system providing information about individual patients accumulated over the course of their "psychiatric life" and kept up-to-date, and a simple system of managerial and administrative counting of cases and items of work done. These two types of requirement are so different, involving different types of universe, record, and file organization, that there is little point in trying to marry them into one system unless there are very special circumstances. Such *duplex* systems are, and will continue to be, the most common, the simplest, and easiest to operate. The clinical record will usually be on hard copy organized in folders for each patient and arranged in some numerical or alphabetical way to accord with local convictions as to what is most suitable to staff needs. The administrative data may be collected on special forms or abstracted manually from the clinical records. For larger systems punch card machines or even a computer may be used to manipulate the file.

Often the local situation is complicated by the information requirements of some higher authority which demands a separate return, or several returns of different types to suit its purposes. Governmental data systems are often themselves duplex, involving a return on each organization and a separate report on each patient or admission, referral, etc. This may mean that locally it is necessary to develop a third or even a fourth data collection system to meet these superimposed central needs. It is at this point, when the information systems become *triplex* or even more *multiplex*, that diminishing returns are obtained for retaining the economy and simplicity of separate single-purpose systems, and serious consideration has to be given to ways of rationalizing the flow of information. Almost invariably the several systems develop idiosyncratically and use overlapping but not identical universes, definitions, and methods. They are likely to be run by different groups of staff because of historical accidents of administration and though individually they may be run with diligence and efficiency, severally they may represent a remarkable waste in duplication of effort. Only rarely will they be sufficiently comparable in content even to permit checking of one against another as a means of testing reliability, much less use of one to supplement the content of another.

Even in situations where the users of information are multiple, it is often possible to satisfy all the needs except the clinical by means of a single system of periodic or continuing data collection on events or transactions organized into a static or cumulative file, but with no attempt at linkage. Semi or fully automatic manipulation is usually essential to efficient use. For the most part, such systems have limited value for sophisticated research but they can provide much useful background statistics in fields like patient movement. If a small number of items of personal and social information are obtained on the patient concerned in each event, for example, current marital status, address, birthplace, race, etc., the usefulness of the file may be greatly enhanced, but much reliance should not be placed upon data of this character unless special precautions are taken to maintain accuracy. Careful investigation of the reliability of data from general data systems of this kind will often disappoint the would-be researcher.

The clinical record system does not lend itself to incorporation into a general data system because of its nature as a cumulative, person based, longitudinal record file, because of its extensive, complicated, and heterogeneous content, and because of its primary use for the here-and-now treatment of the individual patient. Consequently it is relatively little used as a source of input to a general data system though its clinical content is often tempting for research. Until much more efficient and economic methods are found for storing, searching, retrieving, and updating extensive plain language records it is unlikely that alternatives to the hard-copy record in a folder will find general favor. However, it is a logical step to replace the duplex and multiplex approach to satisfying data needs with a *unitary* information system capable of serving all the information needs of clinical and other services in community mental health. The essential step in creating a unitary system is to make the clinical record itself the source of systematic data for the general data system, imposing sufficient standardization to fulfill the systematic requirements. A unitary information system must be cumulative, permitting up-dating of longitudinal records by means of linkage and probably should be based on person records, perhaps with capability for linkage into records of other human groups such as the family. So far almost all attempts at developing unitary systems have had a strong research basis and very few have proved clinically acceptable, but there is no doubt that the technological knowledge is now available. The main part of this chapter describes a unitary system which is moving towards these objectives but it is pertinent first to review some of the implications of advanced information systems in the health field.

THE PLACE OF HEALTH
INFORMATION SYSTEMS

It is an obvious step to extend the principle of the cumulative psychiatric record to other types of health and welfare records and then to combine them into a single comprehensive health record for each individual entering care which would eventually encompass his whole life. Since virtually every individual requires health care at birth, there would be a record for every member of the population at risk of illness in quite a short time. It would be quite practical to link in vital records and eventually census records, so that every member of the population would have a life-time record of his personal and social characteristics, his health and welfare experiences, and any other facet of his life which was appropriate. A fund or bank of data of this extent on the individual could improve clinical service in many ways if it were quickly available and, for research, the ability to classify, collate, and count the multitude of variables relating to each individual would undoubtedly lead to advances in many areas.

The potential of the unitary information system when coupled with the immense power of the modern computer is incalculable. Its capacity for communication, computation, and control is so great that concern is frequently expressed about the political and ethical implications. This is not the place to discuss these questions but it may be noted that, so far as health records are concerned, fears of misuse are partly founded on a misconception of the nature of such systems. Although they could make large amounts of information about individuals available immediately on demand, the key to the information can easily be made burglar-proof. The potential benefits to the health care and welfare of the individual may then be thought to outweigh the risks of misuse. The preservation of doctor-patient confidentiality of the contents of the hard copy medical record is impossible in hospitals today, when dozens and even hundreds of nonmedical personnel must have access to it for their work. Yet the most scurrilous abuses of confidence often arise from casual knowledge gained in the course of legitimate work. The magnetic record could be made much more secure from this type of abuse by incorporation of job-specific triggers for selective recall and other devices making use of the special skills required to interpret it. Nevertheless there are clear dangers and they should be recognized, evaluated, and due precautions taken against them.

The potential power of comprehensive health information systems does not automatically ensure their wise and fruitful use. There are definite constraints which severely limit the situations in which their development might be justified. The most general of these is probably also the most intractable, namely the problem of the quality and accuracy of the input. Inaccurate and incomplete recording can vitiate the use of any information system, whether due to purposeful withholding of information as well-intentioned effort to preserve confidentiality or from any other voluntary or involuntary cause. The mutual benefit to the users of full cooperation must be abundantly clear if motivation to maintain the system is to remain high. A system prone to important degrees of error would be likely quickly to fall into disrepute.

Unreliability is most important in the two fields in which large-scale information systems could be most useful—clinical service and research. Provided there was some assurance of reasonable cooperation, a fully automated clinical record system could have valuable application in a group of mental and general health services covering a well-defined and relatively stable population. There would have to be a high probability that anyone in the area served would enter the reporting system whenever care was sought. There

would have to be prior agreement on standard formats for the record, at least within each specialty, and there would have to be a degree of common administration.

To be of sufficient benefit for health research to justify the investment, all these conditions would have to be met for a risk population the characteristics of which were appropriate to the research to be undertaken. The system would have to be unitary, the clinical record forming the basis of the systematic record, and there would also have to be more stringent rules and procedures for the collection of specialized data which could be changed from time to time to meet current needs. It is evident that such far-reaching constraints could only be met on a limited scale and would only be appropriate in a limited number of instances. Even then it would be necessary to ensure that the standard and complementary methods of direct survey research on the community could be carried out and that facilities were available for laboratory and other specialized techniques to be applied where necessary. In short, so great an investment as a comprehensive information system would not be justified unless the best possible conditions for its exploitation as well as for its implementation were assured. These conditions are the same as those required for successful application of the population or community laboratory concept, in which a growing pool of information accruing from research programs in a variety of fields conducted on the same human groups leads to cross-fertilization and the development of cooperative efforts in pursuit of ideas and hypotheses stretching across the boundaries of several disciplines. Such Meccas of interdisciplinary and multidisciplinary team research are necessarily few and far between and for this reason, wherever they can be created, their enthusiastic encouragement is eminently worthwhile.

THE CASE REGISTER CONCEPT[1]

The essential characteristics of the register concept which distinguish it from all other forms of data collection systems are that it constructs person-rather than event-orientated records and cumulative rather than once-for-all files of information, so that data on events occurring in relation to an individual or changes in his recorded characteristics may be linked together into a temporal sequence in the same record. Strictly, any data collection system which fulfills these criteria is a register. Data collection systems which, though cumulative, do not link events to individuals may be referred to as indexes, and all register systems can be used as indexes where only event data are required.

A further characteristic of registers, but which is not unique to them, is that they draw their input from a defined population of persons. The population may be defined by any one or group of features pertinent to the purpose of the register. For epidemiological purposes this is usually a particular disease or group of diseases (e.g., cancer) or a geographical area. For operational purposes the defining features will normally be the organization under study, such as a single hospital or a system of functionally related services. The input may be a random, selected, or total sample of the population defined as at risk of inclusion.

Important consequences of these characteristics of the register are: (1) data collection is systematic rather than haphazard, (2) data are standardized rather than heterogeneous, (3) data are prospective rather than retrospective, (4) data are cumulative rather than point-related, and (5) records are longitudinal rather than cross-sectional.

At a more philosophical level it may be remarked that medical science uses experimental methods in two main ways. Traditionally, the physician diagnoses and treats his individual patients much as an experimenter conducting a study of one example of a series. He strives to understand the disease process in the individual on the basis of past training and experience of processes in other individuals more or less similar in certain respects. The stages of observation, data collection, judgment, and verification are carried out with varying degrees of skill, thoroughness, and reliability. Increasingly in the recent past, purely laboratory and group methods have been introduced, utilizing selected characteristics of the individual (e.g., serum, urine, electroencephalogram, social class) as examples of more completely documented and measured dimensions of populations which can be placed along gradients of variation known to be statistically or causally associated with the presence or absence of

pathology. This approach, which is also subject to considerable variation in accuracy and reliability, is seen as an *aid* to the traditional methods of the physician. The defects of the one method are, at least theoretically, the virtues of the other. Whereas the physician can observe multiple aspects of the individual over long periods of time, the laboratory and field investigator can only analyze samples of a few characteristics at points in time. On the other hand, the latter can call upon immense series of well-documented and carefully measured data, whereas the physician is limited to his own experience gained from a small number of similar cases, those of his colleagues, and written reports.

The growing complexity and extent of medical knowledge, and the increasing difficulty of making properly verified and reliable advances is of major concern in some fields of medicine. Nowhere is this more evident than in psychiatry, where, in spite of great effort, the scope of knowledge, as opposed to hunch, surmize, and speculation, is relatively narrow. What is required is an application of the scientific method which combines the holistic and longitudinal approach of the physician to the individual with the precision of measurement and large number verification of the population and laboratory investigator. The case register is one such synthetic approach.

The idea of the case register is by no means new (Bellows, 1949). One of the earliest and most extensive uses of registers was in tuberculosis control programs though inadequate reporting has tended to vitiate attempts to use them for epidemiological research (Bahn, 1964). Many registers have been started for reporting cancer cases (Haenszel & Hon, 1956), but have been relatively little used for research because of incomplete coverage and inability to keep them going over sufficiently long periods (United States Department of Health, Education, and Welfare, 1964). Bahn (1964) states that registers for rheumatic fever, venereal disease, and diabetes have suffered from similar defects and indeed, have led to erroneous conclusions on morbidity and survival rates due to selective reporting.

Early applications of register method to mental illness research were limited to mental hospital patients. Norwegian mental hospital statistics have been organized in register form since the 1920s and this register is still yielding valuable contributions (Odegaard, 1964). Reporting of admissions to English mental hospitals has also used the register approach since 1954 (Brooke, 1963). Extension to cover outpatients and other forms of care has taken place only since about 1960, notably by the two American registers in Monroe County, New York, and the State of Maryland.

The Monroe County register began on January 1, 1960, covering all but an estimated two to three percent of county residents seen in the five psychiatric inpatient units and eight outpatient facilities, and by the 50 private psychiatrists which constitute the psychiatric services available (Gardner et al., 1963). The county population numbered 586,000 in 1960, of whom 317,000 were in the city of Rochester and the remainder in the suburban and rural areas around it. The initial rolls (one-day prevalence) amounted to 4,300 persons and an average of 4,900 persons were added each year (Bahn, 1965). The psychiatric services were particularly comprehensive, county residents did not go outside the area for treatment in any numbers, and the state mental hospital was situated near the centre of the community, while the Department of Psychiatry of the University of Rochester provided a location for the project (Gardner et al., 1962). Three types of research use were planned for the register: clinical, epidemiological, and service evaluation, and only individuals were registered who received service under the immediate or ultimate responsibility of a psychiatrist. The data collected were limited to identifying, demographic, and clinical and included: name, maiden name, address, date of birth, race, sex, marital status, social security number (where possible), prior psychiatric service, diagnoses, date of beginning and ending of current service, type of service, and type of treatment (Gardner et al., 1962). Data were punched into two IBM punch cards for each patient and processed on a 101 statistical machine, but later computer storage and processing were introduced, together with extensive reliability checks (Hopkins & Gardner, 1963). A series of studies have been reported from this register, including operational (Gardner, Bahn, & Miles, 1964), demographic (Bodian et al., 1963), clinical (Gardner, Bahn, & Mack, 1963), and nosological types (Babigian et al., 1964).

The Maryland case register was established on July 1, 1961. It was compiled from a very large network of reporting agencies, including 36 institutions (state, private, and Veterans Administration mental hospitals and general hospital psychiatric units), and 65 out-patient clinics (county, state, Veterans Administration, university, etc.) (Phillips, Gorwitz, & Bahn, 1962). Private psychiatrists were not included. The state population was 3.4 million, of which 0.9 million were resident in Baltimore city, 1.5 million in suburban counties, and 0.8 million in rural areas (Bahn et al., 1963). The initial prevalence registration amounted to 21,000 persons and about 14,000 individuals were added each year (Bahn, 1965). The goals of the register were stated in terms of value to the reporting agencies, to the program planner, and to the epidemiologist (Gorwitz et al., 1963). Considering the extensiveness of the reporting system, a large number of items of data were collected, which differed somewhat for the two basic types of reporting agency. Identifying and demographic information included name and maiden name, case number, address, birth date, sex, color, marital status, and social security number. Social data were collected only from hospitals and institutions and were limited to education and religion. The operational data included referral source, details of previous admissions, dates of admission and discharge, number and frequency of outpatient interviews, details of movements in and out of hospital on pass, leave, etc., and disposition. Clinical data encompassed diagnoses, cause of death, symptoms of "problem drinking," type of service received, and condition after treatment (Phillips, Gorwitz, & Bahn, 1962). The register was processed by computer from the start, fully automated matching and linkage being carried out on all incoming data (Phillips, Bahn, & Miyasaki, 1962; Phillips & Bahn, 1963). The register was operated under the auspices of the state government in Baltimore and supported by the United States National Institute of Mental Health. A number of studies have been reported, including epidemiological (Bahn, Gorwitz, & Kramer, 1964), and operational types (Bahn et al., 1965).

Apart from the Monroe County and Maryland registers, a number of others have been started in the United States. Bahn (1962), reporting a conference on case registers held in 1962, noted that the State of Hawaii (population 600,000) was operating a register of persons provided service by the State Division of Mental Health from 1961; residents of Washington Heights in New York City receiving clinical care had been registered since 1956 (population 270,000); Dutchess County, New York, residents (population 170,000) served by a large state mental hospital and a small experimental facility were included in a register from 1960; and one or two other small registers were also in existence. At a similar conference in 1965 only four registers were mentioned: Maryland, Monroe County, Hawaii, and a register covering three counties in North Carolina (population at risk 350,000) which had been started in July 1964 (Bahn, 1965). Work has since been reported from the Dutchess County register (Brandon & Gruenberg, 1966; Kasius, 1966; Patton, 1966). More recently Mazer (1966) has described a register on the small island of Martha's Vineyard (population 5,800) which covers both psychiatric and "parapsychiatric" disorders. Another project which can be classified as a register is the well-known and long-established study on the Danish island of Samsø with a population of 6,200 (Nielsen, Wilsnack, & Stromgren, 1965). A register covering the Camberwell area of London was started on December 31, 1964. Attempts are now being made to produce valid comparative studies based on register areas (Bahn et al., 1965; Wing et al., 1967).

From this review it is clear that the psychiatric case register, as a method of conducting research of various types, is now being fairly widely used. In the relatively new situation of expanding and developing variety in patterns of psychiatric service, the mental hospital as the traditional source of data must be superseded and the register offers a means of covering a multitude of data sources while carefully controlling overlap. At the same time it should be emphasized that its greatest potential lies in longevity. Its most valuable contributions will derive from its cumulative function in amassing longitudinal records of patient experience over major segments of the life-span, thus affording the opportunity of tracing the course of illness under varying conditions from initial recognition to ultimate outcome—an opportunity which, if it existed in the custodial mental hospital, was not much exploited.

THE PSYCHIATRIC CASE REGISTER IN NORTHEAST SCOTLAND

Although it is possible to state the general characteristics of the case register method with reasonable precision, each practical application is unique and can only be fully understood in its particular context. The users whose needs the register is designed to meet vary widely and consequently both the information content and the methodological and technical details also vary with circumstances. In order to exemplify the general principles in a specific example there follows an extended description of the psychiatric case register developed to cover the northeast region of Scotland. This begins with a brief outline of the setting in which the register had to be developed and the user-needs and goals which led to the choice of the register type of information system; then the register system is described and the details of implementation explored; finally, examples of actual uses are given, together with a general discussion of possible future developments and applications.

The Northeast of Scotland

The northeast of Scotland can be likened to a clenched fist thrust forward into the North Sea, which washes the 3,460 square miles of the mainland part of it to the east and north, while to the west and south mountain ranges of the Scottish Highlands form a natural back wall enclosing a fertile and relatively populous lowland plain (Figure 34—1). To this mainland area are added two groups of islands, the Orkneys and Shetlands, each about 90 in number and totalling a little under 1,000 square miles. Both lie well to the north, beyond the northernmost point of the Scottish mainland. The whole region is about 15 percent of the area of Scotland and contains about nine percent of its population. Its focal point is the city of Aberdeen which has about two-fifths of the regional population. From this university city, major fishing port and railway terminus, there radiate the region's lines of communication and transport.

The region has a long history of isolation and cultural separateness reaching back beyond the time of the Roman occupation of Britain.

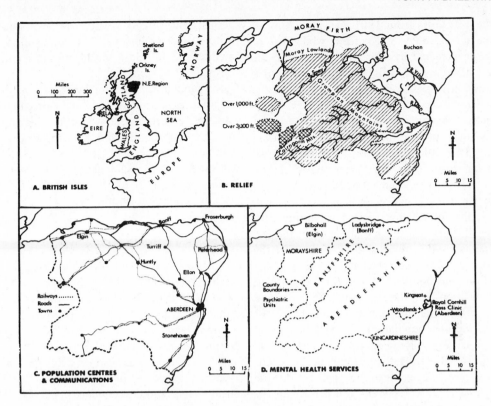

Fig. 34—1. The geography of the northeast of Scotland. (Reproduced with permission from "The Northeast Region of Scotland" by G. Innes and S. M. Bain, in J. A. Baldwin & W. M. Millar (eds.), Community Psychiatry. Boston, Mass.: International Psychiatry Clinics, Little, Brown, 1964.)

Although its people are now less ethnically distinct due to Celtic, Scandinavian, and later, Norman and English colonization, it is still easy to see traces of the original settlers, who came from central Europe, in the appearance of the inhabitants of today. Although the region is predominantly agricultural, there are a variety of industries, of which the most important is fishing. Others of note are whisky distilling, granite quarrying, textile manufacture, shipbuilding, engineering, food preservation, and paper manufacture.

Demography. At the 1961 Census the region had a population of 479,530. Aberdeen city accounted for 185,390. The regionally indigenous proportion was 85 percent while a further nine percent were born elsewhere in Scotland, though these proportions varied between the counties of the region. In addition to the city of Aberdeen, there

were 30 burghs with a population over 1,000, of which three were over 10,000. If all 30 burghs and the city are regarded as urban, the total urban proportion of the population was 62 percent, but the urban proportion was less than one-third in all but two of the counties.

In common with most population groups, there were more females than males overall and in all age groups .except those aged zero-14 years. This youngest age group contained a quarter of the total population, there were 12 percent to 13 percent in each ten year age group up to age 54, and 23 percent were aged 55 and over. In comparison with the population of Scotland, the regional population was slightly older in both sexes. The marital status distribution reflected the higher proportion of aged females, there being over three times as many widowed women as widowed men.

In the 160 years from 1801 the population of Scotland increased by 322 percent while that of the region increased by only 185 percent. In the middle 50 years of this period the Scottish population increased by 55 percent and that of the region 21 percent, but in the last 50 years Scotland's population increased nine percent whereas that of the region fell nearly seven percent. Thus the proportion of the Scottish population formed by the region fell from 16 percent in 1801 to 9.3 percent in 1961.

Although the regional population was at a peak in 1911, that of Aberdeen city has continued to increase, though at a much lower rate in the last 50 years than in the previous hundred. In 1801 the city formed only ten percent of the regional population, and by 1911 35 percent. In contrast, the population of the rest of the mainland declined from its maximum in 1911 by 12 percent, and the population of the Orkney and Shetland Islands fell by 43 percent in the 100 years up to 1961. The rate of decline in the islands is also rising, having been 6.6 percent in the twenty years before 1951 and ten percent in the ten years after that date.

These demographic changes in the region illustrate well the phenomenon of depopulation which is one of its major characteristics (Innes & Bain, 1964). Depopulation began at the periphery of the island groups and only 26 of the 90 Orkney Islands and 19 of the 90 Shetland Islands are now inhabited. Rural depopulation presents as a migration from extreme isolation in the upper glens to relative isolation in the lower glens, from the lower glens to villages, from villages to towns, from the towns to the city, and from the islands to the mainland. Regional depopulation has also been increasing as workers and their families move towards the Glasgow-Edinburgh industrial belt and further south to England, and has particularly affected skilled workers. Depopulation affects mainly the younger age groups and may largely account for the weighing towards the higher end of the age range in the region as compared with Scotland.

Despite these changes the regional population is undoubtedly relatively static in size and composition in comparison with most other parts of the United Kingdom. This feature, coupled with the remarkably high indigenous proportion, the relative isolation from the rest of Scotland, and perhaps the unique origins of the population in hsitory and prehistory, has contributed to the maintenance of close kinship ties in communities throughout the region.

In summary, the northeast region may be regarded as having an isolated, indigenous, stable but slowly declining, slowly urbanizing population of close-knit family and kinship structure, long and idiosyncratic tradition, and unique origins. Geographically, sociologically and demographically it is close to the ideal for an experimental area or population laboratory.

The Mental Health Service System

As elsewhere in the United Kingdom, the mental health services of the region are part of the hospital arm of the National Health Service, the other two arms being the general practitioner services and the public health services. The hospital services of the whole region are organized under a single administrative board which has exclusive responsibility for all aspects of their maintenance and development under the Secretary of State for Scotland. The regional hospital board is assisted by boards of management with responsibility for the day-to-day running of particular hospitals and groups of units. The mental health services of the city of Aberdeen are all under a single board of management while those in other parts of the region are administered by other boards with responsibility for local groups of hospitals. In the whole region there are only two part-time private psychiatrists, most of whose time is devoted to duties in the National Health Service.

The main elements of the mental health service system and their interrelations are shown diagramatically in Figure 34–2. Although the inpatient services centered in the mental hospitals are the most visible part of the present system of psychiatric services, from the point of view of numbers of patients treated or overall impact on psychiatric illness generally, they have assumed a progressively less dominating role in recent years so that they must be seen in the context of the interlocking parts of the whole service organization. As the case register has shown, three out of five patients first entering care in a year are not admitted to inpatient units within one year of entry.

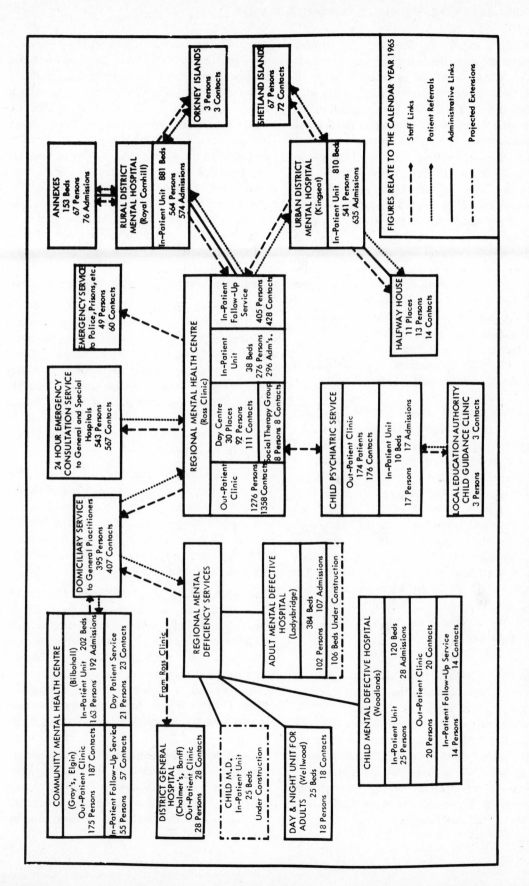

Fig. 34-2. Organization of northeast Scottish psychiatric services. (Reproduced from "The Mental Hospital in the Psychiatric Service: A Case Register Study" by J. A. Baldwin, published for the Nuffield Provincial Hospitals Trust by Oxford University Press, 1971.)

Psychiatric Inpatient Services. The overall staffed bed provision rate in 1965 was 4.30 beds per 1,000 total population or 34 percent of all hospital beds in the region, which compares with 4.04 staffed beds per 1,000 total population for Scotland as a whole in the same year. The level of bed provision has not altered in any important respect in the decade from 1955, but there was an overall increase of 115 beds between 1948 and 1955. There have also been important changes in the distribution of beds between units, such as closure of the small unit in the Royal Infirmary and opening of the much larger Ross Clinic in 1959, and opening of a ten bed unit for children in 1965. Prior to this, there were no beds specifically for emotionally disturbed children in the region and children under 15 years had to be hospitalized outside the region or in ordinary adult psychiatric units, the children's mental deficiency hospital, or in the general wards of the children's hospital, none of which alternatives was considered appropriate by parents, staff, or administration.

Outpatient Services. All the main hospitals run outpatient clinics or outpatient sessions for discharged inpatients (inpatient follow-ups) and by far the greater part of this work is carried out at the Ross Clinic, either by its staff or by visiting psychiatrists from other hospitals. In 1965 Ross Clinic staff also provided clinics at Chalmer's general hospital in Banff, and at the university's Student Health Service unit, while Kingseat and Royal Cornhill Hospitals carried out the quarterly clinics in Shetland and Orkney respectively. The figures for child psychiatry also include patients seen at the Aberdeen City Education Authority Child Guidance Clinic, the only child guidance clinic in the region at that time.

Domiciliary Services. Home visiting of patients by psychiatric consultants at the request of general practitioners is extensive and the greater part of this work is carried out by consultants from the Ross Clinic, though all hospitals participate in varying degrees. Visits by psychiatric social work staff to patient's homes for the purpose of treatment, here referred to as "domiciliary treatment," is active at the Ross Clinic, and Kingseat and Bilbohall Hospitals.

Hospital Emergency Services. These include both "emergency" consultations, mainly at the Casualty Department at Woolmanhill, primarily for the purpose of disposal and very frequently in cases of attempted suicide, and elective consultations in general and special hospitals in the region. This service is almost wholly provided by Ross Clinic staff in the Aberdeen city group of hospitals and is carried out by all grades of staff from registrar and above on a 24-hour duty roster basis. No attempt is made at selection of referrals by priority or by grade of psychiatrist, almost all being seen within a day of referral, but referring staff may request consultation by named psychiatrists. A proportion of patients seen as outpatients at the Ross Clinic are also "emergency" referrals.

Extrahospital Emergency Service. This service, which is provided almost wholly by consultants at the Ross Clinic and Royal Cornhill Hospital, enables psychiatric consultations to be obtained by any agent or person requesting it, mainly police, prisons, mental welfare officers, etc. The Royal Cornhill Hospital is the designated "place of safety" to which persons may be admitted by police or other official agents under the Mental Health (Scotland) Act, 1960.

Mental Deficiency. The regional mental deficiency services are organized under a director and work closely with the psychiatric services. The total of 529 beds was nine percent of all hospital beds or 1.10 per 1,000 population. At all these hospitals a range of services is offered, including outpatient and domiciliary care.

Integrative Character of the Service System. The chart in Figure 34–2 shows many of the administrative links between units and services, and some of the more important staff and patient movements. The principles of balance and integration in their planning and development have been discussed in detail elsewhere (Baldwin & Millar, 1964) and their functional character as an input-output system should be emphasized.

The Referring Services. Of over 2,100 patients entering psychiatric treatment for the first time in 1965 who were registered in the regional psychiatric services, only three dozen were not referred by a formal institution of some kind but came into care through their own agency or that of relatives or friends. The psychiatric services accept demand for their use from a wide variety of organizations ranging from general practitioners working in the community and the general and special hospital services which together refer nearly nine out of ten patients, to the local authority health and welfare services, national agencies, legal agencies, and voluntary agencies. These agencies have been described in detail elsewhere (Baldwin & Millar, 1964). Figure 34–3 summarizes their relationship to the various psychiatric services and the routes by which patients arrive in psychiatric care.

General and Special Hospitals. In 1965 there were 43 hospitals other than mental and mental deficiency in the region. The largest of these are in the city of Aberdeen and most are centered on the extensive site at Foresterhill. Of the 3,456 general and special hospital beds in the region in 1965, 47 percent were in hospitals with 100 or fewer beds. There were no general or special hospitals outside the city of more than 100 beds. Of these 38 smaller hospitals in various parts of the region, including the two groups of islands, about 30 were wholly or partly worked by general practitioners, although it is difficult to give precise figures since many of these units are regularly visited by hospital consultants from the hospitals in the city.

One in four patients entering psychiatric care for the first time in their lives in 1965 were referred by the general and special hospitals service.

General Practitioner Services. About 98 percent of the population are registered with one of 282 general practitioners in the region. The general practitioner forms the primary diagnostic screen from which the majority of referrals to the hospital service in general and the psychiatric services in particular originate. Family doctors initiate psychiatric referrals mainly to out-patient clinics, the domiciliary visiting services, and direct to mental hospitals. Of all patients entering the psychiatric services for the first time in their lives in 1965, over 64 percent were referred by general practitioners. The referral practices and the coverage of the population by general practitioners are therefore of considerable importance in the creation of demand for psychiatric care.

Legal, Social, and Welfare Services. Despite the extensive and well-developed system of national statutory and local voluntary social and welfare services in the region, particularly in Aberdeen city (Baldwin & Millar, 1964), their contribution to the demand for psychiatric care is remarkably small—a total of 16 patients out of over 2,100 who had had no previous care in 1965. Local authority services, such as the education authority child guidance clinic in Aberdeen city, the children's departments, speech therapists, and mental welfare officers referred about three percent of new patients, while legal agencies such as the probation service, courts, police, prisons, and approved schools accounted for four percent.

The Need for a Psychiatric Case Register

Prior to 1963 there was no mental health service information system in existence specifically for the use of mental health service staff in northeast Scotland. There was a national reporting system for admissions to and separations from mental hospitals which was improved in 1963, and there were a number of other periodic and aperiodic returns of various kinds, but none of these was immediately available for research or clinical use, and all were of very limited value either because their content was inappropriate or because their coverage was inadequate. Even the medical records systems were not organized on a regional basis. A patient attending more than one regional unit would have more than one record and units often swapped patients without swapping their records.

There had been a study of patients referred in 1960, conducted by George Innes and Geoffrey Sharp (1962) and followed up for five years, and this had demonstrated the practicality and the clinical usefulness of systematic medical records in the developing system of mental health services in which patients were being referred from one unit to another in increasing numbers and were beginning to accumulate treatment histories going back many years. It was becoming a clinical necessity to have a unit system of psychiatric records for the region as a whole and plans were executed to bring it into being.

The 1960 Cohort Study also demonstrated that to do much detailed epidemiological research on the regional population of 480,000 it would be

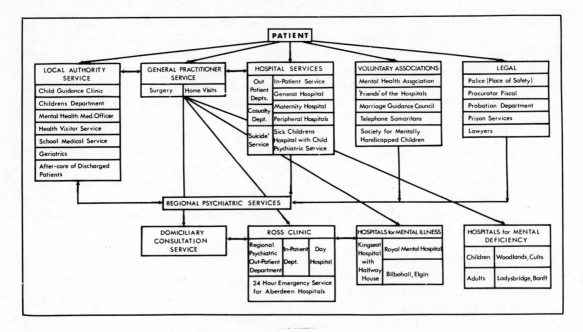

Fig. 34—3. Paths to the psychiatric services in northeast Scotland. (Reproduced with permission from "Paths to the Psychiatric Services" by J. G. Henderson, in J. A. Baldwin & W. M. Millar (eds.), Community Psychiatry. *Boston, Mass.: International Psychiatry Clinics, Little, Brown, 1964.)*

necessary to amass much larger numbers of patients than were referred in any single year, and interest was already focused on longitudinal studies covering a number of years and on detecting trends occurring over long periods.

Operational research was coming into vogue by 1962 and it was obvious that the reporting system confined to mental hospitals was quite inadequate to the regional need for management information about the way in which all the extramural services as well as the hospitals were being used. Planning could not proceed rationally in the virtual absence of information about at least half of the work of the mental health services.

All these user-needs—clinical service, epidemiological research, and operational research—became apparent at about the same time, and it was quickly evident that there was a great deal of overlap in both the types of data required and the risk population to be covered by all three. The population at risk was defined by the hospital board region; it was relatively stable, immobile, and virtually entirely covered by clinical services under a single administrative umbrella.

There was one further type of use which was anticipated as an incidental bonus, and that was as an aid to clinical research. It had been found that many clinicians, with limited time at their disposal, were being discouraged from undertaking even very modest research by the sheer magnitude of the task of collecting data. If they were not completely disheartened by attempts at searching records retrospectively, they were stopped by simply being unable to collect enough cases prospectively or not being able to get adequately representative samples. Indeed, they really could not even measure the representativeness of samples in most cases. It did seem that a searchable file of systematic data of known content and predictable quality would remove to some extent the twin burdens of retrospective searching and measurement of representativeness. If it were possible also to set up a data collection system which did not depend on the vagaries of clinical interest the problems of adequate sampling might also be materially reduced.

Thus it became clear that the common need was for continuous, prospective, systematic data collection yielding a comprehensive and longitudinal picture of total treated psychiatric morbidity in the region. The case register method was especially appropriate to the characteristics of the area and its services, and to the needs of the users. The essential conditions were fulfilled for successfully undertaking a venture capable of reaching the objectives: the features of the geography and demography of the area, previous experience with extensive data collection, the existence of the university medical school and its relationship with the National Health Service, and the integrated regional mental health services.

Special Features of the Northeast Scottish Register

The register system which was clearly required to fulfil the objectives set forth above was *regional* in character. For epidemiological purposes the population at risk of inclusion was that of the Northeastern Regional Hospital Board area while operationally the system of services to be encompassed was the psychiatric and mental deficiency services of the same regional board. These two kinds of definition of the registrable population were largely coincident so that the register would include virtually the whole of the psychiatrically treated morbidity in a geographically defined population. The particular features of the region and its services thus combined to provide the conditions for a register with the following special characteristics: (1) integration with a standardized medical record, (2) availability of more extensive data than had usually been possible, (3) more complete coverage of the risk population than was possible in an area with diversity of service administration, (4) relative ease of follow-up and of avoiding unmeasurable loss of risk population because of the stable and relatively "captive" nature of the population, (5) greater flexibility of the pool of data to meet the needs of a variety of users. To this was added (6) special measures to increase the reliability of the data obtained.

The Standard Record as a Data Source. It has long been suggested that the National Health Service in Britain provides a unique opportunity for the synthesis of health information of all kinds, with obvious benefits for both clinical care and medical and biological research. The idea of a central register of personal health records was put forward by Acheson, Truelove, and Witts (1961) and supported by representatives of many institutions associated with medical research such as the General Register Office (Heasman, 1961), The College of General Practitioners (Pinsent, 1961), and the Statistical Research Unit of the London School of Hygiene and Tropical Medicine (Doll, 1961). Rawnsley and Loudon (1961) pointed out that inpatient statistics for mental hospitals in England and Wales were already based on the register method, and Sir Aubrey Lewis (1961) emphasized that a register would be valuable, if not indispensable, for study of the causes, course, and response to treatment of mental disorders among many other diseases. The trend toward general hospital psychiatric services and treatment in the community made comprehensive data collection more difficult and the increased frequency of readmission strengthened the case for person rather than event records.

The clinical record is a potential source of much invaluable medical and psychosocial information which is hidden in an undecipherable and fragmented jungle of heterogeneous quality, content, and reliability. The difficulties in realizing the potential are enormous. Apart from the general problem of confidentiality, which affects not only psychiatric but all medical information, the task of standardization and collation of worthwhile, reliable data has seemed insuperable. Pioneering work by Acheson (1963) in the Oxford Record Linkage Study on the linkage of vital and health records and by Weir (1964) on the problems of standardization have begun to make inroads and recently interest in this field has increased greatly.

The fact that the new records department of the Aberdeen city group of mental hospitals was in a position to develop a new group records system presented an opportunity for standardization of the record and the possibility that the standard record might be adopted by hospitals in both mental and mental deficiency services throughout the region. Furthermore, if the necessary rigor of systematic data collection could be introduced and maintained and an automatic data handling facility incorporated, the clinical record would assume a value and importance far beyond the individual patient record. Not only would the clinician have a standard record containing a wider range of more reliable information than hitherto, but also the varying data needs of the population research programme could be met, and a greater variety of administrative and operational information could be provided, such as routine statistical reports. Perhaps in the long run even more important, the obstacle to good clinical research of inadequate, unreliable, and inconsistent data would be removed. The pooling of the systematic information from the case records for the whole region into a "data bank" would enable each of the clinical and research staff to have access to the accumulated experience of all.

Availability of Data. Use of the medical record as a data source meant that, in principle, any data which it might contain could form part of the case register. Although in practice it would be necessary to limit the quantity of information processed to the capacity of the data handling facility, many kinds of data (clinical, social, psychological, physical, treatment, etc.) could be included according to need. As the data handling capacity increased it would be possible to extend the data to cover an increasingly wider range of needs and uses. This potential in versatility and flexibility implied an adaptability not hitherto found in psychiatric case register systems.

Completeness of Coverage. Since the whole of institutional psychiatry in the region is administered by the regional hospital board and the only private psychiatry is conducted by two hospital board consultants on a part-time basis, coverage of all the regional services would be virtually assured if the records system were adopted by all the boards' psychiatric and mental deficiency services. A small number of patients from the geographical area of the region were known to go outside it for treatment, almost wholly to Inverness to the north and Montrose to the south. The 1960 Cohort Study had shown that only three percent of all persons referred from the region were involved. Thus population coverage for many purposes would be adequate through the regional services alone and the cooperation of the adjacent services could be obtained for specific purposes in providing information about patients attending from the northeast region.

Follow-up. A common difficulty with the case register method, as with most longitudinal types of population research, is to keep track of individuals once they leave the network of reporting agencies, in order to obtain accurate measures of the study population remaining at risk of reentry to the reporting agencies at any time. The main causes of loss from this risk population are death and movement out of the reporting area. Losses due to death could be obtained by linkage with death registers. In northeast Scotland this problem has been solved on a pilot basis for the 1960 Cohort Study and a general solution should be possible in collaboration with the registration authority. Movement out of the reporting area is extremely difficult to trace, the only suggested solutions being direct survey by field study or by mail, post office notification of change of address, and notification of changes of a patient's general practitioner by the local executive councils who keep the general practitioner registration records. The first of these methods would be costly and could only be carried out periodically at best, while the others would be hard to implement and rather unreliable in practice, and it may never be possible to keep continuous records of these movements. In the absence of satisfactory alternatives, an area like northeast Scotland with little movement across its boundaries is in the most favorable position. The relative stability of the population in numbers and composition also improves the reliability of studies utilizing population data obtained at a decennial census in the intercensal years.

Flexibility and the Data Bank Concept. The register may be thought of as a cumulative information storage, retrieval, and analytic facility or "data bank." The analogy with a financial bank is useful. Not only is it a store where information is kept and from which it can be obtained selectively but also the store grows in value the more and the better the information put into it. Moreover, by putting information into the "bank" or lending it, the user can receive a dividend or interest in the shape of (a) additional data already in the bank relevant to his needs, and (b) rearrangement of his own and the existing data to suit his special purposes. The loan of data by a user does not deprive him of them but adds to the usefulness of the bank to others. In one respect the data bank is better off than a financial bank because users may draw on it at will without risking "overdrawing," without charge or interest, and without the risk of bankrupting the bank, because the data bank does not lose what is taken out of it.

It has to be accepted that the proper conduct of research almost always involves the collection of data matched to its specific objectives. Borrowed data are rarely satisfactory since they rarely fit precisely the needs of a problem for which they were not collected. Similarly, retrospective data are rarely adequate since they are often incomplete and of varying quality. The data bank concept does not contradict this principle since it does not preclude the collection of special data for special purposes. On the contrary, the input system of the data may actually facilitate special data collection. The data bank does provide a more adequate form of retrospective data store since its content is known, its quality is predictable, and it is easily and economically searched. The data bank is also a facility for prospective data collection of relatively "hard" data of an incontrovertible character and in almost universal use, such as patient's date of birth or age, sex, and date of or age at marriage. In these ways the register is more flexible and adaptable as a research tool than the once-for-all type of approach to research data collection.

Reliability. Extensive collections of data almost always incur penalties in larger proportions of error than small, carefully controlled samples. Sources of error in data collection systems of this type may be divided conveniently into five groups: (1) errors introduced by the patient or other informant, such as failure of memory in giving date of marriage or birth, or deliberate or unconscious falsification, such as omission of an illegitimate child; (2) errors due to failure of the recorder, such as mishearing what the patient says, misinterpreting the patient's meaning, assuming information not actually given (e.g., that a woman with a child is in fact married), misrecording, and misspelling; (3) errors introduced subsequent to the data collection procedure, such as miscoding, mispunching, analysis design error, and miscalculation; (4) errors inherent in the system design such as inadequate record matching leading to duplication of counts on persons, and (5) clinical judgmental error, such as variation in diagnostic labeling (Baldwin et al., 1965).

Error types (3) and (4) are well-recognized and usually carefully avoided in good research design and procedure. Types (1) and (2) have long been virtually ignored except for rudimentary precautions, but have recently received more intensive study (Cartwright, 1963). However, adequate measures to prevent their occurrence are still rarely encountered, particularly in large scale reporting systems. For instance, reliance is often placed on nursing and auxiliary staff who are quite without knowledge of the reasons why data are required, or the uses to be made of them, and entirely without training in this unfamiliar mode of approaching patients. Data collection in these circumstances is often an added chore which is resented, at least unconsciously if not actively. Even clerical staff cannot be expected to comprehend the importance and relevance of items which they do not themselves have to utilize in their ordinary work. Medical staff are understandably unwilling to have their interviewing practice hampered by the requirements of a structured form, although they may well come to appreciate the freedom imparted by having factual information available before seeing the patient. For the case register the best solution to this problem was undoubtedly the recruitment of special staff for the specific purpose of data collection.

Structure of the Register. The psychiatric patient often undergoes a prolonged and complicated series of treatment experiences in many different treatment units over many years—often the greater part of his life—frequently returning for more after varying periods of relative health. Thus the psychiatric patient can be regarded as having *episodes* of illness, each consisting of a number of *contacts* with different psychiatric services. The critical functions of the register are to match all the records pertaining to any one individual and link them together in temporal order. This is accomplished in the ordinary unit system of medical records by manually sorting the various papers, visually matching on selected characteristics such as names, date of birth, etc., and then numbering all the papers for an individual with a common unit number. These procedures work quite well if the system is properly designed and operated, and provided the number of records is relatively small, since the records staff accumulate a considerable personal knowledge of the case records which enables matching even with incomplete and unreliable information. However, when the case-load exceeds the memory retention abilities of the records staff, error inevitably increases, though its extent cannot be measured and correction is haphazard. Special attention is therefore given to the problems of person matching and event linkage in the case register and the records system on which it is based.

Matching. Each person is given a unique, sequential five-digit number (the Register Number). In order to ensure that, when an individual presents in any of the regional psychiatric services, any previous record of his previous attendance is located and records of his present attendance incorporated into it, a definite procedure must be carried out if duplicate records, i.e., two or more unit or register numbers for the same person, are to be kept to a minimum. (The converse of two or more persons with the same number can also occur but is unlikely to involve much difficulty if a numerical as well as an alphabetical check is maintained.) An individual's previous record may be many years old, may be located in any of the regional units, and may be under a different name, as when a woman marries or remarries in the interval between treatment episodes. For various reasons the patient may be unable or unwilling to give information about previous treatment, or may even give false or misleading information about previous treatment or identity, or both. A practical matching procedure must therefore be effective in the absence of proper information and even in the presence of erroneous information. For instance, if present surname, sex, and date of birth from two records agree, it would be assumed generally that these records refer to the same individual. Yet surnames are notoriously misspelled (e.g., Stewart and Stuart, Thompson and Thomson, Jonstone and Johnston), aliases are used, and dates of birth are wrongly reported. (In the 1960 Cohort Study, Innes found that date of birth was discrepant in 12 percent of 200 cases on which more than one report of it was available). In general, the larger the number of factors on which agreement can be obtained, the higher the probability of an accurate match. Electronic methods of name matching have been devised to cope with the massive sorting and comparing processes which are required for large files (Newcombe et al., 1959; Phillips et al., 1962; Phillips & Bahn, 1963). In the early stages of development of the register it was impossible to apply such methods because of the absence of sufficiently powerful computing equipment, and an improved form of the usual type of alphabetical card index was generated. The main card for each patient contains several matching factors (present and birth surnames, given names, date and place of birth, sex and marital status, address and changes of address) in addition to the register number and a summary of the linked events in the patient's treatment record. A secondary card containing the patient's birth surname where this differs from present surname is also included in the same alphabetical index and cross-referenced to the main card so that patients presenting with name changes may more easily be picked out. In addition, the procedure for interrogating patients includes rigid instructions to ask the patient to spell present and birth surnames, and a check of stated date of birth against stated age. Preliminary investigation of the effectiveness of the clerical matching procedure has justified the initial trust in it. Examination of the 13,000 cases registered in the first four years of operation, using semiautomated methods, yielded a duplication rate of a little over one in a thousand.

For the research and data processing aspect of the register two further items were collected which could be of particular value for person matching and which might be used experimentally when facilities became available. The National Health Service Number is a unique number assigned to each individual in the United Kingdom at birth and is therefore potentially the ideal matching device (Smith, 1963). The number is complex and of rather variable form and would have to be obtained from an official written record to be of sufficient reliability. Such a record is the "medical card" issued to every subject and presented to the general practitioner on registration with him. Patients are asked if they have their medical cards on entry to the psychiatric services but there is no compulsion and very few people carry their cards. Although patients are asked to bring cards at a later visit, the National Health Service Number was obtained by this method for only 3.6 per cent of a consecutive sample of 2,000 patients registered. Further effort could be made to increase this proportion by, for instance, requesting the number from general practitioners on referral, but it seems doubtful if more than a small minority of numbers could be obtained for any justifiable effort. In contrast, mother's birth surname, which has been shown by Newcombe et al. (1957) to be particularly valuable as a matching factor, was obtained on 67 percent of the same sample and therefore should be quite suitable for person matching. Indeed, this sample included a porportion of patients entering the mental health services who were not asked for their mother's birth surname. The proportion of those who were asked who were able to give it was about 90 percent.

Linkage. The linking together of all the events and records of them relating to an individual and their ordering in temporal sequence is achieved in the case register by means of an adaptation of the method used in the Monroe County register by Miles et al. (1964) and referred to as the contact number. This is an eight-digit code number which specifies in the first two digits the facility the patient is attending at any time while the third digit signifies the type of care (i.e., inpatient, outpatient, daypatient, etc.). The next two digits indicate the numerical position of the contact in relation to other facilities attended during the total psychiatric treatment experience. The final three digits are concerned with the current count of treatment episodes in the patient's life. A loose leaf book register in number order is maintained, showing all the linked contacts for each patient in their correct sequence.

General definitions for the case register are therefore as follows: A *patient* is any person referred to any of the mental health services included in the psychiatric case register. A referral is regarded as initiating a *contact* with the service or unit to which it is made, whether or not the patient actually attends or is attended for treatment. (Intended contacts which are not realized are counted separately and designated *uneventuated contacts*.) Transfer of a patient from one service or unit to another within the regional mental health services constitutes initiation of a new contact which is recorded and counted separately, the prior contact being closed. In certain circumstances a patient can be in contact with more than one mental health service at the same time (e.g., an inpatient in one unit attending a day care program in another). Methods have been developed for dealing with complex situations of this kind which permit the full range of treatment experience to be recorded correctly. A sequential series of such contacts constitutes an *episode* of care, which is thus a period commencing with a referral to a mental health service by an agent outside it and ending when a patient is discharged (or discharges himself) from the regional mental health services or dies. All *discharges* are regarded as referrals from the mental health service in question to an agency outside the service system, such as a general practitioner. A consequence of these definitions is that, with some exceptions, each contact begins with a *referral agent*, all but the first of the episode being another mental health service or unit, and ends with a *disposal*, all but the last of the episode being to another mental health service or unit.

The Case Record. The medical record itself, designed by the records officer in consultation with clinical and research staff, consists of a number of types of forms covering all aspects of clinical work and treatment. The systematic information which is input to the data processing system is contained in four duplicate forms, the first copies going into the case record and the duplicates being used for data processing:

(1) *The Patient Contact Summary Form.* The documentation of the patient begins with the transcription to this form of brief identification details of the patient received from the referral source. This permits an immediate search of the card index for any previous record of psychiatric care. After the patient has been seen by a psychiatrist, diagnoses, disposal, and in-service transfers are noted on this form. An additional Contact Summary is opened for each new regional service contact.

(2) *The Original Patient Detail Form* is more comprehensive and is completed by one of a special staff of interviewers, with the patient, immediately prior to his first psychiatric consultation. This form contains considerable identifying information and service data as well as a comprehensive statement of previous and current medical and psychiatric history.

(3) *The Social Data Form* is also completed in interview with the patient and contains a lengthy enquiry into sociocultural factors.

(4) *Domiciliary and Emergency Contact Form.* Many patients are seen for the first time as emergency cases in their homes and in general hospital and on these occasions a special shortened form, to embrace certain key data, is used. This necessary limitation of data is not critical since a high proportion of these patients enter other parts of the service immediately, and many of the remainder at a later date, when complete information can be gathered.

A fifth form, the Discharge/Transfer Summary Form, was discontinued after a short trial period, as it proved unacceptable to some of the clinical and secretarial staff. The clinical record copies of the forms are filed on a treasury tag in a manila folder in chronological order with the Original Patient Detail Form at the front and the most recent contact forms at the back. Contact forms, follow-up sheets, and forms used by ancillary services such as psychology and social work, are all color-coded for easy identification in a bulky record.

Special records were devised for the child psychiatric services to meet their unique needs, and psychiatric referrals from the Education Authority Child Guidance Clinic are also included.

Operation of the register began with a census of patients in treatment at midnight on December 31, 1962. A 100 percent regional coverage of inpatients and 90 percent of outpatients was obtained, totaling about 3,500 cases. From that date, all persons entering the service system and all types of service contact have been registered. The complete records system could not be brought into use in all units simultaneously and initially reliance had to be placed on the minimal data obtainable from the existing record systems and the Scottish Home and Health Department return on inpatient admissions. Each part of the record was tried out on a pilot basis for periods up to a year before final printing and for the same period the whole system was operated in the regional center (the Ross Clinic) and the smaller mental hospital (Bilbohall) before extension to the main hospitals and other parts of the psychiatric services. Patience was rewarded by complete acceptance and the unified standard record came into use throughout the regional services with

virtually complete coverage by January 1, 1965. The standard documentation has been extended to each new form of service as it has developed, demonstrating the adaptability of the basic system to the changing pattern of psychiatric services. Although the data from the first two years of operation were less than complete, they were adequate for many purposes, and from the beginning of 1965 satisfactory for all the purposes envisaged. About 2,500 persons have been added to the register each year and by the end of 1967 a total of about 17,000 persons had been registered.

The Register Data

Apart from the identifying information described above, the main types of systematic data extracted from the case record for inclusion in the data processing system are personal and social data, patient movement data, and clinical data.

Personal and Social Data

The types of information obtained in this category were determined partly by clinical need and partly by research interest. The general objective was to obtain a description of the social context from which the individual comes, using only characteristics which were likely to be documented reliably. Special attention is given to occupation, including employment status, type of employment, and social class, since this aspect was known to be of importance (Hollingshead & Redlich, 1958) and warranted continuing close study. Data on occupation and employment are obtained for the patient, spouse, and parent or guardian. The histories of upbringing, education, and marriage are fully recorded and sufficient of the information processed to enable retrieval of unusual features such as a disturbed childhood home life, special educational achievement, or multiple marriages. Religious affiliation is noted in terms of church attendance rather than simply a formal statement of denomination. Characteristics of housing, household composition, and family structure are recorded in detail. A history of psychiatric treatment in close family members is also detailed so that, wherever possible, family record linkage can be executed. Lastly, an attempt is made to record evidence of geographical mobility and affiliation with formal community organizations.

Patient Movement Data

Relevant features of the patient's use of the services are included, such as referring agent, dates of notification, referral, and termination of the contact, identity of treating psychiatrist, and preferred and actual disposal. The complete set is repeated for each separate treatment experience with a particular service, consecutive experiences being grouped together as an episode of care. Between 7,500 and 10,000 sets of these data are collected annually. In conjunction with diagnostic information, these data provide a detailed longitudinal picture of the course and outcome of treatment experience and permit ad hoc enquiries to be answered such as tabulations or lists requested by a particular doctor on his own patients. The availability of this "feedback" is considered an important feature since it encourages doctors to undertake small research exercises, and provides a return for collaboration in the system.

Clinical Data

This is the most restricted field of data collection. Only diagnostic classification is collected routinely using the International Statistical Classification (World Health Organization, 1957) with allowance for two diagnoses at the beginning and end of each service contact. No other clinical or treatment information is routinely processed, since this is such a complex and difficult area that it is more appropriately studied by means of special projects directed to specific aspects.

The flexibility of the system permits the addition of new types of information or the modification or exclusion of existing items when they have served their purpose. For instance, plans have been discussed to include psychological test results so that psychologists could undertake research on their own work.

The Interviewer Technique of Data Collection

Previous experience suggested that the best solution to the general problem of unreliability in reports by patient and recorder and incompleteness of records when reliance is placed on staff whose primary duties are unrelated to these matters was to employ special staff and train them for the purpose. Female interviewers were therefore selected on the basis of their general intelligence and maturity to collect the nonclinical information from patients and other informants for the standard case record forms, carry out some aspects of the medical records work and the first steps in the preparation of the data for processing. The systematic data forms are lengthy and to maintain a high degree of reliability a skilled interviewer takes about 20 minutes to complete them. For this purpose patients are asked to come 30 minutes before the scheduled initial psychiatric interview. Training in interviewing is detailed. It begins with a study of specific instructions concerning each item in the data forms and an explanation of its purpose. After practice with the forms on colleagues, sitting-in with skilled interviewers, and discussion, the trainee is ready to interview patients. Periodic monitoring by means of a one-way screen is necessary to maintain standards. Experience shows that people drawn from outside the medical profession and its auxiliaries make the best interviewers, since they do not bring with them specific professional response-sets in handling and relating to patients which can impede the objective collection of data of this kind. Intimate knowledge of all phases of records work and some aspects of the preparation and processing of research data ensure that the interviewers are aware of the purposes of their work and of the special difficulties.

Four full-time interviewers are required to cover the Aberdeen City Group of psychiatric services, including Child Psychiatry and Child Guidance Clinic referrals. Two part-time staff members carry out data collection at Bilbohall and Ladysbridge hospitals in the northerly part of the mainland area, and the mental welfare officers execute this function in the Orkney and Shetland Islands.

Patient Reactions. One aspect of the interviewer technique of data collection in clinical service on which scepticism would be understandable, is the possibility of resentment and noncooperation on the part of patients. In the region as a whole, about 2,300 interviews were conducted by interviewing staff in 1965, the first full year of complete coverage. In all, between 6,000 and 7,000 interviews were carried out in the three years from commencement of the register system in 1963. Despite careful enquiry only two refusals were notified. Allowing for some that may have been missed, the refusal rate could not have been higher than one in a thousand. This is a remarkable tribute to both the cooperation of the patients and the skill and care of the interviewers. It is a record which would not be bettered in any ordinary clinical program. Some of the interviewers express surprise at this experience and even doubt as to its desirability, taking the view that the public should not acquiesce so readily in the demands of institutions. Patients generally seem to find the interview process reassuring rather than stressful and even in the rare instances where difficulty has been experienced in obtaining the patient's complete cooperation, there has not been reported any evidence of ill-effects clinically. A small proportion of very disturbed patients cannot be interviewed initially and sometimes not at all. In these cases, and where the reliability of the patient is doubtful, relatives are interviewed. The rarity of refusal and poor cooperation has meant that a very high proportion of interviews yield complete data.

Staff Reactions. From previous experience of data collection with the 1960 Cohort Study, it was known that, in principle, medical and nursing staff would favor some such scheme as this since there were definite advantages to be gained. In the first place, the kind of routine and systematic data collection carried out by the interviewers was precisely the kind that is found to be tedious by doctors and is often badly done by them. Secondly, if the data are collected at some length and in an easily readable form, they are a distinct asset to the clinician when he comes to see the patient. There have been no adverse opinions expressed about the fact that patients might spend 20 minutes with one of the interviewing staff before seeing the doctor. On occasions, interviews have to be postponed until after the patient has been examined, but this is mainly to ensure that the outpatient session works smoothly and that patients and doctors are not kept waiting.

Effect on Clinical Service. The task of a medical records system is first and foremost to provide the right information about the right individual patient at the time, in the place and in the form it is needed. Important but secondary tasks are to provide data arranged in various ways for research and administration. The medical record based on the unit principle with an automatic search and retrieval capability for systematic data is an adequate foundation for developing a complete service information system. But no information system, however technically sophisticated, can fulfill its proper function if the input to it is insufficiently complete and reliable for the purposes intended. The merit of the interviewer method in the psychiatric services is that it goes to the heart of the input problem. In the outpatient service, where most patients are seen for first full assessment, the systematic information is available to the psychiatrist before he sees the patient. This is a definite advantage to the clinical service and there is a bonus in the saving of time to the clinician in the many cases where he would have had to gather similar information himself. Furthermore, the standard information is available for the patient over the whole of his psychiatric "life," which might cover many years, and is routinely brought up to date. Eventually all patients will have similar complete coverage and any record will be immediately understandable to any clinician. The record itself is designed in such a way that transfer to technologically more advanced forms of storage and retrieval than the case folder will be facilitated.

Although clinical benefits are difficult to measure, acceptance of the method throughout the regional services may be an index of its value.

Effect on Research. Apart from the clear advantages of the register as a "data bank" for the on-going research program, the interviewer system of data collection provides an efficient means of screening patients for special purposes. Psychiatrists use this method to obtain patients with particular attributes for research projects. Interviewers provide a screen by asking standard questions at the end of the normal interview and making arrangements for the investigator to see the patient if the response is positive. The interviewers may also collect specialized data for particular projects, using forms designed for the purpose.

Data Reliability

The chief reason for developing the interviewer method of data collection was to enhance its reliability and extend its completeness. Investigation of data reliability can be directed to any phase of their handling from their origin to checking of proofs of reports. The interviewer technique was introduced mainly to minimize (a) errors introduced by the patient, such as failure of memory in giving date of birth or marriage, or deliberate or unconscious falsification, such as omission of an illegitimate child, and (b) errors introduced by the recorder, such as mishearing what the patient says, misinterpreting the patient's meaning, assuming information not actually given, misrecording, and misspelling. Both may be checked by reference to independent sources of identical information. Such controls should include internal checks, such as one interviewer against another or a patient against his spouse at the same and different times, and interviewers and patients against themselves at different times; and external checks such as clinical interview and other records (e.g., medical and vital records). Investigations of this type should set standards of expectation which will vary with the purpose. For instance, absolute accuracy may be necessary or desirable with some items, such as spelling of names for patient identification, while other items may be acceptable within defined limits, such as age to within two years in adults over 35. In another group of items the patient may be asked only for an opinion which is expected to vary with circumstances.

In addition, irregularly scheduled monitoring sessions, in which each interviewer sees a patient behind a one-way screen while being observed by her colleagues, research staff, visitors, and other interested people, provide an on-going check on reliability and technique. This has shown an increasingly high quality of interviewing and has enabled many detailed points to be standardized.

Three brief studies of data reliability may be summarized here (Baldwin & Innes, 1966). The first was a comparison of interview data on 20 patients first interviewed in 1960 for the Cohort Study by the records clerk first assigned to this work, and then reinterviewed four or five years later by the Aberdeen group of register interviewing staff. The second was a comparison of data on ten patients interviewed by two different members of the register interviewer staff at different times in the period 1964–65. The third was a comparison of some items obtained in 52 consecutive interviews with parents of children seen in the Child Psychiatric Service both by interviewing staff and by the child psychiatrist at about the same time, and of items on the birth history of 24 of these children with the original obstetric record.

Thus, the first study compared data collected at widely different times by independent interviewers. The second compared information obtained by interviewing staff on two occasions closer together in time and not always independently. The third compared a limited amount of rather specialized information obtained independently and at the same time by both interviewer and psychiatrist, and also some historical items elicited at interview with similar data recorded at the time of its occurrence by independent observers. Even from these limited studies some conclusions can be drawn. There was an improvement in the quality of the interview material obtained in the later interviews in the second study. It is probable that this was mainly a function of interviewer rather than patient experience and was consistent with the monitoring observations. Interviewer error may be expected to be virtually eliminated with experience.

Patient error varied widely. Important errors tended to be concentrated in a very few records, whereas minor errors were observed in the majority. It should be noted that there were very few discrepancies in identifying information and, contrary to expectation, none in date of birth. This may have been due to the special precautions taken routinely by interviewers on these items, such as inclusion of checks of age against stated date of birth. Date of marriage, on the other hand, appeared to be discrepant sufficiently often to be unsatisfactory for identifying purposes, unless wide tolerance limits for concordance could be accepted.

Although the numbers in each study were small, the results generally were consistent. The total number of differences not due to factual changes was not small, but very few definitely could be ascribed to interviewer error. Most were the result of error introduced by the patient, presumably either through faulty memory or through deliberate or unconscious falsification. Most were minor errors in reporting dates and ages which would not materially affect the use of the data either for most research or for clinical purposes. The remaining small number were more serious, but it is difficult to see how they could have been avoided. They probably represent the residual element of unreliability after all reasonable precautions have been taken, reduction of which would entail more effort and disturbance than could be justified on economic or ethical grounds. On the basis of these preliminary studies, it was concluded that (a) the interviewers achieved a high degree of consistency, both one with another and with the three independent sources: an independent interviewer, a clinician, and a medical record; (b) not all unreliability in patient-reported information can be eliminated, but there is no evidence of error which is both extensive and important. There are few important errors and a large number of unimportant ones.

The Problem of Underreporting

One of the most intractable problems of register maintenance is that of incomplete reporting leading to selective and inadequate coverage and consequent misinterpretation of results (Bahn, 1964; United States Department of Health, Education, and Welfare, 1964). Underreporting may take a variety of forms and is not always easily detected. Reporting agents may not be aware of failure to complete returns or they may deliberately avoid reporting certain types of information. For instance, clinicians may feel bound to protect the confidentiality of some patient data or even whole records of certain types, or they may be unwilling to have some aspects of their work incorporated in a general data system. Objections of this nature are usually very understandable and in most cases arise from lack of information on the part of the reporting agent on the measures available for protection of confidentiality, or on the importance and value to him of inclusion of the information in the system. Where it is impossible to justify complete reporting of, for instance, certain records, it is often acceptable to include only specified anonymous items, such as sex and age. Even a simple count of excluded cases is preferable to total lack of information since the extent of underreporting can be measured thereby. Nevertheless, conscious underreporting of this type is usually more difficult to eliminate than unconscious omissions which can be detected by means of monitoring devices.

Underreporting is of two main types: incomplete records and missing records. Incomplete records may have certain items of data missing, or whole sections of the record, such as a contact summary, may be omitted. Items may be lacking for several reasons, including inability of the patient to give the information or failure of staff to record an item, such as diagnosis. Sections of a record may be missing because of failure to complete forms, failure to extract completed forms for processing, or occurrence of the events outside the reporting network, such as spells of treatment in services outside the region.

Loss of whole records may be caused by inadequate recording coverage within the system, such as a clinic run independently by a doctor without secretarial help, by medical direction to exclude certain cases, or by exclusive treatment of cases from the population at risk by agencies outside the reporting network. For instance, it was known that a proportion, believed to be about three percent of patients from the region, went to hospitals outside it for treatment.

Measures to Counter Underreporting. The principle for dealing with missing information is that both reporting agents and register staff cannot be expected to act unless they are aware of omissions in detail. In addition to many and repeated discussions with reporting agents to overcome localised difficulties, three systematic approaches to the problems of underreporting have been evolved to cover the main categories of missing information.

(1) *The register status return.* The system design, particularly following computerization, permits routine monitoring of its input at various stages. A check is maintained by verifying staff on receipt of data on each register number. At the end of each week the register numbers allocated by the records department during the week are noted and a weekly count made of numbers on which no data have been received. Register numbers on which no data have been received for four weeks after issue are treated as overdue and numbers which would become overdue in the following week are listed and circulated, together with the counts, to all staff involved. This simple weekly return is effective in keeping the backlog of cases on which no data are available to reasonable proportions.

The computer files of register data are brought up to date periodically, usually at about six-week intervals. These "updating runs" provide an opportunity for correcting errors in the existing files, checking that new information is compatible with the existing records, adding it in, and searching the whole file system for missing records and parts of records. For instance, it is possible to deduce that contacts are missing if the sequence of contact numbers is broken. The type of the missing contact can be specified from the transfer information in the preceding contact. A missing contact at the end of a string can be detected if closure of the last available contact indicates transfer to another service within the system. If contacts within the string are incomplete it can be assumed that closure information is missing. Altogether, seven different categories of missing data can be detected by the computer. Details of each of these are listed according to need at each updating run and used by register and records staff to make up the deficiencies. In addition, 15 types of count of both missing and available information are made and output as a table showing the status of the register as a whole. This monitoring procedure has proved to be a valuable means of quality control. For example, the first time this device was run 2,102 missing contacts were detected from the file of 18,612 available contacts. A year later the same procedure detected only 382 missing contacts from the file of 28,293 available contacts.

(2) *Records department searches.* Not all missing information can be located by computer techniques. All new patients, patients reentering treatment after a period out of care, and many treatment contacts are not predictable from the existing files. For these categories the records department staff depend on a system of notification by referring agents and health service staff. Prior notifications are provisionally recorded in the book register and card index. The whole of the book register is worked through periodically to obtain details of missing confirmations of provisional entries. This essential but laborious clerical procedure could be fully automated only if computing facilities were available on the spot.

(3) *Patients treated outside the service system.* For epidemiological research involving estimates of total treated morbidity in the population at risk, it is necessary to ensure that patients from the geographical area of the region who go to services outside it are included. Data on these patients are of two main types: out-of-region treatment experience of patients who are also treated in the region and who are therefore on the register, and records of patients treated wholly outside the region, and who are not registered. It is routine records department procedure to request information about treatment in other hospitals of patients on the register and sufficient data are usually obtained to complete all contacts, at least in outline. The redesigned national psychiatric inpatient reporting system provides a ready means of access to data on patients from the risk population treated wholly outside the region. The permission of the Scottish Home and Health Department and of each of the hospitals concerned is obtained to include such patients in the register and data from the central punch card file used to make up the main elements of the records. For these patients, only inpatient admissions were available initially and no data could be obtained for patients treated exclusively outside inpatient services. Because of the excessively small numbers involved, no attempt is made to obtain information on patients treated outside Scotland. In general, it is extremely unlikely that significant underreporting results from these omissions. Should additional information be required on patients' treatment experience outside inpatient units, each service would have to be contacted with specific requests on each patient. The return would be too small to justify the effort involved except for special purposes on selected groups.

The redesigned national reporting system did not come into full operation until the middle of 1963, when a census of all patients in care was taken, though all admissions in 1963 were included. For this analysis, admissions in the three years 1963 to 1965 were examined together with all patients resident at the end of 1963 who had been admitted before 1963. A few patients admitted before 1963 and leaving hospital during 1963 will have been missed.

The initial search yielded 707 cards, of which 32 were found to be in error because of miscoding or duplication of existing cards. Of the 675 admissions remaining, 88 were readmissions occurring within one of the three years and a further 55 were readmitted in two or three different years. Of the 532 persons involved, 48 were found to be already on the northeast region register, and a further 39 were placed on the register subsequent to their admission to a hospital outside the region and before the end of 1965.

This left a total of 445 individuals who would have been missed had this search not been undertaken. Of these, 200 were in residence at the end of 1963, all but eight of whom had been in hospital over two years and 120 (60 percent) of whom had been admitted prior to 1948, when the hospital regions came into being.

The average annual number of persons from the region population admitted to hospitals outside the region in 1963 to 1965 was 82, or 3.7 percent of new patients registered in a year. There was no evidence of a real trend in the three years. A fall in numbers of "first" admissions was probably caused by inadequate documentation of previous histories.

Register Data Handling

The interview staff undertake the coding of both their own interview data and the contact information using nearly 50 numerical codes. The coding is verified, providing a complete check on accuracy. Codes are entered into labeled spaces on the duplicate forms arranged to underlie printed headings on the first copy. Self-coding is limited to names and record-keeping numbers, partly to retain simplicity and readability of the clinical record and partly to ensure a check on accuracy by enforcing reconsideration of the accuracy and meaning of the written information during coding.

The initial data collection by interview includes some 126 items of identifying, social, and clinical material requiring five 80-column punch cards for each of 2,500 new patients every year. On every occasion when there is a change in the patient's treatment contact a further two cards are required for 41 additional items of data. This happens 7,500 to 10,000 times a year. The punch card system was designed for processing on a sorter and tabulator with additional procedures on a 542 electronic calculator and a gang punch (see Figure 34–4).

Although satisfactory for some purposes, this method was slow and inefficient for others. For instance, longitudinal analyses involving several pairs of event cards were particularly difficult to carry out. The need to update the card files continuously reduced their availability for processing on the machines to unacceptable levels, so that it was necessary to produce special decks of cards for even relatively straightforward analyses if these were likely to take more than a few days. The

clear answer was to use a computer with a large backing-store to hold all the data permanently. A systems analysis was undertaken (Baldwin, 1964) and arrangements made for programming assistance to place the work on an Elliott 803B computer with magnetic film.[2] Initial programming of updating and simple analyses took about six months, and a further six months were required to develop monitoring and interrogation procedures providing answers to ad hoc enquiries, print-outs of error conditions, and missing information in a form suitable for use by the interviewing and records staff, and the counts for the Register Status Return. Following this period, modifications were made to the computer files to permit greater flexibility and the inclusion of additional data, and a complete set of analysis programs were written to produce edited tables for annual distribution to research, clinical, administrative, and planning staff (Baldwin & Evans, 1966, 1967).

Computer Applications. The punch card system proved to be completely computer compatible. The first step was to study the system structure to find the best method of using the Elliott 803B computer and mangetic film backing-store. Basically the data consist of: (1) the identifying and social data which are relatively unchanging and can be valid over lengthy time periods, and (2) the treatment experience data which are constantly changing by a fixed "quantum" for each experience or "contact." The number of such contact "quanta" for each patient can be predicted only within rather large limits. These two kinds of data were already held on different card types and one of the difficulties with the sorter/tabulator set-up had been to select items from the experience data cards for tabulation against items from the social data cards. Even holding these two kinds of data on separate films there would be no difficulty in item selection from either or both files. However, because of the uncertainty about the length of any particular patient's treatment experience, a method had to be found of dealing with variable length records in a serial backing-store. Not only must an economical method be found for storing, searching, and retrieving the information, but some means would have to be devised for adding new treatment experiences to those already held on the same patient, as well as the experiences of new

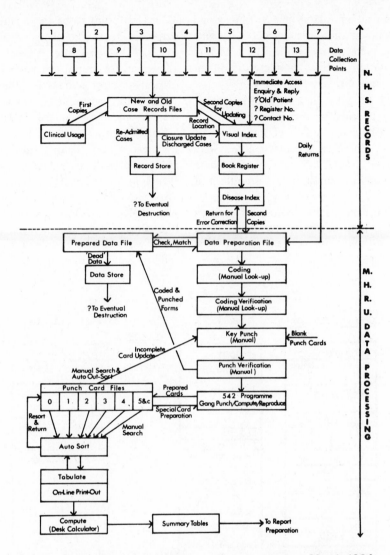

Fig. 34—4. Psychiatric Case Register: Systems diagram, March 1964.

patients. In essence the problem was to find an alternative to leaving "space" on the film for adding in data on psychiatric treatment experience when there was no way of determining how much to leave. It would be very inefficient to store all the information on each patient in register or unit number order on one reel of film since its variable amount would prevent location of any individual record by calculation, and so prevent access except by laboriously going through the whole film item by item.

Variable Length Record Storage. The key to a solution lay in the fact that the identifying and social data are relatively unchanging and of fixed length. By separating off the variable length

treatment experience data there remained a file of fixed length records. The unique register number allocated serially to each record could be used to define the position of the record on the film, data spaces being left for unused numbers. By means of a cross-referencing system in which the address of the variable length record was contained in the fixed length record, the position of any variable length record could be ascertained and the data accessed. Thus, initially two files were required, each stored on different magnetic films (Figure 34—5):

File 1—fixed length—called "Current Social Data File"

File 2—variable length—called "Psychiatric Experience File"

Typically, one reel of 803 magnetic film would hold File 1 data on more than 16,000 patients (i.e., 48,000 punch cards), while a File 2 film would hold about 30,000 complete treatment experiences or contacts.

In addition to the great increase in efficiency of record location afforded by this cross reference or "link" system, the introduction of new types of data on even a subset of patients is a relatively simple procedure. Several different types of data can be held on any patient and there is no limit of practical importance to the quantity. For instance, special surveys carried out on samples of patients can be added in and automatically linked with existing data without loss of generality of the system.

The last point to be taken into account was the situation created by change of an item of data in File 1. The two file system would make no allowance for duplicating items like a change of marital status or address. But the cardinal principle of the case register is to accumulate an on-going record, and any change in an item must be effected without destroying the original. To meet this need a third file on a third film was created to hold social and identifying data superseded by real events in the patient's life. This is File 3—called "Past Social Data File," and since the number of such changes is variable it is also a variable length file using a cross-referencing link in File 1 in the same way as File 2. Files 1 and 3 also contain validity dates defining the time periods over which

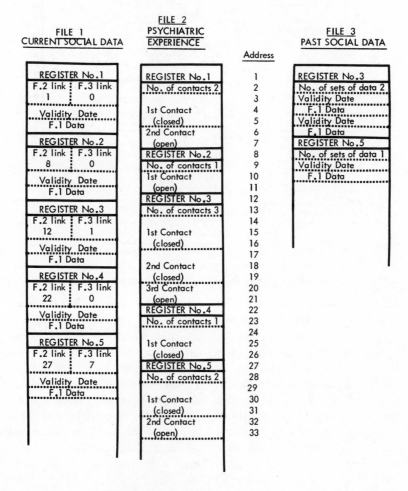

Fig. 34–5. Register data storage on magnetic film. (Reproduced from "The Mental Hospital in the Psychiatric Service: A Case Register Study" by J. A. Baldwin, published for the Nuffield Provincial Hospitals Trust by Oxford University Press, 1971.)

each set of data hold true, so that time related analyses can always utilize social data valid at the specified time.

Updating the System. Having developed a relatively efficient storage method, the next major problem was to work out ways of adding in new information on existing records and creating new records as new patients appeared in treatment. In the case of the fixed length record in File 1, new data have only to be inserted into the appropriate empty space, while replacement of existing data by a new current set with a new validity date involves transfer of the original data to File 3, together with its validity date. File 3 being of the variable length type, insertion of data transferred from File 1 involves rewriting the film and putting in the added data at the correct point in the sequence of register numbers. This has the effect of pushing the remainder of the File 3 data further down the film so that links in File 1 also have to be adjusted. All these operations are carried out in a single pass.

A further pass is required to update File 2, the "Psychiatric Experience File." This is also of variable length type so that the whole of this film also has to be rewritten, inserting new data and altering the links from File 1 to File 2 accordingly.

The programs allow several other important functions to be performed during each pass. During the first, provision is made for correcting social data which are found to be erroneous and for adding in previously missing information. For instance, a date of birth might have been recorded wrongly or only obtained later, or coding or punching errors might come to light in the course of day to day use of the data, or in the records department. Such changes are punched into new cards and the computer extracts the data from the incoming cards and integrates it with existing data.

During the second pass similar changes can be made in File 2, but two further functions are also incorporated. The first is to carry out checks for consistency on incoming data, rejecting any which are impossible and testing for acceptable but improbable features. Initially there were 13 categories of error condition in which cards were rejected, and six of suspect data. Both types are listed so that manual checks can be made later. The second function is to monitor all the data on all three files for each register number in turn, adjusting and checking the correctness of the links

for Files 2 and 3, and listing various categories of missing data, such as missing contacts, missing cards, etc., according to the operator's choice. There are seven categories of missing data which can be selected according to current requirements, and further types could be included if thought useful.

As this updating program has been developed, an increasing number of error checks have been included and also simple frequency counts are possible on specified items. In this way the updating procedures, which are carried out at about six weekly intervals, keep the system in readiness for analysis purposes, systematically improve reliability and completeness of the data, and provide answers to routine inquiries made by clinical, administrative, and research staff. The generality of the system also permits ad hoc projects to be run using existing or specially collected data, and development of the system itself by incorporation of additional data is facilitated.

Implications of Register Automation. Although the steps towards computerization described are really little more than use of the machine to carry out relatively straightforward data processing, much like the sorter, tabulator, and desk calculator, and to simplify and accelerate the clerical work of checking for errors and missing information (Figure 34–6, Phase 1), the potential for further exploitation of automation was very early apparent. The facility for automatic linkage of new data with the existing files provides a very efficient means of carrying out research using nonstandard data collected on defined groups of patients for special purposes. By means of the register and contact numbers alone it is possible to add data from punch cards or extract information for later punching into the same cards or produce samples matched with experimental groups in various ways. Even working "off-line," the benefits are obvious. The possibilities for computerizing the records office work by such procedures as electronic name matching, automatic encoding of data where only dictionary look-up or deduction from rules is required, issuing instructions in anticipation of events, etc., are apparent. The provision of "on-line" facilities with either a local computer or a remote machine with time-sharing and fast serial or random access backing-store and immediate access from a

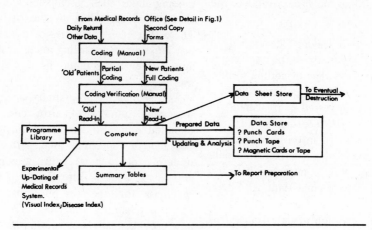

DATA PROCESSING SYSTEMS REVISION – PHASE 1

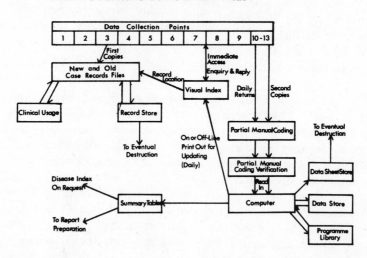

PSYCHIATRIC CASE REGISTER SYSTEMS REVISION – PHASE 2

Fig. 34–6. Psychiatric case register: Computer applications systems diagram.

terminal console (Phase 2 in Figure 34–6), which would allow such developments to take place, was fully recognized by the Flowers Committee in its recommendations for Aberdeen University's Medical Faculty computing needs (Great Britain Council for Scientific Policy and University Grants Committee, 1966).

Applications of the Psychiatric Case Register[3]

The two general classes of use of information systems of the case register type are *research* and *service*, though the extent to which each is practical depends upon the organization and content of the individual register and the purposes for which it was designed. A register based upon special reports unrelated to the case record would be unlikely to yield much of value in the immediate management of the clinical case, while one which was not capable of effecting linkage of records of different individuals in the same family would be of limited value for research in population genetics. It must also be emphasized that few, if any, specific applications of a continuing register system could not be carried out on a once-for-all project basis, though many such projects would probably be much more expensive to execute in isolation. Similarly, for many uses the special characteristic of person records may not be required while for others the cumulative feature of the records may be irrelevant. Many valuable studies may be based on indexes of unlinked data and probably most research is cross-sectional rather than longitudinal and does not require cumulative records. Yet without cumulative person records cohort research is always difficult and usually impossible, and it is because of the lack of such records that knowledge of the temporal patterns of psychiatric illness and disability is noticeable by its poverty of both extent and quality. The unique advantage of the register type of data bank is that it facilitates all these kinds of use, affording the opportunity of exploiting them when required.

Flexibility in development and application is one of the key features of the northeast Scottish register. It is capable of accepting, linking, and manipulating nonstandard data so that the user may incorporate any information which is appropriate to his needs. This is a function of the generality of the system design and yields a great increase in power over a nongeneral system. The following account of current uses of this register is given as a general guide to the types of use for which registers can be designed, but it is by no means exhaustive and the reader will be able to think of other uses specific to his own interests which are not mentioned.

Service Uses. The principal use is, of course, the case record in everyday *Clinical Service* and in this respect the system functions much as any ordinary unit medical record system. Nevertheless, the complex of services through which a patient may be referred implies the need for much more careful attention to updating and rapid transfer of the clinical record between services than is ordinarily necessary in a single hospital. Involvement of the data handling system occurs in relation to the provision of *Service Management Information.* This takes two forms at the moment. First, a series of tables are prepared relating to each year's work for distribution to administrative staff, medical superintendents, and other interested persons. The tables are produced and printed up directly on the computer. They are arranged in volumes relating to the psychiatric and mental deficiency services as a whole and to individual units or groups of units as requested. The tables are numerous but very simple, being designed to yield the most useful information with the least effort at interpretation, for most users are not accustomed to reading tabular material. They are set out with full

definitions interleaved and consist of straightforward counts of the usual dimensions of service use, covering inpatients, outpatients, follow-up, emergency and ward referrals, domiciliary visits, day patients, and so on. Counts are given with percentage distributions by sex, age, diagnosis, referral agent, address, disposal, and a few other useful features like waiting-time. Cohort analyses are also included giving durations in care and outcome. For the main volumes on the services as a whole a section on specifically person analyses is also included.

These *Annual Operational Tables* are an example of routine feedback. It is essential to provide a visible return for the cooperation of staff and administration in the maintenance of the system, though it may be very difficult to know what would be most valuable. Our policy has been to provide a reference volume rather than a report which can be read and then forgotten, though research reports on specific aspects are produced as well. Considerable use is being made of these annual tables. As the educational process proceeds, the least useful material will be omitted, additions will be made wherever the need arises, and gradually more complex indices will be incorporated as people get used to handling them. The aim is to reduce the bulk and increase the pertinence.

The second type of service management information is the *Ad Hoc Inquiry.* We undertake to answer specific requests for information from bona fide users of the system. Examples are numerous. For instance, the Regional Hospital Board wanted to know what additional case-load would result from a realignment of the catchment area of one hospital which they thought would be feasible on appointment of an additional consultant. Numerical confirmation of their supposition was given in a very short time. In another case the regional board was asked to report to the Scottish Home and Health Department on the numbers of children referred by social and legal agencies over several years. These data were supplied at no cost in time or money to the board which would otherwise have had to be collected by asking consultants to search through their records—a process which might have taken weeks or months and have been quite unreliable at the end of the search.

It is part of the role of the research team to carry out research into the functioning of the mental health services. So far as the register is concerned the object is to improve understanding of the operation of service systems in several ways:

1. *Patient movement studies.* These were an obvious starting point and they are now rather routine, if not exactly obsolete. Research reports are issued from time to time summarizing recent trends and investigating special aspects. These act as a supplement to the Annual Operational Tables and give statistical guidelines for planning and administration.

2. *Mathematical models of mental health service function.* We are attempting to develop models, particularly of hospital function, which might be used to evaluate the consequences of planning and administrative proposals. This sort of work is really only possible with extensive data and adequate computing facilities. For instance, in one recent study (Baldwin & Hall, 1967) detailed data were required on each of nine years and dozens of trial computations were carried out, each taking a few hours of computing time, any one of which would have taken several days on a desk calculator with considerably increased risks of error.

3. *Studies of demand for psychiatric care.* Here the interest is in assessment of the factors affecting demand, as well as its dimensions.

(a) *Factors affecting hospitalization.* There has of course been a very significant fall in the proportion of patients entering care who are hospitalized and in the northeast region this is now down to about two patients out of five in the year following initial referral. The social, clinical, and service data in the register have enabled differentiation of which groups are not now receiving inpatient care who did in the past, and useful predictors of hospitalization have been obtained from the data.

(b) *Multiple hospitalization.* A start has been made on a detailed study of readmissions to mental hospital with a view to delineating the characteristics of patients in this very extensive "stage army" and their care pattern, which should enable us to see more clearly how the demand for repeated hospitalization arises and how the hospitals cope with it.

(c) *Interservice demand pattern.* In the complex type of integrated system of services now in existence, the demand for different types of care is

initiated in important measure by the mental health service staff themselves as they move patients from one type of unit or care to another. The system behaves very much like an industry, the output of one part representing the input to another part. Table 34–1, which illustrates in a simple way the importance of counts of persons in relation to counts of events such as referrals or admissions, also shows up the phenomenon of interunit and interservice movements. For instance, 470 of the 2,565 persons entering care in 1965 were admitted to both the Ross Clinic and the mental hospitals in the course of that year. It is important to reach an operational understanding of this phenomenon in quantitative terms if the approach to the provision of services is to be a conscious expression of policy. It is possible to derive useful descriptions by applying an adaptation of the method of input/output economics to this problem.

(d) *Community demand pattern.* This, the most crucial aspect of demand, shades into epidemiology and can equally well be considered under that head. With a total population of less than half a million it is necessary to accumulate cases over a considerable period in order to have enough to carry out statistically viable detailed analyses. In northeast Scotland it will shortly be possible to analyze five-year reported incidence and prevalence rates, which will permit quite detailed examination of social variables such as could not be obtained reliably on very large patient populations and would not yield adequate numbers in short times in small areas.

The point about all these projects is not so much that they have been or are being done, but that they are possible without special arrangements for data collection only because of the register. They all use only standard register data.

An Interregister Comparative Study. A simple initial study comparing results from three register areas: Aberdeen City with Camberwell and Baltimore, has been completed recently (Wing et al., 1967). The most striking finding was the similarity of the results from all three urban areas with about one percent of the adult population in care on one day and a further one percent entering care in the following year in all three areas. There were certain differences in diagnostic distribution and sex and age composition and in the way patients were distributed between different types

TABLE 34–1

Northeast Scottish Psychiatric Services
All adult persons entering care in 1965 who were not in care on last day of 1964

Agency	Inpatients Persons	Contacts	Outpatients Persons	Contacts	Daypatients Persons	Contacts	Other Persons	Contacts	Total Persons	Contacts	Total Individuals
Ross Clinic	222	239	1119	1182	66	77	801	913	2208	2411	1725
Mental Hospitals	1066	1314	224	233	9	9	267	298	1566	1854	1310
Other	–	–	1	1	–	–	4	4	5	5	5
Total	1288	1553	1344	1416	75	86	1072	1215	3779	4270	3040
Total Individuals	1264	–	1337	–	75	–	1046	–	3722	–	2565

of care, but overall the similarities were more in evidence. The point about this study was that the three registers had to reach comparability of their data and in order to do this it was necessary to rerun a number of analyses, the first attempts having shown up defects. This was quite practical using computer files and did not add greatly to the work. With a once-for-all data collection undertaken just for this purpose, it might well have been impossible to make the necessary adjustments. Comparative studies between areas, especially international comparisons, have been very difficult and often unsatisfactory in the past. It may be that the flexibility of the register method will help to get over some of the problems and make such studies more fruitful.

Family linkage studies are just beginning. The chief interest is in three types of relationship: (1) sibs, (2) married couples, and (3) parents and children, in each case where more than one member of the family appears in the register. The initial object will be to obtain measures of referral incidence. Recent work has suggested strongly that the risk of other family members being referred is much increased once one member goes into psychiatric care, though in most cases samples have been small or biased by, for instance, exclusion of unhospitalized cases. This type of study is possible because there is sufficient identifying information in the northeast Scottish register to obtain linkages on a high proportion of cases. The long-term plan is to extend the register to cover other types of social, welfare, and legal agencies to identify and characterize the very high risk families who are known to make extensive use of multiple agencies. There are obvious operational reasons for the importance of this type of so-called psychosocial register, but there are also theoretical considerations in both psychiatry and sociology which could be tested out by this means. In both cases the value of the data would be immeasurably enhanced by the capability of effecting family linkage.

Clinical Research provides several examples of the flexibility of the register: 1. *Use of the interviewer data collection procedure as a screen for prospective sample selection.* By incorporating one or two questions in the routine data gathering interview it is possible to filter out cases on which special studies are being conducted and direct them to the investigating clinical staff. For instance, a study of blackouts among psychiatric referrals was carried out on the basis of the question: "Have you had a blackout, fit, or lost consciousness at any time in the last year?" A study of pregnancy and childbirth has been completed selecting women of child-bearing age for special investigation. The interview can also be used for collection of special data directly as was done for a study of Avitaminosis B12.

2. *Retrospective sample selection.* There have been a lot of small studies based on retrospective samples drawn from the register files, usually as ad hoc enquiries. Having identified the cases the researcher may use standard data from the case register or go back to the case records, or both. A feature of this facility is that it enables one to browse and follow hunches. There are numerous occasions when it is very difficult to know whether a study would be worthwhile carrying out, either because the idea is completely untried or because its feasibility is uncertain. Even with great caution many studies are begun and relatively few finished. The ability to search retrospectively, quickly, and effectively does not absolve the searcher from thinking carefully. Indeed, defining the enquiry has a great disciplinary effect. But it does enable the would-be researcher to disabuse himself of impractical ideas at relatively little cost, and it removes the absolute drudgery and frustration of manual record-searching.

3. *Matched samples.* It is quite easy to draw controls for an experimental group from the register files. For instance, one investigator carried out a careful clinical study of alcoholics. He found that he needed a control group of patients matched for sex, age, and address and to obtain exactly comparable social data on them as he had for his alcoholics. The files were searched by the computer and an exact match for each patient with all the relevant data was obtained in about half an hour.

4. *Representative samples.* Whatever you are studying you usually want to know how representative your sample of patients is of all similar patients. Obviously the register provides a very simple method of measuring representativeness and it can often be done immediately from the routine annual tables.

5. *Data linkage.* Most of the clinical studies which have been conducted in recent years have used register data in one form or another.

Sometimes this is incidental, but more often data on the identified cases are taken out of the "bank" for the use of the researcher. A more advanced and potentially more efficient method which has not yet been fully exploited is to link the experimental data in the computer files and carry out the analyses in the computer. This way the experimenter could get his results fast and his data would be available for anyone else to use if he permitted.

Expected Future Uses

Development plans are now almost entirely dependent on the arrival of more powerful computing facilities in the university. In general this should provide much greater potential for data storage and much faster retrieval. Consequently we shall aim to incorporate more types of data as the needs of users grow. For instance, there is obviously much to be gained from including psychological test results for clinical, research, and administrative uses. We would like to investigate the physical histories of psychiatric patients, both prior to and following psychiatric care to obtain more adequate measures of association between different conditions. This, of course, leads directly to the question of large scale record linkage studies with vital records on the one hand and general health records on the other, and *inter alia*, all the possibilities for research in population genetics which that opens up.

Some of the most interesting possibilities in the field of *Service Uses* are in the automation of more and more of the medical record. We have known for some time what next steps to take—indeed, if the hardware had been available they could have been taken several years ago. With on-line access, either to our own computer or through a remote terminal to a large time-sharing machine, we could be using the computer as a records office, doing all our name matching, updating, tracing of missing data, and so on by this means. Much useful operational work could be done at a detailed level on such things as bed allocation, staff disposition, planned patient follow-up, etc.

There are a number of examples of attempts at storage and retrieval of extensive medical records in plain language. Selective retrieval and visual display with optional hard copy is feasible, though it is uncertain whether the computer is necessarily

the best approach to this problem. It may be that videotape records systems or holography will be more economical and practical. But whatever is eventually developed, the days of the hard copy record are numbered.

At a more directly clinical level, the very fast computational facility of the computer could be used to provide the doctor with almost immediate access to quantitative material on the accumulated experience of his colleagues—providing such information as a probability statement on the outcome for the patient in front of him of a number of alternative dispositions or courses of treatment. Prognostics, expected reactions to drugs, and such like seem more practical than computer-assisted psychiatric diagnosis which is beset by immense difficulties on the input side.

CONCLUSION

The psychiatric case register constitutes a comprehensive, cumulative, regional mental health service information system capable of great flexibility, yielding sophisticated management data, and facilitating a variety of types of clinical and epidemiological research. Its success has depended upon the characteristics of the region, its population, its integrated system of mental health services, and the favorable climate of opinion among the cooperating institutions of the health service, the university, and the funding organizations. It has been developed over a period of years to a pitch of operational readiness which permits rapid and variegated information retrieval sufficient to meet the growing demands of its users. By the end of five years it had only just begun to realize its real potential as a longitudinal record system and its value may be expected to accrue rapidly over the next five. Further development in terms of both inclusion of new types of data and more service orientated utilization is clearly possible, but will depend upon easy access to more sophisticated computing facilities than were available in the early years.

The register method is a powerful research tool which it will take time to learn to use to the full. It has already stimulated useful research which would not otherwise have been undertaken and it has provided information for planning and management commensurate with modern needs.

Its assets and its limitations both stem from its derivation from the clinical record. It can provide information only on treated morbidity, and it is not a substitute for other population research methods. It should be seen as complementary to direct epidemiological and social studies of community on the one hand, and to more specialized clinical, anthropological, sociological, psychological, and laboratory studies on the other. It is a costly technique, demanding of both staff and resources over an indefinite period. Furthermore the cost, complexity, and difficulty of implementation probably increase disproportionately to the size and complexity of the area and the service program to which it is applied. For this reason, it has limited general applicability until the necessary technology becomes cheaper, more acceptable to health service staff, and more widely available. Register areas should be selected for their special features and the form and content of the register geared to their specific needs and characteristics, with only sufficient in common between registers to permit useful comparisons of results to be made. There is much to be said for the concept of the "experimental area" in which expensive research can be concentrated, augmenting existing facilities and complementing work already in progress, rather than diffusing a meagre proportion of limited resources overall.

Notes

Formerly Research Fellow, Department of Mental Health, University of Aberdeen, Scotland, Dr. Baldwin is now Medical Director, University of Oxford Unit of Clinical Epidemiology and Oxford Record Linkage Study, Oxford Regional Hospital Board, Old Road, Headington, Oxford OX3 7LF, England.

1. The remainder of this chapter is based on extracts from *The Mental Hospital in the Psychiatric Service: A Case-Register Study* by J. A. Baldwin, published for the Nuffield Provincial Hospitals Trust by Oxford University Press, 1971. (Extracts reprinted with permission, copyright © 1971 by the Oxford University Press.)

2. The Elliott 803B computer is a "second generation" machine with an 8,000-word core store. It is unique in using magnetic film (35-mm. film coated with iron oxide) instead of magnetic tape as a backing store. Unlike tape, the film is permanently divided into numbered "blocks" so that the exact position of an item in a fixed length record can be derived from knowledge of the number of blocks per record and the number of the record. Since this chapter was written the register has been transferred to a large "third generation" computer,

and more advanced methods of file handling have been implemented. Many of the applications suggested under "Expected Future Uses" (page 815) are now operational.

3. Almost the whole of the program of ongoing research discussed in this section has been completed since this chapter was written. Reference should be made to the following principal publications:

Baldwin, J. A. The Mental Hospital in the Psychiatric Service: A Case-Register Study. Published for the Nuffield Provincial Hospitals Trust by Oxford University Press, 1971.

Baldwin, J. A. (Editor). Aspects of the Epidemiology of Mental Illness: Studies in Record Linkage. Boston, Massachusetts: Little, Brown, 1972.

References

Acheson, E. D. *A central file of morbidity and mortality records for a pilot population.* Oxford, England: Oxford Regional Hospital Board, 1963.

Acheson, E. D., Truelove, S. C., & Witts, L. J. *British Medical Journal*, 1961, 1, 668.

Babigian, H. M., Gardner, E. M., Miles, H. C., & Romano, J. Diagnostic consistency and change in a follow-up study of 1215 patients. Paper presented at the 120th annual meeting of the American Psychiatric Association, Los Angeles, Calif., 1964.

Bahn, A. K. *Psychiatric Case Register Conference, 1962.* Washington, D. C.: Outpatient Studies Section, Biometric Branch, National Institute of Mental Health, 1962.

Bahn, A. K. Experience and philosophy with regard to case registers in health and welfare. Paper presented at the Workshop on Case Registers, American Orthopsychiatric Association, Chicago, Ill., March 1964.

Bahn, A. K. *Psychiatric Case Register Conference, 1965.* Washington, D. C.: Out-patient Studies Section, Office of Biometry, National Institute of Mental Health, 1965.

Bahn, A. K., Gardner, E. A., Alltop, L., Knatterud, G. L., & Solomon, M. Comparative study of rates of admission and prevalence for psychiatric facilities in four register areas. Paper presented at the meeting of the Mental Health and Statistics Section, American Public Health Association, Washington, D. C., 1965.

Bahn, A. K., Gorwitz, K., Klee, G. D., Kramer, M., & Tuerk, I. *Psychiatric care received by individuals in a state during a one year period: Maryland psychiatric case register: Analysis of the first year's experience.* Washington, D. C.: Out-patient Studies Section, Biometrics Branch, National Institute of Mental Health, 1963.

Bahn, A. K., Gorwitz, K., Klee, G. D., & Tuerk, I. Services received by Maryland residents in facilities directed by a psychiatrist. *Public Health Reports*, 1965, 80, 405–416.

Bahn, A. K., Gorwitz, D., & Kramer, M. *A cross-sectional picture of psychiatric care in an entire state.* (Psychiatric Studies and Projects, Vol. 2, No. 3) Washington, D. C.: Mental Hospital Service, American Psychiatric Association, 1964.

Baldwin, J. A. *Automation requirements in the psychiatric morbidity research programme.* Aberdeen, Scotland: Department of Mental Health, University of Aberdeen, 1964.

Baldwin, J. A., & Evans, J. H. *North-east Scottish psychiatric services: Operational tables for the year 1965.* Aberdeen, Scotland: Department of Mental Health, University of Aberdeen, 1966.

Baldwin, J. A., & Evans, J. H. *North-east Scottish psychiatric services: Operational tables for the year 1966.* Aberdeen, Scotland: Department of Mental Health, University of Aberdeen, 1967.

Baldwin, J. A., & Hall, D. J. Estimation of the outcome of a standing mental hospital population. *British Journal of Preventive and Social Medicine*, 1967, 21, 56–65.

Baldwin, J. A., & Innes, G. *The interviewer technique of data collection for the psychiatric case register.* Aberdeen, Scotland: Department of Mental Health, University of Aberdeen, 1966.

Baldwin, J. A., Innes, G., Millar, W. M., Sharp, G. A., & Dorricott, N. A psychiatric case register in north-east Scotland. *British Journal of Preventive and Social Medicine*, 1965, 19, 38–42.

Baldwin, J. A., & Millar, W. M. (eds.) *Community psychiatry.* Boston, Mass.: Little, Brown, 1964.

Bellows, M. T. Case registers. *Public Health Reports*, 1949, 64, 36.

Bodian, C., Gardner, E. A., Willis, E. M., & Bahn, A. K. Socio-economic indicators from census tract data related to rates of mental illness. Paper presented at the annual meeting of the American Statistical Association, Cleveland, O., 1963.

Brandon, S., & Gruenberg, E. M. Measurement of the incidence of chronic severe social breakdown syndrome. *Milbank Memorial Fund Quarterly*, 1966, 44, 129–149.

Brooke, E. M. A cohort study of patients first admitted to mental hospitals in 1945 and 1955. (General Register Office; Studies on Medical and Population Subjects No. 18) London: Her Majesty's Stationery Office, 1963.

Cartwright, A. Memory errors in a morbidity survey. *Milbank Memorial Fund Quarterly*, 1963, 41, 5–24.

Doll, R. *British Medical Journal*, 1961, 1, 1035.

Gardner, E. A., Bahn, A. K., & Mack, M. Suicide and psychiatric care in the aging. Paper presented at the 6th International Congress of Gerontology, Copenhagen, Denmark, August 1963.

Gardner, E. A., Bahn, A. K., & Miles, H. C. Patient experience in psychiatric units of general and state mental hospitals. *Public Health Reports*, 1964, 79, 755–766.

Gardner, E. A., Miles, H. C., Bahn, A. K., & Romano, J. All psychiatric experience in a community. *Archives of General Psychiatry*, 1963, 9, 369–378.

Gardner, E. A., Miles, H. C., Iker, H. P., & Romano, J. A cumulative register of psychiatric services in a community. Paper presented at the meeting of the Mental Health and Statistics Section, American Public Health Association, Washington, D. C., 1962.

Gorwitz, K., Bahn, A. K., Chandler, C. A., & Martin, W. A. Planned uses of a statewide psychiatric register for aiding mental health in the community. *American Journal of Orthopsychiatry*, 1963, 33, 494–500.

Great Britain Council for Scientific Policy and University Grants Committee. *Report of the joint working group on computers for research.* London: Her Majesty's Stationery Office, 1966.

Haenszel, W., & Hon, N. B. Statistical approaches to the study of cancer with particular reference to case registers. *Journal of Chronic Disease*, 1956, 4, 589–599.

Heasman, M. A. *British Medical Journal*, 1961, 1, 821.

Hollingshead, A. B., & Redlich, F. C. *Social class and mental illness: A community study.* New York: Wiley, 1958.

Hopkins, R. A., & Gardner, E. A. Development of a flexible control system in the maintenance of a patient case register. Paper presented at the meeting of the Information Retrieval Section, Conference on Data Acquisition and Processing in Biology and Medicine, Rochester, New York, 1963.

Innes, G., & Bain, S. M. The northeast region of Scotland. In J. A. Baldwin & W. M. Millar (eds.), *Community psychiatry.* Boston, Mass.: Little, Brown, 1964.

Innes, G., & Sharp, G. A. A study of psychiatric patients in north-east Scotland. *Journal of Mental Science*, 1962, 108, 447–456.

Kasius, R. V. Some aspects of patient-flow in the Dutchess County Unit, 1960–1963. *Milbank Memorial Fund Quarterly*, 1966, 44, 194–213.

Lewis, A. *British Medical Journal*, 1961, 1, 1034–1035.

Mazer, M. A psychiatric and parapsychiatric register for an island community. *Archives of General Psychiatry*, 1966, 14, 366–371.

Miles, H. C., Gardner, E. A., Bodian, C., & Romano, J. A cumulative survey of all psychiatric experience in Monroe County, N. Y.: Summary data for the first year (1960). *Psychiatric Quarterly*, 1964, 1–30.

Newcombe, H. B., James, A. P., & Axford, S. J. *Family linkage of vital and health records.* Ontario: Atomic Energy of Canada Limited, Chalk River, 1957.

Newcombe, H. B. Kennedy, J. M., Axford, S. J., & James, A. P. Automatic linkage of vital records. *Science*, 1959, 130, 954–959.

Nielsen, J., Wilsnack, W., & Stromgren, E. Some aspects of community psychiatry. *British Journal of Preventive and Social Medicine*, 1965, 19, 85–93.

Odegaard, O. Pattern of discharge from Norwegian psychiatric hospitals before and after the introduction of the psychotropic drugs. *American Journal of Psychiatry*, 1964, 120, 772–778.

Patton, R. E. Record of mental hospitalization of Dutchess County residents. *Milbank Memorial Fund Quarterly*, 1966, 44, 124–128.

Phillips, W., Jr., & Bahn, A. K. *Experience with computer matching of names.* Washington, D. C.: Communications of the Social Statistics Section, American Statistical Association, 1963.

Phillips, W., Jr., Bahn, A. K., & Miyasaki, M. Person matching by electronic methods. *Communications of the Association for Computing Machinery*, 1962, 5, 404–407.

Phillips, W., Jr., Gorwitz, K., & Bahn, A. K. Electronic maintenance of case registers. *Public Health Reports*, 1962, 77, 503–510.

Pinsent, R. J. F. H. *British Medical Journal*, 1961, 1, 821–822.

Rawnsley, K., & Loudon, J. B. *British Medical Journal*, 1961, 1, 1170.

Smith, A. *Automatic linkage of medical and vital registration records.* Edinburgh, Scotland: Department of Social Medicine, University of Edinburgh, 1963.

United States Department of Health, Education, and Welfare. *Smoking and health: Report of the Advisory Committee to the Surgeon General of the Public Health Service.* (Public Health Service Publication No. 1103) Washington, D. C.: United States Government Printing Office, 1964.

Weir, R. D. What the medical profession expects from the medical records officer. *Medical Record*, 1964, 5.

Wing, J. K., Wing, L., Hailey, A., Bahn, A. K., & Baldwin, J. A. The use of psychiatric services in three urban areas: An international case register study. *Social Psychiatry*, 1967, 2, 158–167.

World Health Organization. *Manual of the international statistical classification of diseases, injuries and causes of death.* (7th rev., 1955) Geneva: World Health Organization, 1957.

35

Mental Health Program Evaluation

Bernard L. Bloom

The purpose of this chapter is to review the field of mental health program evaluation and to discuss and critically examine methods which have recently been used to evaluate a variety of mental health programs. Prior overviews of the field and bibliographic summaries may be found in National Institute of Mental Health (1955), Dent (1966), and Bloom (1963, 1967a, 1968a, 1968b, 1968c). It will be useful at the outset to set the limits of this discussion by defining program evaluation and distinguishing it from other types of evaluation studies (see American Public Health Association, 1960). A mental health program is viewed as the totality of activities which together are designed to meet a set of mental health program objectives. These objectives constitute defined and measurable end results to be achieved by these activities in a finite period of time. Evaluation is the process of determining the value or amount of success in achieving these predetermined objectives (also see Hutchison, 1960, p. 499). Other definitions of the term "evaluation" seem to focus on the same concepts. Arnold suggests that "Evaluation is the feedback mechanism used to assess whether the plans that have been made are being implemented and whether the expected outcomes are occuring" (1966, p. 12). Blenkner indicates that "Soundly conducted evaluative research in casework should enable the members of the profession to determine to what extent they are achieving their objectives, to discover the reasons both for their success and their failures, to point the way toward experimentation with new programs and techniques, and to provide a means of testing their effectiveness" (1950, p. 54). Central to these definitions is the

concept of predetermined and measurable objectives and the emphasis on a quantitative approach to the assessment of attainment. In a well-functioning mental health program, one would expect to see a continuing process of objective setting, activity selection, evaluation, revision of objectives and activities, reevaluation, and so on.

Mental health program evaluation can be distinguished from the evaluation of specific techniques which do not constitute the whole of a mental health program. In practice, however, evaluation of specific techniques, as in the case of behavior modification (for example Krasner & Ullmann, 1966), psychotherapy (for example, Goldstein & Dean, 1966), or mental health education (Davis, 1965) is as important as is the study of the outcomes of total mental health programs.

GENERAL ISSUES IN MENTAL HEALTH PROGRAM EVALUATION

A persistent discrepancy can be seen between the admonitions regarding the necessity for mental health program evaluation on the one hand and the rarity of such evaluations on the other hand. In a recent position statement by the American Psychological Association regarding community mental health centers, it is suggested that "The comprehensive community mental health center should devote an explicit portion of its budget to program evaluation. All centers should inculcate in their staff attention to and respect for research findings. . . . Only through explicit appraisal of program effects can worthy approaches be retained and refined, ineffective ones dropped" (Smith & Hobbs, 1966, pp. 21–22). At a recent conference on professional preparation of clinical psychologists, it was suggested that "... common to both science and service are such attributes as a question-posing attitude, a style of problem-solving, a respect for evidence, and a need for built-in evaluative devices which make for a self-correcting system. . . . The Ph.D. training programs must prepare a clinical psychologist . . . whose psychological activities involve a constant drawing on theory, a conscientious attention to definable procedures, the evaluation of his clinical work through acceptable scientific procedures, and a felt responsibility for reporting his results to his colleagues" (Hoch, Ross, & Winder, 1966, pp. 69, 76). In the recent policy statement on mental health promulgated by the American Public Health Association, it is stated that "the growth and development of mental health services must be justified by demonstration of success in reaching the objectives. Without such demonstration the increased demands for manpower and facilities cannot be supported nor can the optimal direction for growth be confidently explored" (APHA, 1967, pp. 8–9). Yet in a review of existing community health centers, it was noted that "The one area in which there seems to be substantial deficiency across the board is perhaps the most consequential of all, namely, a means of determining the effectiveness of their services" (Glasscote, Sanders, Forstenzer, & Foley, 1964, p. 28). In a more recent review appraising community mental health centers, the situation is described in the same terms. "Quite a lot is known about the numbers and kinds of facilities, and something is known about the units of service that are delivered in them in the course of a year. As yet, almost nothing is known about effectiveness, and this sad observation applies even to the longest-established facilities" (Glasscote, Sussex, Cumming, & Smith, 1969, p. 31). Lest one think that the lack of adequate evaluations is uniquely a characteristic of mental health programs, however, it would be well to recall that in the 1930s when the national program to help handicapped children was rapidly expanding, "not one carefully planned, controlled prospective evaluation study of the long-range restorative power of the program was begun" (James, 1962, p. 1145).

Lumry and Simon (1967) urge the favorable consideration of psychiatric case registers and other long-term data collection systems as an alternative to the continued use of unevaluated treatment modalities which often seem to be employed because of specific therapist's enthusiasm. They note that cross-validations and follow-up studies have rarely confirmed first findings regarding therapeutic efficacy of some particular technique. Furthermore they suggest that available data does not permit practitioners to make adequate discriminations between that kind of patient for whom a particular treatment may be suitable, and that patient for whom the treatment might be harmful or, at best, useless. With the overwhelming support and encouragement on the part of practitioners and scientists for systematic evaluation, the fact that so little acceptable program evaluation is being undertaken can well be questioned.

Problems in Program Evaluation

Blenkner (1950), in addressing this question, has identified a variety of obstacles to evaluative research. She has suggested that practitioners and scientists have significantly different and perhaps contradictory value systems. The practitioner thinks of the unique attributes of his clients, and has a strong drive to help persons in distress, an intuitive and imaginative mind, and a deep identification with others. The scientist, on the other hand, takes a conceptual analytic approach and strives for a rational inductive or deductive solution to clinical problems, always looking for similarities between people in the quest for generalization. While these attributes are not mutually exclusive, it is rare to find them equally well developed in the same person. The scholar-clinician or scientist-practitioner can exist but he seems most uncommon.

Wilner (1968) has suggested three major sources of difficulty in undertaking evaluative research. First, the state of our knowledge regarding etiology and causal processes is very limited. Second, the range of treatment variants offered patients is very narrow, in spite of presumed differences in etiology. Third, the judgment of improvement is exceedingly difficult and complex (also see Blum, 1962). Complicating these more specific factors is the general shortage of mental health professionals with the resultant difficulty in deploying time and resources to the task of systematic program evaluation, the reluctance on the part of many mental health practitioners to withhold treatment from some patients deliberately and consciously, and the lack of research training among psychiatrists. Freeman and Sherwood (1965) have addressed themselves to the general issue of program evaluation in the context of research in juvenile delinquency control and have made a number of additional observations regarding the difficulties in undertaking such studies. They comment that all too often program success has been measured by the amount of service provided rather than by the outcome of such service. In making the necessary transition to measuring program effectiveness in terms of outcome, they suggest that it is imperative to specify program objectives in measurable terms, to think through the presumed relationships between anticipated procedures and desired outcomes, to ascertain cost of alternative services, and to include evaluation studies in program planning.

Rein (1965) in a recent discussion of the power of knowledge as a strategy for reform, has indicated many of its inherent contradictions. In the short run, program evaluation is costly and it may impede action, even though it may be beneficial over the long run. People in need, particularly those who have been traditionally denied service, often view research as a dodge to postpone action. Much research has not yielded new insights nor has it led on its own to the development of new and improved social action programs. In practice, action program planners often must be opportunistic, taking maximum advantage of unpredicted events to modify their programs so as to secure, in their judgment, the best outcome. This kind of program flexibility creates a serious, if not insurmountable, problem for the person assigned to evaluate the program. With changing opportunities for program development, changing power coalitions, and changing political realities, sound evaluation of the consequences of a particular defined program, now undergoing unpredicted change, is near impossible. Yet, Rein continues, research which attempts to be rigorous runs the risk of providing a mass of information from which no coherent plan of action can be drawn.

Conceptually, program evaluation is not difficult to describe. It consists essentially of four steps.

(1) Specify the objectives of the program;

(2) define the relevant parameters, such as the target population, the criteria to be used in defining the disorder and in determining the attainment of the previously specified objectives;

(3) specify the techniques and procedures to be used in attaining the desired objectives; (4) collect the necessary data to answer the following questions: (a) To what extent have the proposed techniques been applied to the target population? (b) To what extent have the original objectives been attained? (c) What other changes have occurred in the community as a result of the program? (d) What are the implications of the results in terms of modification of objectives or techniques? (e) What are the costs?

In practice, however, there are difficulties at every step. Description of the objectives of a program is often unbelievably complex. It is rare that any mental health program has but a single objective, yet in the mental health field the notion of a variety of objectives arranged in some hierarchical organization is not generally acknowledged. For example, many new mental health programs, like new human beings, have as their chief objective sheer survival. The program is publicized, efforts are made to ensure and expand staff, and the program's visibility and power is maximized. Yet because the objective of program survival rarely has public legitimacy, such efforts often have to be bootlegged and disguised in annual reports as community education or the ubiquitous category "other." But the fact that there are multiple objectives of varying degrees of importance is only part of the problem. An agency may have its corporate programatic objectives and the staff may have their personal objectives. There may be short-term objectives which are quite different from long-term objectives. Objectives may differ in degree of rationality yet be equally important in determining program activities. There may be a set of public objectives and quite another set of private objectives. And finally, the degree of awareness of the whole array of program objectives is often highly variable depending on the particular person as well as the particular objective. Since a program can be evaluated only if its objectives are clearly known in advance it is significant that few programs have fully identified their objectives.

Perhaps even prior to the establishment of program objectives is the systematic establishment of clinical objectives in the case of individual patients. Success in accomplishing the objectives of a mental health program can be measured in part in terms of success in achieving service objectives with each client in the system—whether the client is a patient, a relative of a patient, or a consultee. With respect to individual patients, two questions should be at the forefront of one's attention. First, what objectives do you have in treating this patient; and second, by what signs will you know that you have achieved these objectives? If an effort were to be made at answering these two questions for every patient being seen in a clinical setting, and if each clinician would have the opportunity, perhaps on a monthly basis, to update his statements of objectives and acceptable documentation, then considerable progress toward the evaluation of the clinical program could be made.

In the case of clinicians who do not know why they are seeing a patient, or who do know more or less where they are heading but do not know how to tell when they get there, their clinical activities cannot be evaluated. It is up to the professional staff or to the program director or to the lay advisory board or to the county commissioners to decide what to do about this state of affairs. They could decide to tolerate it, to encourage it, or to minimize it. But it may be a sobering realization to such clinicians to know that their work with respect to some particular patient cannot be evaluated—they have undertaken the treatment of a patient with unspecified goals, or with goals stated so abstractly that they cannot pin themselves down to any observable points of reference in order to determine the extent to which the goals have been achieved.

If objectives and signs can be specified, however, for every closed case each clinician could be asked to what extent the desired behavior changes actually took place. Because the signs of improvement are observable, they are subject to verification.

Analysis of the results of such studies along with appropriate follow-up studies would help answer such questions as:

1. What is the general nature of interclinician reliability or agreement in the establishment of treatment goals?

2. In the case of patients for whom there are particular treatment goals, what is the nature and range in the types of behavior deemed suitable to be used to index goal attainment?

3. Are there any changes over time in the treatment objectives of clinicians?

4. What patient or therapist factors are associated with the ability to establish treatment goals and objective signs of success?

5. Are treatment goals related to diagnostic characteristics of patients or to judgments of severity of chronicity?

6. Are certain treatment goals easier to achieve than other goals?

7. In what proportion of cases are treatment goals attained, for how long and at what cost?

8. What patient characteristics are significantly related to the achievement or failure in the achievement of treatment goals?

9. What are the consequences to the goal setting process of a feedback system in which clinicians are informed regarding the general degree of success of their various treatment goals?

10. Are there any significant differences in degree or duration of goal attainment as a function of various types of mental health treatment programs? Are certain goals more easily accomplished by state hospitals than by community mental health centers? Are other goals more easily accomplished in the community? Are certain goals achieved without treatment as easily as with treatment?

A second problem in program evaluation relates to the determination of the amount of success. As has already been indicated, this determination first requires the conversion of statements about program objectives into observable and measurable criteria. It is easy to overlook important program objectives, but it is equally easy to fail to identify variables or methods by which the degree of attainment of program objectives can be estimated. A third difficulty in undertaking program evaluations is that evidence must be presented to show that the program is the cause of the change in the recipient group, if a change can be demonstrated. Ordinarily, some form of control or comparison group design should be utilized in attempting to demonstrate program effectiveness. The need for a control or comparison group is directly related to the established validity of the treatment technique. If it can be shown that the application of a particular technique leads toward the attainment of a specified objective, then evaluation efforts need only deal with the extent to which the technique is being applied. This would be true, for example, in the case of seat belts as a technique for reducing automobile accident fatalities. In this case, the cause-effect relationship has been reasonably established, and one need concentrate primarily on increasing the application of the technique. If the relation between the application of the technique and the attainment of the objectives has not been adequately demonstrated, as is the case in most aspects of community as well as institutional mental health programs, major effort has to be directed toward this demonstration. It is of small consequence to show the extent to which a particular treatment is being provided when the validity of the treatment in attaining the program objectives has not been established. While an ideal study would start with matched samples in which one group would be the recipient and the others would receive no service or different services, such a design is often quite difficult to execute. Short of a matched group design, some form of comparison over time should be undertaken, even though such longitudinal studies always leave open the possibility that observed changes might have occurred without the program. If large enough samples from the recipient group are drawn at frequent enough intervals, and if one knows in advance exactly what one is looking for to determine program effectiveness, it should be possible, however, to make the study of time trends quite productive.

A fourth problem in the evaluation of degree of success in the attainment of program objectives is the tendency to equate the scientific-unscientific dimension with the objective-subjective dimension. Howe has asked, for example, ". . . how 'scientific' is it necessary to be in order to reach conclusions—and conversely, how far is it feasible to go in relying upon subjective judgment?" (1955, p. 226). Burnett and Greenhill have described different levels at which evaluations can be undertaken. Their paper deals with the

evaluation of an inservice training program for nurses, and the authors consider the nurse's self-evaluation as the first level, faculty evaluation as the second level, and obtaining a time sample of nurse interaction as the third level of evaluation. The authors suggest that ". . . any program evaluated at the third level of evaluation should adhere to such principles of scientific method as formulation of the problem, careful planning of research design, delineation of methods of data collection, and logical analysis of experimental results" (1954, p. 1549). The implication which could be drawn by a reader, namely, that evaluations at the first two levels are exempt from the application of the principles of scientific method, would be grossly inaccurate. It would seem from reading many published discussions of mental health program evaluation that utilizing clinical judgment is unscientific by definition. Since, as many authors point out, judgment must often be used, nonscientific methods are justified. Yet there is no reason why clinical or administrative judgment data cannot and should not be scientifically collected and scientifically treated. Two of the most highly regarded and productive fields of psychology, namely, psychophysics and psychoaesthetics are based virtually exclusively upon scientifically collected and analyzed judgment data. While it is true that clinical judgment can easily be treated unscientifically, this is certainly not mandatory. Although it is beyond the scope of this chapter to elaborate this point fully, it might be mentioned that scientific respectability of judgment data can be gained merely by devoting adequate energies to the concept of reliability—both interjudge and interjudgment. Increasing reliability of judgments is essentially the same as precision of definitions, and a precise definition is one of the distinguishing features of science.

TYPES OF PROGRAM EVALUATIONS

Evaluation studies can be categorized according to where one looks for evidence of program success and what kind of information is collected upon which to base judgments of success.

Program Description

One common type of evaluation reported in the literature is that which more appropriately should be called program description. These studies present a narrative account of a program, often of its history as well as of its current functioning. In a sense, program description constitutes a necessary introduction to a program evaluation although it cannot substitute for a program evaluation. While this discussion tends to focus on the consequences of conducting evaluations too late, if at all, a program evaluation can also be undertaken prematurely. A certain degree of program stability is required before it can be appropriately evaluated. During the early history of any new program, a carefully developed narrative account of its vicissitudes is not only highly desirable, but may be far more appropriate than a study of its effectiveness. Yet the director of a new program rarely allocates adequate time to the task of describing and documenting its rapidly shifting characteristics and organizational crises. It is from just such a narrative account that much can be learned which would be of use to others planning similar programs elsewhere. A program diary has all the usefulness of a personal diary. It can capture the day-by-day stresses, the reactions, and the counterreactions in a manner which no retrospective study can hope to do. Events often move so quickly and in such a complex manner that it is unlikely that these issues can be validly described if one waits a year or longer to review one's organizational history.

In some cases there is considerable question whether program stability will be able to be achieved, whether a program inaugurated as a trial will be able to achieve permanence. In these cases, a carefully prepared narrative account is especially useful. While it is always hard to deny the urgency of the clinical needs which lead to the establishment of many programs, administrators might well seriously consider the long-term deleterious consequences of allocating virtually total staff time to service with little, if any, to systematic program description.

Recipient Judgment

A second type of evaluation is based upon judgments about a particular mental health program by the recipients of the services of that program. These are the studies which report that a certain percentage of patients state that they feel better after receiving treatment at a clinic, or a certain percentage of public school teachers report that they can deal with problem pupils more adequately now that they are receiving regular weekly group mental health consultation. While such reports are important, the problems in their interpretation are manifold. There is the difficulty in distinguishing between the valid report and the one given because it is expected. Assuming the validity of the report, there is the problem of determining the extent to which the existence of this specific program is responsible for the report. Such a determination may require the parallel study of a comparison group not receiving consultation. Assuming both the validity of the report and the fact that it is the participation in the program which resulted in the report, one must then determine the report's significance. Since it is not often that an improved self-report is the major goal of a mental health program, the question must be raised as to whether a report of increased effectiveness has any demonstrable parallel in behavior. Does a teacher who reports that she is doing better with her hard-to-manage pupils actually behave any differently toward them than she formerly did? If no significant behavior difference can be demonstrated, how is the importance of the report to be determined? In many ways, then, an evaluation of a primary prevention program which bases its method upon the analysis of judgments made by recipients of service poses especially difficult problems in interpretation.

Expert Judgment

A third type of evaluation is based upon judgments of program effectiveness made by providers of service or by outside professional experts. Included in this group of studies is the time-honored use of clinical judgment. The valid use of professional judgment in assessing program effectiveness requires first that there be some indication of the objective evidence which forms the basis of the judgment, and second that there be some indication of interjudge and interjudgment reliability. The requirement of objective evidence means, in effect, that a method is provided whereby a judgment can be made by someone not directly involved in the provision of the service. This requirement also establishes the feasibility of studying outcome by contrasting treated and untreated groups since judgments of outcome can be made quite independently of information regarding treatment provision. The study of judgment reliability is not only methodologically important, but also important because when reliability of clinical judgment is assessed, it is often disappointingly low. Nor does the practice of pooling clinical judgments to arrive at a judgment by consensus solve the reliability problem. The problem must be dealt with at the level of the instrument used to measure outcome, in this case the clinical judgment itself. What is its reliability? If it is low, that is, if there is interjudge or interjudgment disagreement, what factors account for it? What would be the significance of the finding that professional judgment does not agree with the judgment made by the recipient of the service? Lack of adequate reliability sometimes signifies that judges use different sets of objective data on which to base their judgments. Is there satisfactory agreement on the presence or absence of bits of objective data, regardless of whether this information is employed in making the clinical judgment? What objective data should be searched in order to make a clinical assessment of outcome in each particular program?

Measurement of Community Variables

A final type of program evaluation which has been identified in published literature is based upon an analysis of objective community data without recourse to any intervening interpretive judgments. A community mental health center program is successful if the first-admission rate to the nearby state mental hospital decreases. A state mental hospital program is effective if the length of hospitalization and the readmission rate both decline. A consultative service to a juvenile court is successful if the recidivism rate decreases, etc. Since this kind of data often bears directly on primary objectives, and since its interpretation does not rest so heavily upon required concurrent studies of reliability, this type of evaluation seems to present fewer methodological problems and greater potential usefulness than those previously described. The major consideration in undertaking an evaluation study of this type is to ensure wise choices in the selection of community variables to be measured. These variables must, of course, be amenable to measurement, and must at the same time have direct pertinence to program objectives. If such variables can be identified, program evaluations of this type have some obvious advantages over those discussed earlier.

SOME RECENT MENTAL HEALTH PROGRAM EVALUATIONS

In order to illustrate the issues which have been raised in the previous section, seven recent mental health program evaluation studies will be critically reviewed. The studies which have been selected for review share in common a major strength, i.e., they have been published in sufficient detail to enable the meaningful discussion of specific methodological issues to take place. Problems raised by these particular studies should be viewed as illustrative of more general problems rather than as ad hoc critiques.

The studies which have been selected to illustrate general issues in mental health program evaluation include the evaluation of a program designed to prevent hospitalization of schizophrenics; the evaluation of a day hospital program as an alternative to 24-hour hospitalization; evaluation of the results of a major shift in an outpatient clinic program from emphasis on long-term psychotherapy to emphasis on brief psychotherapy; evaluation of a program of psychotherapy designed to reduce the demand upon medical services in a group-practice prepayment plan general hospital; evaluation of the effects of psychoactive drugs on mental patients treated and discharged from a large state hospital; evaluation of a British community-based psychiatric service program; and evaluation of the differential effectiveness of a group of Veterans Administration hospitals throughout the United States.

The program designed to prevent hospitalization of schizophrenics has been fully reported in a series of papers and one book (Dinitz et al., 1965; Pasamanick et al., 1964; Pasamanick et al., 1967; Scarpitti et al., 1964; see also, Bloom, 1967a), and has earned for the authors the Hofheimer Prize for the outstanding research contribution to the mental health field awarded annually by the American Psychiatric Association. The authors, partly as a test of the community mental health center concept, sought to prevent psychiatric

hospitalization in a group of diagnosed schizophrenics by providing and evaluating two alternative experimental programs, namely, home treatment by public health nurses combined with
medication, or home treatment by public health
nurses combined with placebo. The subjects
consisted of 152 schizophrenic patients destined
for a state hospital treatment program randomly
assigned to either a drug home care group
(N = 57), placebo home care group (N = 41), or
treated at the state hospital as a comparison group
(N = 54). All patients, in addition to having a
diagnosis of schizophrenia of such a severe degree
that hospitalization was thought necessary, met
the following criteria: nonhomicidal and nonsuicidal; age between 18 and 60; willingness on the part
of the family or family surrogate to accept and
supervise the patient at home, and residence
within 60 miles of the research site. Home care
patients were visited by the public health nurse on
the day following their entrance into the program
and on a regular decreasing schedule thereafter. A
battery of psychological tests was administered
periodically along with a variety of behavior rating
scales. Follow-up of patients in the program was
maintained for a maximum of 30 months. The
success of the experimental programs was judged
primarily by the extent to which the patients
could be maintained outside of a hospital setting.

The day hospital program, reported by Zwerling
and Wilder (1964), sought to evaluate the
feasibility of using that type of facility rather than
an inpatient service. Of all patients admitted to the
psychiatric service, 189 were referred to the day
hospital for treatment and a like number, treated
in the inpatient facility, served as a comparison
group. The authors sought to identify those
characteristics of the patients referred to the day
hospital who were unable to be treated there
successfully. The success of the day hospital
program was apparently judged by the extent to
which patients could be treated there without
needing to be transferred to the inpatient service.

The brief psychotherapy evaluation program,
reported by Straker (1968), evaluated the results of
a reorganization of a university-based psychiatric
outpatient clinic which shifted its emphasis from
reconstructive to goal-limited crisis-oriented brief
therapy. Prior to reorganization of the clinic

program there was evidence of poor diagnostic
evaluations, high drop-out rate, poorly planned
therapeutic efforts, poor staff morale, and long
waiting lists. When the new program was
instituted, an effort was made to provide the brief
contact for selected patients. About 20 percent of
the total caseload was so treated, and part of the
evaluation consisted of identifying demographic
characteristics which distinguished between those
patients selected and those not selected for the
new approach. A follow-up of 110 patients was
undertaken two years after a three-month intake
period. Included among these patients were 44
who were treated by the brief psychotherapy
program.

The general hospital project, reported by
Follette and Cummings (1967), investigated the
question of whether there is a change in patient's
utilization pattern of general medical facilities
after brief psychotherapy, comparing the patients
studied with a group who did not receive
psychotherapy. Experimental subjects included
152 cases applying for outpatient psychiatric care
within the prepaid group practice setting. A
comparison group of high medical utilizers who
had never presented themselves for psychiatric
care was identified matched with the experimental
cases on the basis of age, sex, socioeconomic
status, medical utilization, and evidence of
psychological distress as judged from medical
records. Utilization of all forms of medical
facilities was studied for a five-year period
following the initial experimental group member
contact with the psychiatric outpatient facility
and for the same years in the case of the control
group members who had, of course, had no
contact with the psychiatric facility.

The state hospital drug evaluation project was
reported by Heckel, Epps, and Perry (1967). In
order to determine the effects of psychoactive
drugs upon discharged patients, a group of 138
expatients was studied during the fifth or sixth
month following discharge. In addition to
information obtained from the expatients themselves, a relative or other key informant was also
interviewed. This group of patients was subdivided
according to whether they took drugs after
hospital release. Among the patients not taking
drugs were those for whom none had been

prescribed as well as those who avoided taking drugs which were prescribed. Most of the statistical analyses contrast drug users with drug nonusers, although there is some discussion of the demographic variables which distinguished drug users from drug avoiders. Follow-up study extended for a maximum of 15 months following discharge for 100 subjects and additional analyses were made distinguishing between the 68 cases who remained in their home community throughout the follow-up period and the 32 cases who had to return for further inpatient treatment.

The community psychiatric service program evaluation in Chichester, England, has been reported by Grad and Sainsbury (1966), Sainsbury and Grad (1966), and Sainsbury, Walk, and Grad (1966) (see also Bloom, 1967b). The authors sought to evaluate the extent to which a suicide rate increase could be prevented when the community program began, the extent to which hospital admission rates could be reduced, and the extent to which patients could be kept in the community without causing an intolerable burden upon the families of these patients. For most of these studies, the 831 patients referred to the community psychiatric service in Chichester during a one-year period were contrasted with the 585 patients referred to a hospital program in near-by Salisbury. The two communities resemble one another closely in terms of geographic and demographic characteristics and are situated in adjoining counties. In the case of about one third of the community program patients, the closest relative was also interviewed. Two-year follow-up studies of all patients made it possible to study outcome as a function of treatment program.

The study of Veterans Administration psychiatric hospitals was undertaken by Ullmann (1967). Indexing the effectiveness of any particular hospital by the proportion of patients who were successfully discharged within one year and by the extent to which the hospital avoids the build-up of long-term patients, the author attempted to assess the importance of such hospital characteristics as size, staffing pattern, and cost of operation. With this introductory summary of the seven studies, an elaboration of the tasks associated with mental health program evaluation can be undertaken within the context of these examples of recent efforts.

Specification of Program Objectives

The programs described here have a broad range of stated objectives, although in the state hospital drug study and the VA hospital study, the specification of objectiveness seems somewhat unclear. While the VA hospital study has been approached in terms of looking for hospital correlates of rapid patient turnover, it is not clear what role this objective played in the thinking of the hospital administration or professional staff. Rapid turnover is often thought of as associated with superficial treatment and one can be confident that there was no general agreement on the part of the hospital staffs as to the virtue of using this particular method of measuring treatment effectiveness.

The purpose of the state hospital drug program was to determine the effects of psychoactive drugs on discharged state hospital patients. But if the purpose of the postdischarge treatment plan was to maintain the patient outside the hospital, then the prescription of medication had no necessary relationship to this objective.

In many of the studies the objectives are specified clearly enough but with little if any defense. The prevention of hospitalization is a straightforward enough objective but in a sense it is trivial. Hospitalization has been prevented for schizophrenia, or for that matter for every psychiatric disorder, in many parts of the world and in many parts of the United States for generations by the simple fact of inaccessibility of hospitals or unavailability of hospital beds. No study needs to be mounted to determine if hospitalization, per se, can be prevented. Nearly every public psychiatric hospital has its perhaps covert and often fluid admission standards. Some hospitals will not accept drug addicts; others will not accept alcoholics; others will not accept many nonpsychotics, feeling that their facilities need to be reserved for the more seriously disturbed. Admission criteria vary according to the availability of treatment facilities, tending to less discriminating as more facilities are unoccupied. All this is prevention of hospitalization by administrative decision. In their review of the literature pertinent to their own study, Pasamanick et al. (1967) report that a Baltimore study showed that only half of the psychotics in their survey population were institutionalized. The other half were at home or elsewhere in the community, hospitalization having been prevented. Prevention of hospitalization may also suggest that hospitalization is inevitably harmful or antitherapeutic, and that it should be avoided at all costs. Since few people maintain this point of view, it seems clear that studies of the effectiveness of mental health programs in preventing hospitalization really need to be directed to the prevention of *unnecessary* or *indiscriminate* hospitalization, that is, the prevention of hospitalization in those cases where alternative treatment programs are thought to offer a better probability of improvement. In a recent survey of brief hospitalization techniques, for example, Mendel (1966, pp. 314–5) suggests 14 legitimate reasons for hospitalization.

Related observations can be made about recent studies which seek to determine the feasibility of substituting treatment B for treatment A, such as the day hospital substitute for the 24-hour hospital. This substitution is very much of an intervening step, a technique, whereby it is hoped that the amount of psychopathology can ultimately be reduced. The variety of studies in recent years exploring the range of alternatives to psychiatric hospitalization (see Langsley, 1967) suggests virtually unlimited tolerance to treatment procedures on the part of psychiatric patients, and virtually unlimited creativity in the development of alternative treatment procedures on the part of mental health professionals. If the question is whether treatment B can be substituted for treatment A, the answer seems to be invariably "yes." But the question rarely addressed is whether treatment B is better than treatment A. For what kinds of patients and under what kinds of circumstances is a community program superior to a hospital? What types of patients seem to be more effectively helped by inpatient care than as outpatients? Under what circumstances is brief psychotherapy superior to more extensive or intensive contacts, and under what circumstances is long-term therapy the treatment of choice?

Measure of Outcome

For most of the studies considered here, the measurement of outcome has followed quite logically from the identification of program objectives. The chief finding of the Pasamanick prevention of hospitalization project was that 77 percent of the home care–drug patients remained continuously at home while only 34 percent of the home care–placebo patients remained continuously at home. In the day hospital program evaluation, it was reported that of the 189 patients referred to the day treatment center, 125 were deemed acceptable and of these cases nearly 60 percent were treated without recourse to any inpatient care. The brief psychotherapy clinic program evaluation revealed a reduction in drop-outs, elimination of the waiting list, and a remission rate two years after clinic intake of 84 percent. The group practice prepaid insurance program evaluation revealed a significant drop in medical utilization following brief psychotherapy. In the group of 80 patients who applied for psychiatric care and had but a single psychotherapy session, medical utilization was reduced more than 50 percent during the next five years. Results of the evaluation of the Chichester community psychiatric service revealed an unchanged suicide rate when contrasted with the rate in the same community prior to the start of the program and a significantly reduced hospitalization rate when compared with the town of Salisbury which did not have the community based service. This program evaluation also showed that home care sometimes left the patients' families with more problems than the families of patients who had hospital care.

In certain cases, outcome can be measured in various ways and the different measures can yield different results. In the case of the Pasamanick prevention of hospitalization project one might have indexed attainment of objectives not by the all-or-none criterion of prevention of hospitalization but by achieving maximum days out of the hospital during the study period. This measure has been calculated based on the unusually complete data reported by Dinitz et al. (1965), and the results of the analysis are shown in Table 35–1. As might be expected, the home-care drug group was out of the hospital the largest proportion of the study period (90.2 percent). The home-care placebo group was out of the hospital 80.0 percent of the days of the study period. But most surprising is the fact that the hospital control group remained out of the hospital 87.8 percent of the days following their discharge from the

TABLE 35—1
Outcome as Measured by Days Out of Hospital
(see Dinitz, et al., 1965)

	Home Care Drugs	Home Care Placebo	Hospital Controls
Number of Cases*	57	41	54
Average Project Days Per Patient**	556	559	571
Average Number of Days at Home**	501	447	428
Average Number of Days in Hospital**	55	112	143
Percent of Days at Home*	90.2	80.0	75
Average Length of Initial Hospitalization*	–	–	83.4
Average Number of Days After Discharge**	–	–	487.6
Average Number of Days in Hospital After Initial Discharge*	–	–	59.6
Average Number of Days at Home After Initial Discharge*	–	–	428.0
Percent of Days at Home Following Initial Discharge**	–	–	87.8

*Reported in article.
**Calculated from material in article.

hospital—nearly as high as the home-care drug group. These findings might easily argue for the superiority of hospitalization over home care with placebos and can cast a sobering shadow upon the previously reported findings of superiority of home care with drugs.

There are special problems in interpreting the outcome measures in the state hospital drug project and in the Veterans Administration hospital evaluation project specifically because the program objectives were not clearly delineated. The state hospital project is presented as a study of the effects of chemotherapy on released psychiatric patients, with the implied program objective of achieving a more favorable posthospitalization adjustment by means of chemotherapy. The bulk of the statistical analyses, however, contrast characteristics of the patients, the patients' families, and posthospital behavior subdivided as to drug use or nonuse. Among the nonusers, however, are an unspecified number of patients for whom no drugs had been prescribed. The authors report that their sample of 138 patients is equally divided by drug use, i.e., 69 users and 69 nonusers. They also report that 64 of these 138 patients had not been given prescriptions at the time of discharge but information is not presented to make it possible to group the 69 nonusers according to whether thay had been prescribed drugs which they subsequently refused to take or they had simply not been prescribed medication. With this kind of uncertainty, the evaluation project outcome measures appear to bear little relationship to the presumed program objectives.

In the case of the Veterans Administration hospital study, effectiveness of treatment is indexed by various measures of release rates. Yet as any inpatient facility professional staff member will attest, releasing a patient is a complex process, in which the patient's psychiatric status constitutes but one factor taken into consideration. A patient making significant therapeutic progress tends to be discharged more slowly than another patient with an equivalent degree of psychopathology who is not making discernable progress. Patients are often discharged more quickly if receptive and supportive family members can be found in contrast to the patient who is isolated and who has no satisfactory home environment to which to return. Discharge speed is a function of the employability of the patient, of the demand for beds at the admission office, of the assertiveness of the social service staff in making the necessary administrative arrangements, of the availability of follow-up services, of the urgency and frequency of demands for discharge by the patient himself, of the amount of disruption caused by the patient on the ward, which in turn is often a function of the characteristics of the ward personnel, and, of course, of the unique symptomatology of the patient and the interest of the professional staff in that constellation of symptoms.

The authors of the Pasamanick hospitalization prevention project are sufficiently candid in their description of the project findings to raise their own questions about the relationship of outcome measures to program objectives even though this relationship seems, on the surface, quite direct. While avoidance of hospitalization seems like the obvious way of measuring the effects of a program designed to prevent hospitalization, the authors, after presenting a group of sample case histories, indicate that "the perusal of these histories, in the absence of the introductory statement as to whether the outcome was a success or failure, in themselves provide no special clues as to case outcome . . . the histories indicate that successes could almost as likely have been failures" (Pasamanick et al., 1967, p. 245).

Identification of Comparison Groups

Many of the studies identified comparison groups which could be examined in order to evaluate the specific effects of the program under investigation. In some cases, notably the hospitalization prevention project, the day hospital

program, and the medical utilization reduction project, explicit efforts were made to equate these groups as closely as possible with the experimental population, and, in some cases, to employ the technique of random assignment to groups. In the case of the day hospital program evaluation, however, no follow-up or treatment history information is presented regarding the inpatient program comparison group, although it is indicated that the group does not differ significantly from the experimental group with regard to sex, age, religion, marital status, or diagnosis. Except for concluding on the basis of the experimental group-comparison group analysis that the experimental day hospital program patients are representative of the total population, the comparison group does not figure in any subsequent analyses. Evaluation of the day hospital program should involve, of course, a comparison of its results with those of a group treated by a different modality.

In the case of the brief psychotherapy clinic program evaluation, patients treated by the traditional long-term psychiatric methods were available as a comparison group, but since patients were not randomly assigned to short-term or long-term treatment conditions, systematic differences between these two groups undoubtedly exist. This kind of comparison group analysis is useful only for descriptive purposes. It has a very limited role in program evaluation. In the Chichester community psychiatric service program evaluation, experiences with patients in another city served as a comparison population. If one can ensure relative independence of programs in the two cities in question and if the cities and the program clientele are reasonably similar, this method for identifying a comparison group can be quite satisfactory. Neither in the Veterans Administration hospital study nor in the state hospital drug study was a comparison group specifically selected and evaluated. In the absence of comparison groups it is particularly difficult to make valid assertions regarding program effectiveness.

The selection of the comparison group in the case of the medical utilization reduction program illustrates the necessity of holding as many variables constant as is possible except for the variable deliberately being manipulated. In this case, it appears as if one major dimension was not controlled in the comparison group, namely, the requesting of psychiatric treatment. The case for the effectiveness of psychiatric treatment in reducing medical service utilization would have been much more convincingly made if a comparison group of patients who had requested but not received psychiatric treatment could have been identified and followed. With such a group available for analysis it would have been possible to distinguish between the readiness to ask for help in contrast to asking and receiving of help as causally related to subsequent reduced utilization of medical facilities. The very fact of requesting psychotherapeutic care suggests a kind of psychological-mindedness on the part of the experimental group which might auger well for the future regardless of how the request for psychotherapy was handled.

Close examination of the random assignment procedure used in the prevention of hospitalization project illustrates another useful principle, namely, that random assignment of patients to treatment conditions should only be undertaken if the number of cases is quite large. The risk of failure of the randomization procedure decreases with increasing sample size. With relatively few cases in each treatment condition (as in the case of this study with between 41–57 cases in each group) it may be more satisfactory to assign cases to treatment conditions by matching on a set of predetermined relevant criteria. Whenever patients are assigned at random, the experimenter runs the risk of failure of the randomization procedure. In the case of the prevention of hospitalization project, a bias favoring the experimental group resulted from the random assignment. When the characteristics of the home-care placebo group are contrasted with those of the home-care drug group, every difference of any magnitude favors the drug group. In comparison with the home-care placebo group, the home-care drug group includes more married patients, more high school graduates, patients with an average of fewer previous hospitalizations, less rated psychopathology at the time of admission into the study when measured by psychiatrists, and less nurse-rated psychopathology when seen at the first home visit. When all the home care patients are divided according to success or failure of prevention of hospitalization, it can be seen that a higher proportion of

successful cases than of unsuccessful cases had been in the drug group (76 percent versus 33 percent) but, in addition, the successful cases had significantly fewer previous hospitalizations (P = <.10), less rated psychopathology at the start of the project, and a 14-point higher Porteus Maze I.Q. Because of the partial failure of the random assignment procedure, the relative importance of drug utilization versus certain demographic factors cannot be determined. A recent publication of the NIMH Psychopharmacology Research Branch (1968) indicates that there are some predictive variables which are consistently related to short-term symptom reduction in schizophrenic patients whether they receive drugs or placebo.

COMMUNITYWIDE MENTAL HEALTH PROGRAM EVALUATION

One of the significant by-products of the community mental health movement in the United States has been a rapidly growing interest in total community attributes in the evaluation of mental health programs. In a way, this increasing concern for the broad community is a tribute to the farsightedness of the Group for the Advancement of Psychiatry, which in 1949 published an outline for evaluation of a community mental hygiene program (GAP, 1949). This outline proposes a list of questions which can be asked in order to evaluate the effectiveness or the deficiencies of existing mental hygiene activities. The evaluation is seen as a first step, to be followed by long-range planning for improving the situation, followed by implementation of this planning. The questions posed by this outline deal with such general activities thought to influence mental health as prenatal and well-baby clinics, schools and recreational programs, industrial health, welfare agencies, public health, legal and court activities, public relations, the clergy, socioeconomic factors, and special problems of the aged. In addition to these more general programs, the outline also suggests questions regarding treatment facilities and mental health activities of both lay (volunteer) and professional groups. At the statewide level (at a time when most mental health treatment facilities were primarily state-supported) the outline suggests questions regarding state agencies, legislation, and the full range of state services, including mental hospitals, institutions for the retarded, penal institutions, reformatories, and training schools.

Since this GAP report, which served the primary function of identifying the major program area with which evaluations should be concerned, efforts have been directed primarily at elaboration and quantification. Thus, for example, the GAP outline asked whether there are adequate facilities for the care of psychotic patients in public or private general hospitals. Subsequent work by Gruenberg (1962, esp. chapter 8), and Kramer (1966a, 1966b), for example, has resulted in the development of an array of specific questions aimed at the development of a quantitative base to this evaluation.

Recent efforts toward the expanded collection of communitywide data relevant to mental health program planning and evaluation have been concentrated in two general areas, improved collection and analysis of service statistics, and improved collection and analysis of information about the population and the community at risk. Two of the most useful documents dealing with improved service statistics which have appeared in recent years are the manual for evaluation of mental health programs of the Department of Mental Health in Illinois (Slotkin, 1966) and the Southern Regional Conference Mental Health Statistics task force report on comprehensive mental health data (Williams, 1967). The Illinois document deals directly with program evaluation starting with identification of program goals and ending with analyzing data and report writing. Three detailed examples are provided which illustrate many of the principles in the body of the manual. The task force report deals primarily with program description, i.e., with reporting of service statistics and less directly with program evaluation. It provides a thoughtful discussion of many issues in the development of a reliable and useful reporting system integrating information on patients, facilities, and programs. Papers in a recent publication by Pettus (1967a) deal with related general issues in mental health program evaluation.

Recent papers by Moore et al. (1967), Schulberg and Wechsler (1967) and Monroe, Klee, and Brody (1967) have concerned themselves with identifying community characteristics relevant to mental health program planning. Moore and her coauthors have summarized the deliberations of the Committee on Uses of Data for Planning of the Outpatient Advisory Committee of the Biometry Branch, NIMH. Their report suggests that there has been an overemphasis on traditionally collected information regarding patients receiving care at the expense of data that attempts to define broad community mental health needs. They suggest that community-based data systems should include information regarding demographic characteristics of the service area, existing mental health resources, need for local mental health services, and capacity to meet these needs. In describing mental health resources, information should be collected regarding intake policies and waiting list, financing, staffing, and program. In the case of need for local mental health services, information should be routinely collected which can assist in the prompt identification of high risk group members, including those persons involved in normative crises such as school entrance, pregnancies, marriage or retirement, and persons in special atypical crises such as divorce, suicide attempts, employment loss, acute illness, hospitalizations, school drop outs, or accidents. Another group of persons who should be identified are those involved in prolonged stress situations such as psychosis in the family, neglect, chronic unemployment, or cultural deprivation. A community mental health program wishing to have a more complete assessment of need for mental health services should also keep account of psychiatric patients entering the community, particularly being discharged from inpatient facilities, and of those clients in community nonpsychiatric agencies for whom psychiatric problems might constitute a significant although secondary problem.

The recent conference report sponsored by the Committee on Research of the American Psychiatric Association edited by Monroe et al. (1967) bears careful reading. This conference dealt with psychiatric epidemiology and mental health planning and the publication includes a series of reports of empirical studies based primarily on Baltimore, Maryland, data and thoughtful discussions of the issues raised by these studies. The discussions deal with the problems of describing psychiatric service patterns, difficulties of psychiatric epidemiologic studies in the face of an unsatisfactory nosological system, the identification of high risk groups, the virtues and problems associated with psychiatric case registers, other techniques of meaningful data collection, and the uses of biometric data for program planning. In a related paper, Bahn (1965) describes the two facets of a desirable community mental health research program—population surveys and case register studies. In the case of periodic population surveys, Bahn suggests that information be collected regarding demographic, social, and cultural characteristics, mental health status and social role functioning, and community attitudes. Case register studies of patients and their movements into and between identified psychiatric facilities can provide useful complementary information. A recent paper by Michaux et al. (1967) illustrates how information about environmental stresses such as might be collected in periodic population surveys can be related to psychiatric care data.

Review of the literature in recent years indicates a growing concern with the community as a social system and with those particular characteristics of this social system which may have a bearing upon problems of psychopathology and mental health program planning and evaluation. This study of community correlates of mental disorder can be viewed as the ecologic counterpart to the epidemiologic study of individual correlates of mental disorder. Schulberg and Wechsler (1967) have suggested that one of the reasons for the increasing interest in community characteristics has been the federal regulation that states participating in the community mental health centers construction programs be subdivided into catchment areas of between 75,000 and 200,000 population. These areas are ranked in terms of mental health need which is determined by an analysis of extent of mental illness and such related factors as poverty, social disequilibrium, and the needs of particular groups including children, the aged, and the physically and mentally handicapped. These regulations have resulted in the collection and analysis of large amounts of data in many states and local communities which had not formerly studied such information. In Massachusetts, the extent of mental illness was

indexed by a three-year analysis of first admissions from every city and town to state, private, and VA hospitals. When the Massachusetts catchment areas were ranked on this index, it was found that this rank was not significantly correlated with catchment area rank on socioeconomic need, social pathology, and prevalence of welfare recipients. Where there were many welfare recipients, however, there was a significant likelihood that socioeconomic need would be greater and social pathology more common. The lack of significant relationship between extent of mental illness on the one hand, and other community characteristics presumed to be related to this index on the other hand, highlights a series of major methodological problems in the analysis of the community as a social system. How should the extent of mental illness be measured? What should be the geographic unit subjected to study? What factors should be employed in characterizing the community? How can the results of such studies be appropriately utilized for mental health program planning and for the subsequent process of evaluation?

Recent research studies in the community of Pueblo, Colorado, (Bloom, 1966, 1968d) have a bearing on these questions. Pueblo, a community of 120,000 persons, is divided into 34 census tracts. The city lends itself to meaningful census tract subdivision because its population is not randomly distributed within its borders. Furthermore, the tract boundaries have been very successfully drawn so as to enclose quite homogeneous groups with large intertract variance. Thus, for example, census tracts vary from those in which practically no evidence of social disequilibrium exists to those in which 30 percent of persons under age 18 do not live with both parents, nearly one third of marriages are disrupted, and more than two percent of the population has, during a three-year period, been hospitalized for the first time in their lives for psychiatric reasons. This relative homogeneity of census tracts, coupled with their small population (average of 3400) makes them ideal geographic units to study.

Since the early 1950s the community characteristic most commonly studied in its relationship to various mental disorders has been social class (see, for example, Hollingshead & Redlich, 1958, or

Srole et al., 1962). In this connection, a recent review of the evidence linking socioeconomic factors to delinquency by Gordon (1967) indicates that community studies of social class may often err in the manner in which they measure social class. In the case of family income, for example, most studies have used census bureau reports of median family income. Gordon suggests that this cutting point may be much less sensitive to the possible relationship of income to delinquency than, say, the figure indicating the proportion of families with incomes below $1,000 or below $2,000 per year. He suggests, "if the information concerning a dependent variable is concentrated in one tail of the distribution of an independent variable, the full strength of the association will not be revealed unless the independent variable is dichotomized at the optimal point, in the tail" (Gordon, 1967, p. 940). Studies in Pueblo have shown that dimensions other than social class can be identified, however, which may be more highly related to rates of mental disorder than social class. When 42 different characteristics of Pueblo census tracts as shown in Table 35−2 are subjected to a cluster analysis, a socioeconomic affluence cluster is the first to appear. It is comprised of 14 variables including education (variable 1), all five measures of community participation (variables 2 through 6), median income (variable 12), males in the labor force (variable 13), males in white collar jobs (variable 16), value of owner-occupied housing (variable 17), sound housing units (variable 20), housing with bath (variable 23 reversed), housing with central heating (variable 25), and white population with non-Spanish surname (variable 30 reversed). Census tracts high on this cluster score are characterized by people with high education, a considerable amount of community participation, favorable financial, employment, and housing characteristics, and relatively few white persons with Spanish surname. This cluster is highly related to the social class measure based upon education and occupation. The 14 variables comprising this cluster have a mean intercorrelation of 0.71 and together account for nearly half of the initial communality of the 42 variable matrix. If one divides all first-admission psychiatric hospitalizations into four major diagnostic groups and according to whether the hospitalizations occur in public or private (fee-charging) facilities, it is possible to calculate for each census

tract a hospitalization rate by diagnosis and type of facility. When these rates are correlated with the census tract socioeconomic affluence cluster score it is found that admissions rates into private facilities with diagnoses of psychoneuroses and psychosomatic disorders are significantly positively related to affluence (r = +0.54), admission rates into public facilities with diagnoses of personality disorders are significantly negatively related to affluence (r = −0.39), and admission rates into public facilities with diagnoses of acute or chronic brain syndromes are also significantly negatively related to affluence (r = −0.36). Admission rates with diagnoses of functional psychoses into either public or private facilities are not significantly related to census tract affluence. As a consequence of these various relationships between socioeconomic affluence and diagnosis-specific admission rates, for all patients combined, public facility admission rates are significantly negatively related with affluence (r = −0.37) and private facility admission rates are significantly positively related to affluence (r = +0.34). Across all facilities and all patients there is no significant relationship between admission rates and census tract socioeconomic affluence. Thus, as far as social class is concerned, hospitalization with diagnoses of milder psychiatric conditions is associated with higher social class scores, while hospitalization for more serious conditions is associated with lower social class scores. These general relationships have been found in other studies and are consistent with what is known about class structure and socioeconomic affluence. But half of the variance of the initial 42 variable matrix has not yet been accounted for.

The second cluster accounts for half of the remaining variance. This cluster has been named young marrieds and includes high population per household (variable 7), high fertility ratio (variable 10), many children (variable 11), new housing (variable 21), and low male and female median age (variables 32 and 33 reversed). Census tracts high on this cluster score are comprised of relatively large young families in relatively new housing units. The six variables included in the second cluster score have an average intercorrelation of 0.82 and the score on this cluster is not significantly related to the score on the socioeconomic affluence cluster. When the young marrieds cluster score for census tracts is

TABLE 35–2
Pueblo Census Tract Characteristics Selected for Analysis

A. Educational Level
    1. Median Number of School Years Completed by Adults Age 25 and Above

B. Community Participation
    2. Municipal Golf Club Members Per 1,000 Population Age 21 and Above
    3. YMCA Members Per 1,000 Population Age Three and Above
    4. Public Library Card Holders Per 1,000 Population Age Five and Above
    5. Tennis Club Members Per 1,000 Population Age 21 and Above
    6. League of Women Voters Members Per 10,000 Population Age 21 and Above

C. Family Characteristics
    7. Population Per Household
    8. Percent Housing Units Occupied by More Than One Person Per Room
    9. Percent Housing Units Occupied by One Person
    10. Fertility Ratio (Number Children Under Age Five Per Female Age 15–49)
    11. Percent Married Couples With Own Children Under Age Six

D. Economic Characteristics
    12. Median Family Income
    13. Percent Males Over Age 14 in the Labor Force
    14. Percent Females Over Age 14 in the Labor Force
    15. Percent Nonseparated Married Women in the Labor Force
    16. Percent Employed Males in Professional, Technical, and Kindred Occupations
    17. Median Value of Owner Occupied Housing Units
    18. Percent Families Receiving Aid to Dependent Children
    19. Percent Housing Units Owner Occupied

E. Housing Characteristics
    20. Percent All Housing Units Sound
    21. Percent All Housing Units Built Since 1950
    22. Median Number of Rooms Per Housing Unit
    23. Percent Housing Units With Shared or No Bath
    24. Percent All Structures Containing One Housing Unit
    25. Percent All Housing Units With Central Heating
    26. Available Vacant Housing Units Per Total Housing Units

F. Health Characteristics
    27. New TB Case Rates Per 10,000 Population
    28. Cases and Contacts Salmonellosis and Shigellosis Per 10,000 Population
    29. Public Health Nursing Visits Per 10,000 Population

G. Demographic Characteristics
    30. Percent White Population with Spanish Surname
    31. Percent Foreign Born
    32. Male Median Age
    33. Female Median Age
    34. Females Per 100 Males
    35. Percent Population Age Five and Above in 1960 Living in This County in 1955

H. Social Disequilibrium
    36. Familial Disruption (Proportion of Persons Under 18 Not Living With Both Parents)
    37. Marital Disruption (Number of Divorced and Separated Males Per 1,000 Nonseparated Males)
    38. Economic Disruption (Percent of Male Civilian Labor Force Unemployed)
    39. Environmental Disruption (First Response Fire Runs as a Percentage of Total Housing Units)
    40. Education Disruption (Number of Public School Drop-Outs Per 10,000 Population Age 18 and Under)
    41. Juvenile Delinquency (Number of Delinquents on the Active File of the County Probation Department Per 100 Population Age 18 and Under)
    42. Suicide Rate (Cumulated Over Eight Years Ending 1962 as a Proportion of Total Population)

correlated with psychiatric admission rates, all correlations are significantly negative for every diagnostic group whether one looks at private hospital or public hospital rates. The relationship of social class to incidence of psychiatric hospitalization can be further understood, then, by examination of marital and family status. High incidence of psychiatric hospitalizations for psychoneurotic disorders takes place primarily in those census tracts characterized by *both* high socioeconomic affluence *and* low proportion of young families. High incidence of psychiatric hospitalizations for personality disorders occurs in those census tracts in which there are both *low* socioeconomic affluence and *few* young married families.

With three quarters of the initial correlation matrix accounted for by the first two clusters, a third cluster was located which again accounted for half of the remaining variance. This cluster score, named social isolation, was based on six variables, people living alone (variable 9), low proportion of owner-occupied housing (variable 19 reversed), few rooms per housing unit (variable 22 reversed), few single homes (variable 24 reversed), many vacant housing units (variable 26), and high marital disruption (variable 37). Census tracts with high scores on the social isolation cluster tend to include many divorced or separated people living alone in relatively rundown, often one- or two-room multiple dwelling rental housing. These variables have an average intercorrelation of 0.74. As might be expected, census tracts high on the social isolation cluster score are often low on the socioeconomic affluence score. But no significant relationship exists between social isolation cluster scores and young married cluster scores. While the variables comprising the social isolation cluster are not intercorrelated to the same extent as the variables in the other two clusters, and while the social isolation cluster score is significantly related to socioeconomic affluence, nevertheless, for certain diagnoses the social isolation score is much more powerfully related to the incidence of psychiatric hospitalization than either of the first two cluster scores. In the case of hospitalization rates for personality disorders (including all disorders associated with alcoholism), the correlation between public hospital admission rate and census tract social isolation score is +0.78. In the case of private hospital admission rate, the correlation is +0.51. For public and private rates combined, the correlation is +0.70. In the case of hospitalization rates for functional psychoses and for acute and chronic brain syndromes, the correlations with social isolation cluster scores are nearly as high. In contrast to these three major diagnostic groups which are all significantly more common in those census tracts in which there is considerable social isolation, hospitalization rates for psychoneurotic and psychosomatic conditions are independent of social isolation scores.

These findings suggest some useful newer dimensions for characterizing community structure and suggest, furthermore, that social class may be relatively unimportant when identifying salient community characteristics in the study of psychiatric hospitalization patterns for specific diagnoses.

Communitywide studies, such as the one just reviewed, have a direct bearing on program evaluation, first, because of the interest on the part of many mental health programs in reducing the incidence, prevalence, or severity of psychopathology in the total community. Evaluation of this objective can be most easily accomplished by periodic monitoring of psychiatric disability in the community, even though such monitoring presents complex conceptual and methodological problems (see, for example, Blum, 1962). The federally supported comprehensive community mental health centers program (see Glasscote et al., 1964, pp. 1–12, and Smith & Hobbs, 1966) has as one of its fundamental principles that the mental health center will see itself as being concerned with the mental health of the total community it serves.

Second, understanding the pattern of psychiatric disability in the community and the changes in this pattern over time can help in the development and subsequent evaluation of preventive services. In describing the federal community mental health center program, Glasscote et al. mention that a "further major purpose of the program is to *prevent* mental illness and promote mental health. . . . The community mental health center staff will be concerned not only with actual cases of mental disorder but with potential cases. They will be concerned with those social and medical considerations known or believed to influence the development of the disorders" (1964, p. 9). The Pueblo project is an example of the investigation of social factors in the epidemiology of severe (hospitalized) psychiatric disorder. From such studies, hypotheses can be developed (such as that reduction of social isolation may result in the subsequent reduction of certain forms of psychiatric disability) which can form the basis of innovative community-based preventive services. Since these preventive programs have as their objective the reduction of certain specified emotional disorders in those geographic areas where the program has been instituted, continuous monitoring of psychiatric disability and periodic study of the relationships between disability and environmental characteristics can be most pertinent in evaluating the effectiveness of these programs.

TRAINING FOR MENTAL HEALTH PROGRAM EVALUATION

Several recent publications (Bahn, 1965; Baler, 1967; Gruenberg & Leighton, 1965; and Pettus, 1967b) have concerned themselves with training for research and program evaluation particularly in the area of community mental health activities. If the comprehensive community mental health center is to enjoy a better fate than previous efforts at identifying effective modes for the amelioration of behavior disorders, it needs to broaden and strengthen the empirical foundation on which it rests. Wilner (1968) has suggested that in the community mental health center there may be the mechanism for substantial progress in this task. He mentions specifically an encouraging readiness to extend our epidemiologic and ecologic knowledge of the distribution of mental disorders and our understanding of the effectiveness of the variety of services which will be made available to patients, and systematic collection of information regarding both the demands for service as well as the responses to these demands.

Gruenberg and Leighton (1965) have described the potential contribution of the field of epidemiology to the understanding of mental disorders and the importance of understanding this field in the training of mental health professionals. Basing their discussion upon the earlier work of Morris (1964) they have outlined the variety of ways in which the trained epidemiologist can make a significant contribution

to practice and understanding with respect to the mental disorders. Baler (1967) has addressed himself to many of the problems which seem to interfere with community mental health research productivity, particularly in the case of psychologists, and urges that universities do a more adequate job in socializing students for the role of research specialist. Because of the frequent schism between scientist and practitioner, many students are forced to choose between these two professional life styles, and Baler suggests that since there can be no community research apart from community practice, training institutions need to discourage the development of one-sided identity patterns. In order to increase competence in community mental health research, Baler suggests and illustrates expanded classroom instruction activities and community practicum experiences.

Efforts have already begun to increase the competence of empirically-oriented practitioners in the field. One of the most innovative examples of this kind of activity is the development of the Western Conference on the Uses of Mental Health Data under the sponsorship of the Western Interstate Commission for Higher Education and supported by a grant from the National Institute of Mental Health (see Pettus, 1967a, 1967b). This conference, which has a continuous training function for mental health statisticians, program analysts, other users of mental health data, and mental health program administrators and directors was inaugurated in 1965 and has, since that time, identified a population of persons with interests relevant to the conference objectives and has developed and conducted a series of training opportunities for these persons with primary initial emphasis upon mental health program evaluation. The Western Conference is actually the third regional organization devoted to the general purpose of increasing competence of mental health professionals in the quantitative description of mental health program activities. A midwest conference on mental health statistics had been formed ten years earlier, and in southeastern United States, under the sponsorship of the Southern Regional Education Board, the Southern Regional Conference on Mental Health Statistics had been formed in 1959.

If these regional organizations can continue in their training of persons already employed in mental health and related agencies, and if universities can expand their training programs in the direction of improving competence of students to work productively in community mental health research, then one can confidently expect a growing interest in both scientifically and programmatically relevant mental health evaluation.

References

American Public Health Association. Glossary of administrative terms in public health. *American Journal of Public Health*, 1960, 50, 225–226.

American Public Health Association. *Policy statement on mental health.* New York: Author, 1967.

Arnold, M. F. Introduction to PERT. In M. F. Arnold (ed.), *Health program implementation through PERT.* San Francisco: Western Regional Office, APHA, 1966.

Bahn, A. K. An outline for community mental health research. *Community Mental Health Journal*, 1965, 1, 23–28.

Baler, L. A. Training for research in community mental health. *Community Mental Health Journal*, 1967, 3, 250–253.

Blenkner, M. Obstacles to evaluative research in casework: Part I. *Social Casework*, 1950, 31, 54–60.

Bloom, B. L. The mental health statistician and program evaluation. In J. Levy (ed.), *Mental health data collection in the West.* Boulder, Colo.: WICHE, 1963.

Bloom, B. L. A census tract analysis of socially deviant behaviors. *Multivariate Behavioral Research*, 1966, 1, 307–320.

Bloom, B. L. Institute on program evaluation. In C. W. Pettus (ed.), *Proceedings of the first annual meeting: Western conference on the uses of mental health data.* Boulder, Colo.: WICHE, 1967. (a)

Bloom, B. L. Review of E. M. Gruenberg (ed.), Evaluating the effectiveness of mental health services. *Community Mental Health Journal*, 1967, 3, 291–293. (b)

Bloom, B. L. The evaluation of primary prevention programs. In N. S. Greenfield, M. H. Miller, & L. M. Roberts (eds.), *Comprehensive mental health: The challenge of evaluation.* Madison: University of Wisconsin Press, 1968. (a)

Bloom, B. L. Mental health program evaluation 1955–1964. In N. S. Greenfield, M. H. Miller, & L. M. Roberts (eds.), *Comprehensive mental health: The challenge of evaluation.* Madison: University of Wisconsin Press, 1968. (b)

Bloom, B. L. Community mental health statistical programs of the future. In National Institute of Mental Health Biometry Branch, *Selected presentations: National conference on mental health statistics.* (Chicago, Illinois, May 16–19, 1967) Washington, D. C.: United States Government Printing Office, 1968. (c)

Bloom, B. L. An ecologic analysis of psychiatric hospitalizations. *Multivariate Behavioral Research*, 1968, 3, 423–463. (d)

Blum, R. H. Case identification in psychiatric epidemiology methods and problems. *Milbank Memorial Fund Quarterly*, 1962, 40, 253–288.

Burnett, F. M., & Greenhill, M. H. Some problems in the evaluation of an inservice training program in mental health. *American Journal of Public Health*, 1954, 44, 1546–1556.

Davis, J. A. *Education for positive mental health.* Chicago: Aldine, 1965.

Dent, J. K. *A bibliographic index of evaluation in mental health.* (United States Public Health Service Bulletin No. 1545) Washington, D. C.: United States Government Printing Office, 1966.

Dinitz, S., Scarpitti, F. R., Albini, J. L., Lefton, M., & Pasamanick, B. An experimental study in the prevention of hospitalization of schizophrenics. *American Journal of Orthopsychiatry*, 1965, 35, 1–9.

Follette, W., & Cummings, N. A. Psychiatric services and medical utilization in a prepaid health plan setting. *Medical Care*, 1967, 5, 25–35.

Freeman, H. E., & Sherwood, C. C. Research in large-scale intervention programs. *Journal of Social Issues*, 1965, 21, 11–28.

GAP. *An outline for evaluation of a community program in mental hygiene.* (Report No. 8) Topeka, Kan.: Author, 1949.

Glasscote, R., Sanders, D., Forstenzer, H. M., & Foley, A. R. (eds.) *The community mental health center: An analysis of existing models.* Washington, D. C.: American Psychiatric Association, 1964.

Glasscote, R., Sussex, J. N., Cumming, E., & Smith, L. H. *The community mental health center: An interim appraisal.* Washington, D. C.: Joint Information Service, 1969.

Goldstein, A. P., & Dean, S. J. (eds.) *The investigation of psychotherapy: Commentaries and readings.* New York: Wiley, 1966.

Gordon, R. A. Issues in the ecological study of delinquency. *American Sociological Review*, 1967, 32, 927–944.

Grad, J., & Sainsbury, P. Evaluating the community psychiatric service in Chichester: Results. In E. M. Gruenberg (ed.), *Evaluating the effectiveness of mental health services.* New York: Milbank Memorial Fund, 1966.

Gruenberg, E. M. (ed.) *Mental disorders: A guide to control methods.* New York: American Public Health Association, 1962.

Gruenberg, E. M., & Leighton, A. H. Epidemiology and psychiatric training. In S. E. Goldston (ed.), *Concepts of community psychiatry: A framework for training.* (Public Health Service Publication No. 1319) Washington, D. C.: United States Government Printing Office, 1965.

Heckel, R. V., Epps, A. J., & Perry, C. W. *The return home.* Columbia, S. C.: Authors, 1967.

Hoch, E. L., Ross, A. O., & Winder, C. L. (eds.) *Professional preparation of clinical psychologists.* Washington, D. C.: American Psychological Association, 1966.

Hollingshead, A. B., & Redlich, R. C. *Social class and mental illness.* New York: Wiley, 1958.

Howe, L. P. Problems in the evaluation of mental health programs. In R. Kotinsky & H. L. Witmer (eds.), *Community programs for mental health.* Cambridge: Harvard University Press, 1955.

Hutchison, G. B. Evaluation of preventive services. *Journal of Chronic Diseases,* 1960, 11, 497–508.

James, G. Evaluation in public health practice. *American Journal of Public Health,* 1962, 52, 1145–1154.

Kramer, M. *Some implications of trends in the usage of psychiatric facilities for community mental health programs and related research.* (Public Health Service Publication No. 1434) Washington, D. C.: United States Government Printing Office, 1966. (a)

Kramer, M. Mental health statistics of the future. *Eugenics Quarterly,* 1966, 13, 186–204. (b)

Krasner, L., & Ullmann, L. P. (eds.) *Research in behavior modification: New developments and implications.* New York: Holt, Rinehart & Winston, 1966.

Langlsey, D. G. Alternatives to psychiatric hospitalization. In B. L. Bloom & D. Buck (eds.), *Preventive services in mental health programs.* Boulder, Colo.: WICHE, 1967.

Lumry, G. K., & Simon, W. The urgent need for treatment evaluation. *Hospital and Community Psychiatry,* 1967, 18, 262–266.

Mendel, W. Brief hospitalization techniques. In J. Masserman (ed.), *Current psychiatric therapies: 1916, Vol. VI.* New York: Grune & Stratton, 1967.

Michaux, W. W., Gansereit, K. H., McCabe, O. L., & Kurland, A. A. The psychopathology and measurement of environmental stress. *Community Mental Health Journal,* 1967, 3, 358–372.

Monroe, R. R., Klee, G. D., & Brody, E. B. (eds.) *Psychiatric epidemiology and mental health planning.* (Psychiatric Research Report No. 22) Washington, D. C.: American Psychiatric Association, 1967.

Moore, D. N., Bloom, B. L., Gaylin, S., Pepper, M., Pettus, C., Willis, E. M., & Bahn, A. K. Data utilization for local mental health program development. *Community Mental Health Journal,* 1967, 3, 30–32.

Morris, J. H. *Uses of epidemiology.* (2nd ed.) Baltimore: Williams & Wilkins, 1964.

National Institute of Mental Health. *Evaluation in mental health.* (United States Public Health Service Publication No. 413) Washington, D. C.: United States Government Printing Office, 1955.

National Institute of Mental Health, Psychopharmacology Research Branch Collaborative Study Group. Short-term improvements in schizophrenia: The contribution of background factors. *American Journal of Psychiatry,* 1968, 124, 900–909.

Pasamanick, B., Scarpitti, F. R., Lefton, M., Dinitz, S., Wernert, J. J., & McPheeters, H. Home versus hospital care for schizophrenics. *Journal of the American Medical Association,* 1964, 187, 177–181.

Pasamanick, B., Scarpitti, F. R., & Dinitz, S. *Schizophrenics in the community.* New York: Appleton-Century-Crofts, 1967.

Pettus, C. W. (ed.) *Program evaluation in mental health service.* Boulder, Colo.: WICHE, 1967. (a)

Pettus, C. W. (ed.) *Proceedings of the first annual meeting: Western conference on the uses of mental health data.* Boulder, Colo.: WICHE, 1967. (b)

Rein, M. Strategies of planned change. Paper presented at the meeting of the American Orthopsychiatric Association, New York, March 1965.

Sainsbury, P., & Grad, J. Evaluating the community psychiatric service in Chichester: Aims and methods of research. In E. M. Gruenberg (ed.), *Evaluating the effectiveness of mental health services.* New York: Milbank Memorial Fund, 1966.

Sainsbury, P., Walk, D., & Grad, J. Evaluating the Graylingwell hospital community psychiatric service in Chichester: Suicide and community care. In E. M. Gruenberg (ed.), *Evaluating the effectiveness of mental health services.* New York: Milbank Memorial Fund, 1966.

Scarpitti, F. R., Lefton, M., Dinitz, S., & Pasamanick, B. Problems in a home care study for schizophrenics. *Archives of General Psychiatry,* 1964, 10, 143–154.

Schulberg, H. C., & Wechsler, H. The uses and misuses of data in assessing mental health needs. *Community Mental Health Journal,* 1967, 3, 389–395.

Slotkin, E. J. *Manual for evaluation of mental health programs.* Springfield, Ill.: Department of Mental Health, 1966.

Smith, M. B., & Hobbs, N. *The community and the community mental health center.* Washington, D. C.: American Psychological Association, 1966.

Srole, L., Langner, T. S., Michael, S. T., Opler, M. K., & Rennie, T. A. C. *Mental health in the metropolis: The Midtown Manhattan Study.* New York: McGraw-Hill, 1962.

Straker, M. Brief psychotherapy in an outpatient clinic: Evolution and evaluation. *American Journal of Psychiatry,* 1968, 124, 1219–1226.

Ullmann, L. P. *Institution and outcome: A comparative study of psychiatric hospitals.* New York: Pergamon Press, 1967.

Williams, H. B. (ed.) *Toward more comprehensive mental health data.* Atlanta, Ga.: SREB, 1967.

Wilner, D. M. Research and evaluation in social psychiatry. In J. Zubin & F. Freyhan (eds.), *Social psychiatry.* New York: Grune & Stratton, 1968.

Zwerling, J., & Wilder, J. F. An evaluation of the applicability of the day hospital in treatment of acutely disturbed patients. *Israel Annals of Psychiatry and Related Disciplines,* 1964, 2, 162, 185.

V

Training

In the writings on community mental health, we have seen descriptions of the recent attempt to apply ecological sensibilities to human social settings. The rapid and open-ended growth of the new science is due partially to accelerating social change and community need and partially to community mental health's own need for definition. For theory, community mental health has consolidated multidisciplined knowledge, examined history, and looked at its own recent findings; for method, it has adapted past practices to new motivations, thus encouraging experimental leaps. The goals of community mental health, which have been as elusive as the concepts of mental health and well-being themselves, have stubbornly been kept idealistic in broad outline, while research of testable definitions has been encouraged.

Training in community mental health has had to keep pace with accumulating knowledge from the field and continuous revision of concepts of service. At the same time, attempts have been made to equip new practitioners to develop innovative programs of scientific rigor from a nontraditional orientation. In community settings, mental health professionals have found themselves performing new roles and collaborating with and training many new kinds of mental health workers—functions for which they traditionally have not been prepared. The impact of these forces on psychology, psychiatry, social work, and nursing is explored in part V, which is addressed to issues of training.

In their opening chapter, "Manpower Needs and Resources for Community Psychology and Mental Health," Franklyn N. Arnhoff and C. Alan Boneau explore the gross output characteristics and structure of the educational system which produces psychologists, and detail the extensive services long provided by sub-doctorally trained practitioners. By chapter end, background issues arising from social need and demand, and lack of definition in mental health sciences and service (manpower for what?), are tightly interwoven with issues of public policy in higher education.

Hildegard E. Peplau, in "Nursing Education and Community Mental Health," has described the historical and conceptual development of psychiatric nursing and the broad influence that the integration of mental health concepts into all levels of nursing education has had on nursing practice and the community. Nurses with specialized learning in mental health theory and practice have proved unusually flexible and resourceful in defining innovative and productive mental health roles; this is especially so in the community mental health field, where individuals with graduate training in nursing are most likely to find acceptance as colleagues and the opportunity to assume leadership roles in programs of total patient care.

New requirements imposed on social work education programs by the emergence and rapid growth of community mental health are the subject of a chapter by Howard J. Parad and Lydia Rapoport, "Advanced Social Work Educational

Programs in Community Mental Health." The authors detail their findings on current educational programs and program change, primarily at the post-master's level but also at the master's level, drawn from a questionnaire survey of existing programs. The Community Mental Health Program of the University of California School of Social Welfare at Berkeley is described to provide an experimental program model.

In "Training in Community Psychiatry," Raquel E. Cohen and Ralph G. Hirschowitz discuss psychiatric roles in community mental health and analyze the process of training for new roles. The authors survey existing community psychiatry training programs in the United States, describe curriculum content, and detail the ongoing program of the Laboratory of Community Psychiatry at Harvard Medical School. Community psychiatry is described as a field characterized by uncertainty and continual responsiveness to change.

Charles D. Spielberger and Ira Iscoe, writing on "Graduate Education in Community Psychology," have provided a history of community psychology's development and an analysis of community psychological roles. The authors examine current trends in graduate education and field training for the community, describe some unique university programs, and discuss the burden on university departments to offer strong academic foundations and field training experiences to give emerging psychologists the conceptual and methodological tools needed to meet the challenges of the community.

Melvin E. Allerhand and Goldie Lake, in "New Careerists in Community Psychology and Mental Health," have written a personalized description of the training/education and use of nonprofessionals for mental health service delivery and program development in a variety of circumstances. The authors are sensitive to the conflicts potentially engendered in both professional and nonprofessional circles by emphasis on the use of paraprofessional talent, and address themselves to these components of change while developing a detailed treatment of nonprofessional roles, training, and outcomes.

In the volume's final chapter, "Systematic Selection of Psychotherapeutic Talent: Group Assessment of Interpersonal Traits," Gerald Goodman sets forth a procedural model for systematic selection of nonprofessionals to work in a variety of mental health and counseling settings which demand unusual interpersonal sensitivity. The format detailed here, and tested in the Berkeley Interpersonal Relations Project, has potential value for personnel selection in programs directed toward education, training, or immediate fieldwork. Goodman sees an active future for structured group assessment methods, and has provided a useful prototype.

36

Manpower Needs and Resources for Community Psychology and Mental Health

Franklyn N. Arnhoff and C. Alan Boneau

Manpower questions are all too often thought of only in terms of numbers: manpower statistics, although essential, represent only one facet of manpower analysis. However, since it is the numbers that are easiest to obtain, manipulate, and extrapolate, they frequently serve as a palliative or as a defense against dealing with more critical questions. There is one fundamental question which is implicit in all manpower studies and analyses and all efforts evolve from its answer: Manpower for what? For the mental health fields at this point in time, and for psychology in particular, the question must be made explicit and the answers carefully articulated and reconciled, not within the artificial and archaic schisms of the discrete professions, but with the totality of the human health and welfare service system of today and tomorrow. Of necessity, this includes the broader areas of science now actively engaged in behavioral research and experimentation, the political and social arena as it shapes and stresses the educational/manpower matrix, and the increasing army of groups and professions who draw upon and employ the tools, techniques, and methods once entirely the private preserve of a few discrete mental health professions.

"Finally, it is salutary to recall that health manpower is not a goal in itself but a means of providing services to a population. Services should be provided to the extent that they make a worthwhile contribution to the health of a population. In turn, a given program of services can be provided by alternative combinations of health personnel" (Klarman, 1968, p. 15).

In this chapter we shall examine several concepts relevant to manpower problems and manpower supply as they relate to community psychology and more generally to mental health, and illustrate their complexity and interdependency. To set the stage it is fruitful to quote some recent comments by David (1966):

I have a very strong conviction that the frequent failure of manpower experts to come to grips with issues results from their readiness to ignore fundamental conceptions and considerations. This frequently leads them to become, in a sense, 'instant experts' with a predilection for commitments to relatively quick solutions of very difficult human problems. Implicit in this sort of behavior is the notion that somewhere there are hidden panaceas, and if one could only discover them, they could be applied to the solution of manpower problems . . . the manpower characteristics of any society, quantitative and qualitative, are a product of the total life of that society. Dealing with any one strand of that total life with respect to either manpower problems or manpower policies, consequently, leads to an almost frightening entanglement of issues (p. 1).

While such global considerations are constraints upon fragmented approaches to any type of manpower considerations, they are particularly relevant in the human (health) service domain, within which mental health falls. Mental health has been characterized by "Balkanization" of policy, programs, and responsibility for services, functions, and training: a condition enhanced by the open-endedness and uncertainty of the goals of mental health, and the lack of reliable and universally accepted indices or measures of achievement or effectiveness. "These circumstances . . . conspire to frustrate the design of comprehensive strategies for effective development, deployment, and utilization of manpower resources. These circumstances, however, should also serve to deter the ready purchase of paper solutions in aggregate statistical terms for imbalances in manpower demand-supply relations" (David, 1969, p. 7).

Following these preliminary but essential caveats about manpower conceptualizations, we may now move on to develop those issues most immediately germane to community psychology and its relation to the mental health field. The focus on community psychology is not as narrow as may first appear, since, as we shall show, it is impossible to consider this special area independent of all of psychology and all of mental health. The broader issues, including the politics and economics of the total mental health field, have been recently dealt with, in depth, elsewhere (Arnhoff, Rubinstein, & Speisman, 1969).

Any discussion of manpower issues is ultimately related to such fundamental categories as need, supply, demand, and shortages. While all these terms are part of the common language, they frequently lack the precision necessary for our discussion even when interpreted within the framework of economics, the discipline in which manpower analysis is most at home. These terms, moreover, are subject to particular confusion in the arena of mental health. Hence our discussion will focus primarily about these issues in an attempt to clarify them and articulate their current relevance.

MENTAL HEALTH MANPOWER AND THE SUPPLY OF PSYCHOLOGISTS

The professions traditionally associated with the mental health field have been psychiatry, clinical psychology, psychiatric social work, and psychiatric nursing. Although other professional and scientific groups have become increasingly involved in human behavior and mental health concerns, these four groups remain the dominant ones for delivery of broadly defined mental health services. In addition, considerable effort is currently being expended to develop new types of personnel for service delivery; these personnel, currently labeled by the pejorative "subprofessional," represent a new departure in emphasis.

The four primary professional groups are all currently in the throes of reappraisal of their training, selection, functions, professional perquisites, and future status. With the exception of psychiatry, whose members must all possess an M.D. degree as a minimal credential, the other disciplines are having "career ladder" problems as the pressures mount for full recognition of those trained to less than the traditional academic maximum in these respective fields.[1] The rather spectacular growth, development, and annual output of these "four core" disciplines is shown in Table 36–1 which establishes the order of magnitude for these professional groups.

While psychiatry, social work, and nursing are almost entirely service delivery professions, psychology alone has traditionally seen itself as a science *and* as a profession; indeed psychology is a generic science basic to the study of human behavior and hence, mental health. Consequently, vast numbers of undergraduate college students study psychology or even major in psychology as background for further study in other areas. This is rarely true for these other disciplines. Consequently the social impact of the science is far more extensive than the number of advanced degree recipients would imply and the entire educational flow system of psychological education becomes of critical concern for community psychology.

Contrasting the numbers of persons trained to some minimal level in a given discipline with the traditional criteria for professional inclusion and recognition immediately confounds the issue of manpower supply, since who, or what, to include in the labor pool becomes diffuse. "Manpower supply" usually appears to be the most easily considered aspect of the manpower equation and the most amenable to planning. However, supply planning is not only dependent upon resolution of this definitional issue mentioned above, but output into occupations and professions is a direct function of the total input into the educational system. This is in turn related to a complex series of educational steps and progressions which in turn are determined and shaped by national

TABLE 36–1
Selected Growth Data and Projected Production of
Mental Health Professions

Discipline	1950[1]	1969–1970	Expected Annual Output 1969–1970
Psychiatry	7,000	25,000[3]	1,100[7]
Psychology	7,270	28,800[4]	6,100[8]
Social Worker	21,000 (1956)[2]	50,400[5]	8,200[9]
Psychiatric Nurses	10,000	32,900[6]	41,000[10]

[1] NIMH estimates.
[2] Earlier data not available.
[3] Data from American Psychiatric Association—all psychiatric physicians.
[4] American Psychological Association Membership.
[5] National Association Social Workers Membership.
[6] NIMH Biometry Branch, nurses in mental health positions.
[7] Data from American Psychiatric Association. Includes residents completing training from all sources, with 3, 4, or 5 years of training.
[8] All areas of psychology, M.A. and Ph.D. Data from United States Office of Education.
[9] All areas of social work. Data from United States Office of Education.
[10] Total for nursing field. Separate data for psychiatric nurses not available.

policies, economic conditions, immigration policies, value systems and ideologies, individual ability, and motivational factors, etc. (Roe, 1969; Rossi, 1969; Symposium on Manpower Theory, 1967). At the ultimate base for such planning and projections is the birth rate at a given period of time. Furthermore, each field or profession has its unique problems and factors of recruitment and education too lengthy for elaboration here. It is these unique parameters which determine the ultimate "supply potential" for the respective fields.[2]

Although the primary emphasis here is upon mental health and community psychology, the diffuseness of the boundaries of these areas and the extreme range of functions and types of psychologists involved in them precludes restrictive analyses by educational program or professional subspecialty. Consequently, the existing educational system for the total field of psychology will be the point of departure. Examination of the inputs into the educational matrix, and the expected ultimate output, based upon present conditions and institutionalized

professional practices, will serve to illustrate the order of magnitude of the numbers involved at any point in the total system.

The Educational Matrix

According to the United States Office of Education (USOE, 1966), the number of individuals matriculating for the first time in institutions of higher education increased from 670,013 in 1955 to 1,144,882 in 1965 and is expected to reach 1,990,000 in 1975. The number of bachelor's and first professional degrees shows a corresponding increase from 309,514 in 1955–56 to about 536,000 in 1965–66 and is estimated to be about 930,000 in 1975–76.

These projected figures tend to be based upon reasonably hard data such as known birth figures and fairly stable tendencies for increasing enrollments. The war in Vietnam and its sequelae (the draft and economic factors affecting education) while they may distort the above figures somewhat, may well be having a more dramatic effect on graduate enrollments and degrees. The projections which follow, then, will be very heavily affected by topical factors and may well be considerably in error, particularly at the level of the individual discipline such as psychology. The general trends and relationships shown are, however, of more importance than the absolute values.

At the graduate level, according to the same source, master's degrees increased from a total of 59,294 in 1955–56 to 126,200 in 1965–66 and are expected to reach 234,900 in 1975–76. Doctorates totaled 8,903 in 1955–56, about 17,500 in 1965–66, and project to 36,900 in 1975–76.

Against this background, psychology's growth shows variable progress. According to these Office of Education figures, psychology is attracting and will continue to attract a high proportion of individuals at the baccalaureate level. Psychology

captured 1.8 percent of the baccalaureate degrees in 1955–56, 2.8 percent in 1965–66, and a projected 3.7 percent in 1975–76. The other social sciences exhibit a similar growth trend, but so do many other fields. The growth is presented as taking place at the expense of business, home economics, agriculture, engineering, and the allied health professions.

The Office of Education figures project a similar relative growth for psychology at the master's level–1.6 percent of the total master's production in 1955–56, 2.5 percent in 1965–66, and 3.0 percent in 1975–76. But at the doctoral level the Office of Education foresees a relative decline in psychology degrees from 7.1 percent of the total in 1955–56 to a predicted 5.8 percent of the total in 1975–76. Most fields also seem to be experiencing an increase in their relative share of the master's degree production, largely at the

TABLE 36–2
Psychology Degree Production: Actual and Projected*

Year				NAS
Actual	Bachelor's	Master's	Doctor's	Doctorates
1955–56	5,665	973	634	627
1956–57	6,191	1,095	550	723
1957–58	6,930	1,235	572	745
1958–59	7,383	1,257	635	787
1959–60	8,111	1,406	641	773
1960–61	8,524	1,719	703	820
1961–62	9,638	1,832	781	857
1962–63	11,062	1,918	844	892
1963–64	13,359	2,059	939	1,013
1964–65	14,771	2,708	1,004	955
1965–66	15,120	3,100	1,060	1,133
Projected				
1966–67	16,750	3,400	1,130	
1967–68	20,460	3,440	1,270	
1968–69	22,910	3,860	1,410	
1969–70	23,980	4,660	1,470	
1970–71	24,850	5,370	1,480	
1971–72	26,580	5,480	1,590	
1972–73	28,650	5,840	1,880	
1973–74	31,050	6,110	2,060	
1974–75	33,330	6,680	2,090	
1975–76	34,640	7,140	2,140	

*Office of Education, 1966, 1967.

expense of the field of education, in which almost 50 percent of the master's degrees were awarded in 1955–56, but in which only 22 percent of the degrees are projected in 1975–76. The relative loss in percentage of doctorates awarded in psychology is a loss which is shared with the social sciences and humanities in general. Relative growth in doctorate production is projected mainly in the natural sciences, with the largest growth occurring in the field of engineering.

These relative figures tend to obscure the absolute growth occurring in the production of degrees in psychology, a growth tabulated in Table 36–2. The table, which presents figures from the Office of Education report, gives the production of bachelor's, master's, and doctor's degrees separately by years. The figures for the years 1955–56 through approximately 1964–65 are actual counts, while those following are estimates and projections based upon a linear interpolation method. Because of its intrinsic interest, data from another survey on doctorate production in psychology is included as column 4 of the table. These data are from a 1967 report of the National Academy of Sciences entitled *Doctorate Production from United States Universities: 1958–1966.*

The Office of Education figures demonstrate some interesting characteristics for psychology. For example, they show that the proportion of master's production to bachelor's production for two years earlier remains almost stable at 20–25 percent. As we have already seen, these parallel growths represent a relative increase when plotted against the growth of production for all fields. If, however, we assume a six-year lag between the baccalaureate and the doctorate, we find that about 14 percent of the baccalaureate production is converted into doctorate degrees early in the period covered in Table 36–2, but this percentage decreases to about 9 percent later in the table. Although master's degree production is holding up, it is projected that doctorate production will not.

The National Academy of Sciences data are interesting for at least two reasons. The first is the difference in the absolute number of doctorates listed by the two sources. The second is an apparent difference in the rate of growth reported by the two sets of figures. For example, number of doctorates reported by the National Academy of

Sciences in 1957–58 is roughly 20 percent higher than that recorded by the Office of Education. By 1966, however, the discrepancy has narrowed down to about 5 percent. Apparently the figures reported are based on different methods of counting, or different things are being counted. A more careful analysis of the source of these differences highlights the difficulties surrounding attempts to characterize the educational system but it does not seem to clarify the issue to any extent. The Office of Education figures are based upon yearly reports by registrars of the degrees awarded at their respective institutions. For a field such as psychology which may be interdisciplinary in nature and for which the awarding department may be one or more of several within an institution, it is not surprising that a registrar may be somewhat in disagreement with other sources when estimating the number of degrees which are attributed to psychology. It is likely that the criteria for such judgments differ from institution to institution and over time with changes in registrars.

The National Academy of Sciences figures, on the other hand, are based upon questionnaires completed by all doctorate recipients in the United States and the categorization is based upon the field given by the recipient as his major field. Presumably, the recipient knows the field to which he belongs, but NAS automatically assigns all Ed.D's to the field of education even though the recipient may indicate that his major field is a field such as educational or school psychology. This scheme does not necessarily apply to the Office of Education categories, although in practice it may. In short, the relatively less rapid growth rate shown by the National Academy of Sciences figures may be due to the fact that degrees in educational psychology are being excluded by the National Academy of Sciences and not by the Office of Education. A glance at the educational psychology figures reported by the National Academy of Sciences would tend to substantiate this hypothesis. The number of doctorates in educational psychology rose from a small number in 1961 to 225 in 1966. The addition of these educational doctorates to the figures reported by the National Academy of Sciences tends to make the reported growths roughly parallel, but whatever the OE figures are measuring they tend to do it at a rate which is approximately 80 percent of whatever is being measured by the National Academy of Sciences figures. Whether this same underestimation of psychology degrees is characteristic of the Office of Education figures for master's and bachelor's degrees is problematical.

No matter the source of our figures, the final result of the analysis is the same: the relative rate of growth of doctorate production in psychology is low. It is low compared to the growth of bachelor's and master's degrees in psychology. It is low compared with the growth in other fields. Least favorable to psychology are the National Academy figures which indicate that psychology has grown about 5.5 percent per year. This growth rate is less than that for almost every field listed by the National Academy. Table 36–3 compares the growth of psychology with other major areas of specialization.

Both the National Academy figures and those from the Office of Education give a story much the same. In an article appearing in "Manpower Comments" (Scientific Manpower Commission, 1966), is an analysis of the OE figures which compare 1955 and 1965 doctoral production in various fields, the increase being expressed as a percentage of the 1955 production. Psychology doctorates in that period increased by 58 percent. Other increases, however, are 225 percent for biophysics, 312 percent for pathology, 150 percent each for meteorology and oceanography,

and 248 percent for engineering. It is not true that the large percentage increases are necessarily in those fields which were originally fairly small, although that crude generalization merits some consideration. Nevertheless, psychology's rate of growth falls close to the bottom.

Despite the complexities, we can outline a reasonably clear picture of the production of psychology's educational system. Perhaps 20,000 doctorates are projected over the next ten years; again perhaps 60,000 master's degrees will be awarded, and upwards of 250,000 bachelor's degrees in psychology. From several sources including the National Academy of Sciences report we note that approximately 80 percent of the doctorate recipients also were awarded a master's degree. We would assume then that perhaps 15,000 of the 60,000 master's degrees represent individuals who later completed the doctorate. Thus, our production in psychology over the next ten years would be roughly 20,000 doctorates and an additional 45,000 master's degree holders.

We have looked at gross output characteristics. Now let us examine in detail the structure of the system of education which produces psychologists. Recently, one of the authors (Boneau, 1968) presented a sketch of the system in terms of the proportion of individuals who reach identifiable time goals in the course of a voyage through the educational system. We are now in a position to detail this educational flow more precisely by virtue of new data and recent analyses of old.

TABLE 36–3
Yearly Percentage Increase in Various Fields
from 1958–1966*

Field	% Per Year Increase
Engineering	17.7
Professional Fields	10.9
Physical Sciences	9.7
Arts and Humanities	9.5
Education	9.4
Social Sciences (other than Psychology)	7.6
Biological Sciences	7.5
Psychology	5.4

Note: Date from *Doctorate Recipients from United States Universities, 1958–1966,* Publication 1489, Office of Scientific Personnel, National Academy of Sciences–National Research Council, Washington, D. C., 1967.

The system is presented in Figure 36–1 as a flow chart through which the individual students proceed. A student enters from the left at one of the major entrance points and exits at the right. As is indicated there are several alternative pathways down through the system and a possible exit at every level. The system is rendered less abstract by placing it in a contemporary context anchored to the bachelor's degree production in 1965. The system is immediately made somewhat artificial by a focus on only master's production in 1967 and doctorates in 1970. As a matter of course, every student goes through his own version of the system and constructs his own timelines in the process. Thus, the numbers on the diagram which represent numbers of students at various stages do not all represent, say, the original group of bachelor's degree individuals who are the 1965 anchor of our representation. Some of these individuals may have been or will be around for some time. A word should be said about the origin of the numbers exhibited in Figure 36–1; the figures for degrees granted in psychology at the three levels are based upon the Office of Education data previously mentioned.

The system is subdivided into categories representing institutions classified according to the level of training offered. For the sake of the analysis, we consider institutions which offer the bachelor's degree as the highest degree to be different from those which offer the master's or the doctorate as the highest degree. If, as is probably the case, different proportions of students go to graduate school from each of these sources, the distinction is worth making.

According to other Office of Education data (OE, 1967), 696 institutions awarded degrees in psychology in 1964–65. Of these, 495 institutions awarded the bachelor's as the highest degree and, in fact, conferred 5,598 such degrees in psychology. The 101 institutions offering the master's degree as the highest degree awarded 3,549 baccalureate degrees. A total of 5,575 bachelor's degrees were conferred by the 100 institutions which awarded a doctorate in psychology as the highest degree that year.

Of the approximately 15,000 bachelor's awarded in psychology in 1965, some went on to graduate school, others left the system—to employment, to the armed forces, to graduate work in other areas, or to other activities. We could only guess these proportions at present and

have not attempted to. Unpublished data in the APA Office of Educational Affairs indicate that there were approximately 7,000 first-year psychology students in graduate school in 1965–66. Some of these, however, entered without the baccalaureate in psychology. Our best guess as to the number of such individuals comes from a consideration of the fact that 35 percent of those acquiring a doctorate in psychology have a background other than psychology at the baccalaureate level (NAS, 1967). Let us surmise from this that 2,300 entered the psychology system at the graduate school level from the outside in 1965. As a consequence, we may hypothesize that approximately two thirds of the 1965 baccalaureates in psychology left the system after acquiring that degree. The remaining third and the 2,300 outsiders comprise the entering graduate student body for the academic year 1965–66.

At the graduate school level, the system without the undergraduate colleges has fewer institutions involved. The relative number of students in each portion of the system at this level can be estimated with caution on the basis of the proportion of master's degrees awarded by each kind of institution. According to the Office of Education figures for 1964–65, 38 percent of the master's degrees were awarded by institutions conferring no degree higher than a master's degree in psychology. Applying this proportion to the 3,400 degrees for 1967, the numbers in the figure are obtained. With 3,400 master's degrees, however, 3,300 individuals seem to have left the system between initial matriculation and the obtaining of a degree. Three hundred additional will have bypassed the master's degree on the way to the doctorate. This estimate is based upon figures from the National Academy of Sciences and from the Directory of the American Psychological Association, both of which tell us that 20 percent of those with a doctorate seem not to have a master's degree.

Finally, then, approximately 1,500 doctorates are produced in 1970. As sheer guess we assume that a small number, say 200 individuals, leaves the system after being admitted to doctoral candidacy at roughly a postmaster's level. Thus, the 3,700 individuals who have received a master's or who have bypassed it divide into 1,700 remaining in graduate school and 2,000 who make an exit at the time the master's degree is conferred.

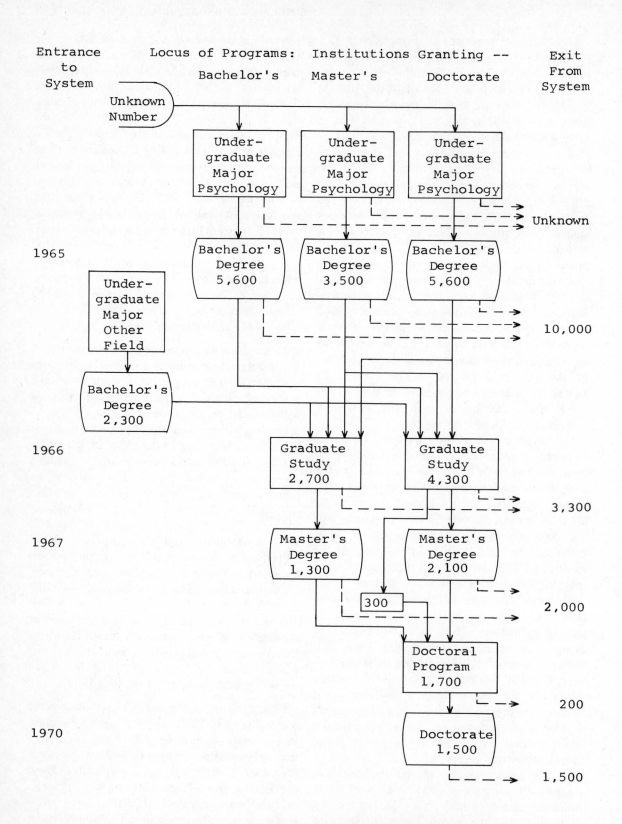

Fig. 36—1. Throughput diagram of the education system for psychologists.

As can be seen from Figure 36—I, we can identify some 17,000 individuals who exit from the psychology educational system with a bachelor's degree or more. We can consider them as the raw materials in a process which eventuates in 1,500 doctorates: only one in 11 of a selected group achieves the credentials necessary for full membership in the American Psychological Association. This ratio is undoubtedly much larger if we consider additional individuals who were in the system but exited prior to the baccalaureate degree. Even considering those who achieved a master's degree as a maximum, we are still looking only at some 3,700 individuals who represent the ultimate professional component of a major undergraudate baccalaureate program or about 22 percent of the initial enrollment. This compares with about 40 percent for the field of physics (American Institute of Physics, 1966).

Considering these data and the educational flow they represent, one cannot but be impressed by the potential input into the field of psychology and the actual, successive attrition that takes place *insofar as organized psychology is concerned.* The doctorate has long been viewed as the requisite for a fully qualified psychologist. This is not to say that only the doctorally trained are active in psychology or psychological work since this is quite untrue. The organized field of psychology, however, has taken no cognizance of other than doctorally trained persons, either through systematic career ladder education, or preparation for specific employment. While it is known that many students major in psychology, as a background for other fields and occupations, the proportion of this group to the total number of majors is not known.

The extreme importance of these facts is highlighted by what is known about less than doctorally trained psychologists—not only the numbers, but also where they work, and what they do.

Subdoctorally Trained Psychologists

The 1957 follow-up of terminal M.A.'s in psychology by Clark found that 63 percent were working as psychologists and an additional 18 percent were in related work. A recent National Institute of Mental Health study (1965) showed that approximately half of the psychologists employed in mental health establishments had less

than the doctoral degree (52.6 percent Ph.D.; 37.9 percent M.A.; 7.6 percent graduate study but no degree; 1.4 percent B.A. or less; 0.5 percent unknown). Only 47.9 percent of those without the Ph.D. were members of APA. Similar data are provided by Wellner (1969) in his survey of state mental hospitals. Of a total of 1,116 psychologists employed in these institutions, only 46 percent had their doctorate, and 9 percent had only the bachelor's degree.

Data from the 1968 National Science Foundation survey (National Science Foundation, 1969) provides the best systematic picture of the areas of psychology in which people with and without a doctorate work, although the sample is limited to those who are known to meet APA membership requirements. Questionnaires were sent to members of the APA and of state and regional psychological organizations as well as to many individuals. It is probable that many people working as "psychologists" are missed because they do not belong to these associations or do not meet the criteria for inclusion. Of the 23,077 usable replies received from people who listed psychology as their primary field of competence, *36 percent (8,248) had less than the doctoral degree.* The data on their reported fields of interest and places of employment are of importance in any discussion of subdoctoral training.

From Table 36—4, it can be seen that the largest group of psychologists is in clinical or counseling and guidance, with approximately 38 percent of all M.A.'s and all Ph.D.'s in these two fields. The remaining subdoctoral people cluster in the other applied areas of school, educational, and industrial and personnel psychology. Of particular note is the area of school psychology in which over 75 percent of the psychologists have less than a doctoral degree. The more traditionally academic areas of experimental, developmental, and personality have proportionately more Ph.D.'s.

Examination of the settings in which psychologists work (Table 36—5) reveals that slightly over half of those with a doctorate are in colleges, universities, or medical schools, but only 17 percent of psychologists in such institutions are trained at the subdoctoral level. M.A.'s predominate in the secondary schools and school systems (78 percent M.A.), junior colleges (64 percent M.A.), state and local government (52 percent

TABLE 36—4
Distribution of Respondents Employed in Psychology,
by Subfield and Highest Degree

Subfield	Total Responding		Doctorate		Subdoctoral		% in subfield with less than doctorate
	N^a	%	N	%	N	%	
Clinical	6,628	28.1	4,552	30.4	2,063	24.3	31.1
Counseling	2,329	9.9	1,393	9.3	936	11.0	40.2
Developmental	963	4.1	754	5.0	207	2.4	21.5
Educational	2,379	10.1	1,510	10.1	868	10.2	36.5
Engineering	573	2.4	300	2.0	272	3.2	47.5
General	189	.8	138	.9	50	.6	26.5
Industrial and Personnel	1,574	6.7	978	6.5	595	7.0	37.8
Personality	370	1.6	327	2.2	43	.5	11.6
School	2,138	9.1	521	3.5	1,615	19.0	75.5
Experimental, Comparative and Physiological	2,421	10.3	2,027	13.6	387	4.6	16.0
Psychometrics	581	2.5	404	2.7	176	2.1	30.3
Social	1,272	5.4	904	6.0	365	4.3	28.7
Other	2,134	9.1	1,149	7.7	906	10.7	42.5
Total	23,551	100.0	14,957	99.9	8,483	99.9	36.0

Note.—Data in Tables 36—4 and 36—5 are from the National Science Foundation's 1968 National Register of Scientific and Technical Personnel.

[a]Includes 23 with no report of degree and 88 with medical degree.

M.A.); and in business and industry (43 percent M.A.). These data support Albee's (1967) observation that the education, guidance, and counseling, etc., of our children are primarily in the hands of people trained at the bachelor's level, and psychological services provided to them tend to be by M.A.'s

All in all, it would seem that much, if not most, of the actual service and applied work in psychology is done by people without the doctoral degree. All current indications are that this situation will continue, *both within the framework of psychology per se and in other groups and professions.*

The immediate relevance of these data and the issues they represent are obvious. The impact of increasingly large numbers of nondoctoral persons employed in psychological services has major planning, educational, and service implications which are shaping and will continue to shape the scientific as well as the professional role and image of psychology (Arnhoff, 1968; Arnhoff & Jenkins, 1969).

Total Supply Pool

Any approach to supply must be concerned with the total available or potentially available persons, *regardless of discipline*, who possess the requisite education, training, and/or experience to perform specific tasks and functions. We have shown that the currently available and projected potentially available supply of psychologists goes far beyond the usual specification of only doctorally trained persons. Since, however, the psychologist (at whatever level of training he possesses) competes in a total manpower market, all other persons offering the same or similar services need also be considered. From the standpoint of the administrator who must fill positions, and the public, who is both consumer and ultimate financial resource, the concern is with services rendered, not necessarily with professional groupings.

In this regard, the tremendous overlap in functions and/or apparent skills among the various health professions and service groups enters into calculation of the available manpower pool. As

TABLE 36–5
Distribution of Psychologists by Type of Employer
and Highest Degree[1]

Type of Employer	All Psychologists		Doctorates		Masters		% in subgroup with doctorate
	N^a	%	N^b	%	N	%	
College or University	8,760	38.0	7,220	48.7	1,469	18.4	82.4
Medical School	803	3.5	675	4.5	121	1.5	84.1
Junior College	490	2.1	175	1.2	313	3.9	35.7
Secondary School	2,715	11.8	562	3.8	2,125	26.6	20.7
Research Center-Educational	42	0.2	30	.2	11	0.1	71.4
Federal Government-Civilian	1,443	6.3	1,069	7.2	360	4.5	74.1
State and Local Government	1,977	8.6	917	6.2	1,022	12.8	46.4
Nonprofit Organization	970	4.2	604	4.1	354	4.4	62.3
Nonprofit Hospital or Clinic	1,318	5.7	780	5.3	514	6.4	59.2
Nonprofit Research Center	30	0.1	28	.2	2	–	93.3
Industry or Business	1,415	6.1	780	5.3	608	7.6	55.1
Private Research Center	2	–	1	–	1	–	50.0
Private Hospital or Clinic	330	1.4	220	1.5	107	1.3	66.7
Self-Employed	1,402	6.1	1,089	7.3	300	3.8	77.7
Military	256	1.1	143	1.0	109	1.4	55.9
Other	176	0.8	91	.6	83	1.0	51.7
Not Employed	744	3.2	319	2.1	408	5.1	42.9
No Report	204	0.9	105	.7	93	1.2	51.5
Total	23,077	100.0	14,808	99.9	8,000	100.0	64.2

Note.–Data provided by the American Psychological Association based upon the 1968 National Register of Scientific and Technical Personnel.
[a]Includes 248 B.A.s and 21 with no report of degree.
[b]Includes 14,794 with academic and 14 with medical doctorates.

long as the manpower supply question remains addressed to such ill-defined, all encompassing issues as "community psychology," "community mental health," or even just "mental health," the manpower supply pool is also broadly defined. This then must include the large number of other professions and groups engaged in the provision of broadly defined psychological services.

Current estimates of the traditional four "core" mental health disciplines give a currently available supply of 25,000 psychiatrists, 28,800 APA psychologists, 50,000 social workers, and 33,000 psychiatric nurses. In addition to these traditional groups we can add: 347,000 physicians, 320,000 lawyers, 325,000 clergymen, 800,000 hospital aides, orderlies, and attendants, 13,500 probation and parole officers, 2,560,000 public school teachers, and so forth. There is ample documentation of the direct involvement and role of each of these groups of people with currently conceived problems of mental health, and this list is certainly minimal. We have then a grossly expanded picture of the numbers of persons actively dealing with problems of human behavior.

It seems appropriate also to mention at this point that despite the cherished belief that any of the psychological service activities are best (i.e., inherently better or more effective) when performed by a member of the profession to which one belongs, there is little if any data to support this position. Not only is there considerable overlap in tasks and functions, but there is also apparently considerable transferability of skills between occupational or professional groups.

Supply and Transferability of Skills

In discussing manpower issues in mental health, Harmon observed that

It is also true that there is a considerable area of transferability of skills. This transferability is in part limited and rigidified by the traditions or customs of the various fields—and that in itself constitutes one of the manpower research problems. Can the definitions of qualifications be made more functional than at present? In theory, of course, they could. In practice—it is quite a different question, partly for technical and partly for what might be broadly termed political reasons. But the fact of change in functioning of various portions of the broad spectrum of mental health manpower is one of the important variables with which any inclusive conceptual scheme must deal. The question occasionally becomes acute when there is a sudden development of demand (need backed by dollars) for national emergency reasons or other reasons. In such crises there almost always occurs some transfer of job functions which would be rare or non-existent in normal times. The transfer demonstrates what is technically possible at any time (Harmon, 1965, pp. 12—13).

From the standpoint of supply, therefore, a vast pool of people is currently involved in mental health services and, under current social conditions, can be expected to increase. As a function of automation and increased industrial productivity per worker, the vast increase in the number of jobs needed for the population will continue to occur in the service fields (Ginzberg, 1968). Health services, including mental health services, will continue to expand and multiply to provide a large proportion of these jobs.

Until greater specification of employment goals occurs, and until the tasks, functions, and competencies of the workers are specified, established, and related to outcome, the mental health groups will continue to experience this overlap in occupational skills, transferability in functions, and the diffusion of professional prerogatives. Attempts of the discrete professions to plan educational curricula, ascertain goals, and establish or maintain professional autonomy must be done within this framework, since this broader framework is reflective of the shifting demands of a larger social structure.

NEED

Clarification and understanding of this term is probably the most important single step that can be taken to increase understanding of manpower issues and to begin to relate manpower to problem solution.

There is no single definition of "need" in manpower usage, and certainly none that is universally accepted. We can, however, begin to come to some better understanding by differentiating two quite different usages. For our purposes, need is defined as professional, scientific, or expert opinion of what is necessary or required to accomplish desired ends. (It is assumed, although often spuriously, that professional or expert opinion is based upon reasonable knowledge and reflects cause-effect relationships, e.g., vitamin D is *needed* to prevent rickets.) This is in contrast to the more common use of the word need: a desire for something, a want to be satisfied, a statement of social philosophy. Closely related, in fact a derivative, is the concept of "needy" as used to refer to the poor, underprivileged, indigent ill, etc.

There is no question that considerable portions of the literature, both popular and professional, dealing with needs in mental health and community mental health are reflections of broad social philosophy and egalitarian concerns, reflective of the current society and culture. As Seely wrote in 1953, the mental health movement "is itself an expression of, and a result of, a revolution in social values" (p. 15), which has now extended into the whole of contemporary society.

There has been to date, however, no serious attempt to separate "objectives explicitly related to mental health and objectives that affect mental health" (Lasswell, 1969, p. 54). The term mental health itself (as is community mental health or community psychology) is more likely an object of sentiment, not of definition. The separation must be made, however, since precision in defining "need" follows directly from this dichotomization, and will permit explicit focus on delineated targets, in contrast to the totality of welfare philosophy and its societal implementation.

It is now a characteristic of the field that *all* activities carried on by psychologists in mental health or community mental health—testing, research, administration, supervision, training, therapy (no matter how defined), community consultation, etc.—are to a greater or lesser degree also performed by others (Arnhoff, 1968). Thus, it is impossible to translate function directly to specific, single personnel types. At this stage of the development of the field, however, it *would* be possible to state services to be delivered and to specify manpower equivalencies necessary: so many of A, *or* B, *or* C, etc., recognizing the interprofessional transferability in functions. This type of approach occurs increasingly in the actual mental health marketplace, and has been incorporated into legislation in the recent Massachusetts Mental Health Act (i.e., position eligibility requirements specified for either a psychiatrist, psychologist, social worker, or nurse). The approach of substitution among health professionals has long been used by economists: "substitution is warranted when it reduces the cost of a given output (the given includes quality)" (Klarman, 1968, p. 2).

A contrasting approach to defining need has been that of professional standards, best exemplified by the Lee-Jones (1933) procedure in medicine: "The steps comprising this procedure are: (1) determining the frequency of occurrence of illnesses in a population (incidence or prevalence is not specified); (2) gathering a consensus among experts regarding the number of services required to treat and diagnose a given illness; (3) estimating the number of services rendered per hour by a provider; (4) securing agreement on the average number of hours that a provider spends per year in caring for patients" (Klarman, 1968, p. 3). Even for physical health the method is extremely controversial. Furthermore, the assumptions made by professionals may not be justified or empirically valid, and they will serve to perpetuate existing professional prerogatives and obsolete concepts and practices. As David (1966, p. 4) has recently observed, "job classification, recruitment practices, and work assignments tend to be perpetuated, frequently beyond the point of relevance."

Regardless of the specific approach to defining need, a statement of need by any occupational group will bear the stamp of the initial conceptualization of the outcomes desired, the methods chosen for implementation, and the services, role functions, and skills provided by the group. (Whether or not society will pay to implement their definition of need will be discussed later, since it is of crucial importance.)

However, until very recently, conceptions of manpower needs in mental health were heavily weighted by individual treatment considerations. The realization has been growing that one-to-one treatment approaches have very limited utility in dealing with the major portion of mental health problems. Community psychology is a response to this in its attempt to establish a broader, ecological approach to prevention rather than treatment.

At the 1961 annual meeting of the National Association for Mental Health, Dr. Rene Dubos discussed the final report of the Joint Commission on Mental Illness and Health. As he has done elsewhere (Dubos, 1959), he remarked that the major advances in control of communicable disease have come from changes in hygiene and sanitation; environmental manipulation rather than medical treatment. Moreover, as Dubos pointed out, no major health problem has ever been brought under control or eliminated by treatment of those already afflicted.

The same sort of analogy is being enunciated today for mental health since the conceptual model seems even more relevant. Despite the problems and limitations of so-called "medical" or organic models of behavior, the basic modern model is essentially a preventive public health approach. Such an approach focuses on the community and population rather than on individuals, and attempts to reduce the target condition by modifying factors believed to be affecting large segments of the community or population. This approach is based upon the conviction, borne out by experience, that early diagnosis and treatment have very limited utility. What is needed is a total systems approach in which the course of events is modified to prevent undesirable results from occurring.

While psychology, and the other disciplines as well, are now coming to accept this broader approach to human behavior, they have not yet reached a clear articulation between such an ecologic-public health approach and their own potential (and limited) roles in such a plan.

It is here that the previous distinction between objectives that affect mental health and objectives explicitly related to mental health become critical for the mental health disciplines, so as to narrow the stage upon which to consider and weigh the caveats of substitution of skills, interprofessional transferability of functions, marketplace economics, etc. Need for psychologists, for example, can then begin to emerge with precision from the continuing confusion which has assumed isomorphism between broadly perceived societal need for psychological services and the specific need for psychologists (Arnhoff, 1968).

DEMAND

Throughout the literature of mental health there exists a confused interchangeability in the terms "need" and "demand." As has been indicated, "need," for the most part, tends to reflect statements of social philosophy which are too imprecise for translation into direct service and/or manpower requirements. Furthermore, "economists and manpower specialists agree that manpower forecasts based even on a finite need for future health services are unrealistic. Instead, they suggest approaching manpower forecasting in terms of *demand* for health services in the classic economic sense of supply and demand. For the most part, demand is the economic expression of need. . . ." (Kissick, 1967, p. 48). The importance of the economic base cannot be overlooked since ultimately what can or will be paid for is a fundamental factor. "It is contrary to rational thinking to assume or to expect that manpower deficits can be eliminated before financial problems are solved" (Brown, 1967, p. 81).

Since the end of World War II and subsequent national efforts devoted to improving mental health, appropriations and expenditures in this area have tended to show a positively accelerating growth curve. It has usually been assumed that this condition will continue to prevail indefinitely, and that about 15 percent minimal increase in funding per year will be provided to maintain this rate. While one may question the wisdom of such assumptions in the past, it is now readily apparent that economic reassessments are in order, are being made, and will alter the previous rates of growth. Consequently, mental health planners are being forced to reconsider the economics of mental health and mental health manpower and to worry about getting more mileage for the dollar. In short, the concept of demand as "need" backed up with dollars to pay becomes a primary reality in manpower planning.

Demand can be, and often is, measured in terms of use, e.g., use of professional services or types of facilities. This approach, however, while useful for some purposes, ignores the question of who pays for what; is subject to Parkinsonian inflation—the more clinics and hospitals, the more patients; and assumes and/or implies that current use is most efficient, parsimonious, economical, or scientifically and professionally justifiable. Furthermore, it tends to exacerbate a fundamental ambiguity that often exists between demand as what a person says he wants, and for which means can be found for payment on the one hand, and professional or egalitarian definitions of need which are totally unanchored to effective delivery or to hopes of accomplishment on the other.[3]

A moment's pause for recapitulation and amplification of some previous points can help to shape the relevance of these disparate considerations for psychology in the human services arena. Along with the continuing and expanding training of new and different types of mental health workers, which involves transfer and substitution of skills from one group to another, the economic trends, concerns, and definitions all unfold against an increasing awareness of and impatience with the entire system of welfare, the gross and pernicious deficiencies in the health and welfare delivery system, and the exclusion of large segments of the population from the reward and services system which has now become a stated right of all citizens (Yolles, 1968). In all the traditional fields and professions, the result of these developments has been reassessment of roles and functions, explorations of lesser-trained personnel within a given professional career-ladder pattern, and an agonizing groping to abstract a basic or "core" professional role which is essentially unique for each group. The current outlines of the social order are rapidly changing, and psychology along with the totality of what has been described as the "mental health consortium" (Freeman & Gertner, 1968), is caught up in the flux. The mandate seems clear: more and more effective delivery of services to the public must occur, and this must be accomplished in shorter periods of time than it takes to train M.D.'s, Ph.D's, and M.S.W.'s, and at lower cost. The services to be delivered, with which community psychology is concerned, can be broadly termed "psychological services" but it is clear that this is not restricted merely to psychology or psychologists.

Within this broader frame of reference, a more critical analysis of the demand dimension may help to reassess and separate out demand for psychologists from the broader demand for psychological services.

Take, for example, analyses of job offerings for psychologists. An offered wage which is significantly lower than the going rate may not really represent a true demand for a Ph.D. psychologist at all, even if Ph.D. is specified. Since the low remuneration drastically reduces the probabilities that it will be filled by a Ph.D., except under unusual and probably highly individualistic circumstances, it should be viewed as a demand for psychological services but not a true demand for Ph.D. level manpower.

In general, however, there has been a tendency to look at all positions, regardless of economic level, as an indication of a demand for a psychologist at the Ph.D. level, even though the public determines what it will pay and what it requires for certain services. Witness the history of the public school teacher and, even more telling, that of the nurse. Although the need for nurses is and has been tremendous, the almost asymptotic salary picture defies traditional supply-demand economics.

Furthermore, examination of the specific position, e.g., task requirements, type of responsibilities, services to be performed, etc., quite often indicates a broader spectrum of potential personnel. While these may be at a comparable professional level to a Ph.D. psychologist, increasingly it is seen that the services desired can be performed by paraprofessional or subprofessional personnel. Clearly then, what emerges is a demand for specified psychological services, not necessarily a specified professional type; this is by virtue of both salary offered and tasks to be performed.

This of course means that in order for one to meaningfully assess the demand for psychologists (or any other category of personnel), job offerings must be analyzed according to type of position, level of training required, and the amount of money offered. At the present time we do not possess the systematic data to permit analyses which would lead to assessment of demand in a more meaningful fashion, nor can we yet determine the level of training required to perform the tasks or services for which a demand exists.

CONCLUSIONS

This chapter has attempted to highlight some of the conceptual issues involved in answering manpower questions, issues which must be examined in order for meaningful manpower

policy for mental health and community psychology to be formulated, and from which manpower strategies may then be developed.[4] Each topic mentioned has only been lightly touched upon rather than extensively analyzed in depth. Yet, it can readily be seen by anyone familiar with the last two decades of mental health literature, especially that of professional psychology from the Boulder Conference (Raimy, 1950) to the present, that no new issues have been uncovered or proposed. Rather, discussions which kept painful decisions or realities merely simmering have now come to critical mass.

The mental health fields and professional psychology as we know them today came about as the result of social need and social pressure post-World War II. They have continued to respond to social need and social pressure, particularly within the past few years, and the existence of community psychology bears testimony to this reactivity and responsibility. But this has all been accomplished with considerable role diffusion and confusion, plus increasing overlap with other fields and conceptual areas. Many of these other fields, however, tend to be social service occupations (broadly defined), rather than scientific ones. The interest and ability patterns of those in social service occupations tend to be quite different from those in scientific occupations (Super, 1967), which raises basic questions for the selection and education of prospective manpower. In addition, the more fundamental questions of the boundaries of professional function and responsibilities, the role of science versus social value systems, and societal responsibilities become of paramount importance.

Basically, however, the essential goal which orients manpower planning for mental health is the delivery of services to the population. Public policy is directed toward this end, not toward the role or development of discrete professions per se. Consequently, it is absolutely essential that each of the professions recognizes that education and training and role functions take cognizance of others engaged in similar pursuits. During periods of economic expansion and development of new areas, with their attendant manpower shortages, such concerns may get short shrift, and have, in mental health.

Times, however, have changed, not only on the economic scene where a leveling off and even a retrenchment is now occurring, but on the part of the public, which is now demanding more adequate delivery of services. The economic scene now demands more mileage for the dollar and a search for cheaper sources of service delivery. Furthermore, public demand, in the face of chronic and insoluable shortages of the traditional mental health professionals, leads to the search for lesser trained (and hence, cheaper) personnel to fill the void.

All the existing mental health disciplines now accept (albeit, grudgingly) the necessity of lesser trained people to perform tasks previously done by the professionals. And it is here that the existing overlap in functions, the existing differences in length of training, cost of training, and differences and discrepancies between existing professional salaries all come to focus on the new mental health workers. Since representatives of the various mental health disciplines have publicly and constantly endorsed meeting society's mental health service needs with people trained at the B.A. and M.A. level, what will be the effect on the existing professions?

The professions seem finally to have abandoned the attitude that the public was better off with nothing if it couldn't obtain M.D.'s or Ph.D.'s to minister to its needs. This step has not as yet brought forth a concerted reevaluation of existing training, manpower, professional overlap, and effects on service delivery. While these issues are causing profound concern and will undoubtedly have profound effect on psychiatry, social work, and nursing, the potential effects on psychology vis-à-vis its role in delivery of mental health services appears even greater than for the others. Despite more than two decades of clinical psychology, it was only in 1969 that psychology officially declared itself a health service profession (Schofield 1969). How this will be implemented, accepted, and competitively compensated in the economic market place remains to be seen. For now, it can only be hoped that community psychology develops and formulates its manpower policies and training requirements within the broadest context of health services delivery systems, manpower supply, and economic reality.

Notes

Final analyses and writing for this chapter were completed in June 1970.

1. For a more extended yet concise analysis of the current scene, see, for example, Freeman and Gertner (1968).

2. For more extended discussion see, for example, Arnhoff, Rubinstein, and Speisman (1969).

3. For further, extended discussions of the issues only alluded to here see, for example, Heistand (1966), Feldstein (1966), and Boulding (1966).

4. On the issue of manpower strategies, Torgerson (1968) has recently given an excellent exposition of the relevant issues for the social work profession. The similarities to psychology are considerable, and their relevance to all of mental health is vast.

References

Albee, G. W. The relation of conceptual models to manpower needs. In E. L. Cowen, E. A. Gardner, & M. Zax (eds.), *Emergent approaches to mental health problems.* New York: Appleton-Century-Crofts, 1967.

American Institute of Physics. *Physics manpower 1966.* New York: Author, 1966.

Arnhoff, F. N., Rubinstein, E. A., & Speisman, J. C. (eds.) *Manpower for mental health.* Chicago: Aldine, 1969.

Arnhoff, F. N., & Jenkins, J. W. Subdoctoral education in psychology: A study of issues and attitudes. *American Psychologist,* 1969, 24, 430–443.

Arnhoff, F. N. Reassessment of the trilogy: Need, supply and demand. *American Psychologist,* 1968, 23, 312–316.

Boneau, C. A. The educational base: Supply for the demand. *American Psychologist,* 1968, 23, 308–311.

Boulding, K. E. The concept of need for health services. *Milbank Memorial Fund Quarterly,* 1966, 44(4), 202–225.

Brown, M. Health manpower. *Hospitals,* 1967, 41, 81–83, 86, 90.

Clark, K. E. *America's psychologists: A survey of a growing profession.* Washington, D. C.: American Psychological Association, 1957.

David, H. A perspective on manpower theory and conceptualization. In F. N. Arnhoff, E. A. Rubinstein, & J. C. Speisman (eds.), *Manpower for mental health.* Chicago: Aldine, 1969.

David, H. Reflections on manpower utilization. In *Utilization of mental health manpower.* (Mental health manpower current statistical and activities report No. 11) Bethesda, Md.: National Institute of Mental Health, 1966.

Dubos, R. J. *Mirage of health.* New York: Anchor Books, 1959.

Dubos, R. J. An outsider's view of Action for mental health. Paper presented at the annual meeting of the National Association for Mental Health, 1961. (Mimeo)

Feldstein, P. J. Research on the demand for health services. *Milbank Memorial Fund Quarterly,* 1966, 44(3), 128–165.

Freeman, H. E., & Gertner, R. S. The changing posture of the mental health consortium. Paper presented at the 45th annual meeting of the American Orthopsychiatric Association, Chicago, March 21, 1968.

Ginzberg, E. *Manpower agenda for America.* New York: McGraw-Hill, 1968.

Harmon, L. R. Conceptual considerations in manpower research and data collection. In *Mental health manpower current statistical and activities report No. 5.* Bethesda, Md.: National Institute of Mental Health, 1965.

Hiestand, D. L. Research into manpower for health service. *Milbank Memorial Fund Quarterly*, 1966, 44(4), 146–181.

Kissick, W. L. Forecasting health manpower needs. *Hospitals*, 1967, 41, 47–51.

Klareman, H. E. Economic aspects of projecting requirements for health manpower. Paper prepared for symposium on Methods of Estimating Medical and Paramedical Personnel Requirements, World Health Organization, Regional Office for Europe, Budapest, October 15–19, 1968. (Mimeo)

Lasswell, H. D. The politics of mental health objectives and manpower assets. In F. N. Arnhoff, E. A. Rubinstein, & J. C. Speisman (eds.), *Manpower for mental health.* Chicago: Aldine, 1969.

Lee, R. I., & Jones, L. W. *The fundamentals of good medical care.* Chicago: University of Chicago Press, 1933.

National Academy of Sciences. *Doctorate Recipients from United States Universities 1958–66.* Washington, D. C.: Author, 1967.

National Institute of Mental Health, Division of Manpower and Training Programs. Selected characteristics of psychologists employed in mental health establishments, 1963. In *Mental health manpower current statistical and activities report No. 4.* Chevy Chase, Md.: National Institute of Mental Health, 1965.

National Science Foundation. *American science manpower 1968.* Washington, D. C.: United States Government Printing Office, 1968.

Office of Education, United States Department of Health, Education, and Welfare. *Projections of educational statistics to 1975–76.* Washington, D. C.: United States Government Printing Office, 1966.

Office of Education, United States Department of Health, Education, and Welfare. *Earned degrees conferred 1964–65.* Washington, D. C.: United States Government Printing Office, 1966.

Raimy, V. C. (ed.) *Training in clinical psychology.* Englewood Cliffs, N. J.: Prentice-Hall, 1950.

Roe, A. Individual motivation and personal factors in career choice. In F. N. Arnhoff, E. A. Rubinstein, & J. C. Speisman (eds.), *Manpower for mental health.* Chicago: Aldine, 1969.

Rossi, P. H. Career patterns: Trends and prospects. In F. N. Arnhoff, E. A. Rubinstein, & J. C. Speisman (eds.), *Manpower for mental health.* Chicago: Aldine, 1969.

Schofield, W. The role of psychology in the delivery of health services. *American Psychologist*, 1969, 24, 565–584.

Scientific Manpower Commission. *Manpower Comments*, 1966, 3(9), 13.

Seeley, J. R. Social values, the mental health movement and mental health. *Annals of the American Academy of Political and Social Sciences*, 1953, 286, 15–24.

Super, D. E. Career development theory and the manpower shortage. In *Mental health manpower.* Vol. 2. *Recruitment, training and utilization.* Sacramento, Calif.: California Department of Mental Hygiene, 1967.

Symposium on manpower theory. Proceedings. *Journal of Human Resources*, 1967, 2, 140–253.

Torgerson, F. G. Toward a manpower strategy. In *Manpower: A community responsibility.* New York: National Commission for Social Work Careers, 1968.

Wellner, A. M. Survey of psychology services in state mental hospitals. *American Psychologist*, 1968, 23, 377–380.

Yolles, S. F. Social policy and the mentally ill. Paper presented at the American Psychiatric Association Mental Hospital Institute, Washington, D. C., October 2, 1968.

37

Nursing Education and Community Mental Health

Hildegard E. Peplau

There are more than 600,000 registered nurses now practicing in the United States—each with a large stake in the promotion of mental health in the community. The nursing profession has moved vigorously, particularly during the last two decades, to improve graduate, undergraduate, and continuing education programs and to include in them theory and techniques essential for professional work with people who have sociopsychiatric problems. While there are no standardized curricula which ensure or guarantee expertise for mental health work, for all of these nurses there are major trends which auger well in this direction. This chapter will discuss these recent developments and show the relation to community mental health.[1]

When the Mental Health Act was passed in 1946 there were very few nurse leaders who were psychiatric nurses. While these few spokesmen kept alive the general idea that there should be more and better preparation of nurses for psychiatric work, both in hospitals and within the community, there was indeed a paucity of knowledge and know-how. The deficit was most glaringly seen in basic nursing curricula. To be sure, this dearth of knowledge was common to all of the professions, not just in nursing. But those disciplines which had an academic base for the preparation of professional practitioners were educating more leaders, producing a literature, and reporting results of research. The situation in nursing was quite different and the primary, critical need was the education of psychiatric nurses at the graduate level. These nurses would

become the leaders who instituted the necessary changes in nursing education and nursing services in psychiatric facilities.

The graduate programs in psychiatric nursing which began in 1943 and, aided by Mental Health Act support, expanded to 33 programs by 1968, were established to prepare leaders—psychiatric nurse educators, administrators, researchers, and clinical specialists. In the first decade, however, these programs were faced with the enormous problem of recruitment of students. The pool of professional nurses who held baccalaureate degrees was indeed small. In 1946 only 5.6 percent of all nursing students were *enrolled* in collegiate programs—the majority obtained diplomas from hospital controlled schools of nursing without academic affiliation (American Nurses Association, 1955–56, p. 75). By 1955 the trend toward collegiate education for nurses showed 15.2 percent enrolled and by 1965 collegiate schools had 22.4 percent of the total enrollment of nursing students (ANA, 1966, p. 81). The establishment of graduate programs under these conditions was an act of faith. Nevertheless, through such programs the long, hard task of preparing psychiatric nurse leaders was begun.

Psychiatric nurses who graduated from master's degree programs in the period 1946–56 were, in effect, pioneers in bringing about drastic revisions in what was being taught to basic nursing students. For it was these students who would be the staff nurses who would carry forward the profession's commitment in the mental health movement. Perhaps the most significant new experience that was introduced into undergraduate curricula was the "nurse-patient relationship study." This learning experience consists in the student talking directly with one psychiatric patient, in a scheduled interview situation, for a period of time—sometimes as much as 45 hours distributed over 15-20 weeks of one hour sessions. The student is expected to obtain interaction data including the verbal transactions that occur, the nurse student's perceptions and reactions to the patient, and other observable phenomena.[2] These data are then reviewed in detail with a psychiatric nurse faculty member, who is herself an expert clinician. Two competencies essential for mental health work derive from this experience: 1) awareness of the behavior of the student nurse as stimuli to or input for the patient; and 2) consciousness in the student of her ability to recall and apply known explanatory theoretical concepts which guide her interventions during the interaction with the patient.

This learning experience opened up two hopeful avenues of control of and assistance to patients. Many nursing textbooks published earlier tended to suggest that somehow the nurse *should* be able to prevent disturbances in patients, that subtle approaches were useful in this regard, but rarely were the directions explicit. The nurse-patient interaction study, however, generated awareness that the reactions of patients were not infrequently stimulated by unwitting behavior of nursing personnel. Control of the stimuli rather than of the responses became self-evident. Moreover, as the relationship between nurse and patient continued over time and was studied in detail, student nurses especially began rather quickly to recognize their own responsibility in facilitating favorable changes in patients. Their predecessors who had not had such supervisory review of inquiry into interactive data felt more helpless in the face of prescribed "shoulds" which were ineffective as guidelines for work with patients. Study of the relation between staff behavior and patient behavior—evoking reactions, contributing to disorientation, perpetuating patterns of difficulty—became a vital aspect of the undergraduate course in nursing of psychiatric patients. One consequence of this focus was that many collegiate students became intrigued with the possibilities of graduate study of psychiatric nursing as depth investigation along similar lines.

There were other forms of impact upon basic nursing programs which resulted from the work of the "first wave" of psychiatric nurse-graduates of master's degree programs. These educators recognized that much of what was taught in the basic clinical nursing course, now entitled "nursing in psychiatric services," ought to be presented earlier in the curriculum. Concepts of growth and personality development, for example, ought to be taught in relation to all clinical courses. As a result, many schools began to develop such courses. In some instances social scientists were employed to teach them. In some schools an experience with healthy children in nursery schools was provided *before* the experience with psychiatric patients. There were two major consequences of this trend. By 1952, the Mental Health Act began to provide "integration grants" which provided schools of nursing with at least one additional faculty member who could work out the details of other sociopsychiatric content to be included in the curriculum prior to the psychiatric experience. Consequently, the time available for study in the psychiatric course could be revamped to include other equally important new developments which were being discussed in graduate programs.

The integration projects had and continue to have a large and constructive influence upon the nursing faculty as a whole and upon all clinical areas other than the psychiatric—maternal-child nursing, public health nursing, and medical-surgical nursing courses. Schmahl has provided an insightful report of one such project as well as a very useful summary of eight integration project reports (Schmahl, 1966, p. 460). By 1966 there were 123 collegiate schools, of a total of 185, at work exploring the inclusion of sociopsychiatric content in the total basic curriculum. Psychiatric nurse faculty members in these projects have worked on committees and with individual faculty members to examine not only clinical courses, but basic sciences, humanities, and other academic subjects in the basic program which contribute to an understanding of behavior related to mental health. No claim is made here that psychiatric nurses *alone* have instituted desirable changes in that direction; they have been a substantial force in this regard. The opportunity for such explorations, moreover, was fortuitious, for the profession of nursing was soon to take a stand on professional nursing education.

In 1965 the American Nurses Association published its "position paper" in which several important principles were enunciated (ANA, 1965, p. 16): "Education for those who work in nursing should take place in institutions of learning within the general system of education." "Minimum preparation for beginning professional nursing practice at the present time should be baccalaureate degree education in nursing." "Minimum preparation for beginning technical nursing practice at the present time should be associate degree education in nursing." This report of the Committee on Education of ANA presents a rationale for the preparation of professional and technical nurses within academic institutions.

Major new emphases which had been evolving in professional nursing practices and which required collegiate education are not unrelated to developments in psychiatric nursing. Six of these that are most important include: 1) teaching of patients or their families using experiential teaching or methods of formal instruction; 2) counseling and guidance of individual patients or groups concerning· sociopsychiatric difficulties (ANA, 1967); 3) interviewing patients to obtain information so as to formulate nursing problems and subsequently to make and revise nursing care plans for each patient; 4) supervision and management of nonprofessional nursing personnel in implementing nursing care plans; 5) interdisciplinary communication so that the nursing care plan is effectively interdigitated with the total patient care plan; and 6) referral of patients to other sources of care, including public health nursing agencies, so that continuity of current and follow-up care obtains. These six functions are far more abstract, ambiguous, and complex than the more concrete, simple tasks—such as bathing, feeding, giving medications—generally associated with professional nursing (Peplau, 1957). Each of these professional functions requires considerable sophistication in the use of sociopsychiatric theory and technique—which the basic nursing student learns in the undergraduate courses which have "integrated" such content or which teach it directly, as in the clinical course—nursing in psychiatric services. Moreover, the entire nursing program provides exposure to the problems of people sick and well, in different environments

such as homes and hospitals, from different socioeconomic classes, of various ages and capacities for learning, and so on. In other words, the preparation of the professional nurse for work in psychiatric and community mental health facilities occurs in the total basic program of nursing education (National League for Nursing, 1958).

The undergraduate course in nursing in psychiatric services includes and has extended the dimensions of content advised in the first report of the WHO Expert Committee on Psychiatric Nursing (World Health Organization, 1956). These include theories which explain intrapersonal, interpersonal, sociological, and community aspects of mental health and illness. These theories are drawn from all of the basic and applied sciences as applicable. Additionally, there are some beginning reports of the results of nursing research which are utilized (Simmons & Henderson, 1964, p. 461).

Professional nursing curricula tend to parallel "clinical learning experiences" with theory courses, thus providing the student with the opportunity to test published theories against direct observations with patients whose behavior is presumably explained by existing theories. At the present time, these clinical educative events provided in a psychiatric setting generally include: 1) a nurse-patient interaction study as previously described; 2) a case study through which the student learns how to obtain and use information and available reports in making a nursing care plan; 3) a sociological study of the patient-staff or patient-visitor interaction with some discussion of the role of professional nurse as "change agent," or of the nurse interventions that might be utilized to disrupt pattern integrations which are problematic and involve two or more patients; 4) participant experiences in ward government, and other "milieu" type activities of patients which are considered beneficial; 5) observation and conferencing of nursing assistants who work under professional nurse guidance; 6) some programs include participation as observer, recorder, or cotherapist in group therapy for patients; 7) follow-up visits to families of at least one discharged patient for several sessions; 8) participation in nursing team and in interdisciplinary team conferences about patients when these are available; and 9) field trips to acquaint the student with a wide variety of mental health resources and their purposes. These theory and clinical courses build upon the base of all preceding liberal arts, science, and nursing courses and are designed to extend rather than merely to repeat or even to "adapt" to psychiatric patients what the student has previously learned. Upon graduation the student will work as a staff nurse in a health facility—a clinic, general hospital, community mental health center, industrial health service, and the like.

The most recent, definitive statement of the workrole of staff nurse appears in the ANA (1967, p. 41) "Statement on Psychiatric Nursing."[3] This statement was formulated from a review of nursing literature on trends and developments already underway in nursing services in psychiatric facilities. It describes the dimensions of function of staff nurse in psychiatric facilities as clinical nursing care, provision of therapeutic milieu, counseling, serving as "symbolic parent," health teaching, social agent, clinical assistance to personnel, technical aspects, and joint planning. It should serve as a guideline in bringing all basic nursing education programs and nursing services substantially nearer to the use of modern practices generally accepted within the profession. The document does not include some still quite unique practices which are beginning to develop. One of these has to do with the use of conditioning techniques by which constructive behavior of patients is observed and then rewarded, or is introduced and rewarded. Nurses are developing such practices particularly now with chronically ill psychiatric patients and mental retardates (Venang, Leanard, & Pierson, 1967).

The ANA "Statement on Psychiatric Nursing" also clarifies the difference between a registered nurse who holds a baccalaureate degree or hospital diploma, and practices general nursing in a psychiatric facility as a *staff nurse*, and one who holds a graduate degree and, having completed work in advanced psychiatric nursing, is called a *psychiatric nurse*. The level of education determines the level of practice. Experience, of course, refines competencies. However, many nurse educators now believe that "learning by doing" is outmoded; learning requires analysis of what has been done in light of the best available theoretical framework, and evaluation of the long-range consequences of nurse actions. The development of graduate programs—at the master's and doctoral

levels—has made possible the use of the designation "psychiatric nurse" as a specialty title that rests upon completion of a graduate degree with emphasis upon theories and practices of psychiatric nursing.

Psychiatric nursing is a specialty within professional nursing and an important component of total patient care in psychiatric services of all types. Psychiatric nursing practices include four major areas at this time: 1) direct psychotherapeutic work with individual patients on a brief or intensive basis; 2) group psychotherapy with patients and families (Armstrong & Rouslin, 1963); 3) social engineering of constructive interactions among patients, visitors, staff, and students in the milieu of home, ward, or unit (Hays & Larson, 1963); and 4) coordination of professional services to patients in a unit, including management of nursing service personnel. Subspecialties are also developing such as psychiatric nursing of adult patients, of children, of mental retardates, and in community mental health. The ANA statement also describes these specialty functions in detail. These complex areas of practice require the psychiatric nurse specialist to have quite lengthy graduate education including supervised clinical work along the dimensions indicated above. Most programs are currently two academic years in length or longer, for the master's degree; several programs now extend to the doctoral level (Berthold, Tschudin, Peplau, Schlotfeldt, & Rogers, 1966).

Graduate education of psychiatric nurses rests upon a philosophy or set of assumptions which speak to the nature of the phenomena for which the nursing practices are intended, and which suggest the direction of the education. One such philosophical overview is presented here (see also ANA, 1967, pp. 4–8).

The clinical interventions of psychiatric nurses are intended to have corrective impact upon the presenting variant of the pathology of a particular patient. Consequently, psychiatric nurses are educated to become sensitive observers. The nurse must hear what a patient is saying and notice accompanying bodily gestures of the patient with whom she is having direct contact. Observed behavior, however, must be interpreted. The psychiatric nurse makes such interpretations during the work with the patient by decoding, by applying known explanatory theories, and/or by drawing inferences concerning presenting phenomena. For example, the concept of anxiety when known by the nurse can be utilized during an interaction with a patient both to interpret what the nurse notices (if it fits this concept definition) and to determine the responses of the nurse to the patient in light of this theory (Peplau, 1962). The presenting need, theme, pattern, or intention of the patient's behavior when inferred from observational data also becomes a basis for the response of the psychiatric nurse. The nurse reponse, therefore, is based upon theory and is a more or less consciously selected one which, if used persistently, in relation to other variants of the same pathology, will tend to have corrective impact upon the various pathologies of the patient. The long-range consequences of nursing interventions upon the further development of mental health in the patient is a prime consideration.

Three major response options are open to psychiatric nurses. The behavior of the patient can be reinforced; this option is useful when the patient's behavior is constructive; it aids and abets development of chronicity when pathology is reinforced. The psychiatric nurse can shed doubt upon a variant of pathological behavior. The third option is for the nurse to stimulate "new" nonpathological behavior.

Pathological behavior can be viewed intrapersonally in terms of four major categories: 1) disorders of the process of thought manifested in the language behavior of the patient; 2) dissociation of feeling or impoverishment due to sensory deprivation; 3) actions that are detrimental to the social order, prevent social relationship, or are self-destructive; and 4) splitting of thought, feelings, and actions, or of dissonant self-views that are incongruent with capacity or achievement.

Each of the foregoing categories suggests major modes of psychiatric nurse interventions. When the nurse takes action, responds to a variant of intrapersonal pathology presented by a patient, the situation becomes an interpersonal one. That is, there arises one of the following interpersonal linkages: The nurse can *complement* the presenting pattern of the patient—the pattern of the nurse "fitting in" as hand to glove. Submission—domination; helplessness—helpfulness, would be two instances. Or, the nurse can participate in a *mutuality* of pattern or need integration. For example, when a patient expresses an acquired need or bids for disrespect or derogation and the nurse gives it. The nurse intervention, however, could be *antagonistic* to the pattern of the patient. For instance, when a patient seeks disapproval but instead the nurse responds with indifference, or approval, or investigation, these interventions are antithetical to the patient's immediate, acquired need for disapproval.

Interpersonal interactions of patient and nurse are intended to have a corrective impact upon the patient's problematic behavior in which a pattern is used recurringly but with variation in the presenting item. This task requires the psychiatric nurse to have a viable theoretical framework available for recall and application during such interactions so that relevant interpretations are made and used to guide nurse responses. Corrective impact derives from a judgment as to when to complement, make mutual, or act antagonistically in relation to a problematic pattern of behavior. Expressions by a patient of submissiveness, helplessness, or acquired needs for disrespect, disapproval, or derogation, when confirmed or ignored by the nurse do not promote constructive changes, although they do reduce anxiety of patients. Moreover, in most cases, merely using the opposites—giving help or approval—tends to increase anxiety and often patients then redouble efforts to obtain confirmation of helplessness or self-derogation. Consequently, an approach called *investigative neutrality* has the advantage of opening a seemingly closed intrapersonally based interpersonal orientation to the patient to new possibilities and at the same time bypassing the need-defense system of a patient.

In disorders of the thought process, the language behavior of the psychiatric nurse is of paramount importance because the nurse statements can, when used recurringly, stabilize or promote favorable change in the difficulties of the patient. When the language of the patient with monotonous regularity includes such statements as "I'm no good"; "I don't know"; "I can't remember"; and "I can't think," the pattern of the patient's thoughts about himself is primarily derogatory. If the nurse says "OK," or "You never know anything I ask you," or merely reflects back "You are no good," or says "Maybe you'll think of it later," the nurse, in effect, is confirming or reinforcing the derogatory self-thought of the patient. On the other hand, if the psychiatric nurse suggests "You will recall," or says, "Is that possible," or if she inquires "What prevents you from remembering?" or some variant of bypassing the self-derogation is used, a corrective effort has been made. Disruption of established but useless self-views of the patient has been started, and a stimulus toward effort at recall has been provided.

If one nurse persists in using such an investigative approach, in time, many patients with whom she has direct contact do recall or do begin to inquire of themselves about barriers to recall. This is not to say that the nurse should repeat stereotyped phrases such as "Is that possible," with deadly monotony. Instead, rich variety in use of synonyms and similar phrases all of which convey the same meaning albeit in different words should be used. The message is held as a constant stimuli or input to the patient; the media change to include different words, gestures, or persons on the nursing staff.

Before continuing a discussion of other modes of intervention which psychiatric nurses are educated to use, a brief explanation about *why* investigative neutrality as suggested above works, might be clarifying. Why does it coerce favorable change in patients, as judged by empirical testing? Perhaps the simplest explanation is found in Sullivan's concept of self-system as "reflected appraisal" (Peary & Gawel, 1953).

This concept suggests a series of steps by which self-system evolves and then is manifested. In most elementary form these steps are 1) appraisals of an infant (child) are made by parents (significant others); 2) these appraisals are at first merely heard by the child. They may at first be repeated verbatim, (a) "Johnny is a bad boy;" then (b) "me a bad boy," and finally (c) "I am a bad boy." 3) the appraisals are incorporated (as shown in (c)), and become accepted self-appraisals; 4) actions to go with the incorporated self-views are evolved as a result of the child observing what parents convey with these verbalized appraisals of the child; 5) situations are set up to confirm and maintain the already incorporated appraisals in subsequent experiences with family, school teachers and pupils, neighbors, and others who may or may not reinforce the already established views which, in time (by age 12), become more organized and less open to revision.

It is these same steps—1) input, 2) processing via hearing, incorporating, acting upon, 3) maintaining via confirming or excluding—which have much to do with any subsequent revision of self-system and therefore of behavior, if not with all learning. Promoting such revision in a favorable direction is a major psychotherapeutic task of psychiatric nurses. So the nurse must be able to observe a patient, from these data derive the operating self-views of that patient, and then respond with an input which will neither confirm nor collide with the operating self-system of the patient but rather open it up for the evolution of new self-views. Such input seems to be more useful when it consists *not* of new pictures painted of the patient and presented to him, but is instead *a persistent stimulus to new work* vis-à-vis the latent capacities of the patient: to take a fresh look at himself and his experiences. The input in this sense is not a *content* (new view) input but an *instrumental* one which, when heard, incorporated, and acted upon by the patient will force him in the direction of a new view of self.

Instrumental inputs are primarily investigative. They force inquiry about a) the structure of an event—"*who* was with you," "*when* did this happen," "*where* did you go,"—and b) upon the content which can be repeated, named or described—"*what* did you say," "what was your feeling," "what was Joe's response to you." Such inputs do not provide an answer to a question, nor an interpretation of an event, nor paint a picture of the patient as actor during an experience, but provide input instruments which—when heard, incorporated, and acted upon by the patient—will force new views upon his focus of attention.

Meanwhile, the nurse must also be attentive to, interpret (to herself), and respond in light of, barriers in the patient which prevent hearing and incorporating the instrumental input. Foremost among these is anxiety which the patient can be helped to name. It appears with considerable regularity that when a nurse asks a patient "are you anxious? (nervous, upset, troubled, uncomfortable, tense, etc.)" the response pattern moves from a) avoidance of the question (changes the subject), b) denial ("no I'm not"), c) doubt ("Maybe I am"), to d) recognition ("yes"). When a "yes" answer is forthcoming with some convincing inference by the nurse of the presence of recognition then, and then only, is it worthwhile to pursue antecedents to anxiety (Peplau, 1962). When a patient is able to name the fact that he is at the moment anxious, the anxiety tends to decrease and ability to notice (hear and see) improves.

Psychiatric nurses also convey "good feelings" such as interest, concern, and tenderness primarily through attitudes, gestures, eye-to-eye contact, and other actions rather than in words. The patient who has dissociated all feelings, or primarily constructive feelings as is more often the case, such as joy and interest, is not likely to hear, retain, or respond to verbalized "good feelings" of the nurse. In fact, a patient who is feeling enraged may experience panic if feelings of tenderness are at that moment verbalized directly by the psychiatric nurse. Collisions between the content of the patient's self-system and immediate perception, and the nurse's need to verbalize feelings of warmth, serve no useful purpose for the patient. When patients, however, have impoverishment of feelings the provision of sensory experience through sight, sound, and color becomes essential.

The modes of intervention that psychiatric nurses use in coping with antisocial actions depend upon the particular stage of acting out in which a patient is at a particular moment. Anticipatory interventions ward off violent outbursts or destructive actions toward self, others, or property. Such interventions require the psychiatric nurse to be sensitively alert to cues to mounting tension so that relief of that tension through verbal means can be instituted early, before the internal demand for relief through action goes beyond the tenuous control of the patient.

A "whole" person tends to have thoughts, actions, and feelings, in relation to particular events that go together harmoniously as a set. Splitting refers to disharmony among these parts of a set, as well as to different self-views which are subject to recall and dissociated. Feelings may be incongruent with thoughts and actions; actions may not be in accord with expressed thoughts and feelings. In order to intervene in an effort to restore harmony the psychiatric nurse needs to recognize the discrepancy in presenting behavior and ask about it so as gradually to bring about constructive change.

One result of failure to cope intelligently with any of the foregoing presenting difficulties of patients is panic. Panic represents massive splitting or splintering of all of the previously held views of the patient. Patients describe the experience vividly often saying "I was split into a million pieces—I was disappearing." This obliteration of the prevailing views of self and the world, and of strategies for retaining some semblance of coherence and stability among views, is a terrifying experience in which the patient, literally, is totally out of control. The interventions of the psychiatric nurse are based upon thorough grasp of the patient's immediate experience to the extent that these are explained in known concepts of panic. The nurse provides "thereness," fluids, and awareness and control of her own anxiety often interpersonally and empathically communicated by the patient. Simple commands—two or three words spoken calmly—are used such as "sit down," "drink this," "say what's happening," or "talk to me." It is of the utmost importance that no "input" is added since the patient is attempting to deal, privately, with a flood of terrifying ideas and cannot handle additional ones. Reduction of outside stimuli is useful. The patient should not be touched or restrained if at all feasible because of the highly private connotations that may be assigned to such staff actions by the patient. A nursing study has shown that as the panic subsides the patient will begin to talk to describe the panic—producing events, and to derive meaning of great usefulness in healthier reorganization of personality (Oden, 1962).

The psychiatric nurse serves as a "model" of a healthy person. As such, the nurse represents herself as a person who can meet her own needs—one who does not use patients for this purpose. Further, the psychiatric nurse uses language to communicate directly, simply, and clearly to patients; the verbal messages are not mixed or inconsistent with nurse's actions. The psychiatric nurse demonstrates that she has self-awareness and self-control and that she is capable of one-way focus on the concerns and difficulties of psychiatrically disturbed persons.

Psychiatric nursing consists of a complex set of interpersonal techniques, based upon sociopsychological theories explanatory of human difficulty, that serve to aid troubled individuals to develop and use their latent capacities for life in the community.

The foregoing presentation speaks primarily to psychotherapeutic work with quite disturbed people, some of whom will be seen in community mental health agencies. Such agencies, however, are providing a broad range of services including prevention, early case finding, early intervention in the form of behavioral modification or counseling, emergencies services, and the like. Nurses, including those having graduate preparation in psychiatric nursing, are being recruited for work in mental health clinics, day-care and night-care facilities, and the more comprehensive mental health centers. The issue being debated within the nursing profession is whether psychiatric nurses, in graduate programs, need a special kind of within-community preparation for such work or whether the present plan of clinical study will suffice for the new tasks required in community mental health centers. Currently, there are two new graduate programs designed to test the former assumption. Several conferences have also been addressed to aspects of this issue (see *Nursing*, 1966, p. 244; *Work Conference,* 1964, p. 71).

The use of community facilities other than the general and psychiatric hospitals has been and continues to be an aspect of collegiate undergraduate education in nursing. Such programs require the student to have course work in public health knowledge and clinical experiences conducted in public health agencies under the supervision of faculty members from the school. Collegiate schools are beginning to build into their curricula more content directly related to nursing in health facilities other than general hospitals. Graduates of these schools often seek, indeed tend to prefer, work in school health services, industry, visiting nurse associations, and other community health agencies.

Undergraduate course work in maternal-child health nursing also prepares the professional nurse for mental health work. The application of theories of personality, growth, and development, to work with children who are sick in hospitals as well as to those who are members of a "pregnant family" is a case in point. The student nurse with increasing frequency has clinical experience with selected families which are studied before, during, and after the birth of an additional child in that family. Such studies require theories explanatory of marital dyads, under varying social conditions, as well as a grasp of principles and strategies useful in child-rearing in relatively healthy families.

Well staffed community mental health centers will require professional nurses who qualify for general practice of nursing and those who, by reason of graduate education, qualify as clinical specialists in psychiatric nursing. The undergraduate program emphasizes the development of intellectual competence, a broad base of theories explanatory of health problems, and beginning clinical competence in nursing practices suggested above. In contrast, the graduate program further develops intellectual competencies such as ability to apply concepts, to analyze data, to see relations, and to consider the long-range consequences of nursing interventions. Interest is concentrated on depth understanding of theories relating more specifically to problems of mental health and mental illness. Similarly, clinical competencies that are developed are focused in terms of prevention and treatment of psychiatric disturbances in people.

Community mental health centers that are already established tend to utilize the services of general nurses and psychiatric nurses, educated along lines described above. Graduates of basic nursing programs are employed as staff nurses in such centers, or may similarly be employed in some other agency which serves as a resource having liaison with the community mental health center. These resources include nurses employed in school systems, in public health agencies, in industry, and in clinics of various kinds. Similarly, psychiatric nurses are employed as staff nurses but expected to function at a higher level (Stokes, 1969, p. 152).[4]

The active role of psychiatric nurses in the development and provision of community based mental health services includes orientation to and evaluation of the characteristics of the catchment area served by the center. All agencies, including public health nursing services that are available within the target area, are seen as resources of both information and services that may be needed. In such a survey, the psychiatric nurses would be particularly interested in the mental health services currently being provided by nurses employed in schools, public health, and other community agencies—such as case finding, follow-up care of discharged patients. Many of these nurses already employed in established formal helping systems have considerable, intimate knowledge of the conditions which interfere with mental health in a particular community and often know families and neighborhoods that are most in need of additional help. Such help might be provided by mental health center staff directly, or further education of nurses in these related resources might enable them to enlarge their services to this group of clients. The evaluation thus seeks to establish concerns, problems, resources, and kinds of suitable help whether to clients or to staff of other agencies.

Psychiatric nurses also participate in the provision of a wide range of activities and center services related to the mental health program. One noticeable trend in community mental health centers is the tendency of all professionals—at generic and specialty levels—to extend traditional roles. As a consequence, much commonality or overlap of role is emerging. While nurses, particularly in inpatient services and home visits, may concern themselves with such traditional nursing activities as managing hygiene, diet, or medications, they are also demonstrating considerable ability to perform other kinds of direct and indirect services which tend to be performed by many other mental health center personnel. Thus, it is common for nurses to provide such *direct services* to clients, families, or community areas, as intake, diagnostic study, referral, family visits and sociological study, individual counseling and psychotherapy, group psychotherapy, family therapy, and the traditional nursing activities previously mentioned. They also are demonstrating ability to provide such *indirect services* as consultation, mental health teaching, supervisory review (of generic mental health workers of all types), various forms of community evaluation, planning, and action, and participation in program planning as members of the center interdisciplinary team.

Thus, one nurse might carry a small case load offering individual psychotherapy and family therapy to several clients, conduct a teaching seminar with a group of industrial nurses and another with a group of policemen, work with one community social action group on a particular local problem, and supervise the work of several other workers on the staff through supervisory review conferences. Another nurse might have an entirely different schedule of activities. A third might spend much of her time in the design and conduct of an emergency service—manning the emergency phone service some of the time, seeing walk-in clients, consulting with public health

nurses or other community health workers concerning continuity of care to the families of clients seen in emergency services, maintaining follow-up review of cases for evaluation,' and supervising new center staff attached to an emergency service. It is not possible to state concretely what any particular nurse in a specific center would do, for that would depend upon the nurse's education and competence, her ability to carve out a productive role in relation to the other professionals and nonprofessionals in that center, and her ability to innovate and expand her competencies utilizing the educative opportunities available.

As was indicated earlier in this paper, the preparation of professional nurses has moved considerable distance toward functions that have much complexity, abstractness, and ambiguity in addition to the more concrete traditional activities associated with the stereotype of nurse. Such preparation of the intellectual and interpersonal competencies of the nurse provide the basis of graduate education in psychiatric nursing, and also for participation in the more innovative, ambiguous, abstract functions related to community mental health. Involvement with a disturbed family for purposes of direct work, either with the family as a whole, the spouses as dyads, or of the individual who is the "identified patient," coupled with programming for activities outside that home, for the adolescents and children in that family, to attenuate effects upon them of the disturbance, is work having little concreteness to it. It requires that the nurse have the theories and competencies referred to earlier as being included in undergraduate and graduate educational programs in nursing. More than any other existing health agency, mental health centers seem to be evolving along lines of participant management and colleagueship. Those centers which are furthest along in this development are beginning to demonstrate Herzberg's principle, that challenging work in which responsibility can be assumed, will motivate the worker to give himself fully to the work and perform ever more effectively (Herzberg, 1968). Similarly, the tendency to be viewed as a colleague—rather than an "ancillary"—is more evident in community mental health centers. Many nurses who want to demonstrate their abilities to extend themselves beyond the stereotype of nurse, who want to have a voice in planning, conduct, and evaluation of their work in relation to the work of others in a total patient care system, find great appeal in community mental health work. For some time now, nurses have been teaching that nursing care is one component of a total complex of services called patient care; that the definition of nursing care is made by nurses and that the interdigitation of nursing with all other components—medical care, social work, psychological services, and the like—in any patient care system, requires colleague-type discussion of an interdisciplinary nature. Nurses are taught that the focus of such colleague discussions in the design of patient care plans requires the interrelation of separate standpoints of the various disciplines, with the focus being upon the problems, needs, and concerns of the client. However, most hospitals and other health agencies are organized along hierarchial lines with the stratification connoting status differentiation—and nursing being one of the ancillaries not often viewed near the top of the pyramid. Hence, the possibility, and in some community mental health centers the realization of colleague relations in planning and executing programs is refreshing and inviting to nurses. Particularly ones from the current generation find it easier "to do their thing"—with encouragement for self-development, self-expression, and demonstration of professional competence—in the new environment of mental health centers. This is not to say that all such centers are oriented toward participant management and colleagueship; indeed, some are not. It depends to considerable extent on the administrator—whether he believes that women can demonstrate intellectual competence, take full responsibility for their actions, and perform as effectively as men; and whether he believes that all disciplines in the health field are as viable and important and socially useful as his own (for additional information see Levine, 1969).

Notes

1. Earlier trends in the development of psychiatric nursing were described in Arieti (1959, pp. 1840–1854) and Freedman and Kaplan (1967, pp. 1625–1628).
2. For an extension of this educative event to continuing education workshops for registered nurses, see Peplau (1964, p. 55).
3. Available from the American Nurses Association, 10 Columbus Circle, New York, New York 10019; $1.00.
4. Available from G. Stokes, Box No. 5083, Grand Central Station, New York New York 10017; $2.25.

References

American Nurses Association. *Facts about nursing.* New York: Author, 1955–56.

American Nurses Association. *A position paper: Educational preparation for nurse practitioners and assistants to nurses.* New York: Author, 1965.

American Nurses Association. *Facts about nursing.* New York: Author, 1966.

American Nurses Association. *Statement on psychiatric nursing.* New York: Author, 1967.

Arieti, S. *American handbook of psychiatry.* Vol. 2. New York: Basic Books, 1959.

Armstrong, S., & Rouslin, S. *Group psychotherapy in nursing practice.* New York: Macmillan, 1963.

Berthold, J. S., Tschudin, M. S., Peplau, H. E., Schlotfeldt, R. M., & Rogers, M. E. A dialogue on approaches to doctoral preparation. *Nursing Forum,* 1966, 5(2), 48–104.

Freedman, A. M., & Kaplan, H. I. *Comprehensive textbook of psychiatry.* New York: Williams & Wilkins, 1967.

Hays, J. S., & Larson, K. *Interacting with patients.* New York: Macmillan, 1963.

Herzberg, F. How do you motivate employees? *Harvard Business Review,* 1968, 46(1), 53–62.

Levine, E. Nurse manpower tomorrow. *American Journal of Nursing,* 1969, 69, 290–296.

National League for Nursing. Concepts of the behavioral sciences in basic nursing education. In *Proceedings of the 1958 regional conferences on psychiatric nursing education.* New York: Author, 1958.

Nursing in community mental health services. (Conference report) Boulder: University of Colorado, 1966.

Oden, G. Panic: A descriptive study. Unpublished master's thesis, College of Nursing, Rutgers, the State University of New Jersey, 1962.

Peary, H. S., & Gawel, M. L. (eds.) *The collected works of Harry Stack Sullivan.* Vol. 1. New York: Norton, 1953.

Peplau, H. E. Interpersonal techniques: The crux of psychiatric nursing. *American Journal of Nursing,* 1962, 62(6), 50–54.

Peplau, H. E. *Basic principles of patient counseling.* Philadelphia, Pa.: Smith, Kline and French Laboratories, 1964.

Schmahl, J. A. *Experiment in change.* New York: Macmillan, 1966.

Simmons, L. W., & Henderson, V. *Nursing research: A survey and assessment.* New York: Appleton-Century-Crofts, 1964.

Stokes, G. A. (ed.) *A giant step: The roles of psychiatric nurses in community mental health practice.* New York: Faculty Press, 1969.

Venang, B., Leanard, P., & Pierson, L. Experience in mental retardation for basic nursing students. *Nursing Forum,* 1967, 6(2), 183–194.

Work conference in graduate education: Psychiatric-mental health nursing. Pittsburgh, Pa.: University of Pittsburgh School of Nursing, 1964.

World Health Organization. *Expert committee on psychiatric nursing.* (Technical Report Series No. 105) New York: Author, 1956.

38

Advanced Social Work Educational Programs in Community Mental Health

Howard J. Parad and Lydia Rapoport

Education for social workers in community mental health poses numerous problems. We are dealing here with a rapidly expanding field of practice of an amorphous character with fluid boundaries and open-ended, newly emerging professional roles and functions. The very nature of the comprehensiveness to be encompassed, pushed by both ideological and legislative dicta, has moved the field far beyond traditional psychiatric care and practice which was able, at an earlier time, to move on an evolutionary basis from individual to family to group approaches. The consequences for education are legion, and the resulting uncertainties concerning goals, methods, and educational patterns are to be expected as part of a necessary transitional stage.

Three consequences are immediately apparent: First, the broadened perspective in community mental health creates an inevitable competition in manpower needs between the needs of the community mental health enterprise and the still larger social welfare enterprise to which social work has a basic commitment. This is true although certain aspects of community mental health and basic social welfare provision and amelioration now merge, and indeed, should support each other. Manpower considerations have to be reexamined from a much broader base to provide for tasks from the level of technician to that of highly sophisticated specialist. Such a spectrum of tasks requires a rationale with appropriate educational goals and models.

Secondly, community mental health practice has to develop increasingly within a broadened interdisciplinary context, since the knowledge now considered relevant is no longer contained within the traditional psychiatric specialities. This requires a greater number of specialists in a wide variety of educational programs, regardless of disciplinary auspices, as well as the development of new patterns of interdisciplinary collaboration in the field.

And, finally, the thrust of education for community mental health, particularly at the advanced level, has to be toward those areas of practice in which roles, formerly carried out on the basis of generalized knowledge and common sense (such as mental health consultation) now need to become more strongly professionalized. This requires increasing scrutiny and systematization of knowledge with the extrapolation of new principles of practice. This chapter deals not, however, with what might be, but with what is to be found in prevailing educational practice in the community mental health field.

Specifically, this chapter has three purposes: (1) To provide an overview of a group of advanced (post-master's) social work educational programs that have community mental health components, (2) to identify some of the practice needs and issues that are related to these programs, and (3) to give a brief description of one such experimental program—the Community Mental Health Program of the University of California School of Social Welfare at Berkeley. While this chapter focuses on programs for trainees already possessing the master's degree in social work, it will include some observations concerning community mental health related programs at the master's level.

Since community mental health involves individual, group, and community approaches to the enhancement and restoration of psychosocial functioning, we assume that the total social work curriculum with its three main sequences—human behavior and the social environment, social welfare policy and services, and the methods of social work practice (including casework, group work, and community organization and planning)—is fundamental to the preparation of the social worker for community mental health practice. And in the light of the ever-present mental health manpower problem, we are also assuming that social work education, at all levels, is relevant to the preparation of community mental health workers, including undergraduate (leading to a bachelor's degree), graduate (leading to a master's degree), and advanced (leading to a third-year certificate or a doctoral degree) programs.

If the social work curriculum, regardless of level, is to prepare its graduates for responsible entry into practice and if—as we believe—community mental health is a vital innovation in today's social welfare scene, then the curriculum must prepare for a variety of roles relating to community mental health.

At the outset it may be helpful to differentiate between "education" and "training" in terms of their relative emphases on theory and practice. As used here, education refers to the development of a broad and fundamental *theoretical* understanding of a given body of professional and scientific knowledge, with emphasis on the mastery of organizing and linking concepts. Training, on the other hand, emphasizes the acquisition and mastery of *skills* in applying that knowledge *in specific practice areas* through more or less structured learning experiences, including, for example, field or practicum assignments. While basic concepts can and should be illustrated, reformulated, and reenforced in the training situation, the emphasis here is mainly on the application and testing of concepts—on learning by doing.

The question immediately arises: What is the proper role for the various types of educational and training facilities vis-à-vis the complex and varying tasks in the rapidly changing community mental health arena? For background purposes it is useful here to attempt a rough typology along three main dimensions: (1) type of facility,

(2) type of certificate or degree granted, (3) type of community mental health task or role for which the trainee is being prepared.

TYPES OF FACILITIES

Broadly speaking, we may outline four major types of educational and training facilities and their corresponding goals and certification procedures.

(1) Agency extension programs involving community training and consultation activities. Examples include community mental health center programs which train nonprofessional indigenous personnel as mental health aides; this type of program does not usually give a formal certificate or diploma. With the help of professional consultants, trainees are prepared for roles in offering psychosocial first aid—for example, through their natural access to people in crises. Within a specific social network, usually in a lower class disadvantaged area, help may be offered in a variety of settings, perhaps through a storefront program in an OEO-sponsored multipurpose neighborhood service center. Techniques may involve some adaptation of short-term crisis intervention (in mental health programs), or the use of militant social action (in community development programs related to civil rights or poverty) and other forms of social advocacy. Many trainees in these programs do not have a high school diploma, but some may be college graduates.

(2) A second type of educational resource is the university or college sponsored undergraduate program with social welfare content, an increasing number of which are now affiliated with the Council on Social Work Education (204 as of July, 1967).[1] College and university educational arrangements differ widely in these programs; many are located within departments of sociology, usually not formally affiliated with a graduate school of social work. Some departments have specialized concentrations in social welfare; others have one or more course offerings; both types usually include some form of field practicum. The diploma may be a liberal arts BA degree or a preprofessional BSW (bachelor of social work or bachelor of social welfare). Such educational programs generally prepare their graduates for

positions as welfare workers or case aides (especially in public assistance, child welfare, and state mental hospital programs), as well as for recreational research, correctional community development, mental health education, psychiatric technology and a variety of other assignments.

(3) The most important educational facility, within the social work profession, is of course the graduate school of social work, accredited by the Council on Social Work Education. There were 64 such schools in the United States in 1967—with a total enrollment of 10,178 full time students (Council on Social Work Education, 1967c). The social work master's curriculum should, at the very least, familiarize entrants in professional social work with the basic concepts and principles of community mental health programming and practice through the previously mentioned curricular sequences. Successful completion of all academic, field work, and research requirements leads to the MSW degree (master of social work) or its equivalent. These programs prepare for core jobs in community mental health practice. Most of these are in the junior or middle range of responsibility and typically involve direct service assignments in casework and group treatment activities. For a smaller number of relatively more experienced MSW graduates there are leadership roles in policy and program planning, community organization, and administration.

(4) A fourth category—the main focus of this chapter—encompasses a wide variety of patterns in post-master's education and training. These programs are sponsored, in some instances, entirely by schools of social work; in others by social welfare and mental health agencies; and in still others jointly by schools and agencies through various partnership arrangements. Some grant certificates in community mental health. In 1967 there were 18 third-year and doctoral programs accredited by the Council on Social Work Education, granting third-year diplomas and DSW or PhD degrees (Council on Social Work Education, 1967b). We shall later discuss these programs in detail.

Typically, the range of post-master's programs includes the following:

(a) Extramural "refresher" courses (variously labeled seminars, workshops, and institutes) sponsored by schools of social work, and such national social welfare organizations as the Family Service Association of America, the Child Welfare League of America, the American Public Welfare Association, the American Association of Psychiatric Clinics for Children, and a wide range of other professional membership groups and national accrediting and coordinating bodies. These vary from single session workshops to institutes that run for one or several weeks. The level of scholarly demand is also variable: in some there may be extensive reading lists and written assignments; in others the learner may be in a relatively passive role, absorbing information from specialists in various fields.

(b) Intramural staff development programs, or in-service training, usually agency sponsored; also characterized by enormous variation, these are designed to enhance the effectiveness of practitioners at many different levels within a given organization.

(c) Third-year (post MSW) programs under agency, clinic, or hospital auspices, leading to some sort of certificate but not related to a university department or school of social work.

(d) Third-year certificate programs sponsored by or affiliated with a school of social work. Virtually all such programs provide a year of preparation for the fourth year in a doctoral sequence. Content with respect to community mental health will be discussed below.

(e) Doctoral programs, under the direct auspices of schools of social work, leading to the degree DSW or PhD, will also be discussed below. Generally, these programs prepare their graduates for key positions as administrators, planners, educators, consultants, researchers, or senior clinical practitioners.[2]

(f) There are also a few postdoctoral programs in multidiscipline settings that prepare for highly specialized and complex roles in education, administration, and research. These are beyond the scope of this chapter.

SURVEY FINDINGS

The following material is based on responses to questionnaires, mailed in December 1967, to (a) all schools of social work (accredited by the Council on Social Work Education) with post-master's programs; (b) selected NIMH-supported advanced clinical training programs that were not affiliated with schools of social work or universities; (c) certain specialized multidiscipline university-affiliated programs, offering advanced education and training to social workers; and (d) selected schools of social work with NIMH-sponsored community mental health training programs designed primarily or exclusively for master's candidates.[3] Since time limitations made it impossible to survey all accredited schools of social work, this chapter makes no pretense of offering a comprehensive report of community mental health education and training at the master's level.[4]

A total of 49 questionnaires were mailed; 40 completed questionnaires were returned by program directors or their assistants.[5] Nineteen respondents reported that they offered advanced (that is, post-master's) programs to social workers; two offered advanced training to disciplines other than social work (although they had social workers on their instructional staff); three indicated that their programs had no relevant community mental health content; one had discontinued its program; one was a coordinating educational board that stimulated regional community mental health training but did not offer a program of its own; and 14 schools of social work indicated availability of some form of community mental health training for certain master's candidates.

The mailed questionnaire, to which (as indicated above) 19 advanced program directors responded, elicited information concerning a wide variety of items, including organizational affiliations, program objectives, course content in community mental health, field placements, faculty composition, admission requirements, and educational problems.

The modal organizational pattern (for eight third-year and doctoral sequences) involved direct sponsorship by a graduate school of social work. In three cases, the advanced program was under the auspices of other university departments (psychiatry or public health); three additional programs were loosely affiliated with but not directly sponsored by university departments; four training programs reported no university affiliation whatsoever; and one newly established experimental program was under the combined auspices of a university's school of social work and psychiatry department. Some program directors indicated that the lack of a formal university affiliation often constituted a source of difficulty in relation to curriculum planning and the

awarding of an appropriate certificate of completion. Third-year programs that were not related to doctoral sequences were somewhat hampered in their recruitment efforts because nonuniversity third-year course credits were usually not transferable for doctoral candidacy requirements.

With respect to educational objectives, the themes repeatedly stressed were the preparation of the advanced student for roles involving leadership and program management in community mental health and the need for training in multidiscipline collaboration. In addition to citing their general objectives in relation to community mental health, most program directors mentioned specific objectives in educating students for specialist roles in policy and program development, clinical practice, administration, research, teaching, mental health consultation, and mental health education. While the most frequently mentioned training components were in the nonclinical areas (community organization and planning, program and policy development), a number of respondents emphasized the importance of good experience in clinical practice to provide a sound base for the trainee's further professional development.

Typical responses concerning objectives include the following: The director of a multidiscipline program (for psychiatrists, psychologists, social workers, and nurses) indicated that his program is "geared to the needs and interests of the community mental health specialist student" who "usually goes on to occupy key positions, in universities and in federal and state governments, in community mental health administration, education, planning, and research." Another university-affiliated program indicated that "although community psychiatry is grounded in clinical work, it necessarily requires additional knowledge and supplemental training in consultant-consultee relationship, administration and community organization processes, theories and techniques of communication and education, and numerous other skills." The coordinator for an advanced social work (third-year) program stated that his program's main objective is "to prepare social workers with post-master's degree experience for positions of leadership and responsibility in comprehensive mental health programs." Finally, the chairman of a university doctoral committee mentioned that his program's objectives are to educate "doctoral students for planning, administrative, and research positions in community mental health."

Nine programs offered one or more courses labeled "community mental health"; in the other programs, community mental health content was diffused in a variety of courses in such areas as community planning, administration, social research, biostatistics, and the social aspects of health care. A number of respondents appended course syllabi which detailed the community mental health components in their curricula. Usually organized as seminars, most of these courses dealt with such diverse subjects as community mental health ideology; historical and international perspectives; epidimiological studies; federal and state legislative provisions; critical analysis of specimen plans for comprehensive mental health centers and consortia; concepts and issues in planning, administration, and finances; utilization of mental health manpower; consultation and training; the use of the "medical model"; short-term crisis intervention; trends and issues in the delivery of mental health services; the interrelationship of mental health and social welfare programming; the changing role of the social worker in community mental health; and methods of program evaluation. In many programs a number of these content areas were covered concurrently with related field and observational experiences.

Field Work

All but a few of the programs offered some type of field training or observational experience in community mental health. In most cases, the students were offered choices among a variety of supplementary experiences in order to tailor the program to their needs and future career interests. The prevailing pattern was the "concurrent" type of field placement for one or more days per week; under this plan the remainder of the student's time was devoted to class attendance, reading, and to the completion of a written project or doctoral dissertation (for those enrolled in degree programs). A few programs offered "blocks" of field training in program planning, consultation, research, and clinical practice; these ranged from a few weeks of "exposure" to carefully structured full-time internships with the more ambitious goal of helping the student to master specific skills in clinical practice, administration, and research. In a few instances, the trainee's field practicum was directly supervised by a faculty member, but in most programs field supervision was the responsibility of a senior staff member in an affiliated training center. In a few experimental programs, where the emphasis was on the innovational use of mental health professionals, the trainee had access to consultation from a faculty advisor but no direct supervision in the field.

While most program directors favored the placement of their students in multidiscipline mental health settings (for example, comprehensive mental health centers, city and county health departments, mental retardation centers, state hospitals, departments of psychiatry in general hospitals, and state departments of mental health), some preferred to assign their students—primarily as consultants—to social welfare programs that were not under medical auspices (for example, OEO-sponsored community action programs, public welfare departments, public schools, correctional authorities, and settlement houses).

In addition to formal field placements, many programs made use of a rich variety of supplemental observational experiences, including live demonstrations in clinical, consultation, and group process techniques, various adaptations of sensitivity training, "in-basket" training in administration, role playing, preceptorship groups, and special short-term research assignments.

In general, systematic field and informal observational experiences—in a real-life human laboratory—were · considered essential for the application, integration, and at times, the elaboration of community mental health theory.

Type of Diploma

The mailed questionnaire also elicited information concerning the type of diploma granted to trainees upon completing the various programs. Fourteen of the 19 programs under review granted some form of formal certification: eight awarded the PhD or DSW degree; six issued special certificates. Three gave no special acknowledgment of program completion at the time of the study (two of these were considering making a change), and two offered an option for a certificate or master's in public health.

As expected, the degree programs extended for a longer period than those which offered certificates; the doctoral programs involved two to three years of full-time study (for those who entered with master's degrees). In many cases, the dissertation, often completed while the student was engaged in full or part-time employment, required a year or more of additional work; however, some programs imposed a five-year limit for the completion of all doctoral requirements.

The nondegree programs required nine to 11 months of full-time study or one or more years of part-time study. For example, a multidiscipline program, focused on the training of child therapists and mental health consultants, required four years of study, on the basis of two half-days per week. A special NIMH-sponsored leadership training program for social workers in mental health settings, over a three-year period, has scheduled intermittent but intensive week-long institutes, plus reading and project assignments, and consultation in the area where the trainee carried out his full-time employment. A psychiatric training center has offered ten to 12 hours of advanced courses per week over a two-year period, with elective opportunities for concentrated study during part of the summer. Finally, one school of social work doctoral program has a unique schedule combining three intensive ten-week periods of summer study with two intervening nine-month clinical and research internships, with concurrent seminars and course work during the internship periods, and a structured research practicum that makes possible the completion of the dissertation within a 27-month period of education and training.

By definition, all programs included in this section were limited to applicants with a master's degree in social work. In accordance with NIMH standards for traineeships, most programs required the applicant to possess a minimum of three years of relevant post-MSW professional experience; two programs specializing in the preparation of administrators and program directors for key positions expected successful applicants to have at least five years of social work practice. One program was beamed to the younger practitioner who had recently completed his master's degree in social work. All respondents indicated their expectation that applicants have requisite qualities of maturity, scholarly ability, and professional promise; some explicitly sought evidence in such areas as the candidate's "commitment to a career in community mental health," "leadership potential," or demonstrated clinical competence in certain fields of social work practice. Ten of the programs were limited to social work applicants, six accepted qualified candidates from all "mental health and associated disciplines," and three accepted psychiatrists, psychologists, and social workers. With one exception, all faculties were multidiscipline, including specialists in biostatistics, economics, education, history, nursing, psychiatry, psychology, public health, social work, and sociology.

Enrollment

An attempt was made to determine the number of students registered in these programs. In the light of the ever-pressing mental health manpower crisis, it is disconcerting to report that only 63 full-time social work students were registered (as of December 1967) in the 19 programs that participated in this informal survey. The number of enrolled students ranged from one to 13, reflecting the highly specialized tutorial nature of these programs which, of course, do not pretend to produce large numbers of personnel. The number of part-time social work students was much larger; there were 146 such students, including 100 in the above-mentioned leadership training program (which allowed its trainees to continue in full-time jobs). According to the Council on Social Work Education, 311 full-time post-master's third-year and fourth-year students were enrolled in American schools of social work as of November 1, 1967.[6] Thus, even if one includes all full-time third-year certificate and doctoral candidates (many of whom are being prepared for teaching careers) in social work programs, the total enrollment is very small in relation to the need for community mental health personnel with advanced education and training.

Problems and Issues

In the final section of the questionnaire, program directors were asked to note problems and issues concerning program objectives, curriculum planning, field experiences, student and faculty recruitment, finances, and other matters. Virtually all respondents commented on the need for higher stipends for trainees, particularly for qualified men with families who simply cannot afford to undertake full-time advanced study without substantial scholarship aid. A recent study of career aspirations, in which social workers in mental health settings were asked what type of practice they would like to be engaged in at the "peak" of their careers, indicated that 74 percent of the male respondents preferred assignments in areas for which post-master's study would probably provide optimal educational preparation (administration, teaching social work, consultation, and research) in contrast to only 37 percent of the female study participants. Thus, it would seem that a substantial up-grading of stipend levels might well serve as an incentive to recruit qualified MSW degree holders for postgraduate study in areas in which they and advanced social work programs have a common interest.[7]

In addition, the need for increased long-term financial support for program development and maintenance was mentioned as a "critical problem" by some respondents. Also noted were problems in recruiting enough highly qualified students (often mentioned in conjunction with the meagerness of stipends for advanced social work students); the heavy investment of faculty time in tailoring individual educational plans; the difficulties (or impossibility) of precisely defining the elusive boundaries of community mental health—which in turn leads to difficulties in judiciously selecting appropriate content from the rapidly developing knowledge from the social and behavioral sciences; the selection of relevant field experiences, especially in administrative roles (how much in mental health and how much in the broader social welfare field?) which afford the student both stimulation and support; the opportunity to develop innovative programs while completing a meaningful learning experience; and the determination of a proper balance of academic and field work. For example, one program director stated, "A major issue among our faculty has been the question of a broad knowledge and theory base versus practical application—of ideas related to the community and social and political processes versus the specifics of community mental health practice."

In regard to program objectives, the director of a third-year sequence with a practicular interest in the young practitioner, commented:

The developing field of community mental health has brought into focus the need for a wide range of services for prevention and treatment, as well as the need for effective delivery of services ensuring continuity of services to all sectors of the community. Collectively, the social workers' functions are manifold as administrator, social planner, educator, researcher, and clinician. Education and training goals for social workers in community mental health should be defined on the basis of a major role emphasis such as a clinician or an administrator and so on, especially for beginning practitioners. In regard to training, it seems difficult to define a systematic course of professional development because of our tendency to view the manpower needs in toto in relation to the vast and comprehensive field of community mental health. A feasible approach might be to define and teach the new concepts applicable, for example, to the clinician in the field of community mental health.

Some respondents discussed the problems (such as faculty resistance to change) in making the transition from a traditional clinical orientation, with emphasis on individual and family therapy, to a broader multifaceted community approach to the mental health needs of a given catchment area, which uses "nonclinical" methods of consultation, group service, community organization, and research. Such a broad approach to post-master's study in community mental health is included in the following description of an advanced program located within a school of social work.

The Berkeley Program

The post-master's program at the School of Social Welfare, University of California at Berkeley, is one experimental model in advanced education in community mental health. The program has been designed to recruit trainees with a broad spectrum of interests in community mental health activities which include career goals in social planning, community organization, administration, consultation, and research. The primary objective of the program is to add to the pool of highly skilled community mental health workers, by preparing seasoned clinicians to take on the responsibility for leadership and specialist roles; second, to join in partnership with practice in the discovery and development of new knowledge and techniques in community mental health; and third, to experiment with a new educational format and method of training in social work on the advanced level.

The criteria for admission to this nine-month program—for which academic credit is given—is an MSW degree plus at least three years of post-master's experience in a clinical setting. The trainee must have a strong scholastic record, personal qualities of creativity, flexibility, and a capacity for leadership, and give evidence of successful mastery of casework or group work skills. In addition, he is expected to demonstrate curiosity about the broader factors affecting community mental health, and have a commitment to influencing social change.

Considerable attention is given to creating a stimulating and productive learning environment in which the trainees can study the problems and methods in community mental health. A milieu is developed in which competition is kept to a minimum and in which learning is measured by the individual's own pace and progress. In order to diminish resistance to learning and to prevent regression to a dependent role, the relationship of the community mental health faculty to the trainees is—to the maximum extent possible—egalitarian. An individualized education plan is developed by ascertaining the trainee's choice of methods, the problem areas in which he wishes to concentrate, as well as his career goals. This plan encompasses both academic course work and field projects.

Academic course work falls into three main areas: (1) social work methods; (2) social and behavioral science theory; and (3) the philosophy of community mental health, its knowledge areas, and concepts. Courses from all departments of the University are open to the trainees from which elective courses can be taken commensurate with career goals.

In the methods area, there are courses in mental health consultation, community organization, social planning, administration, and research. In the area of social and behavioral science theory there is a growing area of knowledge considered to be valuable for community mental health practice. This includes social system theory, bureaucratic theory, human ecology, cultural anthropology, small group theory, reference group theory, theory of planned change, and communications theory.

Since the trainees are preparing for practice, it is important to select those theories and concepts that have special relevance for community mental health practice. The task of pulling together relevant theory for integration into practice is a sizeable one which has not yet been successfully achieved in the community mental health field. To meet this need, the trainees take a course in the behavioral sciences wherein the content is being adapted to mental health practice.

In the field of community mental health there is as yet a paucity of knowledge which is identifiable as its own. Here community mental health resembles public health and criminology, which are also essentially eclectic, all borrowing from wide and diverse disciplines. The knowledge to be taught is dictated by practice demands in the field. In order to pull together the philosophy, theory, and knowledge relevant to community mental health practice, an integrative seminar has been designed which extends over the entire academic year. In this seminar heavy emphasis is placed on public health concepts and principles. The seminar proceeds with an examination of the social, cultural, and environmental factors which affect mental health. Major epidemiological and ecological studies are reviewed. Emphasis is placed on preparing the trainees to study and analyze community mental health problems from several social perspectives, taking into consideration multiple stress factors and their relation to individual, group, and community phenomena.

During the year the trainees are given increasingly more responsibility for conducting the seminar by preparing the presenting material from their own concurrent field projects, research, and readings in order to maximize their opportunity to incorporate new knowledge into their professional understanding. The seminar also provides a place for an appraisal of the present state of knowledge in the field, in order to question the validity of many of the concepts and assumptions that frequently pass for theory.[8] The trainees are also expected to produce a paper of professional quality by the end of the year, based on empirical or bibliographic research. The purpose of this learning experience is to provide another tool to integrate theoretical knowledge and field experience, as well as to foster the discipline of professional communication and writing.

The basic purposes of field work in the Berkeley program are to help the trainees master the methods being taught, and to experience the vicissitudes of the new work roles extant in contemporary community mental health practice. This educational model has certain unique features which depart from the traditional field work model. The areas of novelty refer to the nature of the assignments which are developed in several settings, the nature of supervision, and the concept of the field as a laboratory.

The trainees are assigned to specific field projects which have special learning components for them. The assignments are highly individualized and are geared to expanding the trainees' skill in the methods of their choice. Two types of settings are used for the field projects for each trainee: first, mental health settings which have an articulated community mental health philosophy and a broad range of services of a direct and indirect nature following the community mental health center concept; second, settings that are non-psychiatric in nature, but in which the service has implications for the mental health of its clientele. In this latter type of setting a mental health specialist can make a major impact on the system or its clientele by influencing the administrative process or structure, program policy, the coordination of services, or by carrying out program demonstration or research. Examples of such settings include programs in public health, urban renewal, and economic opportunity, as well as public school and recreation departments, neighborhood or settlement houses, and welfare services.

In the first of the two field assignments the task to be performed is relatively well defined in advance and allows the trainee to become quickly involved in providing an indirect service. In the second assignment, the role to be developed and the problem to be worked on are purposely left relatively undefined. Such a state is frequently a characteristic of actual practice in which a worker will find himself in the future.

The supervision of the trainee's field experience is split into its administrative and educational aspects. The field agency maintains administrative responsibility for the performance of the trainee, while the educational components of supervision are assumed by the teaching faculty, in the form of individual and group tutorials which are held weekly, thus insuring an integrated approach to both course work and field work. The tutorial method of field supervision in the school provides the opportunity for a high degree of conceptual teaching, and enables the program to use settings for field projects which do not have social work supervision available.

It should be noted that the training needs of the program and the manpower needs for experienced people of community agencies have meshed nicely so that there is a congruence of interests. The trainees have been welcomed and are perceived by the agencies as performing needed services which would otherwise be uncovered. In order for faculty members to perform this kind of tutorial teaching, it is necessary for them to become thoroughly acquainted with the agency, its staff, functions, and policies. Furthermore, through their ties with the field they are in an ideal position to recognize current practice problems, issues, and trends, and to bring these into the classroom for examination and discussion. In staffing a training program one tries to recruit a faculty with a diversity of competencies. Since the trainees are advanced, they also bring in their own expertise based on prior professional experience which contributes to the general level of teaching and knowledge.

It is very hard to predict the long-range developments of such specialized programs. It may be that some aspects of knowledge and skill will be absorbed into the master's program, while some other aspects may be suitable for and be incorporated into doctoral study. However, at this point in time, a specialty program of the sort just described seems to be valid and useful for practitioners who wish to make a commitment to a career in community mental health and wish to prepare for such a career by means of advanced education.

Master's Programs

In view of the relatively small proportion of mental health professionals who undertake full-time study in post-master's social work programs, it becomes immediately obvious that we must look to the master's curriculum—supplemented and enriched by a variety of in-service and continuing education programs—for the preparation of the large numbers of community mental health practitioners who are needed to staff the rapidly developing comprehensive centers, not to mention the growing number of related programs that are not formally affiliated with comprehensive mental health center complexes.[9] For this reason, we include in this review some brief observations of a selected group of NIMH-funded master's programs that have community mental health training projects. Fourteen such programs, sponsored by accredited graduate schools of social work, provided informal narrative statements concerning the community mental health components of their classroom and field curricula. As indicated in our introduction, it was not feasible to survey the 64 United States schools of social work which were accredited at the time of this informal review.

As of December 1967 (the time of our original inquiry) only one of the 14 schools offered its master's candidates a course formally entitled "Community Mental Health."[10] This course will be described in some detail because it is unique and could become prototypical for one kind of offering. Its educational rationale was explained as follows:

Here at the university, the School of Social Work has taken the position that community mental health should be an identifiable part of the curriculum. In many respects, one of the most important benefits of this policy is that it makes it possible to explicate the linkage between community mental health and the courses regularly offered in the curriculum. The implicit assumption that much of the material taught in casework, group work, community organization, and administration is relevant for community mental health provided an explicit link between these courses and community mental health. Of course, one additional advantage is that this community mental health component in turn tends to modify and change what is being taught in the more traditional courses.

A background course in mental health services, taught by a faculty member who shares responsibility for this school's course in community mental health, is considered a prerequisite. The community mental health course may be sketchily summarized as follows: First introduced are selected epidemiological and social survey studies of the correlates of various mental health problems (for example, associations between such factors as social class, family breakdown, race, health, and education on the one hand, and schizophrenia, delinquency, and alcoholism on the other). With the knowledge of various groups that are theoretically at high risk, the student examines ways of identifying these groups in a given locality through the use of census data and other demographic documents. A second component of the course deals with innovative mental health programs including short-term crisis intervention services. The master's student then learns about consultee-centered clinical and program consultation. Finally, the student's attention is drawn to the manpower problem, with emphasis on the roles of nonprofessionals in dealing with mental health problems.

A number of brief focused "familiarizing" field experiences have been offered students in conjunction with the study of the above topics. For example, some students have elected to investigate relevant demographic documents in a county planning office. Certain students have chosen to interview practitioners about their use of crisis theory in mental health programs, while others have shown a special interest in learning more about the role of the mental health consultant in the local educational system. And still others have inquired into the use of indigenous personnel in a local Head Start program. By design, students concentrating in all three basic social work methods—casework, group work, and community organization—have enrolled in this course. In addition to the above-mentioned familiarization field experiences, a small number of students (again, in all three social work methods) have had the opportunity for extended field placements in an area community mental health center where a variety of training experiences is offered in brief crisis intervention, consultation, promoting community participation and decision-making, administration (for example, learning the preparation of budgets for a complex of component units of the comprehensive center), and research (for example, helping with a system for processing information and monitoring center operations).

The other 13 schools all offered similar types of community mental health field experience both to first- and second-year students.[11] Five of these schools believed that a good deal of community mental health content was included in a number of courses that were variously entitled "Social

Problems," "Social Policy," "Social Work Methodology," and "Principles of Administration." A few respondents indicated that some of their graduate social work students elected courses in such areas as community psychiatry, mental health consultation, and epidemiology in other university departments. The remaining eight schools in this group stated that community mental health content was taught through the field experience in a community mental health center. In a number of these training centers, the supervisor had a faculty-level appointment, occasionally including responsibility for a limited amount of classroom teaching. One community mental health center, serving as a training resource for three schools in its area, provided an opportunity for the exchange of ideas and experiences among the cooperating institutions.

The newer NIMH-supported programs indicated a good deal of experimentation with the education and training of the multipurpose (also called "generic," "generalist," or "polyvalent") student social worker in recently established comprehensive community mental health centers. The aim of these innovative programs has been to prepare graduate social work practitioners with basic competence in working (simultaneously, if indicated) with individuals, families, groups, and neighborhood and community collectivities through familiarity with—and some degree of mastery of—the techniques of individual and family casework, group process, and community organization. In one such field training center, for example, students spent one day per week in a hospital-based clinical service and one and one-half days in various types of community action settings that were considered relevant to community mental health programming. Learning experiences were designed to enhance the student's progress in "combining community organization and clinical skills and to provide a firsthand opportunity to observe the social and cultural stresses which contribute to mental illness." In the words of the training director, this program "increases the student's interest in participation in bringing about social change. A broader experience helps prevent over-identification with an individual client, promotes a greater interest in groups and more knowledgeable use of various mental health and mental retardation resources."

Another program director described an innovative NIMH-supported field work program, under direct faculty supervision, for master's candidates (with previous social welfare experience) who concentrate in community organization and who have a career interest in community mental health.[12] The first year of training (with concurrent classroom work) has emphasized the acquisition of group work skills as a foundation for the second field work year (again with concurrent classes) which has focused on the application and extension of these skills in a wider neighborhood and community context—for example, in developing indigenous citizen participation on boards and committees, surveying mental health needs, organizing block groups and tenement councils, and mental health educational efforts for lower class families. Unlike the more ambitious multipurpose programs which aim for something like equal competency in casework, group work, and community organization, this program has emphasized the attainment of community organization skills; it has not pretended to offer its trainees more than an exposure or familiarizing experience in individual and family clinical work.

Discussion

The relative merits of these two patterns of master's education and training—the multipurpose "man-for-all-occasions" approach versus concentration in one of the social work methods (with accompanying familiarization learning experiences in the other methods)—has been the subject of lively professional debate rather than a subject for systematic educational research based on an experimental design with adequate follow-up measures of the student's performance in his first job. We hope that some sort of cooperative interschool research could be mounted, with the support of NIMH and the Council on Social Work Education, to provide more information in this vital area. For at the heart of this issue are many fundamental questions. For example: Can the master's program prepare an *effective* mental health-oriented social work generalist who is equipped to perform in a wide variety of practice roles? If so, should the post-master's programs then concentrate on advanced education and training for specialist roles in such discrete areas as clinical practice innovations (for example, in direct preventive crisis intervention where much more systematic work has to be done to advance practice theory), consultation (both individual and program centered), program and policy development (involving intensive study of alternate planning models), administrative management (for executive staff careers in comprehensive centers), or research (with emphasis on the elusive but vital problems of program evaluation)?

Regardless of one's stance toward the recurrent generalist versus specialist dilemma, it is clear that there should be a major thrust in the increase of community mental health content in both class and field in the core master's curriculum. As suggested by one of our respondents, it may well be that the development of special courses in community mental health is a first step toward promoting greater knowledge of and commitment to this rapidly growing field of practice. After such an awareness has been stimulated, it might well be advisable to disseminate units of community mental health content in specific courses within broad curricular sequences concerned with social and behavioral theory, social welfare policy and services, and the methods of social work practice.

Since, on the average, social workers contribute the greatest number of actual man-hours in outpatient mental health settings in comparison with psychiatrists, psychologists, nurses, and other personnel (United States Departmental of Health, Education, and Welfare, 1965a, p. 8), and since the establishment of new mental health programs will continue to create a demand for even more social work personnel, it is urgent that both graduate enrollments and facilities be dramatically increased. As of November 1, 1967, there were 10,178 full-time students in United States schools of social work,[13] far less than the estimated number of unfilled budgeted positions available for MSW graduates in all fields of social work practice, including community mental health.

CONCLUSION

As expected, advanced programs for post-master's social work candidates vary in their approach to community mental health, from attempts to familiarize the advanced student with certain concepts and issues in community mental health

to more sophisticated programs that educate and train personnel for high levels of leadership responsibility. In general, doctoral curricula reported heavy emphasis on the social and behavioral sciences and on research methodology, at least some emphasis on social policy, and relatively less attention to direct practice roles in clinically oriented casework or group work. Graduates of these programs who go into community mental health programs will usually do so at a leadership level, as administrators, directors of training, or research project directors. Most doctoral programs have provided compulsory or elective course work that includes community mental health content (for example, in social welfare planning, administration, and policy courses), while some have provided both academic content and structured field learning experiences that include training in community mental health centers. In general, it seems fair to say that the field work content, with respect to community mental health, is still evolving and is far from being definitively formulated. There was relatively little field work training for consultation and administration roles; where there were field learning opportunities, the emphasis seemed to be on direct clinical practice (especially in the nondegree nonuniversity affiliated programs) perhaps with some chance to do brief crisis therapy or research (usually but not always related to the doctoral dissertation). A few doctoral programs have provided research internships in mental health centers, over and above the data-gathering required for the dissertation.

Problems typically encountered by program directors have included student recruitment, finances (especially the need for higher stipends for married students), questions of professional role blurring, issues in selection of proper content for class and field instruction (especially in programs extending for nine months or less), and the perennial question of where community mental health ends and the broader field of social welfare begins.

While the advanced social work programs (with an all too small collective enrollment) generally concentrated on preparing personnel for specialist or leadership roles, the master's programs (with a current enrollment of more than 10,000 full-time degree candidates) have been experimenting with the development of innovative field centers, some of which are geared to the training of the multipurpose "generalist" social worker. Community mental health content was more clearly defined in the advanced than in the master's curricula. A reasonable case can be made for encouraging the development of master's courses specifically labeled "community mental health" in order to foster greater clarity about both the core and peripheral content of this growing field of professional practice and in order to promote more meaningful connecting links between traditional and innovative curriculum content.

The quantitative and qualitative aspects of the mental health manpower crisis place a premium on (1) the expansion of current social work educational and training programs at all levels, full-time and part-time—from junior college programs for mental health technicians to postdoctoral programs for highly specialized professionals preparing for leadership and research roles, with special attention to the increase of core mental health personnel with master's degrees; (2) increase in federal government support to make possible more scholarship aid at more realistic stipend levels, especially for post-MSW students; (3) greater attention to the specification of the actual content of community mental health for both class and field work, with emphasis on carefully designed field learning experiences in both the clinical and nonclinical areas; (4) the continued encouragement by NIMH of extramural types of continuing education,[14] offered by schools of social work, providing—on a part-time basis—brief but concentrated periods of study (workshops, seminars, and institutes) that not only enable trainees to retain their jobs but to apply (perhaps with the help of traveling consultants) their newly gained knowledge and skills on the job; and (5) the need for systematic evaluative educational research, an ever-present one, particularly through the use of experimental designs to assess the relative merits of some of the prevailing educational models, for example, with respect to the balance of "specialist" and "generalist" components in a variety of community mental health educational and training efforts.

Notes

Howard J. Parad was Dean and Professor, Smith College School for Social Work, Northampton, Massachusetts.

Lydia Rapoport was, until her sudden death on September 6, 1971, Professor and Director, Community Mental Health Training Program, School of Social Welfare, University of California at Berkeley.

1. Listed in "Constituent Members: Colleges and Universities Offering Undergraduate Courses with Social Welfare Content" (Council on Social Work Education, 1967a). See also Merle (1967). Also worthy of mention are the rapidly growing junior college and community college programs, some of which are developing specialized training for mental health aides, psychiatric technicians, and other auxiliary personnel.

2. It is important to emphasize here that a number of top level leadership positions have been created throughout the country by recent legislative and administrative action which follows NIMH policy guidelines. For example, the newly passed Massachusetts community mental health legislation provides for a number of area and regional mental health administrators and assistant administrators who may be recruited from a variety of disciplines—not only from psychiatry but from psychology or social work. The most senior of these social work positions require a professional doctoral degree in social welfare or social work (DSW or PhD). These administrative positions may well involve a status in the community mental health organizational hierarchy that is superordinate to that of the psychiatrist. Thus, the emphasis, in some of the newer legislation, is on the level of program and administrative responsibility inherent in a given status rather than on the disciplinary affiliation of the person in that status.

3. We are grateful to Miss Margaret Daniel and Dr. Milton Wittman of the National Institute of Mental Health for suggesting relevant programs for inclusion in this informal survey. Of course, the authors of this chapter bear sole responsibility for the material presented in this chapter.

4. As of this writing, such a comprehensive study is being planned by the senior author of this chapter.

5. We wish to express our appreciation to Dr. Libbie G. Parad and Mrs. Kathleen Savicki for their assistance in reviewing these questionnaires.

6. According to a Public Health Service report (containing the most recently compiled data), there were an estimated 7,500 social workers (75 percent with graduate degrees) in mental health programs as of 1963. It seems reasonable to estimate that the total as of the time of the present review was larger. In any event, in relation to the total number of social work personnel in mental health settings, the proportion involved in full-time or systematic part-time postmaster's study is very small indeed, especially when we consider the tremendous need for social work personnel with advanced training for key leadership roles as chief social workers, training directors, and consultants to local, state, and regional planning bodies. See United States Department of Health, Education, and Welfare (1965b, p. 1).

7. See United States Department of Health, Education, and Welfare (1965, pp. 8—9). For example, 42 percent of the men and only 10 percent of the women expressed a preference for administrative roles.

8. This is in accord with the position taken by Dr. Gerald Caplan who maintains that "an educational program must be organized within a framework of pioneering practice." Such an approach enhances the possibility for creative innovation and theory building and avoids what Dr. Caplan calls the risk of a trainee becoming "a technician or a conforming disciple." See Caplan (1963, p. 15).

9. It should be stressed, in this context, that unlike the master's academic schedule in education, psychology, or certain other disciplines, the social work master's program extends for two years, not one year. It should also be borne in mind that the master's degree is considered the terminal professional degree by most workers, even though there has been an increase in the number of postmaster's programs.

10. Two schools were in the process of setting up such a course.

11. One graduate school has developed a preliminary rating instrument in an effort to provide a crude rating of the community mental health component in its affiliated field training centers. The provisions of the Community Mental Health Centers Act of 1963 were used as a basis for these ratings on a 5-point scale:

A rating of (1) referred to comprehensive community mental health center programs, fully organized and in day-to-day operation that qualified under the terms of federal legislation; that is, they had, at the very least, the first five components specified in the Act (inpatient and outpatient services, partial hospitalization, emergency care 24 hours per day, consultation, educational, and diagnostic services) as well as appropriate provisions for continuity of care within a coordinated program of services.

A rating of (2) was used for partially operative centers whose programs met all of the above requirements but were still in the advanced stages of planning and financing and were expecting to be fully operative in the near future.

A rating of (3) was given to *noncomprehensive* programs which were clearly considered to be "community mental health" by the professional staff and the community which is served by the program; these programs had a *community* orientation (that is, they offered *preventive* services, *emergency* services, *consultation* to community agencies, thus reflecting a broad view of the mental health needs of a fairly large population group in a given catchment area). These programs, however, did not have all of the five components mentioned above, especially (*a*) inpatient services and (*b*) provisions for continuity of care from inpatient to outpatient and from outpatient to inpatient—along the precare, undercare, aftercare continuum. A rating of (3) would apply to virtually all of the state-supported mental health centers that are part of a network of services in a particular mental health catchment area and are integrated with statewide and regional

mental health planning efforts (that is, in relation to the notions of catchment area, aftercare, or some other aspect of community mental health ideology).

A rating of (4) was applied to more or less traditional multidiscipline mental health clinics (child guidance and adult mental hygiene clinics) that did not have the characteristics outlined in ratings (1), (2), or (3) above.

These clinics were not formally designated as or related to "Community Mental Health Centers." While they had some consultation and community-oriented services, these were relatively limited in scope as compared to centers that were classified with a rating of (3), as outlined above.

A rating of (5) referred to nonmedical programs (for example, child welfare or family service) that were related to local, state, or regional community mental health planning or programming, perhaps by offering contractual services (for example, aftercare programs for the mentally ill). Some family agencies and child welfare services belonged to this category, because they were linked with some type of community mental health board or hospital complex.

A rating of (6) was applied to nonmedical, nonmultidiscipline programs that could be considered a part of mental health services in a community—in a rather broad sense—but were unrelated to current community mental health programming (either directly or through indirect contractual relationships), nor were they involved in any of the community mental health planning endeavors in a given locality, as outlined above.

12. The director of this program appended a note concerning the recurrent problem of where to draw the boundaries of community mental health: "One issue is in relation to the way community mental health is defined and whether our program is to be limited to the distinct types of mental health services listed or should include the integration of mental health concepts and programming as part of a broader agency program. For example, this involves the question of whether developing a tenant organization—in connection with housing conditions—which helps individuals to develop a firmer sense of self and an ability to move along with others should be carried" under the mental health umbrella or under some other type of social welfare auspices.

13. Percentage distributions by concentration were casework, 72.2; group work, 9.9; community organization, 8.4; administration, .6; research, .3; and other, 8.6 ("includes programs in which methods are combined in various patterns of class and field instruction"). See *Statistics on Social Work Education* (Council on Social Work Education, 1967, p. 30). The proportion of students concentrating in community organization has steadily risen in recent years, with a concomitant decline in the proportion concentrating in casework.

14. Relevant in this context is a recently completed study by Miller (1968).

References

Caplan, G. Community psychiatry: Introduction and overview. In S. E. Goldston (ed.), *Concepts of community psychiatry: A framework for training.* (Public Health Service Publication No. 1319) Bethesda, Md.: National Institute of Mental Health, United States Department of Health, Education, and Welfare, 1963.

Council on Social Work Education. *Constituent members: Colleges and universities offering undergraduate courses with social welfare content.* New York: 1967. (a)

Council on Social Work Education. *Schools of social work offering post-master's programs 1967–1968.* New York: 1967. (b)

Council on Social Work Education. *Statistics on social work education.* New York: 1967. (c)

Merle, S. *Survey of undergraduate programs in social welfare: Programs, faculty, students.* New York: Council on Social Work Education, 1967.

Miller, D. Continuing education programs in schools of social work: Report of a survey. Unpublished document, Council on Social Work Education, New York City, December 1968.

United States Department of Health, Education, and Welfare. *Outpatient psychiatric clinics: Data on staff and man-hours, 1965.* (Public Health Service Publication No. 1448) Bethesda, Md.: Author, 1965. (a)

United States Department of Health, Education, and Welfare. Selected characteristics of social workers. In *Mental health manpower.* Bethesda, Md.: May 1965. (b)

39

Training in Community Psychiatry

Raquel E. Cohen and Ralph G. Hirschowitz

INTRODUCTION: SOME PROBLEMS OF DEFINITION

Community psychiatrists in the United States are trained in programs titled social psychiatry, community psychiatry, community mental health, or public health psychiatry. Some preliminary definitions are therefore in order. For the purposes of this paper, we accept the view of the Group for the Advancement of Psychiatry (GAP) Report (1967) that there are "essentially no practitioners of social psychiatry as such." We choose to define social psychiatry as a data-gathering, research, and theory-building enterprise. Community psychiatry, community mental health, and public health psychiatry (or preventive psychiatry) are viewed as alternative toponyms for merging fields in which parameters and objectives are shared. These shared objectives are: reduction of disability from mental illness; reduction of the intensity and duration of mental illness; prevention of mental illness; and the promotion of positive mental health in the community. While differing in audience, emphasis, and disciplinary affiliations,[1] practitioners in these three fields draw from the same reservoir of knowledge, theory, and skills. As Caplan (1967) has recently stated, these fields are characterized by a focus upon: "(a) populations; (b) all etiological factors, social, psychological, and physical; (c) all preventive, treatment, and rehabilitation factors, social, psychological, and physical; (d) correcting pathology, preventing illness, and promoting and maintaining positive mental health; (e) all types of prevention; (f) both service and research; (g) both intramural and extramural;

(h) auspices which include governmental, voluntary community agencies, and private jurisdictions; and, (i) programs in which administrators and workers may be drawn from the ranks of social science, psychiatry, other clinical professions, and administration."

The evolution of a shared rationale for training programs in community psychiatry is sometimes confounded by a "Babel Syndrome" to which Srole (1967) has drawn attention. In order to avoid such a "Babel Syndrome" we present the following schematic guidemap. This schema attempts to define what is central and crucial to the principles and practice of community psychiatry (or community mental health). It also attempts to delineate the perimeter of a field while it incorporates all parent disciplines.

In this cruciate schema ten areas can be identified:

I. Public Health
II. Psychobiological Sciences
III. Social Sciences
IV. Managerial and Political Sciences
A. Skills, methods or techniques that derive from I and/or II.
B. Skills, methods or techniques that derive from II and/or III.
C. Skills, methods or techniques that derive from III and/or IV.
D. Skills, methods or techniques that derive from IV and/or I.
V. Integrating "Center" or "Core"
BZ Boundary Zone

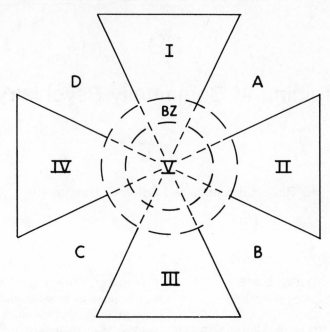

Fig. 39–1. Community psychiatry's crucial center.

I. *Public Health*
    The principles that follow are derived from public health.
    a. The catchment area concept. The concept of catchment area defines
        1. The population for which the community psychiatrist accepts responsibility.
        2. A population base for demographic and epidemiological data-gathering.
        3. The territorial base for ecological exploration.
    b. Principles of prevention.
    c. The concept of risk populations. Since populations may be at risk because of inherent vulnerability or because of overwhelming environmental stress, this concept relates to
    d. Environmental sanitation. This principle permits the identification, control, or modification of environmental influences which are inimical to mental health.
    e. Biostatistical and epidemiological approaches.
    f. Principles of public health administration.
    g. Principles of comprehensive family and community health.

II. *The Psychobiological Sciences*
    These include psychological medicine (psychiatry) as well as clinical and behavioral psychology, human development, and education. To the armamentarium of the community psychiatrist, the psychobiological sciences contribute the following:
    a. Understanding of personality, including human growth and development.
    b. Understanding of psychopathology, mental disorder, and mental illness.
    c. Principles for the diagnosis and management of troubled individuals. Of particular relevance to community psychiatry are methods of diagnosis or treatment which can be used for the effective screening or treatment of large populations. Examples of high quality, low-cost approaches include such diagnostic screening devices as the automated MMPI or the screening questionnaires of Shapiro and Maholick (1967).
    d. Principles of crisis intervention.
    e. Principles of "behavior therapy."
    f. Military psychiatry (Hausman & McK. Rioch, 1967) has contributed such principles as proximity, expectancy, and immediacy to the practice of community psychiatry.

III. *The Social Sciences*
    The social sciences are here defined as

sociology, social psychology, and anthropology. Representative contributions from the social sciences to community psychiatry are:

a. Understanding of social ties and bonds in primary groups, secondary groups, and community networks.

b. Understanding of social learning, socialization, and acculturation processes.

c. Studies of the interrelationship between sociocultural factors and mental illness or mental health.

d. Studies of mental hospitals and human services networks.

e. Studies of social deviants.

f. Studies of "temporary systems."

g. Cross-cultural studies of mental illness.

h. Studies of the organization and dynamics of small groups and communities.

i. Studies of the patterning of role behavior in social systems.

IV. *The Managerial and Political Sciences*
Some contributions are:

a. Principles of formal organization as they relate to such matters as: budgeting, administrative design, personnel practices, and bureaucratic structure.

b. Principles of informal organization, involving such issues as: organizational climate, human relations, and group relations.

c. Techniques for information-processing.

d. Understanding of power and leadership.

e. Principles for the development and maintenance of community mental health constituencies.

f. Methods for the design, implementation, and evaluation of programs.

g. Studies of the intersystemic relationships between community mental health agencies and other public and private agencies.

A-D

We have arbitrarily placed skills in application or practice in these schematic zones. We recognize that theory and practice are inextricably wed; principles are translated into practice and practice generates new theory.

A. *Methods, skills, or techniques derived from public health and/or psychiatry.*
Representative skills in psychiatric casualty management or prevention are:

1. Strategies of "crisis intervention" as they relate to individuals, families, or institutional networks. Public health applications include "prophylactic" interventions with populations-at-risk of crisis, such as the mothers of premature children or children entering school for the first time.

2. A particular technique for prophylactic intervention is "anticipatory guidance" (Caplan, 1964).

3. Crisis theory is applied in change strategies with institutions or the institutionalized. Examples are the strategy of "crisis engineering" (Daniels & Kuldau, 1967) or "purposive disequilibration" (Hirschowitz, 1969).

4. Brief therapies. These therapies represent precise strategies for reaching short-range goals. Decision counseling is one such strategy.

5. Strategies of family intervention which focus upon the mobilization of intrafamilial resources to improve interpersonal competence within the family matrix.

6. Education and consultation. Clustered here are all the methods by which community resources are developed for the prevention or management of emotional disturbance. Examples of such methods and skills are:

a. Mental health education for "firing-line professionals" (e.g. health, education, welfare, correctional, or pastoral professions).

b. Consultation to such target individuals and groups.

c. The development of therapeutic resources in "subprofessionals", "nonprofessionals," or amateur volunteers, via programs of training, education, or consultation.

d. The development, management, and evaluation of responsive innovation.

In summary, all strategies, programmatic and individual, for the development of indigenous helping resources, are grouped in Area A. Community mental health skills involve the application of a "problem orientation" rather than a "method orientation." The framework is ecological rather than clinical and goals may transcend conventional "treatment" to include social competence. As Golann (1967) has emphasized, "community mental health represents movement away from exclusive concern with methods of treatment towards innovative consideration of the 'time of the choice,' the 'location of choice,' and the 'helper of choice' for the reduction of psychological disability" (p. 1759).

B. *Methods, skills, or techniques derived from psychiatry and/or the social sciences.*
Practices here include the following:

1. Techniques for preventive education or remedial intervention that have as their targets: marital couples, or groups of marital couples; families, or groups of families.

2. Mental health education or consultation to schools, other socializing institutions, or resocializing institutions.

3. Mental health consultation to care-giving or human services agencies.

4. Small group intervention techniques.

5. The sociotherapies: milieu therapy, the therapeutic community, and "intentional social systems therapy."

6. Social rehabilitation, community restoration, and tertiary prevention programs.

C. *Methods, skills, or techniques derived from the social sciences and/or managerial sciences.*
In this area the focus is upon change or development in *institutions* that serve the emotionally disturbed. Practices applied here include:

1. Strategies for combating institutionalization and the social breakdown syndrome. Some of the methods employed are:
   a. Training, education, and consultation to promote change from custodial ideologies and practices to community mental health ideologies and practices.
   b. Organizational change such as decentralization, unitization, and delegation.
   c. Brief hospitalization.
   d. Public education programs to combat stigma and prejudice against the mentally ill.
   e. The development of part-care or transitional facilities for psychiatrically disabled or long-institutionalized patients. This includes the development of half-way houses, boarding homes, therapeutic social clubs, and transitional therapeutic groups.
   f. The development of sheltered work opportunities.
   g. The building of bridges and links between the "total institutions" and community agencies by "screening-linking-planning" methods (Hansell, 1967) and by collaborative planning techniques.

2. Community organization and development. Emerging are skills in public relations, public education, negotiation, and practical politics.

3. Applications of "environmental hygiene" and "therapeutic community" principles to community institutions. Technical vehicles are program-centered or consultee-centered administrative consultation (Caplan, 1964) to human services networks.

D. *Methods, skills, and techniques that relate to managerial sciences and/or public health.*
In both Areas C and D, the community psychiatrist practices skills in community penetration, in linking, in the recruitment of constituents, in convening, and in the development and extension of a base of influenced and power within his community. In Area D, practices include:

1. Intelligence, reconnaissance, and research activities. The community psychiatrist gathers essential data about the mental health needs and resources in his catchment area.

2. Program planning and design.

3. Program implementation.

4. Program maintenance, evaluation, and development. Methods, skills, and techniques that are required include the following:
   a. Biostatistical and epidemiological monitering.
   b. Skills in the design of service delivery vehicles and associated supportive and regulative system units.
   c. Skills in the integration of such differentiated units.

d. Political skills to maintain a community mental health enterprise within its task environments.

V. *The Crucial Center*

This is the center or core in which the art, principles, and practice of community psychiatry are mixed, blended, coordinated, and integrated. Here the principles originating in disciplines I-IV and the skills developed in Areas A-D are assimilated and synthesized. In order to integrate these multidisciplinary contributions into a cognate discipline, a generalist orientation and common language are needed. A unifying language, as well as generalizable conceptual models are emerging. Caplan (1968) has proposed three such models all of which interrelate personality and social systems theory. These are:

1. A metabolic or nutritional model. This model conceives of healthy personality development as being dependent upon *adequate and appropriately timed supplies* of physical, psychosocial, and/or sociocultural nutrients.

2. A community organization and development model. This model attempts to define those community properties which are conducive to mental health. A model for community development is offered by which a community could provide necessary supplies for all its members, as and when these are needed.

3. A "socialization or effective role performance model." This model applies social learning and role theory to the reeducation and resocialization of individuals who have been cast in "deviant" or "patient" roles.

Many other attempts at interdisciplinary integration have been made by psychiatrists. Vail has applied social psychological principles in combating "dehumanization and the institutional career" (Vail, 1966) by modification of the physical and psychosocial architecture of mental hospital wards. Daniels and Kuldau (1967) have developed an integrated "intentional social systems therapy" for the modification of socially deviant behavior.

In an attempt to "unfreeze" traditional psychiatric habits of thought and practice, Hansell (1968) has postulated, and supplied a language for, "mental health technology in transition."

Finally, many practitioners and theorists have found that general systems theory offers a language for the multilevel integration of psychobiological, psychosocial, and sociocultural systems of organization. Representative researchers have been Baker and Schulberg (1971) and a representative theoretician is Ruesch (1966).

BZ *Boundary Zone*

As befits the multidisciplinary, emergent field of community psychiatry (or community mental health), this schema recognizes that the margins or boundaries between community psychiatry and its parental, sib, or related disciplines are fluid and permeable. The central zone of community psychiatry is therefore depicted within a circumferential Lewinian "boundary zone" (Lewin, 1936) which permits free ingress and egress of theories, knowledge, and skills. To the extent that such a boundary is selectively permeable, selective in-migration is based upon *field relevance*. The community psychiatrist's strategic location permits him to play a boundary-spanning and cross-fertilizing role.

Reflection on this Cruciate Schema

In presenting this cruciate model, our objectives have been two-fold. We have sought to "cover the territory" by offering examples of the substantive content of community psychiatry (and, therefore, a framework for the community psychiatry training program). Our second objective has been to emphasize the vital, integrating, synthesizing, developing core or center of a community psychiatry training program. In focusing on the center or hub of our schema, we emphasize that this is not a simple cross-roads. The center exerts sociopetal forces and actively *processes* the theories, principles, and skills which it filters in. In addition to processing, ordering, and integrating, the center has generative properties: the system's center abstracts, synthesizes, and generates new theories, research strategies, and heuristic problem-solving approaches. Without such an active, integrating, generating center, a training program will lack order, integration, and vitality.

While Zones I-IV and A-D contribute the necessary content ingredients for a successful training program, it is in Zone V that the *sufficient* conditions are established for the selective assimilation, incorporation, and application of these ingredients.

ON BECOMING A
COMMUNITY PSYCHIATRIST

In his basic training, the psychiatrist will have acquired a focus upon personality systems, while maintaining his "clinical" orientation: diagnosis, treatment, and rehabilitation of the mentally ill patient. As a community psychiatrist, he will accept responsibility for the prevention, treatment, and rehabilitation of *all* mental disorders in a community. The community psychiatrist will work in a multidisciplinary setting; his ability to understand and participate in community health programs will derive from a broad identity base and a general commitment to the needs of a total community. The trainee who is most likely to make a successful transition from a "clinical" to a "community" orientation is a generalist who is not too exclusively invested in his professional "specialist" status or identity.

The typical community psychiatrist will be practicing in an increasingly turbulent environment. He will be expected to survey and solve problems of multifocal complexity in situations he may not previously have encountered. In selecting the trainee, adaptive competence under conditions of turbulence should be weighted. In addition, the trainee with a broad range of experience, training, and education enters a training program with these resources to draw upon. These resources are a foundation upon which to build new areas of expertise.

Learning-Teaching Processes
in the Training Program

The training program must facilitate the acquisition of new knowledge and skills by the trainee. In a full-time training program, the trainee will experience significant conflict as he attempts to enlarge his perceptual and conceptual focus; he will experience role strain as he attempts to extend his role repertoire. In administering a training program, this dissonance and strain should be carefully monitored, anticipated, and controlled. By so doing the anxiety attendant upon cognitive

and role shifts can be maintained at an appropriate working level so that anxieties can be metabolized and constructive learning occur.

In field experience, the community psychiatrist will discover the need to shift cognitive gears rapidly as he moves from one role to another. In learning and practicing consultation, he may be apt to lapse into the more familiar role of therapist; unless suitably prepared, he may have difficulty deciding when to maintain a stance which appears to be coordinate, subordinate, or superordinate to the individuals with whom he is working. Unless he is provided with appropriate conceptual models, cognitive guide maps, a symbolic compass and suitable guidance, he may demonstrate "role-clinging" with impairment of his capacity to absorb new learning. In making the cognitive and role shift from "personality system" to "social system," from "clinical" to "community," and from "therapy" to "consultation," it is helpful for the trainee to realize that existing knowledges and skills will *not be supplanted, but supplemented.* The training program needs to maintain the security operations, and self-esteem of its trainees.

Training Components in a Community
Mental Health Program

Within the boundaries of the training program, new learning is catalyzed and facilitated by interacting with a teaching faculty in a variety of situations:

1. *The classroom seminar.* In seminar settings the trainee will be exposed to new knowledge, new approaches, and new techniques. In seminar interaction, he will be exposed to the resources of experience and education in the other trainees as well as the instructors. As trainees prepare to enter their community and consultee agencies within it, seminars can provide orientation, guide maps, and appropriate expectational sets. Once they enter the boundaries of the community and begin consultation, seminars provide opportunities for information exchange and theoretical elaboration. Vicarious problem solving is encouraged when trainees bring field experience into the classroom setting. The instructor can be helpful in many ways:

as a role model, as a source of nonspecific support, and as a supplier of cognitive maps and reference ideas. As the instructor moves slowly and carefully from a focus on personalities to a focus on environment and social system, he demonstrates to the trainee the relevance of "multifocal" lenses and teaches by "show" as well as "tell."

2. *The role of the advisor within a training staff.* In his relationship with the advisor the trainee receives help, support, guidance, and counsel. The advisor helps the trainee design an optimal package of experiential and cognitive learning so that appropriate increments of knowledge and skill are sequentially absorbed. The advisor can guide the trainee towards appropriate resources at critical transition points in his learning program.

Through the advisor, the trainee can give and receive useful feedback. When the trainee or advisor become aware that the trainee is laboring under too heavy a load of experiential or cognitive input, error amplification can be avoided by appropriate modification of the pace and content of learning.

3. *The supervisory process* Trainees benefit from individual and/or small-group supervision. These can be precise, helpful, supportive transactions in which trainees are helped to prepare for change, reflect on field experience in some depth, and integrate these analytic reflections as they go to and from their weekly field experiences. The skilled supervisor is able to introduce or emphasize working principles as the trainee encounters field problems for which he lacks appropriate working constructs.

4. *Ceremonial encounters.* At significant transition points, such as entry and exit to the program, appropriate ceremonial with exposure to leaders in the community psychiatry field generates commitment, engagement, esprit de corps, and identification.

5. *Informal encounters.* An appropriate organizational climate encourages collaborative learning and problem solving. Such a climate is characterized by experimentalism, innovation, receptivity to new learning, and constructive reciprocity. It is the task of a training program's administrators to function as emotional thermostats to regulate the organizational climate and maintain an appropriately supportive matrix through this learning and formative period.

In learning-teaching encounters, the following educational principles are applied:

1. *The process model of education.* In the training program, the trainee needs to learn good theories which he can apply and upon which he can build; he needs to learn practitioner skills; and he needs to learn to ask questions and build theories of his own, while testing these in research or in action. It is necessary for the training program to offer information, quality theory, and opportunities to translate theory into practice. In his learning-teaching encounters, the trainee should acquire new information, become acquainted with existing theoretical principles, and learn to reflect upon his experience. Above all, he should enlarge his problem-solving repertoire and acquire a causal or analytical approach to problem-solving. For these an outmoded pedagogical model will not prove adequate. Problem solving can be taught in many ways of which we emphasize two:

    a. *The DA-TA model of Wedge.* This is a model for the synthesis of action experience and intelligent reflection (Wedge, 1968). It is based upon field experience ("demonstration by action") combined with learning opportunities that provide "theoretical analysis."

    b. *A process model of education.* This has recently been defined by Miller (1967): "There is ample evidence to support the view that adult learning is not most efficiently achieved by systematic subject instruction; it is accomplished by involving learners in identifying problems and seeking ways to solve them. It does not come in categorial bundles but in a growing need to know. It may initially seem wanting in content that pleases experts, but it ultimately incorporates knowledge in a context that has meaning. . . ."

"The first step in this long process is not to tell them what they need to know, it is to help them to want what they require. It means involving participants in identifying their own educational needs, in selecting the learning experiences most likely to help them to meet their needs, and in assessing whether they have learned what was intended, not merely determining whether they took part in the learning experience, or even whether they liked it" (pp. 322–323).

2. *Cognitive maps. As* he navigates through strange terrain and attempts to define his goal direction, the trainee acquires new guide maps from the teaching staff.

3. *Role models.* In an emerging discipline which lacks traditions, established patterns, or codified skills, it is important that the trainee be exposed to community psychiatrists who can model appropriate role behavior for him. Such modeling can be provided face-to-face or via movies or video tape of staff professionals working in the community.

4. *Selective reinforcement.* In the trial and error process of practicing new skills, consultees, peers, and supervisors provide helpful reinforcement of appropriate strategies. In monitoring error, the selective inattention of a sympathetic supervisor assists the trainee in maintaining centrality of focus.

5. *Involvement, participation, and motivation.* Trainees who are involved in the definition and packaging of their learning experience are likely to be more receptive to learning. The effectiveness of any learning-teaching experience seems to be a function both of its quality and its acceptance by the trainee.

6. *Collaborative problem-solving.* When trainees are involved in collaborative problem-solving, dogmatic solution-minded approaches to problems will be unfrozen and exploratory or causal orientations encouraged. Collaborative problem-solving is an organic approach and facilitates new learning.

7. *Learning is an active not a passive process.* The trainee has to invest and participate in all levels of program planning and implementation.

8. *Case method.* The case method can be applied when trainees submit their problems for collaborative discussion. Although only one trainee is directly involved, other trainees participate whenever a case generalizes well. The instructor may introduce "classical" case problems for discussion from his own experience or from an available storehouse of movies or video tapes. Video tape consultations, in particular, lend themselves to refinement of observational, listening, and interviewing skills.

An elaboration of the "case method," as practiced at the Harvard Business School, awaits exploration.

COMMUNITY PSYCHIATRY TRAINING PROGRAMS IN THE UNITED STATES

History and Development of Training Programs

Community psychiatry training programs have been strongly influenced by the contributions of Paul Lemkau, Erich Lindemann, and Gerald Caplan, who instituted the first formal training programs in this country. The knowledge, skills, researches, and ideologies of these community psychiatry pioneers have enriched all subsequent training programs.

Dr. Lemkau's program was established in 1948 at Johns Hopkins Hospital. In 1954 programs were instituted by Dr. Erich Lindemann at Massachusetts General Hospital and by Dr. Gerald Caplan at the Harvard School of Public Health. Dr. Caplan's Laboratory of Community Psychiatry moved to the Department of Psychiatry of Harvard Medical School in 1965.

In 1956, a division of community psychiatry was established at Columbia University under Dr. Viola Bernard. This division was established under the joint auspices of the Department of Psychiatry and the School of Public Health and Administrative Medicine.

In the early 1960s, three programs were established in California. These were: (1) The Center for Training in Community Psychiatry at

Berkeley under the directorship of Dr. Portia Bell Hume; (2) The Program for Graduate Training in Social and Community Psychiatry at UCLA; and (3) The Division of Social and Community Psychiatry in the Department of Psychiatry of the University of Southern California. In the past decade, other training programs have been established under the following auspices:

1. The Department of Psychiatry, Albert Einstein Hospital.

2. The Langley Porter Neuro-Psychiatric Institute.

3. The Menninger Clinic.

4. The Institute of Pennsylvania Hospital.

5. School of Psychiatry, University of Rochester.

6. Yale University.

7. The College of Medicine, University of Florida.

8. The Southwestern Medical School, University of Texas.

9. Oregon State Hospital, Oregon.

10. The School of Public Health, University of Michigan.

11. The Department of Psychiatry, University of North Carolina.

12. The University of Washington.

13. The Department of Psychiatry, University of Wisconsin.

14. The Maryland Training Program in Community Psychiatry of the Johns Hopkins Hospital.

15. The School of Public Health, Harvard University.

16. The Psychiatry Department, The University of Cincinnati.

Community psychiatry programs are being instituted or extended in many departments of psychiatry; exposure to community psychiatry principles is also increasing in general psychiatry residency programs, but we have not attempted to unravel or define these recent training developments.

The Harvard Visiting Faculty Seminar and the Inter-University Forum for Educators in Community Psychiatry

A significant contribution to residency training programs across the United States had its inception in 1965 at the Laboratory of Community Psychiatry.

The Harvard Visiting Faculty Seminar emerged from developments in the past few years in the field of mental health care in the United States, especially those connected with the Joint Commission, the Kennedy Message, The Community Mental Health Centers Act, and its Regulations. In the fall of 1963–1964 the National Institute of Mental Health sponsored four regional training institutes in community psychiatry for professors of psychiatry from all university departments in this country. These meetings demonstrated urgent interest among psychiatric educators in improving their own understanding and skills in the community field, so as to facilitate developments in community psychiatry in their residency training programs. In direct response to this interest, and to a widespread demand among professors for a mechanism which would provide an opportunity for a systematic and continued study in depth of the issues involved without their having to take prolonged leave from their teaching duties, the Visiting Faculty Seminar was organized at the Laboratory of Community Psychiatry, Harvard Medical School.

This Seminar under the direction of Gerald Caplan met three times a year, for two-week sessions each, for three years. It was financed jointly by the Grant Foundation of New York and by an NIMH training grant, supplemented by NIMH Senior Stipends to each of the participants to pay their travel and per diem expenses.

The participants were 16 professors of psychiatry from medical schools around the country who had responsibility for community psychiatry training in their residency programs. Instead of the usual type of seminar, the program was organized as a joint study group. Some of the participating professors were themselves leading figures with years of experience in the community field and the Harvard organizing group were as interested in learning as any of the visitors.

The two-week programs were organized around central topics: meaning and scope of community psychiatry; ongoing community life in relation to community psychiatry; researches and theories which form a basis for concepts and methods of community psychiatry; studies relating to preventive psychiatry; consultation; planning and evaluation; community organization and development; administration and communication; educational issues in community psychiatry. Specialists who were leading practitioners and researchers in community psychiatry, social science, and allied fields from all over the United States and whose work had a bearing on the central themes of the field were invited in for a day or half a day, and were engaged in an informal dialogue about their work. This then led the total group into discussion about the dominant issues, in which each participant was stimulated to contribute to a material enrichment of ideas on the basis of his own experience and thinking.

As a result of the success of the Visiting Faculty Seminar the participants decided to band together to establish similar study groups for other psychiatric educators. This decision led to the organization in 1967 of the Inter-University Forum for Educators in Community Psychiatry, which is sponsored by the departments of psychiatry of the 17 medical schools of the original participants. Coordination and planning activities are carried out by a committee composed of the participants of the Visiting Faculty Seminar, who are now the chairman and cochairman of the study groups, and Dr. Caplan, with financing from the Commonwealth Fund. Six centers were chosen as sites for the study groups which are supported by individual grants from NIMH:

Baylor University College of Medicine, Houston, Texas
Chairman: Moody Bettis
Cochairmen:
Frank J. Nuckols, Medical College of Alabama; and, William G. Reese, The University of Arkansas School of Medicine.

The University of California School of Medicine, San Francisco, California
Chairman: M. Robert Harris
Cochairman:
Edward C. Frank, The University of Louisville School of Medicine.

The University of Chicago School of Medicine, Chicago, Illinois
Chairman: C. Knight Aldrich
Cochairmen:
Eugene W. Green, The Ohio University College of Medicine; and, Leigh M. Roberts, The University of Wisconsin Medical School.

Duke University Medical Center, Durham, North Carolina
Chairman: Charles Llewellyn

Cochairman:
Edward C. Norman, Tulane University School of Medicine.

The University of Pittsburgh School of Medicine, Pittsburgh, Pennsylvania
Chairman: Jack A. Wolford
Cochairmen:
Richard W. Garnett, Jr., The University of Virginia Medical School; and, Robert M. Reed, Vanderbilt School of Medicine.

The University of Vermont College of Medicine, Burlington, Vermont
Chairman: Hans R. Huessy
Cochairmen:
David Davis, The University of Missouri School of Medicine; and, Allan Z. Schwartzberg, Georgetown University School of Medicine.

The participants in the six study groups were chosen from nominations by chairmen of departments of psychiatry and directors of residency programs in universities, general hospitals, veterans' administration hospitals, state mental hospitals, child psychiatry training programs, and schools of public health with mental health programs. Approximately 90 participants were selected by the coordinating committee and divided among the six centers in such a way that each group would be as heterogeneous as possible in regard to seniority, type of institution or organization, and community psychiatry sophistication and also in regard to their place of origin, subject to keeping traveling expenses as low as feasible. Each group mirrors as wide as possible an experience of urban and rural, as well as of regional and local subcultural issues.

The structure of the programs in the Inter-University Forum are similar to the Visiting Faculty Seminar, except they meet twice a year (instead of three times) for four years (instead of three years). The study groups rotate the topic areas of their sessions drawing on a wide spectrum of national speakers; in addition each center's program includes distinctive features relating to community psychiatry which can be demonstrated within its community setting by local speakers.

The Inter-University Forum, thus, through its participants and chairmen, influences 105 or so residency training programs. It also provides a unique, sustained opportunity for cross-communication and cross-fertilization of ideas about education in community psychiatry across the boundaries of university, state hospital, general hospital, veteran's administration hospital, and community systems.

Review of Training Programs in Community Psychiatry[2]

There are significant differences in program titles. Approximately half the programs are labeled "Programs in Community Psychiatry." Representative of this group are New York Medical College, The University of North Carolina, and the Washington State Program. Some programs are labeled "Programs in Social and Community Psychiatry." Included in this group are the University of California, Los Angeles; the University of Southern California, Los Angeles; and Yale University. Only one program is titled "Training Program in Social Psychiatry." This is Dr. Leighton's program at the Harvard School of Public Health. Three programs are designated "Program in Community Mental Health"—The Center for Training in Community Psychiatry, Los Angeles, the Langley Porter Program, and the Massachusetts General Hospital Program. The Columbia University Division of Community Psychiatry offers four programs—community psychiatry, social psychiatry, public health psychiatry, and administrative psychiatry.

Recruitment

Ten programs are open only to psychiatrists. Four training programs are open to all the mental health professions, included psychiatric nursing. Some programs are available to candidates with doctorates; some admit social workers but no psychiatric nurses. Representative programs that are open to all mental health professionals are the Center for Training in Community Psychiatry and Mental Health Administration of the Department of Mental Hygiene, Berkeley, California, and the Laboratory of Community Psychiatry's program at Harvard Medical School.

Degree Requirements

Some programs make work for a degree a mandatory condition. Master's degrees are offered in public health or in social and community psychiatry. Some programs permit trainees to obtain a degree, but the programs are not highly academic-oriented nor is the attainment of a degree a condition. Some programs are highly practice-oriented and do not offer a degree.

The Influence of Program Auspices, Recruitment, and Academic Requirement

In scanning the various programs, factors which tend to give some programs uniquely distinctive hues include the following:

1. *Academic and/or service orientation.* Some programs are highly academic, emphasizing necessary credit hours, formal examinations, theses, and preparation for formal degrees. One program emphasizes that it is training "leaders and educators." At the opposite pole are programs with an emphatic service orientation. A program whose primary mission is the training of practitioners is the Center for Training in Community Psychiatry at Berkeley. Other programs attempt to integrate both academic and service aspects, and may or may not offer academic degrees. A representative program is that of the laboratory of community psychiatry which does not offer an academic degree but does offer a certificate from Harvard Medical School.

2. *Auspices.* Programs housed in schools of public health are notably academic, emphasizing epidemiological and biostatistical research. Leighton's program in the School of Public Health is a research-oriented program in social psychiatry.

3. *Scope.* Some training programs are broadly conceived and offer to physicians at levels of development from medical student to senior post-graduate. An example is the Albert Einstein program.

4. *The influence of site.* Programs housed in medical schools or general hospitals promote and maintain strong "clinical" affiliations. By contrast, public health programs seek out "populations" for epidemiological studies.

   Programs in large cities provide opportunities for wide-ranging urban experience but not for rural programming. Programs in state hospitals emphasize innovations in tertiary and secondary prevention; programs with catchment area responsibilities permit trainees to learn primary prevention and address the comprehensive needs of a total population.

Heavily academic enterprises may seek out opportunities for research rather than practice. Programs strongly committed to field learning such as the Maryland Program contrast markedly with university programs that strongly emphasize "credit hours."

In general, programs are strongly influenced by the traditions, ideologies, assumptions, and political direction of their host institutions.

Curriculum Content

In attempting to analyze the similarities and differences in the content of training programs, our categories are derived from the schema presented for the systematic analysis of training programs.

The courses offered by 19 training programs[3] have been grouped as follows:

1. Principles and practices derived from public health.
2. Principles and practices derived from psychiatry.
3. Principles and practices derived from the social sciences.
4. Principles and practices derived from the managerial and political sciences.
5. Principles and practices of community psychiatry.

I.   *Public Health*
  A. Twelve programs offer courses in epidemiology of mental illness.
  B. Seven programs offer courses related to biostatistics and related research design.
  C. Three programs offer courses in preventive psychiatry or public health-mental health.
  D. Three programs offer courses in principles, practices, and/or methods of public health.
  E. Two programs offer courses in public health administration.
  F. One program offers a course on personality and environment.

II. *Psychiatry*
  A. Five programs offer courses such as "group methods in community mental health."
  B. Four programs offer courses on family therapy or family intervention.
  C. Four programs offer courses which relate to crisis theory or crisis intervention.
  D. Two programs offer courses on short-term brief therapy.
  E. There are a number of idiosyncratic offerings, offered by only one program, such as "in-hospital consultation," or "psychopathology and behavior."

III. *Social Sciences*
  A. Seven programs offer courses with titles such as community processes, community studies, or community concepts.
  B. Six programs offer courses entitled social sciences in psychiatry or readings or contributions to social psychiatry.
  C. Three programs have course offerings dealing with community problems: the titles are community crises, urban renewal and community problems.
  D. There are two programs which offer courses relating sociocultural factors to mental illness.
  E. This is a miscellaneous grab bag in which "one of a kind" seminars are offered by a single training program. Titles include: "Social Dynamics of Ward Management," "Ego Psychology and Culture," and "Social Systems Analysis."

IV. *Managerial and Political Sciences*
  A. Eight training programs offer courses in areas which relate directly to program or service administration.
  B. Six programs offer courses on program planning, evaluation, and research.
  C. Five programs offer courses on community psychiatry and the law.
  D. In the miscellaneous group are "Principles of Organization and Staff," "Leadership and Administrative Processes," and "Analysis of Patient Care Systems and Mental Health Center Programs."

V.   *The Crucial Center: Community Psychiatry*
  A. Of the 19 programs, nine offer courses on consultation.

B. There are six programs which focus on the use of community resources in mental health.

C. Four programs deal specifically with community organization.

D. In the "miscellaneous" category one or two programs offer courses such as:
   1. History of Community Mental Health
   2. Community Mental Health and Alcoholism
   3. Mental Health Education
   4. Communications Theory or Tools of Communication for Psychiatrists
   5. Social Psychiatry in Theory and Practice
   6. Community Psychiatry
   7. Community Mental Health Theory and Principles of Practice
   8. Community Mental Health Issues and Problems

Reflections on the Data

In scanning the above breakdown, it is apparent that a typical community psychiatry training program offers some or all of the following: epidemiology and biostatistics; crisis theory; approaches to the family; group processes; approaches to community and social systems and the lore of social psychiatry; community psychiatry and the law; program planning and administration; consultation; and aspects of community organization. In most programs, these subjects, together with supervised field experience, constitute a "core program."

THE LABORATORY OF COMMUNITY PSYCHIATRY, BOSTON, MASSACHUSETTS: AN ILLUSTRATIVE PROGRAM

To further elaborate and highlight some of the issues already presented, we would like to describe a representative university-based program. This program (The Laboratory of Community Psychiatry in Boston, Mass.) is presented as a model which embodies the principles we have elaborated. In this full-time program, a year of educational experiences prepares community mental health professionals to assume leadership positions as planners, innovators, administrators, researchers,

and educators. A systematic coverage of current theory and practice in community mental health is provided through required core courses. Opportunities to acquire deeper knowledge in areas of individual choice and interest are provided through elective courses and through participation in community service activities. Individual preferences can also be pursued by cross-registration in courses within other departments of the Harvard University.

The principles that are presented in the didactic teaching are translated into practice in an available regional network of urban and rural community mental health programs and human service systems. Trainees enter the community as trained professionals and are not presented to the agencies as students. Although the agencies are aware that these professionals are spending the year broadening their perspectives in community mental health work, they also know that the trainees have the credentials of established psychiatric professionals. In our view, the graduate student model does not sufficiently capitalize on the accumulated knowledge and skills of the professional trainees. The trainee in community psychiatry seeks learning experiences that are geared toward extension of his repertoire of techniques rather than acquisition of the basic techniques of his discipline. Fellows in training are professional colleagues who work in close collaboration with the more experienced teaching staff.

Generally, trainees come from the fields of psychiatry, psychology, public health, sociology, nursing, or social work. Their background may range from that of resident psychiatric to senior professor. The program therefore attempts to provide the most appropriate individual "fit" for each professional trainee. Individual programs hold in common the following purposes and goals:

1) To incorporate a mental health generalist approach covering broad areas of community mental health knowledge.
2) To acquire a knowledge of basic principles, concepts, and approaches both in the didactic program and through practical experiences.
3) To develop competence in such mental health techniques as consultation, education, linking, and coordination.

4) To develop dynamic concepts of social systems which can be applied to the amelioration of behavioral disorders.

Administrative Structure

The administrative structure that is designed to plan and implement the training program is as follows:

1) Each Fellow has an advisor who may occupy various positions in the training program. Most advisors are professionals who are active in teaching and in community service. They help the trainee design his program, serve as role models, and are able to guide and support the trainee in his learning experiences.

2) The program is characterized by a high level both of differentiation and necessary integration. A coordinating committee regulates the training processes and is composed of advisors, supervisors, and teaching staff. This committee reviews and ratifies the individually designed programs of each trainee. The group has the responsibility for the design and implementation of the total training program. Changes are made in response to the training needs of Fellows (trainees) and the advancing knowledge in the field.

3) The full-time teaching staff is composed of professionals who both teach and participate in community service. These professionals help the Fellows acquire and refine the conceptual and practitioner models of community mental health.

The full-time teaching staff is strengthened by a group of part-time staff. Part-time staff are located in a variety of strategic community agencies who can impart ideas and experience of significant field relevance.

The climate of the Laboratory, like any effective training program, is such that:

1) A setting is provided in which mental health and social science professionals as well as lay individuals knowledgeable in community affairs can teach innovative approaches to community mental health.

2) The teaching staff is encouraged to participate on an active continuous basis in community service.

3) Linkages are facilitated among the multidisciplinary teaching staff so as to coordinate teaching material and to share experiences.

4) It facilitates the presentation of knowledge accumulated from the areas of research, community practice, and empirical findings while maintaining recognition of the field's state of flux and development. The overall emphasis in teaching is upon enhancement of capacities to deal with new and uncertain situations in productive ways.

Core and Elective Activities

The academic year is divided into four quarters of approximately eight weeks each, so that opportunities are provided for appropriate field visits. During the first two quarters a conceptual foundation is built in basic core courses. The last two quarters are more open in design to provide opportunities for the design of electives geared to idiosyncratic individual and subgroup needs.

The weekly schedule, as in any representative program, is divided into three days of didactic teaching, consisting mainly of seminars, lectures, and workshops, and two days of community practice. The didactic courses are designated as core or elective courses. Since all programs have such core courses, a brief outline of them follows:

Community Mental Health. This course provides trainees with an opportunity to integrate principles of public health, mental health, social science, and research. An attempt is made to shift focus from a single-patient approach to a consistent population-oriented view of mental health.

Principles of Mental Health Consultation. This seminar describes the theory, rationale, and techniques of mental health consultation. The focus is on problems of penetrating and assessing the social system of the consultee institutions, on obtaining and maintaining sanction, and on deciding the correct mix of consultation and other interventive techniques.

Fundamentals of Administration. This seminar approaches programmatic strategies in community mental health as an organizational and administrative problem. Illustrations are drawn from such areas as business, industry, politics, government, education, hospitals, and public health. Attention is given to such functions as budgeting, accounting, personnel recruitment, training, administration, manpower, and also to such broader issues as organizational goals, leadership and power, politics, legislation, peer agencies, the federal government, voluntary agencies, administrative alternatives, and bureaucracy.

Planning. This seminar views the planning process as a tool to influence or inhibit change. From this point of view, it examines tactics, trends, and current issues in health and welfare planning. It looks at planning methods historically and compares planning models and typologies. Case material from a variety of systems complements the basic theoretical readings.

Community Affairs. This seminar explores a broad range of theoretical concepts about the nature of the community, its power structure, and its internal dynamics. The relationship of the community to the environment is examined, as well as the techniques used by mental health professionals to effect social change.

The core courses and elective seminars form the foundation on which models for practice are developed. These courses are evaluated through an open feedback communication system between the trainees and the coordinating committee.

The Fellows are encouraged to design and participate in a research project or program which can be accomplished within the year. This exposes the Fellow to broad research issues in the field and enhances awareness of research methodology. These activities may not develop research practitioners but do increase the likelihood that trainees will be sophisticated research consumers within future programs that they may direct.

Trainees are encouraged to reflect upon and crystallize their experiences by writing a paper of publishable quality on some aspect of community mental health. Examples of papers written are Dumont's (1967) and Bloom's (1963), as cited in reference.

Summer Programs

Since the academic year ends in June, it is possible for the trainee to work full-time in a special area of practice, administration, or research during the summer months. This intensive experience provides an opportunity to synthesize the year's seminar and field learning. The Fellow and his advisor develop a concrete plan for this placement so that career-oriented individual choices can be fulfilled.

The following examples indicate the range of possibilities which can be designed to meet the individual needs and interests of a Fellow:

1. Placement with the Office of Administration and Finance of the Commonwealth of Massachusetts—to work with the Committee on Comprehensive Health Planning for the State.
2. Placement with a Department of Psychiatry—to work with senior personnel in the process of developing a community mental health program for a catchment area.
3. Placement with a precepter researcher—to gain a deeper and broader knowledge of research problems and methodologies in connection with on-going research in preventive psychiatry and community mental health methods.
4. Placement with local community action programs—to gain direct experience with community advocacy groups developing programs to meet their own needs.

Other field opportunities are available in such organizations as the Office of Health Affairs, Office of Economic Opportunity, the National Institute of Mental Health, the Office of Health Services and Mental Health Administration, Health, Education, and Welfare, state and local community mental health programs in California, Illinois, New York, Minnesota, and Massachusetts. In each case, the Fellow is responsible to an administrator, senior community worker, or researcher.

Community Service Activities

Through the extensive network of placements with community organizations, Fellows are provided with experiences which stimulate the skills necessary to practice in the mental health field. As trainees master these field experiences, they develop creative adaptations to situations which demand innovative concepts, functions, and roles. A flexible approach to problems and the development of rapid feedback loops between new concepts, pioneering practice, evaluation, and ongoing planning receives supervisory emphasis during these experiences.

Relationships between the community host systems and the training unit are essential for a successful program. These relationships are both formal and informal. The more formal tend generally to be contractual relationships. Some of the models we use for practice in the community agencies are "systems" models, where groups of Fellows operate at many levels within a system. Another approach offers a public health model which is applied in community mental health centers with catchment area responsibilities. In the "systems" approach the teaching staff and Fellows work as a collaborative consultant team with individual consultants operating in the agency at different levels. These levels can include senior administrative personnel, middle management, and line workers. Planning for these intervention practices is done during sessions in the training unit and each staff member and Fellow takes on a specific role and task within the system. This provides an opportunity to develop a variety of techniques, which include:

1. Consultation—ranging from program-centered administrative consultation to client-centered or consultee-centered case consultation.
2. Education—in-service training, continuing education, and supervision.
3. Coordination—helping groups of professionals in human services agencies develop boundary-spanning, linking, collaborative, and coordinating skills.
4. Mediation—helping to resolve communication blocks which exist between administrators and consumers, as part of community organization activities.
5. Innovative service program—design, in participation with policy-makers, of a variety of health, welfare, and educational systems.

Some examples of programs developed within community agencies include: a city-wide program of systematic administrative and case consultation to a visiting nurses association; a program of consultation and in-service training for the administrative, supervisory, guidance, and teaching staffs of a city school department; consultation to an Episcopal diocese (with administrative consultation to the bishop and his headquarters staff; and group and individual consultee-centered consultation to clergymen drawn from a cross section of inner, middle, and outer-city parishes); administrative and program consultation to a model cities program; consultation and in-service training to a community action program.

A method that can be used to coordinate these types of activities within a training program is the "learning-teaching teams" approach. In this approach a small group of staff and trainees enters an agency as a team. In scheduled team meetings the group plans its strategies, monitors its tactical errors, and generates the theories and models required for collaborative problem solving in the field.

Following an alternative model, the trainee operates in a mental health center which has responsibility for a geographic area. In such an area he can have unique experiences by consultation to several agencies active in the local care-giving network. Such a field experience provides the trainee with an opportunity to understand and apply the catchment area concept. He can become familiar with the issues and techniques pertinent to community activities. He works closely with the director of the mental health program and is able to participate in many of his administrative activities. He is also assigned two or three specific subsystems within the catchment area where his intervention may assume the form of consultation, education, program development, and/or coordination. In weekly meetings in the training unit his activities and experiences within the mental health programs can be conceptualized, clarified, and integrated. The teaching staff is generally familiar with the mental health activities of particular catchment area programs and so can act as supervisor of techniques and approaches, while the center director communicates with the Fellow at an administrative level. Examples of experiences in one mental health center are: consultation to the administrator and teachers of a Head Start project; consultation with the counselors of a day-care center; administrative and case-centered consultation to a junior high school (that houses all the children of the city in the ninth grade). Another mental health center provided opportunities to work with a group of parents that wanted to organize a nursery for retarded children; to consult with a group of public health nurses; and to participate in an educational program for teachers in a school system.

Implications Drawn from Experience in a Training Unit

In planning training programs our experience leads us to emphasize two phenomena. Most psychiatric professionals find that the role acquired in dyadic patient-doctor relationships is not adequate for population-centered approaches or community consultation. In the training program such professional's community experience can generate role conflict. Affective distress may then need to be dealt with. In recognition of this role-stress dilemma, it is helpful to facilitate, in orientation activities and supervisory practices, discussion of this conflict. The trainee can then receive anticipatory guidance and avail himself of opportunities to verbalize his experience.

We also find that there has been a gradual shift on the part of trainees as the year progresses from being quite dependent on structured schedules to being more self-directed, choosing areas of learning and practice which are more tailored to individual needs. For this reason it might be suggested that the first two quarters of a year should be firmly structured with well-defined learning experiences, followed by a semistructured sequential portion of the year. To do this successfully, planning sessions should be built into the first months in order to design the last part of the year. All along guidance and suggestions from staff should be available.

A series of activities arises out of this flexible programming design. These experiences revolve around the need for the group to become organized, to choose representatives for committees, to design group courses and activities, to plan curriculum together, and to arrange for occasional guest lecturers. Fellows convene to coordinate efforts and help implement part of the program. This allows a supportive matrix to form, collaborative problem-solving to occur, and informal learning links to develop. These internal organizational activities provide practice in leadership and administration. Fellows are brought closer together, develop esprit de corps, and sustain themselves through some of the critical role transition of their year.

Other Educational Activities

Opportunities can be created for medical students to participate in aspects of a training program. Students can be exposed to some of the basic problems of theory, research, and practice in community mental health. They can also gain first-hand knowledge of community service agencies involved in the prevention and control of mental disorders. Students can be broadly exposed to community mental health practitioners and researchers, and acquire some "social systems clinician" and data-processing skills. In our experience, career changes in community mental health may be promoted by such student exposure.

It should also be possible for psychiatric residents to audit some courses in the training unit as well as participate in field work within the community.

A training program can also provide a congenial base for graduate faculty in search of a productive sabbatical year. Creative packages of learning and/or research experiences can be individually tailored to fit each visiting professor's needs.

In-service Training

Personnel from departments of mental health can participate in the seminars of a training program; such participation provides conceptual models for ongoing projects while bringing current problems into the classroom. Opportunities emerge for the systematic organization of field data and the constructive synthesis of field action and seminar reflection.

We have drawn the profile of a representative training program. In so doing our primary concern has been to describe the most salient facets of its formal training structure.

This focus on formal issues has limited our description of the rich aspects of the ever-twisting kaleidoscope of human interactions within the program. It is however our deep belief that significant learning occurs along many ineffable human dimensions. The informal human relations matrix of a training program provides infinite opportunities for human growth and learning. Although we have not depicted this matrix, much staff time and energy is devoted to the maintenance of a nurturant emotional climate—to the development of a system with generative properties.

CONCLUSION

The authors would like to conclude by sharing some personal dilemmas with the reader:

1. Unlike the Hebridean balladier, we do not know where we are going. From two recent

statements by leaders of the community mental health movement we believe that ours is a shared dilemma.

Caplan (1969) has recently predicted that "hard times" lie ahead for the community mental health movement. He has asserted the needs for reference group consolidation in "sanctuaries for hard times." Yolles (1969) is more tentative in his predictions: "No one can predict whether change in the immediate future will owe its directions to the forces of destruction or to the forces of construction" (p. 3). Whatever the uncertain future holds, Yolles asserts with great emphasis that the psychiatrist "must say farewell to professional isolation in the ivory tower of the private practice of yesterday" (p. 3).

2. Because of the uncertainty about future tasks and task environments, we underscore the need to learn to live and work under conditions of uncertainty. We share with Yolles (1969), Duhl (1969), and others the prediction that the community psychiatrist of tomorrow will need enhanced political and social responsiveness. As he enters the community problem-solving sector, the community psychiatrist will be subjected to tugs and pressures in a field where political, economic, and social forces may not succeed in promoting climates favorable to mental health. The community psychiatrist may be called upon to bear witness on behalf of consumers whose expectations are "don't talk it, do it." The community psychiatrist will be tested, and accepted or rejected, by the *results* he achieves, and not the preciousness of the *methods* that he may employ.

3. While projecting a future task environment of uncertainty and turbulence, we do believe that these will be times of "dynamic disequilibrium"; our age has been described by Drucker (1968) as an "age of discontinuity." Planning under conditions of discontinuity is possible and gains can be maximized in times of apparent disruption or ferment. Our very commitment to crisis theory leads us to believe that it is in times of social and individual disequilibrium that we can best maximize our impact. In our approach to community problem-solving, we stress the need for trainees to acquire exploratory, open-ended, causal-analytic approaches. In order to do this, we wish continually to emphasize the need to tolerate ambiguity, anxiety, and uncertainty so that premature decision-making is avoided.

4. We believe that changing times and tasks require innovative problem-solving, functions, and roles; and we also see a need for active, entrepreneurial promotion of these innovative and experimental approaches.

5. As we continue to explore the multivariant relationship between environment and behavior, we see the need for higher levels of integration between behavioral and human services disciplines. Movement towards shared goals can be facilitated in some of the following ways:

a. By an increased infusion of humanism in service transactions. In this, we endorse the values of Sullivan (1953) ("we are all more simply human than otherwise"); Mills (1963) ("I.B.M. plus reality plus humanism equals the social sciences"); Caplan[4] ("mental health is promoted by a community with high indices of social integration plus a humanistic philosophy"); and Yolles ("as the great innovators in the treatment of mental illness have demonstrated, the history of psychiatry is essentially the history of humanism. Every time humanism is diminished, psychiatry has entered a new ebb" (1969, p. 3)).

b. We foresee that the community mental health movement will find itself merging with and sharing domain with other human service systems. We foresee that such merging, sharing, and creative collaboration will multiply resources and increase human service productivity. In such networks we welcome an expanding role for the citizen-consumer. We foresee that the citizen-consumer will transcend his passive consumer role to become our partner in planning and administration.

We are often confronted with questions we cannot answer. When so confronted it seems most appropriate to listen and reflect. Our consultees and our trainees constantly help us to recognize that consultation and education are transactional processes: learners teach and teachers learn. This transactional process with its generative capacity to *innovate* and *create* provides us with our optimistic conviction that, in community mental health, we can learn to adapt intelligently to the certainty of uncertainty.

Notes

1. Community mental health practitioners are members of the medical nursing, psychological, social work, or education-counseling professions.

2. These are National Institute of Mental Health-supported programs and are listed on pages 896–897.

3. Only the programs about which sufficient curriculum information was available have been included in this analysis.

4. G. Caplan, personal communication.

References

Baker, F., & Schulberg, H. C. Community health care-giving systems: Interorganizational networks. In A. Sheldon, F. Baker, & C. McLaughlin (eds.), *System and medical care.* Cambridge: MIT Press, 1971.

Bloom, B. L. Definitional aspects of crisis concepts. *Journal of Consulting Psychology*, 1963, 27, 498–502.

Caplan, G. *Principles of preventive psychiatry.* New York: Basic Books, 1964.

Caplan, G. Development of community psychiatry concepts. In A. M. Freedman & H. I. Kaplan (eds.), *Comprehensive textbook of psychiatry.* Baltimore: Williams & Wilkins, 1967.

Caplan, G. Conceptual models in community mental health. Laboratory of Community Psychiatry, January 1968. (Mimeo)

Caplan, G. Implications for community psychiatry: Personal reflections. (Epilogue) In R. B. Caplan, *Psychiatry and the community in nineteenth century America.* New York: Basic Books, 1969.

Daniels, D. N., & Kuldau, J. M. Marginal man. The tether of traditional and international social system therapy. *Community Mental Health Journal*, 1967, 3, 16.

Drucker, P. F. *The age of discontinuity.* New York: Harper & Row, 1968.

Duhl, L. J. Health–2000 A.D. *American Journal of Public Health*, 1969, 59, 1809–1815.

Dumont, M. P. Tavern culture: The sustenance of homeless men. *American Journal of Orthopsychiatry*, 1967, 37, 938–945.

GAP Report No. 64. Education for community psychiatry, 1967, 6, 499.

Golann, S. E. Initial findings of the follow-up study of child development counselors. *American Journal of Public Health*, 1967, 57, 1759.

Hansell, N. Casualty management method. *Archives of General Psychiatry*, 1968, 19, 288.

Hansell, N. Patient predicament and clinical service: A system. *Archives of General Psychiatry*, 1967, 17, 205.

Hausman, W., & McK Rioch, D. Military psychiatry. *Archives of General Psychiatry*, 1967, 16, 727–738.

Hirschowitz, R. G. Changing human behavior in the state hospital organization. *Psychiatric Quarterly*, 1969, 43:591–611.

Horowitz, I. L. (ed.), *Power, politics, and people: The collected essays of C. Wright Mills.* New York: Ballantine, 1963.

Lewin, K. *Boundaries of psychological regions, principles of topological psychology.* New York: McGraw-Hill, 1936.

Miller, G. E. Continuing education for what? *Journal of Medical Education*, 1967, 42, 322–323.

Ruesch, J. Social process. *Archives of General Psychiatry*, 1966, 15, 577–589.

Shapiro, D. S., & Maholick, L. T. A community mental health program revisited. *Psychology Report*, 1967, 20, 289–290.

Srole, L. Social psychiatry: A case of the babel syndrome. Paper presented at the meeting of the American Psychopathological Association, New York, February 17, 1967.

Sullivan, H. S. *The interpersonal theory of psychiatry.* (ed. by H. S. Perry & Gawel) New York: Norton, 1953.

Vail, D. G. *Dehumanization and the institutional career.* Springfield, Ill.: Charles C Thomas, 1966.

Wedge, B. Training for leadership in cross-cultural dialogue: The DA-TA model. Paper presented at the Conference on Cross-Cultural Interaction sponsored by the Chief of Chaplains/Office of Naval Research, Washington, D. C., 1968.

Yolles, S. F. Past, present, and 1980: Trend projections. In L. Bellak & H. H. Barten (eds.), *Progress in community mental health.* New York: Grune & Stratton, 1969.

40

Graduate Education in Community Psychology

Charles D. Spielberger and Ira Iscoe

The stresses encountered in a modern industrial society place many new and different demands on the human condition, and significant advances in psychological theory, research, and practice are needed to help man cope with these stresses. Community psychology represents an emerging field and a new frontier for the study of human behavior. The goals of community psychology are broadly concerned with clarifying the complex interrelationships between individuals and their social environment, and with the discovery of more effective ways for coping with the stresses of modern life.

The rapid growth of community psychology during the past decade has been stimulated by widespread dissatisfaction with traditional clinical approaches to mental health problems. Since community psychology lacks at present a coherent body of knowledge of its own, and an established set of practices, there are as yet few meaningful precedents upon which to base graduate training programs in this field. To establish a viable community psychology that will meet the growing needs for an ever broader spectrum of psychological research and services in community settings, radical modification of existing graduate programs in psychology will be required, or entirely new training programs must be created.

In this chapter, we review a number of factors that have influenced the development of community psychology and attempt to clarify some of the new roles that have emerged for psychologists in community settings. We then consider the academic foundations and field training experiences that may help to prepare psychologists to function in the community. Finally, we survey recent trends in graduate education in community psychology and examine directions and prospects for the future.

FACTORS THAT HAVE INFLUENCED THE DEVELOPMENT OF COMMUNITY PSYCHOLOGY

Prior to World War II, most psychologists worked in university settings and were concerned primarily with teaching and with laboratory research. Psychologists associated with mental hospitals and child guidance clinics were few in number and their responsibilities were generally limited to administering and interpreting psychological tests. Following the war, urgent demands to provide care for thousands of military psychiatric casualties stimulated the development of training programs in clinical psychology. Aided by financial support from the Veterans Administration and the National Institute of Mental Health, these efforts resulted in the establishment of doctoral programs in clinical psychology at most major universities.

The rapid growth of clinical psychology in the postwar years led the American Psychological Association to convene a national conference on training in 1949 (Raimy, 1950). At this conference, which was held in Boulder, Colorado, a "scientist-professional" model for graduate education in clinical psychology was adopted. In addition to a broad general education in the field of psychology, this model also emphasized intensive training in the development of professional skills in clinical psychodiagnosis and psychotherapy. While the scientist-professional model continues to provide the general orientation for more than 70 APA-approved doctoral training programs in clinical psychology, our conceptions of the causality and treatment of mental illness have undergone radical change in recent years.

During the decade 1946–55, clinical and counseling psychology were concerned primarily with intrapsychic phenomena. The goals of psychological service were to determine how psychodynamic factors determined deviant behavior so that the personality structure of clients or patients could be modified through appropriate psychotherapeutic treatment procedures. By 1955, many psychologists were convinced that mental health involved something more than the absence of mental illness, and it was apparent that preoccupation with the mentally ill was preventing psychologists from giving needed attention to the full range of community mental health problems.

Growing recognition of limitations in traditional conceptions of mental illness and its treatment stimulated the Education and Training Board of the American Psychological Association to convene a conference in 1955 on Psychology and Mental Health (Strother, 1956). In the conference keynote address, Robert H. Felix, then Director of the National Institute of Mental Health, challenged psychology to broaden its conceptions of mental illness and embrace community-oriented approaches to mental health.

To what extent can non-clinical approaches actually produce changes in people that represent improvement in their mental health? This is the question that constantly bedevils those of us who want to develop public health programs in the mental health field. Each of us knows that there is no justification to attempt to handle all the psychological problems of all people on a treatment basis. It is unlikely that we could ever produce enough therapists to meet this objective. Consequently, we talk about mental health education, child rearing practices, mental health in the schools, and the contribution of other agencies to mental health and prevention (Felix, 1956, pp. 7–8).

Concern about mental illness and mounting evidence of unmet community mental health needs led the United States Congress to pass the Mental Health Study Act of 1955. This Act established the Joint Commission on Mental Illness and Health which was directed to make recommendations for a national mental health program. Although many important mental health problems (e.g., drug addiction, alcoholism, juvenile delinquency, mental retardation) were given little consideration, nevertheless, the studies carried out under the sponsorship of the Joint Commission have profoundly influenced the development of community psychology. In general, these studies showed that: (a) the nation's mental health manpower resources were severely limited (Albee, 1959); (b) mental health services for children and for racial and ethnic minority groups were lacking (Robinson, DeMarche, & Waggle, 1960); and (c) mental health services were typically not accessible at times of major crises and only minimally available to the poor (Gurin, Veroff, & Feld, 1960).

The final report of the Joint Commission (Ewalt, 1961) recommended that new mental health facilities be established in community settings, that educational and consultative services be greatly expanded, and that research and preventive efforts be intensified. These recommendations were embodied in the legislative program of John F. Kennedy, the first American president to deliver a message to Congress specifically related to the mental health of the nation. In response to this message, Congress passed the Mental Health Facilities Act of 1963 which provided funds for the construction of comprehensive community mental health centers throughout the nation. This Act was later amended to provide support for professional staff as well. Thus, responsibility for the treatment of the mentally ill, as well as the arena in which treatment would take place, was to be moved from the mental hospital to the community.

Other New Frontier legislation led to the founding of the Peace Corps in which psychologists have played an active role. The Kennedy years also brought a greater awareness of the problems of poverty and cultural deprivation, and prepared the way for President Johnson's Great Society legislation which created community action programs such as Head Start, Upward Bound, Day Care, VISTA, and the Neighborhood Youth Corps. Thus, the decade 1955–65, which began with Felix's challenge for psychology to embrace a community-oriented public health approach, ended with the enactment of broad-gauged social legislation that provided funds for community-action programs.

During this period, shortages in professional manpower led an increasing number of psychologists to invest significant portions of their time in consulting with community care-givers (e.g., ministers, public health nurses, welfare workers, school personnel) about mental health problems, rather than in working directly with individual clients or patients (Spielberger, 1967). Mental health consultation reflected a significant departure from the traditional clinical role of the mental health professions and an important new dimension for mental health practice.[1] The impact of community-action programs also led to increased demands for psychologists to provide consultation on research and program evaluation, and highlighted the need for appropriate training in this area.

In the Spring of 1965, a conference on the "Education of Psychologists in Community Mental Health" was held in Swampscott, Massachusetts. At this conference, now generally referred to as the Boston Conference (Bennett, 1966), the participants' initial concerns with community mental health evolved into a broader conception which recognized that the community itself must be examined as a social system. It was no longer sufficient to deal only with the mental health problems of individuals who were casualties of the system. In thus facilitating a shift in focus from community mental health to community psychology, the Boston Conference marked the beginning of a new decade characterized by the ever-increasing involvement of psychologists in community affairs.

In the few short years since the Boston Conference, many events have contributed to community psychology, and continue to influence its development. While a detailed review of these events is beyond the scope of this chapter, we might note the general malaise of the cities, the impact of civil rights legislation, widespread campus unrest, and violence in the streets. There is hardly a community institution that is not presently under some kind of attack, and many community agencies have been unable to deal constructively with confrontations put forth by consumers of their professional services.

Recent developments in the community make it necessary to look at essentially old problems in different contexts and to seek new solutions. For example, violence in the streets has always been with us, but its recent increase and the forms of its manifestation have challenged traditional methods of law enforcement. Relationships between the police, the laws they are called upon to enforce, and the citizens they serve have never been more strained. Consequently, the need for communities to develop new standards and better internal controls has never been greater.

The establishment of the Office of Economic Opportunity to conduct the War on Poverty has resulted in a variety of community-based action programs of central importance to community psychology. Programs such as Day Care and Head Start cannot operate in a vacuum; active participation by the families and by the communities of the children who are served is required. The phrase "maximum feasible participation" is frequently used to explain OEO's efforts to involve the poor in the decision-making process with their own communities, and the implications of this concept for policy-making and the redistribution of power are just beginning to be recognized (Kravitz & Kolodner, 1969; Rubin, 1969).

The advent of community mental health centers, especially in the deprived areas of cities, has resulted in drastically changed concepts about psychotherapy and other helping procedures. The poor do not distinguish between social pathology and psychopathology, nor do they appreciate the attempts of the mental health professions to make such distinctions. While Medicare and Medicaid have provided new approaches to the delivery of medical services to the poor, and documented the need for even fuller medical coverage, these programs have also placed such tremendous strains on existing medical resources that we are forced to reexamine our basic assumptions about the training of physicians and other health professionals.

The decade that began in 1965 witnessed the first position paper ever issued by the American Psychological Association (Smith & Hobbs, 1966). This paper pointed to the need for representatives of the community to be actively involved in setting goals and determining basic policies for comprehensive mental health centers if these centers were ever to become effective community agencies. The APA position paper also emphasized the need for community programs to promote positive mental health, as well as to prevent and treat mental illnesses.

For psychologists, the prospect of community involvement poses both a threat and a challenge. With but a few exceptions, the graduate training of psychologists has contained little that would help them to work effectively in the community. Consequently, if psychologists are to be involved in community affairs, graduate education in psychology must provide students with opportunities to learn about communities as social systems, and to understand the sociopolitical realities that confront those who work in community settings.

NEW ROLES FOR PSYCHOLOGISTS IN THE COMMUNITY

The complex new roles that are being assumed in the community by psychologists have been described by such terms as mental health consultant, participant-conceptualizer, social systems evaluator, social change agent, and the like. This diversity of roles clearly indicates that community psychology does not imply a homogeneous group of psychologists with a unified body of knowledge and an established set of professional procedures. Rather, as Scribner (1968, p. 4) has recently suggested, "Community psychology represents the bringing together of various kinds of psychologists who have some concern with the broad question of 'man in society.' "

Cowen (1970) describes two major roles for psychologists in community settings: the "mental health quarterback" and the "social engineer." In consultation with other professionals and lay leaders, the mental health quarterback plans and implements mental health programs and engages in the recruitment and training of nonprofessionals to work on mental health problems. The social engineer is broadly concerned with the primary prevention of mental disorders, and with clarification of what can be done to modify social institutions to produce a healthier and more effective society.

Spielberger and Iscoe (1970) have noted that community-oriented psychologists currently function as mental health consultants, participant-conceptualizers, and social change agents. The major goal of mental health consultation is to assist community care-givers in handling the emotional problems of their clients with greater effectiveness. As a participant-conceptualizer, the psychologist is an expert with special conceptual skills whose task it is to help community leaders analyze and clarify mental health problems in terms of social system variables. As a community change agent, the psychologist attempts to solve the problems he has helped to clarify, either by working directly on the problem himself or training others.

In view of the many new professional roles for psychologists in community settings, Division 27 (Community Psychology) established a Task Force to clarify community mental health goals and priorities. Since the spring of 1968, this Task Force has produced seven position papers, ranging in topic from strategies of intervention and primary prevention to epidemiology and ecology. A preliminary report of the Task Force (Glidewell & Brown, 1969), submitted to the APA Board of Professional Affairs in the fall of 1969, stressed the need to modify physical, biological, and social environmental systems in order to reduce the incidence of mental illness and social pathology. The Task Force Report also recognized the urgent need to train psychologists in a different mold, one more in keeping with the functions they are being called upon to carry out in community settings. It was specifically recommended that university psychology departments give the highest priority to training psychologists who are "competent to design, execute, and be accountable for collaborative experimental social interventions." Similar recommendations with regard to the need for educational innovations in psychology were incorporated in the 1969 Annual Report of Division 27 (Iscoe & Kelly, 1969).

More and more, psychologists are being called upon to participate as mental health consultants and participant-conceptualizers in the planning and development of a variety of community services. As agents of social change, psychologists are being asked to contribute to the modification of existing social structures. The effectiveness of psychologists in these new professional roles will be determined in large measure by the adequacy of their graduate education. Therefore, it is a matter of critical importance to examine the academic foundations on which community psychology is being built and the field experiences that prepare psychologists to function in the many new roles which are being created for them by society's needs.

ACADEMIC FOUNDATIONS OF COMMUNITY PSYCHOLOGY

Community psychology must draw upon the resources of many different areas within psychology for its basic knowledge. Theoretical conceptions and research findings in social psychology, personality, abnormal psychology, developmental psychology, perception, and learning are of particular relevance to community psychology, but utilization of knowledge from these fields will require new integrations. While many of the current techniques and methods of school, industrial, counseling, and clinical psychology are of undeniable value to the community psychologist, such techniques require modification and refinement in order to apply them in a broader community context.

Among the current educational requirements in doctoral psychology programs, what content areas and professional skills are most essential for community psychology? What kinds of educational inputs from other disciplines are needed? It is no longer adequate merely to train clinical psychologists with a community orientation because the knowledge base for clinical psychology is too restricted (Reiff, 1970). For psychologists to function effectively in community settings, the contributions of fields such as sociology, anthropology, social psychiatry, epidemiology, economics, political science, social work, and urban planning are likely to be more relevant than some of the traditional areas within psychology.

The community psychologist requires, at the very least, a basic understanding of community organization if he is to work effectively with care-givers and community leaders as a mental health consultant and participant-conceptualizer, and such knowledge is especially important to the psychologist who is called upon to intervene in complex social systems as a change agent. But in order to accommodate educational inputs from other disciplines, existing doctoral programs must be lengthened or their content must be modified. Since many doctoral programs in clinical psychology already require six to seven years of graduate work, the prospect of extending them is not very attractive.

Despite objections that may be expressed to eliminating traditional courses in psychology, graduate education in community psychology will be forced to become more selective. It may be necessary, for example, to dispense with the more molecular aspects of psychology in order to provide intensive training in the most relevant areas and permit significant contributions from other disciplines. In effect, such changes have been incorporated into the newly established doctoral program in clinical psychology at the City University of New York (Singer & Bard, 1970) in which seminars on "Social Psychopathology" and "Small Group Dynamics and Family Interaction" may be taken instead of more traditional but less relevant courses. There is also a strong emphasis on training in consultation in this program which reflects the "new look" in community-oriented clinical psychology.

Training in research methodology more germane to the problems of community psychology will also be required. For example, courses in demographic and epidemiological methods, biometrics, attitude measurement, and survey research are likely to be more useful than small-sample inferential statistics. Community psychologists who intend to carry out research on social system problems will require knowledge of computer methods for multivariate analysis and for the simulation of complex social processes. In addition, the community psychologist will need to have some understanding of the major research methods in other social science disciplines.

FIELD TRAINING EXPERIENCES IN COMMUNITY PSYCHOLOGY

To prepare graduate students in psychology for work in community settings, Roen (1970) recommends that they be exposed to a broad range of everyday problems of living in the natural environments in which these problems occur. Confrontation with problems at the scene of the action is called for, not merely academic conversations about these problems in the classroom. As Roen has observed, the basic question for psychology has changed from "What is the nature of man?" to the contextual question of "What happens at the interface of inner man and problem world?"

The active involvement of psychologists in the community poses important questions as to the nature of the settings in which practicum training should be carried out, and the kinds of field experiences that are most needed. Many practicum facilities were originally organized as laboratories to meet the needs of academic subspecialties; clients or patients were selected for study and treatment because they had problems which would provide students with opportunities to practice certain techniques. Thus, the choice of practicum agencies often determined the psychological techniques that were learned. Since the field settings in which psychologists are trained profoundly influence the skills they develop and their attitudes toward their professional work, the need to develop facilities that will permit psychologists to make more effective contributions in community settings is apparent. Graduate students in psychology should be exposed to a wide range of applications of psychological knowledge in nontraditional community agencies. It may be useful at this point to describe several innovative community psychology programs and the unique training settings in which these efforts are being carried out.

The University of Rochester requires a year-long, community-oriented practicum of doctoral students in clinical psychology during their final year of training (Cowen, 1970). Students work in Day Care programs located in elementary schools, in settlement houses with adolescents who serve as "companions" to neighborhood children, in programs for training teacher aids to work with emotionally disturbed school children, and in a variety of other community settings. These training assignments bring graduate students closer to the mental health problems of the poor in the environments in which they work and live, while providing a broad spectrum of experiences with a number of community agencies.

The psychology department at the University of Cincinnati established a Psychological Services Center as a major training resource in community

psychology for advanced graduate students (Goodstein & Oseas, 1967). The Center provides consultation for educational institutions, the police department, religious organizations, anti-poverty programs, family service agencies, and various community planning groups. The Center also assists community agencies in preparing research proposals. Students assigned to the Center for practicum training work with community caregivers such as policemen, teachers, ministers, and social workers under the supervision of Center staff.

The Yale University Psycho-Educational Clinic was developed as an integral part of the Yale Psychology Department (Sarason & Levine, 1970). This "clinic" is quite different from conventional mental health facilities in that it serves as a headquarters, rather than as a work setting, for psychology faculty and students who spend their time as consultants, participant-conceptualizers, and change agents in a variety of community agencies. The staff of the clinic has also contributed in many different ways to projects sponsored by the New Haven Community Action Program.

The locus of the multidisciplinary field training program in community psychology at the Duke University Medical Center is a small, rural county in North Carolina (Altrocchi & Eisdorfer, 1970). The coordinating headquarters for this program is in the county health department, but there is active involvement with the entire community. Trainees observe senior mental health consultants in individual and group consultation with school teachers, nurses, policemen, ministers, and other community care-givers. Intensive, supervised experience is provided in individual and group mental health consultation with a variety of community agencies.

The Human Relations Center at Boston University provides a unique multidisciplinary setting for training in community psychology (Lipton & Klein, 1970). Stipends are available for graduate students from such diverse fields as philosophy, theology, law, business, psychology, sociology, social work, nursing, and education. All students take a practicum course in human relations in which a modified T-group approach helps them develop a deeper understanding and greater awareness of themselves and others.

Frequent contact with other disciplines serves to challenge and stimulate students to examine their personal values as well as the prevailing practices in their own field.

The programs described in this chapter represent but a few of the many community-oriented innovations in graduate education in psychology. Others are taking place in clinical, counseling, industrial, school, and social psychology. An opportunity for the exchange of ideas among psychologists involved in training innovations was provided in an informal symposium on community psychology at the University of Texas at Austin in the spring of 1967. In a book based in part on this symposium (Iscoe & Spielberger, 1970), conceptual issues relating to the philosophy and goals of community psychology are discussed, and a number of academic and field training programs in community psychology are described.

CURRENT TRENDS IN GRADUATE EDUCATION AND FIELD TRAINING IN COMMUNITY PSYCHOLOGY

The growth of interest in community psychology is reflected in the dramatic increase in articles and books relating to this area over the past decade and in the founding of Division 27 (Community Psychology) of the American Psychological Association in 1967, which now has more than 800 members. The growing acceptance of graduate education in community psychology in institutions of higher learning is demonstrated in Golann's (1970) surveys of academic departments of psychology. He found that "focused attention" on community psychology, defined in terms of identifiable course content relevant to community mental health, increased from less than 20 percent in 1962 to 44 percent by 1967. Furthermore, in the 1966–67 survey, ten departments reported a "distinguishable curriculum or specialization" in community mental health and community psychology, in contrast to a single department which reported the availability of such intensive training in 1962.

In the spring of 1969, the Division 27 Committee on Manpower and Training conducted a survey of academic and field training opportunities in community psychology. Questionnaires

were sent to APA-accredited doctoral programs and internship settings in clinical and counseling psychology, and to other programs and facilities where it was known that training in community psychology was being undertaken. Information pertaining to current course offerings and field training opportunities in community mental health and community psychology were obtained. In addition, respondents were asked to provide descriptive statements about their training programs, including multidisciplinary emphasis, the availability of stipends, and whether or not an academic degree was awarded by the program.[2]

A summary of the results of the survey of academic institutions offering training in community psychology is presented in Table 40–1. The following brief analysis of the content of the academic programs listed in Table 40–1 was given in the Final Report of the Division 27 Committee on Manpower and Training (Bloom, 1969a, p. 1):

The most common elements include introductions to innovative community-based action programs, case consultation, and preventive services. Least commonly identified as subject matter in academic settings is mental health program administration, national and state legislation, health and welfare agency structure and function and the general area of empirical studies, particularly those dealing with the identification of high-risk groups and community social system analysis.

If programs surveyed by Bloom reporting *both* course sequences and field training opportunities in community psychology may be regarded as having a "distinguishable curriculum or specialization," then the results of the 1969–70 survey may be compared with Golann's 1966–67 survey. In contrast to the ten departments who reported intensive specialization in community psychology in Golann's survey, 20 of the 50 academic programs listed in Table 40–1 reported intensive training according to the specified criteria. In addition, 18 institutions reported portions of courses devoted to community psychology or community mental health plus the availability of field training opportunities.

The Report of the Division 27 Committee on Manpower and Training identified 46 field settings offering training opportunities in community psychology in 1969–70. These include 17 medical centers, 13 community mental health centers

TABLE 40–1

Academic Institutions Offering Course Work and
Field Training in Community Psychology

Insititution	Characteristics of Training		
	Course Sequence	Portions of Courses	Fieldwork
Adelphi University		x	x
University of Arizona		x	
Boston University		x	x
Catholic University of America	x		
University of California at Berkeley		x	x
University of California at Los Angeles	x	x	x
University of Chicago*	x		x
University of Cincinnati	x		x
City College of City University of New York	x		x
University of Colorado	x		x
Columbia Teachers College			x
University of Connecticut		x	x
Denver University			x
Duke University		x	x
Emory University		x	x
University of Florida*	x		x
Florida State University		x	x
Fordham University		x	
University of Georgia			x
University of Houston		x	x
University of Illinois			x
Indiana University*		x	x
University of Kansas	x	x	x
Loyola University	x		
University of Massachusetts	x	x	x
University of Miami			x
University of Michigan*	x	x	x
University of Minnesota		x	x
University of Mississippi		x	x
New York University*	x		x
University of North Carolina		x	x
Northwestern University*		x	
University of Nebraska	x	x	x
Ohio State University		x	
Ohio University		x	x
George Peabody College	x		x
Pennsylvania State University		x	x
University of Pittsburgh	x	x	x
University of Portland	x		x
Purdue University	x	x	x
University of Rochester	x	x	x

	Characteristics of Training		
Institution	Course Sequence	Portions of Courses	Fieldwork
St. Louis University	x		x
Southern Illinois University		x	
State University of New York at Buffalo		x	x
University of Texas*	x		x
University of Utah	x		x
Vanderbilt University*		x	x
West Virginia University		x	x
University of Wisconsin		x	
Yale University	x		x

Note.—Only those institutions reporting courses or field training in community psychology or community mental health are listed. (Adopted with permission from Bloom, 1969.)

*Denotes interdepartmental programs.

and/or child guidance clinics, nine outpatient psychiatric settings, and seven state hospitals. The survey further indicates that the following types of training in community psychology were most often provided in these field settings: supervised experience in case consultation, crisis intervention, and brief psychotherapy. Training was least often provided in mental health program administration and research.

To facilitate constructive changes in graduate education, an Institute on Innovations in Psychological Training was established in 1967 at the University of Colorado. Supported by a training grant from the National Institute of Mental Health, the first institute was held during the summer of 1968 with "Training the psychologists for a Role in Community Change" as its theme. Most of the participants were directors of doctoral training programs in either clinical or social psychology.

As a part of the institute program, visits were made to field settings in which innovative practices in community psychology had been going on for a sufficient length of time for the program to have a reasonable degree of stability. A total of 11 different programs located in various parts of the country were visited, with each participant visiting at least nine settings. In his report on the Institute, Bloom (1969b, p. 5–6) provides the following descriptive analysis of the diverse community activities of the psychologists who staffed the field settings that were visited:

Activities in the facilities visited have moved away from the study of intrapsychic conflict to the study of social epidemiology of mental disorders. The facilities have placed greater emphasis on the development of skills in program planning and administration rather than the development of skills in the provision of clinical services. Diagnostic techniques for studying individuals are no longer as important as techniques for the diagnosis of groups, neighborhoods, and communities at large. Techniques are now increasingly important for community organization and community development rather than techniques of individual intervention. The focus in many of these programs is much more on preventive services than it is on therapeutic services. Staff are deployed much more in the task of consultation than in the task of therapy, and their therapeutic intervention, when it is employed, is much more in terms of groups of patients rather than individual patient. The fundamental knowledge to carry out these activities is shifted from an understanding of intrapsychic systems to an understanding of community social systems and community institutions. All of these changes have potential impact on the ways in which psychologists should be trained.

From Bloom's observations, it is apparent that psychologists in innovative community settings more frequently function as mental health quarterbacks and social engineers (Cowen, 1970) than in more traditional clinical roles. While Bloom noted increased participation by psychologists in community action programs, lack of conceptual clarity and methodological rigor characterized these endeavors. Absence of relevant research and the failure to evaluate the effectiveness of mental programs were identified by Bloom as the major shortcomings in present community efforts. In his words: "The spirit of inquiry seems to have been displaced by the call to action and it is highly problematical whether a field of activity characterized by action without evaluation and conceptualization can become a permanent member of the academic community" (Bloom, 1969b, p. 8).

NEW DIRECTIONS AND FUTURE PROSPECTS FOR GRADUATE EDUCATION IN COMMUNITY PSYCHOLOGY

Community psychology has evolved primarily from clinical psychology and many psychologists who now work in community settings were originally trained as clinicians. Therefore, it is not surprising that the theories and methods of clinical psychology are strongly represented in this emerging field. Indeed, clinical psychology is broadening to a point where some training programs have established community psychology as a subspecialty. Students interested in this subspecialty must acquire many of the same skills that are important in clinical psychology, but perhaps not with the same degree of expertise. In contrast to the traditional clinical psychologist who is an expert in psychodiagnosis and psychotherapy, the community-oriented clinical psychologist requires greater sophistication in mental health consultation and in understanding the community as a social system.

Just as clinical psychology has developed a stronger community orientation, so too have parallel changes occurred in counseling, school, and social psychology. And similar changes may be expected in developmental psychology as it takes on additional applied activities. We do not mean to imply that social and developmental psychologists will render professional services as mental health consultants, but we predict they will assume increasing responsibility for applied research in community settings. While we do not foresee the establishment of entirely new training programs in social and developmental psychology, we anticipate the emergence of a stronger community orientation in these fields.

In his 1969 presidential address to the APA Division of Community Psychology, Kelly advocates an ecological approach to the study of man. Kelly contends that since community psychology is basically different from other fields of psychology, "its socialization will need to be different, namely, the training of the community psychologist demands a critical period in which he learns the styles of work that are going to be relevant for his own adaptation. If the differences in requirements are real, training programs will need to be created so as to reflect these varied conditions." Kelly outlines the following seven basic principles for training in community psychology: "field assessment in the selection of community psychologists, continuous interdisciplinary interaction, the need for longitudinal perspective, the appropriate mixing of theory and practice, the need to take advantage of community events, the identification of community resources, and the continuous updating of the community psychologist."

Can the challenge of community psychology be met by academic departments? To be sure, there will be resistance to changes in curriculum and to giving up professional techniques and procedures that have served us well in working with individual clients and patients. On the basis of his experience as Secretary of Health, Education, and Welfare, John W. Gardner has noted that such resistances are characteristic of all professions: "Professions are subject to the same deadening forces that afflict all other human institutions: an attachment to time-honored ways, reverence for established procedures, a preoccupation with one's own vested interests, and an excessively narrow definition of what is relevant and important" (Gardner, 1968, p. 52). But psychology will undoubtedly continue to be called upon to lend its skills in solving society's problems, and the critical task for academic departments will be to develop training programs that are relevant to community psychology. Graduate education in community psychology will require academic foundations that enable psychologists to function more effectively at the social system level, and field training experiences that will help them develop the professional skills they will need to function as mental health consultants, social engineers, and change agents in a variety of community settings.

It is in the areas of social planning and conceptual analysis, program evaluation, and research on community problems that psychology is likely to make its most unique and significant contributions. Hopefully, the community psychologist of the future will be imbued with a spirit of scientific inquiry, and equipped by his training with the necessary conceptual and methodological tools so that he may carry out much needed research on the community as a social system.

Notes

This chapter is based in part on I. Iscoe and C. D. Spielberger (eds.) *Community Psychology: Perspectives in Training and Research*. New York, Appleton-Century-Crofts, Inc., 1970. We are grateful to Drs. Bernard L. Bloom, Mortimer M. Brown, and Stuart E. Golann for their helpful comments and suggestions, and to Mrs. Helen Thomas, Mrs. Bertha Shanblum, Mrs. Glee Coles, and Mrs. Patty Cox for their assistance in the preparation of the manuscript.

1. No survey of factors that have influenced the development of community psychology would be complete which failed to recognize the pioneering, innovative programs in community psychiatry developed in the early 1950s by Erich Lindemann (e.g., 1944, 1956) at the Harvard Medical School and the Massachusetts General Hospital, and by Gerald Caplan (e.g., 1959, 1961, 1964) at the Harvard School of Public Health. Through the work of Lindemann and Caplan, mental health consultation has become an essential part of the training of psychiatrists, clinical psychologists, and social workers.

2. A copy of the complete report, entitled "Training Opportunities in Community Psychology and Mental Health: 1969–70," is available on request from Dr. Bernard L. Bloom, Department of Psychology, University of Colorado, Boulder, Colorado 80302.

References

Albee, G. W. *Mental health manpower trends.* New York: Basic Books, 1959.

Altrocchi, J., & Eisdorfer, C. Apprentice-collaborator field training in community psychology: The Halifax County Program. In I. Iscoe & C. D. Spielberger (eds.), *Community psychology: Perspectives in training and research.* New York: Appleton-Century-Crofts, 1970.

Bennett, C. C., Anderson, L. S., Cooper, S., Hassol, L., Klein, D. C., & Rosenblum, G. (eds.) *Community psychology: A report of the Boston Conference on the Education of Psychologists for Community Mental Health.* Boston: Boston University Press, 1966.

Bloom, B. L. Training opportunities in community psychology and mental health: 1969–70. (Committee on Manpower and Training, Division of Community Psychology) Washington, D. C.: American Psychological Association, 1969. (Mimeo) (a)

Bloom, B. L. Training the psychologist for a role in community change. (American Psychological Association, Division of Community Psychology) *Newsletter*, 1969, 3, 1–7. (b)

Caplan, G. *Concepts of mental health and consultation.* (Children's Bureau Publication No. 373) Washington, D. C.: United States Department of Health, Education, and Welfare, 1959.

Caplan, G. *An approach to community mental health.* New York: Grune & Stratton, 1961.

Caplan, G. *Principles of preventive psychiatry.* New York: Basic Books, 1964.

Cowen, E. L. Training clinical psychologists for community mental health functions. In I. Iscoe & C. D. Spielberger (eds.), *Community psychology: Perspectives in training and research.* New York: Appleton-Century-Crofts, 1970.

Ewalt, J. *Action for mental health.* New York: Basic Books, 1961.

Gardner, J. W. *No easy victories.* New York: Harper & Row, 1968.

Glidewell, J. C., & Brown, M. *Priorities for psychologists in community mental health: The report of the Task Force on Community Mental Health.* Washington, D. C.: American Psychological Association, 1969.

Felix, R. H. The role of psychology in the mental health effort. In C. R. Strother (ed.), *Psychology and mental health.* Washington, D. C.: American Psychological Association, 1956.

Golann, S. E. Community psychology and mental health: An analysis of strategies and a survey of training. In I. Iscoe & C. D. Spielberger (eds.), *Community psychology: Perspectives in training and research.* New York: Appleton-Century-Crofts, 1970.

Goodstein, L. D., & Oseas, L. The psychological services center: A paradigm for clinical training. *The Clinical Psychologist*, 1967, 20, 92–96.

Gurin, G., Veroff, J., & Feld, S. *Americans view their mental health.* New York: Basic Books, 1960.

Iscoe, I., & Kelly, J. G. Division 27 (Community Psychology) Annual Report. Submitted to Board of Directors and Council of Representatives of the American Psychological Association, September 1969.

Iscoe, I., & Spielberger, C. D. (eds.) *Community psychology: Perspectives in training and research.* New York: Appleton-Century-Crofts, 1970.

Kelly, J. G. Antidotes for arrogance: Training for community psychology. *American Psychologist*, 1970, 25, 524–531.

Kravitz, S., & Kolodner, F. K. Community action: Where has it been? Where will it go? *Annals of the American Academy of Political and Social Science*, 1969, 385, 30–41.

Levine, M. Some postulates of practice in community psychology and their implications for training. In I. Iscoe & C. D. Spielberger (eds.), *Community psychology: Perspectives in training and research.* New York: Appleton-Century-Crofts, 1970.

Lindemann, E. Symptomatology and management of acute grief. *American Journal of Psychiatry*, 1944, 101 141–148.

Lindemann, E. The meaning of crisis in individual and family living. *Teachers College Record*, 1956, 57, 310–315.

Lipton, H., & Klein, D. C. Community psychology training in a multidisciplinary setting. In I. Iscoe & C. D. Spielberger (eds.), *Community psychology: Perspectives in training and research.* New York: Appleton-Century-Crofts, 1970.

Raimy, Y. C., (ed) *Training in clinical psychology.* (Boulder Conference Report) New York: Prentice-Hall, 1950.

Reiff, R. Community psychology, community mental health and social needs: The need for a body of knowledge in community psychology. In I. Iscoe & C. D. Spielberger (eds.), *Community psychology: Perspectives in training and research.* New York: Appleton-Century-Crofts, 1970.

Robinson, R., DeMarche, D. F., & Waggle, M. *Community resources in mental health.* New York: Basic Books, 1960.

Roen, S. R. Educating psychologists for public practice and applied research. In I. Iscoe & C. D. Spielberger (eds.), *Community psychology: Perspectives in training and research.* New York: Appleton-Century-Crofts, 1970.

Rubin, L. B. Maximum feasible participation: The origins, implications, and present status. *Annals of the American Academy of Political and Social Science*, 1969, *385*, 14–30.

Sarason, S. B., & Levine, M. Graduate education and the Yale Psycho-Educational Clinc. In I. Iscoe & C. D. Spielberger (eds.) *Community psychology: Perspectives in training and research.* New York: Appleton-Century-Crofts, 1970.

Scribner, S. What is community psychology made of? (American Psychological Association, Division of Community Psychology) *Newsletter*, 1968, *2*, 4–6.

Singer, J. L., & Bard, M. The psychological foundation of a community oriented clinical psychology training program. In I. Iscoe & C. D. Spielberger (eds.), *Community psychology: Perspectives in training and research.* New York: Appleton-Century-Crofts, 1970.

Smith, M. B., & Hobbs, N. The community and the community mental health center. *American Psychologist*, 1966, *21*, 499–509.

Spielberger, C. D. A mental health consultation program in a small community with limited professional mental health resources. In E. L. Cowen, E. A. Gardner, & M. Zax (eds.), *Emergent approaches to mental health problems.* New York: Appleton-Century-Crofts, 1967, pp. 214–236.

Spielberger, C. D., & Iscoe, I. The current status of training in community psychology. In I. Iscoe & C. D. Spielberger (eds.), *Community psychology: Perspectives in training and research.* New York: Appleton-Century-Crofts, 1970.

Strother, C. R. *Psychology and mental health.* (Stanford Conference Report) Washington, D. C.: American Psychological Association, 1956.

41

New Careerists in Community Psychology and Mental Health

Melvin E. Allerhand and Goldie Lake

INTRODUCTION

This chapter will deal primarily with the new careerist, a special approach to community mental health through the aid of nonprofessionals. Many of the considerations seem readily generalizable to all nonprofessionals involved in the delivery of human services. In thinking about mental health needs, the delivery of mental health services, the professional training institutions, the professionals, and the professional organizations, the contemporary social climate suggests that little change has taken place. Although there are certain very significant steps being taken by a few people and a few institutions to facilitate the extension and revision of mental health services with the help of new careerists and other nonprofessionals, a general inertia about change and a concern about lowering standards represent the stance of the vast majority of professionals and institutions.

The usual delivery of mental health services, and specifically psychological services, to and from the community is from the superprofessional or medical level. If high school, college, graduate education, and professional experience provide the only accepted route of mental health training, then the potential range of functions and value of the new careerist in mental health is either not conceivable or considerably restricted. Population growth and the complexities of society demand a redefinition of the professional role.

Other chapters in this volume will be examining the professional role of the mental health professional in the community, so it seems sufficient to point out, in this chapter, that there

is a difference between the psychologist in the community and the community psychologist. To become a community psychologist, the former anticipates having to choose between retaining status and becoming part of the community. As a community psychologist, he extends his services beyond the white middle and upper classes to the broad community whose mental health needs have, until recently, received primarily lip service. For the latter, we must revise our thinking of the role of the psychologist to include catalytic agent, consultant, and collaborator. With other mental health professionals and personnel, the psychologist will carry out many tasks in direct services, research, teaching, and administration. He may devise approaches and orchestrate more often than discharge actual service. He is likely to share the position of expert with others who may have expert knowledge in poverty or useful first hand experience in how it feels to receive mental health care.

THE CURRENT CONTEXT

Although the utilization of nonprofessionals in the mental health field has been practiced for a number of years (e.g., case aides in social work and child care workers), the concept of the new careerist was strongly promoted in a volume by Pearl and Reissman (1965). Emphasis in that volume is on services in the field of education. There are clear indications of more extensive applicability. In the broad concept of service delivery in mental health for both prevention and treatment it would be possible to include:

1) direct care services; 2) technical services; 3) educational services; 4) communicating services; 5) control services. This chapter will not catalog all possible functions for the nonprofessional since these are readily available[1] nor will it be a scientific typology of the nonprofessional since one is aptly presented by Levinson and Schiller (1966) in which they divide this manpower force into preprofessionals, semiprofessionals, and subprofessionals. It is useful to identify what may be considered a significant dichotomy motivating workers in the new career mental health field. This dichotomy became very evident in a conference jointly sponsored by the National Association of Social Work and the American Psychological Association in 1967.[2] The sides were drawn between new careers as a movement and new careers as a form of modifying the delivery of mental health services. The new careers as a movement emphasizes the *power orientation* which sees the major impact of the use of nonprofessionals as a way of significantly changing the social and institutional structures in mental health. The other approach, viz., the *accommodation orientation*, emphasizes the utilization of nonprofessional as an alternative or strategy in the providing of mental health services. The issue may be cut as one may view a group of new careerists who band together as a union to increase their wages or new careerists who band together to insist that the delivery of service change in order to reach the many people not being served by the current professional techniques. We must quickly add that the same new careerists groups can become interchangeable, i.e., at one point being power oriented and at another point being accommodation oriented.

To identify the arenas of need for such community-oriented experiences, a series of critical events will be described with some potential and existing solutions utilizing the nonprofessional.

Event One: "The Welfare." It is not infrequent that the sources of relief, Aid to Dependent Children, public welfare, etc., are loosely categorized as "the welfare" which appears as a very necessary evil that sucks in people and keeps them there. It offers a bare existence and little chance to break out of this highly dependent, demeaning experience, recognizing the few that both bleed

the welfare system and enjoy the dependency on it. Large metropolitan areas have attempted to develop service to their clients but often do not reach the level of necessary effectiveness. Therefore, programs emphasizing community change, financed both by the federal government and more frequently by private and religious organizations, have been seeking to organize welfare clients into a variety of efforts. The ADC mother and her six or seven children who live in a run down, rat infested apartment house are often plagued and confused by what's happening around them. In order to satisfy manpower needs, workers with various titles have been employed. In the past, these employees usually held the bachelor's degree from some liberal arts college. These workers, however, had gone to clients with a mixture of attitudes aroused by their differences; they, in turn, were viewed by the clients as "the establishment"; opponents rather than allies.

Solutions Using New Careerists. Federal programs of the Head Start and community action variety have included some nonprofessional workers in direct work with both the parents and the children involved in Head Start. Such nonprofessionals, referred to as community aides or outreach aides, have the explicit function in some programs of helping the welfare mother pay attention to how changes in her welfare status may have a direct impact on the educational vitality of her children. Still other indigenous workers may assist a minister in more varied community organization for social change. These kinds of bridge agents act as entree, or, as some say, "advocate" to the community residents for the usually white professional who is attempting to organize the poor for self-help.

A more accommodation-oriented approach to the welfare system is the development of such a nonprofessional as the indigenous store front worker described by Reissman and Halowitz (1967). The function of the welfare aide in a store front or indigenous situation (hair dresser shop, pool parlor, on the streets, etc.) is primarily one of interpreting the service of the agency or program. In some instances the nonprofessional may assume the friendly counseling role, being able to utilize language in a similar cultural context which may increase the client's utilization of the more professional services within the mental health organization.

Event Two: "The Health System." The frequent cry and complaint of the professionals in the health services, including mental health, is that the resident of poverty communities particularly does not follow through on recommendations, misses appointments, appears to the professional as not caring about herself or her children's health, etc. The magnificent advances in health as represented by the technology of the operating room, use of electronic processing of records, etc., has in certain ways outmoded aggravating practices, such as queuing up for outpatient clinic appointments at 8:00 in the morning, and waiting two or two-and-one-half hours to be seen, having an appointment with a different doctor each time, going through a means test (evaluation of ability to pay for health services) whenever a person goes to a different hospital or clinic, etc. With more attention paid to these recipients of clinic help by the government, and exposure by the news media, the degrading treatment and the limited use of available facilities have become more painfully apparent. Hospital administrators and city health departments are moving toward more humane and effective approaches.

Solutions Using Nonprofessionals. Through programs sponsored by the Office of Economic Opportunity, the Children's Bureau, etc., specific nonprofessional positions have been and are being developed. These include direct care functionnaires such as various kinds of interpreters or bridges to the client (e.g., suicide prevention aides, public health aides, hospital aides, mental health aides, nurses' aides). The role of such nonprofessionals is one of carrying out some of the technical tasks previously limited to the professional including taking temperatures, interviewing, interpreting services, etc. Having indigenous workers in the health setting in some instances has evidently increased the utilization of the health facilities, and concommittantly a more positive view of life for the worker (see Halpern, 1969; Fishman, Mitchell, & Wittenberg, 1968; Fishman & McCormack, 1969; Rozowski, 1968). The aides, who often will have these expanded services available to themselves in the comprehensive health center when returning to their communities, present spontaneous testimonials about the care received at the health facility. With such basic needs satisfied, breaking out of poverty seems possible,

or at least can be attended to. These aide activities are primarily an attempt at the accommodating of the health delivery system. There are other indications of change in the structuring of the delivery of service, such as the development of satellite clinics away from the hospital setting and, in a more grandiose fashion, comprehensive health centers including mental health and the parallel and more inclusive approach, the comprehensive center for human resource development.

Event Three: The Public Schools. As a primary prevention phase of the mental health program, the school experience becomes the natural locus for the utilization of the new careerist. Crowded, disorganized, irrelevant experiences within many inner-city public schools has forced our hand in recognizing that there is a very significant teacher shortage, over which there has been a quiet roar for two decades. This, plus the clear inadequacy of the curriculum in preparing youngsters, has revealed itself more so in our blighted areas than in others. These schools have become almost completely irrelevant to the needs and characteristics of many of the rural and urban children, as well as lacking in techniques and methods of teaching what is pertinent. The hard-to-change structure of the public schools is a painful reality in school districts at almost all socioeconomic levels.

Solutions Using Nonprofessionals. Nonprofessionals have been working within the school systems as teacher assistants, as composition readers, and in many instances have found themselves with highly professional responsibilities, viz., direct teaching, introducing new concepts to children, responsibility for a whole class, evaluating a child's achievement, etc. (see Gaines, Allerhand, & Grobsmith, 1968). Attention to the critical nature of the school problem has been forced by the pressure for community control and the related New York teacher strike of 1968; by the teaching profession as reflected in the National Education Association's Non-Conference Year (1967) which focused on auxilliary personnel and the increased attention to teacher assistants in the recent Elementary and Secondary Education Acts enacted by Congress. The primary role of the teacher assistant has been the direct assistant of the teacher in activities directed by that professional. In various ways, such assistance has increased the teacher's effectiveness within the classroom by having the teacher aide or assistant either work with the disturbing child so that the rest of the children can pay attention to the teacher, set up the visual aides so that they will be on hand at the appropriate time for the higher-quality edification of the entire group, or offer more recognizable role model for the poverty children in the class, etc.

Event Four: Applied Behavior Research. Head Start came into being. Children were placed in educational situations much earlier than was usually the case. What happens to these children? What approaches have the most significant effect on their future achievement in the public schools? Such is one example of the ever increasing applied behavioral research that we are constantly reading about not only in journals but even more frequently in the news media. When this research takes place in the poverty communities how can the data be best collected? How can all of this work be carried out requiring so much observation and leg work? We need test administrators. We need research aides.

Solutions using Nonprofessionals. Certain administration of and scoring of psychological tests can be taught to individuals who have limited formal education. It became evident that such nonprofessionals can be so trained in a very limited period of time (Allerhand, 1967). Not only can they successfully administer and score complex tests but they can handle direct observations in the classroom in a manner similar to individuals with much more formal education (Levy & Allerhand, 1968.) These research aides or tester-observers, under the training and ongoing supervision of qualified psychologist-researcher, have given additional minds and hands to the professional researcher through completing, observing, and rating schedules in the preschool classroom, administering readiness, intelligence, and linguistic tests, scoring the tests, discussing their observations, etc. Through such assistance the professional had very usable data for both research and clinical applications.

Such nonprofessionals may also function in the more clerical aspects of research including tabulation of data and punch card operators for computerized data handling.

Beyond the sample of events identified above, one could list: 1) the need for aides to ministers at the prevention level of mental health; 2) the aides to police officers in assisting in crises and interpreting the necessary controls to maintain order; 3) the aides to probation officers to carry out interviewing and interpretive tasks with the adult and juvenile delinquent and so on.

REACHING, SELECTING, TRAINING/ EDUCATING, AND PERMANENTLY INVOLVING THE NEW CAREERIST IN MENTAL HEALTH

It is never as easy as would be desired; but what exciting innovative adventure ever is? As psychologists and other mental health specialists concerned about the community, we must move from our psychological seats to the dynamic strains of the community. As suggested earlier, the community psychologists have to assess where their role begins and ends and where their professional training can best be utilized. Experience demands not only looking at one's own roles, but also initiating organization redevelopment of agencies or institutions through the separating out of aspects of the professional's job resulting in new job definitions and descriptions. Further, some professionals have the difficult task of achieving the acceptance of nonprofessionals by guiding the examination of the personal biases and community prejudices. The economic and social superstructure requires adjustment to these changes. Further examination of approaches to trainers to provide the most rewarding learning environment, and much professional effort, is still necessary to increase the accessibility of the cognitive and social knowledge required by nonprofessionals in their new roles. Work of the University Research Corporation[3] under the leadership of Jacob Fishman and Lonnie Mitchell offers significant assistance and direction. The readjustment for the professionals is painful. Boundaries are not changed only through easily understood, small steps. For example, the Lincoln Hospital strike of nonprofessionals (see *New York Times*, March, 1969).

As psychologists we know that once the change has started, chain reactions may abound. All relationships enter a new phase—not just the nonprofessionals must find ways to further their education but we professionals require paralleled reeducation. Beyond having more information and skill, the nonprofessionals are no longer the same "inner city" indigenous poor persons. Their development as individuals in new subgroups opens previously unavailable doors to practice community organization for change. The entrance of the nonprofessional into the service professions is on one level upon entry and is at another level as the nonprofessional becomes an integral part of these social institutions. With each plateau, new relationships between professional and nonprofessional have to be anticipated and prepared for. While thinking out the steps in the process from selection to regular employment, the realistic planner must immerse himself in the discomfort of the relevant crises and somewhat polarized positions. Only with this sense of the contrasts and counterpoint as a backdrop can effective new ideas and workable plans emerge.

At the NASW-APA Conference on Nonprofessionals the following contrasts and indecisiveness were evidenced: 1) what should they (those who assist the professional) be called—non/sub/un/not/ semi/paraprofessionals in mental health; 2) helping the nonwhite poor become richer versus increasing the nonwhite sense of power to bring about change; 3) the use of nonprofessionals to uplift the poor versus the use of nonprofessionals to increase the needed mental health services in our society; 4) power model versus the accommodation model; 5) the unique value of the individual as an indigenous person versus his becoming a captive of the professional and/or other aspects of the middle class society; 6) a new job versus a new career; 7) training and orientation being captive of the university-based and intellectual community versus such orientation and training being captive of the community; 8) professional's concern over his personal needs and values versus his perceptions of professional needs and values; 9) the retention of power by the rationally educated professional versus the yielding of the power to the unsophisticated indigenous poor person; 10) developing work (in the public works agency style) for the poor versus developing jobs to increase the quality and amount of necessary service in the mental health field; 11) social work versus psychology; 12) action versus passivity. Such items portray the tension points guiding and confusing the professionals who have taken some steps towards using or training new careerists and other nonprofessionals. They are offered to the reader as stimuli for thinking out—"How do I fit into this confusing but visible new direction in mental health and community psychology?"

Reaching the Potential New Careerist

The outreach worker, whether based in a community action agency or the more permanent neighborhood center agency, has attempted to locate the "hard core" poor to participate in some of the new career activities. When we think of the nonprofessional working in the mental health area, we must go beyond the established poor (established on the basis of governmental guidelines) and begin to identify people who have worked steadily but in positions which may be labeled as underemploying their talents. In a number of efforts to locate such potential candidates, the willingness to participate is incredibly high. As has been indicated by many and most effectively demonstrated in a recent volume by Reissman (1968), the poor will respond very favorably when they understand what the middle class and poor are presenting. So in reaching for potential nonprofessional workers, it is most essential to define and describe the characteristics of the position. In addition to the usual description of the work, it is necessary to identify the type of additional supportive services and demands the job will place on the individual worker as he or she leaves the poverty or near-poverty environment in which he has lived. Where middle class individuals have learned the meaning of organizational group support, planning for travel, the sharing of rides, etc., poor people or near-poor people must have this spelled out. As soon as it is spelled out clearly such less "sophisticated" people know quickly what they have to do within their own way of life. The error often made is that such individuals are slow or limited because they cannot behave in terms of the white middle class series of steps. However, when the professional can learn more about the culture, he can see that it is not limited intelligence or ability, but the need to translate the demands of one culture to the situation of your own culture. Many potential candidates for nonprofessional positions have been frustrated by the dead-end type of program that has been developed in the past, i.e., much training and promises, yet no jobs. As such, the specific promise of a job at the end of training is a sine qua non in developing new careers in the mental health arena.

Selecting from the Recruited

The number of Concentrated Employment Programs[4] and other manpower programs approach the selection primarily on the basis of job availability. Although in some of these programs some effort has been made at matching the individual enrollee and the job, the tendency has been (as might be expected with the upper class orientation) that one generates the job and then you look around for individuals who might fit it. Oftentimes in generating jobs, the entry level job is viewed and described in less than glowing terms. There are advantages to locating a group of people who would be interested in a range of positions in mental health. After the group of individuals has been located the series of positions are described to the group. In addition to the description, experiencing the actual locus of work for each of the positions is helpful. This more concrete experiencing of the job situation is particularly important for those entertaining nonprofessionalhood, since it is less likely that the participants have experienced the many small cues about the workings of professionals that middle class children and young adults have available to them in their development. Such professionals are just not as available to poor families, so that selection means helping to create the image of the various positions which then results in a mutual matching of person and position. In such a selection procedure, an ideal model suggests that the initial choice may not be the final choice. The trainee and the supervisor in the job situation can learn more about each other only after a series of experiences and joint problem solving. Thus, the final selection of the job may occur only after a period of careful exploration of what initially seemed to be a good choice. The trainees can often share their experiences and begin to learn about other possibilities that initially did not seem to be interesting or available.

In reviewing the outcomes of many manpower and job training programs for the poor, self-selection seems to be a critical variable, i.e., the original recruitment and selection procedure may be designed to identify and place poor people according to external criteria, yet in the final analysis the person is in the situation of his choice. Although poor people show an initial attraction to many job and training programs, there is a high drop-out rate, or when possible, a shift from one training program to another. Further, with the type of informal communication system in the ghetto, knowledge of the type of programs, the orientation, and attitude of the staff is rather quickly disseminated. With this information, the resident decides whether or not to become available.

The new careerist who often does remain in the training program and subsequent job previously has had high dissatisfaction with other forms of work. The planned self-selection in some of the new career programs seems to have contributed to the even higher retention rates.

Training/Education

Education is constantly going through revision; and that's as it should be since the educational process presses the learner to consider new alternatives. In a situation where the traditional form of becoming a professional is being questioned, the development of a content/process/experiential-learning environment presents more complications. Not only are the professionals faced with the conflict generated by this departure from the educational tract of the past but also someone must establish a new educational format. The breaking down of the teacher-learner into more of a community comprised of experts including experts in poverty, who both plan and implement, seems to be looming up as a good alternative. In the mental health area particularly, professionals (educators and practitioners) tend to make assumptions either on the side that "these people" are repressed and therefore need a lot of focus on bringing their feelings out; or on the side that we can't present content because it's so irrelevant to the real-life experiences or way beyond them that the educational programs are often chaotic and unsatisfactory. The unfolding will be represented in the example of such a program found later in this chapter. Suffice to say, most new career trainees can understand the music (the concept) and learn the skills if we package the training in clearly phrased attractive and concrete experiences.

The ingredients of both simultaneous academic and on-the-job experiences as a part of the total training/education turn out to be on target. The participation of the students in planning and, where relevant, implementation, seems to increase the usefulness of the content and helps to build in the correct timing for certain experiences on the job. For example, in helping to identify a series of lectures on psychology to child-care worker aides, it was evident that getting a cross-section of the trainees to discuss what they were interested in helped focus the kind of presentation to the total group. The moving back and forth between specific psychological content and specific experiences of the trainees (both in their work situation and their here-and-now situation) increase the attention and interest in the content. The gradual increasing of the focus on the work world, as the nonprofessional trainees move through the education program, also seems to offer a useful bridge into the work situation.

The major question of *where* these preparation programs should occur suggests quickly that educational institutions, like many other institutions, should not be restricted by walls. In a statement presented at the University of Oregon (Allerhand, 1968) it was noted that unless we begin to look at the goals of education in terms of the persons who are receiving that education, we will have the increasing disillusionment and sense of irrelevancy that the students are expressing all over the country and world. So with these training programs, if the location happens to be at a community college, a four-year college, or a university, the distinction between a place as a reference or locus of activity defining the totality of the program must be made. Ideally, as we recognize the talents and resources from the different educational facilities, the notion of consortium of educational and other community facilities has taken hold. Thus, one can build a training educational model for a mental health nonprofessional trainee that brings together the best of educational and community resources, and shape such a program to help the trainee move from the strength and awareness of the situation in which he lives, to becoming a competent assistant to the professional, bringing identifiable and

marketable skills to the professional carrying out a type of work in which past experience has been a long-term contributor.

No doubt the type of preplanning and planning committees for these nonprofessional educational programs requires a cross-section of people including the trainees themselves. Such plans must be revised as more knowledge is generated and attended to. As the training program goes on, necessary inputs help revise the program to more closely approximate the needs of the individuals in that specific training program. Ideally the training programs are as mentally healthy as the anticipated mental health of the individuals who have been helped by the nonprofessionals and professionals in that field, a condition that must be worked towards rather than assumed.

How Do We Keep "Them" Involved

Involvement of trainer and trainee in developing training experiences often demands the blurring of the difference between the "we" (trainers, professionals) and the "them" (trainees, nonprofessionals). In most organizations there is a very noticeable pecking order. If we are able to eliminate the pecking order and if we are able to recognize the expertise of the different members of the mental health team, this changed attitude will be recognized by the nonprofessional. In fact, the return to a functional rather than credential, structural view of professionalism might be in order.[5] At times the mental health team is best managed by the nonprofessional and at other times by the social work professional, or the psychologist professional, or the psychiatrist professional, or the psychiatric nurse professional, etc. Such decision should be based on the specific task involved. The respect for one another seems to be the most critical factor in keeping the nonprofessionals involved and interested. Built into a number of the new career programs, and specifically in the guidelines of the Scheuer Amendment to the Economic Opportunity Act of 1964, is the notion of a career ladder with the related expectations of credits and credentials. There is a craving in the new careerist and nonprofessional for a sense of personal gain and a sense of being recognized as more than before by the society, by friends, and by family. The woman who has prostituted herself for a period of time and who at a point in a training program has a feeling she is getting some unique powers as a result of learning about psychology, is viewed by her peers in somewhat of a special light. The mother who has just been at home for many years and then becomes a teacher assistant has a greater sense of personal fulfillment, but beyond such personal growth her children see her as—*a teacher*. The mother of a Head Start youngster who has learned to administer and score an Illinois Test of Psycholinguistic Ability feels quite powerful, particularly as she recognizes that the results of the tests she administered and scored will be used to help individualize the curriculum of a Head Start youngster. These experiences that tie together learning and increased personal worth act as the most significant attractions to continued involvement in work. It moves the view of the entry position in mental health from menial to professional.

A REAL PROGRAM FOR NEW CAREERISTS IN CHILD CARE

Each component of any program training non-professionals, whether in mental health or other areas, whether training poor people or middle class, embodies assessments of previously accepted approaches and ideas, and moves toward sometimes uncharted, innovative designs. (However, the stresses with the former group will be more extreme.) The components, essential to any program, are the following:

1) Guaranteeing of jobs to participants upon successful completion of training;
2) exact job descriptions and the wages involved;
3) the structuring of curricula and the teaching-learning environment so that there is utilization of the positive knowledge gained from life experience, and expansion of this knowledge with progression towards professional skills, attitudes, theories, and practice;
4) the convincing of the community to be served, particularly staff within institutions, of the justification of using nonprofessionals both from the point of view of maintaining and expanding quality service, and from that of accepting the necessity for participating in

a movement to affect socially necessary changes in the treatment of poor people generally and black people in particular, by providing jobs;
5) building on this conviction, developing a method for supervising and incorporating into institutional structures a group of trainees so that the on-job experience is positive for all concerned.

Jobs—Available, Guaranteed, Sufficiently Reimbursed

The cornerstone of "poverty programs" has been the provision of jobs for people who have fluctuated between employment and unemployment, because the jobs offered them have usually been jobs that made few demands beyond possession of physical strength, and in return offered few satisfactions, with pay insufficient to allow them to rise above the poverty level. The nature of these jobs and the position of inner-city minorities in the labor market have demeaned their spirit and crushed their egos. Another difficulty exists in the field of human services, a contradiction between the responsibility of the work and the recognition that is earned. In the human services, the person who works closest with those who need help—the aged, the children, and those in poor physical or mental health—are in exceedingly sensitive and responsible positions. The significance of these roles has often been acknowledged by professionals, but these jobs are still the lowest paid, these people often do not gain official recognition of their important function; and their knowledge of ways to work has depended on small measures of in-service meetings and supervised direction. One program that took cognizance of this situation and attempted to change the direction was conducted by the Child Welfare League of America in 1968—1969. This pilot program set out to provide a sounder base for nonprofessionals in key contact positions with children through preemployment training. The demonstration was funded by the Department of Labor and the Office of Education and conducted simultaneously in five cities—Newark, New York, Baltimore, Chicago, and Cleveland—with the ultimate goal of training and providing employment for 500 child-care workers. The training periods ran for 12 weeks in all the cities except

Cleveland which felt an extended period was necessary and continued the training for an additional eight weeks. Many of the experiences in the various cities were similar in a number of respects.

The response by child care institutions and agencies to the program was supportive in accepting the principle of training, although there were some reservations at the thought that the trainees would be "hard-core." Whatever that designation really means, it conjured up fears that these might not be people anyone would want in direct contact with children. However, the real reluctance occurred when there had to be a firm commitment of jobs, i.e., the economic willingness to stand behind the program, even though this "firm commitment" allowed for an out—the job would not be available unless the trainee met the standards of the employing agency.

Most of the institutions would not make this commitment although they did agree to participate in training people. Those institutions who eagerly promised jobs were in outlying areas where distance, lack of transportation, low wages, and swing and split shifts, combined to reduce the availability of employees from usual sources. In Cleveland, where public transportation did exist, it was costly, running $8 per week or more; between the traveling time and the split shifts, employees might have to be away from home a total of 15 hours in order to earn eight hours pay. Also, if they found a way to leave or return home, it might be in the early hours of the morning or late at night—both dangerous when living in the inner city. Eventually, in order to make the distant jobs available, an arrangement was made to set up an inner-city man in the busing business using funds for trainees' transportation allowances from the Department of Labor (MDTA) and the Bureau of Vocational Rehabilitation to cover a portion of his costs. (The service was impressive enough to be maintained after the conclusion of the program through a combined City of Cleveland-federal government grant.)

The low level of wages was another immediately apparent problem. Those directly responsible for the training program began to question the value of preparing people for jobs that would keep them in the poverty bracket or barely above it. Low as institutional salaries were, those in many city day-care centers were even lower, and this was compounded by poorer working conditions (the overloading in the child-teacher ratio). These were typical of the problems encountered in all the cities. A closer look at one city's experience might give a clearer impression of the intricate nature of training nonprofessionals.

The Cleveland program was influential in raising wage levels in some places. To counter the low entry salary, an effort was made to gain acceptance for crediting the trainees with six months work experience for the period spent in training so that they would enter some of the jobs at the second salary level. One institution raised the salary from $1.44 to $1.84 an hour in recognition of the value of the training. An administrator of another agency, seeing the reaction of the advisory committee to the hourly rate his institution paid, raised the entry salary 15¢ to $1.75 per hour. Several new agencies, upon inquiry about salary levels, were advised that $4,000 was a fair rate for entry-level positions and agreed to establish this as a base pay even though equivalent jobs were commonly $3,600 in already established agencies. However, many salaries in the field still are barely above the nationally designated poverty level.

Lack of guaranteed jobs interfered with the program in a number of ways; there was a considerable and noticeable reduction in the intensity with which some people worked in the classroom and on their attendance; on-job-training supervision was not as thorough as it might have been in some places and this could very well have been a reflection of the lack of firm commitment in hiring.

Matching People and Job

One hundred people were selected for the program solely through the questions, "Do you want to work with children? Do you like children? Have you ever done volunteer work or worked in any way with children?" Those who gave favorable responses were then told everything about the job—location of work, hours, salaries, and full job descriptions. Not content that verbal and written information were sufficient, the training center staff arranged field trips so that each applicant visited a number of agencies where he was interviewed by the director and shown around. Only after this lengthy procedure did people decide whether or not they wanted to participate in the program. After people were in the program, further field trips, exchanges of observations in core[6] groups, and interviews with the prospective supervisors and employers were arranged to help the enrollees determine with which type of child they wished to work; which age group, degree of normalcy or disturbance, etc. Where jobs entailed late hours and weekends, recruiting was done selectively so that people would not be away from their homes, for instance, when their children needed them. Careful interviewing established these facts.

This intensive and careful familiarizing with the work beforehand reduced the number of adjustments and dropouts later in the program. Eighty people out of 100 completed the cycle and graduated from the program, with only seven refusing jobs at the places where they trained. (In November 1969, 60 were working, with almost all in child care institutions.)

Nevertheless, some adjustments still had to be made as people tried out placements. Transportation even in the city was sometimes too involved; some people had to take as many as four buses to get to their jobs. The nature of the jobs, after trying them on for size, presented problems—for example, some people were emotionally unable to cope with the situation at an institution for severely retarded children although originally they had thought they could.

Workshops to Structure Curriculum and On-Job Training Supervision

Because of experience with previous training programs[7] the training center staff had planned workshops with the personnel of various agencies for an interchange on matters of curricula, on personal development of the trainees, and on methods of supervision and agency policy. This led to incorporation of material relevant to each agency's needs, development of sympathy and patience as the agencies were told, of the background of some of the trainees' personal problems; the training center staff learned early in the program of the strengths to be reinforced and the weaknesses with which the trainee needed help.

Supervision and agency policies had to be discussed at length. At the initial meetings with agencies, it had been stressed that the participants were to be regarded as trainees, not employees, with a gradual assumption of responsibility under supervision. But some agencies still veered in one or another direction, either giving the trainees too much responsibility too soon or not giving them any work at all. One of the day-care centers did not permit the trainee even to speak to the children; others gave assignments but no supervision. It appeared upon investigation, however, that at least some of the trainees misunderstood their assignments. When some were told by the agency to observe, they did not realize they should be relating what they saw to the theoretical material they had studied and that these were a continuation of the observations they had been taught to make intially. In addition to this confusion, some of the trainees, being activity-oriented, didn't realize that attendance at staff meetings and in-service meetings, though "interesting," was actually "work." When the situations were clarified, the trainees felt better about their placements and were willing to "wait" for phasing into more active participation.

Investigation did reveal other instances where the trainees were justified in their expression of concern and discontent. Some places, for example, took great care to acquaint the trainees with the children and their backgrounds; others did not. Some agencies invited the trainees to participate in in-service training and staff meetings; others excluded them until it was brought to the attention of the director. At one residential institution the placement was complicated by obvious racial prejudice on the part of some of the staff. This was recognized by the director and he made an effort to see that these feelings and attitudes were examined and overcome. But it was too late to help one person who was hurt so badly she left and went to work in a factory, even though the director tried to dissuade her, feeling she had excellent potential and offering her a job.

Learning went on within the trainee—but also much searching was seen within agency staff and directors. As each changed, a new combination emerged. The inner-city person sensed and learned some of the ways and values of the agencies; the agency personnel realized the special contributions of the trainee in terms of commitment, experience with and concern about children, enthusiasm for a new world of work, etc.

A director of a Cleveland residential children's agency summed up this mutual evolution: "The program was good training for the agency itself. There were rough spots in staff relationships, and some individuals had personal problems." He stressed the need for preparation of staff before trainees arrive—some staff reflected fears of their own jobs, jealousy, concern over exposing children to strangers, fear of lessening their own contact with children. Some were not interested in teaching and were unskilled at it. The director suggested the need to examine in advance how much staff preparation is needed, and to put down on paper all the purposes and concepts and methods of such a training program.

Health

The mental and physical health of some of the trainees seriously affected their participation in this as in previous programs. About 15 percent of those who entered were found to have almost completely incapacitating physical, mental, or emotional problems even after an attempt had been made to screen out people with such problems when they were applicants. Whether this propensity for illness was caused by poverty or was in itself a contributing cause of poverty is irrelevant, but this percentage does reveal one other roadblock for the inner-city person and for the new careers concept—particularly in areas that are as demanding on the total person as child care or other human services.

In cases where physical problems had been neglected or where people had to miss days of work in order to spend endless hours at clinics, waiting to be treated for chronic illnesses, the training center was instrumental in referring the trainees to special supportive services or, through the Bureau of Vocational Rehabilitation, directly to private physicians for care that was more quickly available.

At least ten women in the second cycle were so obese that it constituted a menace to their health and raised the question as to whether they could function on any job. Arrangements were made through the City of Cleveland, Department of Health, for a nutritionist to meet with these women in an effort to reduce their weight. The Bureau of Vocational Rehabilitation financed a series of 11 classes which resulted in a considerable

weight loss. In addition, the course was basic and thorough enough to qualify the women to act as nutrition consultants in their family and community circles. The program had a remarkable effect on the trainees' self-image, and the willpower exerted in this dieting could only have been a result of motivation that came through the knowledge of a waiting job and other personal supports.

Arrangements were made through the Case Western Reserve University psychology department and Cleveland College Psychological Services to Education for four experienced industrial and clinical psychology interns to become part of the training center sustaining faculty. Each met once a week for four months with a core group. Discussion centered on topics that led to understanding of self and had application, as well, to the children. A similar arrangement had been made in a previous program with the School of Applied Social Sciences for a social work consultant to meet with the staff and for a social worker to meet with groups of trainees for particularized instruction and to address the entire group in assemblies. The presence of these professionals served the dual purpose of teaching and of making their personal services easily available to the trainees. Assuming that one progresses more rapidly if one recognizes one's own problems and initiates the seeking of help, it is encouraging that a number of people requested private sessions with the interns.

In these and many other ways, some of the physical and emotional bases for inability to learn and for poor attendance on a job—so many times blamed superficially on attitude and lack of motivation—were traced to their origins, and collective and individualized approaches were brought to bear in eradicating them. The occurence of these problems and their resolution were used as learning situations to prepare the trainees for independent action when they were no longer in the program.

Organization for Learning—the Core[8]

Learning the theory and techniques of child care takes time and practice, but personal problems can interfere with assimilation and mastery here as in any other learning experience.

To create a learning atmosphere, the trainees were grouped into "core" groups led by a "core leader." With the core leader as resource person and friend, the participants helped each other recognize their own problems which prevented them from functioning at the highest level, and shared knowledge about resources and solutions, plus moral support to aid in resolving these problems. The learning process for a small group is highly individualized, and an informal setting like core provided a vehicle for such discussion, for more formal core curriculum, and also for reinforcement of remedial classes and of materials presented in general assemblies of the student body. In addition, the child oriented and academic curricula were discussed in groups and with individuals, so that the material was understood and assimilated. A great deal of time was spent examining field placement experiences and relating child theory to the actual experience. On-going staff relationships and how to function in various situations was another area that received attention.

A degree of cohesiveness developed among the core members that was in a large measure responsible for the development of behavior that would make success on the job possible. Core influence counteracted to some degree such inappropriate behavior as drinking on the job or at the training center, the wearing of extreme clothing and hair styles, noise and disturbances at lectures, and unreasonable absenteeism or tardiness. Sometimes, changes were precipitated by dramatic incidents and reactions of the core members to them. For example, on a field trip in a previous program, one carload of trainees arrived at their destination drunk and belligerent. The other trainees and the young staff member were deeply humiliated. At the ensuing discussion the next day in core, the trainees who had imbibed were gradually convinced—after much long and angry discussion—that their behavior had been inappropriate to the occasion. They apologized, although it was difficult to do, and promised not to behave in a similar fashion again. The entire core was apprehensive about the next field trip and tried to beg off, but their core leader persuaded them to participate and their behavior was exemplary. There has been no recurrence of drunken behavior since this incident.

By the closing of the training period, it was interesting to note that the core members had established such a strong relationship not only with one another but also with their core leaders

and with the core room itself that many of their lunch hours and breaks were taken right there, often in a continuation of a discussion that had begun during class time.

Functions and Qualities of Core Leaders

Within this project, core leaders, with similar ethnic background and clear awareness of the inner-city community, helped bridge the gap between the poor people living within the city and their movement into new situations, helping to chart the way, being alert to difficulties of a personal or job-related nature. Since the core leader was the most important single contact the trainee had, a presentation by a core leader[9] of her functions and qualifications is presented here.

From the moment the trainee enters the core, he is constantly evaluating the core leader as well as the program. Although there is usually satisfactory motivation on the part of the trainee, he combines this with a skepticism that affects his whole relationship to the program in all its facets.

To carry out the role of a core leader, it is absolutely necessary to work toward mutual respect between core leader and trainee. This respect is based upon the trainee's individual and collective evaluation of the core leader's sincerity, attitudes, personal relationships, and general knowledge.

The above respect begins to form when trainees are convinced that the core leader identifies with or is making an honest effort to understand their way of life, day-to-day problems, individual "hang-ups" (whether intellectual, emotional, or otherwise). Pretentiousness is quickly recognized and rejected by those in training.

The core leader who prejudges (and this is difficult to avoid at times) minimizes the opportunity for an accurate understanding of the trainees' motivations and their relationship to general behavior and outlook. This calls for developing, on the part of the core leader, the ability to listen quite carefully, watch, and then come to certain conclusions based on observing those in training over a sustained period of time.

The Negro core leader faces additional evaluating. In the main, he is expected to be aware of his "black" identity and manifest this awareness. Many trainees expect and are constantly looking for signs of what they construe as "Uncle Tomism."

On the other hand, the Negro core leader is expected to compare favorably on an intellectual level with white members of the staff. Trainees seem to want to feel that their core leader can "hold his own" in any group, that his use of the English language is good, and that he can answer and enlighten on a multiplicity of subjects, be it politics, literature, civil rights, or other topical events.

Conversely, the white core leader is constantly under scrutiny for evidences of insincerity, paternalism, opportunism. This results, sometimes, in a reticence on the part of Negro trainees toward the idea of "leveling" with the core leader or with other white staff members.

Essentially, the building of the described relationship between core leaders and trainees goes back to mutual respect. Once that is achieved, it becomes possible for many warm and valid interpersonal relationships to develop. The underlying insecurity on the part of the trainee begins to fall into proper perspective. He begins to recognize it and to deal with it to his benefit.

In these programs I have detected a feeling of loneliness on the part of many of those in training, particularly the women. There seems to be an absence of real ties with individuals other than relatives. The core, I feel, has had a positive effect in that it has given some of the women the opportunity to meet others whose circumstances are similar to theirs. In some cases real friendships have developed and in most instances genuine concern for the rest of the members of the core is evident.

Development of Curriculum

The primary concern in planning the curriculum was the effect of the trainees on the children in the institutions. Toward this end the curriculum was developed in consultation with representatives of the various areas of child-care work and on the basis of the training center's experience over the last two-and-a-half years in conducting other major programs. Specialists from agency personnel and Case Western Reserve University faculty conducted extended workshops, rather than one-session lectures, in the areas of the retarded and emotionally and mentally ill children, and on the emotional problems of all institutionalized children. Because of the amount of information to be assimilated, only those portions of subjects could be included that would provide tools for functioning most effectively in this demanding field. Generic issues were presented to all the enrollees and continued throughout the program; then specifics were added to the basic foundation. The trainees helped in shaping the curriculum by reporting their needs in their field placements (Gaines, Allerhand, & Grobsmith, 1967; Lake, Allerhand, & Grobsmith, 1968).

Academic Curriculum

This same approach was used in the academic subjects where the curriculum was made as functional as possible. Where, in previous programs, the question of academic upgrading was approached with a view to correcting general educational gaps in English and math and in preparing for the High School Equivalency tests, in this cycle the teaching of English was limited to providing a tool necessary to the trainees' ability to function in classroom situations at the training center and to meet job requirements for the writing of case histories and reports. Math was included later in the program only so those who wanted to prepare for the High School Equivalency test and for Civil Service tests would be able to experience success in an area where a large number of people have had difficulties or need a refresher for confidence. Despite the care with which the curriculum was planned, there still was pressure to find time for all that was included and yet allow time for supervised study.

Distinction in Job Function between Professionals and Child-Care Workers

In describing personal attributes for selection, professionals said that they chiefly wanted a person who was able to reach and love a child, but then some trainees were criticized for not being able to articulate what they were doing at staff meetings. It was necessary to remind professionals that those who are warm and capable can gain facility in articulating theory, but it will mainly be the experienced professional, by asking the right questions and observing the daily interactions, who will serve as the guide, interpreter, articulator, and diagnostician. In the institutions and agencies where these were the roles, where the abilities of the nonprofessional and the professional each had a place and the tasks and responsibilities were fairly well defined, there was satisfactory utilization of talents, extension of services to the children, and professional growth in the staff. Where these roles were not clear and "instant professionalism" was expected from nonprofessionals, where people were not observed in action but were judged solely on verbal facility, the on-the-job training was a discouraging experience to the agency and to the trainee and resulted in a transfer of the trainee out of that agency and a discrediting of the program within the agency and the profession.

Other limitations that were commented on, during the first half of the program at least, were a general lack of trainee communication and initiative with the children. The trainees and training staff reaction was that the life style of an inner-city person can lead to withdrawal—a seeming lack of initiative; and guarded communication develops as a defense against being rebuffed and becomes a pattern of functioning. This can be, and was, overcome as the trainee felt he had support, and as he believed that he was really going to be allowed to do responsible work—that he was capable of it and that others respected his capabilities and potential. But it was a development in a participant that did not reveal itself until he was in the program three or four months.

Eventually, as the placements were visited to observe the trainees in their work with children, the supervisors were asked, "Do you notice any difference between the way the trainees work with the children as compared with someone you hire off the street?" The answer invariably was, "Of course. Your trainees never come running to us and say that the children are 'bad.' They don't get upset when the children use foul language or are violent. They don't take it personally. They have learned very well that these children need help and they are patient and quiet with them. That has a wonderful effect on the children."

Even in the matter of vocabulary, the trainees very quickly picked up the professional jargon and took pride in using it properly.

Effect of the Program
on the Trainees

Recognition should be given to the expressions of the participants that the program had "changed their lives." This would be natural from those who now have jobs which they are enjoying, and from those who are already enrolled in school and can see their way to furthering their education—both because they gained confidence through the program that they could do so, and because financial resources were made available to them. But some of those who did not get jobs also felt that they were now better equipped and had the confidence to go out and find a job on their own; in addition, they now had references from the school. This requirement for securing a job is one that most middle class people take for granted; but trainees mentioned it so frequently that we can respect the widespread need for it. People learned to apply for jobs and to obtain information about job prospects so that their selection would be based on reality and lead to more permanence in the job situation.

The best way to assess the value of such a training program would be to follow its range from trainee to family to community to the client children in what can be described as a chain or cascading effect of change. Some brief descriptions might serve this purpose:

Mrs. S. left school when she was 16. Her father had supported her and her motherless brothers and sisters since they were youngsters, and they had all gone to school. But when Mrs. S. entered high school, she was made painfully aware that both of the two dresses she owned were really rags. She was ashamed and quit school in order to work—to help herself and her father. She did day work, then came to Case Western Reserve University and worked in the housekeeping department for seven years. During that time, she eavesdropped on classes and discussions in the corridors, and enjoyed the work, but then the housekeepers were shifted to night work. She endured the isolation and lack of stimulation for two years, but missed the educational stimulus so much that when she heard of the New Careers Child Care Worker Training Program, she applied and was accepted in the program. She decided that she would like to train as a resident mother in a group home, working for the county. Before the program was half over, she had been offered a job as a group mother, but refused because she didn't want to leave the training program and the classes. However, toward the end of the program she did accept the job and became a "mother" of five children. These were children who could not live at home, were not in need of institutionalization, but were not ready to live in foster homes. Several were deeply disturbed, one so badly that the case worker was prepared to visit and help every day, and the psychiatrist was to give special attention to the placement and relationship. The "mother" was so effective that this particular child showed little indication of the behavior that had characterized him as deeply disturbed. In the three months that Mrs. S. has been his mother, the child regressed only once, when she left for a two-day break. Arrangements have been made by the agency to give Mrs. S. release time to attend college in preparation for entering the field of social work.

Mr. L.'s manner and appearance when he came to a previous program frightened people who were accustomed to tough guys—his nose was slashed and put back together with cross stitches, his eyes were yellow and bleary from alcohol, he was ready to fight men or women. He was a nonreader. When he learned how to read in the program, it had a remarkable effect on his personality but it didn't give him enough strength, even with attempts to use other available resources in Cleveland, to overcome his alcoholism. However, he stuck to the program, did get a job, and the staff didn't expect to hear from him again except in follow-up. But in the following program conducted by the training center, the Child Care Program, a Mrs. L.—the sister-in-law of Mr. L.—enrolled. He had convinced her that this was what she must do. She was the wife of a serviceman in Vietnam, the mother of two children. She worked with unwed teen-age mothers, teaching them sewing and typing, and helping them with social activities. Although she was offered a job in child-care work, she decided to work nights, accepted a job in a hospital and enrolled in college full-time during the day. Mr. L. came to the graduation ceremonies, and at that time asked if he couldn't come back into another training program—not for job training, but because the joy of the learning experience, which he had never encountered in public school, was something he wanted to repeat.

Mrs. R. was an exceptional and impressive woman. It was thought that she and her husband might act as parents in a group home, but upon investigation, a social worker found that the husband and a son were considered "belligerent, uncooperative, disturbing, hostile, paranoid," etc. Mrs. R. was offered and accepted two community service jobs, one working full-time with a branch of Ohio State University, teaching nutrition in homes of clients in the inner city, and the other part-time with a Cleveland College program for unwed teenage mothers. Mrs. R. was able to draw into attendance at meetings girls who had never been reached before—her ability to organize, her display of responsibility towards work that had to be done, her regularity of attendance at meetings, and punctuality have earned her respect in the community. Her husband and son glow with pride and accompany her to many of the evening meetings in a demonstration of protection.

Mrs. D. was a ward of the county almost from birth and was raised in institutions and foster homes. She was assigned to do her training in an institution for dependent and neglected children. She established a rapport with a young girl whom no one else was able to reach—the girl responded to suggestions by Mrs. D. and took her accumulation of dirty clothes down to the laundry. Mrs. D. showed her how to wash these clothes and iron them, and the girl did her own laundry and put her clothes away in an orderly manner. Mrs. D. also got her to the point where she started to bathe, to comb her hair, and otherwise to take an interest in her own personal care. Disagreement arose within the staff as to whether Mrs. D. was allowing the girl to manipulate her—Mrs. D. said she had had enough experience herself in such situations to know when she was being "conned"—that this was not the case, but that her own experience had made it possible to empathize with the youngster and thus reach her. The staff felt that Mrs. D. was still working out her own feelings regarding institutions and suggested this was not the place for her to train. She did change to working in a day care center, but eventually decided to take children into her own home as a "foster" day care mother (known in other cities as "family" day care). The question as to whether Mrs. D. might not have had valuable insights to bring to an institution—and whether this might not apply to other inner-city people whose experiences include these backgrounds—is one that might merit investigation by psychologists and social workers.

These few profiles indicate the web of relationships between individual mental health, community mental health, rehabilitation through a program and jobs—rather than rehabilitation first and then jobs—and provision of services by nonprofessionals. The contribution to the mental health of the participant in training programs is obvious—successful participation and jobs provide the substance on which to build belief in oneself; this is augmented by the requirements of training in the area of human service and community participation which demand incorporation into the program curricula, courses that deal with the psychodynamics of development and lay the foundation for self-understanding and the understanding of others. The application of this understanding in the day-to-day provision of service performed by another level of worker in addition to the professional expands the mental health environment affecting the receiver of services. It is this element that is sometimes lost sight of in preparing nonprofessionals for human service careers. The focus many times is on the "service" rather than on the conveying of service in a manner, and on the foundation of knowledge, that contributes to the mental health of the client.

Those programs that provide three to five weeks of training are thinking of the "provision of service" as a function of the nonprofessional and the "affecting of mental health" as a function of the professional. The programs that provide longer training seem to be operating on the premise that the two aspects cannot and should not be divided—that the person in more frequent contact with the client than the professional affects the client one way or another. If he has been taught at least the elements of knowledge that make him aware of human needs, and the effect of interaction on problems, he can from the start act more responsibly and with greater consciousness and sensitivity. He has the foundation, as well, on which to grow professionally.

One of many experiences in the child-care program illustrates this point. Miss B. had worked at a psychiatric hospital for emotionally disturbed children for a time as an entry-level child-care worker. She quit that job, but a few years later, as a trainee in the Child-Care Workers Training Program, found herself back at the same hospital. Although the assignment was the same, that of being a child-care worker, she said it was like working at an entirely different job. The tasks were the same, but her view of the tasks had been altered by her newly acquired education. Before training she thought of the work as menial and custodial—after training she realized that since each task revolved around a child, she could make use of her contact to help that child while she was performing the same outwardly menial and custodial tasks. She knew a word, a gesture, a glance could help her give the child some insight into himself that might lead him to change his behavior or make him happier. The added dimension made the child-care worker value the job and made her more valuable for the job.

From this detailed description of one group of nonprofessionals preparing to work in a phase of community mental health can be drawn some general conclusions: to provide a training program that can ameliorate in a few short months a life-time of warping experiences inflicted by the same society that now turns its attention to making amends is an ambitious undertaking. The situation demands patience, flexibility, resiliency, and empathy on the part of both "trainers" and trainees, with the burden of effort on the part of the trainers who must prove good faith in the face of history.

Within this large framework, many questions of "professionality" must be resolved before a curriculum can be structured: To what extent is the nonprofessional to be educated and for what duties? Which, translated, means is he to be "allowed" to enter into decision-making, and if so, to what extent? While professionals individually and in their organizations are mulling over these questions, the nonprofessionals who now have their feet in the door are resolving this question through assuming the role of decision-makers. But since their number is infinitesimal and limited to pockets of new careerists in a few major cities, these questions remain in the elementary stages of debate among the majority of professionals and are basic to a meaningful development in the use of nonprofessionals in mental health.

Notes

This chapter is *not* a review of the literature nor a formulation of the varied positions on the use of nonprofessionals in mental health and community psychology. A recent publication entitled, "Use of Nonprofessionals in Mental Health Work" (see Grosser,

Henry, & Kelly, 1969) is a most comprehensive attempt at such an overview. We recognize that the nature and sense of these programs also requires at least one more personalized and in-depth account. This chapter is such a detailed examination. It may afford the reader a starting point for further study. It may also generate a search for other feasible ways of extending mental health services to people through a delivery which utilizes their capacity for self-help.

1. By writing Dr. Frank Reissman, New Careers Development Center, New York University, 22 Waverly Place, New York, New York 10003.

2. The Use of Nonprofessionals in Mental Health Work sponsored by the National Association of Social Work and the American Psychological Association, Washington, D. C., May 3–5, 1967.

3. University Research Corporation, 1424 Sixteenth Street, N. W., Washington, D. C. 20036.

4. Concentrated Employment Program (CEP) is an intensive effort initiated by the federal government in 1967 to match poor people and jobs in the private and public sectors.

5. Professionals' adherence to certain credentials and educational procedures at times continues beyond their usefulness. Such procedures may afford support and a frame of reference to the professional as he meets the ambiguity of each special person and events; when the profession rigidly adheres to the credential or the technique so that some of the humanistic values are set aside, the credential or technique must be confronted and revised.

6. The participants were divided by job assignments into groups called cores, under the guidance of a syntonic staff member, for classwork, academic reinforcement, discussion of job-related and personal adjustment problems.

7. Teacher Assistant Training Program for Cleveland Board of Education, Scheuer-AIM Project for Health Aides for City of Cleveland, Aides for Adult Basic Education, Community Service Aides for Mt. Sinai Hospital.

8. This section excerpted from: Lake, Allerhand, & Grobsmith, "New Careers (Scheuer Amendment) Training Program: Final Report. First Section: Description of Program and Results," *Cleveland College Technical Reports*, 1969.

9. Hortense Mitchell, Core Leader, Cleveland College Training Center.

References

Allerhand, M. E. Effectiveness of parents of Head Start children as administrators of psychological tests. *Journal of Consulting Psychology*, 1967, 31, 286.

Fishman, J., Mitchell, L., & Wittenberg, C. *Bakers Dozen: A program of training young people as mental health aides.* Washington, D. C.: Bakers Dozen Community Mental Health Center for Adolescents, Institute for Youth Studies, Howard University, October 1968.

Fishman, J., & McCormack, J. Mental health without walls: Community mental health in the ghetto. In *Current psychiatric therapies.* New York: Grune & Stratton, 1969.

Gaines, E., Allerhand, M., & Grobsmith, M. Teacher assistant training program: Final report and curriculum guide. In *Cleveland College technical reports*, 1967.

Grosser, C., Henry, W., & Kelly, J. *Use of non-professionals in mental health work.* San Francisco: Jossey-Bass, 1969.

Halpern, W. I. The community mental health aide. *Mental Hygiene*, 1969, 53, 78–83.

Lake, G., Allerhand, M., & Grobsmith, M. New careers (Scheuer Amendment) training program: Final report. First section: Description of program and results. In *Cleveland College technical reports*, 1968.

Levinson, P., & Schiller, J. Role analysis of the indigenous non-professional. *Social Work*, 1966, 95–101.

Levy, C., & Allerhand, M. Research and evaluation in early childhood education. Interim report. In *Cleveland College technical reports*, 1968.

Lincoln Hospital strike of nonprofessionals. *New York Times*, March 1969.

Pearl, A., & Reissman, F. *New careers for the poor.* New York: Free Press, 1965.

Reissman, F., & Popper, H. *Up from poverty.* New York: Harper & Row, 1968.

Reissman, F., & Halowitz, E. The neighborhood service center: An innovation in preventive psychiatry. *American Journal of Psychology*, 1967, 123, 1408–1413.

Rozowski, A. Model career development for mental health aides. Unpublished manuscript, University of Southern California, 1968.

42

Systematic Selection of Psychotherapeutic Talent: Group Assessment of Interpersonal Traits

Gerald Goodman

We know very little about selecting nonprofessionals for therapeutic roles. Programs often use the judgment of an interviewer or the information on an application form as selection criteria. The effectiveness of these criteria is rarely studied. Developing reliable selection procedures becomes especially important where training is minimal. Indeed, training may be less important than appropriate selection in programs using nonprofessionals. Interpersonal sensitivity coupled with honesty and courage is probably the basic equipment for therapeutic competence. Such competence is more a matter of untutored talent or interpersonal style than of skill learned during a training course. Using nonprofessionals instead of professionals means replacing the lengthy training of clinical skills with rapid interpersonal procedures (e.g., Truax & Mitchell, 1971; Ivey, 1971) and the reliable selection of untrained therapeutic talent. Putting this concept into practice requires commitment to a specific and public notion of therapeutic talent. It also demands a reliable method for measuring such ability. This difficult requirement might be partially achieved—at best—but only after cumbersome and costly work. No wonder that it is passed over in the expedient-action atmosphere of nonprofessional mental health programs.

The Berkeley Interpersonal Relations Project (Goodman, 1972) was confronted with the task of systematically selecting college students to serve as companions to emotionally troubled elementary school boys. The companionships were established in order to study their therapeutic effectiveness.

Over 100 students applied each year and our research design called for the selection of 50. A search of the literature for relevant methods of research was disappointing. Traditional screening procedures used in selecting students for professional clinical training were inappropriate and seemed more concerned with academic achievement than therapeutic talent. Lacking prior models, we proceeded from scratch. We wanted to build an "exportable" and inexpensive selection method that would be open to research and adaptable to varied program needs and manpower sources. Using multiple structure interviews in which each applicant was seen and rated by a male and female staff member did not generate satisfactory variables. These interviews were useful as a reliable pathology screen, but they showed a constricted view of the applicant's interpersonal style. Various self-description questionnaires and projective tests could only offer weak prediction of field performance and few clues about therapeutic talent. Finding a selection procedure to meet our initial goals seemed unlikely at the end of the pilot program. We were in a dilemma. The information needed for selection was most observable after the counselors were already selected and on the job for a while. Only then did we see a good sample of their interpersonal styles via supervision sessions, reading their accounts of the companionships, and—most keenly—from observing their behavior in small sensitivity-training groups. Training-group sessions provided counselors with a practice group for empathy, self-disclosure, and accepting feelings. Even the initial sessions gave strong clues about the counselors' future field behavior with their boys.

In the midst of our dilemma over selection, we decided to experiment with small group sessions as a context for selecting counselors. It would be in the form of a structured session that could provide consistency between groups and within groups. Each applicant would need an equal opportunity for participation. There were many other problems such as selecting the variables, building an assessment device, establishing rejection criteria, devising the actual group procedure, and preparing a research design to study the entire selection method. Step one was to choose the variables: the interpersonal traits related to untutored therapeutic talent. This step required a clarification of our assumptions.

THERAPEUTIC TALENT

Perhaps there never will be any generally accepted criteria for therapeutic talent. Each system of therapy holds its own view of effective therapist behavior and its own training methods. Clinical training programs in and out of the universities have offered little empirical or theoretical work on therapeutic talent. It appears to be thought of as either a minor variable or an impossible concept. Schools usually select their students with criteria based on academic achievement. Evidence of therapeutic talent is generally missing, and committees, at best, attempt to extrapolate intuitively a few clues about personality into judgments of future success in the therapy role. The major concern is predicting compatibility with a given training program. Of course, a few selected students are eventually screened out because they disappoint their clinical supervisors, evidence pathology, fail academically, or leave by choice— but these factors can be unrelated to therapeutic talent. Thus, therapists are usually brought into professional training on evidence that often has little to do with the critical skills they must actually use in the field.

It is possible to begin forming a model for selection by creating a picture of personal requisites that seem most likely to generate conditions outlined by a therapy theory. Of course, the therapy theory would have to be convertible to a program using nonexperts. This last consideration limits the choice because most systems of therapy imply, specify, or simply generate a therapy environment established by an expert. The medical styles of "patient management" and professional distance have surely influenced the mainstream of psychotherapy practice. Being an expert, omitting personal reactions, and specifying antecedent causes of current distress are necessary conditions or by-products of most therapy theory. The traditional therapist usually attempts to use the "power of knowledge" in understanding his patient better than his patient understands himself. In short, his therapeutic techniques seldom depart from the historical conception of a professional healer. These theories cannot provide a working model for nonprofessional therapists who do not have the expertise to formulate or prescribe.

In contrast, client-centered theory seems to provide an appropriate model for selecting nonprofessional criteria. Each of the necessary and sufficient conditions of therapeutic personality change formulated by Rogers (1957) can be seen in everyday behavior—even though their simultaneous and sustained appearance is less evident outside the therapist's office. Some people are regarded by those close to them as "good listeners," good at knowing what the other person's feelings mean to him. Others are better at being spontaneous, open, "straight," self-disclosing. Some people who do not need many specific conditions to feel positive regard for humans are often described as having "an accepting nature." A few unusual people possess these traits in combination and are clearly seen by many to be "straight," accepting, good listeners. Occasionally, these unusual people should be able to approximate the conditions of client-centered therapy without effort, but with some orientation or slight training they might create this type of therapeutic environment.

This reasoning together with our strong predilections led us to adapt a set of criteria for therapeutic talent based on client-centered theory. We wanted to find people with these traits. Some previous work showed promising results at assessing client-centered conditions from tape recordings of interviews (e.g., Carkhuff & Truax, 1965) and questionnaires (e.g., Barrett-Lennard, 1962), but they are too elaborate for a large scale selection program.

The project's attempt to operationalize and quantify such vague variables as openness, understanding, and acceptance is only a promising first step. We simply manufactured a structured small group situation where students were asked to rate each other after trying to listen and disclose to a stranger (a fellow applicant). The sessions were often stunning, stressful, and revealing for students. However, some major measurement issues must be clarified before this procedure can be used with confidence. For example, the constancy of interpersonal style over time and situation is still a question for study. In addition, variance in the composition assessment groups and disparities between group and dyadic behavior will reduce predictability. Nevertheless, some early informal observations and a few findings suggest that this new technique can be superior to interviews or paper-pencil self-descriptions at quantifying interpersonal traits such as openness, understanding, and acceptance. The procedure will be referred to as GAIT (Group Assessment of Interpersonal Traits).

THE GROUP ASSESSMENT OF INTERPERSONAL TRAITS (GAIT)

Procedure

Seven or eight applicants gather into structured groups where they perform several interpersonal tasks and prepare systematic descriptions of each other. As they enter the room, each applicant receives a written set of instructions and a sociometric rating scale along with a rationale for the entire procedure (available from the author). A warm-up period invites students to ask the *group* a personal question "as if" it were an individual. Anyone who wishes can answer the question in a sentence or two and the exchange is terminated even though applicants may wish to continue the dialogue. Questions and answers continue around the group until all have asked and answered once. Now the applicants are asked to think of two immediate interpersonal concerns that they could share with the group and to state them briefly in writing during a coffee break. The majority of these statements tell of discomfort with alienation, guilt, dependency, self-worth, and honesty; they usually involve girl friends, parents, pals, and siblings. These self-descriptive statements are used as catalysts to start dialogues between pairs of applicants: One person elaborates or explores his own written statement as his partner attempts to understand feelings. Here is an outline of the procedure:

(1) The applicants sit in a circle and wear letter tags. "Mr. A" begins by reading one of his statements to the group. He is designated as "the Discloser."

(2) Any applicant can spontaneously respond to the Discloser and engage him in a five minute dialogue. He is called "the Understander." The remainder of the group should be asked to remain silent. A kitchen timer (bell type) passed from one Discloser to another is an excellent way to structure the procedure.

(3) In the rare instance (about one in 75) where no response is offered to the Discloser's first statement within a minute, the Discloser should be asked to read his second statement.

(4) In order to protect the Disclosers from coercion, Understanders should be asked to avoid giving advice, making judgments, asking questions, or offering interpretations (a difficult request for many applicants). We suggest they reflect feelings, disclose their own relevant thoughts or immediate reactions, or simply "listen very hard" while saying nothing. Nonetheless, questions were the dominant response.

(5) When the five-minute dialogue has terminated, the Understander tries a brief (30 seconds) recap of the interaction with a focus on his own style of listening.

(6) The recap is followed by the Discloser's rereading of his initial statement. This contrast between initial statement and recap gives the group a sharper view of the Understander's grasp of the situation and his success at facilitating the expansion of the problem presented.

(7) The recap ends the first dyadic interaction. A second dyad is formed as "Mr. B" becomes the Discloser and anyone who has not been an Understander responds to him. The group continues to form dyads in this manner until everyone in the circle has performed both tasks.

(8) When finished, the group has observed each of its members performing in the Understander and Discloser roles. All have attempted to solve the problem of being genuine and understanding in a mild stress situation. At this point applicants are asked to rate each other (but not themselves) on sociometric scales describing interpersonal traits: Understanding, Openness, Acceptance, Rigidity,

etc. The same scale is used by attending staff members to rate applicants.

(9) Finally, when the ratings are completed, the group is open for free discussion, with the staff answering questions. The entire procedure takes about an hour and a half.

We realized this task would ask much of applicants, and we told them so. Some would be dissatisfied with their performance, and we also told them that. But a sustained relationship with a troubled boy might ask more of them and cause frequent feelings of self-dissatisfaction. For us, the central product of GAIT is the direct assessment of each applicant's solution for solving two difficult interpersonal problems before he assumes the trials of therapeutic relationship. These interpersonal problems are: (a) how best to take the risk of disclosing an important part of ones self in conditions far from ideal (being assessed by a manufactured group of strangers) and (b) how to enter another person's frame of reference and understand his feelings with few questions, no judgments or interpretations or advice giving (all in five minutes!).

Applicants feeling much anxiety about performing the tasks are left with avenues of escape. They can simply leave the group after reading instructions or during the coffee break; they can also remain and avoid disclosing themselves by reading an abstract or less personal statement to the group. Avoidance of the listening task was

Sociometric Item	Variable Name
1. I feel he understands what others really mean.	*(Understanding)
2. He seems sad, blue, discontented.	(Depressed)
3. He appears honest, frank, emotionally open.	*(Open)
4. I see him as a mild, reserved, quiet person.	(Quiet)
5. He seems warm, patient, and accepting.	*(Accepting-Warm)
6. He appears set in his ways.	(Rigid)
7. I see him as a relaxed, easy-going person.	(Relaxed)
8. A composite of items No. 1, 3, and 5.	*(Therapeutic Talent)

infrequently accomplished by interjecting small lectures on unrelated matters or turning away from the Discloser's statement with unrealistic "quickie" solutions, etc. Those few appearing to need escape were usually rejected through the poor ratings given by other applicants and staff.

The sociometric instrument contains seven statements descriptive of interpersonal style (see Appendix 42–1). It also contains space for rank ordering the applicants on judged potential as successful counselors. The statements are linked with six-step scales ranging from "very much like him" to "very much not like him." Terms in parentheses are variable names; asterisks denote selection criteria variables thought to reflect attributes suggested by client-centered theory.

A Scoring Method and Score Patterns

Scoring procedure will be described in detail here for those who wish to experiment with the GAIT procedure. Two methods for scoring an individual's performance were studied. The first utilizes the mean rating given an applicant on each item by all observers. This score has a potential range of one to six corresponding to the six-statement GAIT scale: "very much not like him" to "very much like him." The second method uses the percentage of observers that rate an individual on the positive half of the six-statement GAIT scale (see Appendix 42–1). It is a simple index of positive endorsement. A "yes" score is given any rating from "I feel this is probably like him, or more like him than not" to "very much like him." The endorsement method of scoring collapses the six-step scale into a two-step dichotomous scale. The potential range is zero to 100 percent. Both types of scores were completed for about 180 applicants on each of the scale items. A comparison of the two methods yielded correlations around .90 with a range of .83 (Open) to .93 (Mild).

The strong correlations between the two sets of scores allowed us to discard one scoring method. Several slight advantages favored the percent of endorsement method. First, raters appeared to be using the scale in a dichotomous fashion, with the majority of responses falling around the point of transition from positive to negative endorsement. Therefore, the percent of endorsement procedure which collapsed the scale into a "yes" or "no" vote seemed a better approximation of the actual rating behavior of the observers. Second, percentage scores are easier to discuss because they do not require external scale referents for meaning, e.g., "81 percent described him as Open" versus "His score on Open was 5.3." All scores used in this chapter are indices of positive endorsement.

Table 42–1 shows the mean percentage of endorsement scores (in rank order) for 179 applicants. Analyses for the separate program years produced very similar results. Similarity of scores for the two program years suggests a stability of observer response and group performance. The rank pattern of scores yields a rough picture of the average applicant's performance or perhaps general group atmosphere.

The trait seen as most characteristic of the average applicant was Open. About eight out of ten observers saw him as more open than closed during the assessment. His rating was probably based on the way he disclosed a personal concern to a peer in front of the group—and possibly on his response to a question during the warm-up period and his stance while trying to understand a fellow applicant. The project staff was impressed by the applicants' willingness to share meaningful concerns with the group. We expected more guarded behavior. Yet, the most frequently mentioned motive for applying (to enhance interpersonal sensitivity) appears consistent with taking the chance of disclosing in a strange environment. Table 42–1 shows that raters are also willing to make socially undesirable descriptions. The average applicant was described as Rigid ("set in his ways") by half the raters. Similar patterns of scores were found in a separate analysis of staff ratings which further weakened the case for an overall positive response set.

Other traits highly characteristic of the average applicant's behavior in the assessment groups were Accepting-Warm and Understanding. Impressions for these ratings were probably drawn from the student's behavior while trying to empathize with a fellow applicant. It should be noted that the applicants were instructed to resist bombarding each other with questions, and to avoid advice-giving or "therapeutic" interpretations. We believed that the avoidance of these behaviors would dramatize the appearance of empathic understanding and acceptance of feelings in dyads discussing personal concerns. Indeed, the entire group procedure is designed to provide unusual opportunity to display and observe acts of self-disclosure, empathy, and acceptance in a demanding situation. It was apparent that these qualities appeared in a more concentrated and visible form than is common to everyday behavior. The high mean scores for Open, Accepting, and Understanding suggest that GAIT provides the appropriate sanctions and arena for studying central elements of interpersonal style.

Later on evidence is presented supporting the GAIT Quiet variable ("mild, reserved, quiet. . . . ") as a reliable predictor of external measurements along the Intra-Extravert or Quiet-Outgoing dimension. The distribution of scores on this variable tends to be bimodal. That is, the groups' ratings often showed strong agreement in describing an individual as either Quiet or not. The mean score near 58 percent suggests a balanced group of applicants with a few more Quiet types—or perhaps a few more made quiet by the structured nature of the groups. Some degree of tension, or excitement, or intense concentration was attributed to half the applicants. These nonrelaxed

TABLE 42–1

Group Assessment Scores

For Male College Student Applicants (N = 179)

Trait	Mean Score	Standard Deviation
Open ("honest, frank, emotionally open")	81.3%	15.9%
Accepting-Warm ("warm, patient, and accepting")	74.0	20.8
Understanding ("understands what others really mean")	72.5	19.0
Quiet ("a mild, reserved, quiet person")	57.7	26.9
Relaxed ("a relaxed, easy-going person")	51.9	21.1
Rigid ("set in his ways")	48.7	22.3
Blue ("sad, blue, discontented")	35.7	22.9

descriptions are assumed to be products of a special risk-taking and problem-solving situation. Applicants were using a part of their interpersonal repertoire usually reserved for more familiar environments.

The least frequently used item was Blue ("sad, blue, discontented"). About two-thirds of the applicants were not seen as even slightly blue. Students were obviously eager to perform their GAIT roles successfully. A few seemed dissatisfied with themselves or the procedure, and probably saddened by the prospect of being rejected.

The last item on the GAIT form uses a rank-order format in place of the six-step scales. All observers are asked to "Indicate in order of preference (1, 2, 3, 4) the four applicants you feel would make the best counselors." An individual's score is based on the frequency of endorsement by others (stated in terms of percent). An individual included in half of the listings receives a score of 50 percent, etc. On occasions where only seven applicants are present, the first three choices are used in the scoring.

Measurement Issues

In our project each applicant was usually described on all the interpersonal items by nine male observers: six student applicants and three staff members. Applicants did not describe themselves. Differences in the characteristics of the subgroups seemed capable of producing two independent sets of ratings. Staff members had more sophisticated and inbred ideas about empathy and self-disclosure and were prone to be more demanding than applicant observers. In addition, staff was about fifteen years older, did not have to perform the GAIT tasks, nor experience the apprehension of being rated. They had witnessed many GAIT groups which allowed wider basis for judgment. One might speculate that these apparently sharp differences in need and experience would produce two distinct sets of data. Actually, the two groups made ratings that were somewhat similar. Correlations of student and staff ratings on 179 applicants ranged from .23 to .52 which were modest but significant at the .01 level (an r of .19 or higher = P < .01 for N of 179). The highest correlations were generated by Quiet (.52), Blue (.44), Accepting-Warm (.43), and Therapeutic Talent (.38). Lower correlations

occurred for Best Counselor (.33), Open (.29), Relaxed (.29), and Understanding (.23). Mean student ratings fell in the more socially desirable direction on every item. Staff described applicants as more Blue, less Relaxed, less Understanding, etc. The set of correlations for these two subgroups who differ in sophistication, age, conceptual bias, and personal involvement in the rating task display some measure of agreement in making abstract judgments from brief samples of very complex behavior.

Interjudge reliability for the three staff raters was computed on all GAIT items and produced a mean coefficient of .51 (Spearman-Brown correction). The mean reliability for staff raters on the three Therapeutic Talent items was about the same at .54. Similar reliabilities for Therapeutic Talent ratings from three observers of mixed-sex GAIT groups were subsequently found by Chinsky & Rappaport (1971)—a mean coefficient of .52; D'Angelli, Chinsky, and Getter (1971) also found a mean coefficient of .52. These identical mean reliabilities are from two separate studies with samples of N = 48, and N = 66. Both studies used advanced clinical psychology graduate students as observer-raters. The consistency of reliabilities over all three studies (.54, .52, and .52) indicates that the current version of GAIT-Therapeutic Talent items is modestly reliable when used by sophisticated observers for same and mixed-sex groups.

Prior to the systematic reliability test of students' ratings of each other, we made informal observations of their data and predicted the reliabilities would be of magnitudes close to those obtained by staff raters. We decided to move directly toward studying the reliability of *combined* student-staff ratings because a single set of GAIT scores would simplify comparison with other instruments. In addition, the combined student-staff scores, if reliable, would provide broader based measures due to the amalgam of vantage points (i.e., combining internal-external, experienced-inexperienced, conceptually homogeneous and heterogeneous subgroups of raters).

A split half reliability study was performed by randomly dividing each set of student raters into subgroups of three or four. Staff raters were randomly split into two and one and randomly assigned to the student subgroups. This procedure typically split the combined pool of student-staff raters into subgroups of four and five. Reliabilities were found to range from .44 to .79 (Table 42–2). Here are the split-half reliabilities for the Therapeutic Talent items followed by the parenthesized findings of Chinsky & Rappaport: Understanding .64 (.70); Accepting-Warm .63 (.41); Open .54 (.56). As mentioned earlier, the Chinsky-Rappaport reliabilities were for mixed-sex participant raters only. Mean reliability for the three items in our study is .60 compared to .56 for the Chinsky-Rappaport study. The only sign of disagreement occurs for the Accepting-Warm item. Taken together, these findings indicate modest to moderate reliability for the principle component of GAIT. As expected, the "high visibility" Quiet item was the most reliable.

A test-retest study of GAIT using 41 male and female UCLA undergraduate semivolunteers provides further reliability findings (Dooley, 1972). Eight groups of seven to nine students took GAIT on two occasions approximately three weeks apart. The study was confined to ratings made by students—no external judges were used. Coefficients ranged from .66 to .86 with a mean of .80. The three Therapeutic Talent items produced a mean of .73 (Understanding .78; Open .71; Accepting-Warmth .69).

It should be remembered that GAIT was developed to fill a void in the systematic selection of potential therapeutic talent based on client-centered theory. Project design required something more reliable and quantifiable than the usual screening interview. A "slice-of-performance" procedure seemed more appropriate to the task than self-descriptive paper and pencil assessment.

TABLE 42–2
Split-Half Reliabilities of Combined
Student-Staff GAIT Ratings[1]

Item	Reliability[2]
Quiet	.79
Understanding	.64
Accepting-Warm	.63
Rigid	.62
Blue	.59
Open	.54
Relaxed	.44

[1] For 174 project applicants.
[2] Using Spearman-Brown correction.

Obviously, GAIT is not a finished product and should be limited to experimental use. Unfortunately, refinement of GAIT's reliability could not be pursued within the rigid deadlines imposed by the program's timetable. For the purposes of this study, GAIT was used as an experimental procedure that showed enough reliability for exploratory use. Actually, the initial reliabilities indicate much promise for the eventual refined measurement of these very complex and subtle interpersonal processes that are important to current thinking in the psychotherapy and community mental health areas. Further study will require scaling, item, and procedural revisions aimed at enhanced reliability along with investigation of potential rating artifacts such as ordinal position of the listener, content of disclosures, etc.

Interrelation of GAIT Items

Evidence for the internal coherence of the measures comes from their intercorrelations (Table 42–3). Correlation patterns make sense—they create designs that fit our intuitive expectations based on item definitions. For example, the Best Potential item (based on upper half rankings as "best counselor" by all raters) is well correlated with Understanding, Accepting-Warm, Open, and Relaxed. It is negatively correlated with Rigid and Blue while showing no patterned relation to Quiet. That is, raters tend to see good counseling potential as requiring more understanding, acceptance, and openness along with less tension, rigidity, and depression. Furthermore, good potential was seen in both quiet and outgoing students.

As expected, the Therapeutic Talent composite formed spurious and equally strong correlations with its three components (Accepting, Open, Understanding). Table 42–3 shows this construct takes on additional meaning in the minds of our observers: someone high on the Therapeutic Talent is less set in his ways, more relaxed, somewhat quiet (reserved-mild), and tends not to be blue or discontented. Observers predict he will become a good counselor.

None of the correlations among traits jarred our expectations: Blue is positively related to Quiet, Rigid appears opposed to Open, etc. On the other hand, some of the intercorrelations approach the limit set by their reliabilities, so the measures are not always sharply distinguished from each other.

TABLE 42–3
Correlations Among GAIT Variables*

	Accepting-Warm	Quiet	Open	Understanding	Relaxed	Blue	Rigid	Best Potential
Therapeutic Talent	.84	.24	.77	.84	.45	−.14	−.61	.69
Accepting-Warm		.35	.48	.54	.49	−.22	−.50	.55
Quiet			.12	.09	−.06	.34	−.32	−.03
Open				.52	.22	.02	−.48	.48
Understanding					.38	−.13	−.54	.65
Relaxed						−.43	−.13	.48
Blue							−.12	−.26
Rigid								−.44
Best Potential								X

*For N = 179, an r of .12 = p of .10, r of .15 = p of .05, r 20 = p .01

But, in general, the set of observations suggests a coherent internal order among the GAIT items.

The Relation of GAIT to Other Indices

The initial design of our project had no provision for the study of GAIT. It was a late arrival, and most of our research on its measurement properties has a patchwork quality. Ideally, study of such complex traits would include various assessment methods with variables that parallel those used in GAIT. A comparison of traits between different methods could reveal patterns of convergence and discrimination yielding powerful evidence for validity questions (Campbell & Fiske, 1959). Falling quite short of this ideal, we decided to look for data at hand that could be considered reasonable parallels of GAIT items. Some tentative findings on the validity of GAIT variables comes from a few ostensibly parallel indices from the applicants' self-descriptions and scores received during later group training sessions. Even weak associations will be presented as clues for further study.

The application form asked students to choose the term that came closest to describing them: "quiet or reserved" versus "outgoing." These self-descriptions were strongly related to the GAIT Quiet score—in the appropriate direction (p < .01). There was also a positive relation between GAIT Quiet and low participation in extracurricular high school activities (p < .05). The ACL (Adjective Check List, Gough & Heilbrun, 1965) was also given to all applicants, and its 25 scales were correlated with the GAIT items. The Exhibit scale (adjectives such as "outspoken" minus "reserved," etc.) showed the strongest ACL correlation with GAIT Quiet: −.28 (p < .01).

Two other ACL scales appeared relevant to GAIT items. ACL-Unfavorability (unfavorable self-description) correlated with GAIT-Blue at .20 (p < .01); and GAIT-Therapeutic Talent showed its strongest negative ACL correlation with Defensive at −.20 (p < .01). It seems that applicants seen as sad and discontented via GAIT show a tendency to describe themselves in unfavorable terms. Applicants described as high on GAIT-Therapeutic Talent prepare nondefensive self-descriptions.

Further study of GAIT's ability to predict external variables was hampered because we failed to collect additional data on rejected applicants. Asking them to come back and fill out a battery of questionnaires after their disappointment seemed a rude imposition that would elicit poor cooperation. The additional data did not seem very important to us at that time—unfortunately, it was. Rejection was determined by low scores on a specific set of GAIT items (see next section). The lack of questionnaire data for rejected students with low GAIT scores did not allow an adequate correlation study of GAIT with the questionnaires. That is, our analyses were generally limited to "medium" and "high" GAIT scores. This shrunken range obviously reduced the probability of locating external correlates. The accepted candidates' data became more accessible to study through the formation of subgroups whose scores fell into the upper and lower thirds on each GAIT item. Thus, "medium" and "high" scores could be compared on relevant external variables to see if the differences suggested any construct validity of GAIT variables.

A group of students receiving very high scores on Accepting-Warm (x = 96%) chose significantly (p < .01) more "person-oriented" (Rosenberg, 1957) vocational goals than a group with medium scores (x = 70%). The high scoring group also described themselves as significantly less Dominant, Exhibiting, Self-confident (p's < .01), and more Deferent on the ACL (p = .05). They also scored slightly lower on ACL Defensive (p = .10). Roughly five months after the GAIT session the high Accepting-Warm group was described as tending to let others be themselves during sensitivity training sessions. They made fewer attempts to influence others and were rated as less assertive and determined (.05). Thus GAIT Accepting-Warm seems to predict persistent related behavior in future group settings, along with mild, unforceful self-descriptions.

The more Quiet group (x = 88%) had significantly fewer person-oriented academic majors and less experience working with children (in camps, projects, etc.) than the "Outgoings" (x Quiet score = 30%). Quiets were a little less involved in extracurricular activities in high school and college as compared to Outgoings (p's < .10). They tended to tell others less about their attitudes (.10) according to the Self-Disclosure Questionnaire (Jourard, 1964). Their ACL scores were lower on Exhibit and Labile, and more Succorant (all at .05). The more Quiet group rated themselves as quiet and mild much more frequently on the initial application form (.01). Five months later, during the sensitivity training sessions, their fellow counselors saw them as less assertive and less disclosing (both at < .05).

Students with high scores on Understanding others' feelings (x = 94) produce somewhat higher scores (p < .10) on the Social Insight Test (Chapin, 1942) in contrast to medium understanders (x = 67%). High understanders also describe people as more complex (.05) on the Philosophies of Human Nature Questionnaire (Wrightsman, 1964).

The group scoring higher on Rigid (x = 63%) came from families with stronger religious commitment (p < .05) than the low Rigid group (x = 16%). High Rigids were somewhat less disclosing to their friends (.10) and saw human nature as less complex and less changeable (.05). They also tended to be described as less open during the later training sessions (.10). Please note that many of the extremely high Rigid scores belonging to rejected applicants were lost to this analysis.

Applicants judged as having superior potential for the counselor role (x = 84%) were slightly older than those rated as having moderate potential. The high potential group had stronger grade point averages (p < .05) and participated in a few more extracurricular activities (.10). The high group was more self-supporting (.05) and described human nature as more altruistic and complex (both at .05).

Few relevant differences were found between the subgroups based on Relaxed and Blue. Actually, few external variables seemed pertinent to these dimensions. The moderately high depressed group described themselves with a few more unfavorable adjectives (.10). It was impossible to form distinct subgroups on the Therapeutic Talent variable because high scores were very common to all accepted applicants, i.e., it was the major acceptance criteria.

In sum, studying GAIT's relation to other indices has offered some encouragement about its validity. The reliability findings, the meaningful intercorrelation matrix, the consistency of the small test-retest sample, the significant correlations between staff and student ratings, have also provided clues to GAIT's promise as a worthwhile new assessment technique. It seems capable of generating indices on a wider range of interpersonal traits than have been used here. Administrative expense may be reduced by eliminating some or all of the professional observers. Eliminating or reducing professional biases in screening nonprofessionals may also reduce the emphasis on selecting applicants who resemble professionals in verbal skills and attitudes (See Lynton, 1967). GAIT is also relatively quick, inexpensive, and easy to score. It is less cumbersome than the individual interview, and appears more reliable and bias-free than interviews. Other studies on the reliability and validity of the GAIT-Therapeutic Talent measure are discussed later in this chapter.

Some Arbitrary Standards for Hiring Applicants

Essentially we wanted students who were described as Open, Accepting, and Understanding by a *majority* of observers. The following acceptance criteria were established on the basis of intuition, practicality, and theoretical biases: (1) a minimum score of 60 percent of Therapeutic Talent; (2) a minimum score of 50 percent on each of the three criterion traits: Understanding, Open, and Accepting-Warm (an applicant scoring below 50 percent on any one of the three traits was rejected); (3) a score of at least 30 percent on the Best Potential variable. The final acceptance criterion was based only on the observations of attending staff. The three staff members were instructed to note any applicants that caused them clear doubt or appeared emotionally unprepared for the job. These concerns were amplified into "staff vetoes." A single staff veto would cause an applicant to be rejected. This apparently harsh criterion was used to bring the clinical skills of the staff into focus as a "pathology screen." The incidence of psychopathology in the applicant group seemed similar to that of a typical student population. This unsystematic observation is supported by Holzberg, Whiting, & Lowy (1964), who found no difference in psychopathology between students wanting to work in mental hospitals and a group of controls. It turned out that 82 percent of the vetoed applicants in our study were independently rejected by the first three GAIT criteria aimed at interpersonal style rather than psychological dysfunction. Thus, the standard scales seem to produce a fairly effective pathology screen that only misses 18% of the rejection based on vetoes by experienced clinicians.

These criteria are demanding. Of 179 applicants submitting to GAIT during the two final program years, 56 failed to meet the standards (a 31 percent rejection rate). Extrapolating this rejection rate to the general population of male students at Berkeley seems inappropriate. We estimate that GAIT would reject a majority of the male student body. Considerable self-selection was already involved in applying to the program. In addition, about 25 percent of those who prepared applications decided to withdraw. Some of these students were discouraged after a preliminary talk with a staff member who clarified project demands. We suspect that persevering applicants viewed the prospect of this interpersonally demanding job with more comfort than the average student; many (about 60 percent) had had prior paid or voluntary experience working with young boys. Just how atypical our applicants were cannot be known. Even if they were special, it is evident that they were not rare.

A Note on Staff Judgment

During the final year we conducted an additional small experiment on professional judgment. In addition to the "staff veto" discussed above, a "staff-choice" vote was studied. The varying group of attending staff members and consultants (usually clinicans) were asked to note those applicants who impressed them as very good prospects for the counselor position. There was high interstaff agreement on this judgment. When at least two of the three staff members voted for an applicant, the designation "staff-choice" was applied. About one-third of the final year applicants received staff-choice labels. This group (N = 36) was compared with all the remaining applicants (N = 67) using data from the application form, the ACL, and GAIT. A similar comparison was made for the "staff veto" group (N = 25) versus all other applicants (N = 78). T-Tests were used.

As expected, the staff choice group also was described by staff as significantly more Open, Understanding, etc. (p's < .01). The most dramatic differences appeared for the Therapeutic Talent and Best Potential scores. We also found that staff had more confidence in Quiet applicants. The "weakest" difference in a GAIT item (.05) was produced by Relaxed. Blue was not significantly related to staff choice. That is, a fine counselor prospect also could be blue or sad according to the professional judges.

A similar picture of the staff choice group appeared when viewed through the separate ratings of student observers. Once again the Blue item was not differentiating. Students described the staff choice group as more Accepting-Warm, Open, Understanding, and less Rigid (all at .01)—also more Quiet, Relaxed, and Best Potential (all at .05). Staff-choice applicants were chosen somewhat more frequently as learning partners by their peers (.10).

Other instruments also showed significant differences between students classified "staff-choice" and the remaining group of accepted applicants. The "staff-choice" students saw human nature as much more Complex (p < .01), more Changeable (.05), and slightly more Altruistic (.10) on Wrightsman's Questionnaire (1964). Their ACL self-descriptions were more Deferent (p = .05) and a bit lower on Exhibit, Dominance, and Self-confidence (all at .10). They describe themselves as self-disclosing more to their girl friends (.05) while being somewhat less concealing about money matters and their bodies (both at .10). Compared with other applicants they are less religiously committed and more of them are in psychotherapy (both at .05). They tend to remember being less close to their mothers during high school years (.10) and appear to have slightly more work experience with young boys (.10). A detailed discussion of these variables and further validity studies relating GAIT scores to companionship process and therapeutic effectiveness can be found in a monograph on companionship therapy (Goodman, 1972).

When the staff-veto group was compared with all other applicants the significant differences were almost perfectly opposite those found for the staff-choice group. Once again, student rater patterns were very close to those of staff raters. When a staff member secretly vetoes an applicant, student observers tend to describe that applicant as emotionally closed, misunderstanding, non-accepting, tense, and rigid; he is also not chosen as Best Potential or learning-partner. He could be either Quiet or Outgoing, and either Blue or not.

Findings on these two special subgroups strengthen previous observations on staff-student similarity in rating behavior. For some programs, the applicants themselves may effectively replace professional observers (or vice versa) in the assessment of interpersonal traits.

The selection criteria we chose predetermined that the group of accepted applicants had significantly higher scores on Accepting-Warm and Understanding than those rejected. Rejected applicants were also rated as significantly more Rigid (p = .01). Comparison of the two groups on personal background characteristics and scores on other instruments revealed the following differences significant at the .05 level or better: Accepted applicants had more volunteer or paid work experiences in the social service area —especially with children. They described themselves as "quiet or reserved" more frequently, said they were less religiously committed, were more self-supporting, had mothers with more formal education, and fathers with less religious commitment. Those accepted by GAIT were more frequently aimed at careers in the clinical or social-helping professions. A few were receiving counseling or psychotherapy compared to none in the rejected group. Self-descriptions (ACL) of the rejected group were higher on Exhibit, Self-confidence, Dominance, and Number Checked. Accepted applicants were higher on Deference and Counseling Readiness.

Of course, the characteristics of the accepted and rejected applicant groups would have changed if different selection criteria were chosen. Programs using different populations, or different goals, or varying therapy procedures may require criteria that differ from those persented here. Several variations are possible: selecting new combinations of scales, modifying the cut-off points, relying solely on staff observer ratings or solely on applicant observations. Criteria could also be established on the basis of a predetermined rejection rate. That is, if program requirements determined that only the top 25 percent of the applicants be accepted, higher cut-off points could be established after running several GAIT groups. Selecting criteria to meet some specific program needs will require pretesting. Lengthening the five minute time limit for Discloser and Understander performances could enhance reliability. A substantial increase (e.g., to ten minutes) would probably extend the session too long for comfort. I suggest that those wishing to experiment with extended performance times attempt two minute increments at first. It may also be possible to enhance reliability by assessing each applicant into two

GAIT sessions with similar or varied group composition.

The use of videotape, film, or sound recording methods on GAIT sessions expands its function as a research tool. For exmaple, sessions that occur before and after a training program can be replayed to a panel of judges in a staggered format that disguises the "before" and "after" condition of the Understander and Discloser performances. Of course, the recordings can also be used as a training device where nonprofessionals, or students in professional training, can observe themselves in a demanding situation.

Prediction of Field Performance with GAIT

The association between ratings of a person's ten minute performance in a GAIT session and measurable changes in his troubled "client's" problems is cluttered with measurement distortions and intervening variables. There is much to dilute predictions. The findings below fall short of establishing GAIT as an unquestionably valid measurement device, but they do begin to suggest that GAIT scores are capable of predicting therapeutic effectiveness.

In our Berkeley study, 30 percent of the applicants with lower GAIT criteria scores were rejected and lost to further research. We could not compare differences in field performance between high and low scoring subjects. Instead, we were limited to a correlational study using those who scored medium and high on the Therapeutic Talent variables. The research question was: Is there any association between change in emotionally troubled boys and the truncated GAIT scores of their college student companions? Four representative change items for boys were arbitrarily selected: (a) two retrospective change scores on self-esteem (positive change in " . . . the way he feels about himself") from the observations of teachers and parents, (b) a pre-post discrepancy measure on the Adjustment Scale of the Adjective Check List (Gough & Heilbrum, 1965) filled out by parents before and after the companionships, and (c) a composite school aggression score built from classmate and teacher response—pre to post—on the Peer Nominations Inventory (Wiggins & Winder 1963). Correlations of these change indices with the Acceptance-Warmth scale were weak and below the level of statistical significance. (See Table 42–4.) It is interesting to note that even these weak correlations generally fall in a systematic pattern: counselors' Acceptance-Warmth is negatively correlated with School Aggression and typically positive with the positive change items. Of the four GAIT variables in Table 42–4, Acceptance-Warmth shows the weakest correlations with boy change.

The Disclosure scores derived from both staff raters and all-raters are significantly (and negatively) related to a lowering of measured School Aggression in boys. The same is seen for Disclosure and gains in parents' ratings of ACL–Adjustment for staff raters—and is almost true for the all-raters scoring procedure.

GAIT Understanding produced a couple of modest correlations with parents' ACL-Adjustment (all-raters scoring procedure) and parents observing gains in their boys' self-esteem (staff-raters).

Therapeutic Talent produced a few more suggestive correlations. Using all-raters it was related (in the appropriate directions) to most of the selected change indices.

Ratings made by the applicants of each other were the poorest predictors of the change items. Staff ratings and the combined staff and applicant ratings did a better job predicting. GAIT scores correlated highest with the parents' ACL-Adjustment score and the composite teacher-classmate School Aggression score. In general, the correlations in Table 42–4 lend some support to GAIT as a valid measure of therapeutic talent in a field situation. Of the 36 correlations shown, 32 fall in a direction that supports a hypothesis holding the GAIT as a successful predictor. Of course, these data do not indicate that the predictions are powerful.

Some further support for the predictive capacity of GAIT-Therapeutic Talent items comes from the work of Chinsky (1968), Chinsky & Rappaport (1971), D'Augelli, Chinsky, & Getter (1971), and Rappaport, Chinsky & Cowen (1971). Chinsky and Rappaport used several assessment procedures as potential predictors of therapeutic ability in student volunteers. Before the college students were assigned to their tasks as therapy group leaders for chronic hospitalized schizophrenic patients, they were assessed on the

TABLE 42—4
Correlation of GAIT Criteria Variables
with Selected Change Scores for Emotionally Troubled Boys

Change Items	GAIT Variables											
	Acceptance-Warmth			Disclosure			Understanding			Therapeutic Talent		
	Applicant Raters	Staff Raters	All Raters	Applicant Raters	Staff Raters	All Raters	Applicant Raters	Staff Raters	All Raters	Applicant Raters	Staff Raters	All Raters
Teachers: positive change in "...the way he feels about himself"	.01	.14	.11	-.15	.08	-.07	.08	.03	.07	-.02	.10	.08
Parents: positive change in "...the way he feels about himself"	-.03	.08	.02	.14	.13	.19	.11	.18	.20*	.09	.17	.20*
Parents: ACL Adjustment Scale	10	.17	.18	.10	.26**	.19	.06	.20**	.17	.11	.26**	.24*
Classmates-Teachers: Composite School Aggression Score	-.04	-.09	-.10	-.10	-.31**	-.24*	-.06	-.07	-.10	-.09	-.19	-.20*

N = 99
* = p of .05 for r of .195
** = p of .01 for r of .254

Whitehorn-Betz A-B Scale, The Internal-External Locus of Control Scale, The Personality Research Form, The Philosophies of Human Nature Questionnaire, Self-Disclosure Questionnaire, Social Insight Test, Adjective Check List, A Semantic Differential Adaptation, and the GAIT. The 30 students led patient groups for 5 to 6 months. Patient improvement was assessed by 16 criterion measures administered before and after the program. The measures tapped: verbal fluency, thought processes, psychomotor, perceptual, motor functioning, and ward behavior. Effectiveness was studied by correlating all criterion measures with all predictor variables. Only 2 of the 85 variables from nine instruments produced significant correlations with any outcome measures. Observer rated GAIT-Accepting-Warmth was significantly associated with factored ward measures rated by hospital staff on the Ellsworth Behavioral Adjustment Scale: Improved Mood (.39, $p < .05$), Cooperation (.41, $p < .05$) and Total Adjustment (.46, $p < .01$). GAIT Understanding correlated with improved Mood at .48. None of student rated GAIT scales were significantly related to patient outcome. This study offers evidence that observer rated GAIT: Acceptance-Warmth and Understanding scores can be effective in selecting nonprofessionals who may generate some improvement in chronic mental hospital patients.

In another study (D'Augelli et al., 1971) observer rated GAIT-Therapeutic Talent was related to style of participation in free discussion group settings. As part of a larger design, individuals were assigned to groups on the basis of their high, medium, or low Therapeutic Talent scores (HTT, MTT, LTT). Style of group participation was assessed on four levels of personal to impersonal behavior on the Group Interaction Profile (Getter, Korn, & Anchor, 1970). They found that HTT groups used significantly more personal discussion than MTT groups ($x^2 = .01$) and that MTT groups used more personal discussion that LTT groups ($x^2 = .001$). Their data seems clarified by a simple comparison of percentage of personal discussion units by the three types of groups: LTT = 3 percent; MTT = 26 percent; HTT = 32 percent.

These findings suggest that groups composed of individuals with higher ratings on GAIT: Open, Accepting-Warmth, and Understanding develop environments where personal concerns are more frequently discussed. Such group environments are probably more therapeutic, but the findings, as presented, do not allow us to discard the hypothesis that the higher GAIT-Open scores produced most of the results. On the other hand, it seems unlikely that a group composed of participants who were high on Open and low on Acceptance-Warmth or Understanding would produce much personal discussion. We can speculate that the "pulling" of personal exploration by good understanders and the safety provided by those strong on acceptance-warmth combined with the propensity for self-disclosure by those scoring high on Open would continue to generate much personal discussion. In sum, these findings suggest that observer rated GAIT-Therapeutic Talent can predict a more therapeutic style of group participation—if one assumes that higher frequencies of personal disclosure are therapeutic.

As mentioned earlier, GAIT was developed and used in our project as a stop-gap device for bringing some order to the customarily haphazard selection of students that might provide therapeutic companionships. We held no illusions and placed no priorities on perfecting reliabilities or seriously investigating validity because other project goals came first and GAIT was not critical to them. Nevertheless, GAIT functioned better than expected which heightened awareness of its potential and captured the interest of our staff. In its present form the best GAIT scales can only claim modest reliability, but the indications are that stronger reliabilities are probable with some revisions of items, scaling, scoring method, and rating procedures. Prediction of field performance is inconclusive and clear formulations on reliability are not currently possible. However, the rather spotty evidence on prediction presented here can be seen as pointing in the direction of validity. That is, weak suggestions of validity do appear through a series of confounding measurement procedures that would probably dilute variables that were known to be valid. These problems could be reduced with designs specifically built to assess GAIT's measurement properties. (None of the findings presented are from studies focused on the psychometrics of GAIT.) With these considerations, the results appear encouraging and clearly urge further study. Obviously, the theoretical and design problems are difficult, but the development of valid measures for theory bound constructs of therapeutic competence would be a major contribution.

POTENTIAL USES OF GAIT

GAIT is a prototype selection procedure that can aid in the selection of applicants for a variety of work roles that demand uncommon interpersonal sensitivity. Ideally, GAIT should be used in programs that have research components to assess its ability to measure and predict. Unfortunately, current programs using nonprofessionals in therapy roles are mostly without research components (Gruver, 1971; Sobey, 1970; Guerney, 1968). Outside of a research context GAIT can still be useful as a device for displaying interpersonal competence and enhancing objective selection. Thus, in its present form, the procedure can offer service in selecting nonprofessionals for work as counselors, group leaders, tutors, etc., in a variety of settings. The structured communication network created by the GAIT procedure can also be used as a standardized performance situation for testing other measures, instructional sets, and training conditions (Rappaport, Gross, and Lepper, 1972).

It is easy to speculate about other potential uses for GAIT as a selection device. Some of the qualities we consider important for therapeutic applications seem needed for work in cross-cultural settings. It would be interesting to study the effectiveness and attrition rates for Peace Corps or VISTA volunteers that score high and low on GAIT criteria. The Job Corps has expressed interest in exploring GAIT as a method for selecting counselors to work in a residential training center. As noted earlier in this chapter, applicants for advanced education in clinical and counseling psychology, psychiatry, pastoral counseling, and psychiatric social work are often selected on data that has little relation to their intended work in therapy situations. GAIT could be refined for use as an adjunct screening device to compliment academic achievement criteria and letters of recommendation. The addition of a structured group assessment procedure would add complexity and expense to the already over-burdened selection programs of graduate schools—but if it really worked, the advantages would be enormous.

GAIT also might be of use to nontraditional mental health programs that emphasize the training of paraprofessionals. The selection criteria for trainability seem related to our criteria for therapeutic talent. At minimum a good candidate for therapy trianing should be open to new experience and posess good "listening" skills. It would also be interesting to see if low scores on GAIT-Rigidity would correlate with successful learning in a therapy training program. There are some parallels in the readiness for therapy training and the readiness for receiving therapy. With some fanciful thinking one could imagine using something like GAIT as a diagnostic aid for those seeking therapy. It might help by providing first-hand samples of interpersonal performance problems or providing evidence for the advisability of group versus individual therapy.

In addition to these potential selection functions of GAIT, there is the possibility of its use as an instrumental feedback device for group psychotherapy, encounter groups, and sensitivity training. Providing individuals with organized feedback on how a group perceives them along dimensions of empathy, openness, rigidity, outgoingness, warmth, etc., may accelerate interpersonal learning—but it could be painful learning. We have started to explore such feedback with clinical psychology graduate students at UCLA.

Another possibility is suggested by the research of D'Augelli et al. described earlier. They found the GAIT: Therapeutic Talent Score to be a significant predictor of personal exploration levels in training groups. Their use of GAIT to predetermine group composition and subsequent group interaction stimulates the exciting possibility of someday insuring the effectiveness of small group process—especially those "one-shot" or weekend groups common to growth centers.

Finally, procedures like GAIT show promise as research tools for pre and post testing of experimental "treatments" in small group settings. Of course, the affects of repeated administration would have to be studied first, and the scales might need modification to enhance the measurement of change.

Some of the previous speculations might be better called "daydreams" considering that GAIT is a new method without a substantial body of research support. But even a conservative speculator would have to predict an active future for structured group assessment methods.

Notes

This work was funded by the Division of Applied Research, National Institute of Mental Health Grant

00992. It was coordinated by Stiles Hall–YMCA in Berkeley and the Institute of Human Development, University of California at Berkeley.

1. Findings on the association of a large set of change items to all GAIT variables are contained in G. Goodman, *Companionship Therapy: Studies in Structured Intimacy.* San Francisco: Jossey-Bass, 1972.

References

Barrett-Lennard, G. T. Dimensions of therapist response. as causal factors in therapeutic change. *Psychological Monographs*, 1962, 76 (Whole No. 562).

Carkhuff, R., & Truax, C. Training in counseling and psychotherapy: An evaluation of an integrated didactic and experiential approach. *Journal of Consulting Psychology*, 1965, 29, 333–336.

Chinsky, J. Nonprofessionals in a mental hospital. Unpublished doctoral dissertation, Department of Psychology, University of Rochester, 1968.

Chinsky, J. M., & Rappaport, J. Evaluation of a technique for the behavioral assessment of nonprofessional mental health workers. *Journal of Clinical Psychology*, 1971, 27, 400–402.

D'Augelli, A. R., Chinsky, J. M., & Getter, H. The effect of group composition and time on sensitivity training. Unpublished manuscript, Department of Psychology, University of Connecticut, 1971.

Goodman, G. *Companionship therapy: Studies in structured intimacy.* San Francisco: Jossey-Bass, 1972.

Gough, H. G., & Heilbrun, A. *The adjective check-list manual.* Palo Alto, Calif.: Consulting Psychologists Press, 1965.

Gruver, G. G. College students as therapeutic agents. *Psychological Bulletin*, 1971, 76(2), 111–127.

Guerney, B. G. (Ed.) *Psychotherapeutic agents.* New York: Holt, Rinehart & Winston, 1969.

Ivey, A. E. *Microcounseling.* Charles Thomas: Springfield, Illinois, 1971.

Lynton, E. The nonprofessional scene. *American Child*, 1967, 49(1), 9–13.

Rappaport, J., Chinsky, J. M., & Cowen, E. L. *Innovations in helping chronic patients: college students in a mental institution.* New York: Academic Press, 1971.

Rappaport, J., Gross, T., & Lepper, C. Modelling, sensitivity training, and instructions: Implications for the training of nonprofessionals. *Journal of Consulting and Clinical Psychology*, accepted for publication 1972.

Rogers, C. The necessary and sufficient conditions of therapeutic personality change. *Journal of Consulting Psychology*, 1957, 21, 95–103.

Rosenberg, M. *Occupations and values.* Glencoe, Ill.: Free Press, 1957.

Sobey, F. *The nonprofessional revolution in mental health.* New York: Columbia University Press, 1970.

Wiggins, J., & Winder, C. L. The peer nominations inventory: An empirically derived sociometric measure of adjustment in preadolescent boys. *Psychological Reports*, 1961, 9(Monogr. Suppl. 5–V9), 643–677.

Appendix 42-1

GROUP DESCRIPTION SCALE

Your Name and Letter _____   Date _____

ITEMS	GROUP MEMBERS								
	A	B	C	D	E	F	G	H	I
1. I feel he understands what others really mean.									
2. He seems sad, blue, discontented.									
3. He appears honest, frank, emotionally open.									
4. I see him as a mild, reserved, quiet person.									
5. He seems warm, patient, and accepting.									
6. He appears set in his ways.									
7. I see him as a relaxed, easy-going person.									
8. He seemed to talk about personally meaningful, hard-to-express feelings.									

+++ I feel this is very much like him.

++ I feel this is like him.

+ I feel this is probably like him, or more like him than not.

- I feel this is probably not like him, or more unlike than like him.

-- I feel this is not like him.

--- I feel this is very much not like him.

	A	B	C	D	E	F	G	H	I
9. Indicate in order of preference (1,2,3,4) the four students you feel would make the best counselors.									

955

INSTRUCTIONS FOR GROUP DESCRIPTION SCALE

We want your impressions of every group member (except yourself). Please give us your best guesses and speculations on the first eight items. Indicate how each person appears to you from his behavior in today's group. Many items have three descriptive words. If one word doesn't seem to fit the pattern of the other two, then just use the other two words. It's the meaning of the item that we want you to use. We cannot elaborate on these items. Answer _every_ item for _every_ person.

Start with the first item, "I feel he understands what others really mean," and rate group member A. Continue using this same item and rate all the members in the group. When you have finished rating each group member on the first item, then move on to the second item, "He seems sad, blue, discontented," and rate each person on this one item. Then proceed to the third item and then on down the page using the same procedure. It is important that you rate all persons on one item before moving on to the next.

Place one or more plus (+) or minus (-) marks in each square to represent the following answers:

+++ I feel this is very much like him.

++ I feel this is like him.

+ I feel this is probably like him, or more like him than not.

- I feel this is probably _not_ like him, or more unlike than like him.

-- I feel this is _not_ like him.

--- I feel this is very much _not_ like him.

After completing items 1-9, tell us which four applicants you feel might make the best Counselors, i.e., which might be most successful with an emotionally troubled person. Indicate your choices in order by numbering them 1 through 4. Since we cannot be certain of what makes a good Counselor, we can't expect you to be sure of your guesses either. Use your intuition so we can compare it with ours.

Name Index

957

Subject Index